General Chemistry
HE 1510

METHODIST UNIVERSITY

CHEMISTRY

create.mheducation.com

ISBN-13: 9781308516837

ISBN-10: 1308516835

Contents

List of Applications

▶▶▶ The opening sentence of this text is, "Chemistry is an active, evolving science that has vital importance to our world, in both the realm of nature and the realm of society." Throughout the text, Chemistry in Action boxes and Chemical Mysteries give specific examples of chemistry as active and evolving in all facets of our lives.

Chemistry in Action

Chemical Mystery

List of Animations

The animations below are correlated to ***Chemistry.*** Within the chapter are icons letting the student and instructor know that an animation is available for a specific topic. Animations can be found online in the Chang Connect site.

Chang Animations

Absorption of Color (23.5)
Acid-Base Titrations (16.4)
Acid Ionization (15.5)
Activation Energy (13.4)
Alpha, Beta, and Gamma Rays (2.2)
α-Particle Scattering (2.2)
Atomic and Ionic Radius (8.3)
Base Ionization (15.6)
Buffer Solutions (16.3)
Catalysis (13.6)
Cathode Ray Tube (2.2)
Chemical Equilibrium (14.1)
Chirality (23.4, 24.2)
Collecting a Gas over Water (5.6)
Diffusion of Gases (5.7)
Dissolution of an Ionic and a Covalent Compound (12.2)
Electron Configurations (7.8)
Equilibrium Vapor Pressure (11.8)
Galvanic Cells (18.2)
The Gas Laws (5.3)
Heat Flow (6.2)
Hybridization (10.4)
Hydration (4.1)
Ionic vs. Covalent Bonding (9.4)
Le Châtelier's Principle (14.5)
Limiting Reagent (3.9)
Line Spectra (7.3)
Making a Solution (4.5)
Millikan Oil Drop (2.2)
Nuclear Fission (19.5)

Neutralization Reactions (4.3)
Orientation of Collision (13.4)
Osmosis (12.6)
Oxidation-Reduction Reactions (4.4)
Packing Spheres (11.4)
Polarity of Molecules (10.2)
Precipitation Reactions (4.2)
Preparing a Solution by Dilution (4.5)
Radioactive Decay (19.3)
Resonance (9.8)
Sigma and Pi Bonds (10.5)
Strong Electrolytes, Weak Electrolytes, and Nonelectrolytes (4.1)
VSEPR (10.1)

More McGraw-Hill Education Animations

Aluminum Production (21.7)
Atomic Line Spectra (7.3)
Cubic Unit Cells and Their Origins (11.4)
Cu/Zn Voltaic Cell (18.2)
Current Generation from a Voltaic Cell (18.2)
Dissociation of Strong and Weak Acids (15.4)
Emission Spectra (7.3)
Formation of Ag_2S by Oxidation-Reduction (4.4)
Formation of an Ionic Compound (2.7)
Formation of a Covalent Bond (9.4)
Influence of Shape on Polarity (10.2)
Ionic and Covalent Bonding (9.4)
Molecular Shape and Orbital Hybridization (10.4)
Operation of a Voltaic Cell (18.2)
Phase Diagrams and the States of Matter (11.9)
Properties of Buffers (16.3)
Reaction of Cu with $AgNO_3$ (4.4)
Reaction of Magnesium and Oxygen (4.4, 9.2)
Rutherford's Experiment (2.2)
VSEPR Theory (10.1)

Preface

The twelfth edition continues the tradition by providing a firm foundation in chemical concepts and principles and to instill in students an appreciation of the vital part chemistry plays in our daily life. It is the responsibility of the textbook authors to assist both instructors and their students in their pursuit of this objective by presenting a broad range of topics in a logical manner. We try to strike a balance between theory and application and to illustrate basic principles with everyday examples whenever possible.

As in previous editions, our goal is to create a text that is clear in explaining abstract concepts, concise so that it does not overburden students with unnecessary extraneous information, yet comprehensive enough so that it prepares students to move on to the next level of learning. The encouraging feedback we have received from instructors and students has convinced us that this approach is effective.

The art program has been extensively revised in this edition. Many of the laboratory apparatuses and scientific instruments were redrawn to enhance the realism of the components. Several of the drawings were updated to reflect advances in the science and applications described in the text; see, for example, the lithium-ion battery depicted in Figure 18.10. Molecular structures were created using ChemDraw, the gold standard in chemical drawing software. Not only do these structures introduce students to the convention used to represent chemical structures in three dimensions that they will see in further coursework, they also provide better continuity with the ChemDraw application they will use in Connect, the online homework and practice system for our text.

In addition to revising the art program, over 100 new photographs are added in this edition. These photos provide a striking look at processes that can be understood by studying the underlying chemistry (see, for example, Figure 19.15, which shows the latest attempt of using lasers to induce nuclear fusion).

Problem Solving

The development of problem-solving skills has always been a major objective of this text. The two major categories of learning are shown next.

Worked examples follow a proven step-by-step strategy and solution.

- **Problem statement** is the reporting of the facts needed to solve the problem based on the question posed.

- **Strategy** is a carefully thought-out plan or method to serve as an important function of learning.

- **Solution** is the process of solving a problem given in a stepwise manner.

- **Check** enables the student to compare and verify with the source information to make sure the answer is reasonable.

- **Practice Exercise** provides the opportunity to solve a similar problem in order to become proficient in this problem type. The Practice Exercises are available in the Connect electronic homework system. The margin note lists additional similar problems to work in the end-of-chapter problem section.

End-of-Chapter Problems are organized in various ways. Each section under a topic heading begins with Review Questions followed by Problems. The Additional Problems section provides more problems not organized by section, followed by the new problem type of Interpreting, Modeling & Estimating.

Many of the examples and end-of-chapter problems present extra tidbits of knowledge and enable the student to solve a chemical problem that a chemist would solve. The examples and problems show students the real world of chemistry and applications to everyday life situations.

Visualization

Graphs and Flow Charts are important in science. In *Chemistry,* flow charts show the thought process of a concept and graphs present data to comprehend the concept. A significant number of Problems and Review of Concepts, including many new to this edition, include graphical data.

Molecular art appears in various formats to serve different needs. Molecular models help to visualize the three-dimensional arrangement of atoms in a molecule. Electrostatic potential maps illustrate the electron density distribution in molecules. Finally, there is the macroscopic to microscopic art helping students understand processes at the molecular level.

Photos are used to help students become familiar with chemicals and understand how chemical reactions appear in reality.

Figures of apparatus enable the student to visualize the practical arrangement in a chemistry laboratory.

Study Aids

Setting the Stage

Each chapter starts with the Chapter Outline and A Look Ahead.

Chapter Outline enables the student to see at a glance the big picture and focus on the main ideas of the chapter.

A Look Ahead provides the student with an overview of concepts that will be presented in the chapter.

Tools to Use for Studying

Useful aids for studying are plentiful in *Chemistry* and should be used constantly to reinforce the comprehension of chemical concepts.

Marginal Notes are used to provide hints and feedback to enhance the knowledge base for the student.

Worked Examples along with the accompanying Practice Exercises are very important tools for learning and mastering chemistry. The problem-solving steps guide the student through the critical thinking necessary for succeeding in chemistry. Using sketches helps student understand the inner workings of a problem. (See Example 6.1 on page 238.) A margin note lists similar problems in the end-of-chapter problems section, enabling the student to apply new skill to other problems of the same type. Answers to the Practice Exercises are listed at the end of the chapter problems.

Review of Concepts enables the student to evaluate if they understand the concept presented in the section.

Key Equations are highlighted within the chapter, drawing the student's eye to material that needs to be understood and retained. The key equations are also presented in the chapter summary materials for easy access in review and study.

Summary of Facts and Concepts provides a quick review of concepts presented and discussed in detail within the chapter.

Key Words are a list of all important terms to help the student understand the language of chemistry.

Testing Your Knowledge

Review of Concepts lets students pause and check to see if they understand the concept presented and discussed in the section occurred. Answers to the Review of Concepts can be found in the Student Solution Manual and online in the accompanying Connect Chemistry companion website.

End-of-Chapter Problems enable the student to practice critical thinking and problem-solving skills. The problems are broken into various types:

- By chapter section. Starting with Review Questions to test basic conceptual understanding, followed by Problems to test the student's skill in solving problems for that particular section of the chapter.

- Additional Problems uses knowledge gained from the various sections and/or previous chapters to solve the problem.

- Interpreting, Modeling & Estimating problems teach students the art of formulating models and estimating ballpark answers based on appropriate assumptions.

Real-Life Relevance

Interesting examples of how chemistry applies to life are used throughout the text. Analogies are used where appropriate to help foster understanding of abstract chemical concepts.

End-of-Chapter Problems pose many relevant questions for the student to solve. Examples include Why do swimming coaches sometimes place a drop of alcohol in a swimmer's ear to draw out water? How does one estimate the pressure in a carbonated soft drink bottle before removing the cap?

Chemistry in Action boxes appear in every chapter on a variety of topics, each with its own story of how chemistry can affect a part of life. The student can learn about the science of scuba diving and nuclear medicine, among many other interesting cases.

Chemical Mystery poses a mystery case to the student. A series of chemical questions provide clues as to how the mystery could possibly be solved. Chemical Mystery will foster a high level of critical thinking using the basic problem-solving steps built up throughout the text.

A Note to the Student

General chemistry is commonly perceived to be more difficult than most other subjects. There is some justification for this perception. For one thing, chemistry has a very specialized vocabulary. At first, studying chemistry is like learning a new language. Furthermore, some of the concepts are abstract. Nevertheless, with diligence you can complete this course successfully, and you might even enjoy it. Here are some suggestions to help you form good study habits and master the material in this text.

- Attend classes regularly and take careful notes.
- If possible, always review the topics discussed in class the same day they are covered in class. Use this book to supplement your notes.
- Think critically. Ask yourself if you really understand the meaning of a term or the use of an equation. A good way to test your understanding is to explain a concept to a classmate or some other person.
- Do not hesitate to ask your instructor or your teaching assistant for help.

The twelfth edition tools for *Chemistry* are designed to enable you to do well in your general chemistry course. The following guide explains how to take full advantage of the text, technology, and other tools.

- Before delving into the chapter, read the chapter *outline* and the chapter *introduction* to get a sense of the important topics. Use the outline to organize your note taking in class.
- At the end of each chapter you will find a summary of facts and concepts, the key equations, and a list of key words, all of which will help you review for exams.

- Definitions of the key words can be studied in context on the pages cited in the end-of-chapter list or in the glossary at the back of the book.
- Careful study of the worked-out examples in the body of each chapter will improve your ability to analyze problems and correctly carry out the calculations needed to solve them. Also take the time to work through the practice exercise that follows each example to be sure you understand how to solve the type of problem illustrated in the example. The answers to the practice exercises appear at the end of the chapter, following the questions and problems. For additional practice, you can turn to similar problems referred to in the margin next to the example.
- The questions and problems at the end of the chapter are organized by section.
- The back inside cover shows a list of important figures and tables with page references. This index makes it convenient to quickly look up information when you are solving problems or studying related subjects in different chapters.

If you follow these suggestions and stay up-to-date with your assignments, you should find that chemistry is challenging, but less difficult and much more interesting than you expected.

—Raymond Chang and Ken Goldsby

CHAPTER

1

Chemistry
The Study of Change

By applying electric fields to push DNA molecules through pores created in graphene, scientists have developed a technique that someday can be used for fast sequencing the four chemical bases according to their unique electrical properties.

CHAPTER OUTLINE

A LOOK AHEAD

▶ We begin with a brief introduction to the study of chemistry and describe its role in our modern society. (1.1 and 1.2)

▶ Next, we become familiar with the scientific method, which is a systematic approach to research in all scientific disciplines. (1.3)

▶ We define matter and note that a pure substance can either be an element or a compound. We distinguish between a homogeneous mixture and a heterogeneous mixture. We also learn that, in principle, all matter can exist in one of three states: solid, liquid, and gas. (1.4 and 1.5)

▶ To characterize a substance, we need to know its physical properties, which can be observed without changing its identity and chemical properties, which can be demonstrated only by chemical changes. (1.6)

▶ Being an experimental science, chemistry involves measurements. We learn the basic SI units and use the SI-derived units for quantities like volume and density. We also become familiar with the three temperature scales: Celsius, Fahrenheit, and Kelvin. (1.7)

▶ Chemical calculations often involve very large or very small numbers and a convenient way to deal with these numbers is the scientific notation. In calculations or measurements, every quantity must show the proper number of significant figures, which are the meaningful digits. (1.8)

▶ We learn that dimensional analysis is useful in chemical calculations. By carrying the units through the entire sequence of calculations, all the units will cancel except the desired one. (1.9)

▶ Solving real-world problems frequently involves making assumptions and simplifications. (1.10)

Chemistry is an active, evolving science that has vital importance to our world, in both the realm of nature and the realm of society. Its roots are ancient, but as we will see, chemistry is every bit a modern science.

We will begin our study of chemistry at the macroscopic level, where we can see and measure the materials of which our world is made. In this chapter, we will discuss the scientific method, which provides the framework for research not only in chemistry but in all other sciences as well. Next we will discover how scientists define and characterize matter. Then we will spend some time learning how to handle numerical results of chemical measurements and solve numerical problems. In Chapter 2, we will begin to explore the microscopic world of atoms and molecules.

The Chinese characters for chemistry mean "The study of change."

1.1 Chemistry: A Science for the Twenty-First Century

Chemistry is *the study of matter and the changes it undergoes.* Chemistry is often called the central science, because a basic knowledge of chemistry is essential for students of biology, physics, geology, ecology, and many other subjects. Indeed, it is central to our way of life; without it, we would be living shorter lives in what we would consider primitive conditions, without automobiles, electricity, computers, CDs, and many other everyday conveniences.

Although chemistry is an ancient science, its modern foundation was laid in the nineteenth century, when intellectual and technological advances enabled scientists to break down substances into ever smaller components and consequently to explain many of their physical and chemical characteristics. The rapid development of increasingly sophisticated technology throughout the twentieth century has given us even greater means to study things that cannot be seen with the naked eye. Using computers and special microscopes, for example, chemists can analyze the structure of atoms and molecules—the fundamental units on which the study of chemistry is based—and design new substances with specific properties, such as drugs and environmentally friendly consumer products.

It is fitting to ask what part the central science will have in the twenty-first century. Almost certainly, chemistry will continue to play a pivotal role in all areas of science and technology. Before plunging into the study of matter and its transformation, let us consider some of the frontiers that chemists are currently exploring (Figure 1.1). Whatever your reasons for taking general chemistry, a good knowledge of the subject will better enable you to appreciate its impact on society and on you as an individual.

1.2 The Study of Chemistry

Compared with other subjects, chemistry is commonly believed to be more difficult, at least at the introductory level. There is some justification for this perception; for one thing, chemistry has a very specialized vocabulary. However, even if this is your first course in chemistry, you already have more familiarity with the subject than you may realize. In everyday conversations we hear words that have a chemical connection, although they may not be used in the scientifically correct sense. Examples are "electronic," "quantum leap," "equilibrium," "catalyst," "chain reaction," and "critical mass." Moreover, if you cook, then you are a practicing chemist! From experience gained in the kitchen, you know that oil and water do not mix and that boiling water left on the stove will evaporate. You apply chemical and physical principles when you use baking soda to leaven bread, choose a pressure cooker to shorten the time it takes to prepare soup, add meat tenderizer to a pot roast, squeeze lemon juice over sliced

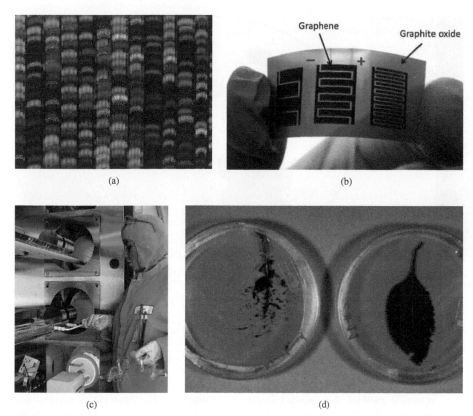

Graphene

Graphite oxide

(a)

(b)

(c)

(d)

Figure 1.1 *(a) The output from an automated DNA sequencing machine. Each lane displays the sequence (indicated by different colors) obtained with a separate DNA sample. (b) A graphene supercapacitor. These materials provide some of the highest known energy-to-volume ratios and response times. (c) Production of photovoltaic cells, used to convert light into electrical current. (d) The leaf on the left was taken from a tobacco plant that was not genetically engineered but was exposed to tobacco horn worms. The leaf on the right was genetically engineered and is barely attacked by the worms. The same technique can be applied to protect the leaves of other types of plants.*

pears to prevent them from turning brown or over fish to minimize its odor, and add vinegar to the water in which you are going to poach eggs. Every day we observe such changes without thinking about their chemical nature. The purpose of this course is to make you think like a chemist, to look at the *macroscopic world*—the things we can see, touch, and measure directly—and visualize the particles and events of the *microscopic world* that we cannot experience without modern technology and our imaginations.

At first some students find it confusing that their chemistry instructor and textbook seem to be continually shifting back and forth between the macroscopic and microscopic worlds. Just keep in mind that the data for chemical investigations most often come from observations of large-scale phenomena, but the explanations frequently lie in the unseen and partially imagined microscopic world of atoms and molecules. In other words, chemists often *see* one thing (in the macroscopic world) and *think* another (in the microscopic world). Looking at the rusted nails in Figure 1.2, for example, a chemist might think about the basic properties of individual atoms of iron and how these units interact with other atoms and molecules to produce the observed change.

4   **Chapter 1** ▪ Chemistry: The Study of Change

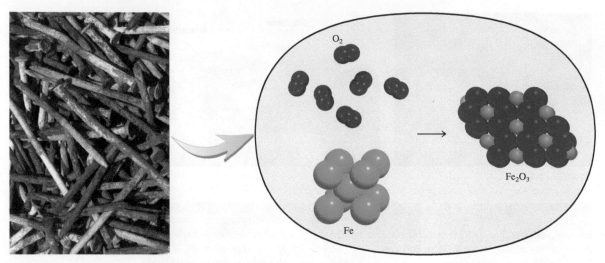

Figure 1.2 *A simplified molecular view of rust (Fe₂O₃) formation from iron (Fe) atoms and oxygen molecules (O₂). In reality, the process requires water and rust also contains water molecules.*

1.3 The Scientific Method

All sciences, including the social sciences, employ variations of what is called the *scientific method, a systematic approach to research.* For example, a psychologist who wants to know how noise affects people's ability to learn chemistry and a chemist interested in measuring the heat given off when hydrogen gas burns in air would follow roughly the same procedure in carrying out their investigations. The first step is to carefully define the problem. The next step includes performing experiments, making careful observations, and recording information, or *data,* about the system—the part of the universe that is under investigation. (In the examples just discussed, the systems are the group of people the psychologist will study and a mixture of hydrogen and air.)

The data obtained in a research study may be both *qualitative, consisting of general observations about the system,* and *quantitative, comprising numbers obtained by various measurements of the system.* Chemists generally use standardized symbols and equations in recording their measurements and observations. This form of representation not only simplifies the process of keeping records, but also provides a common basis for communication with other chemists.

When the experiments have been completed and the data have been recorded, the next step in the scientific method is interpretation, meaning that the scientist attempts to explain the observed phenomenon. Based on the data that were gathered, the researcher formulates a *hypothesis, a tentative explanation for a set of observations.* Further experiments are devised to test the validity of the hypothesis in as many ways as possible, and the process begins anew. Figure 1.3 summarizes the main steps of the research process.

After a large amount of data has been collected, it is often desirable to summarize the information in a concise way, as a law. In science, a *law* is *a concise verbal or mathematical statement of a relationship between phenomena that is always the same under the same conditions.* For example, Sir Isaac Newton's second law of motion, which you may remember from high school science, says that force equals mass times acceleration ($F = ma$). What this law means is that an

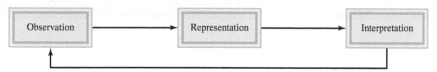

Figure 1.3 *The three levels of studying chemistry and their relationships. Observation deals with events in the macroscopic world; atoms and molecules constitute the microscopic world. Representation is a scientific shorthand for describing an experiment in symbols and chemical equations. Chemists use their knowledge of atoms and molecules to explain an observed phenomenon.*

increase in the mass or in the acceleration of an object will always increase its force proportionally, and a decrease in mass or acceleration will always decrease the force.

Hypotheses that survive many experimental tests of their validity may evolve into theories. A ***theory*** is *a unifying principle that explains a body of facts and/or those laws that are based on them.* Theories, too, are constantly being tested. If a theory is disproved by experiment, then it must be discarded or modified so that it becomes consistent with experimental observations. Proving or disproving a theory can take years, even centuries, in part because the necessary technology may not be available. Atomic theory, which we will study in Chapter 2, is a case in point. It took more than 2000 years to work out this fundamental principle of chemistry proposed by Democritus, an ancient Greek philosopher. A more contemporary example is the search for the Higgs boson discussed on page 6.

Scientific progress is seldom, if ever, made in a rigid, step-by-step fashion. Sometimes a law precedes a theory; sometimes it is the other way around. Two scientists may start working on a project with exactly the same objective, but will end up taking drastically different approaches. Scientists are, after all, human beings, and their modes of thinking and working are very much influenced by their background, training, and personalities.

The development of science has been irregular and sometimes even illogical. Great discoveries are usually the result of the cumulative contributions and experience of many workers, even though the credit for formulating a theory or a law is usually given to only one individual. There is, of course, an element of luck involved in scientific discoveries, but it has been said that "chance favors the prepared mind." It takes an alert and well-trained person to recognize the significance of an accidental discovery and to take full advantage of it. More often than not, the public learns only of spectacular scientific breakthroughs. For every success story, however, there are hundreds of cases in which scientists have spent years working on projects that ultimately led to a dead end, and in which positive achievements came only after many wrong turns and at such a slow pace that they went unheralded. Yet even the dead ends contribute something to the continually growing body of knowledge about the physical universe. It is the love of the search that keeps many scientists in the laboratory.

Review of Concepts

Which of the following statements is true?

(a) A hypothesis always leads to the formulation of a law.

(b) The scientific method is a rigid sequence of steps in solving problems.

(c) A law summarizes a series of experimental observations; a theory provides an explanation for the observations.

CHEMISTRY *in Action*

The Search for the Higgs Boson

In this chapter, we identify mass as a fundamental property of matter, but have you ever wondered: Why does matter even have mass? It might seem obvious that "everything" has mass, but is that a requirement of nature? We will see later in our studies that light is composed of particles that do not have mass when at rest, and physics tells us under different circumstances the universe might not contain *anything* with mass. Yet we know that *our* universe is made up of an uncountable number of particles with mass, and these building blocks are necessary to form the elements that make up the people to ask such questions. The search for the answer to this question illustrates nicely the process we call the scientific method.

Current theoretical models tell us that everything in the universe is based on two types of elementary particles: bosons and fermions. We can distinguish the roles of these particles by considering the building blocks of matter to be constructed from fermions, while bosons are particles responsible for the force that holds the fermions together. In 1964, three different research teams independently proposed mechanisms in which a field of energy permeates the universe, and the interaction of matter with this field is due to a specific boson associated with the field. The greater the number of these bosons, the greater the interaction will be with the field. This interaction is the property we call mass, and the field and the associated boson came to be named for Peter Higgs, one of the original physicists to propose this mechanism.

This theory ignited a frantic search for the "Higgs boson" that became one of the most heralded quests in modern science. The Large Hadron Collider at CERN in Geneva, Switzerland (described on p. 875) was constructed to carry out experiments designed to find evidence for the Higgs boson. In these experiments, protons are accelerated to nearly the speed of light in opposite directions in a circular 17-mile tunnel, and then allowed to collide, generating even more fundamental particles at very high energies. The data are examined for evidence of an excess of particles at an energy consistent with theoretical predictions for the Higgs boson. The ongoing process of theory suggesting experiments that give results used to evaluate and ultimately refine the theory, and so on, is the essence of the scientific method.

Illustration of the data obtained from decay of the Higgs boson into other particles following an 8-TeV collision at the Large Hadron Collider at CERN.

On July 4, 2012, scientists at CERN announced the discovery of the Higgs boson. It takes about 1 trillion proton-proton collisions to produce one Higgs boson event, so it requires a tremendous amount of data obtained from two independent sets of experiments to confirm the findings. In science, the quest for answers is never completely done. Our understanding can always be improved or refined, and sometimes entire tenets of accepted science are replaced by another theory that does a better job explaining the observations. For example, scientists are not sure if the Higgs boson is the only particle that confers mass to matter, or if it is only one of several such bosons predicted by other theories.

But over the long run, the scientific method has proven to be our best way of understanding the physical world. It took 50 years for experimental science to validate the existence of the Higgs boson. This discovery was greeted with great fanfare and recognized the following year with a 2013 Nobel Prize in Physics for Peter Higgs and François Englert, another one of the six original scientists who first proposed the existence of a universal field that gives particles their mass. It is impossible to imagine where science will take our understanding of the universe in the next 50 years, but we can be fairly certain that many of the theories and experiments driving this scientific discovery will be very different than the ones we use today.

1.4 Classifications of Matter

We defined chemistry in Section 1.1 as the study of matter and the changes it undergoes. **Matter** is *anything that occupies space and has mass*. Matter includes things we can see and touch (such as water, earth, and trees), as well as things we cannot (such as air). Thus, everything in the universe has a "chemical" connection.

Chemists distinguish among several subcategories of matter based on composition and properties. The classifications of matter include substances, mixtures, elements, and compounds, as well as atoms and molecules, which we will consider in Chapter 2.

Substances and Mixtures

A *substance* is *a form of matter that has a definite (constant) composition and distinct properties.* Examples are water, ammonia, table sugar (sucrose), gold, and oxygen. Substances differ from one another in composition and can be identified by their appearance, smell, taste, and other properties.

A *mixture* is *a combination of two or more substances in which the substances retain their distinct identities.* Some familiar examples are air, soft drinks, milk, and cement. Mixtures do not have constant composition. Therefore, samples of air collected in different cities would probably differ in composition because of differences in altitude, pollution, and so on.

Mixtures are either homogeneous or heterogeneous. When a spoonful of sugar dissolves in water we obtain a *homogeneous mixture* in which *the composition of the mixture is the same throughout.* If sand is mixed with iron filings, however, the sand grains and the iron filings remain separate (Figure 1.4). This type of mixture is called a *heterogeneous mixture* because *the composition is not uniform.*

Any mixture, whether homogeneous or heterogeneous, can be created and then separated by physical means into pure components without changing the identities of the components. Thus, sugar can be recovered from a water solution by heating the solution and evaporating it to dryness. Condensing the vapor will give us back the water component. To separate the iron-sand mixture, we can use a magnet to remove the iron filings from the sand, because sand is not attracted to the magnet [see Figure 1.4(b)]. After separation, the components of the mixture will have the same composition and properties as they did to start with.

Elements and Compounds

Substances can be either elements or compounds. An *element* is *a substance that cannot be separated into simpler substances by chemical means.* To date, 118 elements have been positively identified. Most of them occur naturally on Earth. The others have been created by scientists via nuclear processes, which are the subject of Chapter 19 of this text.

Figure 1.4 *(a) The mixture contains iron filings and sand. (b) A magnet separates the iron filings from the mixture. The same technique is used on a larger scale to separate iron and steel from nonmagnetic objects such as aluminum, glass, and plastics.*

(a)   (b)

8   **Chapter 1** ▪ Chemistry: The Study of Change

Table 1.1	Some Common Elements and Their Symbols				
Name	**Symbol**	**Name**	**Symbol**	**Name**	**Symbol**
Aluminum	Al	Fluorine	F	Oxygen	O
Arsenic	As	Gold	Au	Phosphorus	P
Barium	Ba	Hydrogen	H	Platinum	Pt
Bismuth	Bi	Iodine	I	Potassium	K
Bromine	Br	Iron	Fe	Silicon	Si
Calcium	Ca	Lead	Pb	Silver	Ag
Carbon	C	Magnesium	Mg	Sodium	Na
Chlorine	Cl	Manganese	Mn	Sulfur	S
Chromium	Cr	Mercury	Hg	Tin	Sn
Cobalt	Co	Nickel	Ni	Tungsten	W
Copper	Cu	Nitrogen	N	Zinc	Zn

For convenience, chemists use symbols of one or two letters to represent the elements. The first letter of a symbol is *always* capitalized, but any following letters are not. For example, Co is the symbol for the element cobalt, whereas CO is the formula for the carbon monoxide molecule. Table 1.1 shows the names and symbols of some of the more common elements; a complete list of the elements and their symbols appears inside the front cover of this book. The symbols of some elements are derived from their Latin names—for example, Au from *aurum* (gold), Fe from *ferrum* (iron), and Na from *natrium* (sodium)—whereas most of them come from their English names. Appendix 1 gives the origin of the names and lists the discoverers of most of the elements.

Atoms of most elements can interact with one another to form compounds. Hydrogen gas, for example, burns in oxygen gas to form water, which has properties that are distinctly different from those of the starting materials. Water is made up of two parts hydrogen and one part oxygen. This composition does not change, regardless of whether the water comes from a faucet in the United States, a lake in Outer Mongolia, or the ice caps on Mars. Thus, water is a **compound,** *a substance composed of atoms of two or more elements chemically united in fixed proportions.* Unlike mixtures, compounds can be separated only by chemical means into their pure components.

The relationships among elements, compounds, and other categories of matter are summarized in Figure 1.5.

Review of Concepts

Which of the following diagrams represent elements and which represent compounds? Each color sphere (or truncated sphere) represents an atom. Different colored atoms indicate different elements.

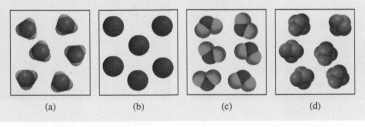

(a)   (b)   (c)   (d)

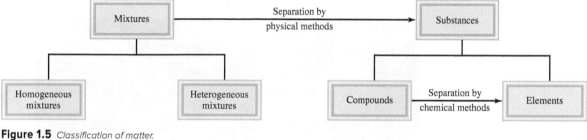

Figure 1.5 *Classification of matter.*

1.5 The Three States of Matter

All substances, at least in principle, can exist in three states: solid, liquid, and gas. As Figure 1.6 shows, gases differ from liquids and solids in the distances between the molecules. In a solid, molecules are held close together in an orderly fashion with little freedom of motion. Molecules in a liquid are close together but are not held so rigidly in position and can move past one another. In a gas, the molecules are separated by distances that are large compared with the size of the molecules.

The three states of matter can be interconverted without changing the composition of the substance. Upon heating, a solid (for example, ice) will melt to form a liquid (water). (The temperature at which this transition occurs is called the *melting point.*) Further heating will convert the liquid into a gas. (This conversion takes place at the *boiling point* of the liquid.) On the other hand, cooling a gas will cause it to condense into a liquid. When the liquid is cooled further, it will freeze into the solid form.

Figure 1.6 *Microscopic views of a solid, a liquid, and a gas.*

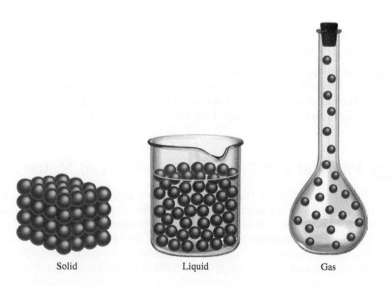

Solid   Liquid   Gas

10   **Chapter 1** ▪ Chemistry: The Study of Change

Figure 1.7 *The three states of matter. A hot poker changes ice into water and steam.*

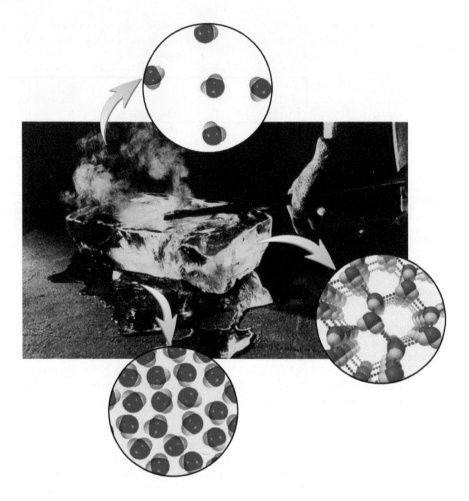

Figure 1.7 shows the three states of water. Note that the properties of water are unique among common substances in that the molecules in the liquid state are more closely packed than those in the solid state.

> ### Review of Concepts
> An ice cube is placed in a closed container. On heating, the ice cube first melts and the water then boils to form steam. Which of the following statements is true?
> (a) The physical appearance of the water is different at every stage of change.
> (b) The mass of water is greatest for the ice cube and least for the steam.

1.6 Physical and Chemical Properties of Matter

Substances are identified by their properties as well as by their composition. Color, melting point, and boiling point are physical properties. A ***physical property*** *can be measured and observed without changing the composition or identity of a substance.* For example, we can measure the melting point of ice by heating a block of ice and recording the temperature at which the ice is converted to water. Water differs from ice only in appearance, not in composition, so this is a physical change; we can freeze the water to recover the original ice. Therefore, the melting point of a substance is a physical property. Similarly, when we say that helium gas is lighter than air, we are referring to a physical property.

On the other hand, the statement "Hydrogen gas burns in oxygen gas to form water" describes a ***chemical property*** of hydrogen, because *to observe this property we must carry out a chemical change,* in this case burning. After the change, the original chemical substance, the hydrogen gas, will have vanished, and all that will be left is a different chemical substance—water. We *cannot* recover the hydrogen from the water by means of a physical change, such as boiling or freezing.

Every time we hard-boil an egg, we bring about a chemical change. When subjected to a temperature of about 100°C, the yolk and the egg white undergo changes that alter not only their physical appearance but their chemical makeup as well. When eaten, the egg is changed again, by substances in our bodies called *enzymes*. This digestive action is another example of a chemical change. What happens during digestion depends on the chemical properties of both the enzymes and the food.

All measurable properties of matter fall into one of two additional categories: extensive properties and intensive properties. The measured value of an ***extensive property*** *depends on how much matter is being considered.* ***Mass,*** which is *the quantity of matter in a given sample of a substance,* is an extensive property. More matter means more mass. Values of the same extensive property can be added together. For example, two copper pennies will have a combined mass that is the sum of the masses of each penny, and the length of two tennis courts is the sum of the lengths of each tennis court. ***Volume,*** defined as *length cubed,* is another extensive property. The value of an extensive quantity depends on the amount of matter.

The measured value of an ***intensive property*** *does not depend on how much matter is being considered.* ***Density,*** defined as *the mass of an object divided by its volume,* is an intensive property. So is temperature. Suppose that we have two beakers of water at the same temperature. If we combine them to make a single quantity of water in a larger beaker, the temperature of the larger quantity of water will be the same as it was in two separate beakers. Unlike mass, length, and volume, temperature and other intensive properties are not additive.

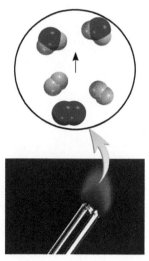

Hydrogen burning in air to form water.

Review of Concepts

The diagram in (a) shows a compound made up of atoms of two elements (represented by the green and red spheres) in the liquid state. Which of the diagrams in (b)–(d) represents a physical change and which diagrams represent a chemical change?

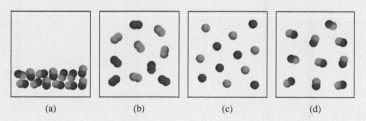

(a)   (b)   (c)   (d)

1.7 Measurement

The measurements chemists make are often used in calculations to obtain other related quantities. Different instruments enable us to measure a substance's properties: The meterstick measures length or scale; the buret, the pipet, the graduated cylinder, and

12   **Chapter 1** ▪ Chemistry: The Study of Change

the volumetric flask measure volume (Figure 1.8); the balance measures mass; the thermometer measures temperature. These instruments provide measurements of **macroscopic properties,** which *can be determined directly.* **Microscopic properties,** *on the atomic or molecular scale, must be determined by an indirect method,* as we will see in Chapter 2.

A measured quantity is usually written as a number with an appropriate unit. To say that the distance between New York and San Francisco by car along a certain route is 5166 is meaningless. We must specify that the distance is 5166 kilometers. The same is true in chemistry; units are essential to stating measurements correctly.

SI Units

For many years, scientists recorded measurements in *metric units,* which are related decimally, that is, by powers of 10. In 1960, however, the General Conference of Weights and Measures, the international authority on units, proposed a revised metric system called the **International System of Units** (abbreviated **SI,** from the French *Système Internationale d'Unites*). Table 1.2 shows the seven SI base units. All other units of measurement can be derived from these base units. Like metric units, SI units are modified in decimal fashion by a series of prefixes, as shown in Table 1.3. We will use both metric and SI units in this book.

Figure 1.8 *Some common measuring devices found in a chemistry laboratory. These devices are not drawn to scale relative to one another. We will discuss the uses of these measuring devices in Chapter 4.*

Volumetric flask   Graduated cylinder   Pipet   Buret

Table 1.2	SI Base Units	
Base Quantity	**Name of Unit**	**Symbol**
Length	meter	m
Mass	kilogram	kg
Time	second	s
Electrical current	ampere	A
Temperature	kelvin	K
Amount of substance	mole	mol
Luminous intensity	candela	cd

Note that a metric prefix simply represents a number:

$$1 \text{ mm} = 1 \times 10^{-3} \text{ m}$$

An astronaut jumping on the surface of the moon.

Table 1.3	Prefixes Used with SI Units			
Prefix	**Symbol**	**Meaning**		**Example**
tera-	T	1,000,000,000,000, or 10^{12}		1 terameter (Tm) = 1×10^{12} m
giga-	G	1,000,000,000, or 10^{9}		1 gigameter (Gm) = 1×10^{9} m
mega-	M	1,000,000, or 10^{6}		1 megameter (Mm) = 1×10^{6} m
kilo-	k	1,000, or 10^{3}		1 kilometer (km) = 1×10^{3} m
deci-	d	1/10, or 10^{-1}		1 decimeter (dm) = 0.1 m
centi-	c	1/100, or 10^{-2}		1 centimeter (cm) = 0.01 m
milli-	m	1/1,000, or 10^{-3}		1 millimeter (mm) = 0.001 m
micro-	μ	1/1,000,000, or 10^{-6}		1 micrometer (μm) = 1×10^{-6} m
nano-	n	1/1,000,000,000, or 10^{-9}		1 nanometer (nm) = 1×10^{-9} m
pico-	p	1/1,000,000,000,000, or 10^{-12}		1 picometer (pm) = 1×10^{-12} m
femto-	f	1/1,000,000,000,000,000, or 10^{-15}		1 femtometer (fm) = 1×10^{-15} m
atto-	a	1/1,000,000,000,000,000,000 or 10^{-18}		1 attometer (am) = 1×10^{-18} m

Measurements that we will utilize frequently in our study of chemistry include time, mass, volume, density, and temperature.

Mass and Weight

The terms "mass" and "weight" are often used interchangeably, although, strictly speaking, they are different quantities. Whereas mass is a measure of the amount of matter in an object, **weight,** technically speaking, is *the force that gravity exerts on an object.* An apple that falls from a tree is pulled downward by Earth's gravity. The mass of the apple is constant and does not depend on its location, but its weight does. For example, on the surface of the moon the apple would weigh only one-sixth what it does on Earth, because the moon's gravity is only one-sixth that of Earth. The moon's smaller gravity enabled astronauts to jump about rather freely on its surface despite their bulky suits and equipment. Chemists are interested primarily in mass, which can be determined readily with a balance; the process of measuring mass, oddly, is called *weighing.*

The SI unit of mass is the *kilogram* (kg). Unlike the units of length and time, which are based on natural processes that can be repeated by scientists anywhere, the kilogram is defined in terms of a particular object (Figure 1.9). In chemistry, however, the smaller *gram* (g) is more convenient:

$$1 \text{ kg} = 1000 \text{ g} = 1 \times 10^{3} \text{ g}$$

Figure 1.9 *The prototype kilogram is made of a platinum-iridium alloy. It is kept in a vault at the International Bureau of Weights and Measures in Sèvres, France. In 2007 it was discovered that the alloy has mysteriously lost about 50 μg!*

14   **Chapter 1** ▪ Chemistry: The Study of Change

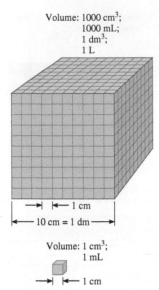

Figure 1.10 *Comparison of two volumes, 1 mL and 1000 mL.*

Volume

The SI unit of length is the *meter* (m), and the SI-derived unit for volume is the *cubic meter* (m³). Generally, however, chemists work with much smaller volumes, such as the cubic centimeter (cm³) and the cubic decimeter (dm³):

$$1 \text{ cm}^3 = (1 \times 10^{-2} \text{ m})^3 = 1 \times 10^{-6} \text{ m}^3$$
$$1 \text{ dm}^3 = (1 \times 10^{-1} \text{ m})^3 = 1 \times 10^{-3} \text{ m}^3$$

Another common unit of volume is the liter (L). A ***liter*** is *the volume occupied by one cubic decimeter.* One liter of volume is equal to 1000 milliliters (mL) or 1000 cm³:

$$1 \text{ L} = 1000 \text{ mL}$$
$$= 1000 \text{ cm}^3$$
$$= 1 \text{ dm}^3$$

and one milliliter is equal to one cubic centimeter:

$$1 \text{ mL} = 1 \text{ cm}^3$$

Figure 1.10 compares the relative sizes of two volumes. Even though the liter is not an SI unit, volumes are usually expressed in liters and milliliters.

Density

The equation for density is

$$\text{density} = \frac{\text{mass}}{\text{volume}}$$

or

$$d = \frac{m}{V} \tag{1.1}$$

where *d, m,* and *V* denote density, mass, and volume, respectively. Because density is an intensive property and does not depend on the quantity of mass present, for a given substance the ratio of mass to volume always remains the same; in other words, *V* increases as *m* does. Density usually decreases with temperature.

The SI-derived unit for density is the kilogram per cubic meter (kg/m³). This unit is awkwardly large for most chemical applications. Therefore, grams per cubic centimeter (g/cm³) and its equivalent, grams per milliliter (g/mL), are more commonly used for solid and liquid densities. Because gas densities are often very low, we express them in units of grams per liter (g/L):

$$1 \text{ g/cm}^3 = 1 \text{ g/mL} = 1000 \text{ kg/m}^3$$
$$1 \text{ g/L} = 0.001 \text{ g/mL}$$

Table 1.4 lists the densities of several substances.

Table 1.4	
Densities of Some Substances at 25°C	
Substance	**Density (g/cm³)**
Air*	0.001
Ethanol	0.79
Water	1.00
Graphite	2.2
Table salt	2.2
Aluminum	2.70
Diamond	3.5
Iron	7.9
Lead	11.3
Mercury	13.6
Gold	19.3
Osmium†	22.6

*Measured at 1 atmosphere.
†Osmium (Os) is the densest element known.

Examples 1.1 and 1.2 show density calculations.

Example 1.1

Gold is a precious metal that is chemically unreactive. It is used mainly in jewelry, dentistry, and electronic devices. A piece of gold ingot with a mass of 301 g has a volume of 15.6 cm^3. Calculate the density of gold.

Solution We are given the mass and volume and asked to calculate the density. Therefore, from Equation (1.1), we write

$$d = \frac{m}{V}$$
$$= \frac{301 \text{ g}}{15.6 \text{ cm}^3}$$
$$= 19.3 \text{ g/cm}^3$$

Practice Exercise A piece of platinum metal with a density of 21.5 g/cm^3 has a volume of 4.49 cm^3. What is its mass?

Gold bars and the solid-state arrangement of the gold atoms.

Similar problems: 1.21, 1.22.

Example 1.2

The density of mercury, the only metal that is a liquid at room temperature, is 13.6 g/mL. Calculate the mass of 5.50 mL of the liquid.

Solution We are given the density and volume of a liquid and asked to calculate the mass of the liquid. We rearrange Equation (1.1) to give

$$m = d \times V$$
$$= 13.6 \frac{\text{g}}{\text{mL}} \times 5.50 \text{ mL}$$
$$= 74.8 \text{ g}$$

Practice Exercise The density of sulfuric acid in a certain car battery is 1.41 g/mL. Calculate the mass of 242 mL of the liquid.

Mercury.

Similar problems: 1.21, 1.22.

Temperature Scales

Three temperature scales are currently in use. Their units are °F (degrees Fahrenheit), °C (degrees Celsius), and K (kelvin). The Fahrenheit scale, which is the most commonly used scale in the United States outside the laboratory, defines the normal freezing and boiling points of water to be exactly 32°F and 212°F, respectively. The Celsius scale divides the range between the freezing point (0°C) and boiling point (100°C) of water into 100 degrees. As Table 1.2 shows, the **kelvin** is *the SI base unit of temperature:* It is the *absolute* temperature scale. By absolute we mean that the zero on the Kelvin scale, denoted by 0 K, is the lowest temperature that can be attained theoretically. On the other hand, 0°F and 0°C are based on the behavior of an arbitrarily chosen substance, water. Figure 1.11 compares the three temperature scales.

The size of a degree on the Fahrenheit scale is only 100/180, or 5/9, of a degree on the Celsius scale. To convert degrees Fahrenheit to degrees Celsius, we write

Note that the Kelvin scale does not have the degree sign. Also, temperatures expressed in kelvins can never be negative.

$$?°C = (°F - 32°F) \times \frac{5°C}{9°F} \qquad (1.2)$$

16   **Chapter 1** ▪ Chemistry: The Study of Change

Figure 1.11 *Comparison of the three temperature scales: Celsius, and Fahrenheit, and the absolute (Kelvin) scales. Note that there are 100 divisions, or 100 degrees, between the freezing point and the boiling point of water on the Celsius scale, and there are 180 divisions, or 180 degrees, between the same two temperature limits on the Fahrenheit scale. The Celsius scale was formerly called the centigrade scale.*

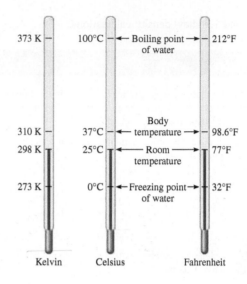

The following equation is used to convert degrees Celsius to degrees Fahrenheit:

$$?°F = \frac{9°F}{5°C} \times (°C) + 32°F \tag{1.3}$$

Both the Celsius and the Kelvin scales have units of equal magnitude; that is, one degree Celsius is equivalent to one kelvin. Experimental studies have shown that absolute zero on the Kelvin scale is equivalent to $-273.15°C$ on the Celsius scale. Thus, we can use the following equation to convert degrees Celsius to kelvin:

$$? K = (°C + 273.15°C) \frac{1 K}{1°C} \tag{1.4}$$

We will frequently find it necessary to convert between degrees Celsius and degrees Fahrenheit and between degrees Celsius and kelvin. Example 1.3 illustrates these conversions.

The Chemistry in Action essay on page 17 shows why we must be careful with units in scientific work.

Magnet suspended above superconductor cooled below its transition temperature by liquid nitrogen.

Example 1.3

(a) Below the transition temperature of $-141°C$, a certain substance becomes a superconductor; that is, it can conduct electricity with no resistance. What is the temperature in degrees Fahrenheit? (b) Helium has the lowest boiling point of all the elements at $-452°F$. Convert this temperature to degrees Celsius. (c) Mercury, the only metal that exists as a liquid at room temperature, melts at $-38.9°C$. Convert its melting point to kelvins.

Solution These three parts require that we carry out temperature conversions, so we need Equations (1.2), (1.3), and (1.4). Keep in mind that the lowest temperature on the Kelvin scale is zero (0 K); therefore, it can never be negative.

(a) This conversion is carried out by writing

$$\frac{9°F}{5°C} \times (-141°C) + 32°F = -222°F$$

(Continued)

CHEMISTRY *in Action*

The Importance of Units

In December 1998, NASA launched the 125-million dollar Mars Climate Orbiter, intended as the red planet's first weather satellite. After a 416-million mi journey, the spacecraft was supposed to go into Mars' orbit on September 23, 1999. Instead, it entered Mars' atmosphere about 100 km (62 mi) lower than planned and was destroyed by heat. The mission controllers said the loss of the spacecraft was due to the failure to convert English measurement units into metric units in the navigation software.

Engineers at Lockheed Martin Corporation who built the spacecraft specified its thrust in pounds, which is an English unit. Scientists at NASA's Jet Propulsion Laboratory, on the other hand, had assumed that thrust data they received were expressed in metric units, as newtons. Normally, pound is the unit for mass. Expressed as a unit for force, however, 1 lb is the force due to gravitational attraction on an object of that mass. To carry out the conversion between pound and newton, we start with 1 lb = 0.4536 kg and from Newton's second law of motion,

$$\begin{aligned} \text{force} &= \text{mass} \times \text{acceleration} \\ &= 0.4536 \text{ kg} \times 9.81 \text{ m/s}^2 \\ &= 4.45 \text{ kg m/s}^2 \\ &= 4.45 \text{ N} \end{aligned}$$

because 1 newton (N) = 1 kg m/s^2. Therefore, instead of converting 1 lb of force to 4.45 N, the scientists treated it as 1 N.

The considerably smaller engine thrust expressed in newtons resulted in a lower orbit and the ultimate destruction of the spacecraft. Commenting on the failure of the Mars mission, one scientist said: "This is going to be the cautionary tale that will be embedded into introduction to the metric system in elementary school, high school, and college science courses till the end of time."

Artist's conception of the Martian Climate Orbiter.

(b) Here we have

$$(-452°F - 32°F) \times \frac{5°C}{9°F} = -269°C$$

(c) The melting point of mercury in kelvins is given by

$$(-38.9°C + 273.15°C) \times \frac{1 \text{ K}}{1°C} = 234.3 \text{ K}$$

Similar problems: 1.24, 1.25, 1.26.

Practice Exercise Convert (a) 327.5°C (the melting point of lead) to degrees Fahrenheit; (b) 172.9°F (the boiling point of ethanol) to degrees Celsius; and (c) 77 K, the boiling point of liquid nitrogen, to degrees Celsius.

Review of Concepts
The density of copper is 8.94 g/cm³ at 20°C and 8.91 g/cm³ at 60°C. This density decrease is the result of which of the following?
  (a) The metal expands.
  (b) The metal contracts.
  (c) The mass of the metal increases.
  (d) The mass of the metal decreases.

1.8 Handling Numbers

Having surveyed some of the units used in chemistry, we now turn to techniques for handling numbers associated with measurements: scientific notation and significant figures.

Scientific Notation

Chemists often deal with numbers that are either extremely large or extremely small. For example, in 1 g of the element hydrogen there are roughly

$$602,200,000,000,000,000,000,000$$

hydrogen atoms. Each hydrogen atom has a mass of only

$$0.00000000000000000000000166 \text{ g}$$

These numbers are cumbersome to handle, and it is easy to make mistakes when using them in arithmetic computations. Consider the following multiplication:

$$0.0000000056 \times 0.00000000048 = 0.000000000000000002688$$

It would be easy for us to miss one zero or add one more zero after the decimal point. Consequently, when working with very large and very small numbers, we use a system called *scientific notation*. Regardless of their magnitude, all numbers can be expressed in the form

$$N \times 10^n$$

where N is a number between 1 and 10 and n, the exponent, is a positive or negative integer (whole number). Any number expressed in this way is said to be written in scientific notation.

Suppose that we are given a certain number and asked to express it in scientific notation. Basically, this assignment calls for us to find n. We count the number of places that the decimal point must be moved to give the number N (which is between 1 and 10). If the decimal point has to be moved to the left, then n is a positive integer; if it has to be moved to the right, n is a negative integer. The following examples illustrate the use of scientific notation:

  (1) Express 568.762 in scientific notation:

$$568.762 = 5.68762 \times 10^2$$

Note that the decimal point is moved to the left by two places and $n = 2$.

  (2) Express 0.00000772 in scientific notation:

$$0.00000772 = 7.72 \times 10^{-6}$$

Here the decimal point is moved to the right by six places and $n = -6$.

Keep in mind the following two points. First, $n = 0$ is used for numbers that are not expressed in scientific notation. For example, 74.6×10^0 ($n = 0$) is equivalent to 74.6. Second, the usual practice is to omit the superscript when $n = 1$. Thus, the scientific notation for 74.6 is 7.46×10 and not 7.46×10^1.

Next, we consider how scientific notation is handled in arithmetic operations.

Any number raised to the power zero is equal to one.

Addition and Subtraction

To add or subtract using scientific notation, we first write each quantity—say, N_1 and N_2—with the same exponent n. Then we combine N_1 and N_2; the exponents remain the same. Consider the following examples:

$$(7.4 \times 10^3) + (2.1 \times 10^3) = 9.5 \times 10^3$$
$$(4.31 \times 10^4) + (3.9 \times 10^3) = (4.31 \times 10^4) + (0.39 \times 10^4)$$
$$= 4.70 \times 10^4$$
$$(2.22 \times 10^{-2}) - (4.10 \times 10^{-3}) = (2.22 \times 10^{-2}) - (0.41 \times 10^{-2})$$
$$= 1.81 \times 10^{-2}$$

Multiplication and Division

To multiply numbers expressed in scientific notation, we multiply N_1 and N_2 in the usual way, but *add* the exponents together. To divide using scientific notation, we divide N_1 and N_2 as usual and subtract the exponents. The following examples show how these operations are performed:

$$(8.0 \times 10^4) \times (5.0 \times 10^2) = (8.0 \times 5.0)(10^{4+2})$$
$$= 40 \times 10^6$$
$$= 4.0 \times 10^7$$
$$(4.0 \times 10^{-5}) \times (7.0 \times 10^3) = (4.0 \times 7.0)(10^{-5+3})$$
$$= 28 \times 10^{-2}$$
$$= 2.8 \times 10^{-1}$$
$$\frac{6.9 \times 10^7}{3.0 \times 10^{-5}} = \frac{6.9}{3.0} \times 10^{7-(-5)}$$
$$= 2.3 \times 10^{12}$$
$$\frac{8.5 \times 10^4}{5.0 \times 10^9} = \frac{8.5}{5.0} \times 10^{4-9}$$
$$= 1.7 \times 10^{-5}$$

Significant Figures

Except when all the numbers involved are integers (for example, in counting the number of students in a class), it is often impossible to obtain the exact value of the quantity under investigation. For this reason, it is important to indicate the margin of error in a measurement by clearly indicating the number of *significant figures,* which are *the meaningful digits in a measured or calculated quantity.* When significant figures are used, the last digit is understood to be uncertain. For example, we might measure the volume of a given amount of liquid using a graduated cylinder with a scale that gives an uncertainty of 1 mL in the measurement. If the volume is found to be 6 mL, then the actual volume is in the range of 5 mL to 7 mL. We represent the volume of the liquid as (6 ± 1) mL. In this case, there is only one significant figure (the digit 6) that is uncertain by either plus or minus 1 mL. For greater accuracy, we might use a graduated cylinder that has finer divisions, so that the volume we measure is now uncertain by only 0.1 mL. If the volume of the liquid is now found to be 6.0 mL, we may express the quantity as (6.0 ± 0.1) mL, and the actual value is somewhere between 5.9 mL and 6.1 mL.

Figure 1.12 *A Fisher Scientific A-200DS Digital Recorder Precision Balance.*

We can further improve the measuring device and obtain more significant figures, but in every case, the last digit is always uncertain; the amount of this uncertainty depends on the particular measuring device we use.

Figure 1.12 shows a modern balance. Balances such as this one are available in many general chemistry laboratories; they readily measure the mass of objects to four decimal places. Therefore, the measured mass typically will have four significant figures (for example, 0.8642 g) or more (for example, 3.9745 g). Keeping track of the number of significant figures in a measurement such as mass ensures that calculations involving the data will reflect the precision of the measurement.

Guidelines for Using Significant Figures

We must always be careful in scientific work to write the proper number of significant figures. In general, it is fairly easy to determine how many significant figures a number has by following these rules:

1. Any digit that is not zero is significant. Thus, 845 cm has three significant figures, 1.234 kg has four significant figures, and so on.

2. Zeros between nonzero digits are significant. Thus, 606 m contains three significant figures, 40,501 kg contains five significant figures, and so on.

3. Zeros to the left of the first nonzero digit are not significant. Their purpose is to indicate the placement of the decimal point. For example, 0.08 L contains one significant figure, 0.0000349 g contains three significant figures, and so on.

4. If a number is greater than 1, then all the zeros written to the right of the decimal point count as significant figures. Thus, 2.0 mg has two significant figures, 40.062 mL has five significant figures, and 3.040 dm has four significant figures. If a number is less than 1, then only the zeros that are at the end of the number and the zeros that are between nonzero digits are significant. This means that 0.090 kg has two significant figures, 0.3005 L has four significant figures, 0.00420 min has three significant figures, and so on.

5. For numbers that do not contain decimal points, the trailing zeros (that is, zeros after the last nonzero digit) may or may not be significant. Thus, 400 cm may have one significant figure (the digit 4), two significant figures (40), or three significant figures (400). We cannot know which is correct without more information. By using scientific notation, however, we avoid this ambiguity. In this particular case, we can express the number 400 as 4×10^2 for one significant figure, 4.0×10^2 for two significant figures, or 4.00×10^2 for three significant figures.

Example 1.4 shows the determination of significant figures.

Example 1.4

Determine the number of significant figures in the following measurements: (a) 394 cm, (b) 5.03 g, (c) 0.714 m, (d) 0.052 kg, (e) 2.720×10^{22} atoms, (f) 3000 mL.

Solution (a) Three , because each digit is a nonzero digit. (b) Three , because zeros between nonzero digits are significant. (c) Three , because zeros to the left of the first nonzero digit do not count as significant figures. (d) Two . Same reason as in (c). (e) Four . Because the number is greater than one, all the zeros written to the right of the decimal point count as significant figures. (f) This is an ambiguous case. The number of significant figures may be four (3.000×10^3), three (3.00×10^3), two

(Continued)

(3.0×10^3), or one (3×10^3). This example illustrates why scientific notation must be used to show the proper number of significant figures.

Similar problems: 1.33, 1.34.

Practice Exercise Determine the number of significant figures in each of the following measurements: (a) 35 mL, (b) 2008 g, (c) 0.0580 m^3, (d) 7.2×10^4 molecules, (e) 830 kg.

A second set of rules specifies how to handle significant figures in calculations.

1. In addition and subtraction, the answer cannot have more digits to the right of the decimal point than either of the original numbers. Consider these examples:

$$
\begin{array}{r}
89.332 \\
+ \ 1.1 \\
\hline
90.432 \\
\end{array}
\quad\longleftarrow \text{ one digit after the decimal point}
$$
$$
90.432 \longleftarrow \text{ round off to } 90.4
$$

$$
\begin{array}{r}
2.097 \\
- \ 0.12 \\
\hline
1.977 \\
\end{array}
\quad\longleftarrow \text{ two digits after the decimal point}
$$
$$
1.977 \longleftarrow \text{ round off to } 1.98
$$

The rounding-off procedure is as follows. To round off a number at a certain point we simply drop the digits that follow if the first of them is less than 5. Thus, 8.724 rounds off to 8.72 if we want only two digits after the decimal point. If the first digit following the point of rounding off is equal to or greater than 5, we add 1 to the preceding digit. Thus, 8.727 rounds off to 8.73, and 0.425 rounds off to 0.43.

2. In multiplication and division, the number of significant figures in the final product or quotient is determined by the original number that has the *smallest* number of significant figures. The following examples illustrate this rule:

$$
2.8 \times 4.5039 = 12.61092 \longleftarrow \text{ round off to } 13
$$
$$
\frac{6.85}{112.04} = 0.0611388789 \longleftarrow \text{ round off to } 0.0611
$$

3. Keep in mind that *exact numbers* obtained from definitions or by counting numbers of objects can be considered to have an infinite number of significant figures. For example, the inch is defined to be exactly 2.54 centimeters; that is,

$$
1 \text{ in} = 2.54 \text{ cm}
$$

Thus, the "2.54" in the equation should not be interpreted as a measured number with three significant figures. In calculations involving conversion between "in" and "cm," we treat both "1" and "2.54" as having an infinite number of significant figures. Similarly, if an object has a mass of 5.0 g, then the mass of nine such objects is

$$
5.0 \text{ g} \times 9 = 45 \text{ g}
$$

The answer has two significant figures because 5.0 g has two significant figures. The number 9 is exact and does not determine the number of significant figures.

Example 1.5 shows how significant figures are handled in arithmetic operations.

Example 1.5

Carry out the following arithmetic operations to the correct number of significant figures: (a) 12,343.2 g + 0.1893 g, (b) 55.67 L − 2.386 L, (c) 7.52 m × 6.9232, (d) 0.0239 kg ÷ 46.5 mL, (e) 5.21×10^3 cm + 2.92×10^2 cm.

(Continued)

Solution In addition and subtraction, the number of decimal places in the answer is determined by the number having the lowest number of decimal places. In multiplication and division, the significant number of the answer is determined by the number having the smallest number of significant figures.

(a)   12,343.2 g
   +   0.1893 g
   ─────────────
      12,343.3893 g ◄──── round off to 12,343.4 g

(b)   55.67 L
   −   2.386 L
   ─────────────
      53.284 L ◄──── round off to 53.28 L

(c) 7.52 m × 6.9232 = 52.06246 m ◄──── round off to 52.1 m

(d) $\dfrac{0.0239 \text{ kg}}{46.5 \text{ mL}}$ = 0.0005139784946 kg/mL ◄──── round off to 0.000514 kg/mL
   or 5.14×10^{-4} kg/mL

(e) First we change 2.92×10^2 cm to 0.292×10^3 cm and then carry out the addition $(5.21 \text{ cm} + 0.292 \text{ cm}) \times 10^3$. Following the procedure in (a), we find the answer is 5.50×10^3 cm.

Practice Exercise Carry out the following arithmetic operations and round off the answers to the appropriate number of significant figures: (a) 26.5862 L + 0.17 L, (b) 9.1 g − 4.682 g, (c) 7.1×10^4 dm × 2.2654×10^2 dm, (d) 6.54 g ÷ 86.5542 mL, (e) $(7.55 \times 10^4 \text{ m}) - (8.62 \times 10^3 \text{ m})$.

Similar problems: 1.35, 1.36.

The preceding rounding-off procedure applies to one-step calculations. In *chain calculations,* that is, calculations involving more than one step, we can get a different answer depending on how we round off. Consider the following two-step calculations:

First step: A × B = C
Second step: C × D = E

Let's suppose that A = 3.66, B = 8.45, and D = 2.11. Depending on whether we round off C to three or four significant figures, we obtain a different number for E:

Method 1	**Method 2**
3.66 × 8.45 = 30.9	3.66 × 8.45 = 30.93
30.9 × 2.11 = 65.2	30.93 × 2.11 = 65.3

However, if we had carried out the calculation as 3.66 × 8.45 × 2.11 on a calculator without rounding off the intermediate answer, we would have obtained 65.3 as the answer for E. Although retaining an additional digit past the number of significant figures for intermediate steps helps to eliminate errors from rounding, this procedure is not necessary for most calculations because the difference between the answers is usually quite small. Therefore, for most examples and end-of-chapter problems where intermediate answers are reported, all answers, intermediate and final, will be rounded.

Accuracy and Precision

In discussing measurements and significant figures, it is useful to distinguish between *accuracy* and *precision.* **Accuracy** tells us *how close a measurement is to the true value of the quantity that was measured.* **Precision** refers to *how closely two or more measurements of the same quantity agree with one another* (Figure 1.13).

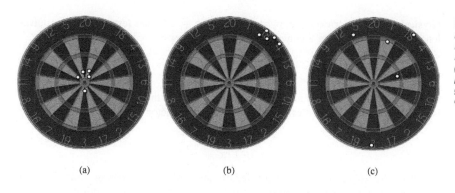

(a)   (b)   (c)

Figure 1.13 *The distribution of holes formed by darts on a dart board shows the difference between precise and accurate. (a) Good accuracy and good precision. (b) Poor accuracy and good precision. (c) Poor accuracy and poor precision.*

The difference between accuracy and precision is a subtle but important one. Suppose, for example, that three students are asked to determine the mass of a piece of copper wire. The results of two successive weighings by each student are

	Student A	Student B	Student C
	1.964 g	1.972 g	2.000 g
	1.978 g	1.968 g	2.002 g
Average value	1.971 g	1.970 g	2.001 g

The true mass of the wire is 2.000 g. Therefore, Student B's results are more *precise* than those of Student A (1.972 g and 1.968 g deviate less from 1.970 g than 1.964 g and 1.978 g from 1.971 g), but neither set of results is very *accurate*. Student C's results are not only the most *precise*, but also the most *accurate*, because the average value is closest to the true value. Highly accurate measurements are usually precise too. On the other hand, highly precise measurements do not necessarily guarantee accurate results. For example, an improperly calibrated meterstick or a faulty balance may give precise readings that are in error.

Review of Concepts

Give the length of the pencil with proper significant figures according to which ruler you use for the measurement.

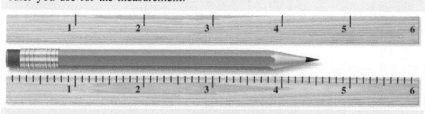

1.9 Dimensional Analysis in Solving Problems

Careful measurements and the proper use of significant figures, along with correct calculations, will yield accurate numerical results. But to be meaningful, the answers also must be expressed in the desired units. The procedure we use to convert between units in solving chemistry problems is called *dimensional analysis* (also called the *factor-label method*). A simple technique requiring little memorization, dimensional analysis is based on the relationship between different units that express the same physical quantity. For example, by definition 1 in = 2.54 cm (exactly). This equivalence enables us to write a conversion factor as follows:

$$\frac{1 \text{ in}}{2.54 \text{ cm}}$$

Because both the numerator and the denominator express the same length, this fraction is equal to 1. Similarly, we can write the conversion factor as

$$\frac{2.54 \text{ cm}}{1 \text{ in}}$$

which is also equal to 1. Conversion factors are useful for changing units. Thus, if we wish to convert a length expressed in inches to centimeters, we multiply the length by the appropriate conversion factor.

$$12.00 \text{ in} \times \frac{2.54 \text{ cm}}{1 \text{ in}} = 30.48 \text{ cm}$$

We choose the conversion factor that cancels the unit inches and produces the desired unit, centimeters. Note that the result is expressed in four significant figures because 2.54 is an exact number.

Next let us consider the conversion of 57.8 meters to centimeters. This problem can be expressed as

$$? \text{ cm} = 57.8 \text{ m}$$

By definition,

$$1 \text{ cm} = 1 \times 10^{-2} \text{ m}$$

Because we are converting "m" to "cm," we choose the conversion factor that has meters in the denominator,

$$\frac{1 \text{ cm}}{1 \times 10^{-2} \text{ m}}$$

and write the conversion as

$$? \text{ cm} = 57.8 \text{ m} \times \frac{1 \text{ cm}}{1 \times 10^{-2} \text{ m}}$$
$$= 5780 \text{ cm}$$
$$= 5.78 \times 10^3 \text{ cm}$$

Note that scientific notation is used to indicate that the answer has three significant figures. Again, the conversion factor 1 cm/1 $\times$ 10^{-2} m contains exact numbers; therefore, it does not affect the number of significant figures.

In general, to apply dimensional analysis we use the relationship

$$\text{given quantity} \times \text{conversion factor} = \text{desired quantity}$$

and the units cancel as follows:

Remember that the unit we want appears in the numerator and the unit we want to cancel appears in the denominator.

$$\text{given unit} \times \frac{\text{desired unit}}{\text{given unit}} = \text{desired unit}$$

In dimensional analysis, the units are carried through the entire sequence of calculations. Therefore, if the equation is set up correctly, then all the units will cancel except the desired one. If this is not the case, then an error must have been made somewhere, and it can usually be spotted by reviewing the solution.

A Note on Problem Solving

At this point you have been introduced to scientific notation, significant figures, and dimensional analysis, which will help you in solving numerical problems. Chemistry is an experimental science and many of the problems are quantitative in nature. The key to success in problem solving is practice. Just as a marathon runner cannot prepare for a race by simply reading books on running and a pianist cannot give a successful concert by only memorizing the musical score, you cannot be sure of your understanding of chemistry without solving problems. The following steps will help to improve your skill at solving numerical problems.

1. Read the question carefully. Understand the information that is given and what you are asked to solve. Frequently it is helpful to make a sketch that will help you to visualize the situation.

2. Find the appropriate equation that relates the given information and the unknown quantity. Sometimes solving a problem will involve more than one step, and you may be expected to look up quantities in tables that are not provided in the problem. Dimensional analysis is often needed to carry out conversions.

3. Check your answer for the correct sign, units, and significant figures.

4. A very important part of problem solving is being able to judge whether the answer is reasonable. It is relatively easy to spot a wrong sign or incorrect units. But if a number (say, 9) is incorrectly placed in the denominator instead of in the numerator, the answer would be too small even if the sign and units of the calculated quantity were correct.

5. One quick way to check the answer is to round off the numbers in the calculation in such a way so as to simplify the arithmetic. The answer you get will not be exact, but it will be close to the correct one.

Example 1.6

A person's average daily intake of glucose (a form of sugar) is 0.0833 pound (lb). What is this mass in milligrams (mg)? (1 lb = 453.6 g.)

Strategy The problem can be stated as

$$? \text{ mg} = 0.0833 \text{ lb}$$

The relationship between pounds and grams is given in the problem. This relationship will enable conversion from pounds to grams. A metric conversion is then needed to convert grams to milligrams (1 mg = 1×10^{-3} g). Arrange the appropriate conversion factors so that pounds and grams cancel and the unit milligrams is obtained in your answer.

Solution The sequence of conversions is

$$\text{pounds} \longrightarrow \text{grams} \longrightarrow \text{milligrams}$$

Using the following conversion factors

$$\frac{453.6 \text{ g}}{1 \text{ lb}} \quad \text{and} \quad \frac{1 \text{ mg}}{1 \times 10^{-3} \text{ g}}$$

(Continued)

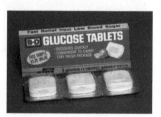

Glucose tablets can provide diabetics with a quick method for raising their blood sugar levels.

Conversion factors for some of the English system units commonly used in the United States for nonscientific measurements (for example, pounds and inches) are provided inside the back cover of this book.

we obtain the answer in one step:

$$? \, \text{mg} = 0.0833 \, \text{lb} \times \frac{453.6 \, \text{g}}{1 \, \text{lb}} \times \frac{1 \, \text{mg}}{1 \times 10^{-3} \, \text{g}} = 3.78 \times 10^4 \, \text{mg}$$

Check As an estimate, we note that 1 lb is roughly 500 g and that 1 g = 1000 mg. Therefore, 1 lb is roughly 5×10^5 mg. Rounding off 0.0833 lb to 0.1 lb, we get 5×10^4 mg, which is close to the preceding quantity.

Similar problem: 1.45.

Practice Exercise A roll of aluminum foil has a mass of 1.07 kg. What is its mass in pounds?

As Examples 1.7 and 1.8 illustrate, conversion factors can be squared or cubed in dimensional analysis.

A cryogenic storage tank for liquid helium.

Example 1.7

A liquid helium storage tank has a volume of 275 L. What is the volume in m^3?

Strategy The problem can be stated as

$$? \, m^3 = 275 \, \text{L}$$

How many conversion factors are needed for this problem? Recall that 1 L = 1000 cm^3 and 1 cm = 1×10^{-2} m.

Solution We need two conversion factors here: one to convert liters to cm^3 and one to convert centimeters to meters:

$$\frac{1000 \, cm^3}{1 \, \text{L}} \quad \text{and} \quad \frac{1 \times 10^{-2} \, m}{1 \, cm}$$

Because the second conversion deals with length (cm and m) and we want volume here, it must therefore be cubed to give

$$\frac{1 \times 10^{-2} \, m}{1 \, cm} \times \frac{1 \times 10^{-2} \, m}{1 \, cm} \times \frac{1 \times 10^{-2} \, m}{1 \, cm} = \left(\frac{1 \times 10^{-2} \, m}{1 \, cm} \right)^3$$

Remember that when a unit is raised to a power, any conversion factor you use must also be raised to that power.

This means that 1 cm^3 = 1×10^{-6} m^3. Now we can write

$$? \, m^3 = 275 \, \text{L} \times \frac{1000 \, cm^3}{1 \, \text{L}} \times \left(\frac{1 \times 10^{-2} \, m}{1 \, cm} \right)^3 = 0.275 \, m^3$$

Check From the preceding conversion factors you can show that 1 L = 1×10^{-3} m^3. Therefore, a 275-L storage tank would be equal to 275×10^{-3} m^3 or 0.275 m^3, which is the answer.

Similar problem: 1.50(d).

Practice Exercise The volume of a room is 1.08×10^8 dm^3. What is the volume in m^3?

Example 1.8

Liquid nitrogen is obtained from liquefied air and is used to prepare frozen goods and in low-temperature research. The density of the liquid at its boiling point ($-196°C$ or 77 K) is 0.808 g/cm^3. Convert the density to units of kg/m^3.

(Continued)

Strategy The problem can be stated as

$$? \, kg/m^3 = 0.808 \, g/cm^3$$

Two separate conversions are required for this problem: g $\longrightarrow$ kg and cm^3 $\longrightarrow$ m^3. Recall that 1 kg = 1000 g and 1 cm = 1×10^{-2} m.

Solution In Example 1.7 we saw that 1 cm^3 = 1×10^{-6} m^3. The conversion factors are

$$\frac{1 \, kg}{1000 \, g} \quad \text{and} \quad \frac{1 \, cm^3}{1 \times 10^{-6} \, m^3}$$

Finally,

$$? \, kg/m^3 = \frac{0.808 \, g}{1 \, cm^3} \times \frac{1 \, kg}{1000 \, g} \times \frac{1 \, cm^3}{1 \times 10^{-6} \, m^3} = 808 \, kg/m^3$$

Check Because 1 m^3 = 1×10^6 cm^3, we would expect much more mass in 1 m^3 than in 1 cm^3. Therefore, the answer is reasonable.

Practice Exercise The density of the lightest metal, lithium (Li), is 5.34×10^2 kg/m^3. Convert the density to g/cm^3.

Liquid nitrogen is used for frozen foods and low-temperature research.

Similar problem: 1.51.

Review of Concepts

The Food and Drug Administration recommends no more than 65 g of daily intake of fat. What is this mass in pounds? (1 lb = 453.6 g.)

1.10 Real-World Problem Solving: Information, Assumptions, and Simplifications

In chemistry, as in other scientific disciplines, it is not always possible to solve a numerical problem exactly. There are many reasons why this is the case. For example, our understanding of a situation is not complete or data are not fully available. In these cases, we must learn to make an intelligent guess. This approach is sometimes called "ball-park estimates," which are simple, quick calculations that can be done on the "back of an envelope." As you can imagine, in many cases the answers are only order-of-magnitude estimates.[†]

In most of the example problems that you have seen so far, as well as the questions given at the end of this and subsequent chapters, the necessary information is provided; however, in order to solve important real-world problems such as those related to medicine, energy, and agriculture, you must be able to determine what information is needed and where to find it. Much of the information you might need can be found in the various tables located throughout the text, and a list of tables and important figures is given on the inside back cover. In many cases, however, you will need to go to outside sources to find the information you need. Although the Internet is a fast way to find information, you must take care that the source is reliable and well referenced. One excellent source is the National Institute of Standards and Technology (NIST).

In order to know what information you need, you will first have to formulate a plan for solving the problem. In addition to the limitations of the theories used in science, typically assumptions are made in setting up and solving the problems based on those theories. These assumptions come at a price, however, as the accuracy of the answer is reduced with increasing simplifications of the problem, as illustrated in Example 1.9.

[†]An order of magnitude is a factor of 10.

Example 1.9

A modern pencil "lead" is actually composed primarily of graphite, a form of carbon. Estimate the mass of the graphite core in a standard No. 2 pencil before it is sharpened.

Strategy Assume that the pencil lead can be approximated as a cylinder. Measurement of a typical unsharpened pencil gives a length of about 18 cm (subtracting the length of the eraser head) and a diameter of roughly 2 mm for the lead. The volume of a cylinder V is given by $V = \pi r^2 l$, where r is the radius and l is the length. Assuming that the lead is pure graphite, you can calculate the mass of the lead from the volume using the density of graphite given in Table 1.4.

Solution Converting the diameter of the lead to units of cm gives

$$2 \text{ mm} \times \frac{1 \text{ cm}}{10 \text{ mm}} = 0.2 \text{ cm}$$

which, along with the length of the lead, gives

$$V = \pi \left(\frac{0.2 \text{ cm}}{2}\right)^2 \times 18 \text{ cm}$$
$$= 0.57 \text{ cm}^3$$

Rearranging Equation (1.1) gives

$$m = d \times V$$
$$= 2.2 \frac{\text{g}}{\text{cm}^3} \times 0.57 \text{ cm}^3$$
$$= 1 \text{ g}$$

Check Rounding off the values used to calculate the volume of the lead gives $3 \times (0.1 \text{ cm})^2 \times 20 \text{ cm} = 0.6 \text{ cm}^3$. Multiplying that volume by roughly 2 g/cm^3 gives around 1 g, which agrees with the value just calculated.

Practice Exercise Estimate the mass of air in a ping pong ball.

Similar problems: 1.105, 1.106, 1.114.

Considering Example 1.9, even if the dimensions of the pencil lead were measured with greater precision, the accuracy of the final answer would be limited by the assumptions made in modeling this problem. The pencil lead is actually a mixture of graphite and clay, where the relative amounts of the two materials determine the softness of the lead, so the density of the material is likely to be different than 2.2 g/cm^3. You could probably find a better value for the density of the mixture used to make No. 2 pencils, but it is not worth the effort in this case.

Key Equations

$d = \dfrac{m}{V}$ (1.1)	Equation for density
$?°C = (°F - 32°F) \times \dfrac{5°C}{9°F}$ (1.2)	Converting °F to °C
$?°F = \dfrac{9°F}{5°C} \times (°C) + 32°F$ (1.3)	Converting °C to °F
$? K = (°C + 273.15°C) \dfrac{1 \text{ K}}{1°C}$ (1.4)	Converting °C to K

Summary of Facts & Concepts

1. The study of chemistry involves three basic steps: observation, representation, and interpretation. Observation refers to measurements in the macroscopic world; representation involves the use of shorthand notation symbols and equations for communication; interpretations are based on atoms and molecules, which belong to the microscopic world.

2. The scientific method is a systematic approach to research that begins with the gathering of information through observation and measurements. In the process, hypotheses, laws, and theories are devised and tested.

3. Chemists study matter and the changes it undergoes. The substances that make up matter have unique physical properties that can be observed without changing their identity and unique chemical properties that, when they are demonstrated, do change the identity of the

substances. Mixtures, whether homogeneous or heterogeneous, can be separated into pure components by physical means.

4. The simplest substances in chemistry are elements. Compounds are formed by the chemical combination of atoms of different elements in fixed proportions.

5. All substances, in principle, can exist in three states: solid, liquid, and gas. The interconversion between these states can be effected by changing the temperature.

6. SI units are used to express physical quantities in all sciences, including chemistry.

7. Numbers expressed in scientific notation have the form $N \times 10^n$, where N is between 1 and 10, and n is a positive or negative integer. Scientific notation helps us handle very large and very small quantities.

Key Words

Accuracy, p. 22
Chemical property, p. 11
Chemistry, p. 2
Compound, p. 8
Density, p. 11
Element, p. 7
Extensive property, p. 11
Heterogeneous mixture, p. 7

Homogeneous mixture, p. 7
Hypothesis, p. 4
Intensive property, p. 11
International System of Units (SI), p. 12
Kelvin, p. 15
Law, p. 4
Liter, p. 14

Macroscopic property, p. 12
Mass, p. 11
Matter, p. 6
Microscopic property, p. 12
Mixture, p. 7
Physical property, p. 10
Precision, p. 22
Qualitative, p. 4

Quantitative, p. 4
Scientific method, p. 4
Significant figures, p. 19
Substance, p. 7
Theory, p. 5
Volume, p. 11
Weight, p. 13

Questions & Problems

Problems available in Connect Plus
Red numbered problems solved in Student Solutions Manual

The Scientific Method
Review Questions

1.1   Explain what is meant by the scientific method.
1.2   What is the difference between qualitative data and quantitative data?

Problems

1.3   Classify the following as qualitative or quantitative statements, giving your reasons. (a) The sun is approximately 93 million mi from Earth. (b) Leonardo da Vinci was a better painter than Michelangelo. (c) Ice is less dense than water. (d) Butter tastes better than margarine. (e) A stitch in time saves nine.

● 1.4   Classify each of the following statements as a hypothesis, a law, or a theory. (a) Beethoven's contribution

to music would have been much greater if he had married. (b) An autumn leaf gravitates toward the ground because there is an attractive force between the leaf and Earth. (c) All matter is composed of very small particles called atoms.

Classification and Properties of Matter
Review Questions

1.5   Give an example for each of the following terms: (a) matter, (b) substance, (c) mixture.

● 1.6   Give an example of a homogeneous mixture and an example of a heterogeneous mixture.

1.7   Using examples, explain the difference between a physical property and a chemical property.

1.8   How does an intensive property differ from an extensive property? Which of the following properties are intensive and which are extensive? (a) length, (b) volume, (c) temperature, (d) mass.

1.9   Give an example of an element and a compound. How do elements and compounds differ?

1.10   What is the number of known elements?

Problems

1.11   Do the following statements describe chemical or physical properties? (a) Oxygen gas supports combustion. (b) Fertilizers help to increase agricultural production. (c) Water boils below 100°C on top of a mountain. (d) Lead is denser than aluminum. (e) Uranium is a radioactive element.

1.12   Does each of the following describe a physical change or a chemical change? (a) The helium gas inside a balloon tends to leak out after a few hours. (b) A flashlight beam slowly gets dimmer and finally goes out. (c) Frozen orange juice is reconstituted by adding water to it. (d) The growth of plants depends on the sun's energy in a process called photosynthesis. (e) A spoonful of table salt dissolves in a bowl of soup.

1.13   Give the names of the elements represented by the chemical symbols Li, F, P, Cu, As, Zn, Cl, Pt, Mg, U, Al, Si, Ne. (See Table 1.1 and the inside front cover.)

1.14   Give the chemical symbols for the following elements: (a) cesium, (b) germanium, (c) gallium, (d) strontium, (e) uranium, (f) selenium, (g) neon, (h) cadmium. (See Table 1.1 and the inside front cover.)

1.15   Classify each of the following substances as an element or a compound: (a) hydrogen, (b) water, (c) gold, (d) sugar.

1.16   Classify each of the following as an element, a compound, a homogeneous mixture, or a heterogeneous mixture: (a) water from a well, (b) argon gas, (c) sucrose, (d) a bottle of red wine, (e) chicken noodle soup, (f) blood flowing in a capillary, (g) ozone.

Measurement
Review Questions

1.17   Name the SI base units that are important in chemistry. Give the SI units for expressing the following: (a) length, (b) volume, (c) mass, (d) time, (e) energy, (f) temperature.

1.18   Write the numbers represented by the following prefixes: (a) mega-, (b) kilo-, (c) deci-, (d) centi-, (e) milli-, (f) micro-, (g) nano-, (h) pico-.

1.19   What units do chemists normally use for density of liquids and solids? For gas density? Explain the differences.

1.20   Describe the three temperature scales used in the laboratory and in everyday life: the Fahrenheit scale, the Celsius scale, and the Kelvin scale.

Problems

1.21   Bromine is a reddish-brown liquid. Calculate its density (in g/mL) if 586 g of the substance occupies 188 mL.

1.22   The density of methanol, a colorless organic liquid used as solvent, is 0.7918 g/mL. Calculate the mass of 89.9 mL of the liquid.

1.23   Convert the following temperatures to degrees Celsius or Fahrenheit: (a) 95°F, the temperature on a hot summer day; (b) 12°F, the temperature on a cold winter day; (c) a 102°F fever; (d) a furnace operating at 1852°F; (e) −273.15°C (theoretically the lowest attainable temperature).

1.24   (a) Normally the human body can endure a temperature of 105°F for only short periods of time without permanent damage to the brain and other vital organs. What is this temperature in degrees Celsius? (b) Ethylene glycol is a liquid organic compound that is used as an antifreeze in car radiators. It freezes at −11.5°C. Calculate its freezing temperature in degrees Fahrenheit. (c) The temperature on the surface of the sun is about 6300°C. What is this temperature in degrees Fahrenheit? (d) The ignition temperature of paper is 451°F. What is the temperature in degrees Celsius?

1.25   Convert the following temperatures to kelvin: (a) 113°C, the melting point of sulfur, (b) 37°C, the normal body temperature, (c) 357°C, the boiling point of mercury.

1.26   Convert the following temperatures to degrees Celsius: (a) 77 K, the boiling point of liquid nitrogen, (b) 4.2 K, the boiling point of liquid helium, (c) 601 K, the melting point of lead.

Handling Numbers
Review Questions

1.27   What is the advantage of using scientific notation over decimal notation?

1.28   Define significant figure. Discuss the importance of using the proper number of significant figures in measurements and calculations.

Problems

1.29   Express the following numbers in scientific notation: (a) 0.000000027, (b) 356, (c) 47,764, (d) 0.096.

1.30   Express the following numbers as decimals: (a) 1.52×10^{-2}, (b) 7.78×10^{-8}.

1.31   Express the answers to the following calculations in scientific notation:
(a) $145.75 + (2.3 \times 10^{-1})$
(b) $79,500 \div (2.5 \times 10^2)$
(c) $(7.0 \times 10^{-3}) - (8.0 \times 10^{-4})$
(d) $(1.0 \times 10^4) \times (9.9 \times 10^6)$

1.32 Express the answers to the following calculations in scientific notation:

(a) $0.0095 + (8.5 \times 10^{-3})$

(b) $653 \div (5.75 \times 10^{-8})$

(c) $850{,}000 - (9.0 \times 10^{5})$

(d) $(3.6 \times 10^{-4}) \times (3.6 \times 10^{6})$

1.33 What is the number of significant figures in each of the following measurements?

(a) 4867 mi

(b) 56 mL

(c) 60,104 tons

(d) 2900 g

(e) 40.2 g/cm^3

(f) 0.0000003 cm

(g) 0.7 min

(h) 4.6×10^{19} atoms

1.34 How many significant figures are there in each of the following? (a) 0.006 L, (b) 0.0605 dm, (c) 60.5 mg, (d) 605.5 cm^2, (e) 960×10^{-3} g, (f) 6 kg, (g) 60 m.

1.35 Carry out the following operations as if they were calculations of experimental results, and express each answer in the correct units with the correct number of significant figures:

(a) 5.6792 m + 0.6 m + 4.33 m

(b) 3.70 g − 2.9133 g

(c) 4.51 cm × 3.6666 cm

(d) $(3 \times 10^{4}$ g $+ 6.827$ g$)/(0.043$ cm$^3 - 0.021$ cm$^3)$

1.36 Carry out the following operations as if they were calculations of experimental results, and express each answer in the correct units with the correct number of significant figures:

(a) 7.310 km ÷ 5.70 km

(b) $(3.26 \times 10^{-3}$ mg$) - (7.88 \times 10^{-5}$ mg$)$

(c) $(4.02 \times 10^{6}$ dm$) + (7.74 \times 10^{7}$ dm$)$

(d) $(7.8$ m $- 0.34$ m$)/(1.15$ s $+ 0.82$ s$)$

1.37 Three students (A, B, and C) are asked to determine the volume of a sample of ethanol. Each student measures the volume three times with a graduated cylinder. The results in milliliters are: A (87.1, 88.2, 87.6); B (86.9, 87.1, 87.2); C (87.6, 87.8, 87.9). The true volume is 87.0 mL. Comment on the precision and the accuracy of each student's results.

1.38 Three apprentice tailors (X, Y, and Z) are assigned the task of measuring the seam of a pair of trousers. Each one makes three measurements. The results in inches are X (31.5, 31.6, 31.4); Y (32.8, 32.3, 32.7); Z (31.9, 32.2, 32.1). The true length is 32.0 in. Comment on the precision and the accuracy of each tailor's measurements.

Dimensional Analysis

Problems

1.39 Carry out the following conversions: (a) 22.6 m to decimeters, (b) 25.4 mg to kilograms, (c) 556 mL to liters, (d) 10.6 kg/m^3 to g/cm^3.

1.40 Carry out the following conversions: (a) 242 lb to milligrams, (b) 68.3 cm^3 to cubic meters, (c) 7.2 m^3 to liters, (d) 28.3 μg to pounds.

1.41 The average speed of helium at 25°C is 1255 m/s. Convert this speed to miles per hour (mph).

1.42 How many seconds are there in a solar year (365.24 days)?

1.43 How many minutes does it take light from the sun to reach Earth? (The distance from the sun to Earth is 93 million mi; the speed of light = 3.00×10^{8} m/s.)

1.44 A jogger runs a mile in 8.92 min. Calculate the speed in (a) in/s, (b) m/min, (c) km/h. (1 mi = 1609 m; 1 in = 2.54 cm.)

1.45 A 6.0-ft person weighs 168 lb. Express this person's height in meters and weight in kilograms. (1 lb = 453.6 g; 1 m = 3.28 ft.)

1.46 The speed limit on parts of the German autobahn was once set at 286 kilometers per hour (km/h). Calculate the speed limit in miles per hour (mph).

1.47 For a fighter jet to take off from the deck of an aircraft carrier, it must reach a speed of 62 m/s. Calculate the speed in miles per hour (mph).

1.48 The "normal" lead content in human blood is about 0.40 part per million (that is, 0.40 g of lead per million grams of blood). A value of 0.80 part per million (ppm) is considered to be dangerous. How many grams of lead are contained in 6.0×10^{3} g of blood (the amount in an average adult) if the lead content is 0.62 ppm?

1.49 Carry out the following conversions: (a) 1.42 light-years to miles (a light-year is an astronomical measure of distance—the distance traveled by light in a year, or 365 days; the speed of light is 3.00×10^{8} m/s). (b) 32.4 yd to centimeters. (c) 3.0×10^{10} cm/s to ft/s.

1.50 Carry out the following conversions: (a) 70 kg, the average weight of a male adult, to pounds. (b) 14 billion years (roughly the age of the universe) to seconds. (Assume there are 365 days in a year.) (c) 7 ft 6 in, the height of the basketball player Yao Ming, to meters. (d) 88.6 m^3 to liters.

1.51 Aluminum is a lightweight metal (density = 2.70 g/cm^3) used in aircraft construction, high-voltage transmission lines, beverage cans, and foils. What is its density in kg/m^3?

1.52 Ammonia gas is used as a refrigerant in large-scale cooling systems. The density of ammonia gas under certain conditions is 0.625 g/L. Calculate its density in g/cm^3.

32   **Chapter 1** ▪ Chemistry: The Study of Change

Additional Problems

1.53   Give one qualitative and one quantitative statement about each of the following: (a) water, (b) carbon, (c) iron, (d) hydrogen gas, (e) sucrose (cane sugar), (f) table salt (sodium chloride), (g) mercury, (h) gold, (i) air.

● 1.54   Which of the following statements describe physical properties and which describe chemical properties? (a) Iron has a tendency to rust. (b) Rainwater in industrialized regions tends to be acidic. (c) Hemoglobin molecules have a red color. (d) When a glass of water is left out in the sun, the water gradually disappears. (e) Carbon dioxide in air is converted to more complex molecules by plants during photosynthesis.

1.55   In 2008, about 95.0 billion lb of sulfuric acid were produced in the United States. Convert this quantity to tons.

● 1.56   In determining the density of a rectangular metal bar, a student made the following measurements: length, 8.53 cm; width, 2.4 cm; height, 1.0 cm; mass, 52.7064 g. Calculate the density of the metal to the correct number of significant figures.

● 1.57   Calculate the mass of each of the following: (a) a sphere of gold with a radius of 10.0 cm [the volume of a sphere with a radius r is $V = (4/3)\pi r^3$; the density of gold = 19.3 g/cm^3], (b) a cube of platinum of edge length 0.040 mm (the density of platinum = 21.4 g/cm^3), (c) 50.0 mL of ethanol (the density of ethanol = 0.798 g/mL).

● 1.58   A cylindrical glass bottle 21.5 cm in length is filled with cooking oil of density 0.953 g/mL. If the mass of the oil needed to fill the bottle is 1360 g, calculate the inner diameter of the bottle.

● 1.59   The following procedure was used to determine the volume of a flask. The flask was weighed dry and then filled with water. If the masses of the empty flask and filled flask were 56.12 g and 87.39 g, respectively, and the density of water is 0.9976 g/cm^3, calculate the volume of the flask in cm^3.

1.60   The speed of sound in air at room temperature is about 343 m/s. Calculate this speed in miles per hour. (1 mi = 1609 m.)

● 1.61   A piece of silver (Ag) metal weighing 194.3 g is placed in a graduated cylinder containing 242.0 mL of water. The volume of water now reads 260.5 mL. From these data calculate the density of silver.

1.62   The experiment described in Problem 1.61 is a crude but convenient way to determine the density of some solids. Describe a similar experiment that would enable you to measure the density of ice. Specifically, what would be the requirements for the liquid used in your experiment?

● 1.63   A lead sphere of diameter 48.6 cm has a mass of 6.852×10^5 g. Calculate the density of lead.

● 1.64   Lithium is the least dense metal known (density: 0.53 g/cm^3). What is the volume occupied by 1.20×10^3 g of lithium?

● 1.65   The medicinal thermometer commonly used in homes can be read ±0.1°F, whereas those in the doctor's office may be accurate to ±0.1°C. In degrees Celsius, express the percent error expected from each of these thermometers in measuring a person's body temperature of 38.9°C.

● 1.66   Vanillin (used to flavor vanilla ice cream and other foods) is the substance whose aroma the human nose detects in the smallest amount. The threshold limit is 2.0×10^{-11} g per liter of air. If the current price of 50 g of vanillin is $112, determine the cost to supply enough vanillin so that the aroma could be detected in a large aircraft hangar with a volume of 5.0×10^7 ft^3.

● 1.67   At what temperature does the numerical reading on a Celsius thermometer equal that on a Fahrenheit thermometer?

● 1.68   Suppose that a new temperature scale has been devised on which the melting point of ethanol (−117.3°C) and the boiling point of ethanol (78.3°C) are taken as 0°S and 100°S, respectively, where S is the symbol for the new temperature scale. Derive an equation relating a reading on this scale to a reading on the Celsius scale. What would this thermometer read at 25°C?

● 1.69   A resting adult requires about 240 mL of pure oxygen/min and breathes about 12 times every minute. If inhaled air contains 20 percent oxygen by volume and exhaled air 16 percent, what is the volume of air per breath? (Assume that the volume of inhaled air is equal to that of exhaled air.)

● 1.70   (a) Referring to Problem 1.69, calculate the total volume (in liters) of air an adult breathes in a day. (b) In a city with heavy traffic, the air contains 2.1×10^{-6} L of carbon monoxide (a poisonous gas) per liter. Calculate the average daily intake of carbon monoxide in liters by a person.

● 1.71   Three different 25.0-g samples of solid pellets are added to 20.0 mL of water in three different measuring cylinders. The results are shown here. Given the densities of the three metals used, identify the cylinder that contains each sample of solid pellets: A (2.9 g/cm^3), B (8.3 g/cm^3), and C (3.3 g/cm^3).

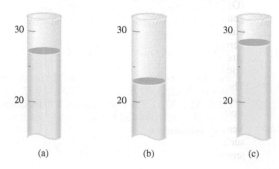

     (a)   (b)   (c)

1.72 The circumference of an NBA-approved basketball is 29.6 in. Given that the radius of Earth is about 6400 km, how many basketballs would it take to circle around the equator with the basketballs touching one another? Round off your answer to an integer with three significant figures.

1.73 A student is given a crucible and asked to prove whether it is made of pure platinum. She first weighs the crucible in air and then weighs it suspended in water (density = 0.9986 g/mL). The readings are 860.2 g and 820.2 g, respectively. Based on these measurements and given that the density of platinum is 21.45 g/cm^3, what should her conclusion be? (*Hint:* An object suspended in a fluid is buoyed up by the mass of the fluid displaced by the object. Neglect the buoyance of air.)

1.74 The surface area and average depth of the Pacific Ocean are 1.8×10^8 km^2 and 3.9×10^3 m, respectively. Calculate the volume of water in the ocean in liters.

1.75 The unit "troy ounce" is often used for precious metals such as gold (Au) and platinum (Pt). (1 troy ounce = 31.103 g.) (a) A gold coin weighs 2.41 troy ounces. Calculate its mass in grams. (b) Is a troy ounce heavier or lighter than an ounce? (1 lb = 16 oz; 1 lb = 453.6 g.)

1.76 Osmium (Os) is the densest element known (density = 22.57 g/cm^3). Calculate the mass in pounds and in kilograms of an Os sphere 15 cm in diameter (about the size of a grapefruit). See Problem 1.57 for volume of a sphere.

1.77 Percent error is often expressed as the absolute value of the difference between the true value and the experimental value, divided by the true value:

$$\text{percent error} = \frac{|\text{true value} - \text{experimental value}|}{|\text{true value}|} \times 100\%$$

The vertical lines indicate absolute value. Calculate the percent error for the following measurements: (a) The density of alcohol (ethanol) is found to be 0.802 g/mL. (True value: 0.798 g/mL.) (b) The mass of gold in an earring is analyzed to be 0.837 g. (True value: 0.864 g.)

1.78 The natural abundances of elements in the human body, expressed as percent by mass, are: oxygen (O), 65 percent; carbon (C), 18 percent; hydrogen (H), 10 percent; nitrogen (N), 3 percent; calcium (Ca), 1.6 percent; phosphorus (P), 1.2 percent; all other elements, 1.2 percent. Calculate the mass in grams of each element in the body of a 62-kg person.

1.79 The men's world record for running a mile outdoors (as of 1999) is 3 min 43.13 s. At this rate, how long would it take to run a 1500-m race? (1 mi = 1609 m.)

1.80 Venus, the second closest planet to the sun, has a surface temperature of 7.3×10^2 K. Convert this temperature to °C and °F.

1.81 Chalcopyrite, the principal ore of copper (Cu), contains 34.63 percent Cu by mass. How many grams of Cu can be obtained from 5.11×10^3 kg of the ore?

1.82 It has been estimated that 8.0×10^4 tons of gold (Au) have been mined. Assume gold costs $948 per ounce. What is the total worth of this quantity of gold?

1.83 A 1.0-mL volume of seawater contains about 4.0×10^{-12} g of gold. The total volume of ocean water is 1.5×10^{21} L. Calculate the total amount of gold (in grams) that is present in seawater, and the worth of the gold in dollars (see Problem 1.82). With so much gold out there, why hasn't someone become rich by mining gold from the ocean?

1.84 Measurements show that 1.0 g of iron (Fe) contains 1.1×10^{22} Fe atoms. How many Fe atoms are in 4.9 g of Fe, which is the total amount of iron in the body of an average adult?

1.85 The thin outer layer of Earth, called the crust, contains only 0.50 percent of Earth's total mass and yet is the source of almost all the elements (the atmosphere provides elements such as oxygen, nitrogen, and a few other gases). Silicon (Si) is the second most abundant element in Earth's crust (27.2 percent by mass). Calculate the mass of silicon in kilograms in Earth's crust. (The mass of Earth is 5.9×10^{21} tons. 1 ton = 2000 lb; 1 lb = 453.6 g.)

1.86 The radius of a copper (Cu) atom is roughly 1.3×10^{-10} m. How many times can you divide evenly a piece of 10-cm copper wire until it is reduced to two separate copper atoms? (Assume there are appropriate tools for this procedure and that copper atoms are lined up in a straight line, in contact with each other. Round off your answer to an integer.)

1.87 One gallon of gasoline in an automobile's engine produces on the average 9.5 kg of carbon dioxide, which is a greenhouse gas, that is, it promotes the warming of Earth's atmosphere. Calculate the annual production of carbon dioxide in kilograms if there are 250 million cars in the United States and each car covers a distance of 5000 mi at a consumption rate of 20 miles per gallon.

1.88 A sheet of aluminum (Al) foil has a total area of 1.000 ft^2 and a mass of 3.636 g. What is the thickness of the foil in millimeters? (Density of Al = 2.699 g/cm^3.)

1.89 Comment on whether each of the following is a homogeneous mixture or a heterogeneous mixture: (a) air in a closed bottle and (b) air over New York City.

1.90 Chlorine is used to disinfect swimming pools. The accepted concentration for this purpose is 1 ppm chlorine, or 1 g of chlorine per million grams of water. Calculate the volume of a chlorine solution (in milliliters) a homeowner should add to her swimming pool if the solution contains 6.0 percent chlorine by mass and there are 2.0×10^4 gallons of water in the pool. (1 gallon = 3.79 L; density of liquids = 1.0 g/mL.)

• 1.91 An aluminum cylinder is 10.0 cm in length and has a radius of 0.25 cm. If the mass of a single Al atom is 4.48×10^{-23} g, calculate the number of Al atoms present in the cylinder. The density of aluminum is 2.70 g/cm^3.

• 1.92 A pycnometer is a device for measuring the density of liquids. It is a glass flask with a close-fitting ground glass stopper having a capillary hole through it. (a) The volume of the pycnometer is determined by using distilled water at 20°C with a known density of 0.99820 g/mL. First, the water is filled to the rim. With the stopper in place, the fine hole allows the excess liquid to escape. The pycnometer is then carefully dried with filter paper. Given that the masses of the empty pycnometer and the same one filled with water are 32.0764 g and 43.1195 g, respectively, calculate the volume of the pycnometer. (b) If the mass of the pycnometer filled with ethanol at 20°C is 40.8051 g, calculate the density of ethanol. (c) Pycnometers can also be used to measure the density of solids. First, small zinc granules weighing 22.8476 g are placed in the pycnometer, which is then filled with water. If the combined mass of the pycnometer plus the zinc granules and water is 62.7728 g, what is the density of zinc?

• 1.93 In 1849 a gold prospector in California collected a bag of gold nuggets plus sand. Given that the density of gold and sand are 19.3 g/cm^3 and 2.95 g/cm^3, respectively, and that the density of the mixture is 4.17 g/cm^3, calculate the percent by mass of gold in the mixture.

• 1.94 The average time it takes for a molecule to diffuse a distance of x cm is given by

$$t = \frac{x^2}{2D}$$

where t is the time in seconds and D is the diffusion coefficient. Given that the diffusion coefficient of glucose is 5.7×10^{-7} cm^2/s, calculate the time it would take for a glucose molecule to diffuse 10 μm, which is roughly the size of a cell.

• 1.95 A human brain weighs about 1 kg and contains about 10^{11} cells. Assuming that each cell is completely filled with water (density = 1 g/mL), calculate the length of one side of such a cell if it were a cube. If the cells are spread out in a thin layer that is a single cell thick, what is the surface area in square meters?

• 1.96 (a) Carbon monoxide (CO) is a poisonous gas because it binds very strongly to the oxygen carrier hemoglobin in blood. A concentration of 8.00×10^2 ppm by volume of carbon monoxide is considered lethal to humans. Calculate the volume in liters occupied by carbon monoxide in a room that measures 17.6 m long, 8.80 m wide, and 2.64 m high at this concentration. (b) Prolonged exposure to mercury (Hg) vapor can cause neurological disorders and respiratory problems. For safe air quality control, the concentration of mercury vapor must be under 0.050 mg/m^3. Convert this number to g/L. (c) The general test for type II diabetes is that the blood sugar (glucose) level should be below 120 mg per deciliter (mg/dL). Convert this number to micrograms per milliliter (μg/mL).

1.97 A bank teller is asked to assemble "one-dollar" sets of coins for his clients. Each set is made of three quarters, one nickel, and two dimes. The masses of the coins are: quarter: 5.645 g; nickel: 4.967 g; dime: 2.316 g. What is the maximum number of sets that can be assembled from 33.871 kg of quarters, 10.432 kg of nickels, and 7.990 kg of dimes? What is the total mass (in g) of the assembled sets of coins?

• 1.98 A graduated cylinder is filled to the 40.00-mL mark with a mineral oil. The masses of the cylinder before and after the addition of the mineral oil are 124.966 g and 159.446 g, respectively. In a separate experiment, a metal ball bearing of mass 18.713 g is placed in the cylinder and the cylinder is again filled to the 40.00-mL mark with the mineral oil. The combined mass of the ball bearing and mineral oil is 50.952 g. Calculate the density and radius of the ball bearing. [The volume of a sphere of radius r is $(4/3)\pi r^3$.]

1.99 A chemist in the nineteenth century prepared an unknown substance. In general, do you think it would be more difficult to prove that it is an element or a compound? Explain.

• 1.100 Bronze is an alloy made of copper (Cu) and tin (Sn) used in applications that require low metal-on-metal friction. Calculate the mass of a bronze cylinder of radius 6.44 cm and length 44.37 cm. The composition of the bronze is 79.42 percent Cu and 20.58 percent Sn and the densities of Cu and Sn are 8.94 g/cm^3 and 7.31 g/cm^3, respectively. What assumption should you make in this calculation?

1.101 You are given a liquid. Briefly describe steps you would take to show whether it is a pure substance or a homogeneous mixture.

1.102 A chemist mixes two liquids A and B to form a homogeneous mixture. The densities of the liquids are 2.0514 g/mL for A and 2.6678 g/mL for B. When she drops a small object into the mixture, she finds that the object becomes suspended in the liquid; that is, it neither sinks nor floats. If the mixture is made of 41.37 percent A and 58.63 percent B by volume, what is the density of the metal? Can this procedure be used in general to determine the densities of solids? What assumptions must be made in applying this method?

1.103 Tums is a popular remedy for acid indigestion. A typical Tums tablet contains calcium carbonate plus some inert substances. When ingested, it reacts with the gastric juice (hydrochloric acid) in the stomach to give off carbon dioxide gas. When a 1.328-g tablet reacted with 40.00 mL of hydrochloric acid (density: 1.140 g/mL), carbon dioxide gas was given off and the resulting solution weighed 46.699 g. Calculate the number of liters of carbon dioxide gas released if its density is 1.81 g/L.

1.104 A 250-mL glass bottle was filled with 242 mL of water at 20°C and tightly capped. It was then left outdoors overnight, where the average temperature was −5°C. Predict what would happen. The density of water at 20°C is 0.998 g/cm^3 and that of ice at −5°C is 0.916 g/cm^3.

Interpreting, Modeling & Estimating

1.105 What is the mass of one mole of ants? (*Useful information:* A mole is the unit used for atomic and subatomic particles. It is approximately 6×10^{23}. A 1-cm-long ant weighs about 3 mg.)

1.106 How much time (in years) does an 80-year-old person spend sleeping during his or her life span?

1.107 Estimate the daily amount of water (in gallons) used indoors by a family of four in the United States.

1.108 Public bowling alleys generally stock bowling balls from 8 to 16 lb, where the mass is given in whole numbers. Given that regulation bowling balls have a diameter of 8.6 in, which (if any) of these bowling balls would you expect to float in water?

1.109 Fusing "nanofibers" with diameters of 100–300 nm gives junctures with very small volumes that would potentially allow the study of reactions involving only a few molecules. Estimate the volume in liters of the junction formed between two such fibers with internal diameters of 200 nm. The scale reads 1 μm.

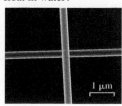
1 μm

1.110 Estimate the annual consumption of gasoline by passenger cars in the United States.

1.111 Estimate the total amount of ocean water in liters.

1.112 Estimate the volume of blood in an adult in liters.

1.113 How far (in feet) does light travel in one nanosecond?

1.114 Estimate the distance (in miles) covered by an NBA player in a professional basketball game.

1.115 In water conservation, chemists spread a thin film of a certain inert material over the surface of water to cut down on the rate of evaporation of water in reservoirs. This technique was pioneered by Benjamin Franklin three centuries ago. Franklin found that 0.10 mL of oil could spread over the surface of water about 40 m^2 in area. Assuming that the oil forms a *monolayer,* that is, a layer that is only one molecule thick, estimate the length of each oil molecule in nanometers. (1 nm = 1×10^{-9} m.)

Answers to Practice Exercises

1.1 96.5 g. **1.2** 341 g. **1.3** (a) 621.5°F, (b) 78.3°C, (c) −196°C. **1.4** (a) Two, (b) four, (c) three, (d) two, (e) three or two. **1.5** (a) 26.76 L, (b) 4.4 g, (c) 1.6×10^7 dm^2, (d) 0.0756 g/mL, (e) 6.69×10^4 m. **1.6** 2.36 lb. **1.7** 1.08×10^5 m^3. **1.8** 0.534 g/cm^3. **1.9** Roughly 0.03 g.

CHEMICAL *MYSTERY*

The Disappearance of the Dinosaurs

Dinosaurs dominated life on Earth for millions of years and then disappeared very suddenly. To solve the mystery, paleontologists studied fossils and skeletons found in rocks in various layers of Earth's crust. Their findings enabled them to map out which species existed on Earth during specific geologic periods. They also revealed no dinosaur skeletons in rocks formed immediately after the Cretaceous period, which dates back some

65 million years. It is therefore assumed that the dinosaurs became extinct about 65 million years ago.

Among the many hypotheses put forward to account for their disappearance were disruptions of the food chain and a dramatic change in climate caused by violent volcanic eruptions. However, there was no convincing evidence for any one hypothesis until 1977. It was then that a group of paleontologists working in Italy obtained some very puzzling data at a site near Gubbio. The chemical analysis of a layer of clay deposited above sediments formed during the Cretaceous period (and therefore a layer that records events occurring *after* the Cretaceous period) showed a surprisingly high content of the element iridium (Ir). Iridium is very rare in Earth's crust but is comparatively abundant in asteroids.

This investigation led to the hypothesis that the extinction of dinosaurs occurred as follows. To account for the quantity of iridium found, scientists suggested that a large asteroid several miles in diameter hit Earth about the time the dinosaurs disappeared. The impact of the asteroid on Earth's surface must have been so tremendous that it literally vaporized a large quantity of surrounding rocks, soils, and other objects. The resulting dust and debris floated through the air and blocked the sunlight for months or perhaps years. Without ample sunlight most plants could not grow, and the fossil record confirms that many types of plants did indeed die out at this time. Consequently, of course, many plant-eating animals perished, and then, in turn, meat-eating animals began to starve. Dwindling food sources would obviously affect large animals needing great amounts of food more quickly and more severely than small animals. Therefore, the huge dinosaurs, the largest of which might have weighed as much as 30 tons, vanished due to lack of food.

Chemical Clues

1. How does the study of dinosaur extinction illustrate the scientific method?

2. Suggest two ways that would enable you to test the asteroid collision hypothesis.

3. In your opinion, is it justifiable to refer to the asteroid explanation as the theory of dinosaur extinction?

4. Available evidence suggests that about 20 percent of the asteroid's mass turned to dust and spread uniformly over Earth after settling out of the upper atmosphere. This dust amounted to about 0.02 g/cm^2 of Earth's surface. The asteroid very likely had a density of about 2 g/cm^3. Calculate the mass (in kilograms and tons) of the asteroid and its radius in meters, assuming that it was a sphere. (The area of Earth is 5.1×10^{14} m^2; 1 lb = 453.6 g.) (Source: *Consider a Spherical Cow—A Course in Environmental Problem Solving* by J. Harte, University Science Books, Mill Valley, CA 1988. Used with permission.)

CHAPTER

2

Atoms, Molecules, and Ions

Illustration depicting Marie and Pierre Curie at work in their laboratory. The Curies studied and identified many radioactive elements.

A LOOK AHEAD

▶ We begin with a historical perspective of the search for the fundamental units of matter. The modern version of atomic theory was laid by John Dalton in the nineteenth century, who postulated that elements are composed of extremely small particles, called atoms. All atoms of a given element are identical, but they are different from atoms of all other elements. (2.1)

▶ We note that, through experimentation, scientists have learned that an atom is composed of three elementary particles: proton, electron, and neutron. The proton has a positive charge, the electron has a negative charge, and the neutron has no charge. Protons and neutrons are located in a small region at the center of the atom, called the nucleus, while electrons are spread out about the nucleus at some distance from it. (2.2)

▶ We will learn the following ways to identify atoms. Atomic number is the number of protons in a nucleus; atoms of different elements have different atomic numbers. Isotopes are atoms of the same element having a different number of neutrons. Mass number is the sum of the number of protons and neutrons in an atom. Because an atom is electrically neutral, the number of protons is equal to the number of electrons in it. (2.3)

▶ Next we will see how elements can be grouped together according to their chemical and physical properties in a chart called the periodic table. The periodic table enables us to classify elements (as metals, metalloids, and nonmetals) and correlate their properties in a systematic way. (2.4)

▶ We will see that atoms of most elements interact to form compounds, which are classified as molecules or ionic compounds made of positive (cations) and negative (anions) ions. (2.5)

▶ We learn to use chemical formulas (molecular and empirical) to represent molecules and ionic compounds and models to represent molecules. (2.6)

▶ We learn a set of rules that help us name the inorganic compounds. (2.7)

▶ Finally, we will briefly explore the organic world to which we will return in a later chapter. (2.8)

Since ancient times humans have pondered the nature of matter. Our modern ideas of the structure of matter began to take shape in the early nineteenth century with Dalton's atomic theory. We now know that all matter is made of atoms, molecules, and ions. All of chemistry is concerned in one way or another with these species.

2.1 The Atomic Theory

In the fifth century B.C. the Greek philosopher Democritus expressed the belief that all matter consists of very small, indivisible particles, which he named *atomos* (meaning uncuttable or indivisible). Although Democritus' idea was not accepted by many of his contemporaries (notably Plato and Aristotle), somehow it endured. Experimental evidence from early scientific investigations provided support for the notion of "atomism" and gradually gave rise to the modern definitions of elements and compounds. In 1808 an English scientist and school teacher, John Dalton,[†] formulated a precise definition of the indivisible building blocks of matter that we call atoms.

Dalton's work marked the beginning of the modern era of chemistry. The hypotheses about the nature of matter on which Dalton's atomic theory is based can be summarized as follows:

1. Elements are composed of extremely small particles called atoms.

2. All atoms of a given element are identical, having the same size, mass, and chemical properties. The atoms of one element are different from the atoms of all other elements.

3. Compounds are composed of atoms of more than one element. In any compound, the ratio of the numbers of atoms of any two of the elements present is either an integer or a simple fraction.

4. A chemical reaction involves only the separation, combination, or rearrangement of atoms; it does not result in their creation or destruction.

Figure 2.1 is a schematic representation of the last three hypotheses.

Dalton's concept of an atom was far more detailed and specific than Democritus'. The second hypothesis states that atoms of one element are different from atoms of all other elements. Dalton made no attempt to describe the structure or composition of atoms—he had no idea what an atom is really like. But he did realize that the

---

[†]John Dalton (1766–1844). English chemist, mathematician, and philosopher. In addition to the atomic theory, he also formulated several gas laws and gave the first detailed description of color blindness, from which he suffered. Dalton was described as an indifferent experimenter, and singularly wanting in the language and power of illustration. His only recreation was lawn bowling on Thursday afternoons. Perhaps it was the sight of those wooden balls that provided him with the idea of the atomic theory.

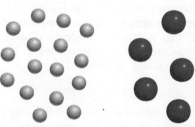

Atoms of element X   Atoms of element Y

Compounds of elements X and Y

(a)   (b)

Figure 2.1 *(a) According to Dalton's atomic theory, atoms of the same element are identical, but atoms of one element are different from atoms of other elements. (b) Compound formed from atoms of elements X and Y. In this case, the ratio of the atoms of element X to the atoms of element Y is 2:1. Note that a chemical reaction results only in the rearrangement of atoms, not in their destruction or creation.*

40   **Chapter 2** ▪ Atoms, Molecules, and Ions

Carbon monoxide

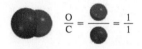

Carbon dioxide

Ratio of oxygen in
carbon monoxide to
oxygen in carbon dioxide: 1:2

Figure 2.2 *An illustration of the law of multiple proportions.*

different properties shown by elements such as hydrogen and oxygen can be explained by assuming that hydrogen atoms are not the same as oxygen atoms.

The third hypothesis suggests that, to form a certain compound, we need not only atoms of the right kinds of elements, but specific numbers of these atoms as well. This idea is an extension of a law published in 1799 by Joseph Proust,[†] a French chemist. Proust's **law of definite proportions** states that *different samples of the same compound always contain its constituent elements in the same proportion by mass.* Thus, if we were to analyze samples of carbon dioxide gas obtained from different sources, we would find in each sample the same ratio by mass of carbon to oxygen. It stands to reason, then, that if the ratio of the masses of different elements in a given compound is fixed, the ratio of the atoms of these elements in the compound also must be constant.

Dalton's third hypothesis supports another important law, the **law of multiple proportions.** According to the law, *if two elements can combine to form more than one compound, the masses of one element that combine with a fixed mass of the other element are in ratios of small whole numbers.* Dalton's theory explains the law of multiple proportions quite simply: Different compounds made up of the same elements differ in the number of atoms of each kind that combine. For example, carbon forms two stable compounds with oxygen, namely, carbon monoxide and carbon dioxide. Modern measurement techniques indicate that one atom of carbon combines with one atom of oxygen in carbon monoxide and with two atoms of oxygen in carbon dioxide. Thus, the ratio of oxygen in carbon monoxide to oxygen in carbon dioxide is 1:2. This result is consistent with the law of multiple proportions (Figure 2.2).

Dalton's fourth hypothesis is another way of stating the **law of conservation of mass,**[‡] which is that *matter can be neither created nor destroyed.* Because matter is made of atoms that are unchanged in a chemical reaction, it follows that mass must be conserved as well. Dalton's brilliant insight into the nature of matter was the main stimulus for the rapid progress of chemistry during the nineteenth century.

Review of Concepts

The atoms of elements A (blue) and B (orange) form two compounds shown here. Do these compounds obey the law of multiple proportions?

2.2 The Structure of the Atom

On the basis of Dalton's atomic theory, we can define an **atom** as *the basic unit of an element that can enter into chemical combination.* Dalton imagined an atom that was both extremely small and indivisible. However, a series of investigations that began in the 1850s and extended into the twentieth century clearly demonstrated that atoms actually possess internal structure; that is, they are made up of even smaller particles, which are called *subatomic particles.* This research led to the discovery of three such particles—electrons, protons, and neutrons.

[†]Joseph Louis Proust (1754–1826). French chemist. Proust was the first person to isolate sugar from grapes.

[‡]According to Albert Einstein, mass and energy are alternate aspects of a single entity called *mass-energy.* Chemical reactions usually involve a gain or loss of heat and other forms of energy. Thus, when energy is lost in a reaction, for example, mass is also lost. Except for nuclear reactions (see Chapter 19), however, changes of mass in chemical reactions are too small to detect. Therefore, for all practical purposes mass is conserved.

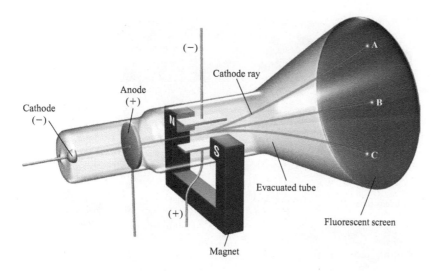

Figure 2.3 *A cathode ray tube with an electric field perpendicular to the direction of the cathode rays and an external magnetic field. The symbols N and S denote the north and south poles of the magnet. The cathode rays will strike the end of the tube at A in the presence of a magnetic field, at C in the presence of an electric field, and at B when there are no external fields present or when the effects of the electric field and magnetic field cancel each other.*

The Electron

In the 1890s, many scientists became caught up in the study of **radiation,** *the emission and transmission of energy through space in the form of waves.* Information gained from this research contributed greatly to our understanding of atomic structure. One device used to investigate this phenomenon was a cathode ray tube, the forerunner of the television tube (Figure 2.3). It is a glass tube from which most of the air has been evacuated. When the two metal plates are connected to a high-voltage source, the negatively charged plate, called the *cathode,* emits an invisible ray. The cathode ray is drawn to the positively charged plate, called the *anode,* where it passes through a hole and continues traveling to the other end of the tube. When the ray strikes the specially coated surface, it produces a strong fluorescence, or bright light.

In some experiments, two electrically charged plates and a magnet were added to the *outside* of the cathode ray tube (see Figure 2.3). When the magnetic field is on and the electric field is off, the cathode ray strikes point A. When only the electric field is on, the ray strikes point C. When both the magnetic and the electric fields are off or when they are both on but balanced so that they cancel each other's influence, the ray strikes point B. According to electromagnetic theory, a moving charged body behaves like a magnet and can interact with electric and magnetic fields through which it passes. Because the cathode ray is attracted by the plate bearing positive charges and repelled by the plate bearing negative charges, it must consist of negatively charged particles. We know these *negatively charged particles* as **electrons.** Figure 2.4 shows the effect of a bar magnet on the cathode ray.

▶▶ Animation
Cathode Ray Tube

Electrons are normally associated with atoms. However, they can also be studied individually.

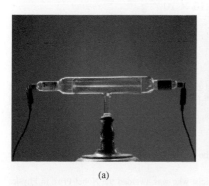

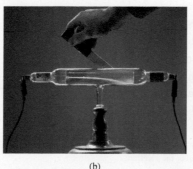

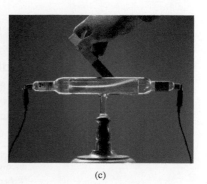

(a)   (b)   (c)

Figure 2.4 *(a) A cathode ray produced in a discharge tube traveling from the cathode (left) to the anode (right). The ray itself is invisible, but the fluorescence of a zinc sulfide coating on the glass causes it to appear green. (b) The cathode ray is bent downward when a bar magnet is brought toward it. (c) When the polarity of the magnet is reversed, the ray bends in the opposite direction.*

Figure 2.5 *Schematic diagram of Millikan's oil drop experiment.*

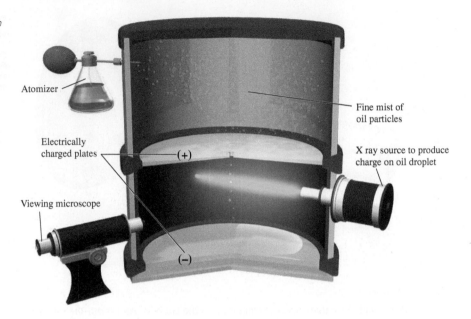

Atomizer

Fine mist of oil particles

Electrically charged plates

(+)

X ray source to produce charge on oil droplet

Viewing microscope

(−)

▶▶ Animation
Millikan Oil Drop

An English physicist, J. J. Thomson,[†] used a cathode ray tube and his knowledge of electromagnetic theory to determine the ratio of electric charge to the mass of an individual electron. The number he came up with was -1.76×10^8 C/g, where C stands for *coulomb,* which is the unit of electric charge. Thereafter, in a series of experiments carried out between 1908 and 1917, R. A. Millikan[‡] succeeded in measuring the charge of the electron with great precision. His work proved that the charge on each electron was exactly the same. In his experiment, Millikan examined the motion of single tiny drops of oil that picked up static charge from ions in the air. He suspended the charged drops in air by applying an electric field and followed their motions through a microscope (Figure 2.5). Using his knowledge of electrostatics, Millikan found the charge of an electron to be -1.6022×10^{-19} C. From these data he calculated the mass of an electron:

$$\text{mass of an electron} = \frac{\text{charge}}{\text{charge/mass}}$$
$$= \frac{-1.6022 \times 10^{-19}\,\text{C}}{-1.76 \times 10^8\,\text{C/g}}$$
$$= 9.10 \times 10^{-28}\,\text{g}$$

This is an exceedingly small mass.

Radioactivity

In 1895 the German physicist Wilhelm Röntgen[§] noticed that cathode rays caused glass and metals to emit very unusual rays. This highly energetic radiation penetrated matter, darkened covered photographic plates, and caused a variety of substances to

[†]Joseph John Thomson (1856–1940). British physicist who received the Nobel Prize in Physics in 1906 for discovering the electron.

[‡]Robert Andrews Millikan (1868–1953). American physicist who was awarded the Nobel Prize in Physics in 1923 for determining the charge of the electron.

[§]Wilhelm Konrad Röntgen (1845–1923). German physicist who received the Nobel Prize in Physics in 1901 for the discovery of X rays.

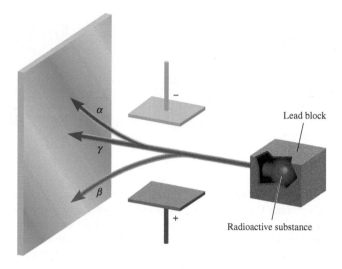

Figure 2.6 *Three types of rays emitted by radioactive elements. β rays consist of negatively charged particles (electrons) and are therefore attracted by the positively charged plate. The opposite holds true for α rays— they are positively charged and are drawn to the negatively charged plate. Because γ rays have no charges, their path is unaffected by an external electric field.*

fluoresce. Because these rays could not be deflected by a magnet, they could not contain charged particles as cathode rays do. Röntgen called them X rays because their nature was not known.

Not long after Röntgen's discovery, Antoine Becquerel,[†] a professor of physics in Paris, began to study the fluorescent properties of substances. Purely by accident, he found that exposing thickly wrapped photographic plates to a certain uranium compound caused them to darken, even without the stimulation of cathode rays. Like X rays, the rays from the uranium compound were highly energetic and could not be deflected by a magnet, but they differed from X rays because they arose spontaneously. One of Becquerel's students, Marie Curie,[‡] suggested the name ***radioactivity*** to describe this *spontaneous emission of particles and/or radiation.* Since then, any element that spontaneously emits radiation is said to be *radioactive.*

Three types of rays are produced by the *decay,* or breakdown, of radioactive substances such as uranium. Two of the three are deflected by oppositely charged metal plates (Figure 2.6). ***Alpha (α) rays*** consist of *positively charged particles,* called ***α particles,*** and therefore are deflected by the positively charged plate. ***Beta (β) rays,*** or ***β particles,*** are electrons and are deflected by the negatively charged plate. The third type of radioactive radiation consists of high-energy rays called ***gamma (γ) rays.*** Like X rays, γ rays have no charge and are not affected by an external field.

▶▶ **Animation**
Alpha, Beta, and Gamma Rays

The Proton and the Nucleus

By the early 1900s, two features of atoms had become clear: They contain electrons, and they are electrically neutral. To maintain electric neutrality, an atom must contain an equal number of positive and negative charges. Therefore, Thomson proposed that an atom could be thought of as a uniform, positive sphere of matter in which electrons are embedded like raisins in a cake (Figure 2.7). This so-called "plum-pudding" model was the accepted theory for a number of years.

Positive charge spread over the entire sphere

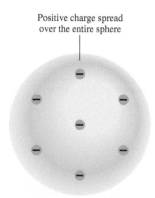

[†]Antoine Henri Becquerel (1852–1908). French physicist who was awarded the Nobel Prize in Physics in 1903 for discovering radioactivity in uranium.

[‡]Marie (Marya Sklodowska) Curie (1867–1934). Polish-born chemist and physicist. In 1903 she and her French husband, Pierre Curie, were awarded the Nobel Prize in Physics for their work on radioactivity. In 1911, she again received the Nobel prize, this time in chemistry, for her work on the radioactive elements radium and polonium. She is one of only three people to have received two Nobel prizes in science. Despite her great contribution to science, her nomination to the French Academy of Sciences in 1911 was rejected by one vote because she was a woman! Her daughter Irene, and son-in-law Frederic Joliot-Curie, shared the Nobel Prize in Chemistry in 1935.

Figure 2.7 *Thomson's model of the atom, sometimes described as the "plum-pudding" model, after a traditional English dessert containing raisins. The electrons are embedded in a uniform, positively charged sphere.*

44   **Chapter 2** ▪ Atoms, Molecules, and Ions

Figure 2.8 *(a) Rutherford's experimental design for measuring the scattering of α particles by a piece of gold foil. Most of the α particles passed through the gold foil with little or no deflection. A few were deflected at wide angles. Occasionally an α particle was turned back. (b) Magnified view of α particles passing through and being deflected by nuclei.*

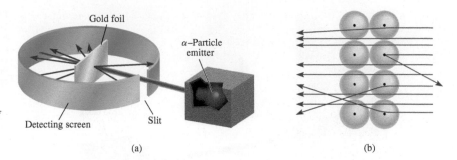

(a)   (b)

▶▶ Animation
α-Particle Scattering

▶▶ Animation
Rutherford's Experiment

In 1910 the New Zealand physicist Ernest Rutherford,[†] who had studied with Thomson at Cambridge University, decided to use α particles to probe the structure of atoms. Together with his associate Hans Geiger[‡] and an undergraduate named Ernest Marsden,[§] Rutherford carried out a series of experiments using very thin foils of gold and other metals as targets for α particles from a radioactive source (Figure 2.8). They observed that the majority of particles penetrated the foil either undeflected or with only a slight deflection. But every now and then an α particle was scattered (or deflected) at a large angle. In some instances, an α particle actually bounced back in the direction from which it had come! This was a most surprising finding, for in Thomson's model the positive charge of the atom was so diffuse that the positive α particles should have passed through the foil with very little deflection. To quote Rutherford's initial reaction when told of this discovery: "It was as incredible as if you had fired a 15-inch shell at a piece of tissue paper and it came back and hit you."

Rutherford was later able to explain the results of the α-scattering experiment in terms of a new model for the atom. According to Rutherford, most of the atom must be empty space. This explains why the majority of α particles passed through the gold foil with little or no deflection. The atom's positive charges, Rutherford proposed, are all concentrated in the **nucleus,** which is *a dense central core within the atom.* Whenever an α particle came close to a nucleus in the scattering experiment, it experienced a large repulsive force and therefore a large deflection. Moreover, an α particle traveling directly toward a nucleus would be completely repelled and its direction would be reversed.

*The positively charged particles in the nucleus are called **protons.*** In separate experiments, it was found that each proton carries the same *quantity* of charge as an electron and has a mass of 1.67262×10^{-24} g—about 1840 times the mass of the oppositely charged electron.

At this stage of investigation, scientists perceived the atom as follows: The mass of a nucleus constitutes most of the mass of the entire atom, but the nucleus occupies only about $1/10^{13}$ of the volume of the atom. We express atomic (and molecular) dimensions in terms of the SI unit called the *picometer (pm),* where

A common non-SI unit for atomic length is the angstrom (Å; 1 Å = 100 pm).

$$1 \text{ pm} = 1 \times 10^{-12} \text{ m}$$

[†]Ernest Rutherford (1871–1937). New Zealand physicist. Rutherford did most of his work in England (Manchester and Cambridge Universities). He received the Nobel Prize in Chemistry in 1908 for his investigations into the structure of the atomic nucleus. His often-quoted comment to his students was that "all science is either physics or stamp-collecting."

[‡]Johannes Hans Wilhelm Geiger (1882–1945). German physicist. Geiger's work focused on the structure of the atomic nucleus and on radioactivity. He invented a device for measuring radiation that is now commonly called the Geiger counter.

[§]Ernest Marsden (1889–1970). English physicist. It is gratifying to know that at times an undergraduate can assist in winning a Nobel prize. Marsden went on to contribute significantly to the development of science in New Zealand.

A typical atomic radius is about 100 pm, whereas the radius of an atomic nucleus is only about 5×10^{-3} pm. You can appreciate the relative sizes of an atom and its nucleus by imagining that if an atom were the size of a sports stadium, the volume of its nucleus would be comparable to that of a small marble. Although the protons are confined to the nucleus of the atom, the electrons are conceived of as being spread out about the nucleus at some distance from it.

The concept of atomic radius is useful experimentally, but we should not infer that atoms have well-defined boundaries or surfaces. We will learn later that the outer regions of atoms are relatively "fuzzy."

If the size of an atom were expanded to that of this sports stadium, the size of the nucleus would be that of a marble.

The Neutron

Rutherford's model of atomic structure left one major problem unsolved. It was known that hydrogen, the simplest atom, contains only one proton and that the helium atom contains two protons. Therefore, the ratio of the mass of a helium atom to that of a hydrogen atom should be 2:1. (Because electrons are much lighter than protons, their contribution to atomic mass can be ignored.) In reality, however, the ratio is 4:1. Rutherford and others postulated that there must be another type of subatomic particle in the atomic nucleus; the proof was provided by another English physicist, James Chadwick,[†] in 1932. When Chadwick bombarded a thin sheet of beryllium with α particles, a very high-energy radiation similar to γ rays was emitted by the metal. Later experiments showed that the rays actually consisted of a third type of subatomic particles, which Chadwick named **neutrons,** because they proved to be *electrically neutral particles having a mass slightly greater than that of protons.* The mystery of the mass ratio could now be explained. In the helium nucleus there are two protons and two neutrons, but in the hydrogen nucleus there is only one proton and no neutrons; therefore, the ratio is 4:1.

Figure 2.9 shows the location of the elementary particles (protons, neutrons, and electrons) in an atom. There are other subatomic particles, but the electron, the

---

[†]James Chadwick (1891–1972). British physicist. In 1935 he received the Nobel Prize in Physics for proving the existence of neutrons.

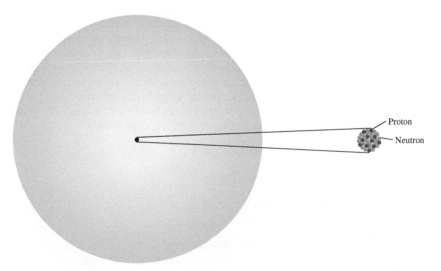

Figure 2.9 *The protons and neutrons of an atom are packed in an extremely small nucleus. Electrons are shown as "clouds" around the nucleus.*

Proton

Neutron

Table 2.1	Mass and Charge of Subatomic Particles		
		Charge	
Particle	Mass (g)	Coulomb	Charge Unit
Electron*	9.10938×10^{-28}	-1.6022×10^{-19}	-1
Proton	1.67262×10^{-24}	$+1.6022 \times 10^{-19}$	$+1$
Neutron	1.67493×10^{-24}	0	0

*More refined measurements have given us a more accurate value of an electron's mass than Millikan's.

proton, and the neutron are the three fundamental components of the atom that are important in chemistry. Table 2.1 shows the masses and charges of these three elementary particles.

2.3   Atomic Number, Mass Number, and Isotopes

All atoms can be identified by the number of protons and neutrons they contain. The **atomic number (Z)** is *the number of protons in the nucleus of each atom of an element.* In a neutral atom the number of protons is equal to the number of electrons, so the atomic number also indicates the number of electrons present in the atom. The chemical identity of an atom can be determined solely from its atomic number. For example, the atomic number of fluorine is 9. This means that each fluorine atom has 9 protons and 9 electrons. Or, viewed another way, every atom in the universe that contains 9 protons is correctly named "fluorine."

The **mass number (A)** is *the total number of neutrons and protons present in the nucleus of an atom of an element.* Except for the most common form of hydrogen, which has one proton and no neutrons, all atomic nuclei contain both protons and neutrons. In general, the mass number is given by

Protons and neutrons are collectively called *nucleons.*

$$\begin{aligned}
\text{mass number} &= \text{number of protons} + \text{number of neutrons} \\
&= \text{atomic number} + \text{number of neutrons}
\end{aligned} \tag{2.1}$$

The number of neutrons in an atom is equal to the difference between the mass number and the atomic number, or $(A - Z)$. For example, if the mass number of a particular boron atom is 12 and the atomic number is 5 (indicating 5 protons in the nucleus), then the number of neutrons is $12 - 5 = 7$. Note that all three quantities (atomic number, number of neutrons, and mass number) must be positive integers, or whole numbers.

Atoms of a given element do not all have the same mass. Most elements have two or more **isotopes,** *atoms that have the same atomic number but different mass numbers.* For example, there are three isotopes of hydrogen. One, simply known as hydrogen, has one proton and no neutrons. The *deuterium* isotope contains one proton and one neutron, and *tritium* has one proton and two neutrons. The accepted way to denote the atomic number and mass number of an atom of an element (X) is as follows:

$$\text{mass number} \searrow \atop \text{atomic number} \nearrow {}^{A}_{Z}\text{X}$$

Thus, for the isotopes of hydrogen, we write

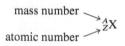

$${}^{1}_{1}\text{H} \qquad {}^{2}_{1}\text{H} \qquad {}^{3}_{1}\text{H}$$
$$\text{hydrogen} \quad \text{deuterium} \quad \text{tritium}$$

${}^{1}_{1}\text{H} \qquad {}^{2}_{1}\text{H} \qquad {}^{3}_{1}\text{H}$

As another example, consider two common isotopes of uranium with mass numbers of 235 and 238, respectively:

$$^{235}_{92}U \qquad ^{238}_{92}U$$

The first isotope is used in nuclear reactors and atomic bombs, whereas the second isotope lacks the properties necessary for these applications. With the exception of hydrogen, which has different names for each of its isotopes, isotopes of elements are identified by their mass numbers. Thus, the preceding two isotopes are called uranium-235 (pronounced "uranium two thirty-five") and uranium-238 (pronounced "uranium two thirty-eight").

The chemical properties of an element are determined primarily by the protons and electrons in its atoms; neutrons do not take part in chemical changes under normal conditions. Therefore, isotopes of the same element have similar chemistries, forming the same types of compounds and displaying similar reactivities.

Example 2.1 shows how to calculate the number of protons, neutrons, and electrons using atomic numbers and mass numbers.

Example 2.1

Give the number of protons, neutrons, and electrons in each of the following species: (a) $^{20}_{11}Na$, (b) $^{22}_{11}Na$, (c) ^{17}O, and (d) carbon-14.

Strategy Recall that the superscript denotes the mass number (A) and the subscript denotes the atomic number (Z). Mass number is always greater than atomic number. (The only exception is $^{1}_{1}H$, where the mass number is equal to the atomic number.) In a case where no subscript is shown, as in parts (c) and (d), the atomic number can be deduced from the element symbol or name. To determine the number of electrons, remember that because atoms are electrically neutral, the number of electrons is equal to the number of protons.

Solution

(a) The atomic number is 11, so there are 11 protons. The mass number is 20, so the number of neutrons is $20 - 11 = 9$. The number of electrons is the same as the number of protons; that is, 11.

(b) The atomic number is the same as that in (a), or 11. The mass number is 22, so the number of neutrons is $22 - 11 = 11$. The number of electrons is 11. Note that the species in (a) and (b) are chemically similar isotopes of sodium.

(c) The atomic number of O (oxygen) is 8, so there are 8 protons. The mass number is 17, so there are $17 - 8 = 9$ neutrons. There are 8 electrons.

(d) Carbon-14 can also be represented as ^{14}C. The atomic number of carbon is 6, so there are $14 - 6 = 8$ neutrons. The number of electrons is 6.

Similar problems: 2.15, 2.16.

Practice Exercise How many protons, neutrons, and electrons are in the following isotope of copper: ^{63}Cu?

Review of Concepts

(a) What is the atomic number of an element if one of its isotopes has 117 neutrons and a mass number of 195?

(b) Which of the following two symbols provides more information? ^{17}O or $_8O$.

48   **Chapter 2** ▪ Atoms, Molecules, and Ions

2.4 The Periodic Table

More than half of the elements known today were discovered between 1800 and 1900. During this period, chemists noted that many elements show strong similarities to one another. Recognition of periodic regularities in physical and chemical behavior and the need to organize the large volume of available information about the structure and properties of elemental substances led to the development of the *periodic table, a chart in which elements having similar chemical and physical properties are grouped together.* Figure 2.10 shows the modern periodic table in which the elements are arranged by atomic number (shown above the element symbol) in *horizontal rows* called *periods* and in *vertical columns* known as *groups* or *families,* according to similarities in their chemical properties. Note that elements 113–118 have recently been synthesized, although they have not yet been named.

The elements can be divided into three categories—metals, nonmetals, and metalloids. A *metal* is *a good conductor of heat and electricity* while a *nonmetal* is usually *a poor conductor of heat and electricity.* A *metalloid* has *properties that are intermediate between those of metals and nonmetals.* Figure 2.10 shows that the majority of known elements are metals; only 17 elements are nonmetals, and 8 elements are metalloids. From left to right across any period, the physical and chemical properties of the elements change gradually from metallic to nonmetallic.

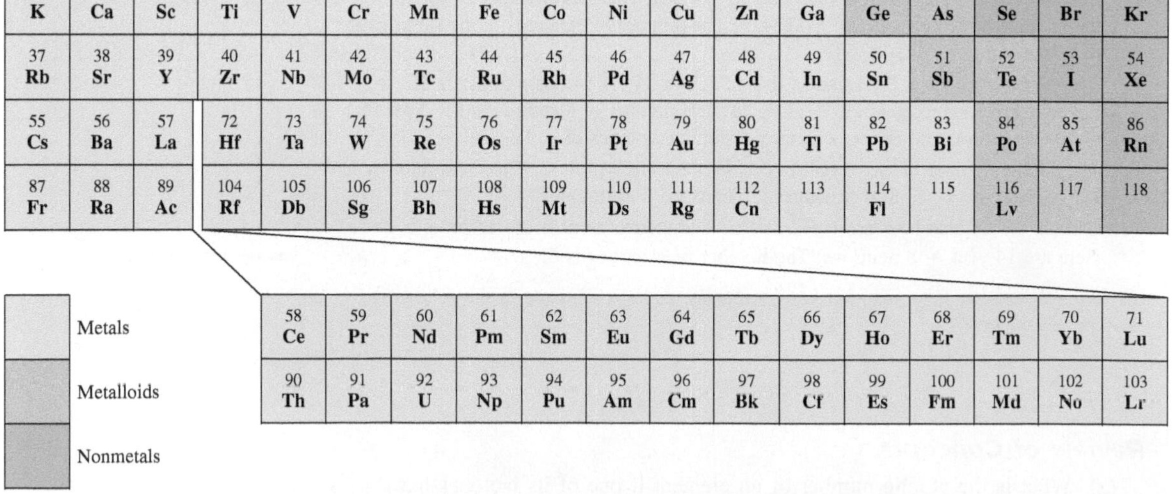

Figure 2.10 *The modern periodic table. The elements are arranged according to the atomic numbers above their symbols. With the exception of hydrogen (H), nonmetals appear at the far right of the table. The two rows of metals beneath the main body of the table are conventionally set apart to keep the table from being too wide. Actually, cerium (Ce) should follow lanthanum (La), and thorium (Th) should come right after actinium (Ac). The 1–18 group designation has been recommended by the International Union of Pure and Applied Chemistry (IUPAC) but is not yet in wide use. In this text, we use the standard U.S. notation for group numbers (1A–8A and 1B–8B). No names have yet been assigned to elements 113, 115, 117, and 118.*

CHEMISTRY *in Action*

Distribution of Elements on Earth and in Living Systems

The majority of elements are naturally occurring. How are these elements distributed on Earth, and which are essential to living systems?

Earth's crust extends from the surface to a depth of about 40 km (about 25 mi). Because of technical difficulties, scientists have not been able to study the inner portions of Earth as easily as the crust. Nevertheless, it is believed that there is a solid core consisting mostly of iron at the center of Earth. Surrounding the core is a layer called the *mantle,* which consists of hot fluid containing iron, carbon, silicon, and sulfur.

Of the 83 elements that are found in nature, 12 make up 99.7 percent of Earth's crust by mass. They are, in decreasing order of natural abundance, oxygen (O), silicon (Si), aluminum (Al), iron (Fe), calcium (Ca), magnesium (Mg), sodium (Na), potassium (K), titanium (Ti), hydrogen (H), phosphorus (P), and manganese (Mn). In discussing the natural abundance of the elements, we should keep in mind that (1) the elements are not evenly distributed throughout Earth's crust, and (2) most elements occur in combined forms. These facts provide the basis for most methods of obtaining pure elements from their compounds, as we will see in later chapters.

The accompanying table lists the essential elements in the human body. Of special interest are the *trace elements,* such as iron (Fe), copper (Cu), zinc (Zn), iodine (I), and cobalt (Co), which together make up about 0.1 percent of the body's mass. These elements are necessary for biological functions such as growth, transport of oxygen for metabolism, and defense against disease. There is a delicate balance in the amounts of these elements in our bodies. Too much or too little over an extended period of time can lead to serious illness, retardation, or even death.

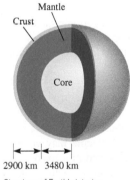

Mantle
Crust
Core

2900 km   3480 km

Structure of Earth's interior.

Essential Elements in the Human Body

Element	Percent by Mass*	Element	Percent by Mass*
Oxygen	65	Sodium	0.1
Carbon	18	Magnesium	0.05
Hydrogen	10	Iron	<0.05
Nitrogen	3	Cobalt	<0.05
Calcium	1.6	Copper	<0.05
Phosphorus	1.2	Zinc	<0.05
Potassium	0.2	Iodine	<0.05
Sulfur	0.2	Selenium	<0.01
Chlorine	0.2	Fluorine	<0.01

*Percent by mass *gives the mass of the element in grams present in a 100-g sample.*

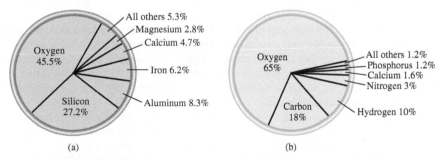

(a)   (b)

(a) Natural abundance of the elements in percent by mass. For example, oxygen's abundance is 45.5 percent. This means that in a 100-g sample of Earth's crust there are, on the average, 45.5 g of the element oxygen.
(b) Abundance of elements in the human body in percent by mass.

50   **Chapter 2** ▪ Atoms, Molecules, and Ions

Elements are often referred to collectively by their periodic table group number (Group 1A, Group 2A, and so on). However, for convenience, some element groups have been given special names. *The Group 1A elements (Li, Na, K, Rb, Cs, and Fr) are called **alkali metals,** and the Group 2A elements (Be, Mg, Ca, Sr, Ba, and Ra) are called **alkaline earth metals.** Elements in Group 7A (F, Cl, Br, I, and At) are known as **halogens,** and elements in Group 8A (He, Ne, Ar, Kr, Xe, and Rn) are called **noble gases,** or *rare gases*.

The periodic table is a handy tool that correlates the properties of the elements in a systematic way and helps us to make predictions about chemical behavior. We will take a closer look at this keystone of chemistry in Chapter 8.

The Chemistry in Action essay on p. 49 describes the distribution of the elements on Earth and in the human body.

Review of Concepts

In viewing the periodic table, do chemical properties change more markedly across a period or down a group?

2.5 Molecules and Ions

Of all the elements, only the six noble gases in Group 8A of the periodic table (He, Ne, Ar, Kr, Xe, and Rn) exist in nature as single atoms. For this reason, they are called *monatomic* (meaning a single atom) gases. Most matter is composed of molecules or ions formed by atoms.

Molecules

We will discuss the nature of chemical bonds in Chapters 9 and 10.

A **molecule** is an *aggregate of at least two atoms in a definite arrangement held together by chemical forces* (also called *chemical bonds*). A molecule may contain atoms of the same element or atoms of two or more elements joined in a fixed ratio, in accordance with the law of definite proportions stated in Section 2.1. Thus, a molecule is not necessarily a compound, which, by definition, is made up of two or more elements (see Section 1.4). Hydrogen gas, for example, is a pure element, but it consists of molecules made up of two H atoms each. Water, on the other hand, is a molecular compound that contains hydrogen and oxygen in a ratio of two H atoms and one O atom. Like atoms, molecules are electrically neutral.

The hydrogen molecule, symbolized as H_2, is called a **diatomic molecule** because it *contains only two atoms*. Other elements that normally exist as diatomic molecules are nitrogen (N_2) and oxygen (O_2), as well as the Group 7A elements—fluorine (F_2), chlorine (Cl_2), bromine (Br_2), and iodine (I_2). Of course, a diatomic molecule can contain atoms of different elements. Examples are hydrogen chloride (HCl) and carbon monoxide (CO).

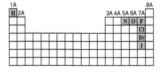

Elements that exist as diatomic molecules.

The vast majority of molecules contain more than two atoms. They can be atoms of the same element, as in ozone (O_3), which is made up of three atoms of oxygen, or they can be combinations of two or more different elements. *Molecules containing more than two atoms are called **polyatomic molecules.*** Like ozone, water (H_2O) and ammonia (NH_3) are polyatomic molecules.

Ions

An **ion** is *an atom or a group of atoms that has a net positive or negative charge.* The number of positively charged protons in the nucleus of an atom remains the same during ordinary chemical changes (called chemical reactions), but negatively charged electrons may be lost or gained. The loss of one or more electrons from a neutral atom results in a **cation,** *an ion with a net positive charge.* For example, a sodium atom (Na) can readily lose an electron to become a sodium cation, which is represented by Na^+:

In Chapter 8 we will see why atoms of different elements gain (or lose) a specific number of electrons.

Na Atom	Na^+ Ion
11 protons	11 protons
11 electrons	10 electrons

On the other hand, an **anion** is *an ion whose net charge is negative* due to an increase in the number of electrons. A chlorine atom (Cl), for instance, can gain an electron to become the chloride ion Cl^-:

Cl Atom	Cl^- Ion
17 protons	17 protons
17 electrons	18 electrons

Sodium chloride (NaCl), ordinary table salt, is called an **ionic compound** because it is *formed from cations and anions.*

An atom can lose or gain more than one electron. Examples of ions formed by the loss or gain of more than one electron are Mg^{2+}, Fe^{3+}, S^{2-}, and N^{3-}. These ions, as well as Na^+ and Cl^-, are called **monatomic ions** because they *contain only one atom.* Figure 2.11 shows the charges of a number of monatomic ions. With very few exceptions, metals tend to form cations and nonmetals form anions.

In addition, two or more atoms can combine to form an ion that has a net positive or net negative charge. **Polyatomic ions** such as OH^- (hydroxide ion), CN^- (cyanide ion), and NH_4^+ (ammonium ion) are *ions containing more than one atom.*

Review of Concepts

(a) What does S_8 signify? How does it differ from 8S?

(b) Determine the number of protons and electrons for the following ions:
(a) P^{3-} and (b) Ti^{4+}.

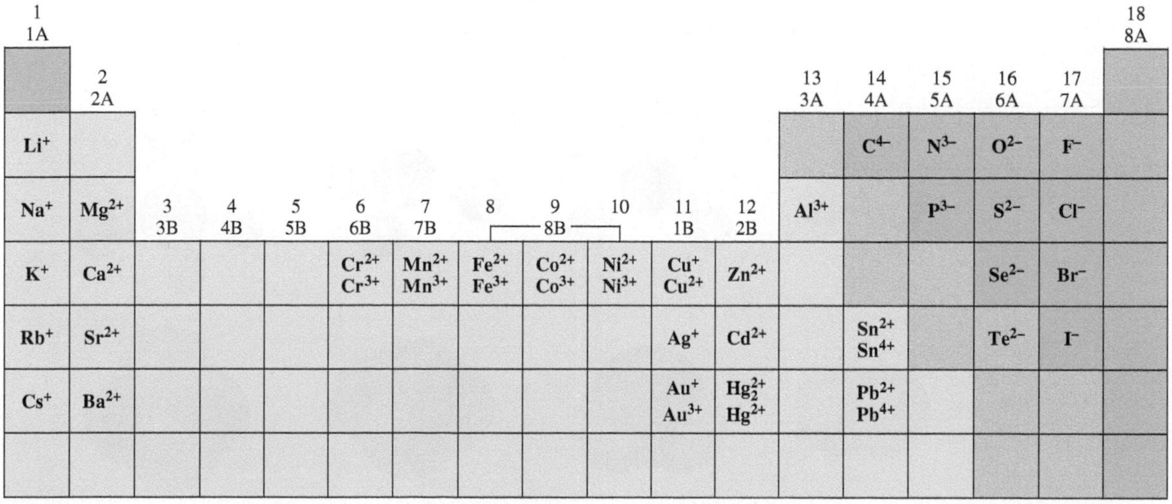

Figure 2.11 *Common monatomic ions arranged according to their positions in the periodic table. Note that the Hg_2^{2+} ion contains two atoms.*

52   **Chapter 2** ▪ Atoms, Molecules, and Ions

2.6 Chemical Formulas

Chemists use **chemical formulas** to *express the composition of molecules and ionic compounds in terms of chemical symbols.* By composition we mean not only the elements present but also the ratios in which the atoms are combined. Here we are concerned with two types of formulas: molecular formulas and empirical formulas.

Molecular Formulas

A **molecular formula** *shows the exact number of atoms of each element in the smallest unit of a substance.* In our discussion of molecules, each example was given with its molecular formula in parentheses. Thus, H_2 is the molecular formula for hydrogen, O_2 is oxygen, O_3 is ozone, and H_2O is water. The subscript numeral indicates the number of atoms of an element present. There is no subscript for O in H_2O because there is only one atom of oxygen in a molecule of water, and so the number "one" is omitted from the formula. Note that oxygen (O_2) and ozone (O_3) are allotropes of oxygen. An **allotrope** is *one of two or more distinct forms of an element.* Two allotropic forms of the element carbon—diamond and graphite—are dramatically different not only in properties but also in their relative cost.

Molecular Models

Molecules are too small for us to observe directly. An effective means of visualizing them is by the use of molecular models. Two standard types of molecular models are currently in use: *ball-and-stick* models and *space-filling* models (Figure 2.12). In ball-and-stick model kits, the atoms are wooden or plastic balls with holes in them. Sticks or springs are used to represent chemical bonds. The angles they form between atoms approximate the bond angles in actual molecules. With the exception of the H atom, the balls are all the same size and each type of atom is represented by a specific color. In space-filling models, atoms are represented by truncated balls held together by snap

See back endpaper for color codes for atoms.

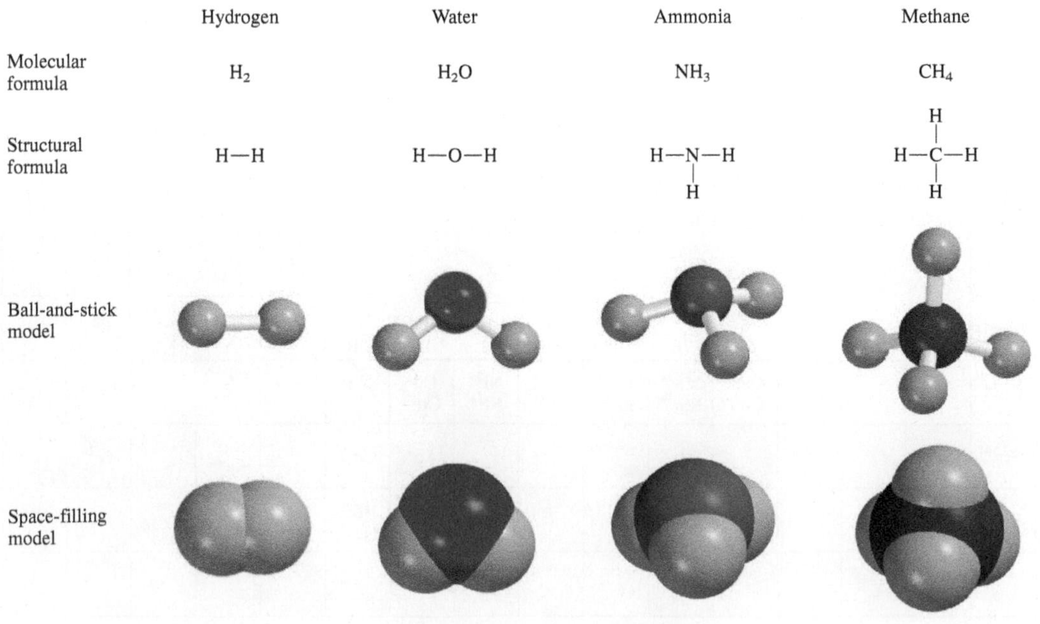

	Hydrogen	Water	Ammonia	Methane
Molecular formula	H_2	H_2O	NH_3	CH_4
Structural formula	H—H	H—O—H	H—N—H $\|$ H	H $\|$ H—C—H $\|$ H
Ball-and-stick model				
Space-filling model				

Figure 2.12 *Molecular and structural formulas and molecular models of four common molecules.*

fasteners, so that the bonds are not visible. The balls are proportional in size to atoms. The first step toward building a molecular model is writing the ***structural formula,*** which *shows how atoms are bonded to one another in a molecule.* For example, it is known that each of the two H atoms is bonded to an O atom in the water molecule. Therefore, the structural formula of water is H—O—H. A line connecting the two atomic symbols represents a chemical bond.

Ball-and-stick models show the three-dimensional arrangement of atoms clearly, and they are fairly easy to construct. However, the balls are not proportional to the size of atoms. Furthermore, the sticks greatly exaggerate the space between atoms in a molecule. Space-filling models are more accurate because they show the variation in atomic size. Their drawbacks are that they are time-consuming to put together and they do not show the three-dimensional positions of atoms very well. Molecular modeling software can also be used to create ball-and-stick and space-filling models. We will use both models extensively in this text.

Empirical Formulas

The molecular formula of hydrogen peroxide, a substance used as an antiseptic and as a bleaching agent for textiles and hair, is H_2O_2. This formula indicates that each hydrogen peroxide molecule consists of two hydrogen atoms and two oxygen atoms. The ratio of hydrogen to oxygen atoms in this molecule is 2:2 or 1:1. The empirical formula of hydrogen peroxide is HO. Thus, the ***empirical formula*** *tells us which elements are present and the simplest whole-number ratio of their atoms,* but not necessarily the actual number of atoms in a given molecule. As another example, consider the compound hydrazine (N_2H_4), which is used as a rocket fuel. The empirical formula of hydrazine is NH_2. Although the ratio of nitrogen to hydrogen is 1:2 in both the molecular formula (N_2H_4) and the empirical formula (NH_2), only the molecular formula tells us the actual number of N atoms (two) and H atoms (four) present in a hydrazine molecule.

Empirical formulas are the *simplest* chemical formulas; they are written by reducing the subscripts in the molecular formulas to the smallest possible whole numbers. Molecular formulas are the *true* formulas of molecules. If we know the molecular formula, we also know the empirical formula, but the reverse is not true. Why, then, do chemists bother with empirical formulas? As we will see in Chapter 3, when chemists analyze an unknown compound, the first step is usually the determination of the compound's empirical formula. With additional information, it is possible to deduce the molecular formula.

For many molecules, the molecular formula and the empirical formula are one and the same. Some examples are water (H_2O), ammonia (NH_3), carbon dioxide (CO_2), and methane (CH_4).

Examples 2.2 and 2.3 deal with writing molecular formulas from molecular models and writing empirical formulas from molecular formulas.

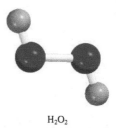

H_2O_2

The word "empirical" means "derived from experiment." As we will see in Chapter 3, empirical formulas are determined experimentally.

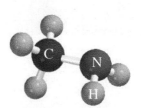

Methylamine

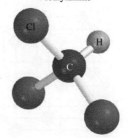

Chloroform

Similar problems: 2.47, 2.48.

Example 2.2

Write the molecular formula of methylamine, a colorless gas used in the production of pharmaceuticals and pesticides, from its ball-and-stick model, shown in the margin.

Solution Refer to the labels (also see back end papers). There are five H atoms, one C atom, and one N atom. Therefore, the molecular formula is CH_5N. However, the standard way of writing the molecular formula for methylamine is CH_3NH_2 because it shows how the atoms are joined in the molecule.

Practice Exercise Write the molecular formula of chloroform, which is used as a solvent and a cleaning agent. The ball-and-stick model of chloroform is shown in the margin.

54   **Chapter 2** ▪ Atoms, Molecules, and Ions

Example 2.3

Write the empirical formulas for the following molecules: (a) diborane (B_2H_6), used in rocket propellants; (b) dimethyl fumarate ($C_8H_{12}O_4$), a substance used to treat psoriasis, a skin disease; and (c) vanillin ($C_8H_8O_3$), a flavoring agent used in foods and beverages.

Strategy Recall that to write the empirical formula, the subscripts in the molecular formula must be converted to the smallest possible whole numbers.

Solution

(a) There are two boron atoms and six hydrogen atoms in diborane. Dividing the subscripts by 2, we obtain the empirical formula BH_3.

(b) In dimethyl fumarate there are 8 carbon atoms, 12 hydrogen atoms, and 4 oxygen atoms. Dividing the subscripts by 4, we obtain the empirical formula C_2H_3O. Note that if we had divided the subscripts by 2, we would have obtained the formula $C_4H_6O_2$. Although the ratio of carbon to hydrogen to oxygen atoms in $C_4H_6O_2$ is the same as that in C_2H_3O (2:3:1), $C_4H_6O_2$ is not the simplest formula because its subscripts are not in the smallest whole-number ratio.

(c) Because the subscripts in $C_8H_8O_3$ are already the smallest possible whole numbers, the empirical formula for vanillin is the same as its molecular formula.

Practice Exercise Write the empirical formula for caffeine ($C_8H_{10}N_4O_2$), a stimulant found in tea and coffee.

Similar problems: 2.45, 2.46.

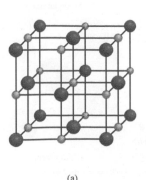

Sodium metal reacting with chlorine gas to form sodium chloride.

Formula of Ionic Compounds

The formulas of ionic compounds are usually the same as their empirical formulas because ionic compounds do not consist of discrete molecular units. For example, a solid sample of sodium chloride (NaCl) consists of equal numbers of Na^+ and Cl^- ions arranged in a three-dimensional network (Figure 2.13). In such a compound there is a 1:1 ratio of cations to anions so that the compound is electrically neutral. As you can see in Figure 2.13, no Na^+ ion in NaCl is associated with just one particular Cl^- ion. In fact, each Na^+ ion is equally held by six surrounding Cl^- ions and vice versa. Thus, NaCl is the empirical formula for sodium chloride. In other ionic compounds, the actual structure may be different, but the arrangement of cations and anions is such that the compounds are all electrically neutral. Note that the charges on the cation and anion are not shown in the formula for an ionic compound.

For ionic compounds to be electrically neutral, the sum of the charges on the cation and anion in each formula unit must be zero. If the charges on the cation and anion are numerically different, we apply the following rule to make the formula

(a)   (b)   (c)

Figure 2.13 *(a) Structure of solid NaCl. (b) In reality, the cations are in contact with the anions. In both (a) and (b), the smaller spheres represent Na^+ ions and the larger spheres, Cl^- ions. (c) Crystals of NaCl.*

electrically neutral: *The subscript of the cation is numerically equal to the charge on the anion, and the subscript of the anion is numerically equal to the charge on the cation.* If the charges are numerically equal, then no subscripts are necessary. This rule follows from the fact that because the formulas of ionic compounds are usually empirical formulas, the subscripts must always be reduced to the smallest ratios. Let us consider some examples.

- **Potassium Bromide.** The potassium cation K^+ and the bromine anion Br^- combine to form the ionic compound potassium bromide. The sum of the charges is $+1 + (-1) = 0$, so no subscripts are necessary. The formula is KBr.

- **Zinc Iodide.** The zinc cation Zn^{2+} and the iodine anion I^- combine to form zinc iodide. The sum of the charges of one Zn^{2+} ion and one I^- ion is $+2 + (-1) = +1$. To make the charges add up to zero we multiply the -1 charge of the anion by 2 and add the subscript "2" to the symbol for iodine. Therefore the formula for zinc iodide is ZnI_2.

- **Aluminum Oxide.** The cation is Al^{3+} and the oxygen anion is O^{2-}. The following diagram helps us determine the subscripts for the compound formed by the cation and the anion:

Refer to Figure 2.11 for charges of cations and anions.

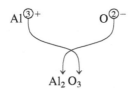

The sum of the charges is $2(+3) + 3(-2) = 0$. Thus, the formula for aluminum oxide is Al_2O_3.

Note that in each of the three examples, the subscripts are in the smallest ratios.

Example 2.4

Magnesium nitride is used to prepare Borazon, a very hard compound employed in cutting tools and machine parts. Write the formula of magnesium nitride, containing the Mg^{2+} and N^{3-} ions.

Strategy Our guide for writing formulas for ionic compounds is electrical neutrality; that is, the total charge on the cation(s) must be equal to the total charge on the anion(s). Because the charges on the Mg^{2+} and N^{3-} ions are not equal, we know the formula cannot be MgN. Instead, we write the formula as Mg_xN_y, where x and y are subscripts to be determined.

Solution To satisfy electrical neutrality, the following relationship must hold:

$$(+2)x + (-3)y = 0$$

Solving, we obtain $x/y = 3/2$. Setting $x = 3$ and $y = 2$, we write

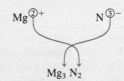

Check The subscripts are reduced to the smallest whole-number ratio of the atoms because the chemical formula of an ionic compound is usually its empirical formula.

Similar problems: 2.43, 2.44.

Practice Exercise Write the formulas of the following ionic compounds: (a) chromium sulfate (containing the Cr^{3+} and SO_4^{2-} ions) and (b) titanium oxide (containing the Ti^{4+} and O^{2-} ions).

When magnesium burns in air, it forms both magnesium oxide and magnesium nitride.

56   **Chapter 2** ▪ Atoms, Molecules, and Ions

Review of Concepts

Match each of the diagrams shown here with the following ionic compounds: Al_2O_3, LiH, Na_2S, $Mg(NO_3)_2$. (Green spheres represent cations and red spheres represent anions.)

(a)   (b)   (c)   (d)

2.7 Naming Compounds

When chemistry was a young science and the number of known compounds was small, it was possible to memorize their names. Many of the names were derived from their physical appearance, properties, origin, or application—for example, milk of magnesia, laughing gas, limestone, caustic soda, lye, washing soda, and baking soda.

Today the number of known compounds is well over 66 million. Fortunately, it is not necessary to memorize their names. Over the years chemists have devised a clear system for naming chemical substances. The rules are accepted worldwide, facilitating communication among chemists and providing a useful way of labeling an overwhelming variety of substances. Mastering these rules now will prove beneficial almost immediately as we proceed with our study of chemistry.

To begin our discussion of chemical *nomenclature,* the naming of chemical compounds, we must first distinguish between inorganic and organic compounds. ***Organic compounds*** *contain carbon, usually in combination with elements such as hydrogen, oxygen, nitrogen, and sulfur.* All other compounds are classified as ***inorganic compounds.*** For convenience, some carbon-containing compounds, such as carbon monoxide (CO), carbon dioxide (CO_2), carbon disulfide (CS_2), compounds containing the cyanide group (CN^-), and carbonate (CO_3^{2-}) and bicarbonate (HCO_3^-) groups are considered to be inorganic compounds. Section 2.8 gives a brief introduction to organic compounds.

For names and symbols of the elements, see front endpapers.

To organize and simplify our venture into naming compounds, we can divide inorganic compounds into four categories: ionic compounds, molecular compounds, acids and bases, and hydrates.

Ionic Compounds

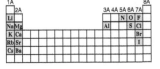

The most reactive metals (green) and the most reactive nonmetals (blue) combine to form ionic compounds.

In Section 2.5 we learned that ionic compounds are made up of cations (positive ions) and anions (negative ions). With the important exception of the ammonium ion, NH_4^+, all cations of interest to us are derived from metal atoms. Metal cations take their names from the elements. For example,

Element		Name of Cation	
Na	sodium	Na^+	sodium ion (or sodium cation)
K	potassium	K^+	potassium ion (or potassium cation)
Mg	magnesium	Mg^{2+}	magnesium ion (or magnesium cation)
Al	aluminum	Al^{3+}	aluminum ion (or aluminum cation)

▶▶ Animation
Formation of an Ionic Compound

Many ionic compounds are ***binary compounds,*** or *compounds formed from just two elements.* For binary compounds, the first element named is the metal cation, followed by the nonmetallic anion. Thus, NaCl is sodium chloride. The anion is named by taking the first part of the element name (chlorine) and adding "-ide."

Table 2.2	The "-ide" Nomenclature of Some Common Monatomic Anions According to Their Positions in the Periodic Table			
Group 4A	**Group 5A**	**Group 6A**	**Group 7A**
C carbide (C^{4-})*	N nitride (N^{3-})	O oxide (O^{2-})	F fluoride (F^-)
Si silicide (Si^{4-})	P phosphide (P^{3-})	S sulfide (S^{2-})	Cl chloride (Cl^-)
		Se selenide (Se^{2-})	Br bromide (Br^-)
		Te telluride (Te^{2-})	I iodide (I^-)

*The word "carbide" is also used for the anion C_2^{2-}.

Potassium bromide (KBr), zinc iodide (ZnI_2), and aluminum oxide (Al_2O_3) are also binary compounds. Table 2.2 shows the "-ide" nomenclature of some common monatomic anions according to their positions in the periodic table.

The "-ide" ending is also used for certain anion groups containing different elements, such as hydroxide (OH^-) and cyanide (CN^-). Thus, the compounds LiOH and KCN are named lithium hydroxide and potassium cyanide, respectively. These and a number of other such ionic substances are called ***ternary compounds,*** meaning *compounds consisting of three elements.* Table 2.3 lists alphabetically the names of a number of common cations and anions.

Certain metals, especially the *transition metals,* can form more than one type of cation. Take iron as an example. Iron can form two cations: Fe^{2+} and Fe^{3+}. An older nomenclature system that is still in limited use assigns the ending "-ous" to the cation with fewer positive charges and the ending "-ic" to the cation with more positive charges:

The transition metals are the elements in Groups 1B and 3B–8B (see Figure 2.10).

$$Fe^{2+} \qquad \text{ferrous ion}$$
$$Fe^{3+} \qquad \text{ferric ion}$$

The names of the compounds that these iron ions form with chlorine would thus be

$$FeCl_2 \qquad \text{ferrous chloride}$$
$$FeCl_3 \qquad \text{ferric chloride}$$

This method of naming ions has some distinct limitations. First, the "-ous" and "-ic" suffixes do not provide information regarding the actual charges of the two cations involved. Thus, the ferric ion is Fe^{3+}, but the cation of copper named cupric has the formula Cu^{2+}. In addition, the "-ous" and "-ic" designations provide names for only two different elemental cations. Some metallic elements can assume three or more different positive charges in compounds. Therefore, it has become increasingly common to designate different cations with Roman numerals. This is called the Stock[†] system. In this system, the Roman numeral I indicates one positive charge, II means two positive charges, and so on. For example, manganese (Mn) atoms can assume several different positive charges:

FeCl$_2$ (left) and FeCl$_3$ (right).

Keep in mind that the Roman numerals refer to the charges on the metal cations.

$$Mn^{2+}: MnO \qquad \text{manganese(II) oxide}$$
$$Mn^{3+}: Mn_2O_3 \qquad \text{manganese(III) oxide}$$
$$Mn^{4+}: MnO_2 \qquad \text{manganese(IV) oxide}$$

These names are pronounced "manganese-two oxide," "manganese-three oxide," and "manganese-four oxide." Using the Stock system, we denote the ferrous ion

[†]Alfred E. Stock (1876–1946). German chemist. Stock did most of his research in the synthesis and characterization of boron, beryllium, and silicon compounds. He was the first scientist to explore the dangers of mercury poisoning.

Table 2.3	Names and Formulas of Some Common Inorganic Cations and Anions

Cation	Anion
aluminum (Al^{3+})	bromide (Br^-)
ammonium (NH_4^+)	carbonate (CO_3^{2-})
barium (Ba^{2+})	chlorate (ClO_3^-)
cadmium (Cd^{2+})	chloride (Cl^-)
calcium (Ca^{2+})	chromate (CrO_4^{2-})
cesium (Cs^+)	cyanide (CN^-)
chromium(III) or chromic (Cr^{3+})	dichromate ($Cr_2O_7^{2-}$)
cobalt(II) or cobaltous (Co^{2+})	dihydrogen phosphate ($H_2PO_4^-$)
copper(I) or cuprous (Cu^+)	fluoride (F^-)
copper(II) or cupric (Cu^{2+})	hydride (H^-)
hydrogen (H^+)	hydrogen carbonate or bicarbonate (HCO_3^-)
iron(II) or ferrous (Fe^{2+})	hydrogen phosphate (HPO_4^{2-})
iron(III) or ferric (Fe^{3+})	hydrogen sulfate or bisulfate (HSO_4^-)
lead(II) or plumbous (Pb^{2+})	hydroxide (OH^-)
lithium (Li^+)	iodide (I^-)
magnesium (Mg^{2+})	nitrate (NO_3^-)
manganese(II) or manganous (Mn^{2+})	nitride (N^{3-})
mercury(I) or mercurous (Hg_2^{2+})*	nitrite (NO_2^-)
mercury(II) or mercuric (Hg^{2+})	oxide (O^{2-})
potassium (K^+)	permanganate (MnO_4^-)
rubidium (Rb^+)	peroxide (O_2^{2-})
silver (Ag^+)	phosphate (PO_4^{3-})
sodium (Na^+)	sulfate (SO_4^{2-})
strontium (Sr^{2+})	sulfide (S^{2-})
tin(II) or stannous (Sn^{2+})	sulfite (SO_3^{2-})
zinc (Zn^{2+})	thiocyanate (SCN^-)

*Mercury(I) exists as a pair as shown.

Nontransition metals such as tin (Sn) and lead (Pb) can also form more than one type of cations.

and the ferric ion as iron(II) and iron(III), respectively; ferrous chloride becomes iron(II) chloride, and ferric chloride is called iron(III) chloride. In keeping with modern practice, we will favor the Stock system of naming compounds in this textbook.

Examples 2.5 and 2.6 illustrate how to name ionic compounds and write formulas for ionic compounds based on the information given in Figure 2.11 and Tables 2.2 and 2.3.

Example 2.5

Name the following compounds: (a) $Fe(NO_3)_2$, (b) Na_2HPO_4, and (c) $(NH_4)_2SO_3$.

Strategy Our reference for the names of cations and anions is Table 2.3. Keep in mind that if a metal can form cations of different charges (see Figure 2.11), we need to use the Stock system.

(Continued)

Solution

(a) The nitrate ion (NO_3^-) bears one negative charge, so the iron ion must have two positive charges. Because iron forms both Fe^{2+} and Fe^{3+} ions, we need to use the Stock system and call the compound iron(II) nitrate.

(b) The cation is Na^+ and the anion is HPO_4^{2-} (hydrogen phosphate). Because sodium only forms one type of ion (Na^+), there is no need to use sodium(I) in the name. The compound is sodium hydrogen phosphate.

(c) The cation is NH_4^+ (ammonium ion) and the anion is SO_3^{2-} (sulfite ion). The compound is ammonium sulfite.

Similar problems: 2.57(b), (e), (f).

Practice Exercise Name the following compounds: (a) PbO and (b) LiClO$_3$.

Example 2.6

Write chemical formulas for the following compounds: (a) mercury(I) nitrate, (b) cesium oxide, and (c) strontium nitride.

Strategy We refer to Table 2.3 for the formulas of cations and anions. Recall that the Roman numerals in the Stock system provide useful information about the charges of the cation.

Solution

(a) The Roman numeral shows that the mercury ion bears a +1 charge. According to Table 2.3, however, the mercury(I) ion is diatomic (that is, Hg_2^{2+}) and the nitrate ion is NO_3^-. Therefore, the formula is $Hg_2(NO_3)_2$.

(b) Each oxide ion bears two negative charges, and each cesium ion bears one positive charge (cesium is in Group 1A, as is sodium). Therefore, the formula is Cs_2O.

(c) Each strontium ion (Sr^{2+}) bears two positive charges, and each nitride ion (N^{3-}) bears three negative charges. To make the sum of the charges equal zero, we must adjust the numbers of cations and anions:

$$3(+2) + 2(-3) = 0$$

Thus, the formula is Sr_3N_2.

Note that the subscripts of this ionic compound are not reduced to the smallest ratio because the Hg(I) ion exists as a pair or dimer.

Similar problems: 2.59(a), (b), (d), (h), (i).

Practice Exercise Write formulas for the following ionic compounds: (a) rubidium sulfate and (b) barium hydride.

Molecular Compounds

Unlike ionic compounds, molecular compounds contain discrete molecular units. They are usually composed of nonmetallic elements (see Figure 2.10). Many molecular compounds are binary compounds. Naming binary molecular compounds is similar to naming binary ionic compounds. We place the name of the first element in the formula first, and the second element is named by adding *-ide* to the root of the element name. Some examples are

HCl	hydrogen chloride
HBr	hydrogen bromide
SiC	silicon carbide

60   **Chapter 2** ▪ Atoms, Molecules, and Ions

Table 2.4

Greek Prefixes Used in Naming Molecular Compounds

Prefix	Meaning
mono-	1
di-	2
tri-	3
tetra-	4
penta-	5
hexa-	6
hepta-	7
octa-	8
nona-	9
deca-	10

It is quite common for one pair of elements to form several different compounds. In these cases, confusion in naming the compounds is avoided by the use of Greek prefixes to denote the number of atoms of each element present (Table 2.4). Consider the following examples:

CO	carbon monoxide
CO_2	carbon dioxide
SO_2	sulfur dioxide
SO_3	sulfur trioxide
NO_2	nitrogen dioxide
N_2O_4	dinitrogen tetroxide

The following guidelines are helpful in naming compounds with prefixes:

- The prefix "mono-" may be omitted for the first element. For example, PCl_3 is named phosphorus trichloride, not monophosphorus trichloride. Thus, the absence of a prefix for the first element usually means there is only one atom of that element present in the molecule.

- For oxides, the ending "a" in the prefix is sometimes omitted. For example, N_2O_4 may be called dinitrogen tetroxide rather than dinitrogen tetraoxide.

Exceptions to the use of Greek prefixes are molecular compounds containing hydrogen. Traditionally, many of these compounds are called either by their common, nonsystematic names or by names that do not specifically indicate the number of H atoms present:

B_2H_6	diborane
CH_4	methane
SiH_4	silane
NH_3	ammonia
PH_3	phosphine
H_2O	water
H_2S	hydrogen sulfide

Binary compounds containing carbon and hydrogen are organic compounds; they do not follow the same naming conventions. We will discuss the naming of organic compounds in Chapter 24.

Note that even the order of writing the elements in the formulas for hydrogen compounds is irregular. In water and hydrogen sulfide, H is written first, whereas it appears last in the other compounds.

Writing formulas for molecular compounds is usually straightforward. Thus, the name arsenic trifluoride means that there are three F atoms and one As atom in each molecule, and the molecular formula is AsF_3. Note that the order of elements in the formula is the same as in its name.

Example 2.7

Name the following molecular compounds: (a) PBr_5 and (b) As_2O_5.

Strategy We refer to Table 2.4 for the prefixes used in naming molecular compounds.

Solution

(a) Because there are five bromine atoms present, the compound is phosphorus pentabromide.

(b) There are two arsenic atoms and five oxygen atoms present, so the compound is diarsenic pentoxide. Note that the "a" is omitted in "penta."

Similar problems: 2.57(c), (i), (j).

Practice Exercise Name the following molecular compounds: (a) NF_3 and (b) Cl_2O_7.

Example 2.8

Write chemical formulas for the following molecular compounds: (a) bromine trifluoride and (b) diboron trioxide.

Strategy We refer to Table 2.4 for the prefixes used in naming molecular compounds.

Solution

(a) Because there are three fluorine atoms and one bromine atom present, the formula is BrF_3.

(b) There are two boron atoms and three oxygen atoms present, so the formula is B_2O_3.   Similar problems: 2.59(g), (j).

Practice Exercise Write chemical formulas for the following molecular compounds: (a) sulfur tetrafluoride and (b) dinitrogen pentoxide.

Figure 2.14 summarizes the steps for naming ionic and binary molecular compounds.

Review of Concepts

Why is it that the name for $SeCl_2$, selenium dichloride, contains a prefix, but the name for $SrCl_2$, strontium chloride, does not?

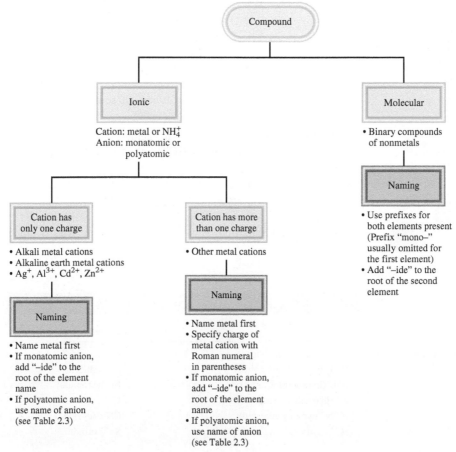

Figure 2.14 *Steps for naming ionic and binary molecular compounds.*

62 **Chapter 2** ▪ Atoms, Molecules, and Ions

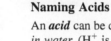

HCl

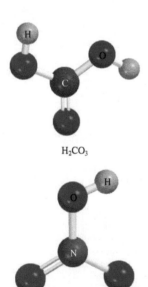

H_3O^+

Cl^-

When dissolved in water, the HCl molecule is converted to the H^+ and Cl^- ions. The H^+ ion is associated with one or more water molecules, and is usually represented as H_3O^+.

H_2CO_3

HNO_3

Note that these acids all exist as molecular compounds in the gas phase.

Acids and Bases

Naming Acids

An **acid** can be described as *a substance that yields hydrogen ions (H^+) when dissolved in water.* (H^+ is equivalent to one proton, and is often referred to that way.) Formulas for acids contain one or more hydrogen atoms as well as an anionic group. Anions whose names end in "-ide" form acids with a "hydro-" prefix and an "-ic" ending, as shown in Table 2.5. In some cases two different names seem to be assigned to the same chemical formula.

HCl	hydrogen chloride
HCl	hydrochloric acid

The name assigned to the compound depends on its physical state. In the gaseous or pure liquid state, HCl is a molecular compound called hydrogen chloride. When it is dissolved in water, the molecules break up into H^+ and Cl^- ions; in this state, the substance is called hydrochloric acid.

Oxoacids are acids that *contain hydrogen, oxygen, and another element (the central element).* The formulas of oxoacids are usually written with the H first, followed by the central element and then O. We use the following five common acids as our references in naming oxoacids:

H_2CO_3	carbonic acid
$HClO_3$	chloric acid
HNO_3	nitric acid
H_3PO_4	phosphoric acid
H_2SO_4	sulfuric acid

Often two or more oxoacids have the same central atom but a different number of O atoms. Starting with our reference oxoacids whose names all end with "-ic," we use the following rules to name these compounds.

1. Addition of one O atom to the "-ic" acid: The acid is called "per . . . -ic" acid. Thus, adding an O atom to $HClO_3$ changes chloric acid to perchloric acid, $HClO_4$.

2. Removal of one O atom from the "-ic" acid: The acid is called "-ous" acid. Thus, nitric acid, HNO_3, becomes nitrous acid, HNO_2.

3. Removal of two O atoms from the "-ic" acid: The acid is called "hypo . . . -ous" acid. Thus, when $HBrO_3$ is converted to $HBrO$, the acid is called hypobromous acid.

Table 2.5	Some Simple Acids	
Acid		**Corresponding Anion**
HF (hydrofluoric acid)		F^- (fluoride)
HCl (hydrochloric acid)		Cl^- (chloride)
HBr (hydrobromic acid)		Br^- (bromide)
HI (hydroiodic acid)		I^- (iodide)
HCN (hydrocyanic acid)		CN^- (cyanide)
H_2S (hydrosulfuric acid)		S^{2-} (sulfide)

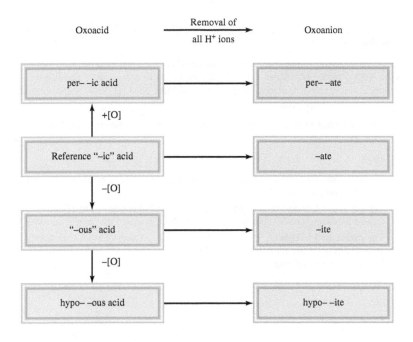

Figure 2.15 *Naming oxoacids and oxoanions.*

The rules for naming *oxoanions, anions of oxoacids,* are as follows:

1. When all the H ions are removed from the "-ic" acid, the anion's name ends with "-ate." For example, the anion CO_3^{2-} derived from H_2CO_3 is called carbonate.

2. When all the H ions are removed from the "-ous" acid, the anion's name ends with "-ite." Thus, the anion ClO_2^- derived from $HClO_2$ is called chlorite.

3. The names of anions in which one or more but not all the hydrogen ions have been removed must indicate the number of H ions present. For example, consider the anions derived from phosphoric acid:

H_3PO_4	phosphoric acid
$H_2PO_4^-$	dihydrogen phosphate
HPO_4^{2-}	hydrogen phosphate
PO_4^{3-}	phosphate

Note that we usually omit the prefix "mono-" when there is only one H in the anion. Figure 2.15 summarizes the nomenclature for the oxoacids and oxoanions, and Table 2.6 gives the names of the oxoacids and oxoanions that contain chlorine.
Example 2.9 deals with the nomenclature for an oxoacid and an oxoanion.

H_3PO_4

Table 2.6	Names of Oxoacids and Oxoanions That Contain Chlorine
Acid	**Corresponding Anion**
$HClO_4$ (perchloric acid)	ClO_4^- (perchlorate)
$HClO_3$ (chloric acid)	ClO_3^- (chlorate)
$HClO_2$ (chlorous acid)	ClO_2^- (chlorite)
$HClO$ (hypochlorous acid)	ClO^- (hypochlorite)

64   **Chapter 2** ▪ Atoms, Molecules, and Ions

Example 2.9

Name the following oxoacid and oxoanions: (a) H_2SO_3, a very unstable acid formed when $SO_2(g)$ reacts with water, (b) $H_2AsO_4^-$, once used to control ticks and lice on livestock, and (c) SeO_3^{2-}, used to manufacture colorless glass. H_3AsO_4 is arsenic acid, and H_2SeO_4 is selenic acid.

Strategy We refer to Figure 2.15 and Table 2.6 for the conventions used in naming oxoacids and oxoanions.

Solution

(a) We start with our reference acid, sulfuric acid (H_2SO_4). Because H_2SO_3 has one fewer O atom, it is called sulfurous acid.

(b) Because H_3AsO_4 is arsenic acid, the AsO_4^{3-} ion is named arsenate. The $H_2AsO_4^-$ anion is formed by adding two H^+ ions to AsO_4^{3-}, so $H_2AsO_4^-$ is called dihydrogen arsenate.

(c) The parent acid is H_2SeO_3. Because the acid has one fewer O atom than selenic acid (H_2SeO_4), it is called selenous acid. Therefore, the SeO_3^{2-} anion derived from H_2SeO_3 is called selenite.

Similar problems: 2.58(f).

Practice Exercise Name the following oxoacid and oxoanion: (a) HBrO and (b) HSO_4^-.

Naming Bases

A *base* can be described as *a substance that yields hydroxide ions (OH^-) when dissolved in water.* Some examples are

NaOH	sodium hydroxide
KOH	potassium hydroxide
$Ba(OH)_2$	barium hydroxide

Ammonia (NH_3), a molecular compound in the gaseous or pure liquid state, is also classified as a common base. At first glance this may seem to be an exception to the definition of a base. But note that as long as a substance *yields* hydroxide ions when dissolved in water, it need not contain hydroxide ions in its structure to be considered a base. In fact, when ammonia dissolves in water, NH_3 reacts partially with water to yield NH_4^+ and OH^- ions. Thus, it is properly classified as a base.

Review of Concepts

Why is the following question ambiguous: What is the name of HF? What additional information is needed to answer the question?

Hydrates

Hydrates are *compounds that have a specific number of water molecules attached to them.* For example, in its normal state, each unit of copper(II) sulfate has five water molecules associated with it. The systematic name for this compound is copper(II) sulfate pentahydrate, and its formula is written as $CuSO_4 \cdot 5H_2O$. The water molecules can be driven off by heating. When this occurs, the resulting compound is $CuSO_4$, which is sometimes called *anhydrous* copper(II) sulfate; "anhydrous" means that the compound no longer has water molecules associated with it (Figure 2.16). Some other hydrates are

$BaCl_2 \cdot 2H_2O$	barium chloride dihydrate
$LiCl \cdot H_2O$	lithium chloride monohydrate
$MgSO_4 \cdot 7H_2O$	magnesium sulfate heptahydrate
$Sr(NO_3)_2 \cdot 4H_2O$	strontium nitrate tetrahydrate

Figure 2.16 $CuSO_4 \cdot 5H_2O$ *(left) is blue; $CuSO_4$ (right) is white.*

Table 2.7	Common and Systematic Names of Some Compounds	
Formula	**Common Name**	**Systematic Name**
H_2O	Water	Dihydrogen monoxide
NH_3	Ammonia	Trihydrogen nitride
CO_2	Dry ice	Solid carbon dioxide
NaCl	Table salt	Sodium chloride
N_2O	Laughing gas	Dinitrogen monoxide
$CaCO_3$	Marble, chalk, limestone	Calcium carbonate
CaO	Quicklime	Calcium oxide
$Ca(OH)_2$	Slaked lime	Calcium hydroxide
$NaHCO_3$	Baking soda	Sodium hydrogen carbonate
$Na_2CO_3 \cdot 10H_2O$	Washing soda	Sodium carbonate decahydrate
$MgSO_4 \cdot 7H_2O$	Epsom salt	Magnesium sulfate heptahydrate
$Mg(OH)_2$	Milk of magnesia	Magnesium hydroxide
$CaSO_4 \cdot 2H_2O$	Gypsum	Calcium sulfate dihydrate

Familiar Inorganic Compounds

Some compounds are better known by their common names than by their systematic chemical names. Familiar examples are listed in Table 2.7.

2.8 Introduction to Organic Compounds

The simplest type of organic compounds is the *hydrocarbons,* which contain only carbon and hydrogen atoms. The hydrocarbons are used as fuels for domestic and industrial heating, for generating electricity and powering internal combustion engines, and as starting materials for the chemical industry. One class of hydrocarbons is called the *alkanes.* Table 2.8 shows the names, formulas, and molecular models of the first 10 *straight-chain* alkanes, in which the carbon chains have no branches. Note that all the names end with -*ane.* Starting with C_5H_{12}, we use the Greek prefixes in Table 2.4 to indicate the number of carbon atoms present.

The chemistry of organic compounds is largely determined by the *functional groups,* which consist of one or a few atoms bonded in a specific way. For example, when an H atom in methane is replaced by a hydroxyl group (—OH), an amino group (—NH_2), and a carboxyl group (—COOH), the following molecules are generated:

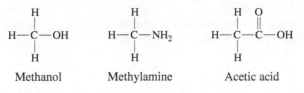

Methanol   Methylamine   Acetic acid

CH_3OH

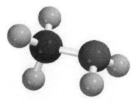

CH_3NH_2

CH_3COOH

Table 2.8	The First Ten Straight-Chain Alkanes	
Name	**Formula**	**Molecular Model**
Methane	CH_4	
Ethane	C_2H_6	
Propane	C_3H_8	
Butane	C_4H_{10}	
Pentane	C_5H_{12}	
Hexane	C_6H_{14}	
Heptane	C_7H_{16}	
Octane	C_8H_{18}	
Nonane	C_9H_{20}	
Decane	$C_{10}H_{22}$	

The chemical properties of these molecules can be predicted based on the reactivity of the functional groups. Although the nomenclature of the major classes of organic compounds and their properties in terms of the functional groups will not be discussed until Chapter 24, we will frequently use organic compounds as examples to illustrate chemical bonding, acid-base reactions, and other properties throughout the book.

Review of Concepts

How many different molecules can you generate by replacing one H atom with a hydroxyl group (—OH) in butane (see Table 2.8)?

Key Equation

mass number = number of protons + number of neutrons

= atomic number + number of neutrons   (2.1)

Summary of Facts & Concepts

1. Modern chemistry began with Dalton's atomic theory, which states that all matter is composed of tiny, indivisible particles called atoms; that all atoms of the same element are identical; that compounds contain atoms of different elements combined in whole-number ratios; and that atoms are neither created nor destroyed in chemical reactions (the law of conservation of mass).

2. Atoms of constituent elements in a particular compound are always combined in the same proportions by mass (law of definite proportions). When two elements can combine to form more than one type of compound, the masses of one element that combine with a fixed mass of the other element are in a ratio of small whole numbers (law of multiple proportions).

3. An atom consists of a very dense central nucleus containing protons and neutrons, with electrons moving about the nucleus at a relatively large distance from it.

4. Protons are positively charged, neutrons have no charge, and electrons are negatively charged. Protons and neutrons have roughly the same mass, which is about 1840 times greater than the mass of an electron.

5. The atomic number of an element is the number of protons in the nucleus of an atom of the element; it determines the identity of an element. The mass number is the sum of the number of protons and the number of neutrons in the nucleus.

6. Isotopes are atoms of the same element with the same number of protons but different numbers of neutrons.

7. Chemical formulas combine the symbols for the constituent elements with whole-number subscripts to show the type and number of atoms contained in the smallest unit of a compound.

8. The molecular formula conveys the specific number and type of atoms combined in each molecule of a compound. The empirical formula shows the simplest ratios of the atoms combined in a molecule.

9. Chemical compounds are either molecular compounds (in which the smallest units are discrete, individual molecules) or ionic compounds, which are made of cations and anions.

10. The names of many inorganic compounds can be deduced from a set of simple rules. The formulas can be written from the names of the compounds.

11. Organic compounds contain carbon and elements like hydrogen, oxygen, and nitrogen. Hydrocarbon is the simplest type of organic compound.

Key Words

Acid, p. 62
Alkali metals, p. 50
Alkaline earth metals, p. 50
Allotrope, p. 52
Alpha (α) particles, p. 43
Alpha (α) rays, p. 43
Anion, p. 51
Atom, p. 40
Atomic number (Z), p. 46
Base, p. 64
Beta (β) particles, p. 43
Beta (β) rays, p. 43
Binary compound, p. 56
Cation, p. 51

Chemical formula, p. 52
Diatomic molecule, p. 50
Electron, p. 41
Empirical formula, p. 53
Families, p. 48
Gamma (γ) rays, p. 43
Groups, p. 48
Halogens, p. 50
Hydrate, p. 64
Inorganic
  compounds, p. 56
Ion, p. 50
Ionic compound, p. 51
Isotope, p. 46

Law of conservation of
  mass, p. 40
Law of definite
  proportions, p. 40
Law of multiple
  proportions, p. 40
Mass number (A), p. 46
Metal, p. 48
Metalloid, p. 48
Molecular formula, p. 52
Molecule, p. 50
Monatomic ion, p. 51
Neutron, p. 45
Noble gases, p. 50

Nonmetal, p. 48
Nucleus, p. 44
Organic compound, p. 56
Oxoacid, p. 62
Oxoanion, p. 63
Periods, p. 48
Periodic table, p. 48
Polyatomic ion, p. 51
Polyatomic molecule, p. 50
Proton, p. 44
Radiation, p. 41
Radioactivity, p. 43
Structural formula, p. 53
Ternary compound, p. 57

Questions & Problems

● *Problems available in Connect Plus*
Red numbered problems solved in Student Solutions Manual

Structure of the Atom
Review Questions

2.1 Define the following terms: (a) α particle, (b) β particle, (c) γ ray, (d) X ray.

2.2 Name the types of radiation known to be emitted by radioactive elements.

2.3 Compare the properties of the following: α particles, cathode rays, protons, neutrons, electrons.

2.4 What is meant by the term "fundamental particle"?

2.5 Describe the contributions of the following scientists to our knowledge of atomic structure: J. J. Thomson, R. A. Millikan, Ernest Rutherford, James Chadwick.

2.6 Describe the experimental basis for believing that the nucleus occupies a very small fraction of the volume of the atom.

Problems

● 2.7 The diameter of a helium atom is about 1×10^2 pm. Suppose that we could line up helium atoms side by side in contact with one another. Approximately how many atoms would it take to make the distance from end to end 1 cm?

2.8 Roughly speaking, the radius of an atom is about 10,000 times greater than that of its nucleus. If an atom were magnified so that the radius of its nucleus became 2.0 cm, about the size of a marble, what would be the radius of the atom in miles? (1 mi = 1609 m.)

Atomic Number, Mass Number, and Isotopes
Review Questions

2.9 Use the helium-4 isotope to define atomic number and mass number. Why does a knowledge of atomic number enable us to deduce the number of electrons present in an atom?

2.10 Why do all atoms of an element have the same atomic number, although they may have different mass numbers?

2.11 What do we call atoms of the same elements with different mass numbers?

2.12 Explain the meaning of each term in the symbol $_Z^A X$.

Problems

● 2.13 What is the mass number of an iron atom that has 28 neutrons?

● **2.14** Calculate the number of neutrons in ^{239}Pu.

● 2.15 For each of the following species, determine the number of protons and the number of neutrons in the nucleus:
$_2^3$He, $_2^4$He, $_{12}^{24}$Mg, $_{12}^{25}$Mg, $_{22}^{48}$Ti, $_{35}^{79}$Br, $_{78}^{195}$Pt

● **2.16** Indicate the number of protons, neutrons, and electrons in each of the following species:
$_7^{15}$N, $_{16}^{33}$S, $_{29}^{63}$Cu, $_{38}^{84}$Sr, $_{56}^{130}$Ba, $_{74}^{186}$W, $_{80}^{202}$Hg

● 2.17 Write the appropriate symbol for each of the following isotopes: (a) $Z = 11$, $A = 23$; (b) $Z = 28$, $A = 64$.

● **2.18** Write the appropriate symbol for each of the following isotopes: (a) $Z = 74$, $A = 186$; (b) $Z = 80$, $A = 201$.

The Periodic Table
Review Questions

2.19 What is the periodic table, and what is its significance in the study of chemistry?

2.20 State two differences between a metal and a nonmetal.

2.21 Write the names and symbols for four elements in each of the following categories: (a) nonmetal, (b) metal, (c) metalloid.

● 2.22 Define, with two examples, the following terms: (a) alkali metals, (b) alkaline earth metals, (c) halogens, (d) noble gases.

Problems

2.23 Elements whose names end with -*ium* are usually metals; sodium is one example. Identify a nonmetal whose name also ends with -*ium*.

2.24 Describe the changes in properties (from metals to nonmetals or from nonmetals to metals) as we move (a) down a periodic group and (b) across the periodic table from left to right.

2.25 Consult a handbook of chemical and physical data (ask your instructor where you can locate a copy of the handbook) to find (a) two metals less dense than water, (b) two metals more dense than mercury, (c) the densest known solid metallic element, (d) the densest known solid nonmetallic element.

● **2.26** Group the following elements in pairs that you would expect to show similar chemical properties: K, F, P, Na, Cl, and N.

Molecules and Ions
Review Questions

2.27 What is the difference between an atom and a molecule?

2.28 What are allotropes? Give an example. How are allotropes different from isotopes?

2.29 Describe the two commonly used molecular models.

2.30   Give an example of each of the following: (a) a mona-tomic cation, (b) a monatomic anion, (c) a polyatomic cation, (d) a polyatomic anion.

Problems

• 2.31   Which of the following diagrams represent diatomic molecules, polyatomic molecules, molecules that are not compounds, molecules that are compounds, or an elemental form of the substance?

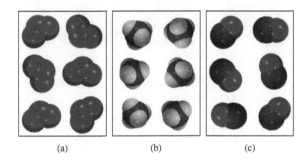

(a)   (b)   (c)

• **2.32**   Which of the following diagrams represent diatomic molecules, polyatomic molecules, molecules that are not compounds, molecules that arc compounds, or an elemental form of the substance?

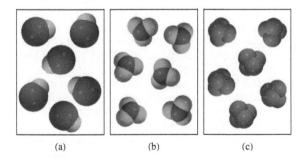

(a)   (b)   (c)

• 2.33   Identify the following as elements or compounds: NH_3, N_2, S_8, NO, CO, CO_2, H_2, SO_2.

• 2.34   Give two examples of each of the following: (a) a diatomic molecule containing atoms of the same element, (b) a diatomic molecule containing atoms of different elements, (c) a polyatomic molecule containing atoms of the same element, (d) a polyatomic molecule containing atoms of different elements.

• 2.35   Give the number of protons and electrons in each of the following common ions: Na^+, Ca^{2+}, Al^{3+}, Fe^{2+}, I^-, F^-, S^{2-}, O^{2-}, and N^{3-}.

• **2.36**   Give the number of protons and electrons in each of the following common ions: K^+, Mg^{2+}, Fe^{3+}, Br^-, Mn^{2+}, C^{4-}, Cu^{2+}.

Chemical Formulas
Review Questions

2.37   What does a chemical formula represent? What is the ratio of the atoms in the following molecular formulas? (a) NO, (b) NCl_3, (c) N_2O_4, (d) P_4O_6

2.38   Define molecular formula and empirical formula. What are the similarities and differences between the empirical formula and molecular formula of a compound?

2.39   Give an example of a case in which two molecules have different molecular formulas but the same empirical formula.

2.40   What does P_4 signify? How does it differ from 4P?

2.41   What is an ionic compound? How is electrical neutrality maintained in an ionic compound?

2.42   Explain why the chemical formulas of ionic compounds are usually the same as their empirical formulas.

Problems

• 2.43   Write the formulas for the following ionic compounds: (a) sodium oxide, (b) iron sulfide (containing the Fe^{2+} ion), (c) cobalt sulfate (containing the Co^{3+} and SO_4^{2-} ions), and (d) barium fluoride. (*Hint:* See Figure 2.11.)

• **2.44**   Write the formulas for the following ionic compounds: (a) copper bromide (containing the Cu^+ ion), (b) manganese oxide (containing the Mn^{3+} ion), (c) mercury iodide (containing the Hg_2^{2+} ion), and (d) magnesium phosphate (containing the PO_4^{3-} ion). (*Hint:* See Figure 2.11.)

• 2.45   What are the empirical formulas of the following compounds? (a) C_2N_2, (b) C_6H_6, (c) C_9H_{20}, (d) P_4O_{10}, (e) B_2H_6

• **2.46**   What are the empirical formulas of the following compounds? (a) Al_2Br_6, (b) $Na_2S_2O_4$, (c) N_2O_5, (d) $K_2Cr_2O_7$

• 2.47   Write the molecular formula of glycine, an amino acid present in proteins. The color codes are: black (carbon), blue (nitrogen), red (oxygen), and gray (hydrogen).

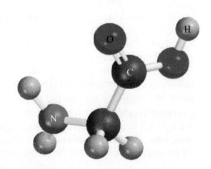

70   Chapter 2 ▪ Atoms, Molecules, and Ions

● **2.48**   Write the molecular formula of ethanol. The color codes are: black (carbon), red (oxygen), and gray (hydrogen).

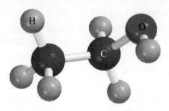

● 2.49   Which of the following compounds are likely to be ionic? Which are likely to be molecular? $SiCl_4$, LiF, $BaCl_2$, B_2H_6, KCl, C_2H_4

● **2.50**   Which of the following compounds are likely to be ionic? Which are likely to be molecular? CH_4, NaBr, BaF_2, CCl_4, ICl, CsCl, NF_3

Naming Inorganic Compounds

Review Questions

2.51   What is the difference between inorganic compounds and organic compounds?

2.52   What are the four major categories of inorganic compounds?

2.53   Give an example each for a binary compound and a ternary compound.

2.54   What is the Stock system? What are its advantages over the older system of naming cations?

2.55   Explain why the formula HCl can represent two different chemical systems.

2.56   Define the following terms: acids, bases, oxoacids, oxoanions, and hydrates.

Problems

● 2.57   Name these compounds: (a) Na_2CrO_4, (b) K_2HPO_4, (c) HBr (gas), (d) HBr (in water), (e) Li_2CO_3, (f) $K_2Cr_2O_7$, (g) NH_4NO_2, (h) PF_3, (i) PF_5, (j) P_4O_6, (k) CdI_2, (l) $SrSO_4$, (m) $Al(OH)_3$, (n) $Na_2CO_3 \cdot 10H_2O$.

● **2.58**   Name these compounds: (a) KClO, (b) Ag_2CO_3, (c) $FeCl_2$, (d) $KMnO_4$, (e) $CsClO_3$, (f) HIO, (g) FeO, (h) Fe_2O_3, (i) $TiCl_4$, (j) NaH, (k) Li_3N, (l) Na_2O, (m) Na_2O_2, (n) $FeCl_3 \cdot 6H_2O$.

● 2.59   Write the formulas for the following compounds: (a) rubidium nitrite, (b) potassium sulfide, (c) sodium hydrogen sulfide, (d) magnesium phosphate, (e) calcium hydrogen phosphate, (f) potassium dihydrogen phosphate, (g) iodine heptafluoride, (h) ammonium sulfate, (i) silver perchlorate, (j) boron trichloride.

● 2.60   Write the formulas for the following compounds: (a) copper(I) cyanide, (b) strontium chlorite, (c) perbromic acid, (d) hydroiodic acid, (e) disodium ammonium phosphate, (f) lead(II) carbonate, (g) tin(II) fluoride, (h) tetraphosphorus decasulfide, (i) mercury(II) oxide, (j) mercury(I) iodide, (k) selenium hexafluoride.

2.61   Sulfur (S) and fluorine (F) form several different compounds. One of them, SF_6, contains 3.55 g of F for every gram of S. Use the law of multiple proportions to determine n, which represents the number of F atoms in SF_n, given that it contains 2.37 g of F for every gram of S.

2.62   Name the following compounds.

2.63   Pair the following species that contain the same number of electrons: Ar, Sn^{4+}, F^-, Fe^{3+}, P^{3-}, V, Ag^+, N^{3-}.

2.64   Write the correct symbols for the atoms that contain: (a) 25 protons, 25 electrons, and 27 neutrons; (b) 10 protons, 10 electrons, and 12 neutrons; (c) 47 protons, 47 electrons, and 60 neutrons; (d) 53 protons, 53 electrons, and 74 neutrons; (e) 94 protons, 94 electrons, and 145 neutrons.

Additional Problems

2.65   A sample of a uranium compound is found to be losing mass gradually. Explain what is happening to the sample.

● 2.66   In which one of the following pairs do the two species resemble each other most closely in chemical properties? Explain. (a) ^1_1H and $^1_1H^+$, (b) $^{14}_7N$ and $^{14}_7N^{3-}$, (c) $^{12}_6C$ and $^{13}_6C$.

● 2.67   One isotope of a metallic element has mass number 65 and 35 neutrons in the nucleus. The cation derived from the isotope has 28 electrons. Write the symbol for this cation.

2.68   One isotope of a nonmetallic element has mass number 127 and 74 neutrons in the nucleus. The anion derived from the isotope has 54 electrons. Write the symbol for this anion.

● 2.69   Determine the molecular and empirical formulas of the compounds shown here. (Black spheres are carbon and gray spheres are hydrogen.)

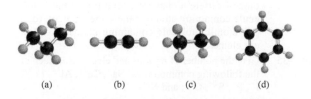

(a)   (b)   (c)   (d)

2.70   What is wrong with or ambiguous about the phrase "four molecules of NaCl"?

2.71 The following phosphorus sulfides are known: P_4S_3, P_4S_7, and P_4S_{10}. Do these compounds obey the law of multiple proportions?

2.72 Which of the following are elements, which are molecules but not compounds, which are compounds but not molecules, and which are both compounds and molecules? (a) SO_2, (b) S_8, (c) Cs, (d) N_2O_5, (e) O, (f) O_2, (g) O_3, (h) CH_4, (i) KBr, (j) S, (k) P_4, (l) LiF

2.73 The following table gives numbers of electrons, protons, and neutrons in atoms or ions of a number of elements. Answer the following: (a) Which of the species are neutral? (b) Which are negatively charged? (c) Which are positively charged? (d) What are the conventional symbols for all the species?

Atom or Ion of Element	A	B	C	D	E	F	G
Number of electrons	5	10	18	28	36	5	9
Number of protons	5	7	19	30	35	5	9
Number of neutrons	5	7	20	36	46	6	10

2.74 Identify the elements represented by the following symbols and give the number of protons and neutrons in each case: (a) $^{20}_{10}X$, (b) $^{63}_{29}X$, (c) $^{107}_{47}X$, (d) $^{182}_{74}X$, (e) $^{203}_{84}X$, (f) $^{234}_{94}X$.

2.75 Each of the following pairs of elements will react to form an ionic compound. Write the formulas and name these compounds: (a) barium and oxygen, (b) calcium and phosphorus, (c) aluminum and sulfur, (d) lithium and nitrogen.

2.76 Match the descriptions [(a)–(h)] with each of the following elements: P, Cu, Kr, Sb, Cs, Al, Sr, Cl. (a) A transition metal, (b) a nonmetal that forms a −3 ion, (c) a noble gas, (d) an alkali metal, (e) a metal that forms a +3 ion, (f) a metalloid, (g) an element that exists as a diatomic gas molecule, (h) an alkaline earth metal.

2.77 Explain why anions are always larger than the atoms from which they are derived, whereas cations are always smaller than the atoms from which they are derived. (*Hint:* Consider the electrostatic attraction between protons and electrons.)

2.78 (a) Describe Rutherford's experiment and how it led to the structure of the atom. How was he able to estimate the number of protons in a nucleus from the scattering of the α particles? (b) Consider the ^{23}Na atom. Given that the radius and mass of the nucleus are 3.04×10^{-15} m and 3.82×10^{-23} g, respectively, calculate the density of the nucleus in g/cm^3. The radius of a ^{23}Na atom is 186 pm. Calculate the density of the space occupied by the electrons in the sodium atom. Do your results support Rutherford's model of an atom? [The volume of a sphere of radius r is $(4/3)\pi r^3$.]

2.79 Caffeine, shown here, is a psychoactive stimulant drug. Write the molecular formula and empirical formula of the compound.

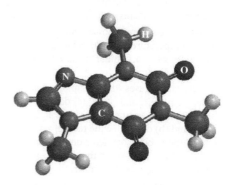

2.80 Acetaminophen, shown here, is the active ingredient in Tylenol. Write the molecular formula and empirical formula of the compound.

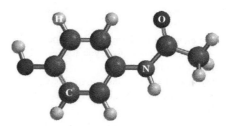

2.81 What is wrong with the chemical formula for each of the following compounds: (a) magnesium iodate [$Mg(IO_4)_2$], (b) phosphoric acid (H_3PO_3), (c) barium sulfite (BaS), (d) ammonium bicarbonate (NH_3HCO_3)?

2.82 What is wrong with the names (in parentheses) for each of the following compounds: $SnCl_4$ (tin chloride), (b) Cu_2O [copper(II) oxide], (c) $Co(NO_3)_2$ (cobalt nitrate), (d) $Na_2Cr_2O_7$ (sodium chromate)?

2.83 Fill in the blanks in the following table.

Symbol		$^{54}_{26}Fe^{2+}$			
Protons	5			79	86
Neutrons	6		16	117	136
Electrons	5		18	79	
Net charge			−3		0

2.84 (a) Which elements are most likely to form ionic compounds? (b) Which metallic elements are most likely to form cations with different charges?

2.85 Write the formula of the common ion derived from each of the following: (a) Li, (b) S, (c) I, (d) N, (e) Al, (f) Cs, (g) Mg

72   **Chapter 2** ▪ Atoms, Molecules, and Ions

2.86 Which of the following symbols provides more information about the atom: ^{23}Na or $_{11}Na$? Explain.

● **2.87** Write the chemical formulas and names of binary acids and oxoacids that contain Group 7A elements. Do the same for elements in Groups 3A, 4A, 5A, and 6A.

2.88 Of the 118 elements known, only two are liquids at room temperature (25°C). What are they? (*Hint:* One element is a familiar metal and the other element is in Group 7A.)

● **2.89** For the noble gases (the Group 8A elements), $_2^4He$, $_{10}^{20}Ne$, $_{18}^{40}Ar$, $_{36}^{84}Kr$, and $_{54}^{132}Xe$, (a) determine the number of protons and neutrons in the nucleus of each atom, and (b) determine the ratio of neutrons to protons in the nucleus of each atom. Describe any general trend you discover in the way this ratio changes with increasing atomic number.

● **2.90** List the elements that exist as gases at room temperature. (*Hint:* Most of these elements can be found in Groups 5A, 6A, 7A, and 8A.)

2.91 The Group 1B metals, Cu, Ag, and Au, are called coinage metals. What chemical properties make them specially suitable for making coins and jewelry?

2.92 The elements in Group 8A of the periodic table are called noble gases. Can you suggest what "noble" means in this context?

● **2.93** The formula for calcium oxide is CaO. What are the formulas for magnesium oxide and strontium oxide?

● **2.94** A common mineral of barium is barytes, or barium sulfate ($BaSO_4$). Because elements in the same periodic group have similar chemical properties, we might expect to find some radium sulfate ($RaSO_4$) mixed with barytes since radium is the last member of Group 2A. However, the only source of radium compounds in nature is in uranium minerals. Why?

2.95 List five elements each that are (a) named after places, (b) named after people, (c) named after a color. (*Hint:* See Appendix 1.)

2.96 One isotope of a nonmetallic element has mass number 77 and 43 neutrons in the nucleus. The anion derived from the isotope has 36 electrons. Write the symbol for this anion.

2.97 Fluorine reacts with hydrogen (H) and deuterium (D) to form hydrogen fluoride (HF) and deuterium fluoride (DF), where deuterium ($_1^2H$) is an isotope of hydrogen. Would a given amount of fluorine react with different masses of the two hydrogen isotopes? Does this violate the law of definite proportion? Explain.

● **2.98** Predict the formula and name of a binary compound formed from the following elements: (a) Na and H, (b) B and O, (c) Na and S, (d) Al and F, (e) F and O, (f) Sr and Cl.

● **2.99** Identify each of the following elements: (a) a halogen whose anion contains 36 electrons, (b) a radioactive noble gas with 86 protons, (c) a Group 6A element whose anion contains 36 electrons, (d) an alkali metal cation that contains 36 electrons, (e) a Group 4A cation that contains 80 electrons.

● **2.100** Write the molecular formulas for and names of the following compounds.

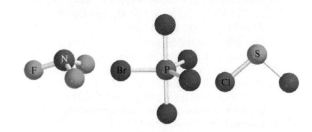

2.101 Show the locations of (a) alkali metals, (b) alkaline earth metals, (c) the halogens, and (d) the noble gases in the following outline of a periodic table. Also draw dividing lines between metals and metalloids and between metalloids and nonmetals.

● **2.102** Fill the blanks in the following table.

Cation	Anion	Formula	Name
			Magnesium bicarbonate
		$SrCl_2$	
Fe^{3+}	NO_2^-		
			Manganese(II) chlorate
		$SnBr_4$	
Co^{2+}	PO_4^{3-}		
Hg_2^{2+}	I^-		
		Cu_2CO_3	
			Lithium nitride
Al^{3+}	S^{2-}		

● **2.103** Some compounds are better known by their common names than by their systematic chemical names. Give the chemical formulas of the following substances: (a) dry ice, (b) table salt, (c) laughing gas, (d) marble (chalk, limestone), (e) quicklime, (f) slaked lime, (g) baking soda, (h) washing soda, (i) gypsum, (j) milk of magnesia.

• **2.104** On p. 40 it was pointed out that mass and energy are alternate aspects of a single entity called *mass-energy*. The relationship between these two physical quantities is Einstein's famous equation, $E = mc^2$, where E is energy, m is mass, and c is the speed of light. In a combustion experiment, it was found that 12.096 g of hydrogen molecules combined with 96.000 g of oxygen molecules to form water and released 1.715×10^3 kJ of heat. Calculate the corresponding mass change in this process and comment on whether the law of conservation of mass holds for ordinary chemical processes. (*Hint:* The Einstein equation can be used to calculate the change in mass as a result of the change in energy. 1 J = 1 kg m^2/s^2 and $c = 3.00 \times 10^8$ m/s.)

• **2.105** Draw all possible structural formulas of the following hydrocarbons: CH_4, C_2H_6, C_3H_8, C_4H_{10}, and C_5H_{12}.

2.106 (a) Assuming nuclei are spherical in shape, show that its radius r is proportional to the cube root of mass number (A). (b) In general, the radius of a nucleus is given by $r = r_0 A^{1/3}$, where r_0 is a proportionality constant given by 1.2×10^{-15} m. Calculate the volume of the $^7_3$Li nucleus. (c) Given that the radius of a Li atom is 152 pm, calculate the fraction of the atom's volume occupied by the nucleus. Does your result support Rutherford's model of an atom?

• **2.107** Draw two different structural formulas based on the molecular formula C_2H_6O. Is the fact that you can have more than one compound with the same molecular formula consistent with Dalton's atomic theory?

• **2.108** Ethane and acetylene are two gaseous hydrocarbons. Chemical analyses show that in one sample of ethane, 2.65 g of carbon are combined with 0.665 g of hydrogen, and in one sample of acetylene, 4.56 g of carbon are combined with 0.383 g of hydrogen. (a) Are these results consistent with the law of multiple proportions? (b) Write reasonable molecular formulas for these compounds.

• **2.109** A cube made of platinum (Pt) has an edge length of 1.0 cm. (a) Calculate the number of Pt atoms in the cube. (b) Atoms are spherical in shape. Therefore, the Pt atoms in the cube cannot fill all of the available space. If only 74 percent of the space inside the cube is taken up by Pt atoms, calculate the radius in picometers of a Pt atom. The density of

Pt is 21.45 g/cm^3 and the mass of a single Pt atom is 3.240×10^{-22} g. [The volume of a sphere of radius r is $(4/3)\pi r^3$.]

• **2.110** A monatomic ion has a charge of +2. The nucleus of the parent atom has a mass number of 55. If the number of neutrons in the nucleus is 1.2 times that of the number of protons, what is the name and symbol of the element?

• **2.111** In the following 2 × 2 crossword, each letter must be correct four ways: horizontally, vertically, diagonally, and by itself. When the puzzle is complete, the four spaces will contain the overlapping symbols of 10 elements. Use capital letters for each square. There is only one correct solution.*

1	2
3	4

Horizontal

1–2: Two-letter symbol for a metal used in ancient times

3–4: Two-letter symbol for a metal that burns in air and is found in Group 5A

Vertical

1–3: Two-letter symbol for a metalloid

2–4: Two-letter symbol for a metal used in U.S. coins

Single Squares

1: A colorful nonmetal

2: A colorless gaseous nonmetal

3: An element that makes fireworks green

4: An element that has medicinal uses

Diagonal

1–4: Two-letter symbol for an element used in electronics

2–3: Two-letter symbol for a metal used with Zr to make wires for superconducting magnets

• **2.112** Name the following acids.

---

*Reproduced with permission of S. J. Cyvin of the University of Trondheim (Norway). This puzzle appeared in *Chemical & Engineering News,* December 14, 1987 (p. 86) and in *Chem Matters,* October 1988.

74   **Chapter 2** ▪ Atoms, Molecules, and Ions

2.113   Calculate the density of the nucleus of a $_{26}^{56}$Fe atom, given that the nuclear mass is 9.229×10^{-23} g. From your result, comment on the fact that any nucleus containing more than one proton must have neutrons present as well. (*Hint:* See Problem 2.106.)

2.114   Element X reacts with element Y to form an ionic compound containing X^{4+} and Y^{2-} ions. Write a formula for the compound and suggest in which periodic groups these elements are likely to be found. Name a representative compound.

2.115   Methane, ethane, and propane are shown in Table 2.8. Show that the following data are consistent with the law of multiple proportions.

	Mass of Carbon in 1 g Sample	Mass of Hydrogen in 1 g Sample
Methane	0.749 g	0.251 g
Ethane	0.799 g	0.201 g
Propane	0.817 g	0.183 g

Interpreting, Modeling & Estimating

2.116   In the Rutherford scattering experiment, an α particle is heading directly toward a gold nucleus. The particle will come to a halt when its kinetic energy is completely converted to electrical potential energy. When this happens, how close will the α particle with a kinetic energy of 6.0×10^{-14} J be from the nucleus? [According to Coulomb's law, the electrical potential energy between two charged particles is $E = kQ_1Q_2/r$, where Q_1 and Q_2 are the charges (in coulombs) of the α particle and the gold nucleus, r is the distance of separation in meters, and k is a constant equal to 9.0×10^9 kg $\cdot$ m^3/s$^2 \cdot$ C^2. Joule (J) is the unit of energy where 1 J $= 1$ kg $\cdot$ m^2/s^2.]

2.117   Estimate the relative sizes of the following species: Li, Li$^+$, Li$^-$.

2.118   Compare the atomic size of the following two magnesium isotopes: ^{24}Mg and ^{26}Mg.

2.119   Using visible light, we humans cannot see any object smaller than 2×10^{-5} cm with an unaided eye. Roughly how many silver atoms must be lined up for us to see the atoms?

2.120   If the size of the nucleus of an atom were that of a pea, how far would the electrons be (on average) from the nucleus in meters?

2.121   Sodium and potassium are roughly equal in natural abundance in Earth's crust and most of their compounds are soluble. However, the composition of seawater is much higher in sodium than potassium. Explain.

2.122   One technique proposed for recycling plastic grocery bags is to heat them at 700°C and high pressure to form carbon microspheres that can be used in a number of applications. Electron microscopy shows some representative carbon microspheres obtained in this manner, where the scale is given in the bottom right corner of the figure. Determine the number of carbon atoms in a typical carbon microsphere.

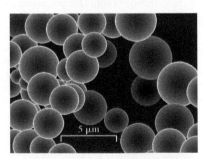

Answers to Practice Exercises

2.1 29 protons, 34 neutrons, and 29 electrons. **2.2** CHCl$_3$. **2.3** C$_4$H$_5$N$_2$O. **2.4** (a) Cr$_2$(SO$_4$)$_3$, (b) TiO$_2$. **2.5** (a) Lead(II) oxide, (b) lithium chlorate. **2.6** (a) Rb$_2$SO$_4$, (b) BaH$_2$. **2.7** (a) Nitrogen trifluoride, (b) dichlorine heptoxide. **2.8** (a) SF$_4$, (b) N$_2$O$_5$. **2.9** (a) Hypobromous acid, (b) hydrogen sulfate ion.

CHAPTER

Mass Relationships in Chemical Reactions

Fireworks are chemical reactions noted for the spectacular colors rather than the energy or useful substances they produce.

CHAPTER OUTLINE

A LOOK AHEAD

▶ We begin by studying the mass of an atom, which is based on the carbon-12 isotope scale. An atom of the carbon-12 isotope is assigned a mass of exactly 12 atomic mass units (amu). To work with the more convenient scale of grams, we use the molar mass. The molar mass of carbon-12 has a mass of exactly 12 grams and contains an Avogadro's number (6.022×10^{23}) of atoms. The molar masses of other elements are also expressed in grams and contain the same number of atoms. (3.1 and 3.2)

▶ Our discussion of atomic mass leads to molecular mass, which is the sum of the masses of the constituent atoms present. We learn that the most direct way to determine atomic and molecular mass is by the use of a mass spectrometer. (3.3 and 3.4)

▶ To continue our study of molecules and ionic compounds, we learn how to calculate the percent composition of these species from their chemical formulas. (3.5)

▶ We will see how the empirical and molecular formulas of a compound are determined by experiment. (3.6)

▶ Next, we learn how to write a chemical equation to describe the outcome of a chemical reaction. A chemical equation must be balanced so that we have the same number and type of atoms for the reactants, the starting materials, and the products, the substances formed at the end of the reaction. (3.7)

▶ Building on our knowledge of chemical equations, we then proceed to study the mass relationships of chemical reactions. A chemical equation enables us to use the mole method to predict the amount of product(s) formed, knowing how much the reactant(s) was used. We will see that a reaction's yield depends on the amount of limiting reagent (a reactant that is used up first) present. (3.8 and 3.9)

▶ We will learn that the actual yield of a reaction is almost always less than that predicted from the equation, called the theoretical yield, because of various complications. (3.10)

76   **Chapter 3** ▪ Mass Relationships in Chemical Reactions

I n this chapter, we will consider the masses of atoms and molecules and what happens to them when chemical changes occur. Our guide for this discussion will be the law of conservation of mass.

3.1 Atomic Mass

In this chapter, we will use what we have learned about chemical structure and formulas in studying the mass relationships of atoms and molecules. These relationships in turn will help us to explain the composition of compounds and the ways in which composition changes.

Section 3.4 describes a method for determining atomic mass.

The mass of an atom depends on the number of electrons, protons, and neutrons it contains. Knowledge of an atom's mass is important in laboratory work. But atoms are extremely small particles—even the smallest speck of dust that our unaided eyes can detect contains as many as 1×10^{16} atoms! Clearly we cannot weigh a single atom, but it is possible to determine the mass of one atom *relative* to another experimentally. The first step is to assign a value to the mass of one atom of a given element so that it can be used as a standard.

One atomic mass unit is also called one dalton.

By international agreement, ***atomic mass*** (sometimes called *atomic weight*) is *the mass of the atom in atomic mass units (amu)*. One ***atomic mass unit*** is defined as *a mass exactly equal to one-twelfth the mass of one carbon-12 atom.* Carbon-12 is the carbon isotope that has six protons and six neutrons. Setting the atomic mass of carbon-12 at 12 amu provides the standard for measuring the atomic mass of the other elements. For example, experiments have shown that, on average, a hydrogen atom is only 8.400 percent as massive as the carbon-12 atom. Thus, if the mass of one carbon-12 atom is exactly 12 amu, the atomic mass of hydrogen must be 0.08400×12 amu or 1.008 amu. Similar calculations show that the atomic mass of oxygen is 16.00 amu and that of iron is 55.85 amu. Thus, although we do not know just how much an average iron atom's mass is, we know that it is approximately 56 times as massive as a hydrogen atom.

Average Atomic Mass

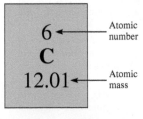

When you look up the atomic mass of carbon in a table such as the one on the inside front cover of this book, you will find that its value is not 12.00 amu but 12.01 amu. The reason for the difference is that most naturally occurring elements (including carbon) have more than one isotope. This means that when we measure the atomic mass of an element, we must generally settle for the *average* mass of the naturally occurring mixture of isotopes. For example, the natural abundances of carbon-12 and carbon-13 are 98.90 percent and 1.10 percent, respectively. The atomic mass of carbon-13 has been determined to be 13.00335 amu. Thus, the average atomic mass of carbon can be calculated as follows:

$$\text{average atomic mass of natural carbon} = (0.9890)(12\text{ amu}) + (0.0110)(13.00335\text{ amu})$$
$$= 12.01\text{ amu}$$

Note that in calculations involving percentages, we need to convert percentages to fractions. For example, 98.90 percent becomes 98.90/100, or 0.9890. Because there are many more carbon-12 atoms than carbon-13 atoms in naturally occurring carbon, the average atomic mass is much closer to 12 amu than to 13 amu.

It is important to understand that when we say that the atomic mass of carbon is 12.01 amu, we are referring to the *average* value. If carbon atoms could be examined individually, we would find either an atom of atomic mass exactly 12 amu or one of 13.00335 amu, but never one of 12.01 amu. Example 3.1 shows how to calculate the average atomic mass of an element.

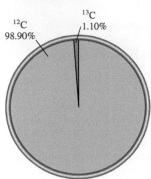

Natural abundances of C-12 and C-13 isotopes.

Example 3.1

Boron is used in the manufacture of ceramics and polymers such as fiberglass. The atomic masses of its two stable isotopes, $^{10}_{5}B$ (19.80 percent) and $^{11}_{5}B$ (80.20 percent), are 10.0129 amu and 11.0093 amu, respectively. The boron-10 isotope is also important as a neutron-capturing agent in nuclear reactors. Calculate the average atomic mass of boron.

Strategy Each isotope contributes to the average atomic mass based on its relative abundance. Multiplying the mass of an isotope by its fractional abundance (not percent) will give the contribution to the average atomic mass of that particular isotope.

Solution First the percent abundances are converted to fractions: 19.80 percent to 19.80/100 or 0.1980 and 80.20 percent to 80.20/100 or 0.8020. We find the contribution to the average atomic mass for each isotope, and then add the contributions together to obtain the average atomic mass.

$$(0.1980)(10.0129 \text{ amu}) + (0.8020)(11.0093 \text{ amu}) = 10.8129 \text{ amu}$$

Check The average atomic mass should be between the two isotopic masses; therefore, the answer is reasonable. Note that because there are more $^{11}_{5}B$ isotopes than $^{10}_{5}B$ isotopes, the average atomic mass is closer to 11.0093 amu than to 10.0129 amu.

Practice Exercise The atomic masses of the two stable isotopes of copper, $^{63}_{29}Cu$ (69.17 percent) and $^{65}_{29}Cu$ (30.83 percent), are 62.9296 amu and 64.9278 amu, respectively. Calculate the average atomic mass of copper.

Boron and the solid-state structure of boron.

The atomic masses of many elements have been accurately determined to five or six significant figures. However, for our purposes we will normally use atomic masses accurate only to four significant figures (see table of atomic masses inside the front cover). For simplicity, we will omit the word "average" when we discuss the atomic masses of the elements.

Review of Concepts

There are two stable isotopes of iridium: ^{191}Ir (190.96 amu) and ^{193}Ir (192.96 amu). If you were to randomly pick an iridium atom from a large collection of iridium atoms, which isotope are you more likely to select?

Similar problems: 3.5, 3.6.

3.2 Avogadro's Number and the Molar Mass of an Element

Atomic mass units provide a relative scale for the masses of the elements. But because atoms have such small masses, no usable scale can be devised to weigh them in calibrated units of atomic mass units. In any real situation, we deal with macroscopic samples containing enormous numbers of atoms. Therefore, it is convenient to have a special unit to describe a very large number of atoms. The idea of a unit to denote a particular number of objects is not new. For example, the pair (2 items), the dozen (12 items), and the gross (144 items) are all familiar units. Chemists measure atoms and molecules in moles.

In the SI system the ***mole (mol)*** is *the amount of a substance that contains as many elementary entities (atoms, molecules, or other particles) as there are atoms in exactly 12 g (or 0.012 kg) of the carbon-12 isotope.* The actual number of atoms in 12 g of carbon-12 is determined experimentally. This number is called ***Avogadro's***

The adjective formed from the noun "mole" is "molar."

Figure 3.1 *One mole each of several common elements. Carbon (black charcoal powder), sulfur (yellow powder), iron (as nails), copper wires, and mercury (shiny liquid metal).*

number (N_A*),* in honor of the Italian scientist Amedeo Avogadro.[†] The currently accepted value is

$$N_A = 6.0221413 \times 10^{23}$$

Generally, we round Avogadro's number to 6.022×10^{23}. Thus, just as 1 dozen oranges contains 12 oranges, 1 mole of hydrogen atoms contains 6.022×10^{23} H atoms. Figure 3.1 shows samples containing 1 mole each of several common elements.

The enormity of Avogadro's number is difficult to imagine. For example, spreading 6.022×10^{23} oranges over the entire surface of Earth would produce a layer 9 mi into space! Because atoms (and molecules) are so tiny, we need a huge number to study them in manageable quantities.

In calculations, the units of molar mass are g/mol or kg/mol.

We have seen that 1 mole of carbon-12 atoms has a mass of exactly 12 g and contains 6.022×10^{23} atoms. This mass of carbon-12 is its *molar mass (*$\mathcal{M}$*),* defined as *the mass (in grams or kilograms) of 1 mole of units* (such as atoms or molecules) *of a substance.* Note that the molar mass of carbon-12 (in grams) is numerically equal to its atomic mass in amu. Likewise, the atomic mass of sodium (Na) is 22.99 amu and its molar mass is 22.99 g; the atomic mass of phosphorus is 30.97 amu and its molar mass is 30.97 g; and so on. If we know the atomic mass of an element, we also know its molar mass.

The molar masses of the elements are given on the inside front cover of the book.

Knowing the molar mass and Avogadro's number, we can calculate the mass of a single atom in grams. For example, we know the molar mass of carbon-12 is 12 g and there are 6.022×10^{23} carbon-12 atoms in 1 mole of the substance; therefore, the mass of one carbon-12 atom is given by

$$\frac{12 \text{ g carbon-12 atoms}}{6.022 \times 10^{23} \text{ carbon-12 atoms}} = 1.993 \times 10^{-23} \text{ g}$$

[†]Lorenzo Romano Amedeo Carlo Avogadro di Quaregua e di Cerreto (1776–1856). Italian mathematical physicist. He practiced law for many years before he became interested in science. His most famous work, now known as Avogadro's law (see Chapter 5), was largely ignored during his lifetime, although it became the basis for determining atomic masses in the late nineteenth century.

Mass of element (m)	$\xrightarrow{m/\mathcal{M}}$ $\xleftarrow{n\mathcal{M}}$	Number of moles of element (n)	$\xrightarrow{nN_A}$ $\xleftarrow{N/N_A}$	Number of atoms of element (N)

Figure 3.2 *The relationships between mass (m in grams) of an element and number of moles of an element (n) and between number of moles of an element and number of atoms (N) of an element. $\mathcal{M}$ is the molar mass (g/mol) of the element and N_A is Avogadro's number.*

We can use the preceding result to determine the relationship between atomic mass units and grams. Because the mass of every carbon-12 atom is exactly 12 amu, the number of atomic mass units equivalent to 1 gram is

$$\frac{\text{amu}}{\text{gram}} = \frac{12 \text{ amu}}{1 \text{ carbon-12 atom}} \times \frac{1 \text{ carbon-12 atom}}{1.993 \times 10^{-23} \text{ g}}$$
$$= 6.022 \times 10^{23} \text{ amu/g}$$

Thus,

$$1 \text{ g} = 6.022 \times 10^{23} \text{ amu}$$

and

$$1 \text{ amu} = 1.661 \times 10^{-24} \text{ g}$$

This example shows that Avogadro's number can be used to convert from the atomic mass units to mass in grams and vice versa.

The notions of Avogadro's number and molar mass enable us to carry out conversions between mass and moles of atoms and between moles and number of atoms (Figure 3.2). We will employ the following conversion factors in the calculations:

$$\frac{1 \text{ mol X}}{\text{molar mass of X}} \quad \text{and} \quad \frac{1 \text{ mol X}}{6.022 \times 10^{23} \text{ X atoms}}$$

After some practice, you can use the equations in Figure 3.2 in calculations: $n = m/\mathcal{M}$ and $N = nN_A$.

where X represents the symbol of an element. Using the proper conversion factors we can convert one quantity to another, as Examples 3.2–3.4 show.

Example 3.2

Helium (He) is a valuable gas used in industry, low-temperature research, deep-sea diving tanks, and balloons. How many moles of He atoms are in 6.46 g of He?

Strategy We are given grams of helium and asked to solve for moles of helium. What conversion factor do we need to convert between grams and moles? Arrange the appropriate conversion factor so that grams cancel and the unit moles is obtained for your answer.

Solution The conversion factor needed to convert between grams and moles is the molar mass. In the periodic table (see inside front cover) we see that the molar mass of He is 4.003 g. This can be expressed as

$$1 \text{ mol He} = 4.003 \text{ g He}$$

From this equality, we can write two conversion factors

$$\frac{1 \text{ mol He}}{4.003 \text{ g He}} \quad \text{and} \quad \frac{4.003 \text{ g He}}{1 \text{ mol He}}$$

(Continued)

A scientific research helium balloon.

80   **Chapter 3** ▪ Mass Relationships in Chemical Reactions

The conversion factor on the left is the correct one. Grams will cancel, leaving the unit mol for the answer, that is,

$$6.46 \text{ g He} \times \frac{1 \text{ mol He}}{4.003 \text{ g He}} = 1.61 \text{ mol He}$$

Thus, there are 1.61 moles of He atoms in 6.46 g of He.

Check Because the given mass (6.46 g) is larger than the molar mass of He, we expect to have more than 1 mole of He.

Practice Exercise How many moles of magnesium (Mg) are there in 87.3 g of Mg?

Similar problem: 3.15.

Example 3.3

Zinc (Zn) is a silvery metal that is used in making brass (with copper) and in plating iron to prevent corrosion. How many grams of Zn are in 0.356 mole of Zn?

Strategy We are trying to solve for grams of zinc. What conversion factor do we need to convert between moles and grams? Arrange the appropriate conversion factor so that moles cancel and the unit grams are obtained for your answer.

Solution The conversion factor needed to convert between moles and grams is the molar mass. In the periodic table (see inside front cover) we see the molar mass of Zn is 65.39 g. This can be expressed as

$$1 \text{ mol Zn} = 65.39 \text{ g Zn}$$

From this equality, we can write two conversion factors

$$\frac{1 \text{ mol Zn}}{65.39 \text{ g Zn}} \quad \text{and} \quad \frac{65.39 \text{ g Zn}}{1 \text{ mol Zn}}$$

The conversion factor on the right is the correct one. Moles will cancel, leaving unit of grams for the answer. The number of grams of Zn is

$$0.356 \text{ mol Zn} \times \frac{65.39 \text{ g Zn}}{1 \text{ mol Zn}} = 23.3 \text{ g Zn}$$

Thus, there are 23.3 g of Zn in 0.356 mole of Zn.

Check Does a mass of 23.3 g for 0.356 mole of Zn seem reasonable? What is the mass of 1 mole of Zn?

Similar problem: 3.16.

Practice Exercise Calculate the number of grams of lead (Pb) in 12.4 moles of lead.

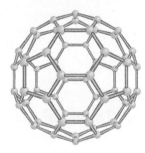

Zinc.

Example 3.4

The C_{60} molecule is called buckminsterfullerene because its shape resembles the geodesic domes designed by the visionary architect R. Buckminster Fuller. What is the mass (in grams) of one C_{60} molecule?

Strategy The question asks for the mass of one C_{60} molecule. Determine the moles of C atoms in one C_{60} molecule, and then use the molar mass of C to calculate the mass of one molecule in grams.

Buckminsterfullerene (C_{60}) or "buckyball."

(Continued)

Solution Because one C_{60} molecule contains 60 C atoms, and 1 mole of C contains 6.022×10^{23} C atoms and has a mass of 12.011 g, we can calculate the mass of one C_{60} molecule as follows:

$$1 \text{ } \cancel{C_{60}\text{ molecule}} \times \frac{60 \text{ } \cancel{\text{C atoms}}}{1 \text{ } \cancel{C_{60}\text{ molecule}}} \times \frac{1 \text{ } \cancel{\text{mol C}}}{6.022 \times 10^{23} \text{ } \cancel{\text{C atoms}}} \times \frac{12.01 \text{ g}}{1 \text{ } \cancel{\text{mol C}}} = 1.197 \times 10^{-21} \text{ g}$$

Check Because 6.022×10^{23} atoms of C have a mass 12.01 g, a molecule containing only 60 carbon atoms should have a significantly smaller mass.

Similar problems: 3.20, 3.21.

Practice Exercise Gold atoms form small clusters containing a fixed number of atoms. What is the mass (in grams) of one Au_{31} cluster?

Review of Concepts

Referring to the periodic table in the inside front cover and Figure 3.2, determine which of the following contains the largest number of atoms: (a) 7.68 g of He, (b) 112 g of Fe, and (c) 389 g of Hg.

3.3 Molecular Mass

If we know the atomic masses of the component atoms, we can calculate the mass of a molecule. The **molecular mass** (sometimes called *molecular weight*) is *the sum of the atomic masses (in amu) in the molecule.* For example, the molecular mass of H_2O is

$$2(\text{atomic mass of H}) + \text{atomic mass of O}$$

or

$$2(1.008 \text{ amu}) + 16.00 \text{ amu} = 18.02 \text{ amu}$$

In general, we need to multiply the atomic mass of each element by the number of atoms of that element present in the molecule and sum over all the elements. Example 3.5 illustrates this approach.

Example 3.5

Calculate the molecular masses (in amu) of the following compounds: (a) sulfur dioxide (SO_2), a gas that is responsible for acid rain, and (b) caffeine ($C_8H_{10}N_4O_2$), a stimulant present in tea, coffee, and cola beverages.

Strategy How do atomic masses of different elements combine to give the molecular mass of a compound?

Solution To calculate molecular mass, we need to sum all the atomic masses in the molecule. For each element, we multiply the atomic mass of the element by the number of atoms of that element in the molecule. We find atomic masses in the periodic table (inside front cover).

(a) There are two O atoms and one S atom in SO_2, so that

$$\text{molecular mass of } SO_2 = 32.07 \text{ amu} + 2(16.00 \text{ amu})$$
$$= 64.07 \text{ amu}$$

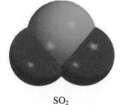

SO_2

(Continued)

Similar problems: 3.23, 3.24.

(b) There are eight C atoms, ten H atoms, four N atoms, and two O atoms in caffeine, so the molecular mass of $C_8H_{10}N_4O_2$ is given by

$$8(12.01 \text{ amu}) + 10(1.008 \text{ amu}) + 4(14.01 \text{ amu}) + 2(16.00 \text{ amu}) = 194.20 \text{ amu}$$

Practice Exercise   What is the molecular mass of methanol (CH_4O)?

From the molecular mass we can determine the molar mass of a molecule or compound. The molar mass of a compound (in grams) is numerically equal to its molecular mass (in amu). For example, the molecular mass of water is 18.02 amu, so its molar mass is 18.02 g. Note that 1 mole of water weighs 18.02 g and contains 6.022×10^{23} H_2O *molecules,* just as 1 mole of elemental carbon contains 6.022×10^{23} carbon *atoms.*

As Examples 3.6 and 3.7 show, a knowledge of the molar mass enables us to calculate the numbers of moles and individual atoms in a given quantity of a compound.

Example 3.6

Methane (CH_4) is the principal component of natural gas. How many moles of CH_4 are present in 6.07 g of CH_4?

Strategy   We are given grams of CH_4 and asked to solve for moles of CH_4. What conversion factor do we need to convert between grams and moles? Arrange the appropriate conversion factor so that grams cancel and the unit moles are obtained for your answer.

Solution   The conversion factor needed to convert between grams and moles is the molar mass. First we need to calculate the molar mass of CH_4, following the procedure in Example 3.5:

$$\begin{aligned} \text{molar mass of } CH_4 &= 12.01 \text{ g} + 4(1.008 \text{ g}) \\ &= 16.04 \text{ g} \end{aligned}$$

Because

$$1 \text{ mol } CH_4 = 16.04 \text{ g } CH_4$$

the conversion factor we need should have grams in the denominator so that the unit g will cancel, leaving the unit mol in the numerator:

$$\frac{1 \text{ mol } CH_4}{16.04 \text{ g } CH_4}$$

We now write

$$6.07 \text{ g } \cancel{CH_4} \times \frac{1 \text{ mol } CH_4}{16.04 \text{ g } \cancel{CH_4}} = 0.378 \text{ mol } CH_4$$

Thus, there is 0.378 mole of CH_4 in 6.07 g of CH_4.

Check   Should 6.07 g of CH_4 equal less than 1 mole of CH_4? What is the mass of 1 mole of CH_4?

Practice Exercise   Calculate the number of moles of chloroform ($CHCl_3$) in 198 g of chloroform.

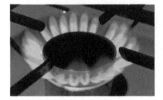

CH_4

Methane gas burning on a cooking range.

Similar problem: 3.26.

Example 3.7

How many hydrogen atoms are present in 25.6 g of urea [$(NH_2)_2CO$], which is used as a fertilizer, in animal feed, and in the manufacture of polymers? The molar mass of urea is 60.06 g.

Strategy We are asked to solve for atoms of hydrogen in 25.6 g of urea. We cannot convert directly from grams of urea to atoms of hydrogen. How should molar mass and Avogadro's number be used in this calculation? How many moles of H are in 1 mole of urea?

Solution To calculate the number of H atoms, we first must convert grams of urea to moles of urea using the molar mass of urea. This part is similar to Example 3.2. The molecular formula of urea shows there are four moles of H atoms in one mole of urea molecule, so the mole ratio is 4:1. Finally, knowing the number of moles of H atoms, we can calculate the number of H atoms using Avogadro's number. We need two conversion factors: molar mass and Avogadro's number. We can combine these conversions

$$\text{grams of urea} \longrightarrow \text{moles of urea} \longrightarrow \text{moles of H} \longrightarrow \text{atoms of H}$$

into one step:

$$25.6 \text{ g } (NH_2)_2CO \times \frac{1 \text{ mol } (NH_2)_2CO}{60.06 \text{ g } (NH_2)_2CO} \times \frac{4 \text{ mol H}}{1 \text{ mol } (NH_2)_2CO} \times \frac{6.022 \times 10^{23} \text{ H atoms}}{1 \text{ mol H}}$$

$$= 1.03 \times 10^{24} \text{ H atoms}$$

Check Does the answer look reasonable? How many atoms of H would 60.06 g of urea contain?

Practice Exercise How many H atoms are in 72.5 g of isopropanol (rubbing alcohol), C_3H_8O?

Urea.

Similar problems: 3.27, 3.28.

Finally, note that for ionic compounds like NaCl and MgO that do not contain discrete molecular units, we use the term *formula mass* instead. The formula unit of NaCl consists of one Na^+ ion and one Cl^- ion. Thus, the formula mass of NaCl is the mass of one formula unit:

$$\text{formula mass of NaCl} = 22.99 \text{ amu} + 35.45 \text{ amu}$$
$$= 58.44 \text{ amu}$$

and its molar mass is 58.44 g.

Note that the combined mass of a Na^+ ion and a Cl^- ion is equal to the combined mass of a Na atom and a Cl atom.

Review of Concepts
Determine the molecular mass and the molar mass of citric acid, $H_3C_6H_5O_7$.

3.4 The Mass Spectrometer

The most direct and most accurate method for determining atomic and molecular masses is mass spectrometry, which is depicted in Figure 3.3. In one type of a *mass spectrometer*, a gaseous sample is bombarded by a stream of high-energy electrons. Collisions between the electrons and the gaseous atoms (or molecules) produce positive ions by dislodging an electron from each atom or molecule. These positive

84   **Chapter 3** ▪ Mass Relationships in Chemical Reactions

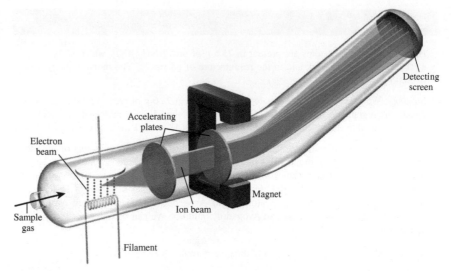

Figure 3.3 *Schematic diagram of one type of mass spectrometer.*

ions (of mass *m* and charge *e*) are accelerated by two oppositely charged plates as they pass through the plates. The emerging ions are deflected into a circular path by a magnet. The radius of the path depends on the charge-to-mass ratio (that is, *e/m*). Ions of smaller *e/m* ratio trace a wider curve than those having a larger *e/m* ratio, so that ions with equal charges but different masses are separated from one another. The mass of each ion (and hence its parent atom or molecule) is determined from the magnitude of its deflection. Eventually the ions arrive at the detector, which registers a current for each type of ion. The amount of current generated is directly proportional to the number of ions, so it enables us to determine the relative abundance of isotopes.

The first mass spectrometer, developed in the 1920s by the English physicist F. W. Aston,[†] was crude by today's standards. Nevertheless, it provided indisputable evidence of the existence of isotopes—neon-20 (atomic mass 19.9924 amu and natural abundance 90.92 percent) and neon-22 (atomic mass 21.9914 amu and natural abundance 8.82 percent). When more sophisticated and sensitive mass spectrometers became available, scientists were surprised to discover that neon has a third stable isotope with an atomic mass of 20.9940 amu and natural abundance 0.257 percent (Figure 3.4). This example illustrates how very important experimental accuracy is to a quantitative science like chemistry. Early experiments failed to detect neon-21 because its natural abundance is just 0.257 percent. In other words, only 26 in 10,000 Ne atoms are neon-21. The masses of molecules can be determined in a similar manner by the mass spectrometer.

Note that it is possible to determine the molar mass of a compound without knowing its chemical formula.

Review of Concepts

Explain how the mass spectrometer enables chemists to determine the average atomic mass of chlorine, which has two stable isotopes (^{35}Cl and ^{37}Cl).

[†]Francis William Aston (1877–1945). English chemist and physicist. He was awarded the Nobel Prize in Chemistry in 1922 for developing the mass spectrometer.

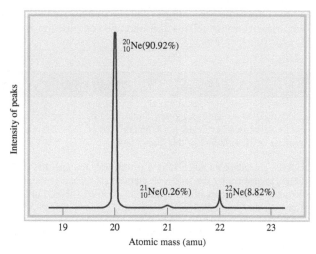

Figure 3.4 *The mass spectrum of the three isotopes of neon.*

3.5 Percent Composition of Compounds

As we have seen, the formula of a compound tells us the numbers of atoms of each element in a unit of the compound. However, suppose we needed to verify the purity of a compound for use in a laboratory experiment. From the formula we could calculate what percent of the total mass of the compound is contributed by each element. Then, by comparing the result to the percent composition obtained experimentally for our sample, we could determine the purity of the sample.

The **percent composition by mass** is the *percent by mass of each element in a compound*. Percent composition is obtained by dividing the mass of each element in 1 mole of the compound by the molar mass of the compound and multiplying by 100 percent. Mathematically, the percent composition of an element in a compound is expressed as

$$\text{percent composition of an element} = \frac{n \times \text{molar mass of element}}{\text{molar mass of compound}} \times 100\% \quad (3.1)$$

where n is the number of moles of the element in 1 mole of the compound. For example, in 1 mole of hydrogen peroxide (H_2O_2) there are 2 moles of H atoms and 2 moles of O atoms. The molar masses of H_2O_2, H, and O are 34.02 g, 1.008 g, and 16.00 g, respectively. Therefore, the percent composition of H_2O_2 is calculated as follows:

$$\%H = \frac{2 \times 1.008 \text{ g H}}{34.02 \text{ g } H_2O_2} \times 100\% = 5.926\%$$

$$\%O = \frac{2 \times 16.00 \text{ g O}}{34.02 \text{ g } H_2O_2} \times 100\% = 94.06\%$$

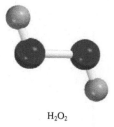

H_2O_2

The sum of the percentages is 5.926% + 94.06% = 99.99%. The small discrepancy from 100 percent is due to the way we rounded off the molar masses of the elements. If we had used the empirical formula HO for the calculation, we

86   **Chapter 3** ▪ Mass Relationships in Chemical Reactions

would have obtained the same percentages. This is so because both the molecular formula and empirical formula tell us the percent composition by mass of the compound.

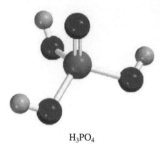

H_3PO_4

Similar problem: 3.40.

Example 3.8

Phosphoric acid (H_3PO_4) is a colorless, syrupy liquid used in detergents, fertilizers, toothpastes, and in carbonated beverages for a "tangy" flavor. Calculate the percent composition by mass of H, P, and O in this compound.

Strategy Recall the procedure for calculating a percentage. Assume that we have 1 mole of H_3PO_4. The percent by mass of each element (H, P, and O) is given by the combined molar mass of the atoms of the element in 1 mole of H_3PO_4 divided by the molar mass of H_3PO_4, then multiplied by 100 percent.

Solution The molar mass of H_3PO_4 is 97.99 g. The percent by mass of each of the elements in H_3PO_4 is calculated as follows:

$$\%H = \frac{3(1.008 \text{ g}) \text{ H}}{97.99 \text{ g } H_3PO_4} \times 100\% = 3.086\%$$

$$\%P = \frac{30.97 \text{ g P}}{97.99 \text{ g } H_3PO_4} \times 100\% = 31.61\%$$

$$\%O = \frac{4(16.00 \text{ g}) \text{ O}}{97.99 \text{ g } H_3PO_4} \times 100\% = 65.31\%$$

Check Do the percentages add to 100 percent? The sum of the percentages is (3.086% + 31.61% + 65.31%) = 100.01%. The small discrepancy from 100 percent is due to the way we rounded off.

Practice Exercise Calculate the percent composition by mass of each of the elements in sulfuric acid (H_2SO_4).

The procedure used in the example can be reversed if necessary. Given the percent composition by mass of a compound, we can determine the empirical formula of the compound (Figure 3.5). Because we are dealing with percentages and the sum of all the percentages is 100 percent, it is convenient to assume that we started with 100 g of a compound, as Example 3.9 shows.

Example 3.9

Ascorbic acid (vitamin C) cures scurvy. It is composed of 40.92 percent carbon (C), 4.58 percent hydrogen (H), and 54.50 percent oxygen (O) by mass. Determine its empirical formula.

Strategy In a chemical formula, the subscripts represent the ratio of the number of moles of each element that combine to form one mole of the compound. How can we convert from mass percent to moles? If we assume an exactly 100-g sample of the compound, do we know the mass of each element in the compound? How do we then convert from grams to moles?

Solution If we have 100 g of ascorbic acid, then each percentage can be converted directly to grams. In this sample, there will be 40.92 g of C, 4.58 g of H, and 54.50 g of O. Because the subscripts in the formula represent a mole ratio, we need to convert the grams of each element to moles. The conversion factor needed is the

(Continued)

```
┌─────────────┐
│    Mass     │
│   percent   │
└─────────────┘
       │ Convert to grams and
       ↓ divide by molar mass
┌─────────────┐
│  Moles of   │
│ each element│
└─────────────┘
       │ Divide by the smallest
       ↓ number of moles
┌─────────────┐
│ Mole ratios │
│ of elements │
└─────────────┘
       │ Change to
       ↓ integer subscripts
┌─────────────┐
│  Empirical  │
│   formula   │
└─────────────┘
```

Figure 3.5 *Procedure for calculating the empirical formula of a compound from its percent compositions.*

molar mass of each element. Let n represent the number of moles of each element so that

$$n_C = 40.92 \text{ g C} \times \frac{1 \text{ mol C}}{12.01 \text{ g C}} = 3.407 \text{ mol C}$$

$$n_H = 4.58 \text{ g H} \times \frac{1 \text{ mol H}}{1.008 \text{ g H}} = 4.54 \text{ mol H}$$

$$n_O = 54.50 \text{ g O} \times \frac{1 \text{ mol O}}{16.00 \text{ g O}} = 3.406 \text{ mol O}$$

Thus, we arrive at the formula $C_{3.407}H_{4.54}O_{3.406}$, which gives the identity and the mole ratios of atoms present. However, chemical formulas are written with whole numbers. Try to convert to whole numbers by dividing all the subscripts by the smallest subscript (3.406):

$$C: \frac{3.407}{3.406} \approx 1 \quad H: \frac{4.54}{3.406} = 1.33 \quad O: \frac{3.406}{3.406} = 1$$

where the $\approx$ sign means "approximately equal to." This gives $CH_{1.33}O$ as the formula for ascorbic acid. Next, we need to convert 1.33, the subscript for H, into an integer. This can be done by a trial-and-error procedure:

$$1.33 \times 1 = 1.33$$
$$1.33 \times 2 = 2.66$$
$$1.33 \times 3 = 3.99 \approx 4$$

Because 1.33×3 gives us an integer (4), we multiply all the subscripts by 3 and obtain $C_3H_4O_3$ as the empirical formula for ascorbic acid.

Check Are the subscripts in $C_3H_4O_3$ reduced to the smallest whole numbers?

Practice Exercise Determine the empirical formula of a compound having the following percent composition by mass: K: 24.75 percent; Mn: 34.77 percent; O: 40.51 percent.

The molecular formula of ascorbic acid is $C_6H_8O_6$.

Similar problems: 3.49, 3.50.

Chemists often want to know the actual mass of an element in a certain mass of a compound. For example, in the mining industry, this information will tell the scientists about the quality of the ore. Because the percent composition by mass of the elements in the substance can be readily calculated, such a problem can be solved in a rather direct way.

Example 3.10

Chalcopyrite ($CuFeS_2$) is a principal mineral of copper. Calculate the number of kilograms of Cu in 3.71×10^3 kg of chalcopyrite.

Strategy Chalcopyrite is composed of Cu, Fe, and S. The mass due to Cu is based on its percentage by mass in the compound. How do we calculate mass percent of an element?

Solution The molar masses of Cu and $CuFeS_2$ are 63.55 g and 183.5 g, respectively. The mass percent of Cu is therefore

$$\%Cu = \frac{\text{molar mass of Cu}}{\text{molar mass of } CuFeS_2} \times 100\%$$

$$= \frac{63.55 \text{ g}}{183.5 \text{ g}} \times 100\% = 34.63\%$$

To calculate the mass of Cu in a 3.71×10^3 kg sample of $CuFeS_2$, we need to convert the percentage to a fraction (that is, convert 34.63 percent to 34.63/100, or 0.3463) and write

$$\text{mass of Cu in } CuFeS_2 = 0.3463 \times (3.71 \times 10^3 \text{ kg}) = 1.28 \times 10^3 \text{ kg}$$

(Continued)

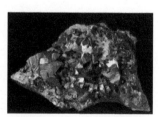

Chalcopyrite.

88   **Chapter 3** ▪ Mass Relationships in Chemical Reactions

Similar problem: 3.45.

Check As a ball-park estimate, note that the mass percent of Cu is roughly 33 percent, so that a third of the mass should be Cu; that is, $\frac{1}{3} \times 3.71 \times 10^3$ kg $\approx 1.24 \times 10^3$ kg. This quantity is quite close to the answer.

Practice Exercise Calculate the number of grams of Al in 371 g of Al_2O_3.

Review of Concepts

Without doing detailed calculations, estimate whether the percent composition by mass of Sr is greater than or smaller than that of O in strontium nitrate [$Sr(NO_3)_2$].

3.6 Experimental Determination of Empirical Formulas

The fact that we can determine the empirical formula of a compound if we know the percent composition enables us to identify compounds experimentally. The procedure is as follows. First, chemical analysis tells us the number of grams of each element present in a given amount of a compound. Then, we convert the quantities in grams to number of moles of each element. Finally, using the method given in Example 3.9, we find the empirical formula of the compound.

As a specific example, let us consider the compound ethanol. When ethanol is burned in an apparatus such as that shown in Figure 3.6, carbon dioxide (CO_2) and water (H_2O) are given off. Because neither carbon nor hydrogen was in the inlet gas, we can conclude that both carbon (C) and hydrogen (H) were present in ethanol and that oxygen (O) may also be present. (Molecular oxygen was added in the combustion process, but some of the oxygen may also have come from the original ethanol sample.)

The masses of CO_2 and of H_2O produced can be determined by measuring the increase in mass of the CO_2 and H_2O absorbers, respectively. Suppose that in one experiment the combustion of 11.5 g of ethanol produced 22.0 g of CO_2 and 13.5 g of H_2O. We can calculate the mass of carbon and hydrogen in the original 11.5-g sample of ethanol as follows:

$$\text{mass of C} = 22.0 \text{ g } CO_2 \times \frac{1 \text{ mol } CO_2}{44.01 \text{ g } CO_2} \times \frac{1 \text{ mol } C}{1 \text{ mol } CO_2} \times \frac{12.01 \text{ g C}}{1 \text{ mol } C}$$

$$= 6.00 \text{ g C}$$

$$\text{mass of H} = 13.5 \text{ g } H_2O \times \frac{1 \text{ mol } H_2O}{18.02 \text{ g } H_2O} \times \frac{2 \text{ mol } H}{1 \text{ mol } H_2O} \times \frac{1.008 \text{ g H}}{1 \text{ mol } H}$$

$$= 1.51 \text{ g H}$$

Figure 3.6 *Apparatus for determining the empirical formula of ethanol. The absorbers are substances that can retain water and carbon dioxide, respectively. CuO is used to ensure complete combustion of all carbon to CO_2.*

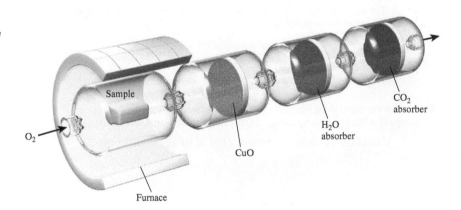

Thus, 11.5 g of ethanol contains 6.00 g of carbon and 1.51 g of hydrogen. The remainder must be oxygen, whose mass is

$$\begin{aligned} \text{mass of O} &= \text{mass of sample} - (\text{mass of C} + \text{mass of H}) \\ &= 11.5 \text{ g} - (6.00 \text{ g} + 1.51 \text{ g}) \\ &= 4.0 \text{ g} \end{aligned}$$

The number of moles of each element present in 11.5 g of ethanol is

$$\text{moles of C} = 6.00 \text{ g C} \times \frac{1 \text{ mol C}}{12.01 \text{ g C}} = 0.500 \text{ mol C}$$

$$\text{moles of H} = 1.51 \text{ g H} \times \frac{1 \text{ mol H}}{1.008 \text{ g H}} = 1.50 \text{ mol H}$$

$$\text{moles of O} = 4.0 \text{ g O} \times \frac{1 \text{ mol O}}{16.00 \text{ g O}} = 0.25 \text{ mol O}$$

The formula of ethanol is therefore $C_{0.50}H_{1.5}O_{0.25}$ (we round off the number of moles to two significant figures). Because the number of atoms must be an integer, we divide the subscripts by 0.25, the smallest subscript, and obtain for the empirical formula C_2H_6O.

Now we can better understand the word "empirical," which literally means "based only on observation and measurement." The empirical formula of ethanol is determined from analysis of the compound in terms of its component elements. No knowledge of how the atoms are linked together in the compound is required.

It happens that the molecular formula of ethanol is the same as its empirical formula.

Determination of Molecular Formulas

The formula calculated from percent composition by mass is always the empirical formula because the subscripts in the formula are always reduced to the smallest whole numbers. To calculate the actual, molecular formula we must know the *approximate* molar mass of the compound in addition to its empirical formula. Knowing that the molar mass of a compound must be an integral multiple of the molar mass of its empirical formula, we can use the molar mass to find the molecular formula, as Example 3.11 demonstrates.

Example 3.11

A sample of a compound contains 30.46 percent nitrogen and 69.54 percent oxygen by mass, as determined by a mass spectrometer. In a separate experiment, the molar mass of the compound is found to be between 90 g and 95 g. Determine the molecular formula and the accurate molar mass of the compound.

Strategy To determine the molecular formula, we first need to determine the empirical formula. Comparing the empirical molar mass to the experimentally determined molar mass will reveal the relationship between the empirical formula and molecular formula.

Solution We start by assuming that there are 100 g of the compound. Then each percentage can be converted directly to grams; that is, 30.46 g of N and 69.54 g of O. Let n represent the number of moles of each element so that

$$n_N = 30.46 \text{ g N} \times \frac{1 \text{ mol N}}{14.01 \text{ g N}} = 2.174 \text{ mol N}$$

$$n_O = 69.54 \text{ g O} \times \frac{1 \text{ mol O}}{16.00 \text{ g O}} = 4.346 \text{ mol O}$$

(Continued)

N₂O₄

Similar problems: 3.52, 3.53, 3.54.

Thus, we arrive at the formula $N_{2.174}O_{4.346}$, which gives the identity and the ratios of atoms present. However, chemical formulas are written with whole numbers. Try to convert to whole numbers by dividing the subscripts by the smaller subscript (2.174). After rounding off, we obtain NO_2 as the empirical formula.

The molecular formula might be the same as the empirical formula or some integral multiple of it (for example, two, three, four, or more times the empirical formula). Comparing the ratio of the molar mass to the molar mass of the empirical formula will show the integral relationship between the empirical and molecular formulas. The molar mass of the empirical formula NO_2 is

$$\text{empirical molar mass} = 14.01 \text{ g} + 2(16.00 \text{ g}) = 46.01 \text{ g}$$

Next, we determine the ratio between the molar mass and the empirical molar mass

$$\frac{\text{molar mass}}{\text{empirical molar mass}} = \frac{90 \text{ g}}{46.01 \text{ g}} \approx 2$$

The molar mass is twice the empirical molar mass. This means that there are two NO_2 units in each molecule of the compound, and the molecular formula is $(NO_2)_2$ or N_2O_4.

The actual molar mass of the compound is two times the empirical molar mass, that is, 2(46.01 g) or 92.02 g, which is between 90 g and 95 g.

Check Note that in determining the molecular formula from the empirical formula, we need only know the *approximate* molar mass of the compound. The reason is that the true molar mass is an integral multiple (1×, 2×, 3×, . . .) of the empirical molar mass. Therefore, the ratio (molar mass/empirical molar mass) will always be close to an integer.

Practice Exercise A sample of a compound containing boron (B) and hydrogen (H) contains 6.444 g of B and 1.803 g of H. The molar mass of the compound is about 30 g. What is its molecular formula?

Review of Concepts

What is the molecular formula of a compound containing only carbon and hydrogen if combustion of 1.05 g of the compound produces 3.30 g CO_2 and 1.35 g H_2O and its molar mass is about 70 g?

3.7 Chemical Reactions and Chemical Equations

Having discussed the masses of atoms and molecules, we turn next to what happens to atoms and molecules in a ***chemical reaction,*** *a process in which a substance (or substances) is changed into one or more new substances.* To communicate with one another about chemical reactions, chemists have devised a standard way to represent them using chemical equations. A ***chemical equation*** *uses chemical symbols to show what happens during a chemical reaction.* In this section, we will learn how to write chemical equations and balance them.

Writing Chemical Equations

Consider what happens when hydrogen gas (H_2) burns in air (which contains oxygen, O_2) to form water (H_2O). This reaction can be represented by the chemical equation

$$H_2 + O_2 \longrightarrow H_2O \tag{3.2}$$

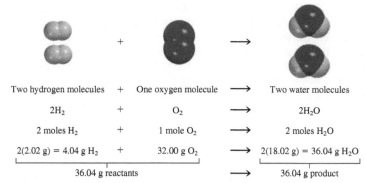

Figure 3.7 *Three ways of representing the combustion of hydrogen. In accordance with the law of conservation of mass, the number of each type of atom must be the same on both sides of the equation.*

where the "plus" sign means "reacts with" and the arrow means "to yield." Thus, this symbolic expression can be read: "Molecular hydrogen reacts with molecular oxygen to yield water." The reaction is assumed to proceed from left to right as the arrow indicates.

Equation (3.2) is not complete, however, because there are twice as many oxygen atoms on the left side of the arrow (two) as on the right side (one). To conform with the law of conservation of mass, there must be the same number of each type of atom on both sides of the arrow; that is, we must have as many atoms after the reaction ends as we did before it started. We can *balance* Equation (3.2) by placing the appropriate coefficient (2 in this case) in front of H_2 and H_2O:

We use the law of conservation of mass as our guide in balancing chemical equations.

$$2H_2 + O_2 \longrightarrow 2H_2O$$

When the coefficient is 1, as in the case of O_2, it is not shown.

This *balanced chemical equation* shows that "two hydrogen molecules can combine or react with one oxygen molecule to form two water molecules" (Figure 3.7). Because the ratio of the number of molecules is equal to the ratio of the number of moles, the equation can also be read as "2 moles of hydrogen molecules react with 1 mole of oxygen molecules to produce 2 moles of water molecules." We know the mass of a mole of each of these substances, so we can also interpret the equation as "4.04 g of H_2 react with 32.00 g of O_2 to give 36.04 g of H_2O." These three ways of reading the equation are summarized in Figure 3.7.

We refer to H_2 and O_2 in Equation (3.2) as **reactants,** which are *the starting materials in a chemical reaction.* Water is the **product,** which is *the substance formed as a result of a chemical reaction.* A chemical equation, then, is just the chemist's shorthand description of a reaction. In a chemical equation, the reactants are conventionally written on the left and the products on the right of the arrow:

$$\text{reactants} \longrightarrow \text{products}$$

To provide additional information, chemists often indicate the physical states of the reactants and products by using the letters *g, l,* and *s* to denote gas, liquid, and solid, respectively. For example,

$$2CO(g) + O_2(g) \longrightarrow 2CO_2(g)$$
$$2HgO(s) \longrightarrow 2Hg(l) + O_2(g)$$

The procedure for balancing chemical equations is shown on p. 92.

To represent what happens when sodium chloride (NaCl) is added to water, we write

$$NaCl(s) \xrightarrow{H_2O} NaCl(aq)$$

where *aq* denotes the aqueous (that is, water) environment. Writing H_2O above the arrow symbolizes the physical process of dissolving a substance in water, although it is sometimes left out for simplicity.

Knowing the states of the reactants and products is especially useful in the laboratory. For example, when potassium bromide (KBr) and silver nitrate ($AgNO_3$) react in an aqueous environment, a solid, silver bromide (AgBr), is formed. This reaction can be represented by the equation:

$$KBr(aq) + AgNO_3(aq) \longrightarrow KNO_3(aq) + AgBr(s)$$

If the physical states of reactants and products are not given, an uninformed person might try to bring about the reaction by mixing solid KBr with solid $AgNO_3$. These solids would react very slowly or not at all. Imagining the process on the microscopic level, we can understand that for a product like silver bromide to form, the Ag^+ and Br^- ions would have to come in contact with each other. However, these ions are locked in place in their solid compounds and have little mobility. (Here is an example of how we explain a phenomenon by thinking about what happens at the molecular level, as discussed in Section 1.2.)

Balancing Chemical Equations

Suppose we want to write an equation to describe a chemical reaction that we have just carried out in the laboratory. How should we go about doing it? Because we know the identities of the reactants, we can write their chemical formulas. The identities of products are more difficult to establish. For simple reactions it is often possible to guess the product(s). For more complicated reactions involving three or more products, chemists may need to perform further tests to establish the presence of specific compounds.

Once we have identified all the reactants and products and have written the correct formulas for them, we assemble them in the conventional sequence—reactants on the left separated by an arrow from products on the right. The equation written at this point is likely to be *unbalanced;* that is, the number of each type of atom on one side of the arrow differs from the number on the other side. In general, we can balance a chemical equation by the following steps:

1. Identify all reactants and products and write their correct formulas on the left side and right side of the equation, respectively.

2. Begin balancing the equation by trying different coefficients to make the number of atoms of each element the same on both sides of the equation. We can change the coefficients (the numbers preceding the formulas) but not the subscripts (the numbers within formulas). Changing the subscripts would change the identity of the substance. For example, $2NO_2$ means "two molecules of nitrogen dioxide," but if we double the subscripts, we have N_2O_4, which is the formula of dinitrogen tetroxide, a completely different compound.

3. First, look for elements that appear only once on each side of the equation with the same number of atoms on each side: The formulas containing these elements must have the same coefficient. Therefore, there is no need to adjust the coefficients of these elements at this point. Next, look for elements that appear only once on each side of the equation but in unequal numbers of atoms. Balance these elements. Finally, balance elements that appear in two or more formulas on the same side of the equation.

4. Check your balanced equation to be sure that you have the same total number of each type of atoms on both sides of the equation arrow.

Let's consider a specific example. In the laboratory, small amounts of oxygen gas can be prepared by heating potassium chlorate ($KClO_3$). The products are oxygen gas (O_2) and potassium chloride (KCl). From this information, we write

$$KClO_3 \longrightarrow KCl + O_2$$

Heating potassium chlorate produces oxygen, which supports the combustion of a wood splint.

(For simplicity, we omit the physical states of reactants and products.) All three elements (K, Cl, and O) appear only once on each side of the equation, but only for K and Cl do we have equal numbers of atoms on both sides. Thus, $KClO_3$ and KCl must have the same coefficient. The next step is to make the number of O atoms the same on both sides of the equation. Because there are three O atoms on the left and two O atoms on the right of the equation, we can balance the O atoms by placing a 2 in front of $KClO_3$ and a 3 in front of O_2.

$$2KClO_3 \longrightarrow KCl + 3O_2$$

Finally, we balance the K and Cl atoms by placing a 2 in front of KCl:

$$2KClO_3 \longrightarrow 2KCl + 3O_2 \tag{3.3}$$

As a final check, we can draw up a balance sheet for the reactants and products where the number in parentheses indicates the number of atoms of each element:

Reactants	Products
K (2)	K (2)
Cl (2)	Cl (2)
O (6)	O (6)

Note that this equation could also be balanced with coefficients that are multiples of 2 (for $KClO_3$), 2 (for KCl), and 3 (for O_2); for example,

$$4KClO_3 \longrightarrow 4KCl + 6O_2$$

However, it is common practice to use the *simplest* possible set of whole-number coefficients to balance the equation. Equation (3.3) conforms to this convention.

Now let us consider the combustion (that is, burning) of the natural gas component ethane (C_2H_6) in oxygen or air, which yields carbon dioxide (CO_2) and water. The unbalanced equation is

$$C_2H_6 + O_2 \longrightarrow CO_2 + H_2O$$

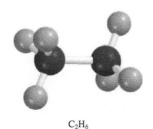

C_2H_6

We see that the number of atoms is not the same on both sides of the equation for any of the elements (C, H, and O). In addition, C and H appear only once on each side of the equation; O appears in two compounds on the right side (CO_2 and H_2O). To balance the C atoms, we place a 2 in front of CO_2:

$$C_2H_6 + O_2 \longrightarrow 2CO_2 + H_2O$$

To balance the H atoms, we place a 3 in front of H_2O:

$$C_2H_6 + O_2 \longrightarrow 2CO_2 + 3H_2O$$

At this stage, the C and H atoms are balanced, but the O atoms are not because there are seven O atoms on the right-hand side and only two O atoms on the left-hand side of the equation. This inequality of O atoms can be eliminated by writing $\frac{7}{2}$ in front of the O_2 on the left-hand side:

$$C_2H_6 + \tfrac{7}{2}O_2 \longrightarrow 2CO_2 + 3H_2O$$

The "logic" for using $\frac{7}{2}$ as a coefficient is that there were seven oxygen atoms on the right-hand side of the equation, but only a pair of oxygen atoms (O_2) on the left. To balance them we ask how many *pairs* of oxygen atoms are needed to equal seven oxygen atoms. Just as 3.5 pairs of shoes equal seven shoes, $\frac{7}{2}O_2$ molecules equal seven O atoms. As the following tally shows, the equation is now balanced:

Reactants	Products
C (2)	C (2)
H (6)	H (6)
O (7)	O (7)

However, we normally prefer to express the coefficients as whole numbers rather than as fractions. Therefore, we multiply the entire equation by 2 to convert $\frac{7}{2}$ to 7:

$$2C_2H_6 + 7O_2 \longrightarrow 4CO_2 + 6H_2O$$

The final tally is

Reactants	Products
C (4)	C (4)
H (12)	H (12)
O (14)	O (14)

Note that the coefficients used in balancing the last equation are the smallest possible set of whole numbers.

In Example 3.12 we will continue to practice our equation-balancing skills.

Example 3.12

When aluminum metal is exposed to air, a protective layer of aluminum oxide (Al_2O_3) forms on its surface. This layer prevents further reaction between aluminum and oxygen, and it is the reason that aluminum beverage cans do not corrode. [In the case of iron, the rust, or iron(III) oxide, that forms is too porous to protect the iron metal underneath, so rusting continues.] Write a balanced equation for the formation of Al_2O_3.

Strategy Remember that the formula of an element or compound cannot be changed when balancing a chemical equation. The equation is balanced by placing the appropriate coefficients in front of the formulas. Follow the procedure described on p. 92.

Solution The unbalanced equation is

$$Al + O_2 \longrightarrow Al_2O_3$$

In a balanced equation, the number and types of atoms on each side of the equation must be the same. We see that there is one Al atom on the reactants side and there are two Al atoms on the product side. We can balance the Al atoms by placing a coefficient of 2 in front of Al on the reactants side.

$$2Al + O_2 \longrightarrow Al_2O_3$$

There are two O atoms on the reactants side, and three O atoms on the product side of the equation. We can balance the O atoms by placing a coefficient of $\frac{3}{2}$ in front of O_2 on the reactants side.

$$2Al + \tfrac{3}{2}O_2 \longrightarrow Al_2O_3$$

(Continued)

This is a balanced equation. However, equations are normally balanced with the smallest set of *whole*-number coefficients. Multiplying both sides of the equation by 2 gives whole-number coefficients.

$$2(2Al + \tfrac{3}{2}O_2 \longrightarrow Al_2O_3)$$

or

$$4Al + 3O_2 \longrightarrow 2Al_2O_3$$

Check For an equation to be balanced, the number and types of atoms on each side of the equation must be the same. The final tally is

Reactants	Products
Al (4)	Al (4)
O (6)	O (6)

The equation is balanced. Also, the coefficients are reduced to the simplest set of whole numbers.

Practice Exercise Balance the equation representing the reaction between iron(III) oxide, Fe_2O_3, and carbon monoxide (CO) to yield iron (Fe) and carbon dioxide (CO_2).

Similar problems: 3.59, 3.60.

Review of Concepts

Which parts of the equation shown here are essential for a balanced equation and which parts are helpful if we want to carry out the reaction in the laboratory?

$$BaH_2(s) + 2H_2O(l) \longrightarrow Ba(OH)_2(aq) + 2H_2(g)$$

3.8 Amounts of Reactants and Products

A basic question raised in the chemical laboratory is "How much product will be formed from specific amounts of starting materials (reactants)?" Or in some cases, we might ask the reverse question: "How much starting material must be used to obtain a specific amount of product?" To interpret a reaction quantitatively, we need to apply our knowledge of molar masses and the mole concept. *Stoichiometry* is *the quantitative study of reactants and products in a chemical reaction.*

Whether the units given for reactants (or products) are moles, grams, liters (for gases), or some other units, we use moles to calculate the amount of product formed in a reaction. This approach is called the *mole method,* which means simply that *the stoichiometric coefficients in a chemical equation can be interpreted as the number of moles of each substance.* For example, industrially ammonia is synthesized from hydrogen and nitrogen as follows:

$$N_2(g) + 3H_2(g) \longrightarrow 2NH_3(g)$$

The stoichiometric coefficients show that one molecule of N_2 reacts with three molecules of H_2 to form two molecules of NH_3. It follows that the relative numbers of moles are the same as the relative number of molecules:

$N_2(g)$	+	$3H_2(g)$	$\longrightarrow$	$2NH_3(g)$
1 molecule		3 molecules		2 molecules
6.022×10^{23} molecules		$3(6.022 \times 10^{23}$ molecules)		$2(6.022 \times 10^{23}$ molecules)
1 mol		3 mol		2 mol

The synthesis of NH_3 from H_2 and N_2.

Thus, this equation can also be read as "1 mole of N_2 gas combines with 3 moles of H_2 gas to form 2 moles of NH_3 gas." In stoichiometric calculations, we say that three moles of H_2 are equivalent to two moles of NH_3, that is,

$$3 \text{ mol } H_2 \mathrel{\hat{=}} 2 \text{ mol } NH_3$$

where the symbol $\hat{=}$ means "stoichiometrically equivalent to" or simply "equivalent to." This relationship enables us to write the conversion factors

$$\frac{3 \text{ mol } H_2}{2 \text{ mol } NH_3} \quad \text{and} \quad \frac{2 \text{ mol } NH_3}{3 \text{ mol } H_2}$$

Similarly, we have $1 \text{ mol } N_2 \mathrel{\hat{=}} 2 \text{ mol } NH_3$ and $1 \text{ mol } N_2 \mathrel{\hat{=}} 3 \text{ mol } H_2$.

Let's consider a simple example in which 6.0 moles of H_2 react completely with N_2 to form NH_3. To calculate the amount of NH_3 produced in moles, we use the conversion factor that has H_2 in the denominator and write

$$\text{moles of } NH_3 \text{ produced} = 6.0 \text{ mol } H_2 \times \frac{2 \text{ mol } NH_3}{3 \text{ mol } H_2}$$
$$= 4.0 \text{ mol } NH_3$$

Now suppose 16.0 g of H_2 react completely with N_2 to form NH_3. How many grams of NH_3 will be formed? To do this calculation, we note that the link between H_2 and NH_3 is the mole ratio from the balanced equation. So we need to first convert grams of H_2 to moles of H_2, then to moles of NH_3, and finally to grams of NH_3. The conversion steps are

$$\text{grams of } H_2 \longrightarrow \text{moles of } H_2 \longrightarrow \text{moles of } NH_3 \longrightarrow \text{grams of } NH_3$$

First, we convert 16.0 g of H_2 to number of moles of H_2, using the molar mass of H_2 as the conversion factor:

$$\text{moles of } H_2 = 16.0 \text{ g } H_2 \times \frac{1 \text{ mol } H_2}{2.016 \text{ g } H_2}$$
$$= 7.94 \text{ mol } H_2$$

Next, we calculate the number of moles of NH_3 produced.

$$\text{moles of } NH_3 = 7.94 \text{ mol } H_2 \times \frac{2 \text{ mol } NH_3}{3 \text{ mol } H_2}$$
$$= 5.29 \text{ mol } NH_3$$

Finally, we calculate the mass of NH_3 produced in grams using the molar mass of NH_3 as the conversion factor

$$\text{grams of } NH_3 = 5.29 \text{ mol } NH_3 \times \frac{17.03 \text{ g } NH_3}{1 \text{ mol } NH_3}$$
$$= 90.1 \text{ g } NH_3$$

These three separate calculations can be combined in a single step as follows:

$$\text{grams of } NH_3 = 16.0 \text{ g } H_2 \times \frac{1 \text{ mol } H_2}{2.016 \text{ g } H_2} \times \frac{2 \text{ mol } NH_3}{3 \text{ mol } H_2} \times \frac{17.03 \text{ g } NH_3}{1 \text{ mol } NH_3}$$
$$= 90.1 \text{ g } NH_3$$

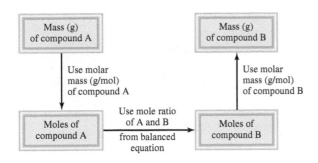

Figure 3.8 *The procedure for calculating the amounts of reactants or products in a reaction using the mole method.*

Similarly, we can calculate the mass in grams of N_2 consumed in this reaction. The conversion steps are

$$\text{grams of } H_2 \longrightarrow \text{moles of } H_2 \longrightarrow \text{moles of } N_2 \longrightarrow \text{grams of } N_2$$

By using the relationship 1 mol $N_2 \simeq$ 3 mol H_2, we write

$$\text{grams of } N_2 = 16.0 \text{ g } H_2 \times \frac{1 \text{ mol } H_2}{2.016 \text{ g } H_2} \times \frac{1 \text{ mol } N_2}{3 \text{ mol } H_2} \times \frac{28.02 \text{ g } N_2}{1 \text{ mol } N_2}$$
$$= 74.1 \text{ g } N_2$$

The general approach for solving stoichiometry problems is summarized next.

1. Write a balanced equation for the reaction.
2. Convert the given amount of the reactant (in grams or other units) to number of moles.
3. Use the mole ratio from the balanced equation to calculate the number of moles of product formed.
4. Convert the moles of product to grams (or other units) of product.

Figure 3.8 shows these steps. Sometimes we may be asked to calculate the amount of a reactant needed to form a specific amount of product. In those cases, we can reverse the steps shown in Figure 3.8.

Examples 3.13 and 3.14 illustrate the application of this approach.

Example 3.13

The food we eat is degraded, or broken down, in our bodies to provide energy for growth and function. A general overall equation for this very complex process represents the degradation of glucose ($C_6H_{12}O_6$) to carbon dioxide (CO_2) and water (H_2O):

$$C_6H_{12}O_6 + 6O_2 \longrightarrow 6CO_2 + 6H_2O$$

If 856 g of $C_6H_{12}O_6$ is consumed by a person over a certain period, what is the mass of CO_2 produced?

Strategy Looking at the balanced equation, how do we compare the amounts of $C_6H_{12}O_6$ and CO_2? We can compare them based on the *mole ratio* from the balanced equation. Starting with grams of $C_6H_{12}O_6$, how do we convert to moles of $C_6H_{12}O_6$? Once moles of CO_2 are determined using the mole ratio from the balanced equation, how do we convert to grams of CO_2?

Solution We follow the preceding steps and Figure 3.8.

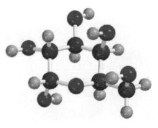

$C_6H_{12}O_6$

(Continued)

98 **Chapter 3** ▪ Mass Relationships in Chemical Reactions

Step 1: The balanced equation is given in the problem.

Step 2: To convert grams of $C_6H_{12}O_6$ to moles of $C_6H_{12}O_6$, we write

$$856 \text{ g } \cancel{C_6H_{12}O_6} \times \frac{1 \text{ mol } C_6H_{12}O_6}{180.2 \text{ g } \cancel{C_6H_{12}O_6}} = 4.750 \text{ mol } C_6H_{12}O_6$$

Step 3: From the mole ratio, we see that 1 mol $C_6H_{12}O_6 \simeq 6$ mol CO_2. Therefore, the number of moles of CO_2 formed is

$$4.750 \text{ } \cancel{\text{mol } C_6H_{12}O_6} \times \frac{6 \text{ mol } CO_2}{1 \text{ } \cancel{\text{mol } C_6H_{12}O_6}} = 28.50 \text{ mol } CO_2$$

Step 4: Finally, the number of grams of CO_2 formed is given by

$$28.50 \text{ } \cancel{\text{mol } CO_2} \times \frac{44.01 \text{ g } CO_2}{1 \text{ } \cancel{\text{mol } CO_2}} = 1.25 \times 10^3 \text{ g } CO_2$$

After some practice, we can combine the conversion steps

grams of $C_6H_{12}O_6 \longrightarrow$ moles of $C_6H_{12}O_6 \longrightarrow$ moles of $CO_2 \longrightarrow$ grams of CO_2

into one equation:

$$\text{mass of } CO_2 = 856 \text{ g } \cancel{C_6H_{12}O_6} \times \frac{1 \text{ } \cancel{\text{mol } C_6H_{12}O_6}}{180.2 \text{ g } \cancel{C_6H_{12}O_6}} \times \frac{6 \text{ } \cancel{\text{mol } CO_2}}{1 \text{ } \cancel{\text{mol } C_6H_{12}O_6}} \times \frac{44.01 \text{ g } CO_2}{1 \text{ } \cancel{\text{mol } CO_2}}$$
$$= 1.25 \times 10^3 \text{ g } CO_2$$

Check Does the answer seem reasonable? Should the mass of CO_2 produced be larger than the mass of $C_6H_{12}O_6$ reacted, even though the molar mass of CO_2 is considerably less than the molar mass of $C_6H_{12}O_6$? What is the mole ratio between CO_2 and $C_6H_{12}O_6$?

Practice Exercise Methanol (CH_3OH) burns in air according to the equation

$$2CH_3OH + 3O_2 \longrightarrow 2CO_2 + 4H_2O$$

If 209 g of methanol are used up in a combustion process, what is the mass of H_2O produced?

Similar problem: 3.72.

Example 3.14

All alkali metals react with water to produce hydrogen gas and the corresponding alkali metal hydroxide. A typical reaction is that between lithium and water:

$$2Li(s) + 2H_2O(l) \longrightarrow 2LiOH(aq) + H_2(g)$$

How many grams of Li are needed to produce 9.89 g of H_2?

Strategy The question asks for number of grams of reactant (Li) to form a specific amount of product (H_2). Therefore, we need to reverse the steps shown in Figure 3.8. From the equation we see that 2 mol Li $\simeq$ 1 mol H_2.

Solution The conversion steps are

grams of $H_2 \longrightarrow$ moles of $H_2 \longrightarrow$ moles of Li $\longrightarrow$ grams of Li

Lithium reacting with water to produce hydrogen gas.

(Continued)

Combining these steps into one equation, we write

$$9.89 \text{ g } H_2 \times \frac{1 \text{ mol } H_2}{2.016 \text{ g } H_2} \times \frac{2 \text{ mol } Li}{1 \text{ mol } H_2} \times \frac{6.941 \text{ g } Li}{1 \text{ mol } Li} = 68.1 \text{ g } Li$$

Check There are roughly 5 moles of H_2 in 9.89 g H_2, so we need 10 moles of Li. From the approximate molar mass of Li (7 g), does the answer seem reasonable?

Similar problem: 3.66.

Practice Exercise The reaction between nitric oxide (NO) and oxygen to form nitrogen dioxide (NO_2) is a key step in photochemical smog formation:

$$2NO(g) + O_2(g) \longrightarrow 2NO_2(g)$$

How many grams of O_2 are needed to produce 2.21 g of NO_2?

Review of Concepts

Which of the following statements is correct for the equation shown here?

$$4NH_3(g) + 5O_2(g) \longrightarrow 4NO(g) + 6H_2O(g)$$

(a) 6 g of H_2O are produced for every 4 g of NH_3 reacted.
(b) 1 mole of NO is produced per mole of NH_3 reacted.
(c) 2 moles of NO are produced for every 3 moles of O_2 reacted.

▶▶▶ Animation
Limiting Reagent

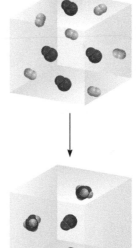

Before reaction has started

After reaction is complete

● H_2 ● CO   ● CH_3OH

Figure 3.9 *At the start of the reaction, there were six H_2 molecules and four CO molecules. At the end, all the H_2 molecules are gone and only one CO molecule is left. Therefore, H_2 molecule is the limiting reagent and CO is the excess reagent. Each molecule can also be treated as one mole of the substance in this reaction.*

3.9 Limiting Reagents

When a chemist carries out a reaction, the reactants are usually not present in exact **stoichiometric amounts,** that is, *in the proportions indicated by the balanced equation.* Because the goal of a reaction is to produce the maximum quantity of a useful compound from the starting materials, frequently a large excess of one reactant is supplied to ensure that the more expensive reactant is completely converted to the desired product. Consequently, some reactant will be left over at the end of the reaction. *The reactant used up first in a reaction* is called the **limiting reagent,** because the maximum amount of product formed depends on how much of this reactant was originally present. When this reactant is used up, no more product can be formed. *Excess reagents* are the *reactants present in quantities greater than necessary to react with the quantity of the limiting reagent.*

The concept of the limiting reagent is analogous to the relationship between men and women in a dance contest at a club. If there are 14 men and only 9 women, then only 9 female/male pairs can compete. Five men will be left without partners. The number of women thus *limits* the number of men that can dance in the contest, and there is an *excess* of men.

Consider the industrial synthesis of methanol (CH_3OH) from carbon monoxide and hydrogen at high temperatures:

$$CO(g) + 2H_2(g) \longrightarrow CH_3OH(g)$$

Suppose initially we have 4 moles of CO and 6 moles of H_2 (Figure 3.9). One way to determine which of two reactants is the limiting reagent is to calculate the number of moles of CH_3OH obtained based on the initial quantities of CO and H_2. From the

100   **Chapter 3** ▪ Mass Relationships in Chemical Reactions

preceding definition, we see that only the limiting reagent will yield the *smaller* amount of the product. Starting with 4 moles of CO, we find the number of moles of CH_3OH produced is

$$4 \text{ mol CO} \times \frac{1 \text{ mol } CH_3OH}{1 \text{ mol CO}} = 4 \text{ mol } CH_3OH$$

and starting with 6 moles of H_2, the number of moles of CH_3OH formed is

$$6 \text{ mol } H_2 \times \frac{1 \text{ mol } CH_3OH}{2 \text{ mol } H_2} = 3 \text{ mol } CH_3OH$$

Because H_2 results in a smaller amount of CH_3OH, it must be the limiting reagent. Therefore, CO is the excess reagent.

In stoichiometric calculations involving limiting reagents, the first step is to decide which reactant is the limiting reagent. After the limiting reagent has been identified, the rest of the problem can be solved as outlined in Section 3.8. Example 3.15 illustrates this approach.

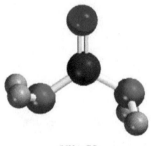

$(NH_2)_2CO$

Example 3.15

The synthesis of urea, $[(NH_2)_2CO]$, is considered to be the first recognized example of preparing a biological compound from nonbiological reactants, challenging the notion that biological processes involved a "vital force" present only in living systems. Today urea is produced industrially by reacting ammonia with carbon dioxide:

$$2NH_3(g) + CO_2(g) \longrightarrow (NH_2)_2CO(aq) + H_2O(l)$$

In one process, 637.2 g of NH_3 are treated with 1142 g of CO_2. (a) Which of the two reactants is the limiting reagent? (b) Calculate the mass of $(NH_2)_2CO$ formed. (c) How much excess reagent (in grams) is left at the end of the reaction?

(a) Strategy The reactant that produces fewer moles of product is the limiting reagent because it limits the amount of product that can be formed. How do we convert from the amount of reactant to amount of product? Perform this calculation for each reactant, then compare the moles of product, $(NH_2)_2CO$, formed by the given amounts of NH_3 and CO_2 to determine which reactant is the limiting reagent.

Solution We carry out two separate calculations. First, starting with 637.2 g of NH_3, we calculate the number of moles of $(NH_2)_2CO$ that could be produced if all the NH_3 reacted according to the following conversions:

grams of NH_3 $\longrightarrow$ moles of NH_3 $\longrightarrow$ moles of $(NH_2)_2CO$

Combining these conversions in one step, we write

$$\text{moles of } (NH_2)_2CO = 637.2 \text{ g } NH_3 \times \frac{1 \text{ mol } NH_3}{17.03 \text{ g } NH_3} \times \frac{1 \text{ mol } (NH_2)_2CO}{2 \text{ mol } NH_3}$$
$$= 18.71 \text{ mol } (NH_2)_2CO$$

Second, for 1142 g of CO_2, the conversions are

grams of CO_2 $\longrightarrow$ moles of CO_2 $\longrightarrow$ moles of $(NH_2)_2CO$

The number of moles of $(NH_2)_2CO$ that could be produced if all the CO_2 reacted is

$$\text{moles of } (NH_2)_2CO = 1142 \text{ g } CO_2 \times \frac{1 \text{ mol } CO_2}{44.01 \text{ g } CO_2} \times \frac{1 \text{ mol } (NH_2)_2CO}{1 \text{ mol } CO_2}$$
$$= 25.95 \text{ mol } (NH_2)_2CO$$

(Continued)

It follows, therefore, that NH_3 must be the limiting reagent because it produces a smaller amount of $(NH_2)_2CO$.

(b) Strategy We determined the moles of $(NH_2)_2CO$ produced in part (a), using NH_3 as the limiting reagent. How do we convert from moles to grams?

Solution The molar mass of $(NH_2)_2CO$ is 60.06 g. We use this as a conversion factor to convert from moles of $(NH_2)_2CO$ to grams of $(NH_2)_2CO$:

$$\text{mass of } (NH_2)_2CO = 18.71 \text{ mol } (NH_2)_2CO \times \frac{60.06 \text{ g } (NH_2)_2CO}{1 \text{ mol } (NH_2)_2CO}$$
$$= 1124 \text{ g } (NH_2)_2CO$$

Check Does your answer seem reasonable? 18.71 moles of product are formed. What is the mass of 1 mole of $(NH_2)_2CO$?

(c) Strategy Working backward, we can determine the amount of CO_2 that reacted to produce 18.71 moles of $(NH_2)_2CO$. The amount of CO_2 left over is the difference between the initial amount and the amount reacted.

Solution Starting with 18.71 moles of $(NH_2)_2CO$, we can determine the mass of CO_2 that reacted using the mole ratio from the balanced equation and the molar mass of CO_2. The conversion steps are

$$\text{moles of } (NH_2)_2CO \longrightarrow \text{moles of } CO_2 \longrightarrow \text{grams of } CO_2$$

so that

$$\text{mass of } CO_2 \text{ reacted} = 18.71 \text{ mol } (NH_2)_2CO \times \frac{1 \text{ mol } CO_2}{1 \text{ mol } (NH_2)_2CO} \times \frac{44.01 \text{ g } CO_2}{1 \text{ mol } CO_2}$$
$$= 823.4 \text{ g } CO_2$$

The amount of CO_2 remaining (in excess) is the difference between the initial amount (1142 g) and the amount reacted (823.4 g):

$$\text{mass of } CO_2 \text{ remaining} = 1142 \text{ g} - 823.4 \text{ g} = 319 \text{ g}$$

Similar problem: 3.86.

Practice Exercise The reaction between aluminum and iron(III) oxide can generate temperatures approaching 3000°C and is used in welding metals:

$$2Al + Fe_2O_3 \longrightarrow Al_2O_3 + 2Fe$$

In one process, 124 g of Al are reacted with 601 g of Fe_2O_3. (a) Calculate the mass (in grams) of Al_2O_3 formed. (b) How much of the excess reagent is left at the end of the reaction?

Example 3.15 brings out an important point. In practice, chemists usually choose the more expensive chemical as the limiting reagent so that all or most of it will be converted to products in the reaction. In the synthesis of urea, NH_3 is invariably the limiting reagent because it is more expensive than CO_2. At other times, an excess of one reagent is used to help drive the reaction to completion, or to compensate for a side reaction that consumes that reagent. Synthetic chemists often have to calculate the amount of reagents to use based on this need to have one or more components in excess, as Example 3.16 shows.

Example 3.16

The reaction between alcohols and halogen compounds to form ethers is important in organic chemistry, as illustrated here for the reaction between methanol (CH_3OH) and methyl bromide (CH_3Br) to form dimethylether (CH_3OCH_3), which is a useful precursor to other organic compounds and an aerosol propellant.

$$CH_3OH + CH_3Br + LiC_4H_9 \longrightarrow CH_3OCH_3 + LiBr + C_4H_{10}$$

This reaction is carried out in a dry (water-free) organic solvent, and the butyl lithium (LiC_4H_9) serves to remove a hydrogen ion from CH_3OH. Butyl lithium will also react with any residual water in the solvent, so the reaction is typically carried out with 2.5 molar equivalents of that reagent. How many grams of CH_3Br and LiC_4H_9 will be needed to carry out the preceding reaction with 10.0 g of CH_3OH?

Solution We start with the knowledge that CH_3OH and CH_3Br are present in stoichiometric amounts and that LiC_4H_9 is the excess reagent. To calculate the quantities of CH_3Br and LiC_4H_9 needed, we proceed as shown in Example 3.14.

$$\text{grams of } CH_3Br = 10.0 \text{ g } CH_3OH \times \frac{1 \text{ mol } CH_3OH}{32.04 \text{ g } CH_3OH} \times \frac{1 \text{ mol } CH_3Br}{1 \text{ mol } CH_3OH} \times \frac{94.93 \text{ g } CH_3Br}{1 \text{ mol } CH_3Br}$$

$$= 29.6 \text{ g } CH_3Br$$

$$\text{grams of } LiC_4H_9 = 10.0 \text{ g } CH_3OH \times \frac{1 \text{ mol } CH_3OH}{32.04 \text{ g } CH_3OH} \times \frac{2.5 \text{ mol } LiC_4H_9}{1 \text{ mol } CH_3OH} \times \frac{64.05 \text{ g } LiC_4H_9}{1 \text{ mol } LiC_4H_9}$$

$$= 50.0 \text{ g } LiC_4H_9$$

Similar problems: 3.137, 3.138.

Practice Exercise The reaction between benzoic acid (C_6H_5COOH) and octanol ($C_8H_{17}OH$) to yield octyl benzoate ($C_6H_5COOC_8H_{17}$) and water

$$C_6H_5COOH + C_8H_{17}OH \longrightarrow C_6H_5COOC_8H_{17} + H_2O$$

is carried out with an excess of $C_8H_{17}OH$ to help drive the reaction to completion and maximize the yield of product. If an organic chemist wants to use 1.5 molar equivalents of $C_8H_{17}OH$, how many grams of $C_8H_{17}OH$ would be required to carry out the reaction with 15.7 g of C_6H_5COOH?

Review of Concepts

Consider the following reaction:

$$2NO(g) + O_2(g) \longrightarrow 2NO_2(g)$$

Starting with the reactants shown in (a), which of the diagrams shown in (b)–(d) best represents the situation in which the limiting reagent has completely reacted?

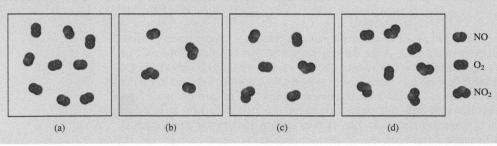

(a)   (b)   (c)   (d)

● NO
● O_2
● NO_2

3.10 Reaction Yield

The amount of limiting reagent present at the start of a reaction determines the ***theoretical yield*** of the reaction, that is, *the amount of product that would result if all the limiting reagent reacted.* The theoretical yield, then, is the *maximum* obtainable yield, predicted by the balanced equation. In practice, the ***actual yield,*** or *the amount of product actually obtained from a reaction,* is almost always less than the theoretical yield. There are many reasons for the difference between actual and theoretical yields. For instance, many reactions are reversible, and so they do not proceed 100 percent from left to right. Even when a reaction is 100 percent complete, it may be difficult to recover all of the product from the reaction medium (say, from an aqueous solution). Some reactions are complex in the sense that the products formed may react further among themselves or with the reactants to form still other products. These additional reactions will reduce the yield of the first reaction.

To determine how efficient a given reaction is, chemists often figure the ***percent yield,*** which describes *the proportion of the actual yield to the theoretical yield.* It is calculated as follows:

> Keep in mind that the theoretical yield is the yield that you calculate using the balanced equation. The actual yield is the yield obtained by carrying out the reaction.

$$\%\,\text{yield} = \frac{\text{actual yield}}{\text{theoretical yield}} \times 100\% \tag{3.4}$$

Percent yields may range from a fraction of 1 percent to 100 percent. Chemists strive to maximize the percent yield in a reaction. Factors that can affect the percent yield include temperature and pressure. We will study these effects later.

In Example 3.17 we will calculate the yield of an industrial process.

Example 3.17

Titanium is a strong, lightweight, corrosion-resistant metal that is used in rockets, aircraft, jet engines, and bicycle frames. It is prepared by the reaction of titanium(IV) chloride with molten magnesium between 950°C and 1150°C:

$$TiCl_4(g) + 2Mg(l) \longrightarrow Ti(s) + 2MgCl_2(l)$$

In a certain industrial operation 3.54×10^7 g of $TiCl_4$ are reacted with 1.13×10^7 g of Mg. (a) Calculate the theoretical yield of Ti in grams. (b) Calculate the percent yield if 7.91×10^6 g of Ti are actually obtained.

(a) Strategy Because there are two reactants, this is likely to be a limiting reagent problem. The reactant that produces fewer moles of product is the limiting reagent. How do we convert from amount of reactant to amount of product? Perform this calculation for each reactant, then compare the moles of product, Ti, formed.

Solution Carry out two separate calculations to see which of the two reactants is the limiting reagent. First, starting with 3.54×10^7 g of $TiCl_4$, calculate the number of moles of Ti that could be produced if all the $TiCl_4$ reacted. The conversions are

$$\text{grams of } TiCl_4 \longrightarrow \text{moles of } TiCl_4 \longrightarrow \text{moles of Ti}$$

(Continued)

104   **Chapter 3** ▪ Mass Relationships in Chemical Reactions

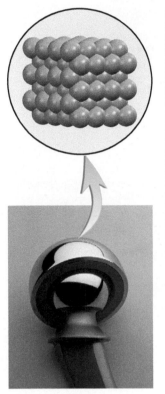

An artificial hip joint made of titanium and the structure of solid titanium.

so that

$$\text{moles of Ti} = 3.54 \times 10^7 \text{ g TiCl}_4 \times \frac{1 \text{ mol TiCl}_4}{189.7 \text{ g TiCl}_4} \times \frac{1 \text{ mol Ti}}{1 \text{ mol TiCl}_4}$$

$$= 1.87 \times 10^5 \text{ mol Ti}$$

Next, we calculate the number of moles of Ti formed from 1.13×10^7 g of Mg. The conversion steps are

$$\text{grams of Mg} \longrightarrow \text{moles of Mg} \longrightarrow \text{moles of Ti}$$

and we write

$$\text{moles of Ti} = 1.13 \times 10^7 \text{ g Mg} \times \frac{1 \text{ mol Mg}}{24.31 \text{ g Mg}} \times \frac{1 \text{ mol Ti}}{2 \text{ mol Mg}}$$

$$= 2.32 \times 10^5 \text{ mol Ti}$$

Therefore, $TiCl_4$ is the limiting reagent because it produces a smaller amount of Ti. The mass of Ti formed is

$$1.87 \times 10^5 \text{ mol Ti} \times \frac{47.88 \text{ g Ti}}{1 \text{ mol Ti}} = 8.95 \times 10^6 \text{ g Ti}$$

(b) Strategy The mass of Ti determined in part (a) is the theoretical yield. The amount given in part (b) is the actual yield of the reaction.

Solution The percent yield is given by

$$\% \text{yield} = \frac{\text{actual yield}}{\text{theoretical yield}} \times 100\%$$

$$= \frac{7.91 \times 10^6 \text{ g}}{8.95 \times 10^6 \text{ g}} \times 100\%$$

$$= 88.4\%$$

Similar problems: 3.89, 3.90.

Check Should the percent yield be less than 100 percent?

Practice Exercise Industrially, vanadium metal, which is used in steel alloys, can be obtained by reacting vanadium(V) oxide with calcium at high temperatures:

$$5\text{Ca} + \text{V}_2\text{O}_5 \longrightarrow 5\text{CaO} + 2\text{V}$$

In one process, 1.54×10^3 g of V_2O_5 react with 1.96×10^3 g of Ca. (a) Calculate the theoretical yield of V. (b) Calculate the percent yield if 803 g of V are obtained.

Industrial processes usually involve huge quantities (thousands to millions of tons) of products. Thus, even a slight improvement in the yield can significantly reduce the cost of production. A case in point is the manufacture of chemical fertilizers, discussed in the Chemistry in Action essay on p. 105.

Review of Concepts

Can the percent yield ever exceed the theoretical yield of a reaction?

CHEMISTRY *in Action*

Chemical Fertilizers

Feeding the world's rapidly increasing population requires that farmers produce ever-larger and healthier crops. Every year they add hundreds of millions of tons of chemical fertilizers to the soil to increase crop quality and yield. In addition to carbon dioxide and water, plants need at least six elements for satisfactory growth. They are N, P, K, Ca, S, and Mg. The preparation and properties of several nitrogen- and phosphorus-containing fertilizers illustrate some of the principles introduced in this chapter.

Nitrogen fertilizers contain nitrate (NO_3^-) salts, ammonium (NH_4^+) salts, and other compounds. Plants can absorb nitrogen in the form of nitrate directly, but ammonium salts and ammonia (NH_3) must first be converted to nitrates by the action of soil bacteria. The principal raw material of nitrogen fertilizers is ammonia, prepared by the reaction between hydrogen and nitrogen:

$$3H_2(g) + N_2(g) \longrightarrow 2NH_3(g)$$

(This reaction will be discussed in detail in Chapters 13 and 14.) In its liquid form, ammonia can be injected directly into the soil.

Alternatively, ammonia can be converted to ammonium nitrate, NH_4NO_3, ammonium sulfate, $(NH_4)_2SO_4$, or ammonium hydrogen phosphate, $(NH_4)_2HPO_4$, in the following acid-base reactions:

$$NH_3(aq) + HNO_3(aq) \longrightarrow NH_4NO_3(aq)$$
$$2NH_3(aq) + H_2SO_4(aq) \longrightarrow (NH_4)_2SO_4(aq)$$
$$2NH_3(aq) + H_3PO_4(aq) \longrightarrow (NH_4)_2HPO_4(aq)$$

Liquid ammonia being applied to the soil before planting.

Another method of preparing ammonium sulfate requires two steps:

$$2NH_3(aq) + CO_2(aq) + H_2O(l) \longrightarrow (NH_4)_2CO_3(aq) \quad (1)$$
$$(NH_4)_2CO_3(aq) + CaSO_4(aq) \longrightarrow$$
$$(NH_4)_2SO_4(aq) + CaCO_3(s) \quad (2)$$

This approach is desirable because the starting materials— carbon dioxide and calcium sulfate—are less costly than sulfuric acid. To increase the yield, ammonia is made the limiting reagent in Reaction (1) and ammonium carbonate is made the limiting reagent in Reaction (2).

The table lists the percent composition by mass of nitrogen in some common fertilizers. The preparation of urea was discussed in Example 3.15.

Percent Composition by Mass of Nitrogen in Five Common Fertilizers

Fertilizer	% N by Mass
NH_3	82.4
NH_4NO_3	35.0
$(NH_4)_2SO_4$	21.2
$(NH_4)_2HPO_4$	21.2
$(NH_2)_2CO$	46.7

Several factors influence the choice of one fertilizer over another: (1) cost of the raw materials needed to prepare the fertilizer; (2) ease of storage, transportation, and utilization; (3) percent composition by mass of the desired element; and (4) suitability of the compound, that is, whether the compound is soluble in water and whether it can be readily taken up by plants. Considering all these factors together, we find that NH_4NO_3 is the most important nitrogen-containing fertilizer in the world, even though ammonia has the highest percentage by mass of nitrogen.

Phosphorus fertilizers are derived from phosphate rock, called *fluorapatite*, $Ca_5(PO_4)_3F$. Fluorapatite is insoluble in water, so it must first be converted to water-soluble calcium dihydrogen phosphate [$Ca(H_2PO_4)_2$]:

$$2Ca_5(PO_4)_3F(s) + 7H_2SO_4(aq) \longrightarrow$$
$$3Ca(H_2PO_4)_2(aq) + 7CaSO_4(aq) + 2HF(g)$$

For maximum yield, fluorapatite is made the limiting reagent in this reaction.

The reactions we have discussed for the preparation of fertilizers all appear relatively simple, yet much effort has been expended to improve the yields by changing conditions such as temperature, pressure, and so on. Industrial chemists usually run promising reactions first in the laboratory and then test them in a pilot facility before putting them into mass production.

106   **Chapter 3** ▪ Mass Relationships in Chemical Reactions

Key Equations

percent composition of an element in a compound =

$$\frac{n \times \text{molar mass of element}}{\text{molar mass of compound}} \times 100\% \quad (3.1)$$

$$\%\text{yield} = \frac{\text{actual yield}}{\text{theoretical yield}} \times 100\% \quad (3.4)$$

Summary of Facts & Concepts

1. Atomic masses are measured in atomic mass units (amu), a relative unit based on a value of exactly 12 for the C-12 isotope. The atomic mass given for the atoms of a particular element is the average of the naturally occurring isotope distribution of that element. The molecular mass of a molecule is the sum of the atomic masses of the atoms in the molecule. Both atomic mass and molecular mass can be accurately determined with a mass spectrometer.

2. A mole is Avogadro's number (6.022×10^{23}) of atoms, molecules, or other particles. The molar mass (in grams) of an element or a compound is numerically equal to its mass in atomic mass units (amu) and contains Avogadro's number of atoms (in the case of elements), molecules (in the case of molecular substances), or simplest formula units (in the case of ionic compounds).

3. The percent composition by mass of a compound is the percent by mass of each element present. If we know the percent composition by mass of a compound, we can deduce the empirical formula of the compound and also the molecular formula of the compound if the approximate molar mass is known.

4. Chemical changes, called chemical reactions, are represented by chemical equations. Substances that undergo change—the reactants—are written on the left and the substances formed—the products—appear to the right of the arrow. Chemical equations must be balanced, in accordance with the law of conservation of mass. The number of atoms of each element in the reactants must equal the number in the products.

5. Stoichiometry is the quantitative study of products and reactants in chemical reactions. Stoichiometric calculations are best done by expressing both the known and unknown quantities in terms of moles and then converting to other units if necessary. A limiting reagent is the reactant that is present in the smallest stoichiometric amount. It limits the amount of product that can be formed. The amount of product obtained in a reaction (the actual yield) may be less than the maximum possible amount (the theoretical yield). The ratio of the two multiplied by 100 percent is expressed as the percent yield.

Key Words

Actual yield, p. 103
Atomic mass, p. 76
Atomic mass unit (amu), p. 76
Avogadro's number (N_A), p. 77
Chemical equation, p. 90

Chemical reaction, p. 90
Excess reagent, p. 99
Limiting reagent, p. 99
Molar mass ($\mathcal{M}$), p. 78
Mole (mol), p. 77

Mole method, p. 95
Molecular mass, p. 81
Percent composition by mass, p. 85
Percent yield, p. 103

Product, p. 91
Reactant, p. 91
Stoichiometric amount, p. 99
Stoichiometry, p. 95
Theoretical yield, p. 103

Questions & Problems

● *Problems available in Connect Plus*
Red numbered problems solved in Student Solutions Manual

Atomic Mass
Review Questions

3.1   What is an atomic mass unit? Why is it necessary to introduce such a unit?

3.2   What is the mass (in amu) of a carbon-12 atom? Why is the atomic mass of carbon listed as 12.01 amu in the table on the inside front cover of this book?

3.3   Explain clearly what is meant by the statement "The atomic mass of gold is 197.0 amu."

3.4 What information would you need to calculate the average atomic mass of an element?

Problems

3.5 The atomic masses of $^{35}_{17}Cl$ (75.53 percent) and $^{37}_{17}Cl$ (24.47 percent) are 34.968 amu and 36.956 amu, respectively. Calculate the average atomic mass of chlorine. The percentages in parentheses denote the relative abundances.

3.6 The atomic masses of $^{6}_{3}Li$ and $^{7}_{3}Li$ are 6.0151 amu and 7.0160 amu, respectively. Calculate the natural abundances of these two isotopes. The average atomic mass of Li is 6.941 amu.

3.7 What is the mass in grams of 13.2 amu?

3.8 How many amu are there in 8.4 g?

Avogadro's Number and Molar Mass

Review Questions

3.9 Define the term "mole." What is the unit for mole in calculations? What does the mole have in common with the pair, the dozen, and the gross? What does Avogadro's number represent?

3.10 What is the molar mass of an atom? What are the commonly used units for molar mass?

Problems

3.11 Earth's population is about 7.2 billion. Suppose that every person on Earth participates in a process of counting identical particles at the rate of two particles per second. How many years would it take to count 6.0×10^{23} particles? Assume that there are 365 days in a year.

3.12 The thickness of a piece of paper is 0.0036 in. Suppose a certain book has an Avogadro's number of pages; calculate the thickness of the book in light-years. (*Hint:* See Problem 1.49 for the definition of light-year.)

3.13 How many atoms are there in 5.10 moles of sulfur (S)?

3.14 How many moles of cobalt (Co) atoms are there in 6.00×10^9 (6 billion) Co atoms?

3.15 How many moles of calcium (Ca) atoms are in 77.4 g of Ca?

3.16 How many grams of gold (Au) are there in 15.3 moles of Au?

3.17 What is the mass in grams of a single atom of each of the following elements? (a) Hg, (b) Ne.

3.18 What is the mass in grams of a single atom of each of the following elements? (a) As, (b) Ni.

3.19 What is the mass in grams of 1.00×10^{12} lead (Pb) atoms?

3.20 A modern penny weighs 2.5 g but contains only 0.063 g of copper (Cu). How many copper atoms are present in a modern penny?

3.21 Which of the following has more atoms: 1.10 g of hydrogen atoms or 14.7 g of chromium atoms?

3.22 Which of the following has a greater mass: 2 atoms of lead or 5.1×10^{-23} mole of helium.

Molecular Mass
Problems

3.23 Calculate the molecular mass or formula mass (in amu) of each of the following substances: (a) CH_4, (b) NO_2, (c) SO_3, (d) C_6H_6, (e) NaI, (f) K_2SO_4, (g) $Ca_3(PO_4)_2$.

3.24 Calculate the molar mass of the following substances: (a) Li_2CO_3, (b) CS_2, (c) $CHCl_3$ (chloroform), (d) $C_6H_8O_6$ (ascorbic acid, or vitamin C), (e) KNO_3, (f) Mg_3N_2.

3.25 Calculate the molar mass of a compound if 0.372 mole of it has a mass of 152 g.

3.26 How many molecules of ethane (C_2H_6) are present in 0.334 g of C_2H_6?

3.27 Calculate the number of C, H, and O atoms in 1.50 g of glucose ($C_6H_{12}O_6$), a sugar.

3.28 Dimethyl sulfoxide [$(CH_3)_2SO$], also called DMSO, is an important solvent that penetrates the skin, enabling it to be used as a topical drug-delivery agent. Calculate the number of C, S, H, and O atoms in 7.14×10^3 g of dimethyl sulfoxide.

3.29 Pheromones are a special type of compound secreted by the females of many insect species to attract the males for mating. One pheromone has the molecular formula $C_{19}H_{38}O$. Normally, the amount of this pheromone secreted by a female insect is about 1.0×10^{-12} g. How many molecules are there in this quantity?

3.30 The density of water is 1.00 g/mL at 4°C. How many water molecules are present in 2.56 mL of water at this temperature?

Mass Spectrometry
Review Questions

3.31 Describe the operation of a mass spectrometer.

3.32 Describe how you would determine the isotopic abundance of an element from its mass spectrum.

Problems

3.33 Carbon has two stable isotopes, $^{12}_{6}C$ and $^{13}_{6}C$, and fluorine has only one stable isotope, $^{19}_{9}F$. How many peaks would you observe in the mass spectrum of the positive ion of CF_4^+? Assume that the ion does not break up into smaller fragments.

3.34 Hydrogen has two stable isotopes, $^{1}_{1}H$ and $^{2}_{1}H$, and sulfur has four stable isotopes, $^{32}_{16}S$, $^{33}_{16}S$, $^{34}_{16}S$, and $^{36}_{16}S$.

How many peaks would you observe in the mass spectrum of the positive ion of hydrogen sulfide, H_2S^+? Assume no decomposition of the ion into smaller fragments.

Percent Composition and Chemical Formulas
Review Questions

3.35   Use ammonia (NH_3) to explain what is meant by the percent composition by mass of a compound.

3.36   Describe how the knowledge of the percent composition by mass of an unknown compound can help us identify the compound.

3.37   What does the word "empirical" in empirical formula mean?

3.38   If we know the empirical formula of a compound, what additional information do we need to determine its molecular formula?

Problems

● 3.39   Tin (Sn) exists in Earth's crust as SnO_2. Calculate the percent composition by mass of Sn and O in SnO_2.

● 3.40   For many years chloroform ($CHCl_3$) was used as an inhalation anesthetic in spite of the fact that it is also a toxic substance that may cause severe liver, kidney, and heart damage. Calculate the percent composition by mass of this compound.

● 3.41   Cinnamic alcohol is used mainly in perfumery, particularly in soaps and cosmetics. Its molecular formula is $C_9H_{10}O$. (a) Calculate the percent composition by mass of C, H, and O in cinnamic alcohol. (b) How many molecules of cinnamic alcohol are contained in a sample of mass 0.469 g?

3.42   All of the substances listed here are fertilizers that contribute nitrogen to the soil. Which of these is the richest source of nitrogen on a mass percentage basis?

(a) Urea, $(NH_2)_2CO$

(b) Ammonium nitrate, NH_4NO_3

(c) Guanidine, $HNC(NH_2)_2$

(d) Ammonia, NH_3

● 3.43   Allicin is the compound responsible for the characteristic smell of garlic. An analysis of the compound gives the following percent composition by mass: C: 44.4 percent; H: 6.21 percent; S: 39.5 percent; O: 9.86 percent. Calculate its empirical formula. What is its molecular formula given that its molar mass is about 162 g?

3.44   Peroxyacylnitrate (PAN) is one of the components of smog. It is a compound of C, H, N, and O. Determine the percent composition of oxygen and the empirical formula from the following percent composition by mass: 19.8 percent C, 2.50 percent H, 11.6 percent N. What is its

molecular formula given that its molar mass is about 120 g?

● 3.45   The formula for rust can be represented by Fe_2O_3. How many moles of Fe are present in 24.6 g of the compound?

● 3.46   How many grams of sulfur (S) are needed to react completely with 246 g of mercury (Hg) to form HgS?

● 3.47   Calculate the mass in grams of iodine (I_2) that will react completely with 20.4 g of aluminum (Al) to form aluminum iodide (AlI_3).

● 3.48   Tin(II) fluoride (SnF_2) is often added to toothpaste as an ingredient to prevent tooth decay. What is the mass of F in grams in 24.6 g of the compound?

● 3.49   What are the empirical formulas of the compounds with the following compositions? (a) 2.1 percent H, 65.3 percent O, 32.6 percent S, (b) 20.2 percent Al, 79.8 percent Cl.

● 3.50   What are the empirical formulas of the compounds with the following compositions? (a) 40.1 percent C, 6.6 percent H, 53.3 percent O, (b) 18.4 percent C, 21.5 percent N, 60.1 percent K.

● 3.51   The anticaking agent added to Morton salt is calcium silicate, $CaSiO_3$. This compound can absorb up to 2.5 times its mass of water and still remains a free-flowing powder. Calculate the percent composition of $CaSiO_3$.

● 3.52   The empirical formula of a compound is CH. If the molar mass of this compound is about 78 g, what is its molecular formula?

● 3.53   The molar mass of caffeine is 194.19 g. Is the molecular formula of caffeine $C_4H_5N_2O$ or $C_8H_{10}N_4O_2$?

● 3.54   Monosodium glutamate (MSG), a food-flavor enhancer, has been blamed for "Chinese restaurant syndrome," the symptoms of which are headaches and chest pains. MSG has the following composition by mass: 35.51 percent C, 4.77 percent H, 37.85 percent O, 8.29 percent N, and 13.60 percent Na. What is its molecular formula if its molar mass is about 169 g?

Chemical Reactions and Chemical Equations
Review Questions

3.55   Use the formation of water from hydrogen and oxygen to explain the following terms: chemical reaction, reactant, product.

3.56   What is the difference between a chemical reaction and a chemical equation?

3.57   Why must a chemical equation be balanced? What law is obeyed by a balanced chemical equation?

3.58   Write the symbols used to represent gas, liquid, solid, and the aqueous phase in chemical equations.

Problems

3.59   Balance the following equations using the method outlined in Section 3.7:
(a) $C + O_2 \longrightarrow CO$
(b) $CO + O_2 \longrightarrow CO_2$
(c) $H_2 + Br_2 \longrightarrow HBr$
(d) $K + H_2O \longrightarrow KOH + H_2$
(e) $Mg + O_2 \longrightarrow MgO$
(f) $O_3 \longrightarrow O_2$
(g) $H_2O_2 \longrightarrow H_2O + O_2$
(h) $N_2 + H_2 \longrightarrow NH_3$
(i) $Zn + AgCl \longrightarrow ZnCl_2 + Ag$
(j) $S_8 + O_2 \longrightarrow SO_2$
(k) $NaOH + H_2SO_4 \longrightarrow Na_2SO_4 + H_2O$
(l) $Cl_2 + NaI \longrightarrow NaCl + I_2$
(m) $KOH + H_3PO_4 \longrightarrow K_3PO_4 + H_2O$
(n) $CH_4 + Br_2 \longrightarrow CBr_4 + HBr$

3.60   Balance the following equations using the method outlined in Section 3.7:
(a) $N_2O_5 \longrightarrow N_2O_4 + O_2$
(b) $KNO_3 \longrightarrow KNO_2 + O_2$
(c) $NH_4NO_3 \longrightarrow N_2O + H_2O$
(d) $NH_4NO_2 \longrightarrow N_2 + H_2O$
(e) $NaHCO_3 \longrightarrow Na_2CO_3 + H_2O + CO_2$
(f) $P_4O_{10} + H_2O \longrightarrow H_3PO_4$
(g) $HCl + CaCO_3 \longrightarrow CaCl_2 + H_2O + CO_2$
(h) $Al + H_2SO_4 \longrightarrow Al_2(SO_4)_3 + H_2$
(i) $CO_2 + KOH \longrightarrow K_2CO_3 + H_2O$
(j) $CH_4 + O_2 \longrightarrow CO_2 + H_2O$
(k) $Be_2C + H_2O \longrightarrow Be(OH)_2 + CH_4$
(l) $Cu + HNO_3 \longrightarrow Cu(NO_3)_2 + NO + H_2O$
(m) $S + HNO_3 \longrightarrow H_2SO_4 + NO_2 + H_2O$
(n) $NH_3 + CuO \longrightarrow Cu + N_2 + H_2O$

Amounts of Reactants and Products

Review Questions

3.61   On what law is stoichiometry based? Why is it essential to use balanced equations in solving stoichiometric problems?

3.62   Describe the steps involved in the mole method.

Problems

3.63   Which of the following equations best represents the reaction shown in the diagram?
(a) $8A + 4B \longrightarrow C + D$
(b) $4A + 8B \longrightarrow 4C + 4D$
(c) $2A + B \longrightarrow C + D$
(d) $4A + 2B \longrightarrow 4C + 4D$
(e) $2A + 4B \longrightarrow C + D$

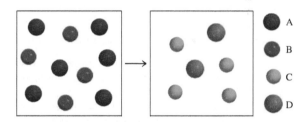

3.64   Which of the following equations best represents the reaction shown in the diagram?
(a) $A + B \longrightarrow C + D$
(b) $6A + 4B \longrightarrow C + D$
(c) $A + 2B \longrightarrow 2C + D$
(d) $3A + 2B \longrightarrow 2C + D$
(e) $3A + 2B \longrightarrow 4C + 2D$

3.65   Consider the combustion of carbon monoxide (CO) in oxygen gas:

$$2CO(g) + O_2(g) \longrightarrow 2CO_2(g)$$

Starting with 3.60 moles of CO, calculate the number of moles of CO_2 produced if there is enough oxygen gas to react with all of the CO.

3.66   Silicon tetrachloride ($SiCl_4$) can be prepared by heating Si in chlorine gas:

$$Si(s) + 2Cl_2(g) \longrightarrow SiCl_4(l)$$

In one reaction, 0.507 mole of $SiCl_4$ is produced. How many moles of molecular chlorine were used in the reaction?

3.67   Ammonia is a principal nitrogen fertilizer. It is prepared by the reaction between hydrogen and nitrogen.

$$3H_2(g) + N_2(g) \longrightarrow 2NH_3(g)$$

In a particular reaction, 6.0 moles of NH_3 were produced. How many moles of H_2 and how many moles of N_2 were reacted to produce this amount of NH_3?

3.68   Certain race cars use methanol (CH_3OH, also called wood alcohol) as a fuel. The combustion of methanol occurs according to the following equation:

$$2CH_3OH(l) + 3O_2(g) \longrightarrow 2CO_2(g) + 4H_2O(l)$$

In a particular reaction, 9.8 moles of CH_3OH are reacted with an excess of O_2. Calculate the number of moles of H_2O formed.

110   **Chapter 3** ▪ Mass Relationships in Chemical Reactions

● **3.69**   The annual production of sulfur dioxide from burning coal and fossil fuels, auto exhaust, and other sources is about 26 million tons. The equation for the reaction is

$$S(s) + O_2(g) \longrightarrow SO_2(g)$$

How much sulfur (in tons), present in the original materials, would result in that quantity of SO_2?

● **3.70**   When baking soda (sodium bicarbonate or sodium hydrogen carbonate, $NaHCO_3$) is heated, it releases carbon dioxide gas, which is responsible for the rising of cookies, donuts, and bread. (a) Write a balanced equation for the decomposition of the compound (one of the products is Na_2CO_3). (b) Calculate the mass of $NaHCO_3$ required to produce 20.5 g of CO_2.

● **3.71**   If chlorine bleach is mixed with other cleaning products containing ammonia, the toxic gas $NCl_3(g)$ can form according to the equation:

$$3NaClO(aq) + NH_3(aq) \longrightarrow 3NaOH(aq) + NCl_3(g)$$

When 2.94 g of NH_3 reacts with an excess of NaClO according to the preceding reaction, how many grams of NCl_3 are formed?

● **3.72**   Fermentation is a complex chemical process of wine making in which glucose is converted into ethanol and carbon dioxide:

$$\underset{\text{glucose}}{C_6H_{12}O_6} \longrightarrow \underset{\text{ethanol}}{2C_2H_5OH} + 2CO_2$$

Starting with 500.4 g of glucose, what is the maximum amount of ethanol in grams and in liters that can be obtained by this process? (Density of ethanol = 0.789 g/mL.)

● **3.73**   Each copper(II) sulfate unit is associated with five water molecules in crystalline copper(II) sulfate pentahydrate ($CuSO_4 \cdot 5H_2O$). When this compound is heated in air above 100°C, it loses the water molecules and also its blue color:

$$CuSO_4 \cdot 5H_2O \longrightarrow CuSO_4 + 5H_2O$$

If 9.60 g of $CuSO_4$ are left after heating 15.01 g of the blue compound, calculate the number of moles of H_2O originally present in the compound.

● **3.74**   For many years the recovery of gold—that is, the separation of gold from other materials—involved the use of potassium cyanide:

$$4Au + 8KCN + O_2 + 2H_2O \longrightarrow$$
$$4KAu(CN)_2 + 4KOH$$

What is the minimum amount of KCN in moles needed to extract 29.0 g (about an ounce) of gold?

● **3.75**   Limestone ($CaCO_3$) is decomposed by heating to quicklime (CaO) and carbon dioxide. Calculate how many grams of quicklime can be produced from 1.0 kg of limestone.

● **3.76**   Nitrous oxide (N_2O) is also called "laughing gas." It can be prepared by the thermal decomposition of ammonium nitrate (NH_4NO_3). The other product is H_2O. (a) Write a balanced equation for this reaction. (b) How many grams of N_2O are formed if 0.46 mole of NH_4NO_3 is used in the reaction?

● **3.77**   The fertilizer ammonium sulfate [$(NH_4)_2SO_4$] is prepared by the reaction between ammonia (NH_3) and sulfuric acid:

$$2NH_3(g) + H_2SO_4(aq) \longrightarrow (NH_4)_2SO_4(aq)$$

How many kilograms of NH_3 are needed to produce 1.00×10^5 kg of $(NH_4)_2SO_4$?

● **3.78**   A common laboratory preparation of oxygen gas is the thermal decomposition of potassium chlorate ($KClO_3$). Assuming complete decomposition, calculate the number of grams of O_2 gas that can be obtained from 46.0 g of $KClO_3$. (The products are KCl and O_2.)

Limiting Reagents
Review Questions

3.79   Define limiting reagent and excess reagent. What is the significance of the limiting reagent in predicting the amount of the product obtained in a reaction? Can there be a limiting reagent if only one reactant is present?

3.80   Give an everyday example that illustrates the limiting reagent concept.

Problems

● 3.81   Consider the reaction

$$2A + B \longrightarrow C$$

(a) In the diagram here that represents the reaction, which reactant, A or B, is the limiting reagent? (b) Assuming complete reaction, draw a molecular-model representation of the amounts of reactants and products left after the reaction. The atomic arrangement in C is ABA.

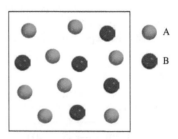

3.82   Consider the reaction

$$N_2 + 3H_2 \longrightarrow 2NH_3$$

Assuming each model represents 1 mole of the substance, show the number of moles of the product and the excess reagent left after the complete reaction.

H₂

N₂

NH₃

● 3.83 Nitric oxide (NO) reacts with oxygen gas to form nitrogen dioxide (NO₂), a dark-brown gas:

$$2NO(g) + O_2(g) \longrightarrow 2NO_2(g)$$

In one experiment 0.886 mole of NO is mixed with 0.503 mole of O₂. Calculate which of the two reactants is the limiting reagent. Calculate also the number of moles of NO₂ produced.

● **3.84** Ammonia and sulfuric acid react to form ammonium sulfate. (a) Write an equation for the reaction. (b) Determine the starting mass (in g) of each reactant if 20.3 g of ammonium sulfate is produced and 5.89 g of sulfuric acid remains unreacted.

● 3.85 Propane (C₃H₈) is a component of natural gas and is used in domestic cooking and heating. (a) Balance the following equation representing the combustion of propane in air:

$$C_3H_8 + O_2 \longrightarrow CO_2 + H_2O$$

(b) How many grams of carbon dioxide can be produced by burning 3.65 moles of propane? Assume that oxygen is the excess reagent in this reaction.

● **3.86** Consider the reaction

$$MnO_2 + 4HCl \longrightarrow MnCl_2 + Cl_2 + 2H_2O$$

If 0.86 mole of MnO₂ and 48.2 g of HCl react, which reagent will be used up first? How many grams of Cl₂ will be produced?

Reaction Yield

Review Questions

3.87 Why is the theoretical yield of a reaction determined only by the amount of the limiting reagent?

3.88 Why is the actual yield of a reaction almost always smaller than the theoretical yield?

Problems

● 3.89 Hydrogen fluoride is used in the manufacture of Freons (which destroy ozone in the stratosphere) and in the production of aluminum metal. It is prepared by the reaction

$$CaF_2 + H_2SO_4 \longrightarrow CaSO_4 + 2HF$$

In one process, 6.00 kg of CaF₂ are treated with an excess of H₂SO₄ and yield 2.86 kg of HF. Calculate the percent yield of HF.

● 3.90 Nitroglycerin (C₃H₅N₃O₉) is a powerful explosive. Its decomposition may be represented by

$$4C_3H_5N_3O_9 \longrightarrow 6N_2 + 12CO_2 + 10H_2O + O_2$$

This reaction generates a large amount of heat and many gaseous products. It is the sudden formation of these gases, together with their rapid expansion, that produces the explosion. (a) What is the maximum amount of O₂ in grams that can be obtained from 2.00×10^2 g of nitroglycerin? (b) Calculate the percent yield in this reaction if the amount of O₂ generated is found to be 6.55 g.

● 3.91 Titanium(IV) oxide (TiO₂) is a white substance produced by the action of sulfuric acid on the mineral ilmenite (FeTiO₃):

$$FeTiO_3 + H_2SO_4 \longrightarrow TiO_2 + FeSO_4 + H_2O$$

Its opaque and nontoxic properties make it suitable as a pigment in plastics and paints. In one process, 8.00×10^3 kg of FeTiO₃ yielded 3.67×10^3 kg of TiO₂. What is the percent yield of the reaction?

3.92 Ethylene (C₂H₄), an important industrial organic chemical, can be prepared by heating hexane (C₆H₁₄) at 800°C:

$$C_6H_{14} \longrightarrow C_2H_4 + \text{other products}$$

If the yield of ethylene production is 42.5 percent, what mass of hexane must be reacted to produce 481 g of ethylene?

● 3.93 When heated, lithium reacts with nitrogen to form lithium nitride:

$$6Li(s) + N_2(g) \longrightarrow 2Li_3N(s)$$

What is the theoretical yield of Li₃N in grams when 12.3 g of Li are heated with 33.6 g of N₂? If the actual yield of Li₃N is 5.89 g, what is the percent yield of the reaction?

3.94 Disulfide dichloride (S₂Cl₂) is used in the vulcanization of rubber, a process that prevents the slippage of rubber molecules past one another when stretched. It is prepared by heating sulfur in an atmosphere of chlorine:

$$S_8(l) + 4Cl_2(g) \longrightarrow 4S_2Cl_2(l)$$

What is the theoretical yield of S₂Cl₂ in grams when 4.06 g of S₈ are heated with 6.24 g of Cl₂? If the actual yield of S₂Cl₂ is 6.55 g, what is the percent yield?

112   **Chapter 3** ▪ Mass Relationships in Chemical Reactions

Additional Problems

3.95   Gallium is an important element in the production of semiconductors. The average atomic mass of $_{31}^{69}$Ga (68.9256 amu) and $_{31}^{71}$Ga (70.9247 amu) is 69.72 amu. Calculate the natural abundances of the gallium isotopes.

3.96   Rubidium is used in "atomic clocks" and other precise electronic equipment. The average atomic mass of $_{37}^{85}$Rb (84.912 amu) and $_{37}^{87}$Rb (86.909 amu) is 85.47 amu. Calculate the natural abundances of the rubidium isotopes.

● 3.97   The following diagram represents the products (CO_2 and H_2O) formed after the combustion of a hydrocarbon (a compound containing only C and H atoms). Write an equation for the reaction. (*Hint:* The molar mass of the hydrocarbon is about 30 g.)

CO_2

H_2O

● 3.98   Consider the reaction of hydrogen gas with oxygen gas:

$$2H_2(g) + O_2(g) \longrightarrow 2H_2O(g)$$

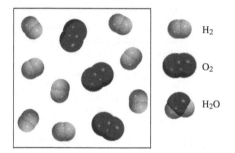

H_2

O_2

H_2O

Assuming complete reaction, which of the diagrams shown next represents the amounts of reactants and products left after the reaction?

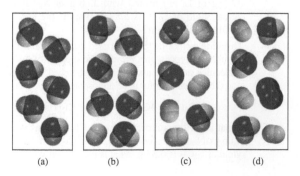

(a)   (b)   (c)   (d)

3.99   Ethylene reacts with hydrogen chloride to form ethyl chloride:

$$C_2H_4(g) + HCl(g) \longrightarrow C_2H_5Cl(g)$$

Calculate the mass of ethyl chloride formed if 4.66 g of ethylene reacts with an 89.4 percent yield.

3.100   Write balanced equations for the following reactions described in words.

(a) Pentane burns in oxygen to form carbon dioxide and water.

(b) Sodium bicarbonate reacts with hydrochloric acid to form carbon dioxide, sodium chloride, and water.

(c) When heated in an atmosphere of nitrogen, lithium forms lithium nitride.

(d) Phosphorus trichloride reacts with water to form phosphorus acid and hydrogen chloride.

(e) Copper(II) oxide heated with ammonia will form copper, nitrogen gas, and water.

● 3.101   Industrially, nitric acid is produced by the Ostwald process represented by the following equations:

$$4NH_3(g) + 5O_2(g) \longrightarrow 4NO(g) + 6H_2O(l)$$
$$2NO(g) + O_2(g) \longrightarrow 2NO_2(g)$$
$$2NO_2(g) + H_2O(l) \longrightarrow HNO_3(aq) + HNO_2(aq)$$

What mass of NH_3 (in g) must be used to produce 1.00 ton of HNO_3 by the above procedure, assuming an 80 percent yield in each step? (1 ton = 2000 lb; 1 lb = 453.6 g.)

3.102   A sample of a compound of Cl and O reacts with an excess of H_2 to give 0.233 g of HCl and 0.403 g of H_2O. Determine the empirical formula of the compound.

3.103   How many grams of H_2O will be produced from the complete combustion of 26.7 g of butane (C_4H_{10})?

3.104   A 26.2-g sample of oxalic acid hydrate ($H_2C_2O_4 \cdot 2H_2O$) is heated in an oven until all the water is driven off. How much of the anhydrous acid is left?

● 3.105   The atomic mass of element X is 33.42 amu. A 27.22-g sample of X combines with 84.10 g of another element Y to form a compound XY. Calculate the atomic mass of Y.

● 3.106   How many moles of O are needed to combine with 0.212 mole of C to form (a) CO and (b) CO_2?

3.107   A research chemist used a mass spectrometer to study the two isotopes of an element. Over time, she recorded a number of mass spectra of these isotopes. On analysis, she noticed that the ratio of the taller peak (the more abundant isotope) to the shorter peak (the less abundant isotope) gradually increased with time. Assuming that the mass spectrometer was functioning normally, what do you think was causing this change?

3.108   The aluminum sulfate hydrate [$Al_2(SO_4)_3 \cdot xH_2O$] contains 8.10 percent Al by mass. Calculate x, that is, the number of water molecules associated with each $Al_2(SO_4)_3$ unit.

3.109 The explosive nitroglycerin ($C_3H_5N_3O_9$) has also been used as a drug to treat heart patients to relieve pain (angina pectoris). We now know that nitroglycerin produces nitric oxide (NO), which causes muscles to relax and allows the arteries to dilate. If each nitroglycerin molecule releases one NO per atom of N, calculate the mass percent of NO available from nitroglycerin.

3.110 The carat is the unit of mass used by jewelers. One carat is exactly 200 mg. How many carbon atoms are present in a 24-carat diamond?

3.111 An iron bar weighed 664 g. After the bar had been standing in moist air for a month, exactly one-eighth of the iron turned to rust (Fe_2O_3). Calculate the final mass of the iron bar and rust.

3.112 A certain metal oxide has the formula MO where M denotes the metal. A 39.46-g sample of the compound is strongly heated in an atmosphere of hydrogen to remove oxygen as water molecules. At the end, 31.70 g of the metal is left over. If O has an atomic mass of 16.00 amu, calculate the atomic mass of M and identify the element.

3.113 An impure sample of zinc (Zn) is treated with an excess of sulfuric acid (H_2SO_4) to form zinc sulfate ($ZnSO_4$) and molecular hydrogen (H_2). (a) Write a balanced equation for the reaction. (b) If 0.0764 g of H_2 is obtained from 3.86 g of the sample, calculate the percent purity of the sample. (c) What assumptions must you make in (b)?

3.114 One of the reactions that occurs in a blast furnace, where iron ore is converted to cast iron, is

$$Fe_2O_3 + 3CO \longrightarrow 2Fe + 3CO_2$$

Suppose that 1.64×10^3 kg of Fe are obtained from a 2.62×10^3-kg sample of Fe_2O_3. Assuming that the reaction goes to completion, what is the percent purity of Fe_2O_3 in the original sample?

3.115 Carbon dioxide (CO_2) is the gas that is mainly responsible for global warming (the greenhouse effect). The burning of fossil fuels is a major cause of the increased concentration of CO_2 in the atmosphere. Carbon dioxide is also the end product of metabolism (see Example 3.13). Using glucose as an example of food, calculate the annual human production of CO_2 in grams, assuming that each person consumes 5.0×10^2 g of glucose per day. The world's population is 7.2 billion, and there are 365 days in a year.

3.116 Carbohydrates are compounds containing carbon, hydrogen, and oxygen in which the hydrogen to oxygen ratio is 2:1. A certain carbohydrate contains 40.0 percent carbon by mass. Calculate the empirical and molecular formulas of the compound if the approximate molar mass is 178 g.

3.117 Which of the following has the greater mass: 0.72 g of O_2 or 0.0011 mole of chlorophyll ($C_{55}H_{72}MgN_4O_5$)?

3.118 Analysis of a metal chloride XCl_3 shows that it contains 67.2 percent Cl by mass. Calculate the molar mass of X and identify the element.

3.119 Hemoglobin ($C_{2952}H_{4664}N_{812}O_{832}S_8Fe_4$) is the oxygen carrier in blood. (a) Calculate its molar mass. (b) An average adult has about 5.0 L of blood. Every milliliter of blood has approximately 5.0×10^9 erythrocytes, or red blood cells, and every red blood cell has about 2.8×10^8 hemoglobin molecules. Calculate the mass of hemoglobin molecules in grams in an average adult.

3.120 Myoglobin stores oxygen for metabolic processes in muscle. Chemical analysis shows that it contains 0.34 percent Fe by mass. What is the molar mass of myoglobin? (There is one Fe atom per molecule.)

3.121 Calculate the number of cations and anions in each of the following compounds: (a) 0.764 g of CsI, (b) 72.8 g of $K_2Cr_2O_7$, (c) 6.54 g of $Hg_2(NO_3)_2$.

3.122 A mixture of NaBr and Na_2SO_4 contains 29.96 percent Na by mass. Calculate the percent by mass of each compound in the mixture.

3.123 Consider the reaction $3A + 2B \longrightarrow 3C$. A student mixed 4.0 moles of A with 4.0 moles of B and obtained 2.8 moles of C. What is the percent yield of the reaction?

3.124 Balance the following equation shown in molecular models.

3.125 Aspirin or acetyl salicylic acid is synthesized by reacting salicylic acid with acetic anhydride:

$$C_7H_6O_3 \;+\; C_4H_6O_3 \longrightarrow C_9H_8O_4 + C_2H_4O_2$$

salicylic acid   acetic anhydride   aspirin   acetic acid

(a) How much salicylic acid is required to produce 0.400 g of aspirin (about the content in a tablet), assuming acetic anhydride is present in excess? (b) Calculate the amount of salicylic acid needed if only 74.9 percent of salicylic acid is converted to aspirin. (c) In one experiment, 9.26 g of salicylic acid is reacted with 8.54 g of acetic anhydride. Calculate the theoretical yield of aspirin and the percent yield if only 10.9 g of aspirin is produced.

3.126 Calculate the percent composition by mass of all the elements in calcium phosphate [$Ca_3(PO_4)_2$], a major component of bone.

3.127 Lysine, an essential amino acid in the human body, contains C, H, O, and N. In one experiment, the complete combustion of 2.175 g of lysine gave 3.94 g CO_2 and 1.89 g H_2O. In a separate experiment, 1.873 g of lysine gave 0.436 g NH_3. (a) Calculate the empirical formula of lysine. (b) The approximate molar mass of lysine is 150 g. What is the molecular formula of the compound?

3.128 Does 1 g of hydrogen molecules contain as many H atoms as 1 g of hydrogen atoms?

114   **Chapter 3** ▪ Mass Relationships in Chemical Reactions

3.129   Avogadro's number has sometimes been described as a conversion factor between amu and grams. Use the fluorine atom (19.00 amu) as an example to show the relation between the atomic mass unit and the gram.

3.130   The natural abundances of the two stable isotopes of hydrogen (hydrogen and deuterium) are ^1_1H: 99.985 percent and ^2_1H: 0.015 percent. Assume that water exists as either H_2O or D_2O. Calculate the number of D_2O molecules in exactly 400 mL of water. (Density = 1.00 g/mL.)

3.131   A compound containing only C, H, and Cl was examined in a mass spectrometer. The highest mass peak seen corresponds to an ion mass of 52 amu. The most abundant mass peak seen corresponds to an ion mass of 50 amu and is about three times as intense as the peak at 52 amu. Deduce a reasonable molecular formula for the compound and explain the positions and intensities of the mass peaks mentioned. (*Hint:* Chlorine is the only element that has isotopes in comparable abundances: $^{35}_{17}Cl$: 75.5 percent; $^{35}_{17}Cl$: 24.5 percent. For H, use ^1_1H; for C, use $^{12}_1C$.)

3.132   In the formation of carbon monoxide, CO, it is found that 2.445 g of carbon combine with 3.257 g of oxygen. What is the atomic mass of oxygen if the atomic mass of carbon is 12.01 amu?

3.133   What mole ratio of molecular chlorine (Cl_2) to molecular oxygen (O_2) would result from the breakup of the compound Cl_2O_7 into its constituent elements?

3.134   Which of the following substances contains the greatest mass of chlorine? (a) 5.0 g Cl_2, (b) 60.0 g $NaClO_3$, (c) 0.10 mol KCl, (d) 30.0 g $MgCl_2$, (e) 0.50 mol Cl_2.

3.135   A compound made up of C, H, and Cl contains 55.0 percent Cl by mass. If 9.00 g of the compound contain 4.19×10^{23} H atoms, what is the empirical formula of the compound?

● **3.136**   Platinum forms two different compounds with chlorine. One contains 26.7 percent Cl by mass, and the other contains 42.1 percent Cl by mass. Determine the empirical formulas of the two compounds.

3.137   The following reaction is stoichiometric as written

$$C_4H_9Cl + NaOC_2H_5 \longrightarrow C_4H_8 + C_2H_5OH + NaCl$$

but it is often carried out with an excess of $NaOC_2H_5$ to react with any water present in the reaction mixture that might reduce the yield. If the reaction shown was carried out with 6.83 g of C_4H_9Cl, how many grams of $NaOC_2H_5$ would be needed to have a 50 percent molar excess of that reactant?

3.138   Compounds containing ruthenium(II) and bipyridine, $C_{10}H_8N_2$, have received considerable interest

because of their role in systems that convert solar energy to electricity. The compound $[Ru(C_{10}H_8N_2)_3]Cl_2$ is synthesized by reacting $RuCl_3 \cdot 3H_2O(s)$ with three molar equivalents of $C_{10}H_8N_2(s)$, along with an excess of triethylamine, $N(C_2H_5)_3(l)$, to convert ruthenium(III) to ruthenium(II). The density of triethylamine is 0.73 g/mL, and typically eight molar equivalents are used in the synthesis. (a) Assuming that you start with 6.5 g of $RuCl_3 \cdot 3H_2O$, how many grams of $C_{10}H_8N_2$ and what volume of $N(C_2H_5)_3$ should be used in the reaction? (b) Given that the yield of this reaction is 91 percent, how many grams of $[Ru(C_{10}H_8N_2)_3]Cl_2$ will be obtained?

● 3.139   Heating 2.40 g of the oxide of metal X (molar mass of X = 55.9 g/mol) in carbon monoxide (CO) yields the pure metal and carbon dioxide. The mass of the metal product is 1.68 g. From the data given, show that the simplest formula of the oxide is X_2O_3 and write a balanced equation for the reaction.

3.140   A compound X contains 63.3 percent manganese (Mn) and 36.7 percent O by mass. When X is heated, oxygen gas is evolved and a new compound Y containing 72.0 percent Mn and 28.0 percent O is formed. (a) Determine the empirical formulas of X and Y. (b) Write a balanced equation for the conversion of X to Y.

● 3.141   The formula of a hydrate of barium chloride is $BaCl_2 \cdot xH_2O$. If 1.936 g of the compound gives 1.864 g of anhydrous $BaSO_4$ upon treatment with sulfuric acid, calculate the value of x.

3.142   It is estimated that the day Mt. St. Helens erupted (May 18, 1980), about 4.0×10^5 tons of SO_2 were released into the atmosphere. If all the SO_2 were eventually converted to sulfuric acid, how many tons of H_2SO_4 were produced?

3.143   Cysteine, shown here, is one of the 20 amino acids found in proteins in humans. Write the molecular formula and calculate its percent composition by mass.

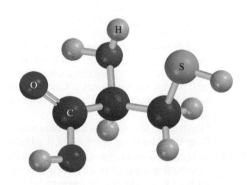

3.144 Isoflurane, shown here, is a common inhalation anesthetic. Write its molecular formula and calculate its percent composition by mass.

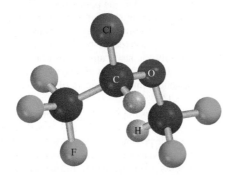

3.145 A mixture of $CuSO_4 \cdot 5H_2O$ and $MgSO_4 \cdot 7H_2O$ is heated until all the water is lost. If 5.020 g of the mixture gives 2.988 g of the anhydrous salts, what is the percent by mass of $CuSO_4 \cdot 5H_2O$ in the mixture?

3.146 When 0.273 g of Mg is heated strongly in a nitrogen (N_2) atmosphere, a chemical reaction occurs. The product of the reaction weighs 0.378 g. Calculate the empirical formula of the compound containing Mg and N. Name the compound.

3.147 A mixture of methane (CH_4) and ethane (C_2H_6) of mass 13.43 g is completely burned in oxygen. If the total mass of CO_2 and H_2O produced is 64.84 g, calculate the fraction of CH_4 in the mixture.

3.148 Leaded gasoline contains an additive to prevent engine "knocking." On analysis, the additive compound is found to contain carbon, hydrogen, and lead (Pb) (hence, "leaded gasoline"). When 51.36 g of this compound are burned in an apparatus such as that shown in Figure 3.6, 55.90 g of CO_2 and 28.61 g of H_2O are produced. Determine the empirical formula of the gasoline additive.

3.149 Because of its detrimental effect on the environment, the lead compound described in Problem 3.148 has been replaced by methyl *tert*-butyl ether (a compound of C, H, and O) to enhance the performance of gasoline. (This compound is also being phased out because of its contamination of drinking water.) When 12.1 g of the compound are burned in an apparatus like the one shown in Figure 3.6, 30.2 g of CO_2 and 14.8 g of H_2O are formed. What is the empirical formula of the compound?

3.150 Suppose you are given a cube made of magnesium (Mg) metal of edge length 1.0 cm. (a) Calculate the number of Mg atoms in the cube. (b) Atoms are spherical in shape. Therefore, the Mg atoms in the cube cannot fill all of the available space. If only 74 percent of the space inside the cube is taken up by Mg atoms, calculate the radius in picometers of a Mg atom. (The density of Mg is

1.74 g/cm^3 and the volume of a sphere of radius r is $\frac{4}{3}\pi r^3$.)

3.151 A certain sample of coal contains 1.6 percent sulfur by mass. When the coal is burned, the sulfur is converted to sulfur dioxide. To prevent air pollution, this sulfur dioxide is treated with calcium oxide (CaO) to form calcium sulfite ($CaSO_3$). Calculate the daily mass (in kilograms) of CaO needed by a power plant that uses 6.60×10^6 kg of coal per day.

3.152 Air is a mixture of many gases. However, in calculating its "molar mass" we need consider only the three major components: nitrogen, oxygen, and argon. Given that one mole of air at sea level is made up of 78.08 percent nitrogen, 20.95 percent oxygen, and 0.97 percent argon, what is the molar mass of air?

3.153 (a) Determine the mass of calcium metal that contains the same number of moles as 89.6 g of zinc metal. (b) Calculate the number of moles of molecular fluorine that has the same mass as 36.9 moles of argon. (c) What is the mass of sulfuric acid that contains 0.56 mole of oxygen atoms? (d) Determine the number of moles of phosphoric acid that contains 2.12 g of hydrogen atoms.

3.154 A major industrial use of hydrochloric acid is in metal pickling. This process involves the removal of metal oxide layers from metal surfaces to prepare them for coating. (a) Write an equation between iron(III) oxide, which represents the rust layer over iron, and HCl to form iron(III) chloride and water. (b) If 1.22 moles of Fe_2O_3 and 289.2 g of HCl react, how many grams of $FeCl_3$ will be produced?

3.155 Octane (C_8H_{18}) is a component of gasoline. Complete combustion of octane yields H_2O and CO_2. Incomplete combustion produces H_2O and CO, which not only reduces the efficiency of the engine using the fuel but is also toxic. In a certain test run, 1.000 gal of octane is burned in an engine. The total mass of CO, CO_2, and H_2O produced is 11.53 kg. Calculate the efficiency of the process; that is, calculate the fraction of octane converted to CO_2. The density of octane is 2.650 kg/gal.

3.156 Industrially, hydrogen gas can be prepared by reacting propane gas (C_3H_8) with steam at about 400°C. The products are carbon monoxide (CO) and hydrogen gas (H_2). (a) Write a balanced equation for the reaction. (b) How many kilograms of H_2 can be obtained from 2.84×10^3 kg of propane?

3.157 In a natural product synthesis, a chemist prepares a complex biological molecule entirely from nonbiological starting materials. The target molecules are often known to have some promise as therapeutic agents, and the organic reactions that are developed along the way benefit all chemists. The overall synthesis, however, requires many steps, so it is important to have the best possible percent yields at each step. What is the overall percent yield for such a synthesis that has 24 steps with an 80 percent yield at each step?

3.158 What is wrong or ambiguous with each of the statements here?

(a) NH_4NO_2 is the limiting reagent in the reaction

$$NH_4NO_2(s) \longrightarrow N_2(g) + 2H_2O(l)$$

(b) The limiting reagents for the reaction shown here are NH_3 and NaCl.

$$NH_3(aq) + NaCl(aq) + H_2CO_3(aq) \longrightarrow \\ NaHCO_3(aq) + NH_4Cl(aq)$$

3.159 (a) For molecules having small molecular masses, mass spectrometry can be used to identify their formulas. To illustrate this point, identify the molecule that most likely accounts for the observation of a peak in a mass spectrum at: 16 amu, 17 amu, 18 amu, and 64 amu. (b) Note that there are (among others) two likely molecules that would give rise to a peak at 44 amu, namely, C_3H_8 and CO_2. In such cases, a chemist might try to look for other peaks generated when some of the molecules break apart in the spectrometer. For example, if a chemist sees a peak at 44 amu and also one at 15 amu, which molecule is producing the 44-amu peak? Why? (c) Using the following precise atomic masses— ^1H (1.00797 amu), ^{12}C (12.00000 amu), and ^{16}O (15.99491 amu)—how precisely must the masses of C_3H_8 and CO_2 be measured to distinguish between them?

3.160 Potash is any potassium mineral that is used for its potassium content. Most of the potash produced in the United States goes into fertilizer. The major sources of potash are potassium chloride (KCl) and potassium sulfate (K_2SO_4). Potash production is often reported as the potassium oxide (K_2O) equivalent or the amount of K_2O that could be made from a given mineral. (a) If KCl costs $0.55 per kg, for what price (dollar per kg) must K_2SO_4 be sold to supply the same amount of potassium on a per dollar basis? (b) What mass (in kg) of K_2O contains the same number of moles of K atoms as 1.00 kg of KCl?

3.161 A 21.496-g sample of magnesium is burned in air to form magnesium oxide and magnesium nitride. When the products are treated with water, 2.813 g of gaseous ammonia are generated. Calculate the amounts of magnesium nitride and magnesium oxide formed.

3.162 A certain metal M forms a bromide containing 53.79 percent Br by mass. What is the chemical formula of the compound?

3.163 A sample of iron weighing 15.0 g was heated with potassium chlorate ($KClO_3$) in an evacuated container. The oxygen generated from the decomposition of $KClO_3$ converted some of the Fe to Fe_2O_3. If the combined mass of Fe and Fe_2O_3 was 17.9 g, calculate the mass of Fe_2O_3 formed and the mass of $KClO_3$ decomposed.

3.164 A sample containing NaCl, Na_2SO_4, and $NaNO_3$ gives the following elemental analysis: Na: 32.08 percent; O: 36.01 percent; Cl: 19.51 percent. Calculate the mass percent of each compound in the sample.

3.165 A sample of 10.00 g of sodium reacts with oxygen to form 13.83 g of sodium oxide (Na_2O) and sodium peroxide (Na_2O_2). Calculate the percent composition of the mixture.

Interpreting, Modeling & Estimating

3.166 While most isotopes of light elements such as oxygen and phosphorus contain relatively equal numbers of protons and neutrons, recent results indicate that a new class of isotopes called neutron-rich isotopes can be prepared. These neutron-rich isotopes push the limits of nuclear stability as the large number of neutrons approach the "neutron drip line." They may play a critical role in the nuclear reactions of stars. An unusually heavy isotope of aluminum ($^{43}_{13}Al$) has been reported. How many more neutrons does this atom contain compared to an average aluminum atom?

3.167 Without doing any detailed calculations, arrange the following substances in the increasing order of number of moles: 20.0 g Cl, 35.0 g Br, and 94.0 g I.

3.168 Without doing any detailed calculations, estimate which element has the highest percent composition by mass in each of the following compounds:

(a) $Hg(NO_3)_2$

(b) NF_3

(c) $K_2Cr_2O_7$

(d) $C_{2952}H_{4664}N_{812}O_{832}S_8Fe_4$

3.169 Consider the reaction

$$6Li(s) + N_2(g) \longrightarrow 2Li_3N(s)$$

Without doing any detailed calculations, choose one of the following combinations in which nitrogen is the limiting reagent:

(a) 44 g Li and 38 g N_2

(b) 1380 g Li and 842 g N_2

(c) 1.1 g Li and 0.81 g N_2

3.170 Estimate how high in miles you can stack up an Avogadro's number of oranges covering the entire Earth.

3.171 The following is a crude but effective method for estimating the *order of magnitude* of Avogadro's number using stearic acid ($C_{18}H_{36}O_2$) shown here. When stearic acid is added to water, its molecules collect at the surface and form a monolayer; that is, the layer is only one molecule thick. The cross-sectional area of each stearic acid molecule has been measured to be 0.21 nm^2. In one experiment it is found that 1.4×10^{-4} g of stearic acid is needed to form a monolayer over water in a dish of diameter 20 cm. Based on these measurements, what is Avogadro's number?

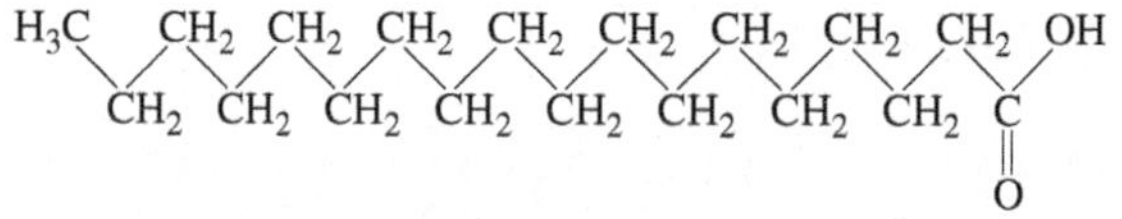

$$H_3C \underset{CH_2}{\overset{CH_2}{\diagup}} \underset{CH_2}{\overset{CH_2}{\diagdown}} \underset{CH_2}{\overset{CH_2}{\diagup}} \underset{CH_2}{\overset{CH_2}{\diagdown}} \underset{CH_2}{\overset{CH_2}{\diagup}} \underset{CH_2}{\overset{CH_2}{\diagdown}} \underset{CH_2}{\overset{CH_2}{\diagup}} \underset{CH_2}{\overset{CH_2}{\diagdown}} \underset{\underset{O}{\overset{\|}{C}}}{\overset{OH}{\diagup}}$$

Answers to Practice Exercises

3.1 63.55 amu. **3.2** 3.59 moles. **3.3** 2.57×10^3 g.
3.4 1.0×10^{-20} g. **3.5** 32.04 amu. **3.6** 1.66 moles.
3.7 5.81×10^{24} H atoms. **3.8** H: 2.055%; S: 32.69%; O: 65.25%. **3.9** $KMnO_4$ (potassium permanganate).

3.10 196 g. **3.11** B_2H_6. **3.12** $Fe_2O_3 + 3CO \rightarrow 2Fe + 3CO_2$.
3.13 235 g. **3.14** 0.769 g. **3.15** (a) 234 g, (b) 234 g.
3.16 25.1 g. **3.17** (a) 863 g, (b) 93.0%.

CHAPTER

4

Reactions in Aqueous Solutions

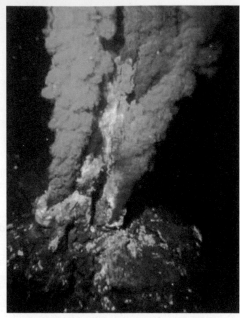

Black smokers form when superheated water, rich in minerals, flows out onto the ocean floor through the lava from an ocean volcano. The hydrogen sulfide present converts the metal ions to insoluble metal sulfides.

A LOOK AHEAD

▶ We begin by studying the properties of solutions prepared by dissolving substances in water, called aqueous solutions. Aqueous solutions can be classified as nonelectrolyte or electrolyte, depending on their ability to conduct electricity. (4.1)

▶ We will see that precipitation reactions are those in which the product is an insoluble compound. We learn to represent these reactions using ionic equations and net ionic equations. (4.2)

▶ Next, we learn acid-base reactions, which involve the transfer of proton (H^+) from an acid to a base. (4.3)

▶ We then learn oxidation-reduction (redox) reactions in which electrons are transferred between reactants. We will see that there are several types of redox reactions. (4.4)

▶ To carry out quantitative studies of solutions, we learn how to express the concentration of a solution in molarity. (4.5)

▶ Finally, we will apply our knowledge of the mole method from Chapter 3 to the three types of reactions studied here. We will see how gravimetric analysis is used to study precipitation reactions, and the titration technique is used to study acid-base and redox reactions. (4.6, 4.7, and 4.8)

Many chemical reactions and virtually all biological processes take place in water. In this chapter, we will discuss three major categories of reactions that occur in aqueous solutions: precipitation reactions, acid-base reactions, and redox reactions. In later chapters, we will study the structural characteristics and properties of water—the so-called *universal solvent*—and its solutions.

4.1 General Properties of Aqueous Solutions

A *solution* is a *homogeneous mixture of two or more substances.* The *solute* is *the substance present in a smaller amount,* and the *solvent* is *the substance present in a larger amount.* A solution may be gaseous (such as air), solid (such as an alloy), or liquid (seawater, for example). In this section we will discuss only *aqueous solutions,* in which *the solute initially is a liquid or a solid and the solvent is water.*

Electrolytic Properties

All solutes that dissolve in water fit into one of two categories: electrolytes and nonelectrolytes. An *electrolyte* is *a substance that, when dissolved in water, results in a solution that can conduct electricity.* A *nonelectrolyte* *does not conduct electricity when dissolved in water.* Figure 4.1 shows an easy and straightforward method of distinguishing between electrolytes and nonelectrolytes. A pair of inert electrodes (copper or platinum) is immersed in a beaker of water. To light the bulb, electric current must flow from one electrode to the other, thus completing the circuit. Pure water is a very poor conductor of electricity. However, if we add a small amount of sodium chloride (NaCl), the bulb will glow as soon as the salt dissolves in the water. Solid NaCl, an ionic compound, breaks up into Na^+ and Cl^- ions when it dissolves in water. The Na^+ ions are attracted to the negative electrode, and the Cl^- ions to the positive electrode. This movement sets up an electric current that is equivalent to the flow of electrons along a metal wire. Because the NaCl solution conducts electricity, we say that NaCl is an electrolyte. Pure water contains very few ions, so it cannot conduct electricity.

Comparing the lightbulb's brightness for the same molar amounts of dissolved substances helps us distinguish between strong and weak electrolytes. A characteristic of strong electrolytes is that the solute is assumed to be 100 percent dissociated into ions in solution. (By *dissociation* we mean the breaking up of the

Tap water does conduct electricity because it contains many dissolved ions.

▶▶ Animation
Strong Electrolytes, Weak Electrolytes, and Nonelectrolytes

(a)

(b)

(c)

Figure 4.1 *An arrangement for distinguishing between electrolytes and nonelectrolytes. A solution's ability to conduct electricity depends on the number of ions it contains. (a) A nonelectrolyte solution does not contain ions, and the lightbulb is not lit. (b) A weak electrolyte solution contains a small number of ions, and the lightbulb is dimly lit. (c) A strong electrolyte solution contains a large number of ions, and the lightbulb is brightly lit. The molar amounts of the dissolved solutes are equal in all three cases.*

Table 4.1	Classification of Solutes in Aqueous Solution	
Strong Electrolyte	**Weak Electrolyte**	**Nonelectrolyte**
HCl	CH_3COOH	$(NH_2)_2CO$ (urea)
HNO_3	HF	CH_3OH (methanol)
$HClO_4$	HNO_2	C_2H_5OH (ethanol)
H_2SO_4*	NH_3	$C_6H_{12}O_6$ (glucose)
NaOH	$H_2O^\dagger$	$C_{12}H_{22}O_{11}$ (sucrose)
$Ba(OH)_2$		
Ionic compounds		

*H_2SO_4 has two ionizable H^+ ions, but only one of the H^+ ions is totally ionized.
†Pure water is an extremely weak electrolyte.

compound into cations and anions.) Thus, we can represent sodium chloride dissolving in water as

$$NaCl(s) \xrightarrow{H_2O} Na^+(aq) + Cl^-(aq)$$

This equation says that all sodium chloride that enters the solution ends up as Na^+ and Cl^- ions; there are no undissociated NaCl units in solution.

Table 4.1 lists examples of strong electrolytes, weak electrolytes, and nonelectrolytes. Ionic compounds, such as sodium chloride, potassium iodide (KI), and calcium nitrate [$Ca(NO_3)_2$], are strong electrolytes. It is interesting to note that human body fluids contain many strong and weak electrolytes.

Water is a very effective solvent for ionic compounds. Although water is an electrically neutral molecule, it has a positive region (the H atoms) and a negative region (the O atom), or positive and negative "poles"; for this reason it is a *polar* solvent. When an ionic compound such as sodium chloride dissolves in water, the three-dimensional network of ions in the solid is destroyed. The Na^+ and Cl^- ions are separated from each other and undergo **hydration,** *the process in which an ion is surrounded by water molecules arranged in a specific manner.* Each Na^+ ion is surrounded by a number of water molecules orienting their negative poles toward the cation. Similarly, each Cl^- ion is surrounded by water molecules with their positive poles oriented toward the anion (Figure 4.2). Hydration helps to stabilize ions in solution and prevents cations from combining with anions.

 Animation
Hydration

Acids and bases are also electrolytes. Some acids, including hydrochloric acid (HCl) and nitric acid (HNO_3), are strong electrolytes. These acids are assumed to ionize completely in water; for example, when hydrogen chloride gas dissolves in water, it forms hydrated H^+ and Cl^- ions:

$$HCl(g) \xrightarrow{H_2O} H^+(aq) + Cl^-(aq)$$

In other words, *all* the dissolved HCl molecules separate into hydrated H^+ and Cl^- ions. Thus, when we write HCl(aq), it is understood that it is a solution of only H^+(aq)

Figure 4.2 *Hydration of Na^+ and Cl^- ions.*

and $Cl^-(aq)$ ions and that there are no hydrated HCl molecules present. On the other hand, certain acids, such as acetic acid (CH_3COOH), which gives vinegar its tart flavor, do not ionize completely and are weak electrolytes. We represent the ionization of acetic acid as

$$CH_3COOH(aq) \rightleftharpoons CH_3COO^-(aq) + H^+(aq)$$

where CH_3COO^- is called the acetate ion. We use the term *ionization* to describe the separation of acids and bases into ions. By writing the formula of acetic acid as CH_3COOH, we indicate that the ionizable proton is in the COOH group.

The ionization of acetic acid is written with a double arrow to show that it is a ***reversible reaction;*** that is, *the reaction can occur in both directions.* Initially, a number of CH_3COOH molecules break up into CH_3COO^- and H^+ ions. As time goes on, some of the CH_3COO^- and H^+ ions recombine into CH_3COOH molecules. Eventually, a state is reached in which the acid molecules ionize as fast as the ions recombine. Such a chemical state, in which no net change can be observed (although activity is continuous on the molecular level), is called *chemical equilibrium.* Acetic acid, then, is a weak electrolyte because its ionization in water is incomplete. By contrast, in a hydrochloric acid solution the H^+ and Cl^- ions have no tendency to recombine and form molecular HCl. We use a single arrow to represent complete ionizations.

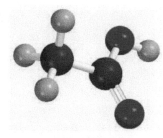

CH_3COOH

There are different types of chemical equilibrium. We will return to this very important topic in Chapter 14.

Review of Concepts

The diagrams here show three compounds AB_2 (a), AC_2 (b), and AD_2 (c) dissolved in water. Which is the strongest electrolyte and which is the weakest? (For simplicity, water molecules are not shown.)

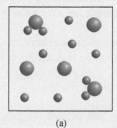   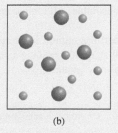   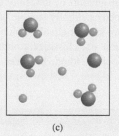

(a)   (b)   (c)

4.2 Precipitation Reactions

One common type of reaction that occurs in aqueous solution is the ***precipitation reaction,*** which *results in the formation of an insoluble product, or precipitate.* A ***precipitate*** is *an insoluble solid that separates from the solution.* Precipitation reactions usually involve ionic compounds. For example, when an aqueous solution of lead(II) nitrate [$Pb(NO_3)_2$] is added to an aqueous solution of potassium iodide (KI), a yellow precipitate of lead(II) iodide (PbI_2) is formed:

$$Pb(NO_3)_2(aq) + 2KI(aq) \longrightarrow PbI_2(s) + 2KNO_3(aq)$$

Potassium nitrate remains in solution. Figure 4.3 shows this reaction in progress.

The preceding reaction is an example of a ***metathesis reaction*** (also called a double-displacement reaction), *a reaction that involves the exchange of parts between the two compounds.* (In this case, the cations in the two compounds exchange anions, so Pb^{2+} ends up with I^- as PbI_2 and K^+ ends up with NO_3^- as

Animation
Precipitation Reactions

122   **Chapter 4 ▪ Reactions in Aqueous Solutions**

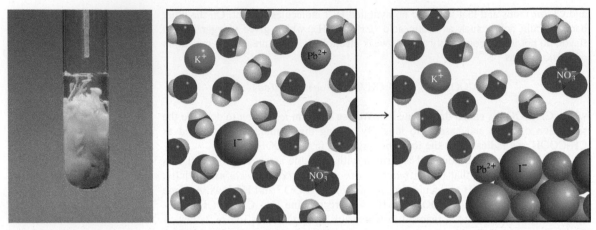

Figure 4.3 *Formation of yellow PbI₂ precipitate as a solution of Pb(NO₃)₂ is added to a solution of KI.*

KNO₃.) As we will see, the precipitation reactions discussed in this chapter are examples of metathesis reactions.

Solubility

How can we predict whether a precipitate will form when a compound is added to a solution or when two solutions are mixed? It depends on the *solubility* of the solute, which is defined as *the maximum amount of solute that will dissolve in a given quantity of solvent at a specific temperature.* Chemists refer to substances as soluble, slightly soluble, or insoluble in a qualitative sense. A substance is said to be soluble if a fair amount of it visibly dissolves when added to water. If not, the substance is described as slightly soluble or insoluble. All ionic compounds are strong electrolytes, but they are not equally soluble.

Table 4.2 classifies a number of common ionic compounds as soluble or insoluble. Keep in mind, however, that even insoluble compounds dissolve to a certain extent. Figure 4.4 shows several precipitates.

Table 4.2	Solubility Rules for Common Ionic Compounds in Water at 25°C
Soluble Compounds	**Insoluble Exceptions**
Compounds containing alkali metal ions (Li⁺, Na⁺, K⁺, Rb⁺, Cs⁺) and the ammonium ion (NH₄⁺)	
Nitrates (NO₃⁻), acetates (CH₃COO⁻), bicarbonates (HCO₃⁻), chlorates (ClO₃⁻), and perchlorates (ClO₄⁻)	
Halides (Cl⁻, Br⁻, I⁻)	Halides of Ag⁺, Hg₂²⁺, and Pb²⁺
Sulfates (SO₄²⁻)	Sulfates of Ag⁺, Ca²⁺, Sr²⁺, Ba²⁺, Hg₂²⁺, and Pb²⁺
Insoluble Compounds	**Soluble Exceptions**
Carbonates (CO₃²⁻), phosphates (PO₄³⁻), chromates (CrO₄²⁻), sulfides (S²⁻)	Compounds containing alkali metal ions and the ammonium ion
Hydroxides (OH⁻)	Compounds containing alkali metal ions and the Ba²⁺ ion

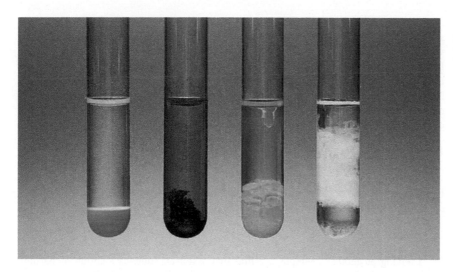

Figure 4.4 *Appearance of several precipitates. From left to right: CdS, PbS, Ni(OH)₂, and Al(OH)₃.*

Example 4.1 applies the solubility rules in Table 4.2.

Example 4.1

Classify the following ionic compounds as soluble or insoluble: (a) silver sulfate (Ag_2SO_4), (b) calcium carbonate ($CaCO_3$), (c) sodium phosphate (Na_3PO_4).

Strategy Although it is not necessary to memorize the solubilities of compounds, you should keep in mind the following useful rules: All ionic compounds containing alkali metal cations; the ammonium ion; and the nitrate, bicarbonate, and chlorate ions are soluble. For other compounds, we need to refer to Table 4.2.

Solution

(a) According to Table 4.2, Ag_2SO_4 is insoluble.

(b) This is a carbonate and Ca is a Group 2A metal. Therefore, $CaCO_3$ is insoluble.

(c) Sodium is an alkali metal (Group 1A) so Na_3PO_4 is soluble.

Similar problems: 4.19, 4.20.

Practice Exercise Classify the following ionic compounds as soluble or insoluble: (a) CuS, (b) Ca(OH)₂, (c) Zn(NO₃)₂.

Molecular Equations, Ionic Equations, and Net Ionic Equations

The equation describing the precipitation of lead(II) iodide on page 121 is called a ***molecular equation*** because *the formulas of the compounds are written as though all species existed as molecules or whole units.* A molecular equation is useful because it identifies the reagents [that is, lead(II) nitrate and potassium iodide]. If we wanted to bring about this reaction in the laboratory, we would use the molecular equation. However, a molecular equation does not describe in detail what actually is happening in solution.

As pointed out earlier, when ionic compounds dissolve in water, they break apart into their component cations and anions. To be more realistic, the equations should show the dissociation of dissolved ionic compounds into ions. Therefore, returning to the reaction between potassium iodide and lead(II) nitrate, we would write

$$Pb^{2+}(aq) + 2NO_3^-(aq) + 2K^+(aq) + 2I^-(aq) \longrightarrow$$
$$PbI_2(s) + 2K^+(aq) + 2NO_3^-(aq)$$

124   **Chapter 4 ▪** Reactions in Aqueous Solutions

Figure 4.5 *Formation of BaSO₄ precipitate.*

The preceding equation is an example of an ***ionic equation,*** which *shows dissolved species as free ions.* To see whether a precipitate might form from this solution, we first combine the cation and anion from different compounds; that is, PbI_2 and KNO_3. Referring to Table 4.2, we see that PbI_2 is an insoluble compound and KNO_3 is soluble. Therefore, the dissolved KNO_3 remains in solution as separate K^+ and NO_3^- ions, which are called ***spectator ions,*** or *ions that are not involved in the overall reaction.* Because spectator ions appear on both sides of an equation, they can be eliminated from the ionic equation

$$Pb^{2+}(aq) + 2\cancel{NO_3^-(aq)} + 2\cancel{K^+(aq)} + 2I^-(aq) \longrightarrow$$
$$PbI_2(s) + 2\cancel{K^+(aq)} + 2\cancel{NO_3^-(aq)}$$

Finally, we end up with the ***net ionic equation,*** which *shows only the species that actually take part in the reaction:*

$$Pb^{2+}(aq) + 2I^-(aq) \longrightarrow PbI_2(s)$$

Looking at another example, we find that when an aqueous solution of barium chloride ($BaCl_2$) is added to an aqueous solution of sodium sulfate (Na_2SO_4), a white precipitate is formed (Figure 4.5). Treating this as a metathesis reaction, the products are $BaSO_4$ and $NaCl$. From Table 4.2 we see that only $BaSO_4$ is insoluble. Therefore, we write the molecular equation as

$$BaCl_2(aq) + Na_2SO_4(aq) \longrightarrow BaSO_4(s) + 2NaCl(aq)$$

The ionic equation for the reaction is

$$Ba^{2+}(aq) + 2Cl^-(aq) + 2Na^+(aq) + SO_4^{2-}(aq) \longrightarrow$$
$$BaSO_4(s) + 2Na^+(aq) + 2Cl^-(aq)$$

Canceling the spectator ions (Na^+ and Cl^-) on both sides of the equation gives us the net ionic equation

$$Ba^{2+}(aq) + SO_4^{2-}(aq) \longrightarrow BaSO_4(s)$$

The following four steps summarize the procedure for writing ionic and net ionic equations:

1. Write a balanced molecular equation for the reaction, using the correct formulas for the reactant and product ionic compounds. Refer to Table 4.2 to decide which of the products is insoluble and therefore will appear as a precipitate.

2. Write the ionic equation for the reaction. The compound that does not appear as the precipitate should be shown as free ions.

3. Identify and cancel the spectator ions on both sides of the equation. Write the net ionic equation for the reaction.

4. Check that the charges and number of atoms balance in the net ionic equation.

These steps are applied in Example 4.2.

Example 4.2

Predict what happens when a potassium phosphate (K_3PO_4) solution is mixed with a calcium nitrate [$Ca(NO_3)_2$] solution. Write a net ionic equation for the reaction.

(Continued)

Precipitate formed by the reaction between K₃PO₄ (aq) and Ca(NO₃)₂(aq).

Strategy From the given information, it is useful to first write the unbalanced equation

$$K_3PO_4(aq) + Ca(NO_3)_2(aq) \longrightarrow ?$$

What happens when ionic compounds dissolve in water? What ions are formed from the dissociation of K_3PO_4 and $Ca(NO_3)_2$? What happens when the cations encounter the anions in solution?

Solution In solution, K_3PO_4 dissociates into K^+ and PO_4^{3-} ions and $Ca(NO_3)_2$ dissociates into Ca^{2+} and NO_3^- ions. According to Table 4.2, calcium ions (Ca^{2+}) and phosphate ions (PO_4^{3-}) will form an insoluble compound, calcium phosphate $[Ca_3(PO_4)_2]$, while the other product, KNO_3, is soluble and remains in solution. Therefore, this is a precipitation reaction. We follow the stepwise procedure just outlined.

Step 1: The balanced molecular equation for this reaction is

$$2K_3PO_4(aq) + 3Ca(NO_3)_2(aq) \longrightarrow Ca_3(PO_4)_2(s) + 6KNO_3(aq)$$

Step 2: To write the ionic equation, the soluble compounds are shown as dissociated ions:

$$6K^+(aq) + 2PO_4^{3-}(aq) + 3Ca^{2+}(aq) + 6NO_3^-(aq) \longrightarrow$$
$$6K^+(aq) + 6NO_3^-(aq) + Ca_3(PO_4)_2(s)$$

Step 3: Canceling the spectator ions (K^+ and NO_3^-) on each side of the equation, we obtain the net ionic equation:

$$3Ca^{2+}(aq) + 2PO_4^{3-}(aq) \longrightarrow Ca_3(PO_4)_2(s)$$

Step 4: Note that because we balanced the molecular equation first, the net ionic equation is balanced as to the number of atoms on each side and the number of positive ($+6$) and negative (-6) charges on the left-hand side is the same.

Similar problems: 4.21, 4.22.

Practice Exercise Predict the precipitate produced by mixing an $Al(NO_3)_3$ solution with a NaOH solution. Write the net ionic equation for the reaction.

Review of Concepts

Which of the diagrams here accurately describes the reaction between $Ca(NO_3)_2(aq)$ and $Na_2CO_3(aq)$? For simplicity, only the Ca^{2+} (yellow) and CO_3^{2-} (blue) ions are shown.

(a)

(b)

(c)

The Chemistry in Action essay on p. 126 discusses some practical problems associated with precipitation reactions.

CHEMISTRY *in Action*

An Undesirable Precipitation Reaction

Limestone ($CaCO_3$) and dolomite ($CaCO_3 \cdot MgCO_3$), which are widespread on Earth's surface, often enter the water supply. According to Table 4.2, calcium carbonate is insoluble in water. However, in the presence of dissolved carbon dioxide (from the atmosphere), calcium carbonate is converted to soluble calcium bicarbonate [$Ca(HCO_3)_2$]:

$$CaCO_3(s) + CO_2(aq) + H_2O(l) \longrightarrow Ca^{2+}(aq) + 2HCO_3^-(aq)$$

where HCO_3^- is the bicarbonate ion.

Water containing Ca^{2+} and/or Mg^{2+} ions is called *hard water*, and water that is mostly free of these ions is called *soft water*. Hard water is unsuitable for some household and industrial uses.

When water containing Ca^{2+} and HCO_3^- ions is heated or boiled, the solution reaction is reversed to produce the $CaCO_3$ precipitate

$$Ca^{2+}(aq) + 2HCO_3^-(aq) \longrightarrow CaCO_3(s) + CO_2(aq) + H_2O(l)$$

and gaseous carbon dioxide is driven off:

$$CO_2(aq) \longrightarrow CO_2(g)$$

Solid calcium carbonate formed in this way is the main component of the scale that accumulates in boilers, water heaters, pipes, and teakettles. A thick layer of scale reduces heat transfer and decreases the efficiency and durability of boilers, pipes, and appliances. In household hot-water pipes it can restrict or

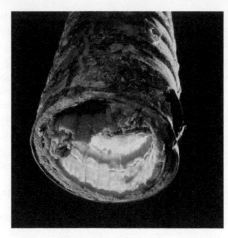

Boiler scale almost fills this hot-water pipe. The deposits consist mostly of $CaCO_3$ with some $MgCO_3$.

totally block the flow of water. A simple method used by plumbers to remove scale deposits is to introduce a small amount of hydrochloric acid, which reacts with (and therefore dissolves) $CaCO_3$:

$$CaCO_3(s) + 2HCl(aq) \longrightarrow CaCl_2(aq) + H_2O(l) + CO_2(g)$$

In this way, $CaCO_3$ is converted to soluble $CaCl_2$.

4.3 Acid-Base Reactions

Acids and bases are as familiar as aspirin and milk of magnesia although many people do not know their chemical names—acetylsalicylic acid (aspirin) and magnesium hydroxide (milk of magnesia). In addition to being the basis of many medicinal and household products, acid-base chemistry is important in industrial processes and essential in sustaining biological systems. Before we can discuss acid-base reactions, we need to know more about acids and bases themselves.

General Properties of Acids and Bases

In Section 2.7 we defined acids as substances that ionize in water to produce H^+ ions and bases as substances that ionize in water to produce OH^- ions. These definitions were formulated in the late nineteenth century by the Swedish chemist

Svante Arrhenius[†] to classify substances whose properties in aqueous solutions were well known.

Acids

- Acids have a sour taste; for example, vinegar owes its sourness to acetic acid, and lemons and other citrus fruits contain citric acid.
- Acids cause color changes in plant dyes; for example, they change the color of litmus from blue to red.
- Acids react with certain metals, such as zinc, magnesium, and iron, to produce hydrogen gas. A typical reaction is that between hydrochloric acid and magnesium:

$$2HCl(aq) + Mg(s) \longrightarrow MgCl_2(aq) + H_2(g)$$

- Acids react with carbonates and bicarbonates, such as Na_2CO_3, $CaCO_3$, and $NaHCO_3$, to produce carbon dioxide gas (Figure 4.6). For example,

$$2HCl(aq) + CaCO_3(s) \longrightarrow CaCl_2(aq) + H_2O(l) + CO_2(g)$$
$$HCl(aq) + NaHCO_3(s) \longrightarrow NaCl(aq) + H_2O(l) + CO_2(g)$$

- Aqueous acid solutions conduct electricity.

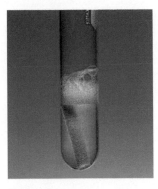

Figure 4.6 *A piece of blackboard chalk, which is mostly $CaCO_3$, reacts with hydrochloric acid.*

Bases

- Bases have a bitter taste.
- Bases feel slippery; for example, soaps, which contain bases, exhibit this property.
- Bases cause color changes in plant dyes; for example, they change the color of litmus from red to blue.
- Aqueous base solutions conduct electricity.

Brønsted Acids and Bases

Arrhenius' definitions of acids and bases are limited in that they apply only to aqueous solutions. Broader definitions were proposed by the Danish chemist Johannes Brønsted[‡] in 1932; a **Brønsted acid** is *a proton donor*, and a **Brønsted base** is *a proton acceptor*. Note that Brønsted's definitions do not require acids and bases to be in aqueous solution.

Hydrochloric acid is a Brønsted acid because it donates a proton in water:

$$HCl(aq) \longrightarrow H^+(aq) + Cl^-(aq)$$

Note that the H^+ ion is a hydrogen atom that has lost its electron; that is, it is just a bare proton. The size of a proton is about 10^{-15} m, compared to a diameter of 10^{-10} m for an average atom or ion. Such an exceedingly small charged particle cannot exist as a separate entity in aqueous solution owing to its strong attraction

---

[†]Svante August Arrhenius (1859–1927). Swedish chemist. Arrhenius made important contributions in the study of chemical kinetics and electrolyte solutions. He also speculated that life had come to Earth from other planets, a theory now known as *panspermia*. Arrhenius was awarded the Nobel Prize in Chemistry in 1903.

[‡]Johannes Nicolaus Brønsted (1879–1947). Danish chemist. In addition to his theory of acids and bases, Brønsted worked on thermodynamics and the separation of mercury isotopes. In some texts, Brønsted acids and bases are called Brønsted-Lowry acids and bases. Thomas Martin Lowry (1874–1936). English chemist. Brønsted and Lowry developed essentially the same acid-base theory independently in 1923.

128   **Chapter 4** ▪ Reactions in Aqueous Solutions

Figure 4.7 *Ionization of HCl in water to form the hydronium ion and the chloride ion.*

$$HCl \quad + \quad H_2O \quad \longrightarrow \quad H_3O^+ \quad + \quad Cl^-$$

for the negative pole (the O atom) in H_2O. Consequently, the proton exists in the hydrated form, as shown in Figure 4.7. Therefore, the ionization of hydrochloric acid should be written as

$$HCl(aq) + H_2O(l) \longrightarrow H_3O^+(aq) + Cl^-(aq)$$

The *hydrated proton, H_3O^+*, is called the **hydronium ion.** This equation shows a reaction in which a Brønsted acid (HCl) donates a proton to a Brønsted base (H_2O).

Experiments show that the hydronium ion is further hydrated so that the proton may have several water molecules associated with it. Because the acidic properties of the proton are unaffected by the degree of hydration, in this text we will generally use $H^+(aq)$ to represent the hydrated proton. This notation is for convenience, but H_3O^+ is closer to reality. Keep in mind that both notations represent the same species in aqueous solution.

Acids commonly used in the laboratory include hydrochloric acid (HCl), nitric acid (HNO_3), acetic acid (CH_3COOH), sulfuric acid (H_2SO_4), and phosphoric acid (H_3PO_4). The first three are **monoprotic acids;** that is, *each unit of the acid yields one hydrogen ion upon ionization:*

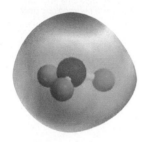

Electrostatic potential map of the H_3O^+ ion. In the rainbow color spectrum representation, the most electron-rich region is red and the most electron-poor region is blue.

In most cases, acids start with H in the formula or have a COOH group.

$$HCl(aq) \longrightarrow H^+(aq) + Cl^-(aq)$$
$$HNO_3(aq) \longrightarrow H^+(aq) + NO_3^-(aq)$$
$$CH_3COOH(aq) \rightleftharpoons CH_3COO^-(aq) + H^+(aq)$$

As mentioned earlier, because the ionization of acetic acid is incomplete (note the double arrows), it is a weak electrolyte. For this reason it is called a weak acid (see Table 4.1). On the other hand, HCl and HNO_3 are strong acids because they are strong electrolytes, so they are completely ionized in solution (note the use of single arrows).

Sulfuric acid (H_2SO_4) is a **diprotic acid** because *each unit of the acid gives up two H^+ ions,* in two separate steps:

$$H_2SO_4(aq) \longrightarrow H^+(aq) + HSO_4^-(aq)$$
$$HSO_4^-(aq) \rightleftharpoons H^+(aq) + SO_4^{2-}(aq)$$

H_2SO_4 is a strong electrolyte or strong acid (the first step of ionization is complete), but HSO_4^- is a weak acid or weak electrolyte, and we need a double arrow to represent its incomplete ionization.

Triprotic acids, which *yield three H^+ ions,* are relatively few in number. The best known triprotic acid is phosphoric acid, whose ionizations are

$$H_3PO_4(aq) \rightleftharpoons H^+(aq) + H_2PO_4^-(aq)$$
$$H_2PO_4^-(aq) \rightleftharpoons H^+(aq) + HPO_4^{2-}(aq)$$
$$HPO_4^{2-}(aq) \rightleftharpoons H^+(aq) + PO_4^{3-}(aq)$$

All three species (H_3PO_4, $H_2PO_4^-$, and HPO_4^{2-}) in this case are weak acids, and we use the double arrows to represent each ionization step. Anions such as $H_2PO_4^-$ and HPO_4^{2-} are found in aqueous solutions of phosphates such as NaH_2PO_4 and Na_2HPO_4. Table 4.3 lists several common strong and weak acids.

Table 4.3	
Some Common Strong and Weak Acids	
Strong Acids	
Hydrochloric acid	HCl
Hydrobromic acid	HBr
Hydroiodic acid	HI
Nitric acid	HNO_3
Sulfuric acid	H_2SO_4
Perchloric acid	$HClO_4$
Weak Acids	
Hydrofluoric acid	HF
Nitrous acid	HNO_2
Phosphoric acid	H_3PO_4
Acetic acid	CH_3COOH

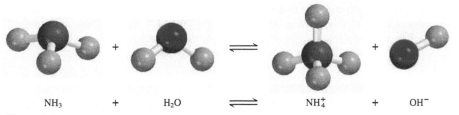

$$NH_3 \quad + \quad H_2O \quad \rightleftharpoons \quad NH_4^+ \quad + \quad OH^-$$

Figure 4.8 *Ionization of ammonia in water to form the ammonium ion and the hydroxide ion.*

Review of Concepts

Which of the following diagrams best represents a weak acid? Which represents a very weak acid? Which represents a strong acid? The proton exists in water as the hydronium ion. All acids are monoprotic. (For simplicity, water molecules are not shown.)

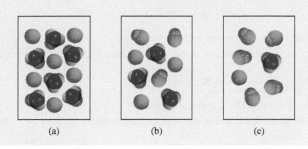

(a)   (b)   (c)

Table 4.1 shows that sodium hydroxide (NaOH) and barium hydroxide [Ba(OH)$_2$] are strong electrolytes. This means that they are completely ionized in solution:

$$NaOH(s) \xrightarrow{H_2O} Na^+(aq) + OH^-(aq)$$
$$Ba(OH)_2(s) \xrightarrow{H_2O} Ba^{2+}(aq) + 2OH^-(aq)$$

The OH$^-$ ion can accept a proton as follows:

$$H^+(aq) + OH^-(aq) \longrightarrow H_2O(l)$$

Thus, OH$^-$ is a Brønsted base.

Ammonia (NH$_3$) is classified as a Brønsted base because it can accept a H$^+$ ion (Figure 4.8):

$$NH_3(aq) + H_2O(l) \rightleftharpoons NH_4^+(aq) + OH^-(aq)$$

Ammonia is a weak electrolyte (and therefore a weak base) because only a small fraction of dissolved NH$_3$ molecules react with water to form NH$_4^+$ and OH$^-$ ions.

The most commonly used strong base in the laboratory is sodium hydroxide. It is cheap and soluble. (In fact, all of the alkali metal hydroxides are soluble.) The most commonly used weak base is aqueous ammonia solution, which is sometimes erroneously called ammonium hydroxide. There is no evidence that the species NH$_4$OH actually exists other than the NH$_4^+$ and OH$^-$ ions in solution. All of the Group 2A elements form hydroxides of the type M(OH)$_2$, where M denotes an alkaline earth metal. Of these hydroxides, only Ba(OH)$_2$ is soluble.

Note that this bottle of aqueous ammonia is erroneously labeled.

Magnesium and calcium hydroxides are used in medicine and industry. Hydroxides of other metals, such as $Al(OH)_3$ and $Zn(OH)_2$ are insoluble and are not used as bases.

Example 4.3 classifies substances as Brønsted acids or Brønsted bases.

Example 4.3

Classify each of the following species in aqueous solution as a Brønsted acid or base: (a) HBr, (b) NO_2^-, (c) HCO_3^-.

Strategy What are the characteristics of a Brønsted acid? Does it contain at least an H atom? With the exception of ammonia, most Brønsted bases that you will encounter at this stage are anions.

Solution

(a) We know that HCl is an acid. Because Br and Cl are both halogens (Group 7A), we expect HBr, like HCl, to ionize in water as follows:

$$HBr(aq) \longrightarrow H^+(aq) + Br^-(aq)$$

Therefore HBr is a Brønsted acid.

(b) In solution the nitrite ion can accept a proton from water to form nitrous acid:

$$NO_2^-(aq) + H^+(aq) \longrightarrow HNO_2(aq)$$

This property makes NO_2^- a Brønsted base.

(c) The bicarbonate ion is a Brønsted acid because it ionizes in solution as follows:

$$HCO_3^-(aq) \rightleftharpoons H^+(aq) + CO_3^{2-}(aq)$$

It is also a Brønsted base because it can accept a proton to form carbonic acid:

$$HCO_3^-(aq) + H^+(aq) \rightleftharpoons H_2CO_3(aq)$$

Comment The HCO_3^- species is said to be *amphoteric* because it possesses both acidic and basic properties. The double arrows show that this is a reversible reaction.

Practice Exercise Classify each of the following species as a Brønsted acid or base: (a) SO_4^{2-}, (b) HI.

Similar problems: 4.31, 4.32.

Acid-Base Neutralization

▶▶ Animation
Neutralization Reactions

A *neutralization reaction* is *a reaction between an acid and a base.* Generally, aqueous acid-base reactions produce water and a *salt,* which is *an ionic compound made up of a cation other than H^+ and an anion other than OH^- or O^{2-}:*

$$\text{acid} + \text{base} \longrightarrow \text{salt} + \text{water}$$

The substance we know as table salt, NaCl, is a product of the acid-base reaction

Acid-base reactions generally go to completion.

$$HCl(aq) + NaOH(aq) \longrightarrow NaCl(aq) + H_2O(l)$$

However, because both the acid and the base are strong electrolytes, they are completely ionized in solution. The ionic equation is

$$H^+(aq) + Cl^-(aq) + Na^+(aq) + OH^-(aq) \longrightarrow Na^+(aq) + Cl^-(aq) + H_2O(l)$$

Therefore, the reaction can be represented by the net ionic equation

$$H^+(aq) + OH^-(aq) \longrightarrow H_2O(l)$$

Both Na^+ and Cl^- are spectator ions.

If we had started the preceding reaction with equal molar amounts of the acid and the base, at the end of the reaction we would have only a salt and no leftover acid or base. This is a characteristic of acid-base neutralization reactions.

A reaction between a weak acid such as hydrocyanic acid (HCN) and a strong base is

$$HCN(aq) + NaOH(aq) \longrightarrow NaCN(aq) + H_2O(l)$$

Because HCN is a weak acid, it does not ionize appreciably in solution. Thus, the ionic equation is written as

$$HCN(aq) + Na^+(aq) + OH^-(aq) \longrightarrow Na^+(aq) + CN^-(aq) + H_2O(l)$$

and the net ionic equation is

$$HCN(aq) + OH^-(aq) \longrightarrow CN^-(aq) + H_2O(l)$$

Note that only Na^+ is a spectator ion; OH^- and CN^- are not.

The following are also examples of acid-base neutralization reactions, represented by molecular equations:

$$HF(aq) + KOH(aq) \longrightarrow KF(aq) + H_2O(l)$$
$$H_2SO_4(aq) + 2NaOH(aq) \longrightarrow Na_2SO_4(aq) + 2H_2O(l)$$
$$HNO_3(aq) + NH_3(aq) \longrightarrow NH_4NO_3(aq)$$

The last equation looks different because it does not show water as a product. However, if we express $NH_3(aq)$ as $NH_4^+(aq)$ and $OH^-(aq)$, as discussed earlier, then the equation becomes

$$HNO_3(aq) + NH_4^+(aq) + OH^-(aq) \longrightarrow NH_4NO_3(aq) + H_2O(l)$$

Example 4.4

Write molecular, ionic, and net ionic equations for each of the following acid-base reactions:

(a) hydrobromic acid(aq) + barium hydroxide(aq) $\longrightarrow$

(b) sulfuric acid(aq) + potassium hydroxide(aq) $\longrightarrow$

Strategy The first step is to identify the acids and bases as strong or weak. We see that HBr is a strong acid and H_2SO_4 is a strong acid for the first step ionization and a weak acid for the second step ionization. Both $Ba(OH)_2$ and KOH are strong bases.

Solution

(a) Molecular equation:

$$2HBr(aq) + Ba(OH)_2(aq) \longrightarrow BaBr_2(aq) + 2H_2O(l)$$

Ionic equation:

$$2H^+(aq) + 2Br^-(aq) + Ba^{2+}(aq) + 2OH^-(aq) \longrightarrow$$
$$Ba^{2+}(aq) + 2Br^-(aq) + 2H_2O(l)$$

(Continued)

Net ionic equation:

$$2H^+(aq) + 2OH^-(aq) \longrightarrow 2H_2O(l)$$

or

$$H^+(aq) + OH^-(aq) \longrightarrow H_2O(l)$$

Both Ba^{2+} and Br^- are spectator ions.

(b) Molecular equation:

$$H_2SO_4(aq) + 2KOH(aq) \longrightarrow K_2SO_4(aq) + 2H_2O(l)$$

Ionic equation:

$$H^+(aq) + HSO_4^-(aq) + 2K^+(aq) + 2OH^-(aq) \longrightarrow$$
$$2K^+(aq) + SO_4^{2-}(aq) + 2H_2O(l)$$

Net ionic equation:

$$H^+(aq) + HSO_4^-(aq) + 2OH^-(aq) \longrightarrow SO_4^{2-}(aq) + 2H_2O(l)$$

Note that because HSO_4^- is a weak acid and does not ionize appreciably in water, the only spectator ion is K^+.

Practice Exercise Write a molecular equation, an ionic equation, and a net ionic equation for the reaction between aqueous solutions of phosphoric acid and sodium hydroxide.

Similar problem: 4.33(b).

Acid-Base Reactions Leading to Gas Formation

Certain salts like carbonates (containing the CO_3^{2-} ion), bicarbonates (containing the HCO_3^- ion), sulfites (containing the SO_3^{2-} ion), and sulfides (containing the S^{2-} ion) react with acids to form gaseous products. For example, the molecular equation for the reaction between sodium carbonate (Na_2CO_3) and $HCl(aq)$ is (see Figure 4.6)

$$Na_2CO_3(aq) + 2HCl(aq) \longrightarrow 2NaCl(aq) + H_2CO_3(aq)$$

Carbonic acid is unstable and if present in solution in sufficient concentrations decomposes as follows:

$$H_2CO_3(aq) \longrightarrow H_2O(l) + CO_2(g)$$

Similar reactions involving other mentioned salts are

$$NaHCO_3(aq) + HCl(aq) \longrightarrow NaCl(aq) + H_2O(l) + CO_2(g)$$
$$Na_2SO_3(aq) + 2HCl(aq) \longrightarrow 2NaCl(aq) + H_2O(l) + SO_2(g)$$
$$K_2S(aq) + 2HCl(aq) \longrightarrow 2KCl(aq) + H_2S(g)$$

4.4 Oxidation-Reduction Reactions

▶▶ Animation
Oxidation-Reduction Reactions

Whereas acid-base reactions can be characterized as proton-transfer processes, the class of reactions called *oxidation-reduction,* or *redox, reactions* are considered *electron-transfer reactions.* Oxidation-reduction reactions are very much a part of the world around us. They range from the burning of fossil fuels to the action of household

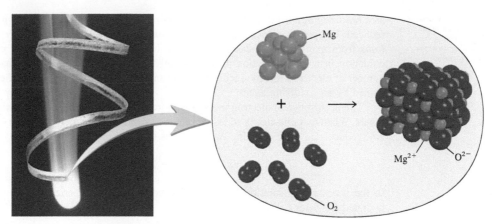

Figure 4.9 *Magnesium burns in oxygen to form magnesium oxide.*

bleach. Additionally, most metallic and nonmetallic elements are obtained from their ores by the process of oxidation or reduction.

Many important redox reactions take place in water, but not all redox reactions occur in aqueous solution. We begin our discussion with a reaction in which two elements combine to form a compound. Consider the formation of magnesium oxide (MgO) from magnesium and oxygen (Figure 4.9):

$$2Mg(s) + O_2(g) \longrightarrow 2MgO(s)$$

Magnesium oxide (MgO) is an ionic compound made up of Mg^{2+} and O^{2-} ions. In this reaction, two Mg atoms give up or transfer four electrons to two O atoms (in O_2). For convenience, we can think of this process as two separate steps, one involving the loss of four electrons by the two Mg atoms and the other being the gain of four electrons by an O_2 molecule:

$$2Mg \longrightarrow 2Mg^{2+} + 4e^-$$
$$O_2 + 4e^- \longrightarrow 2O^{2-}$$

Each of these steps is called a **half-reaction,** which *explicitly shows the electrons involved in a redox reaction.* The sum of the half-reactions gives the overall reaction:

$$2Mg + O_2 + 4e^- \longrightarrow 2Mg^{2+} + 2O^{2-} + 4e^-$$

or, if we cancel the electrons that appear on both sides of the equation,

$$2Mg + O_2 \longrightarrow 2Mg^{2+} + 2O^{2-}$$

Finally, the Mg^{2+} and O^{2-} ions combine to form MgO:

$$2Mg^{2+} + 2O^{2-} \longrightarrow 2MgO$$

The term **oxidation reaction** refers to the *half-reaction that involves loss of electrons.* Chemists originally used "oxidation" to denote the combination of elements with oxygen. However, it now has a broader meaning that includes reactions not involving oxygen. A **reduction reaction** is a *half-reaction that involves gain of electrons.* In the formation of magnesium oxide, magnesium is oxidized. It is said to act

▶▶ **Animation**
Reaction of Magnesium and Oxygen

▶▶ **Animation**
Formation of Ag_2S by Oxidation-Reduction

Note that in an oxidation half-reaction, electrons appear as the product; in a reduction half-reaction, electrons appear as the reactant.

A useful mnemonic for redox is OILRIG: Oxidation Is Loss (of electrons) and Reduction Is Gain (of electrons).

134   **Chapter 4** ▪ Reactions in Aqueous Solutions

Oxidizing agents are always reduced and reducing agents are always oxidized. This statement may be somewhat confusing, but it is simply a consequence of the definitions of the two processes.

as a ***reducing agent*** because it *donates electrons* to oxygen and causes oxygen to be reduced. Oxygen is reduced and acts as an ***oxidizing agent*** because it *accepts electrons* from magnesium, causing magnesium to be oxidized. Note that the extent of oxidation in a redox reaction must be equal to the extent of reduction; that is, the number of electrons lost by a reducing agent must be equal to the number of electrons gained by an oxidizing agent.

The occurrence of electron transfer is more apparent in some redox reactions than others. When metallic zinc is added to a solution containing copper(II) sulfate ($CuSO_4$), zinc reduces Cu^{2+} by donating two electrons to it:

$$Zn(s) + CuSO_4(aq) \longrightarrow ZnSO_4(aq) + Cu(s)$$

In the process, the solution loses the blue color that characterizes the presence of hydrated Cu^{2+} ions (Figure 4.10):

$$Zn(s) + Cu^{2+}(aq) \longrightarrow Zn^{2+}(aq) + Cu(s)$$

The Zn bar is in aqueous solution of $CuSO_4$

Cu^{2+} ions are converted to Cu atoms. Zn atoms enter the solution as Zn^{2+} ions.

When a piece of copper wire is placed in an aqueous $AgNO_3$ solution Cu atoms enter the solution as Cu^{2+} ions, and Ag^+ ions are converted to solid Ag.

(a)   (b)

Figure 4.10 *Metal displacement reactions in solution. (a) First beaker: A zinc strip is placed in a blue $CuSO_4$ solution. Immediately Cu^{2+} ions are reduced to metallic Cu in the form of a dark layer. Second beaker: In time, most of the Cu^{2+} ions are reduced and the solution becomes colorless. (b) First beaker: A piece of Cu wire is placed in a colorless $AgNO_3$ solution. Ag^+ ions are reduced to metallic Ag. Second beaker: As time progresses, most of the Ag^+ ions are reduced and the solution acquires the characteristic blue color due to the presence of hydrated Cu^{2+} ions.*

The oxidation and reduction half-reactions are

$$Zn \longrightarrow Zn^{2+} + 2e^-$$
$$Cu^{2+} + 2e^- \longrightarrow Cu$$

Similarly, metallic copper reduces silver ions in a solution of silver nitrate ($AgNO_3$):

    ▶▶ **Animation**
Reaction of Cu with $AgNO_3$

$$Cu(s) + 2AgNO_3(aq) \longrightarrow Cu(NO_3)_2(aq) + 2Ag(s)$$

or

$$Cu(s) + 2Ag^+(aq) \longrightarrow Cu^{2+}(aq) + 2Ag(s)$$

Oxidation Number

The definitions of oxidation and reduction in terms of loss and gain of electrons apply to the formation of ionic compounds such as MgO and the reduction of Cu^{2+} ions by Zn. However, these definitions do not accurately characterize the formation of hydrogen chloride (HCl) and sulfur dioxide (SO_2):

$$H_2(g) + Cl_2(g) \longrightarrow 2HCl(g)$$
$$S(s) + O_2(g) \longrightarrow SO_2(g)$$

Because HCl and SO_2 are not ionic but molecular compounds, no electrons are actually transferred in the formation of these compounds, as they are in the case of MgO. Nevertheless, chemists find it convenient to treat these reactions as redox reactions because experimental measurements show that there is a partial transfer of electrons (from H to Cl in HCl and from S to O in SO_2).

To keep track of electrons in redox reactions, it is useful to assign oxidation numbers to the reactants and products. An atom's *oxidation number,* also called *oxidation state,* signifies the *number of charges the atom would have in a molecule (or an ionic compound) if electrons were transferred completely.* For example, we can rewrite the previous equations for the formation of HCl and SO_2 as follows:

$$\overset{0}{H_2}(g) + \overset{0}{Cl_2}(g) \longrightarrow \overset{+1\,-1}{2HCl}(g)$$

$$\overset{0}{S}(s) + \overset{0}{O_2}(g) \longrightarrow \overset{+4\,-2}{SO_2}(g)$$

The numbers above the element symbols are the oxidation numbers. In both of the reactions shown, there is no charge on the atoms in the reactant molecules. Thus, their oxidation number is zero. For the product molecules, however, it is assumed that complete electron transfer has taken place and that atoms have gained or lost electrons. The oxidation numbers reflect the number of electrons "transferred."

Oxidation numbers enable us to identify elements that are oxidized and reduced at a glance. The elements that show an increase in oxidation number—hydrogen and sulfur in the preceding examples—are oxidized. Chlorine and oxygen are reduced, so their oxidation numbers show a decrease from their initial values. Note that the sum of the oxidation numbers of H and Cl in HCl (+1 and −1) is zero. Likewise, if we add the oxidation numbers of S (+4) and two atoms of O [2 × (−2)], the total is zero. The reason is that the HCl and SO_2 molecules are neutral, so the charges must cancel.

We use the following rules to assign oxidation numbers:

1. In free elements (that is, in the uncombined state), each atom has an oxidation number of zero. Thus, each atom in H_2, Br_2, Na, Be, K, O_2, and P_4 has the same oxidation number: zero.

2. For ions composed of only one atom (that is, monatomic ions), the oxidation number is equal to the charge on the ion. Thus, Li^+ ion has an oxidation number of $+1$; Ba^{2+} ion, $+2$; Fe^{3+} ion, $+3$; I^- ion, -1; O^{2-} ion, -2; and so on. All alkali metals have an oxidation number of $+1$ and all alkaline earth metals have an oxidation number of $+2$ in their compounds. Aluminum has an oxidation number of $+3$ in all its compounds.

3. The oxidation number of oxygen in most compounds (for example, MgO and H_2O) is -2, but in hydrogen peroxide (H_2O_2) and peroxide ion (O_2^{2-}), it is -1.

4. The oxidation number of hydrogen is $+1$, except when it is bonded to metals in binary compounds. In these cases (for example, LiH, NaH, CaH_2), its oxidation number is -1.

5. Fluorine has an oxidation number of -1 in *all* its compounds. Other halogens (Cl, Br, and I) have negative oxidation numbers when they occur as halide ions in their compounds. When combined with oxygen—for example in oxoacids and oxoanions (see Section 2.7)—they have positive oxidation numbers.

6. In a neutral molecule, the sum of the oxidation numbers of all the atoms must be zero. In a polyatomic ion, the sum of oxidation numbers of all the elements in the ion must be equal to the net charge of the ion. For example, in the ammonium ion, NH_4^+, the oxidation number of N is -3 and that of H is $+1$. Thus, the sum of the oxidation numbers is $-3 + 4(+1) = +1$, which is equal to the net charge of the ion.

7. Oxidation numbers do not have to be integers. For example, the oxidation number of O in the superoxide ion, O_2^-, is $-\frac{1}{2}$.

We apply the preceding rules to assign oxidation numbers in Example 4.5.

Example 4.5

Assign oxidation numbers to all the elements in the following compounds and ion: (a) Li_2O, (b) HNO_3, (c) $Cr_2O_7^{2-}$.

Strategy In general, we follow the rules just listed for assigning oxidation numbers. Remember that all alkali metals have an oxidation number of $+1$, and in most cases hydrogen has an oxidation number of $+1$ and oxygen has an oxidation number of -2 in their compounds.

Solution

(a) By rule 2 we see that lithium has an oxidation number of $+1$ (Li^+) and oxygen's oxidation number is -2 (O^{2-}).

(b) This is the formula for nitric acid, which yields a H^+ ion and a NO_3^- ion in solution. From rule 4 we see that H has an oxidation number of $+1$. Thus the other group (the nitrate ion) must have a net oxidation number of -1. Oxygen has an

(Continued)

oxidation number of -2, and if we use x to represent the oxidation number of nitrogen, then the nitrate ion can be written as

$$[N^{(x)}O_3^{(2-)}]^-$$

so that $x + 3(-2) = -1$

or $x = +5$

(c) From rule 6 we see that the sum of the oxidation numbers in the dichromate ion $Cr_2O_7^{2-}$ must be -2. We know that the oxidation number of O is -2, so all that remains is to determine the oxidation number of Cr, which we call y. The dichromate ion can be written as

$$[Cr_2^{(y)}O_7^{(2-)}]^{2-}$$

so that $2(y) + 7(-2) = -2$

or $y = +6$

Check In each case, does the sum of the oxidation numbers of all the atoms equal the net charge on the species?

Similar problems: 4.47, 4.49.

Practice Exercise Assign oxidation numbers to all the elements in the following compound and ion: (a) PF_3, (b) MnO_4^-.

Figure 4.11 shows the known oxidation numbers of the familiar elements, arranged according to their positions in the periodic table. We can summarize the content of this figure as follows:

- Metallic elements have only positive oxidation numbers, whereas nonmetallic elements may have either positive or negative oxidation numbers.
- The highest oxidation number an element in Groups 1A–7A can have is its group number. For example, the halogens are in Group 7A, so their highest possible oxidation number is $+7$.
- The transition metals (Groups 1B, 3B–8B) usually have several possible oxidation numbers.

Types of Redox Reactions

Among the most common oxidation-reduction reactions are combination, decomposition, combustion, and displacement reactions. A more involved type is called disproportionation reactions, which will also be discussed in this section.

Combination Reactions

A *combination reaction* is *a reaction in which two or more substances combine to form a single product.* Figure 4.12 shows some combination reactions. For example,

Not all combination reactions are redox in nature. The same holds for decomposition reactions.

$$\overset{0}{S}(s) + \overset{0}{O_2}(g) \longrightarrow \overset{+4\ -2}{SO_2}(g)$$

$$2\overset{0}{Al}(s) + 3\overset{0}{Br_2}(l) \longrightarrow 2\overset{+3\ -1}{AlBr_3}(s)$$

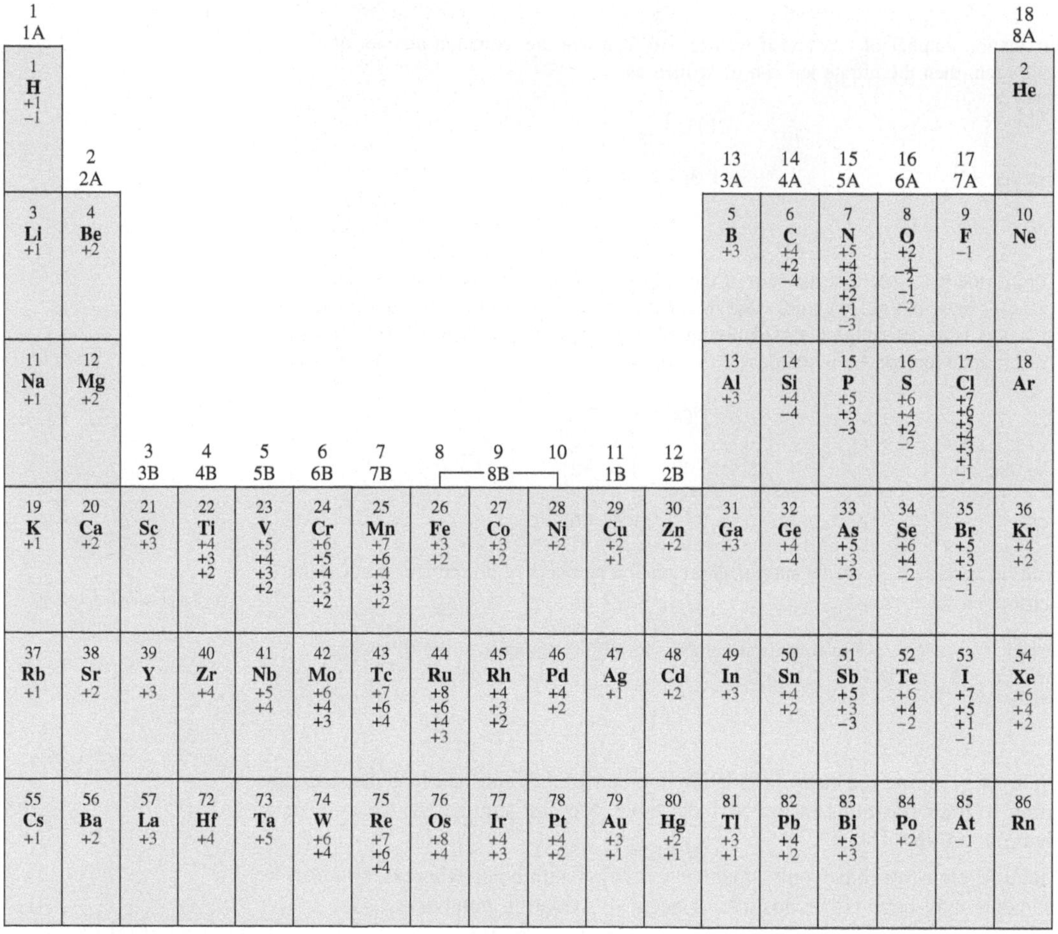

138   **Chapter 4** ▪ Reactions in Aqueous Solutions

Periodic table — oxidation numbers of elements in their compounds

Group headers: 1/1A, 2/2A, 3/3B, 4/4B, 5/5B, 6/6B, 7/7B, 8/9/10 (8B), 11/1B, 12/2B, 13/3A, 14/4A, 15/5A, 16/6A, 17/7A, 18/8A

Period 1

1 H: +1, −1	2 He

Period 2

| 3 Li: +1 | 4 Be: +2 | 5 B: +3 | 6 C: +4, +2, −4 | 7 N: +5, +4, +3, +2, +1, −3 | 8 O: +2, −$\frac{1}{2}$, −1, −2 | 9 F: −1 | 10 Ne |

Period 3

| 11 Na: +1 | 12 Mg: +2 | 13 Al: +3 | 14 Si: +4, −4 | 15 P: +5, +3, −3 | 16 S: +6, +4, +2, −2 | 17 Cl: +7, +6, +5, +4, +3, +1, −1 | 18 Ar |

Period 4

| 19 K: +1 | 20 Ca: +2 | 21 Sc: +3 | 22 Ti: +4, +3, +2 | 23 V: +5, +4, +3, +2 | 24 Cr: +6, +5, +4, +3, +2 | 25 Mn: +7, +6, +4, +3, +2 | 26 Fe: +3, +2 | 27 Co: +3, +2 | 28 Ni: +2 | 29 Cu: +2, +1 | 30 Zn: +2 | 31 Ga: +3 | 32 Ge: +4, −4 | 33 As: +5, +3, −3 | 34 Se: +6, +4, −2 | 35 Br: +5, +3, +1, −1 | 36 Kr: +4, +2 |

Period 5

| 37 Rb: +1 | 38 Sr: +2 | 39 Y: +3 | 40 Zr: +4 | 41 Nb: +5, +4 | 42 Mo: +6, +4, +3 | 43 Tc: +7, +6, +4 | 44 Ru: +8, +6, +4, +3 | 45 Rh: +4, +3, +2 | 46 Pd: +4, +2 | 47 Ag: +1 | 48 Cd: +2 | 49 In: +3 | 50 Sn: +4, +2 | 51 Sb: +5, +3, −3 | 52 Te: +6, +4, −2 | 53 I: +7, +5, +1, −1 | 54 Xe: +6, +4, +2 |

Period 6

| 55 Cs: +1 | 56 Ba: +2 | 57 La: +3 | 72 Hf: +4 | 73 Ta: +5 | 74 W: +6, +4 | 75 Re: +7, +6, +4 | 76 Os: +8, +4 | 77 Ir: +4, +3 | 78 Pt: +4, +2 | 79 Au: +3, +1 | 80 Hg: +2, +1 | 81 Tl: +3, +1 | 82 Pb: +4, +2 | 83 Bi: +5, +3 | 84 Po: +2 | 85 At: −1 | 86 Rn |

Figure 4.11 *The oxidation numbers of elements in their compounds. The more common oxidation numbers are in color.*

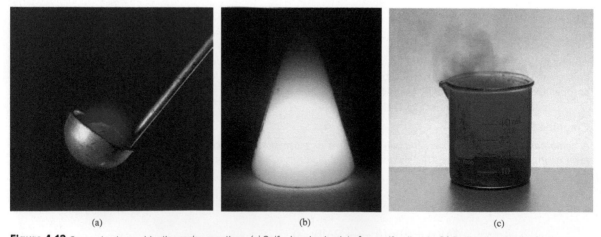

Figure 4.12 *Some simple combination redox reactions. (a) Sulfur burning in air to form sulfur dioxide. (b) Sodium burning in chlorine to form sodium chloride. (c) Aluminum reacting with bromine to form aluminum bromide.*

(a)   (b)

Decomposition Reactions

Decomposition reactions are the opposite of combination reactions. Specifically, a *decomposition reaction* is *the breakdown of a compound into two or more components* (Figure 4.13). For example,

We show oxidation numbers only for elements that are oxidized or reduced.

All combustion reactions are redox processes.

$$\overset{+2\ -2}{2HgO}(s) \longrightarrow \overset{0}{2Hg}(l) + \overset{0}{O_2}(g)$$

$$\overset{+5\ -2}{2KClO_3}(s) \longrightarrow \overset{-1}{2KCl}(s) + \overset{0}{3O_2}(g)$$

$$\overset{+1\ -1}{2NaH}(s) \longrightarrow \overset{0}{2Na}(s) + \overset{0}{H_2}(g)$$

Combustion Reactions

A *combustion reaction* is *a reaction in which a substance reacts with oxygen, usually with the release of heat and light to produce a flame.* The reactions between magnesium and sulfur with oxygen described earlier are combustion reactions. Another example is the burning of propane (C_3H_8), a component of natural gas that is used for domestic heating and cooking:

$$C_3H_8(g) + 5O_2(g) \longrightarrow 3CO_2(g) + 4H_2O(l)$$

Assigning an oxidation number to C atoms in organic compounds is more involved. Here, we focus only on the oxidation number of O atoms, which changes from 0 to −2.

Displacement Reactions

In a *displacement reaction,* an ion (or atom) in a compound is replaced by an ion (or atom) of another element: Most displacement reactions fit into one of three subcategories: hydrogen displacement, metal displacement, or halogen displacement.

1. Hydrogen Displacement. All alkali metals and some alkaline earth metals (Ca, Sr, and Ba), which are the most reactive of the metallic elements, will displace hydrogen from cold water (Figure 4.14):

$$\overset{0}{2Na}(s) + \overset{+1}{2H_2O}(l) \longrightarrow \overset{+1\ +1}{2NaOH}(aq) + \overset{0}{H_2}(g)$$

$$\overset{0}{Ca}(s) + \overset{+1}{2H_2O}(l) \longrightarrow \overset{+2\ +1}{Ca(OH)_2}(s) + \overset{0}{H_2}(g)$$

(a)

(b)

140   **Chapter 4** ▪ Reactions in Aqueous Solutions

(a)	(b)	(c)

Figure 4.15 *Reactions of (a) iron (Fe), (b) zinc (Zn), and (c) magnesium (Mg) with hydrochloric acid to form hydrogen gas and the metal chlorides (FeCl₂, ZnCl₂, MgCl₂). The reactivity of these metals is reflected in the rate of hydrogen gas evolution, which is slowest for the least reactive metal, Fe, and fastest for the most reactive metal, Mg.*

Many metals, including those that do not react with water, are capable of displacing hydrogen from acids. For example, zinc (Zn) and magnesium (Mg) do not react with cold water but do react with hydrochloric acid, as follows:

$$\overset{0}{\text{Zn}}(s) \ + \ 2\overset{+1}{\text{H}}\text{Cl}(aq) \ \longrightarrow \ \overset{+2}{\text{Zn}}\text{Cl}_2(aq) \ + \ \overset{0}{\text{H}}_2(g)$$

$$\overset{0}{\text{Mg}}(s) \ + \ 2\overset{+1}{\text{H}}\text{Cl}(aq) \ \longrightarrow \ \overset{+2}{\text{Mg}}\text{Cl}_2(aq) \ + \ \overset{0}{\text{H}}_2(g)$$

Figure 4.15 shows the reactions between hydrochloric acid (HCl) and iron (Fe), zinc (Zn), and magnesium (Mg). These reactions are used to prepare hydrogen gas in the laboratory.

2. Metal Displacement. A metal in a compound can be displaced by another metal in the elemental state. We have already seen examples of zinc replacing copper ions and copper replacing silver ions (see p. 134). Reversing the roles of the metals would result in no reaction. Thus, copper metal will not displace zinc ions from zinc sulfate, and silver metal will not displace copper ions from copper nitrate.

An easy way to predict whether a metal or hydrogen displacement reaction will actually occur is to refer to an ***activity series*** (sometimes called the *electrochemical series*), shown in Figure 4.16. Basically, an activity series is *a convenient summary of the results of many possible displacement reactions* similar to the ones already discussed. According to this series, any metal above hydrogen will displace it from water or from an acid, but metals below hydrogen will not react with either water or an acid. In fact, any metal listed in the series will react with any metal (in a compound) below it. For example, Zn is above Cu, so zinc metal will displace copper ions from copper sulfate.

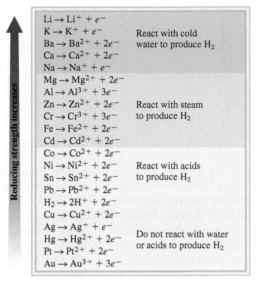

$$Li \rightarrow Li^+ + e^-$$
$$K \rightarrow K^+ + e^-$$
$$Ba \rightarrow Ba^{2+} + 2e^-$$
$$Ca \rightarrow Ca^{2+} + 2e^-$$
$$Na \rightarrow Na^+ + e^-$$
React with cold water to produce H_2

$$Mg \rightarrow Mg^{2+} + 2e^-$$
$$Al \rightarrow Al^{3+} + 3e^-$$
$$Zn \rightarrow Zn^{2+} + 2e^-$$
$$Cr \rightarrow Cr^{3+} + 3e^-$$
$$Fe \rightarrow Fe^{2+} + 2e^-$$
$$Cd \rightarrow Cd^{2+} + 2e^-$$
React with steam to produce H_2

$$Co \rightarrow Co^{2+} + 2e^-$$
$$Ni \rightarrow Ni^{2+} + 2e^-$$
$$Sn \rightarrow Sn^{2+} + 2e^-$$
$$Pb \rightarrow Pb^{2+} + 2e^-$$
$$H_2 \rightarrow 2H^+ + 2e^-$$
$$Cu \rightarrow Cu^{2+} + 2e^-$$
React with acids to produce H_2

$$Ag \rightarrow Ag^+ + e^-$$
$$Hg \rightarrow Hg^{2+} + 2e^-$$
$$Pt \rightarrow Pt^{2+} + 2e^-$$
$$Au \rightarrow Au^{3+} + 3e^-$$
Do not react with water or acids to produce H_2

Reducing strength increases

Figure 4.16 *The activity series for metals. The metals are arranged according to their ability to displace hydrogen from an acid or water. Li (lithium) is the most reactive metal, and Au (gold) is the least reactive.*

Metal displacement reactions find many applications in metallurgical processes, the goal of which is to separate pure metals from their ores. For example, vanadium is obtained by treating vanadium(V) oxide with metallic calcium:

$$V_2O_5(s) + 5Ca(l) \longrightarrow 2V(l) + 5CaO(s)$$

Similarly, titanium is obtained from titanium(IV) chloride according to the reaction

$$TiCl_4(g) + 2Mg(l) \longrightarrow Ti(s) + 2MgCl_2(l)$$

In each case, the metal that acts as the reducing agent lies above the metal that is reduced (that is, Ca is above V and Mg is above Ti) in the activity series. We will see more examples of this type of reaction in Chapter 18.

3. Halogen Displacement. Another activity series summarizes the halogens' behavior in halogen displacement reactions:

$$F_2 > Cl_2 > Br_2 > I_2$$

The power of these elements as oxidizing agents decreases as we move down Group 7A from fluorine to iodine, so molecular fluorine can replace chloride, bromide, and iodide ions in solution. In fact, molecular fluorine is so reactive that it also attacks water; thus these reactions cannot be carried out in aqueous solutions. On the other hand, molecular chlorine can displace bromide and iodide ions in aqueous solution. The displacement equations are

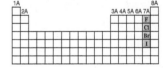

The halogens.

$$\overset{0}{Cl_2}(g) + 2\overset{-1}{KBr}(aq) \longrightarrow 2\overset{-1}{KCl}(aq) + \overset{0}{Br_2}(l)$$

$$\overset{0}{Cl_2}(g) + 2\overset{-1}{NaI}(aq) \longrightarrow 2\overset{-1}{NaCl}(aq) + \overset{0}{I_2}(s)$$

142   Chapter 4 • Reactions in Aqueous Solutions

The ionic equations are

$$\overset{0}{Cl_2}(g) + 2\overset{-1}{Br}(aq) \longrightarrow 2\overset{-1}{Cl^-}(aq) + \overset{0}{Br_2}(l)$$

$$\overset{0}{Cl_2}(g) + 2\overset{-1}{I^-}(aq) \longrightarrow 2\overset{-1}{Cl^-}(aq) + \overset{0}{I_2}(s)$$

Molecular bromine, in turn, can displace iodide ion in solution:

$$\overset{0}{Br_2}(l) + 2\overset{-1}{I^-}(aq) \longrightarrow 2\overset{-1}{Br^-}(aq) + \overset{0}{I_2}(s)$$

Reversing the roles of the halogens produces no reaction. Thus, bromine cannot displace chloride ions, and iodine cannot displace bromide and chloride ions.

The halogen displacement reactions have a direct industrial application. The halogens as a group are the most reactive of the nonmetallic elements. They are all strong oxidizing agents. As a result, they are found in nature in the combined state (with metals) as halides and never as free elements. Of these four elements, chlorine is by far the most important industrial chemical. In 2010 the amount of chlorine produced in the United States was about 25 billion pounds, making chlorine the tenth-ranking industrial chemical. The annual production of bromine is only one-hundredth that of chlorine, while the amounts of fluorine and iodine produced are even less.

Recovering the halogens from their halides requires an oxidation process, which is represented by

$$2X^- \longrightarrow X_2 + 2e^-$$

Bromine is a fuming red liquid.

where X denotes a halogen element. Seawater and natural brine (for example, underground water in contact with salt deposits) are rich sources of Cl^-, Br^-, and I^- ions. Minerals such as fluorite (CaF_2) and cryolite (Na_3AlF_6) are used to prepare fluorine. Because fluorine is the strongest oxidizing agent known, there is no way to convert F^- ions to F_2 by chemical means. The only way to carry out the oxidation is by electrolytic means, the details of which will be discussed in Chapter 18. Industrially, chlorine, like fluorine, is produced electrolytically.

Bromine is prepared industrially by oxidizing Br^- ions with chlorine, which is a strong enough oxidizing agent to oxidize Br^- ions but not water:

$$2Br^-(aq) \longrightarrow Br_2(l) + 2e^-$$

One of the richest sources of Br^- ions is the Dead Sea—about 4000 parts per million (ppm) by mass of all dissolved substances in the Dead Sea is Br. Following the oxidation of Br^- ions, bromine is removed from the solution by blowing air over the solution, and the air-bromine mixture is then cooled to condense the bromine (Figure 4.17).

Figure 4.17 *The industrial manufacture of liquid bromine by oxidizing an aqueous solution containing Br^- ions with chlorine gas.*

Iodine is also prepared from seawater and natural brine by the oxidation of I^- ions with chlorine. Because Br^- and I^- ions are invariably present in the same source, they are both oxidized by chlorine. However, it is relatively easy to separate Br_2 from I_2 because iodine is a solid that is sparingly soluble in water. The air-blowing procedure will remove most of the bromine formed but will not affect the iodine present.

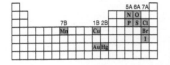

Elements that are most likely to undergo disproportionation reactions.

Disproportionation Reaction

A special type of redox reaction is the disproportionation reaction. In a ***disproportionation reaction,*** *an element in one oxidation state is simultaneously oxidized and reduced.* One reactant in a disproportionation reaction *always* contains an element that can have at least three oxidation states. The element itself is in an intermediate oxidation state; that is, both higher and lower oxidation states exist for that element

in the products. The decomposition of hydrogen peroxide is an example of a disproportionation reaction:

$$\overset{-1}{2H_2O_2}(aq) \longrightarrow \overset{-2}{2H_2O}(l) + \overset{0}{O_2}(g)$$

Note that the oxidation number of H
remains unchanged at +1.

Here the oxidation number of oxygen in the reactant (-1) both increases to zero in
O_2 and decreases to -2 in H_2O. Another example is the reaction between molecular
chlorine and NaOH solution:

$$\overset{0}{Cl_2}(g) + 2OH^-(aq) \longrightarrow \overset{+1}{ClO^-}(aq) + \overset{-1}{Cl^-}(aq) + H_2O(l)$$

This reaction describes the formation of household bleaching agents, for it is the
hypochlorite ion (ClO^-) that oxidizes the color-bearing substances in stains, converting them to colorless compounds.

Finally, it is interesting to compare redox reactions and acid-base reactions. They
are analogous in that acid-base reactions involve the transfer of protons while redox
reactions involve the transfer of electrons. However, while acid-base reactions are
quite easy to recognize (because they always involve an acid and a base), there is no
simple procedure for identifying a redox process. The only sure way is to compare
the oxidation numbers of all the elements in the reactants and products. Any change
in oxidation number *guarantees* that the reaction is redox in nature.

The classification of different types of redox reactions is illustrated in Example 4.6.

Example 4.6

Classify the following redox reactions and indicate changes in the oxidation numbers of
the elements:
(a) $2N_2O(g) \longrightarrow 2N_2(g) + O_2(g)$
(b) $6Li(s) + N_2(g) \longrightarrow 2Li_3N(s)$
(c) $Ni(s) + Pb(NO_3)_2(aq) \longrightarrow Pb(s) + Ni(NO_3)_2(aq)$
(d) $2NO_2(g) + H_2O(l) \longrightarrow HNO_2(aq) + HNO_3(aq)$

Strategy Review the definitions of combination reactions, decomposition reactions,
displacement reactions, and disproportionation reactions.

Solution

(a) This is a decomposition reaction because one reactant is converted to two different
products. The oxidation number of N changes from $+1$ to 0, while that of O
changes from -2 to 0.

(b) This is a combination reaction (two reactants form a single product). The oxidation
number of Li changes from 0 to $+1$ while that of N changes from 0 to -3.

(c) This is a metal displacement reaction. The Ni metal replaces (reduces) the Pb^{2+} ion. The
oxidation number of Ni increases from 0 to $+2$ while that of Pb decreases from $+2$ to 0.

(d) The oxidation number of N is $+4$ in NO_2 and it is $+3$ in HNO_2 and $+5$ in HNO_3.
Because the oxidation number of the *same* element both increases and decreases,
this is a disproportionation reaction.

Similar problems: 4.55, 4.56.

Practice Exercise Identify the following redox reactions by type:
(a) $Fe + H_2SO_4 \longrightarrow FeSO_4 + H_2$
(b) $S + 3F_2 \longrightarrow SF_6$
(c) $2CuCl \longrightarrow Cu + CuCl_2$
(d) $2Ag + PtCl_2 \longrightarrow 2AgCl + Pt$

CHEMISTRY *in Action*

Breathalyzer

Every year in the United States about 25,000 people are killed and 500,000 more are injured as a result of drunk driving. In spite of efforts to educate the public about the dangers of driving while intoxicated and stiffer penalties for drunk driving offenses, law enforcement agencies still have to devote a great deal of work to removing drunk drivers from America's roads.

The police often use a device called a breathalyzer to test drivers suspected of being drunk. The chemical basis of this device is a redox reaction. A sample of the driver's breath is drawn into the breathalyzer, where it is treated with an acidic solution of potassium dichromate. The alcohol (ethanol) in the breath is converted to acetic acid as shown in the following equation:

$$3CH_3CH_2OH \ + \ 2K_2Cr_2O_7 \ + \ 8H_2SO_4 \longrightarrow$$

ethanol   potassium   sulfuric
       dichromate   acid
       (orange yellow)

$$3CH_3COOH \ + \ 2Cr_2(SO_4)_3 \ + \ 2K_2SO_4 \ + \ 11H_2O$$

acetic acid   chromium(III)   potassium
       sulfate (green)   sulfate

In this reaction, the ethanol is oxidized to acetic acid and the chromium(VI) in the orange-yellow dichromate ion is reduced

A driver being tested for blood alcohol content with a handheld breathalyzer.

to the green chromium(III) ion (see Figure 4.22). The driver's blood alcohol level can be determined readily by measuring the degree of this color change (read from a calibrated meter on the instrument). The current legal limit of blood alcohol content is 0.08 percent by mass. Anything higher constitutes intoxication.

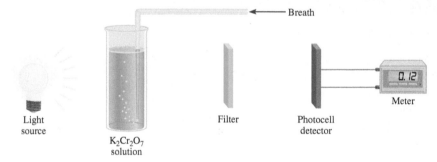

Breath

Light source

$K_2Cr_2O_7$ solution

Filter

Photocell detector

Meter

Schematic diagram of a breathalyzer. The alcohol in the driver's breath is reacted with a potassium dichromate solution. The change in the absorption of light due to the formation of chromium(III) sulfate is registered by the detector and shown on a meter, which directly displays the alcohol content in blood. The filter selects only one wavelength of light for measurement.

Review of Concepts

Which of the following combination reactions is not a redox reaction?

(a) $2Mg(s) \ + \ O_2(g) \longrightarrow 2MgO(s)$
(b) $H_2(g) \ + \ F_2(g) \longrightarrow 2HF(g)$
(c) $NH_3(g) \ + \ HCl(g) \longrightarrow NH_4Cl(s)$
(d) $2Na(s) \ + \ S(s) \longrightarrow Na_2S(s)$

The above Chemistry in Action essay describes how law enforcement makes use of a redox reaction to apprehend drunk drivers.

4.5 Concentration of Solutions

To study solution stoichiometry, we must know how much of the reactants are present in a solution and also how to control the amounts of reactants used to bring about a reaction in aqueous solution.

The **concentration of a solution** is *the amount of solute present in a given amount of solvent, or a given amount of solution.* (For this discussion, we will assume the solute is a liquid or a solid and the solvent is a liquid.) The concentration of a solution can be expressed in many different ways, as we will see in Chapter 12. Here we will consider one of the most commonly used units in chemistry, **molarity (M),** or **molar concentration,** which is *the number of moles of solute per liter of solution.* Molarity is defined as

$$\text{molarity} = \frac{\text{moles of solute}}{\text{liters of solution}} \qquad (4.1)$$

Equation (4.1) can also be expressed algebraically as

$$M = \frac{n}{V} \qquad (4.2)$$

Keep in mind that volume (V) is liters of solution, not liters of solvent. Also, the molarity of a solution depends on temperature.

where n denotes the number of moles of solute and V is the volume of the solution in liters.

A 1.46 molar glucose ($C_6H_{12}O_6$) solution, written as 1.46 M $C_6H_{12}O_6$, contains 1.46 moles of the solute ($C_6H_{12}O_6$) in 1 L of the solution. Of course, we do not always work with solution volumes of 1 L. Thus, a 500-mL solution containing 0.730 mole of $C_6H_{12}O_6$ also has a concentration of 1.46 M:

$$\text{molarity} = \frac{0.730 \text{ mol } C_6H_{12}O_6}{500 \text{ mL soln}} \times \frac{1000 \text{ mL soln}}{1 \text{ L soln}} = 1.46 \text{ } M \text{ } C_6H_{12}O_6$$

Note that concentration, like density, is an intensive property, so its value does not depend on how much of the solution is present.

It is important to keep in mind that molarity refers only to the amount of solute originally dissolved in water and does not take into account any subsequent processes, such as the dissociation of a salt or the ionization of an acid. Consider what happens when a sample of potassium chloride (KCl) is dissolved in enough water to make a 1 M solution:

$$KCl(s) \xrightarrow{H_2O} K^+(aq) + Cl^-(aq)$$

Because KCl is a strong electrolyte, it undergoes complete dissociation in solution. Thus, a 1 M KCl solution contains 1 mole of K^+ ions and 1 mole of Cl^- ions, and no KCl units are present. The concentrations of the ions can be expressed as $[K^+] = 1$ M and $[Cl^-] = 1$ M, where the square brackets [ ] indicate that the concentration is expressed in molarity. Similarly, in a 1 M barium nitrate $[Ba(NO_3)_2]$ solution

$$Ba(NO_3)_2(s) \xrightarrow{H_2O} Ba^{2+}(aq) + 2NO_3^-(aq)$$

we have $[Ba^{2+}] = 1$ M and $[NO_3^-] = 2$ M and no $Ba(NO_3)_2$ units at all.

The procedure for preparing a solution of known molarity is as follows. First, the solute is accurately weighed and transferred to a volumetric flask through a funnel

▶▶ Animation
Making a Solution

146   **Chapter 4** ▪ Reactions in Aqueous Solutions

Figure 4.18 *Preparing a solution of known molarity. (a) A known amount of a solid solute is transferred into the volumetric flask; then water is added through a funnel. (b) The solid is slowly dissolved by gently swirling the flask. (c) After the solid has completely dissolved, more water is added to bring the level of solution to the mark. Knowing the volume of the solution and the amount of solute dissolved in it, we can calculate the molarity of the prepared solution.*

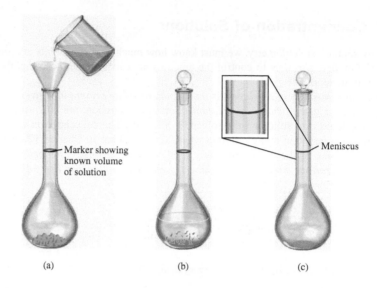

Marker showing known volume of solution

Meniscus

(a)   (b)   (c)

(Figure 4.18). Next, water is added to the flask, which is carefully swirled to dissolve the solid. After *all* the solid has dissolved, more water is added slowly to bring the level of solution exactly to the volume mark. Knowing the volume of the solution in the flask and the quantity of compound (the number of moles) dissolved, we can calculate the molarity of the solution using Equation (4.1). Note that this procedure does not require knowing the amount of water added, as long as the volume of the final solution is known.

Examples 4.7 and 4.8 illustrate the applications of Equations (4.1) and (4.2).

A $K_2Cr_2O_7$ solution.

Example 4.7

How many grams of potassium dichromate ($K_2Cr_2O_7$) are required to prepare a 250-mL solution whose concentration is 2.16 *M*?

Strategy How many moles of $K_2Cr_2O_7$ does a 1-L (or 1000 mL) 2.16 *M* $K_2Cr_2O_7$ solution contain? A 250-mL solution? How would you convert moles to grams?

Solution The first step is to determine the number of moles of $K_2Cr_2O_7$ in 250 mL or 0.250 L of a 2.16 *M* solution. Rearranging Equation (4.1) gives

$$\text{moles of solute} = \text{molarity} \times \text{L soln}$$

Thus,

$$\text{moles of } K_2Cr_2O_7 = \frac{2.16 \text{ mol } K_2Cr_2O_7}{1 \text{ L soln}} \times 0.250 \text{ L soln}$$
$$= 0.540 \text{ mol } K_2Cr_2O_7$$

The molar mass of $K_2Cr_2O_7$ is 294.2 g, so we write

$$\text{grams of } K_2Cr_2O_7 \text{ needed} = 0.540 \text{ mol } K_2Cr_2O_7 \times \frac{294.2 \text{ g } K_2Cr_2O_7}{1 \text{ mol } K_2Cr_2O_7}$$
$$= 159 \text{ g } K_2Cr_2O_7$$

(Continued)

Check As a ball-park estimate, the mass should be given by [molarity (mol/L) × volume (L) × molar mass (g/mol)] or [2 mol/L × 0.25 L × 300 g/mol] = 150 g. So the answer is reasonable.

Similar problems: 4.65, 4.68.

Practice Exercise What is the molarity of an 85.0-mL ethanol (C_2H_5OH) solution containing 1.77 g of ethanol?

Example 4.8

A chemist needs to add 3.81 g of glucose to a reaction mixture. Calculate the volume in milliliters of a 2.53 M glucose solution she should use for the addition.

Strategy We must first determine the number of moles contained in 3.81 g of glucose and then use Equation (4.2) to calculate the volume.

Solution From the molar mass of glucose, we write

$$3.81 \text{ g } C_6H_{12}O_6 \times \frac{1 \text{ mol } C_6H_{12}O_6}{180.2 \text{ g } C_6H_{12}O_6} = 2.114 \times 10^{-2} \text{ mol } C_6H_{12}O_6$$

Note that we have carried an additional digit past the number of significant figures for the intermediate step.

Next, we calculate the volume of the solution that contains 2.114×10^{-2} mole of the solute. Rearranging Equation (4.2) gives

$$
\begin{aligned}
V &= \frac{n}{M} \\
&= \frac{2.114 \times 10^{-2} \text{ mol } C_6H_{12}O_6}{2.53 \text{ mol } C_6H_{12}O_6/\text{L soln}} \times \frac{1000 \text{ mL soln}}{1 \text{ L soln}} \\
&= 8.36 \text{ mL soln}
\end{aligned}
$$

Check One liter of the solution contains 2.53 moles of $C_6H_{12}O_6$. Therefore, the number of moles in 8.36 mL or 8.36×10^{-3} L is (2.53 mol $\times 8.36 \times 10^{-3}$) or 2.12×10^{-2} mol. The small difference is due to the different ways of rounding off.

Similar problem: 4.67.

Practice Exercise What volume (in milliliters) of a 0.315 M NaOH solution contains 6.22 g of NaOH?

Dilution of Solutions

Concentrated solutions are often stored in the laboratory stockroom for use as needed. Frequently we dilute these "stock" solutions before working with them. *Dilution* is *the procedure for preparing a less concentrated solution from a more concentrated one.*

Suppose that we want to prepare 1 L of a 0.400 M $KMnO_4$ solution from a solution of 1.00 M $KMnO_4$. For this purpose we need 0.400 mole of $KMnO_4$. Because there is 1.00 mole of $KMnO_4$ in 1 L of a 1.00 M $KMnO_4$ solution, there is 0.400 mole of $KMnO_4$ in 0.400 L of the same solution:

$$\frac{1.00 \text{ mol}}{1 \text{ L soln}} = \frac{0.400 \text{ mol}}{0.400 \text{ L soln}}$$

Therefore, we must withdraw 400 mL from the 1.00 M $KMnO_4$ solution and dilute it to 1000 mL by adding water (in a 1-L volumetric flask). This method gives us 1 L of the desired solution of 0.400 M $KMnO_4$.

In carrying out a dilution process, it is useful to remember that adding more solvent to a given amount of the stock solution changes (decreases) the concentration

▶▶ Animation
Preparing a Solution by Dilution

Two KMnO₄ solutions of different concentrations.

148   **Chapter 4** ▪ Reactions in Aqueous Solutions

Figure 4.19 *The dilution of a more concentrated solution (a) to a less concentrated one (b) does not change the total number of solute particles (18).*

(a)   (b)

of the solution without changing the number of moles of solute present in the solution (Figure 4.19). In other words,

$$\text{moles of solute before dilution} = \text{moles of solute after dilution}$$

Molarity is defined as moles of solute in 1 liter of solution, so the number of moles of solute is given by [see Equation (4.2)]

$$\underbrace{\frac{\text{moles of solute}}{\text{liters of soln}}}_{M} \times \underbrace{\text{volume of soln (in liters)}}_{V} = \underbrace{\text{moles of solute}}_{n}$$

or

$$MV = n$$

Because all the solute comes from the original stock solution, we can conclude that n remains the same; that is,

$$\underset{\substack{\text{moles of solute}\\\text{before dilution}}}{M_i V_i} = \underset{\substack{\text{moles of solute}\\\text{after dilution}}}{M_f V_f} \tag{4.3}$$

where M_i and M_f are the initial and final concentrations of the solution in molarity and V_i and V_f are the initial and final volumes of the solution, respectively. Of course, the units of V_i and V_f must be the same (mL or L) for the calculation to work. To check the reasonableness of your results, be sure that $M_i > M_f$ and $V_f > V_i$.

We apply Equation (4.3) in Example 4.9.

Example 4.9

Describe how you would prepare 5.00×10^2 mL of a 1.75 M H_2SO_4 solution, starting with an 8.61 M stock solution of H_2SO_4.

Strategy Because the concentration of the final solution is less than that of the original one, this is a dilution process. Keep in mind that in dilution, the concentration of the solution decreases but the number of moles of the solute remains the same.

Solution We prepare for the calculation by tabulating our data:

$$M_i = 8.61\ M \qquad M_f = 1.75\ M$$
$$V_i = ? \qquad\qquad V_f = 5.00 \times 10^2\ \text{mL}$$

(Continued)

Substituting in Equation (4.3),

$$(8.61\,M)(V_i) = (1.75\,M)(5.00 \times 10^2\,\text{mL})$$
$$V_i = \frac{(1.75\,M)(5.00 \times 10^2\,\text{mL})}{8.61\,M}$$
$$= 102\,\text{mL}$$

Thus, we must dilute 102 mL of the 8.61 M H_2SO_4 solution with sufficient water to give a final volume of 5.00×10^2 mL in a 500-mL volumetric flask to obtain the desired concentration.

Check The initial volume is less than the final volume, so the answer is reasonable.

Similar problems: 4.75, 4.76.

Practice Exercise How would you prepare 2.00×10^2 mL of a 0.866 M NaOH solution, starting with a 5.07 M stock solution?

Review of Concepts

What is the final concentration of a 0.6 M NaCl solution if its volume is doubled and the number of moles of solute is tripled?

Now that we have discussed the concentration and dilution of solutions, we can examine the quantitative aspects of reactions in aqueous solution, or *solution stoichiometry*. Sections 4.6–4.8 focus on two techniques for studying solution stoichiometry: gravimetric analysis and titration. These techniques are important tools of **quantitative analysis,** which is *the determination of the amount or concentration of a substance in a sample.*

4.6 Gravimetric Analysis

Gravimetric analysis is *an analytical technique based on the measurement of mass.* One type of gravimetric analysis experiment involves the formation, isolation, and mass determination of a precipitate. Generally, this procedure is applied to ionic compounds. First, a sample substance of unknown composition is dissolved in water and allowed to react with another substance to form a precipitate. Then the precipitate is filtered off, dried, and weighed. Knowing the mass and chemical formula of the precipitate formed, we can calculate the mass of a particular chemical component (that is, the anion or cation) of the original sample. Finally, from the mass of the component and the mass of the original sample, we can determine the percent composition by mass of the component in the original compound.

A reaction that is often studied in gravimetric analysis, because the reactants can be obtained in pure form, is

$$AgNO_3(aq) + NaCl(aq) \longrightarrow NaNO_3(aq) + AgCl(s)$$

The net ionic equation is

$$Ag^+(aq) + Cl^-(aq) \longrightarrow AgCl(s)$$

The precipitate is silver chloride (see Table 4.2). As an example, let us say that we wanted to determine *experimentally* the percent by mass of Cl in NaCl. First, we would accurately weigh out a sample of NaCl and dissolve it in water. Next, we would add enough AgNO₃ solution to the NaCl solution to cause the precipitation of all

This procedure would enable us to determine the purity of the NaCl sample.

150   **Chapter 4** ▪ Reactions in Aqueous Solutions

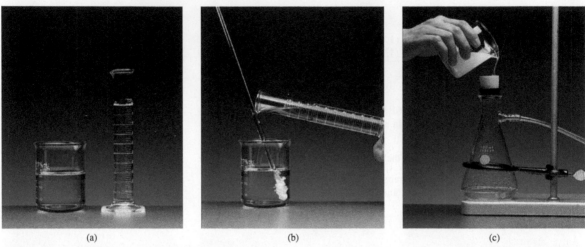

(a)   (b)   (c)

Figure 4.20 *Basic steps for gravimetric analysis. (a) A solution containing a known amount of NaCl in a beaker. (b) The precipitation of AgCl upon the addition of AgNO₃ solution from a measuring cylinder. In this reaction, AgNO₃ is the excess reagent and NaCl is the limiting reagent. (c) The solution containing the AgCl precipitate is filtered through a preweighed sintered-disk crucible, which allows the liquid (but not the precipitate) to pass through. The crucible is then removed from the apparatus, dried in an oven, and weighed again. The difference between this mass and that of the empty crucible gives the mass of the AgCl precipitate.*

the Cl^- ions present in solution as AgCl. In this procedure, NaCl is the limiting reagent and $AgNO_3$ the excess reagent. The AgCl precipitate is separated from the solution by filtration, dried, and weighed. From the measured mass of AgCl, we can calculate the mass of Cl using the percent by mass of Cl in AgCl. Because this same amount of Cl was present in the original NaCl sample, we can calculate the percent by mass of Cl in NaCl. Figure 4.20 shows how this procedure is performed.

Gravimetric analysis is a highly accurate technique, because the mass of a sample can be measured accurately. However, this procedure is applicable only to reactions that go to completion, or have nearly 100 percent yield. Thus, if AgCl were slightly soluble instead of being insoluble, it would not be possible to remove all the Cl^- ions from the NaCl solution and the subsequent calculation would be in error.

Example 4.10 shows the calculations involved in a gravimetric experiment.

Example 4.10

A 0.5662-g sample of an ionic compound containing chloride ions and an unknown metal is dissolved in water and treated with an excess of $AgNO_3$. If 1.0882 g of AgCl precipitate forms, what is the percent by mass of Cl in the original compound?

Strategy We are asked to calculate the percent by mass of Cl in the unknown sample, which is

$$\%Cl = \frac{\text{mass of Cl}}{0.5662 \text{ g sample}} \times 100\%$$

The only source of Cl^- ions is the original compound. These chloride ions eventually end up in the AgCl precipitate. Can we calculate the mass of the Cl^- ions if we know the percent by mass of Cl in AgCl?

(Continued)

Solution The molar masses of Cl and AgCl are 35.45 g and 143.4 g, respectively. Therefore, the percent by mass of Cl in AgCl is given by

$$\%Cl = \frac{35.45 \text{ g Cl}}{143.4 \text{ g AgCl}} \times 100\%$$
$$= 24.72\%$$

Next, we calculate the mass of Cl in 1.0882 g of AgCl. To do so we convert 24.72 percent to 0.2472 and write

$$\text{mass of Cl} = 0.2472 \times 1.0882 \text{ g}$$
$$= 0.2690 \text{ g}$$

Because the original compound also contained this amount of Cl^- ions, the percent by mass of Cl in the compound is

$$\%Cl = \frac{0.2690 \text{ g}}{0.5662 \text{ g}} \times 100\%$$
$$= 47.51\%$$

Check AgCl is about 25 percent chloride by mass, so the roughly 1 g of AgCl precipitate that formed corresponds to about 0.25 g of chloride, which is a little less than half of the mass of the original sample. Therefore, the calculated percent chloride of 47.51 percent is reasonable.

Similar problem: 4.82.

Practice Exercise A sample of 0.3220 g of an ionic compound containing the bromide ion (Br^-) is dissolved in water and treated with an excess of $AgNO_3$. If the mass of the AgBr precipitate that forms is 0.6964 g, what is the percent by mass of Br in the original compound?

Note that gravimetric analysis does not establish the whole identity of the unknown. Thus, in Example 4.10 we still do not know what the cation is. However, knowing the percent by mass of Cl greatly helps us to narrow the possibilities. Because no two compounds containing the same anion (or cation) have the same percent composition by mass, comparison of the percent by mass obtained from gravimetric analysis with that calculated from a series of known compounds would reveal the identity of the unknown.

Review of Concepts

Calculate the mass of AgBr formed if a solution containing 6.00 g of KBr is treated with an excess of $AgNO_3$.

4.7 Acid-Base Titrations

Quantitative studies of acid-base neutralization reactions are most conveniently carried out using a technique known as titration. In *titration,* *a solution of accurately known concentration,* called a *standard solution,* *is added gradually to another solution of unknown concentration, until the chemical reaction between the two solutions is complete.* If we know the volumes of the standard and unknown solutions used in the titration, along with the concentration of the standard solution, we can calculate the concentration of the unknown solution.

Potassium hydrogen phthalate (KHP).

KHP is a weak acid.

Sodium hydroxide is one of the bases commonly used in the laboratory. However, it is difficult to obtain solid sodium hydroxide in a pure form because it has a tendency to absorb water from air, and its solution reacts with carbon dioxide. For these reasons, a solution of sodium hydroxide must be *standardized* before it can be used in accurate analytical work. We can standardize the sodium hydroxide solution by titrating it against an acid solution of accurately known concentration. The acid often chosen for this task is a monoprotic acid called potassium hydrogen phthalate (KHP), for which the molecular formula is $KHC_8H_4O_4$ (molar mass = 204.2 g). KHP is a white, soluble solid that is commercially available in highly pure form. The reaction between KHP and sodium hydroxide is

$$KHC_8H_4O_4(aq) + NaOH(aq) \longrightarrow KNaC_8H_4O_4(aq) + H_2O(l)$$

and the net ionic equation is

$$HC_8H_4O_4^-(aq) + OH^-(aq) \longrightarrow C_8H_4O_4^{2-}(aq) + H_2O(l)$$

The procedure for the titration is shown in Figure 4.21. First, a known amount of KHP is transferred to an Erlenmeyer flask and some distilled water is added to make up a solution. Next, NaOH solution is carefully added to the KHP solution from a buret until we reach the **equivalence point,** that is, *the point at which the acid has completely reacted with or been neutralized by the base.* The equivalence point is usually signaled by a sharp change in the color of an indicator in the acid solution. In acid-base titrations, **indicators** are *substances that have distinctly different colors in acidic and basic media.* One commonly used indicator is phenolphthalein, which is colorless in acidic and neutral solutions but reddish pink in basic solutions. At the equivalence point, all the KHP present has been neutralized by the added NaOH and the solution is still colorless. However, if we add just one more drop of NaOH solution from the buret, the solution will immediately turn pink because the solution is now basic. Example 4.11 illustrates such a titration.

Figure 4.21 *(a) Apparatus for acid-base titration. A NaOH solution is added from the buret to a KHP solution in an Erlenmeyer flask. (b) A reddish-pink color appears when the equivalence point is reached. The color here has been intensified for visual display.*

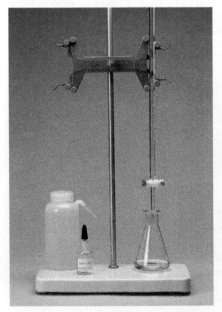

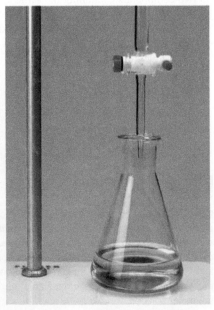

(a)   (b)

Example 4.11

In a titration experiment, a student finds that 23.48 mL of a NaOH solution are needed to neutralize 0.5468 g of KHP. What is the concentration (in molarity) of the NaOH solution?

Strategy We want to determine the molarity of the NaOH solution. What is the definition of molarity?

$$\underset{\text{want to calculate}}{\text{molarity of NaOH}} = \frac{\overset{\text{need to find}}{\text{mol NaOH}}}{\underset{\text{given}}{\text{L soln}}}$$

The volume of NaOH solution is given in the problem. Therefore, we need to find the number of moles of NaOH to solve for molarity. From the preceding equation for the reaction between KHP and NaOH shown in the text we see that 1 mole of KHP neutralizes 1 mole of NaOH. How many moles of KHP are contained in 0.5468 g of KHP?

Solution First we calculate the number of moles of KHP consumed in the titration:

$$\text{moles of KHP} = 0.5468 \text{ g KHP} \times \frac{1 \text{ mol KHP}}{204.2 \text{ g KHP}}$$
$$= 2.678 \times 10^{-3} \text{ mol KHP}$$

Recall that KHP is $KHC_8H_4O_4$.

Because 1 mol KHP $\simeq$ 1 mol NaOH, there must be 2.678×10^{-3} mole of NaOH in 23.48 mL of NaOH solution. Finally, we calculate the number of moles of NaOH in 1 L of the solution or the molarity as follows:

$$\text{molarity of NaOH soln} = \frac{2.678 \times 10^{-3} \text{ mol NaOH}}{23.48 \text{ mL soln}} \times \frac{1000 \text{ mL soln}}{1 \text{ L soln}}$$
$$= 0.1141 \text{ mol NaOH/1 L soln} = \boxed{0.1141 \ M}$$

Similar problems: 4.89, 4.90.

Practice Exercise How many grams of KHP are needed to neutralize 18.64 mL of a 0.1004 *M* NaOH solution?

The neutralization reaction between NaOH and KHP is one of the simplest types of acid-base neutralization known. Suppose, though, that instead of KHP, we wanted to use a diprotic acid such as H_2SO_4 for the titration. The reaction is represented by

$$2NaOH(aq) + H_2SO_4(aq) \longrightarrow Na_2SO_4(aq) + 2H_2O(l)$$

Because 2 mol NaOH $\simeq$ 1 mol H_2SO_4, we need twice as much NaOH to react completely with a H_2SO_4 solution of the *same* molar concentration and volume as a monoprotic acid like HCl. On the other hand, we would need twice the amount of HCl to neutralize a $Ba(OH)_2$ solution compared to a NaOH solution having the same concentration and volume because 1 mole of $Ba(OH)_2$ yields 2 moles of OH^- ions:

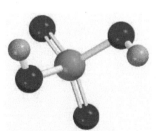

H_2SO_4 has two ionizable protons.

$$2HCl(aq) + Ba(OH)_2(aq) \longrightarrow BaCl_2(aq) + 2H_2O(l)$$

In calculations involving acid-base titrations, regardless of the acid or base that takes place in the reaction, keep in mind that the total number of moles of H^+ ions that have reacted at the equivalence point must be equal to the total number of moles of OH^- ions that have reacted.

Example 4.12 shows the titration of a NaOH solution with a diprotic acid.

154   **Chapter 4** ▪ Reactions in Aqueous Solutions

Example 4.12

The sodium hydroxide solution standardized in Example 4.11 is used to titrate 25.00 mL of a sulfuric acid solution. The titration requires 43.79 mL of the 0.1172 M NaOH solution to completely neutralize the acid. What is the concentration of the H_2SO_4 solution?

Strategy We want to calculate the concentration of the H_2SO_4 solution. Starting with the volume of NaOH solution required to neutralize the acid, we calculate the moles of NaOH.

$$\underset{\text{measured}}{\nearrow} \text{L soln} \times \frac{\text{mol NaOH}}{\text{L soln}} \underset{\text{given}}{\nwarrow} = \overset{\overset{\text{want to find}}{\swarrow}}{\text{mol NaOH}}$$

From the equation for the neutralization reaction just shown, we see that 2 moles of NaOH neutralize 1 mole of H_2SO_4. How many moles of NaOH are contained in 43.79 mL of a 0.1172 M NaOH solution? How many moles of H_2SO_4 would this quantity of NaOH neutralize? What would be the concentration of the H_2SO_4 solution?

Solution First, we calculate the number of moles of NaOH contained in 43.79 mL of solution:

$$43.79 \text{ mL} \times \frac{1 \text{ L soln}}{1000 \text{ mL soln}} \times \frac{0.1172 \text{ mol NaOH}}{\text{L soln}} = 5.132 \times 10^{-3} \text{ mol NaOH}$$

From the stoichiometry we see that 1 mol $H_2SO_4 \simeq 2$ mol NaOH. Therefore, the number of moles of H_2SO_4 reacted must be

$$5.132 \times 10^{-3} \text{ mol NaOH} \times \frac{1 \text{ mol H}_2\text{SO}_4}{2 \text{ mol NaOH}} = 2.566 \times 10^{-3} \text{ mol H}_2\text{SO}_4$$

From the definition of molarity [see Equation (4.1)], we have

$$\text{molarity} = \frac{\text{moles of solute}}{\text{liters of soln}}$$

So the molarity of the H_2SO_4 solution is

$$\frac{2.566 \times 10^{-3} \text{ mol H}_2\text{SO}_4}{25 \text{ mL} \times (1 \text{ L}/1000 \text{ mL})} = 0.1026 \, M \text{ H}_2\text{SO}_4$$

Similar problem: 4.91(b), (c).

Practice Exercise If 60.2 mL of 0.427 M KOH solution are required to neutralize 10.1 mL of H_2SO_4 solution, what is the concentration of the H_2SO_4 solution in molarity?

Review of Concepts

A NaOH solution is initially mixed with an acid solution shown in (a). Which of the diagrams shown in (b)–(d) corresponds to one of the following acids: HCl, H_2SO_4, H_3PO_4? Color codes: Blue spheres (OH^- ions); red spheres (acid molecules); green spheres (anions of the acids). Assume all the acid-base neutralization reactions go to completion.

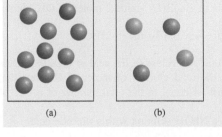 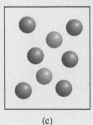 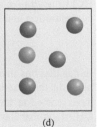

(a)   (b)   (c)   (d)

Figure 4.22 *Left to right: Solutions containing the MnO_4^-, Mn^{2+}, $Cr_2O_7^{2-}$, and Cr^{3+} ions.*

4.8 Redox Titrations

As mentioned earlier, redox reactions involve the transfer of electrons, and acid-base reactions involve the transfer of protons. Just as an acid can be titrated against a base, we can titrate an oxidizing agent against a reducing agent, using a similar procedure. We can, for example, carefully add a solution containing an oxidizing agent to a solution containing a reducing agent. The *equivalence point* is reached when the reducing agent is completely oxidized by the oxidizing agent.

Like acid-base titrations, redox titrations normally require an indicator that clearly changes color. In the presence of large amounts of reducing agent, the color of the indicator is characteristic of its reduced form. The indicator assumes the color of its oxidized form when it is present in an oxidizing medium. At or near the equivalence point, a sharp change in the indicator's color will occur as it changes from one form to the other, so the equivalence point can be readily identified.

There are not as many redox indicators as there are acid-base indicators.

Two common oxidizing agents are potassium permanganate ($KMnO_4$) and potassium dichromate ($K_2Cr_2O_7$). As Figure 4.22 shows, the colors of the permanganate and dichromate anions are distinctly different from those of the reduced species:

$$\underset{\text{purple}}{MnO_4^-} \longrightarrow \underset{\substack{\text{light} \\ \text{pink}}}{Mn^{2+}}$$

$$\underset{\substack{\text{orange} \\ \text{yellow}}}{Cr_2O_7^{2-}} \longrightarrow \underset{\text{green}}{Cr^{3+}}$$

Thus, these oxidizing agents can themselves be used as an *internal* indicator in a redox titration because they have distinctly different colors in the oxidized and reduced forms.

Redox titrations require the same type of calculations (based on the mole method) as acid-base neutralizations. The difference is that the equations and the stoichiometry tend to be more complex for redox reactions. The following is an example of a redox titration.

Example 4.13

A 16.42-mL volume of 0.1327 *M* $KMnO_4$ solution is needed to oxidize 25.00 mL of a $FeSO_4$ solution in an acidic medium. What is the concentration of the $FeSO_4$ solution in molarity? The net ionic equation is

$$5Fe^{2+} + MnO_4^- + 8H^+ \longrightarrow Mn^{2+} + 5Fe^{3+} + 4H_2O$$

(Continued)

Addition of a $KMnO_4$ solution from a buret to a $FeSO_4$ solution.

CHEMISTRY *in Action*

Metal from the Sea

Magnesium is a valuable, lightweight metal used as a structural material as well as in alloys, in batteries, and in chemical synthesis. Although magnesium is plentiful in Earth's crust, it is cheaper to "mine" the metal from seawater. Magnesium forms the second most abundant cation in the sea (after sodium); there are about 1.3 g of magnesium in a kilogram of seawater. The process for obtaining magnesium from seawater employs all three types of reactions discussed in this chapter: precipitation, acid-base, and redox reactions.

In the first stage in the recovery of magnesium, limestone ($CaCO_3$) is heated at high temperatures to produce quicklime, or calcium oxide (CaO):

$$CaCO_3(s) \longrightarrow CaO(s) + CO_2(g)$$

When calcium oxide is treated with seawater, it forms calcium hydroxide [$Ca(OH)_2$], which is slightly soluble and ionizes to give Ca^{2+} and OH^- ions:

$$CaO(s) + H_2O(l) \longrightarrow Ca^{2+}(aq) + 2OH^-(aq)$$

The surplus hydroxide ions cause the much less soluble magnesium hydroxide to precipitate:

$$Mg^{2+}(aq) + 2OH^-(aq) \longrightarrow Mg(OH)_2(s)$$

The solid magnesium hydroxide is filtered and reacted with hydrochloric acid to form magnesium chloride ($MgCl_2$):

$$Mg(OH)_2(s) + 2HCl(aq) \longrightarrow MgCl_2(aq) + 2H_2O(l)$$

After the water is evaporated, the solid magnesium chloride is melted in a steel cell. The molten magnesium chloride contains

Magnesium hydroxide was precipitated from processed seawater in settling ponds at the Dow Chemical Company once operated in Freeport, Texas.

both Mg^{2+} and Cl^- ions. In a process called *electrolysis*, an electric current is passed through the cell to reduce the Mg^{2+} ions and oxidize the Cl^- ions. The half-reactions are

$$Mg^{2+} + 2e^- \longrightarrow Mg$$
$$2Cl^- \longrightarrow Cl_2 + 2e^-$$

The overall reaction is

$$MgCl_2(l) \longrightarrow Mg(l) + Cl_2(g)$$

This is how magnesium metal is produced. The chlorine gas generated can be converted to hydrochloric acid and recycled through the process.

Strategy We want to calculate the molarity of the $FeSO_4$ solution. From the definition of molarity

$$\text{molarity of } FeSO_4 = \frac{\text{mol } FeSO_4}{\text{L soln}}$$

want to calculate   need to find   given

(Continued)

The volume of the $FeSO_4$ solution is given in the problem. Therefore, we need to find the number of moles of $FeSO_4$ to solve for the molarity. From the net ionic equation, what is the stoichiometric equivalence between Fe^{2+} and MnO_4^-? How many moles of $KMnO_4$ are contained in 16.42 mL of 0.1327 M $KMnO_4$ solution?

Solution The number of moles of $KMnO_4$ in 16.42 mL of the solution is

$$\text{moles of } KMnO_4 = \frac{0.1327 \text{ mol } KMnO_4}{1000 \text{ mL soln}} \times 16.42 \text{ mL}$$
$$= 2.179 \times 10^{-3} \text{ mol } KMnO_4$$

From the net ionic equation we see that 5 mol $Fe^{2+} \simeq 1$ mol MnO_4^-. Therefore, the number of moles of $FeSO_4$ oxidized is

$$\text{moles } FeSO_4 = 2.179 \times 10^{-3} \text{ mol } KMnO_4^- \times \frac{5 \text{ mol } FeSO_4}{1 \text{ mol } KMnO_4}$$
$$= 1.090 \times 10^{-2} \text{ mol } FeSO_4$$

The concentration of the $FeSO_4$ solution in moles of $FeSO_4$ per liter of solution is

$$\text{molarity of } FeSO_4 = \frac{\text{mol } FeSO_4}{\text{L soln}}$$
$$= \frac{1.090 \times 10^{-2} \text{ mol } FeSO_4}{25.00 \text{ mL soln}} \times \frac{1000 \text{ mL soln}}{1 \text{ L soln}}$$
$$= 0.4360 \ M$$

Similar problems: 4.95, 4.96.

Practice Exercise How many milliliters of a 0.206 M HI solution are needed to reduce 22.5 mL of a 0.374 M $KMnO_4$ solution according to the following equation:

$$10HI + 2KMnO_4 + 3H_2SO_4 \longrightarrow 5I_2 + 2MnSO_4 + K_2SO_4 + 8H_2O$$

The Chemistry in Action essay on p. 156 describes an industrial process that involves the types of reactions discussed in this chapter.

Review of Concepts

If a solution of a reducing agent is titrated with a solution of an oxidizing agent, and the initial concentrations of the two solutions are the same, does that mean that the equivalence point will be reached when an equal volume of oxidizing has been added? Explain.

Key Equations

$$\text{molarity} = \frac{\text{moles of solute}}{\text{liters of solution}} \quad (4.1) \qquad \text{Calculating molarity}$$

$$M = \frac{n}{V} \quad (4.2) \qquad \text{Calculating molarity}$$

$$M_i V_i = M_f V_f \quad (4.3) \qquad \text{Dilution of solution}$$

Summary of Facts & Concepts

1. Aqueous solutions are electrically conducting if the solutes are electrolytes. If the solutes are nonelectrolytes, the solutions do not conduct electricity.

2. Three major categories of chemical reactions that take place in aqueous solution are precipitation reactions, acid-base reactions, and oxidation-reduction reactions.

3. From general rules about solubilities of ionic compounds, we can predict whether a precipitate will form in a reaction.

4. Arrhenius acids ionize in water to give H^+ ions, and Arrhenius bases ionize in water to give OH^- ions. Brønsted acids donate protons, and Brønsted bases accept protons.

5. The reaction of an acid and a base is called neutralization.

6. In redox reactions, oxidation and reduction always occur simultaneously. Oxidation is characterized by the loss of electrons, reduction by the gain of electrons.

7. Oxidation numbers help us keep track of charge distribution and are assigned to all atoms in a compound or ion according to specific rules. Oxidation can be defined as an increase in oxidation number; reduction can be defined as a decrease in oxidation number.

8. Many redox reactions can be subclassified as combination, decomposition, combustion, displacement, or disproportionation reactions.

9. The concentration of a solution is the amount of solute present in a given amount of solution. Molarity expresses concentration as the number of moles of solute in 1 L of solution.

10. Adding a solvent to a solution, a process known as dilution, decreases the concentration (molarity) of the solution without changing the total number of moles of solute present in the solution.

11. Gravimetric analysis is a technique for determining the identity of a compound and/or the concentration of a solution by measuring mass. Gravimetric experiments often involve precipitation reactions.

12. In acid-base titration, a solution of known concentration (say, a base) is added gradually to a solution of unknown concentration (say, an acid) with the goal of determining the unknown concentration. The point at which the reaction in the titration is complete, as shown by the change in the indicator's color, is called the equivalence point.

13. Redox titrations are similar to acid-base titrations. The point at which the oxidation-reduction reaction is complete is called the equivalence point.

Key Words

Activity series, p. 140
Aqueous solution, p. 119
Brønsted acid, p. 127
Brønsted base, p. 127
Combination reaction, p. 137
Combustion reaction, p. 139
Concentration of a
   solution, p. 145
Decomposition reaction, p. 139
Dilution, p. 147
Diprotic acid, p. 128
Displacement reaction, p. 139
Disproportionation
   reaction, p. 142

Electrolyte, p. 119
Equivalence point, p. 152
Gravimetric analysis, p. 149
Half-reaction, p. 133
Hydration, p. 120
Hydronium ion, p. 128
Indicator, p. 152
Ionic equation, p. 124
Metathesis reaction, p. 121
Molar concentration, p. 145
Molarity (M), p. 145
Molecular equation, p. 123
Monoprotic acid, p. 128

Net ionic equation, p. 124
Neutralization reaction, p. 130
Nonelectrolyte, p. 119
Oxidation number, p. 135
Oxidation reaction, p. 133
Oxidation-reduction
   reaction, p. 132
Oxidation state, p. 135
Oxidizing agent, p. 134
Precipitate, p. 121
Precipitation reaction, p. 121
Quantitative analysis, p. 149
Redox reaction, p. 132

Reducing agent, p. 134
Reduction reaction, p. 133
Reversible reaction, p. 121
Salt, p. 130
Solubility, p. 122
Solute, p. 119
Solution, p. 119
Solvent, p. 119
Spectator ion, p. 124
Standard solution, p. 151
Titration, p. 151
Triprotic acid, p. 128

Questions & Problems

  ● *Problems available in Connect Plus*
  Red numbered problems solved in Student Solutions Manual

Properties of Aqueous Solutions
Review Questions

4.1   Define solute, solvent, and solution by describing the process of dissolving a solid in a liquid.

4.2   What is the difference between a nonelectrolyte and an electrolyte? Between a weak electrolyte and a strong electrolyte?

4.3   Describe hydration. What properties of water enable its molecules to interact with ions in solution?

4.4   What is the difference between the following symbols in chemical equations: $\longrightarrow$ and $\rightleftharpoons$?

4.5 Water is an extremely weak electrolyte and therefore cannot conduct electricity. Why are we often cautioned not to operate electrical appliances when our hands are wet?

4.6 Sodium sulfate (Na_2SO_4) is a strong electrolyte. What species are present in $Na_2SO_4(aq)$?

Problems

4.7 The aqueous solutions of three compounds are shown in the diagram. Identify each compound as a nonelectrolyte, a weak electrolyte, and a strong electrolyte.

  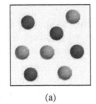

(a)   (b)   (c)

4.8 Which of the following diagrams best represents the hydration of NaCl when dissolved in water? The Cl^- ion is larger in size than the Na^+ ion.

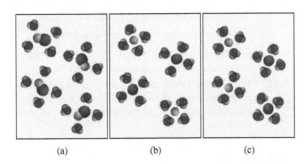

(a)   (b)   (c)

4.9 Identify each of the following substances as a strong electrolyte, weak electrolyte, or nonelectrolyte: (a) H_2O, (b) KCl, (c) HNO_3, (d) CH_3COOH, (e) $C_{12}H_{22}O_{11}$.

4.10 Identify each of the following substances as a strong electrolyte, weak electrolyte, or nonelectrolyte: (a) $Ba(NO_3)_2$, (b) Ne, (c) NH_3, (d) NaOH.

4.11 The passage of electricity through an electrolyte solution is caused by the movement of (a) electrons only, (b) cations only, (c) anions only, (d) both cations and anions.

4.12 Predict and explain which of the following systems are electrically conducting: (a) solid NaCl, (b) molten NaCl, (c) an aqueous solution of NaCl.

4.13 You are given a water-soluble compound X. Describe how you would determine whether it is an electrolyte or a nonelectrolyte. If it is an electrolyte, how would you determine whether it is strong or weak?

4.14 Explain why a solution of HCl in benzene does not conduct electricity but in water it does.

Precipitation Reactions
Review Questions

4.15 What is the difference between an ionic equation and a molecular equation?

4.16 What is the advantage of writing net ionic equations?

Problems

4.17 Two aqueous solutions of $AgNO_3$ and NaCl are mixed. Which of the following diagrams best represents the mixture? For simplicity, water molecules are not shown. (Color codes are: Ag^+ = gray, Cl^- = orange, Na^+ = green, NO_3^- = blue.)

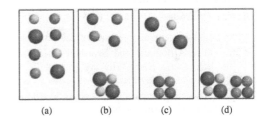

(a)   (b)   (c)   (d)

4.18 Two aqueous solutions of KOH and $MgCl_2$ are mixed. Which of the following diagrams best represents the mixture? For simplicity, water molecules are not shown. (Color codes are: K^+ = purple, OH^- = red, Mg^{2+} = green, Cl^- = orange.)

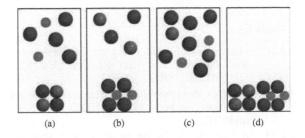

(a)   (b)   (c)   (d)

4.19 Characterize the following compounds as soluble or insoluble in water: (a) $Ca_3(PO_4)_2$, (b) $Mn(OH)_2$, (c) $AgClO_3$, (d) K_2S.

4.20 Characterize the following compounds as soluble or insoluble in water: (a) $CaCO_3$, (b) $ZnSO_4$, (c) $Hg(NO_3)_2$, (d) $HgSO_4$, (e) NH_4ClO_4.

160 Chapter 4 • Reactions in Aqueous Solutions

4.21 Write ionic and net ionic equations for the following reactions:

(a) $AgNO_3(aq) + Na_2SO_4(aq) \longrightarrow$

(b) $BaCl_2(aq) + ZnSO_4(aq) \longrightarrow$

(c) $(NH_4)_2CO_3(aq) + CaCl_2(aq) \longrightarrow$

4.22 Write ionic and net ionic equations for the following reactions:

(a) $Na_2S(aq) + ZnCl_2(aq) \longrightarrow$

(b) $K_3PO_4(aq) + 3Sr(NO_3)_2(aq) \longrightarrow$

(c) $Mg(NO_3)_2(aq) + 2NaOH(aq) \longrightarrow$

4.23 Which of the following processes will likely result in a precipitation reaction? (a) Mixing a $NaNO_3$ solution with a $CuSO_4$ solution. (b) Mixing a $BaCl_2$ solution with a K_2SO_4 solution. Write a net ionic equation for the precipitation reaction.

4.24 With reference to Table 4.2, suggest one method by which you might separate (a) K^+ from Ag^+, (b) Ba^{2+} from Pb^{2+}, (c) NH_4^+ from Ca^{2+}, (d) Ba^{2+} from Cu^{2+}. All cations are assumed to be in aqueous solution, and the common anion is the nitrate ion.

Acid-Base Reactions
Review Questions

4.25 List the general properties of acids and bases.

4.26 Give Arrhenius' and Brønsted's definitions of an acid and a base. Why are Brønsted's definitions more useful in describing acid-base properties?

4.27 Give an example of a monoprotic acid, a diprotic acid, and a triprotic acid.

4.28 What are the characteristics of an acid-base neutralization reaction?

4.29 What factors qualify a compound as a salt? Specify which of the following compounds are salts: CH_4, NaF, NaOH, CaO, $BaSO_4$, HNO_3, NH_3, KBr?

4.30 Identify the following as a weak or strong acid or base: (a) NH_3, (b) H_3PO_4, (c) LiOH, (d) HCOOH (formic acid), (e) H_2SO_4, (f) HF, (g) $Ba(OH)_2$.

Problems

4.31 Identify each of the following species as a Brønsted acid, base, or both: (a) HI, (b) CH_3COO^-, (c) $H_2PO_4^-$, (d) HSO_4^-.

4.32 Identify each of the following species as a Brønsted acid, base, or both: PO_4^{3-}, (b) ClO_2^-, (c) NH_4^+, (d) HCO_3^-.

4.33 Balance the following equations and write the corresponding ionic and net ionic equations (if appropriate):

(a) $HBr(aq) + NH_3(aq) \longrightarrow$

(b) $Ba(OH)_2(aq) + H_3PO_4(aq) \longrightarrow$

(c) $HClO_4(aq) + Mg(OH)_2(s) \longrightarrow$

4.34 Balance the following equations and write the corresponding ionic and net ionic equations (if appropriate):

(a) $CH_3COOH(aq) + KOH(aq) \longrightarrow$

(b) $H_2CO_3(aq) + NaOH(aq) \longrightarrow$

(c) $HNO_3(aq) + Ba(OH)_2(aq) \longrightarrow$

Oxidation-Reduction Reactions
Review Questions

4.35 Give an example of a combination redox reaction, a decomposition redox reaction, and a displacement redox reaction.

4.36 All combustion reactions are redox reactions. True or false? Explain.

4.37 What is an oxidation number? How is it used to identify redox reactions? Explain why, except for ionic compounds, oxidation number does not have any physical significance.

4.38 (a) Without referring to Figure 4.11, give the oxidation numbers of the alkali and alkaline earth metals in their compounds. (b) Give the highest oxidation numbers that the Groups 3A–7A elements can have.

4.39 How is the activity series organized? How is it used in the study of redox reactions?

4.40 Use the following reaction to define redox reaction, half-reaction, oxidizing agent, reducing agent:

$$4Na(s) + O_2(g) \longrightarrow 2Na_2O(s)$$

4.41 Is it possible to have a reaction in which oxidation occurs and reduction does not? Explain.

4.42 What is the requirement for an element to undergo disproportionation reactions? Name five common elements that are likely to take part in such reactions.

Problems

4.43 For the complete redox reactions given here, (i) break down each reaction into its half-reactions; (ii) identify the oxidizing agent; (iii) identify the reducing agent.

(a) $2Sr + O_2 \longrightarrow 2SrO$

(b) $2Li + H_2 \longrightarrow 2LiH$

(c) $2Cs + Br_2 \longrightarrow 2CsBr$

(d) $3Mg + N_2 \longrightarrow Mg_3N_2$

4.44 For the complete redox reactions given here, write the half-reactions and identify the oxidizing and reducing agents.

(a) $4Fe + 3O_2 \longrightarrow 2Fe_2O_3$

(b) $Cl_2 + 2NaBr \longrightarrow 2NaCl + Br_2$

(c) $Si + 2F_2 \longrightarrow SiF_4$

(d) $H_2 + Cl_2 \longrightarrow 2HCl$

4.45 Arrange the following species in order of increasing oxidation number of the sulfur atom: (a) H_2S, (b) S_8, (c) H_2SO_4, (d) S^{2-}, (e) HS^-, (f) SO_2, (g) SO_3.

4.46 Phosphorus forms many oxoacids. Indicate the oxidation number of phosphorus in each of the following acids: (a) HPO_3, (b) H_3PO_2, (c) H_3PO_3, (d) H_3PO_4, (e) $H_4P_2O_7$, (f) $H_5P_3O_{10}$.

4.47 Give the oxidation number of the underlined atoms in the following molecules and ions: (a) $\underline{Cl}F$, (b) $\underline{I}F_7$, (c) $\underline{C}H_4$, (d) $\underline{C}_2H_2$, (e) $\underline{C}_2H_4$, (f) $K_2\underline{C}rO_4$, (g) $K_2\underline{C}r_2O_7$, (h) $K\underline{Mn}O_4$, (i) $NaH\underline{C}O_3$, (j) $\underline{Li}_2$, (k) $Na\underline{I}O_3$, (l) $K\underline{O}_2$, (m) $P\underline{F}_6^-$, (n) $K\underline{Au}Cl_4$.

4.48 Give the oxidation number for the following species: H_2, Se_8, P_4, O, U, As_4, B_{12}.

4.49 Give oxidation numbers for the underlined atoms in the following molecules and ions: (a) $\underline{Cs}_2O$, (b) $Ca\underline{I}_2$, (c) $\underline{Al}_2O_3$, (d) $H_3\underline{As}O_3$, (e) $\underline{Ti}O_2$, (f) $\underline{Mo}O_4^{2-}$, (g) $\underline{Pt}Cl_4^{2-}$, (h) $\underline{Pt}Cl_6^{2-}$, (i) $\underline{Sn}F_2$, (j) $\underline{Cl}F_3$, (k) $\underline{Sb}F_6^-$.

4.50 Give the oxidation numbers of the underlined atoms in the following molecules and ions: (a) $Mg_3\underline{N}_2$, (b) $Cs\underline{O}_2$, (c) $Ca\underline{C}_2$, (d) $\underline{C}O_3^{2-}$, (e) $\underline{C}_2O_4^{2-}$, (f) $Zn\underline{O}_2^{2-}$, (g) $Na\underline{B}H_4$, (h) $\underline{W}O_4^{2-}$.

4.51 Nitric acid is a strong oxidizing agent. State which of the following species is *least* likely to be produced when nitric acid reacts with a strong reducing agent such as zinc metal, and explain why: N_2O, NO, NO_2, N_2O_4, N_2O_5, NH_4^+.

4.52 Which of the following metals can react with water? (a) Au, (b) Li, (c) Hg, (d) Ca, (e) Pt.

4.53 On the basis of oxidation number considerations, one of the following oxides would not react with molecular oxygen: NO, N_2O, SO_2, SO_3, P_4O_6. Which one is it? Why?

4.54 Predict the outcome of the reactions represented by the following equations by using the activity series, and balance the equations.

(a) $Cu(s) + HCl(aq) \longrightarrow$

(b) $I_2(s) + NaBr(aq) \longrightarrow$

(c) $Mg(s) + CuSO_4(aq) \longrightarrow$

(d) $Cl_2(g) + KBr(aq) \longrightarrow$

4.55 Classify the following redox reactions:

(a) $2H_2O_2 \longrightarrow 2H_2O + O_2$

(b) $Mg + 2AgNO_3 \longrightarrow Mg(NO_3)_2 + 2Ag$

(c) $NH_4NO_2 \longrightarrow N_2 + 2H_2O$

(d) $H_2 + Br_2 \longrightarrow 2HBr$

4.56 Classify the following redox reactions:

(a) $P_4 + 10Cl_2 \longrightarrow 4PCl_5$

(b) $2NO \longrightarrow N_2 + O_2$

(c) $Cl_2 + 2KI \longrightarrow 2KCl + I_2$

(d) $3HNO_2 \longrightarrow HNO_3 + H_2O + 2NO$

4.57 Which of the following are redox processes?

(a) $CO_2 \longrightarrow CO_3^{2-}$

(b) $VO_3 \longrightarrow VO_2$

(c) $SO_3 \longrightarrow SO_4^{2-}$

(d) $NO_2^- \longrightarrow NO_3^-$

(e) $Cr^{3+} \longrightarrow CrO_4^{2-}$

4.58 Of the following, which is most likely to be the strongest oxidizing agent? O_2, O_2^+, O_2^-, O_2^{2-}.

Concentration of Solutions
Review Questions

4.59 Write the equation for calculating molarity. Why is molarity a convenient concentration unit in chemistry?

4.60 Describe the steps involved in preparing a solution of known molar concentration using a volumetric flask.

Problems

4.61 Calculate the mass of KI in grams required to prepare 5.00×10^2 mL of a 2.80 M solution.

4.62 Describe how you would prepare 250 mL of a 0.707 M $NaNO_3$ solution.

4.63 How many moles of $MgCl_2$ are present in 60.0 mL of 0.100 M $MgCl_2$ solution?

4.64 How many grams of KOH are present in 35.0 mL of a 5.50 M solution?

4.65 Calculate the molarity of each of the following solutions: (a) 29.0 g of ethanol (C_2H_5OH) in 545 mL of solution, (b) 15.4 g of sucrose ($C_{12}H_{22}O_{11}$) in 74.0 mL of solution, (c) 9.00 g of sodium chloride (NaCl) in 86.4 mL of solution.

4.66 Calculate the molarity of each of the following solutions: (a) 6.57 g of methanol (CH_3OH) in 1.50×10^2 mL of solution, (b) 10.4 g of calcium chloride ($CaCl_2$) in 2.20×10^2 mL of solution, (c) 7.82 g of naphthalene ($C_{10}H_8$) in 85.2 mL of benzene solution.

4.67 Calculate the volume in mL of a solution required to provide the following: (a) 2.14 g of sodium chloride from a 0.270 M solution, (b) 4.30 g of ethanol from a 1.50 M solution, (c) 0.85 g of acetic acid (CH_3COOH) from a 0.30 M solution.

4.68 Determine how many grams of each of the following solutes would be needed to make 2.50×10^2 mL of a 0.100 M solution: (a) cesium iodide (CsI), (b) sulfuric acid (H_2SO_4), (c) sodium carbonate (Na_2CO_3), (d) potassium dichromate ($K_2Cr_2O_7$), (e) potassium permanganate ($KMnO_4$).

4.69 What volume of 0.416 M $Mg(NO_3)_2$ should be added to 255 mL of 0.102 M KNO_3 to produce a solution with a concentration of 0.278 M NO_3^- ions? Assume volumes are additive.

162   Chapter 4 ▪ Reactions in Aqueous Solutions

4.70   Barium hydroxide, often used to titrate weak organic acids, is obtained as the octahydrate, $Ba(OH)_2 \cdot 8H_2O$. What mass of $Ba(OH)_2 \cdot 8H_2O$ would be required to make 500.0 mL of a solution that is 0.1500 M in hydroxide ions?

Dilution of Solutions

Review Questions

4.71   Describe the basic steps involved in diluting a solution of known concentration.

4.72   Write the equation that enables us to calculate the concentration of a diluted solution. Give units for all the terms.

Problems

4.73   Describe how to prepare 1.00 L of 0.646 M HCl solution, starting with a 2.00 M HCl solution.

4.74   Water is added to 25.0 mL of a 0.866 M KNO_3 solution until the volume of the solution is exactly 500 mL. What is the concentration of the final solution?

4.75   How would you prepare 60.0 mL of 0.200 M HNO_3 from a stock solution of 4.00 M HNO_3?

4.76   You have 505 mL of a 0.125 M HCl solution and you want to dilute it to exactly 0.100 M. How much water should you add? Assume volumes are additive.

4.77   A 35.2-mL, 1.66 M $KMnO_4$ solution is mixed with 16.7 mL of 0.892 M $KMnO_4$ solution. Calculate the concentration of the final solution.

4.78   A 46.2-mL, 0.568 M calcium nitrate $[Ca(NO_3)_2]$ solution is mixed with 80.5 mL of 1.396 M calcium nitrate solution. Calculate the concentration of the final solution.

Gravimetric Analysis

Review Questions

4.79   Describe the basic steps involved in gravimetric analysis. How does this procedure help us determine the identity of a compound or the purity of a compound if its formula is known?

4.80   Distilled water must be used in the gravimetric analysis of chlorides. Why?

Problems

4.81   If 30.0 mL of 0.150 M $CaCl_2$ is added to 15.0 mL of 0.100 M $AgNO_3$, what is the mass in grams of AgCl precipitate?

4.82   A sample of 0.6760 g of an unknown compound containing barium ions (Ba^{2+}) is dissolved in water and treated with an excess of Na_2SO_4. If the mass of the $BaSO_4$ precipitate formed is 0.4105 g, what is

the percent by mass of Ba in the original unknown compound?

4.83   How many grams of NaCl are required to precipitate most of the Ag^+ ions from 2.50×10^2 mL of 0.0113 M $AgNO_3$ solution? Write the net ionic equation for the reaction.

4.84   The concentration of sulfate in water can be determined by adding a solution of barium chloride to precipitate the sulfate ion. Write the net ionic equation for this reaction. Treating a 145-mL sample of water with excess $BaCl_2(aq)$ precipitated 0.330 g of $BaSO_4$. Determine the concentration of sulfate in the original water sample.

Acid-Base Titrations

Review Questions

4.85   Describe the basic steps involved in an acid-base titration. Why is this technique of great practical value?

4.86   How does an acid-base indicator work?

4.87   A student carried out two titrations using a NaOH solution of unknown concentration in the buret. In one titration she weighed out 0.2458 g of KHP (see p. 152) and transferred it to an Erlenmeyer flask. She then added 20.00 mL of distilled water to dissolve the acid. In the other titration she weighed out 0.2507 g of KHP but added 40.00 mL of distilled water to dissolve the acid. Assuming no experimental error, would she obtain the same result for the concentration of the NaOH solution?

4.88   Would the volume of a 0.10 M NaOH solution needed to titrate 25.0 mL of a 0.10 M HNO_2 (a weak acid) solution be different from that needed to titrate 25.0 mL of a 0.10 M HCl (a strong acid) solution?

Problems

4.89   A quantity of 18.68 mL of a KOH solution is needed to neutralize 0.4218 g of KHP. What is the concentration (in molarity) of the KOH solution?

4.90   Calculate the concentration (in molarity) of a NaOH solution if 25.0 mL of the solution are needed to neutralize 17.4 mL of a 0.312 M HCl solution.

4.91   Calculate the volume in mL of a 1.420 M NaOH solution required to titrate the following solutions:
   (a) 25.00 mL of a 2.430 M HCl solution
   (b) 25.00 mL of a 4.500 M H_2SO_4 solution
   (c) 25.00 mL of a 1.500 M H_3PO_4 solution

4.92   What volume of a 0.500 M HCl solution is needed to neutralize each of the following:
   (a) 10.0 mL of a 0.300 M NaOH solution
   (b) 10.0 mL of a 0.200 M $Ba(OH)_2$ solution

Redox Titrations

Review Questions

4.93 What are the similarities and differences between acid-base titrations and redox titrations?

4.94 Explain why potassium permanganate ($KMnO_4$) and potassium dichromate ($K_2Cr_2O_7$) can serve as internal indicators in redox titrations.

Problems

4.95 Iron(II) can be oxidized by an acidic $K_2Cr_2O_7$ solution according to the net ionic equation:

$$Cr_2O_7^{2-} + 6Fe^{2+} + 14H^+ \longrightarrow 2Cr^{3+} + 6Fe^{3+} + 7H_2O$$

If it takes 26.0 mL of 0.0250 M $K_2Cr_2O_7$ to titrate 25.0 mL of a solution containing Fe^{2+}, what is the molar concentration of Fe^{2+}?

4.96 The SO_2 present in air is mainly responsible for the acid rain phenomenon. Its concentration can be determined by titrating against a standard permanganate solution as follows:

$$5SO_2 + 2MnO_4^- + 2H_2O \longrightarrow 5SO_4^{2-} + 2Mn^{2+} + 4H^+$$

Calculate the number of grams of SO_2 in a sample of air if 7.37 mL of 0.00800 M $KMnO_4$ solution are required for the titration.

4.97 A sample of iron ore (containing only Fe^{2+} ions) weighing 0.2792 g was dissolved in dilute acid solution, and all the Fe(II) was converted to Fe(III) ions. The solution required 23.30 mL of 0.0194 M $K_2Cr_2O_7$ for titration. Calculate the percent by mass of iron in the ore. (*Hint:* See Problem 4.95 for the balanced equation.)

4.98 The concentration of a hydrogen peroxide solution can be conveniently determined by titration against a standardized potassium permanganate solution in an acidic medium according to the following equation:

$$2MnO_4^- + 5H_2O_2 + 6H^+ \longrightarrow 5O_2 + 2Mn^{2+} + 8H_2O$$

If 36.44 mL of a 0.01652 M $KMnO_4$ solution are required to oxidize 25.00 mL of a H_2O_2 solution, calculate the molarity of the H_2O_2 solution.

4.99 Oxalic acid ($H_2C_2O_4$) is present in many plants and vegetables. If 24.0 mL of 0.0100 M $KMnO_4$ solution is needed to titrate 1.00 g of a sample of $H_2C_2O_4$ to the equivalence point, what is the percent by mass of $H_2C_2O_4$ in the sample? The net ionic equation is

$$2MnO_4^- + 16H^+ + 5C_2O_4^{2-} \longrightarrow 2Mn^{2+} + 10CO_2 + 8H_2O$$

4.100 A 15.0-mL sample of an oxalic acid solution requires 25.2 mL of 0.149 M NaOH for neutralization. Calculate the volume of a 0.122 M $KMnO_4$ solution needed to react with a second 15.0-mL sample of the oxalic acid solution. (*Hint:* Oxalic acid is a diprotic acid. See Problem 4.99 for redox equation.)

4.101 Iodate ion, IO_3^-, oxidizes SO_3^{2-} in acidic solution. The half-reaction for the oxidation is

$$SO_3^{2-} + H_2O \longrightarrow SO_4^{2-} + 2H^+ + 2e^-$$

A 100.0-mL sample of solution containing 1.390 g of KIO_3 reacts with 32.5 mL of 0.500 M Na_2SO_3. What is the final oxidation state of the iodine after the reaction has occurred?

4.102 Calcium oxalate (CaC_2O_4), the main component of kidney stones, is insoluble in water. For this reason it can be used to determine the amount of Ca^{2+} ions in fluids such as blood. The calcium oxalate isolated from blood is dissolved in acid and titrated against a standardized $KMnO_4$ solution, as shown in Problem 4.99. In one test it is found that the calcium oxalate isolated from a 10.0-mL sample of blood requires 24.2 mL of 9.56×10^{-4} M $KMnO_4$ for titration. Calculate the number of milligrams of calcium per milliliter of blood.

Additional Problems

4.103 Classify the following reactions according to the types discussed in the chapter:
(a) $Cl_2 + 2OH^- \longrightarrow Cl^- + ClO^- + H_2O$
(b) $Ca^{2+} + CO_3^{2-} \longrightarrow CaCO_3$
(c) $NH_3 + H^+ \longrightarrow NH_4^+$
(d) $2CCl_4 + CrO_4^{2-} \longrightarrow 2COCl_2 + CrO_2Cl_2 + 2Cl^-$
(e) $Ca + F_2 \longrightarrow CaF_2$
(f) $2Li + H_2 \longrightarrow 2LiH$
(g) $Ba(NO_3)_2 + Na_2SO_4 \longrightarrow 2NaNO_3 + BaSO_4$
(h) $CuO + H_2 \longrightarrow Cu + H_2O$
(i) $Zn + 2HCl \longrightarrow ZnCl_2 + H_2$
(j) $2FeCl_2 + Cl_2 \longrightarrow 2FeCl_3$
(k) $LiOH + HNO_3 \longrightarrow LiNO_3 + H_2O$

4.104 Oxygen (O_2) and carbon dioxide (CO_2) are colorless and odorless gases. Suggest two chemical tests that would enable you to distinguish between these two gases.

4.105 Which of the following aqueous solutions would you expect to be the best conductor of electricity at 25°C? Explain your answer.
(a) 0.20 M NaCl
(b) 0.60 M CH_3COOH
(c) 0.25 M HCl
(d) 0.20 M $Mg(NO_3)_2$

• **4.106** A 5.00×10^2-mL sample of 2.00 M HCl solution is treated with 4.47 g of magnesium. Calculate the concentration of the acid solution after all the metal has reacted. Assume that the volume remains unchanged.

4.107 Shown here are two aqueous solutions containing various ions. The volume of each solution is 200 mL. (a) Calculate the mass of the precipitate (in g) after the solutions are mixed. (b) What are the concentrations (in M) of the ions in the final solution? Treat each sphere as 0.100 mol. Assume the volumes are additive.

4.108 Shown here are two aqueous solutions containing various ions. The volume of each solution is 200 mL. (a) Calculate the mass of the precipitate (in g) after the solutions are mixed. (b) What are the concentrations (in M) of the ions in the final solution? Treat each sphere as 0.100 mol. Assume the volumes are additive.

• **4.109** Calculate the volume of a 0.156 M $CuSO_4$ solution that would react with 7.89 g of zinc.

• **4.110** Sodium carbonate (Na_2CO_3) is available in very pure form and can be used to standardize acid solutions. What is the molarity of a HCl solution if 28.3 mL of the solution are required to react with 0.256 g of Na_2CO_3?

• **4.111** A 3.664-g sample of a monoprotic acid was dissolved in water. It took 20.27 mL of a 0.1578 M NaOH solution to neutralize the acid. Calculate the molar mass of the acid.

• **4.112** Acetic acid (CH_3COOH) is an important ingredient of vinegar. A sample of 50.0 mL of a commercial vinegar is titrated against a 1.00 M NaOH solution. What is the concentration (in M) of acetic acid present in the vinegar if 5.75 mL of the base are needed for the titration?

• **4.113** A 15.00-mL solution of potassium nitrate (KNO_3) was diluted to 125.0 mL, and 25.00 mL of this solution were then diluted to 1.000×10^3 mL. The concentration of the final solution is 0.00383 M. Calculate the concentration of the original solution.

4.114 When 2.50 g of a zinc strip were placed in a $AgNO_3$ solution, silver metal formed on the surface of the strip. After some time had passed, the strip was removed from the solution, dried, and weighed. If the mass of the strip was 3.37 g, calculate the mass of Ag and Zn metals present.

• **4.115** Calculate the mass of the precipitate formed when 2.27 L of 0.0820 M $Ba(OH)_2$ are mixed with 3.06 L of 0.0664 M Na_2SO_4.

• **4.116** Calculate the concentration of the acid (or base) remaining in solution when 10.7 mL of 0.211 M HNO_3 are added to 16.3 mL of 0.258 M NaOH.

4.117 (a) Describe a preparation for magnesium hydroxide [$Mg(OH)_2$] and predict its solubility. (b) Milk of magnesia contains mostly $Mg(OH)_2$ and is effective in treating acid (mostly hydrochloric acid) indigestion. Calculate the volume of a 0.035 M HCl solution (a typical acid concentration in an upset stomach) needed to react with two spoonfuls (approximately 10 mL) of milk of magnesia [at 0.080 g $Mg(OH)_2$/mL].

• **4.118** A 1.00-g sample of a metal X (that is known to form X^{2+} ions) was added to 0.100 L of 0.500 M H_2SO_4. After all the metal had reacted, the remaining acid required 0.0334 L of 0.500 M NaOH solution for neutralization. Calculate the molar mass of the metal and identify the element.

4.119 Carbon dioxide in air can be removed by an aqueous metal hydroxide solution such as LiOH and $Ba(OH)_2$. (a) Write equations for the reactions. (Carbon dioxide reacts with water to form carbonic acid.) (b) Calculate the mass of CO_2 that can be removed by 5.00×10^2 mL of a 0.800 M LiOH and a 0.800 M $Ba(OH)_2$ solution. (c) Which solution would you choose for use in a space capsule and which for use in a submarine?

4.120 The molecular formula of malonic acid is $C_3H_4O_4$. If a solution containing 0.762 g of the acid requires 12.44 mL of 1.174 M NaOH for neutralization, how many ionizable H atoms are present in the molecule?

4.121 A quantitative definition of solubility is the maximum number of grams of a solute that will dissolve in a given volume of water at a particular temperature. Describe an experiment that would enable you to determine the solubility of a soluble compound.

• **4.122** A 60.0-mL 0.513 M glucose ($C_6H_{12}O_6$) solution is mixed with 120.0 mL of 2.33 M glucose solution. What is the concentration of the final solution? Assume the volumes are additive.

4.123 An ionic compound X is only slightly soluble in water. What test would you employ to show that the compound does indeed dissolve in water to a certain extent?

4.124 A student is given an unknown that is either iron(II) sulfate or iron(III) sulfate. Suggest a chemical procedure for determining its identity. (Both iron compounds are water soluble.)

4.125 You are given a colorless liquid. Describe three chemical tests you would perform on the liquid to show that it is water.

4.126 Using the apparatus shown in Figure 4.1, a student found that a sulfuric acid solution caused the lightbulb to glow brightly. However, after the addition of a certain amount of a barium hydroxide [$Ba(OH)_2$] solution, the light began to dim even though $Ba(OH)_2$ is also a strong electrolyte. Explain.

4.127 The molar mass of a certain metal carbonate, MCO_3, can be determined by adding an excess of HCl acid to react with all the carbonate and then "back titrating" the remaining acid with a NaOH solution. (a) Write an equation for these reactions. (b) In a certain experiment, 20.00 mL of 0.0800 M HCl were added to a 0.1022-g sample of MCO_3. The excess HCl required 5.64 mL of 0.1000 M NaOH for neutralization. Calculate the molar mass of the carbonate and identify M.

4.128 A 5.012-g sample of an iron chloride hydrate was dried in an oven. The mass of the anhydrous compound was 3.195 g. The compound was then dissolved in water and reacted with an excess of $AgNO_3$. The AgCl precipitate formed weighed 7.225 g. What is the formula of the original compound?

4.129 You are given a soluble compound of unknown molecular formula. (a) Describe three tests that would show that the compound is an acid. (b) Once you have established that the compound is an acid, describe how you would determine its molar mass using a NaOH solution of known concentration. (Assume the acid is monoprotic.) (c) How would you find out whether the acid is weak or strong? You are provided with a sample of NaCl and an apparatus like that shown in Figure 4.1 for comparison.

4.130 You are given two colorless solutions, one containing NaCl and the other sucrose ($C_{12}H_{22}O_{11}$). Suggest a chemical and a physical test that would allow you to distinguish between these two solutions.

• 4.131 The concentration of lead ions (Pb^{2+}) in a sample of polluted water that also contains nitrate ions (NO_3^-) is determined by adding solid sodium sulfate

(Na_2SO_4) to exactly 500 mL of the water. (a) Write the molecular and net ionic equations for the reaction. (b) Calculate the molar concentration of Pb^{2+} if 0.00450 g of Na_2SO_4 was needed for the complete precipitation of Pb^{2+} ions as $PbSO_4$.

4.132 Hydrochloric acid is not an oxidizing agent in the sense that sulfuric acid and nitric acid are. Explain why the chloride ion is not a strong oxidizing agent like SO_4^{2-} and NO_3^-.

4.133 Explain how you would prepare potassium iodide (KI) by means of (a) an acid-base reaction and (b) a reaction between an acid and a carbonate compound.

4.134 Sodium reacts with water to yield hydrogen gas. Why is this reaction not used in the laboratory preparation of hydrogen?

4.135 Describe how you would prepare the following compounds: (a) $Mg(OH)_2$, (b) AgI, (c) $Ba_3(PO_4)_2$.

4.136 Someone spilled concentrated sulfuric acid on the floor of a chemistry laboratory. To neutralize the acid, would it be preferable to pour concentrated sodium hydroxide solution or spray solid sodium bicarbonate over the acid? Explain your choice and the chemical basis for the action.

4.137 Describe in each case how you would separate the cations or anions in an aqueous solution of: (a) $NaNO_3$ and $Ba(NO_3)_2$, (b) $Mg(NO_3)_2$ and KNO_3, (c) KBr and KNO_3, (d) K_3PO_4 and KNO_3, (e) Na_2CO_3 and $NaNO_3$.

4.138 The following are common household compounds: table salt (NaCl), table sugar (sucrose), vinegar (contains acetic acid), baking soda ($NaHCO_3$), washing soda ($Na_2CO_3 \cdot 10H_2O$), boric acid (H_3BO_3, used in eyewash), epsom salt ($MgSO_4 \cdot 7H_2O$), sodium hydroxide (used in drain openers), ammonia, milk of magnesia [$Mg(OH)_2$], and calcium carbonate. Based on what you have learned in this chapter, describe test(s) that would enable you to identify each of these compounds.

4.139 Sulfites (compounds containing the SO_3^{2-} ions) are used as preservatives in dried fruit and vegetables and in wine making. In an experiment to test the presence of sulfite in fruit, a student first soaked several dried apricots in water overnight and then filtered the solution to remove all solid particles. She then treated the solution with hydrogen peroxide (H_2O_2) to oxidize the sulfite ions to sulfate ions. Finally, the sulfate ions were precipitated by treating the solution with a few drops of a barium chloride ($BaCl_2$) solution. Write a balanced equation for each of the preceding steps.

• **4.140** A 0.8870-g sample of a mixture of NaCl and KCl is dissolved in water, and the solution is then treated with an excess of $AgNO_3$ to yield 1.913 g of AgCl. Calculate the percent by mass of each compound in the mixture.

4.141   Based on oxidation number consideration, explain why carbon monoxide (CO) is flammable but carbon dioxide (CO_2) is not.

4.142   Which of the diagrams shown here corresponds to the reaction between $AgOH(s)$ and $HNO_3(aq)$? Write a balanced equation for the reaction. The green spheres represent the Ag^+ ions and the red spheres represent the NO_3^- ions.

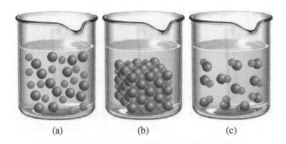

(a)   (b)   (c)

● 4.143   Chlorine forms a number of oxides with the following oxidation numbers: +1, +3, +4, +6, and +7. Write a formula for each of these compounds.

● 4.144   A useful application of oxalic acid is the removal of rust (Fe_2O_3) from, say, bathtub rings according to the reaction

$$Fe_2O_3(s) + 6H_2C_2O_4(aq) \longrightarrow$$
$$2Fe(C_2O_4)_3^{3-}(aq) + 3H_2O + 6H^+(aq)$$

Calculate the number of grams of rust that can be removed by 5.00×10^2 mL of a 0.100 M solution of oxalic acid.

● 4.145   Acetylsalicylic acid ($C_9H_8O_4$) is a monoprotic acid commonly known as "aspirin." A typical aspirin tablet, however, contains only a small amount of the acid. In an experiment to determine its composition, an aspirin tablet was crushed and dissolved in water. It took 12.25 mL of 0.1466 M NaOH to neutralize the solution. Calculate the number of grains of aspirin in the tablet. (One grain = 0.0648 g.)

4.146   A 0.9157-g mixture of $CaBr_2$ and NaBr is dissolved in water, and $AgNO_3$ is added to the solution to form AgBr precipitate. If the mass of the precipitate is 1.6930 g, what is the percent by mass of NaBr in the original mixture?

4.147   Hydrogen halides (HF, HCl, HBr, HI) are highly reactive compounds that have many industrial and laboratory uses. (a) In the laboratory, HF and HCl can be generated by reacting CaF_2 and NaCl with concentrated sulfuric acid. Write appropriate equations for the reactions. (*Hint:* These are not redox reactions.) (b) Why is it that HBr and HI cannot be prepared similarly, that is, by reacting NaBr and NaI with concentrated sulfuric acid? (*Hint:* H_2SO_4 is a stronger oxidizing agent than both Br_2 and I_2.) (c) HBr can be prepared by reacting phosphorus tribromide (PBr_3) with water. Write an equation for this reaction.

● 4.148   A 325-mL sample of solution contains 25.3 g of $CaCl_2$. (a) Calculate the molar concentration of Cl^- in this solution. (b) How many grams of Cl^- are in 0.100 L of this solution?

● 4.149   Phosphoric acid (H_3PO_4) is an important industrial chemical used in fertilizers, in detergents, and in the food industry. It is produced by two different methods. In the *electric furnace method*, elemental phosphorus (P_4) is burned in air to form P_4O_{10}, which is then reacted with water to give H_3PO_4. In the *wet process*, the mineral phosphate rock fluorapatite [$Ca_5(PO_4)_3F$] is reacted with sulfuric acid to give H_3PO_4 (and HF and $CaSO_4$). Write equations for these processes and classify each step as precipitation, acid-base, or redox reaction.

● 4.150   Ammonium nitrate (NH_4NO_3) is one of the most important nitrogen-containing fertilizers. Its purity can be analyzed by titrating a solution of NH_4NO_3 with a standard NaOH solution. In one experiment a 0.2041-g sample of industrially prepared NH_4NO_3 required 24.42 mL of 0.1023 M NaOH for neutralization.

   (a) Write a net ionic equation for the reaction.

   (b) What is the percent purity of the sample?

4.151   Is the following reaction a redox reaction? Explain.

$$3O_2(g) \longrightarrow 2O_3(g)$$

4.152   What is the oxidation number of O in HFO?

4.153   Use molecular models like those in Figures 4.7 and 4.8 to represent the following acid-base reactions:

   (a) $OH^- + H_3O^+ \longrightarrow 2H_2O$

   (b) $NH_4^+ + NH_2^- \longrightarrow 2NH_3$

   Identify the Brønsted acid and base in each case.

4.154   The alcohol content in a 10.0-g sample of blood from a driver required 4.23 mL of 0.07654 M $K_2Cr_2O_7$ for titration. Should the police prosecute the individual for drunken driving? (*Hint:* See the Chemistry in Action essay on p. 144.)

4.155   On standing, a concentrated nitric acid gradually turns yellow in color. Explain. (*Hint:* Nitric acid slowly decomposes. Nitrogen dioxide is a colored gas.)

4.156   Describe the laboratory preparation for the following gases: (a) hydrogen, (b) oxygen, (c) carbon dioxide, and (d) nitrogen. Indicate the physical states of the reactants and products in each case. [*Hint:* Nitrogen can be obtained by heating ammonium nitrite (NH_4NO_2).]

4.157   Referring to Figure 4.18, explain why one must first dissolve the solid completely before making up the solution to the correct volume.

4.158   Can the following decomposition reaction be characterized as an acid-base reaction? Explain.

$$NH_4Cl(s) \longrightarrow NH_3(g) + HCl(g)$$

4.159   Give a chemical explanation for each of the following: (a) When calcium metal is added to a sulfuric acid solution, hydrogen gas is generated. After a few minutes, the reaction slows down and eventually stops even though none of the reactants is used up. Explain. (b) In the activity series, aluminum is above hydrogen, yet the metal appears to be unreactive toward steam and hydrochloric acid. Why? (c) Sodium and potassium lie above copper in the activity series. Explain why Cu^{2+} ions in a $CuSO_4$ solution are not converted to metallic copper upon the addition of these metals. (d) A metal M reacts slowly with steam. There is no visible change when it is placed in a pale green iron(II) sulfate solution. Where should we place M in the activity series? (e) Before aluminum metal was obtained by electrolysis, it was produced by reducing its chloride ($AlCl_3$) with an active metal. What metals would you use to produce aluminum in that way?

● 4.160   The recommended procedure for preparing a very dilute solution is not to weigh out a very small mass or measure a very small volume of a stock solution. Instead, it is done by a series of dilutions. A sample of 0.8214 g of $KMnO_4$ was dissolved in water and made up to the volume in a 500-mL volumetric flask. A 2.000-mL sample of this solution was transferred to a 1000-mL volumetric flask and diluted to the mark with water. Next, 10.00 mL of the diluted solution were transferred to a 250-mL flask and diluted to the mark with water. (a) Calculate the concentration (in molarity) of the final solution. (b) Calculate the mass of $KMnO_4$ needed to directly prepare the final solution.

● 4.161   The following "cycle of copper" experiment is performed in some general chemistry laboratories. The series of reactions starts with copper and ends with metallic copper. The steps are as follows: (1) A piece of copper wire of known mass is allowed to react with concentrated nitric acid [the products are copper(II) nitrate, nitrogen dioxide, and water]. (2) The copper(II) nitrate is treated with a sodium hydroxide solution to form copper(II) hydroxide precipitate. (3) On heating, copper(II) hydroxide decomposes to yield copper(II) oxide. (4) The copper(II) oxide is reacted with concentrated sulfuric acid to yield copper(II) sulfate. (5) Copper(II) sulfate is treated with an excess of zinc metal to form metallic copper. (6) The remaining zinc metal is removed by treatment with hydrochloric acid, and metallic copper is filtered, dried, and weighed. (a) Write a balanced equation for each step and classify the reactions. (b) Assuming that a student started with 65.6 g of copper, calculate the theoretical yield at each step. (c) Considering the nature of the steps, comment on why it is possible to recover most of the copper used at the start.

4.162   A quantity of 25.0 mL of a solution containing both Fe^{2+} and Fe^{3+} ions is titrated with 23.0 mL of

0.0200 M $KMnO_4$ (in dilute sulfuric acid). As a result, all of the Fe^{2+} ions are oxidized to Fe^{3+} ions. Next, the solution is treated with Zn metal to convert all of the Fe^{3+} ions to Fe^{2+} ions. Finally, the solution containing only the Fe^{2+} ions requires 40.0 mL of the same $KMnO_4$ solution for oxidation to Fe^{3+}. Calculate the molar concentrations of Fe^{2+} and Fe^{3+} in the original solution. The net ionic equation is

$$MnO_4^- + 5Fe^{2+} + 8H^+ \longrightarrow Mn^{2+} + 5Fe^{3+} + 4H_2O$$

4.163   Use the periodic table framework shown to show the names and positions of two metals that can (a) displace hydrogen from cold water, (b) displace hydrogen from steam, and (c) displace hydrogen from acid. Also show two metals that can react neither with water nor acid.

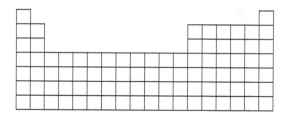

4.164   Referring to the Chemistry in Action essay on page 156, answer the following questions: (a) Identify the precipitation, acid-base, and redox processes. (b) Instead of calcium oxide, why don't we simply add sodium hydroxide to seawater to precipitate magnesium hydroxide? (c) Sometimes a mineral called dolomite (a mixture of $CaCO_3$ and $MgCO_3$) is substituted for limestone to bring about the precipitation of magnesium hydroxide. What is the advantage of using dolomite?

● 4.165   A 22.02-mL solution containing 1.615 g $Mg(NO_3)_2$ is mixed with a 28.64-mL solution containing 1.073 g NaOH. Calculate the concentrations of the ions remaining in solution after the reaction is complete. Assume volumes are additive.

● 4.166   Chemical tests of four metals A, B, C, and D show the following results.

(a) Only B and C react with 0.5 M HCl to give H_2 gas.

(b) When B is added to a solution containing the ions of the other metals, metallic A, C, and D are formed.

(c) A reacts with 6 M HNO_3 but D does not.

Arrange the metals in the increasing order as reducing agents. Suggest four metals that fit these descriptions.

4.167   The antibiotic gramicidin A can transport Na^+ ions into a certain cell at the rate of 5.0×10^7 Na^+ ions s^{-1}. Calculate the time in seconds to transport enough Na^+ ions to increase its concentration by 8.0×10^{-3} M in a cell whose intracellular volume is 2.0×10^{-10} mL.

168   **Chapter 4** ▪ Reactions in Aqueous Solutions

4.168   Shown here are two aqueous solutions containing various ions. The volume of each solution is 600 mL. (a) Write a net ionic equation for the reaction after the solutions are mixed. (b) Calculate the mass of the precipitates formed and the concentrations of the ions in the mixed solution. Treat each sphere as 0.0500 mol.

Cu^{2+}

SO_4^{2-}

Ba^{2+}

OH^-

Interpreting, Modeling & Estimating

4.169   Many proteins contain metal ions for structural and/or redox functions. Which of the following metals fit into one or both categories: Ca, Cu, Fe, Mg, Mn, Ni, Zn?

4.170   The fastest way to introduce therapeutic agents into the bloodstream is by direct delivery into a vein (intravenous therapy, or IV therapy). A clinical researcher wishes to establish an initial concentration of 6×10^{-4} mmol/L in the bloodstream of an adult male participating in a trial study of a new drug. The drug serum is prepared in the hospital's pharmacy at a concentration of 1.2×10^{-3} mol/L. How much of the serum should be introduced intravenously in order to achieve the desired initial blood concentration of the drug?

4.171   Public water supplies are often "fluoridated" by the addition of compounds such as NaF, H_2SiF_6, and Na_2SiF_6. It is well established that fluoride helps prevent tooth decay; however, care must be taken not to exceed safe levels of fluoride, which can stain or etch tooth enamel (dental fluorosis). A safe and effective concentration of fluoride in drinking water is generally considered to be around 1 mg/L. How much fluoride would a person consume by drinking fluoridated water in 1 year? What would be the equivalent mass as sodium fluoride?

4.172   Potassium superoxide (KO_2), a useful source of oxygen employed in breathing equipment, reacts with water to form potassium hydroxide, hydrogen peroxide, and oxygen. Furthermore, potassium superoxide also reacts with carbon dioxide to form potassium carbonate and oxygen. (a) Write equations for these two reactions and comment on the effectiveness of potassium superoxide in this application. (b) Focusing only on the reaction between KO_2 and CO_2, estimate the amount of KO_2 needed to sustain a worker in a polluted environment for 30 min. See Problem 1.69 for useful information.

4.173   Muriatic acid, a commercial-grade hydrochloric acid used for cleaning masonry surfaces, is typically around 10 percent HCl by mass and has a density of 1.2 g/cm³. A 0.5-in layer of boiler scale has accumulated on a 6.0-ft section of hot water pipe with an internal diameter of 2.0 in (see the Chemistry in Action essay on p. 126). What is the minimum volume of muriatic acid in gallons that would be needed to remove the boiler scale?

● 4.174   Because acid-base and precipitation reactions discussed in this chapter all involve ionic species, their progress can be monitored by measuring the electrical conductance of the solution. Match the following reactions with the diagrams shown here. The electrical conductance is shown in arbitrary units.

(1) A 1.0 *M* KOH solution is added to 1.0 L of 1.0 *M* CH_3COOH.

(2) A 1.0 *M* NaOH solution is added to 1.0 L of 1.0 *M* HCl.

(3) A 1.0 M BaCl$_2$ solution is added to 1.0 L of 1.0 M K$_2$SO$_4$.

(4) A 1.0 M NaCl solution is added to 1.0 L of 1.0 M AgNO$_3$.

(5) A 1.0 M CH$_3$COOH solution is added to 1.0 L of 1.0 M NH$_3$.

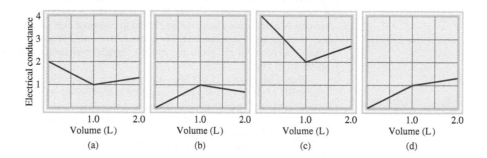

(a)   (b)   (c)   (d)

Answers to Practice Exercises

4.1 (a) Insoluble, (b) insoluble, (c) soluble. **4.2** Al^{3+}(aq) + 3OH$^-$(aq) $\longrightarrow$ Al(OH)$_3$(s). **4.3** (a) Brønsted base, (b) Brønsted acid. **4.4** Molecular equation: H$_3$PO$_4$(aq) + 3NaOH(aq) $\longrightarrow$ Na$_3$PO$_4$(aq) + 3H$_2$O(l); ionic equation: H$_3$PO$_4$(aq) + 3Na$^+$(aq) + 3OH$^-$(aq) $\longrightarrow$ 3Na$^+$(aq) + PO$_4^{3-}$(aq) + 3H$_2$O(l); net ionic equation: H$_3$PO$_4$(aq) + 3OH$^-$(aq) $\longrightarrow$ PO$_4^{3-}$(aq) + 3H$_2$O(l). **4.5** (a) P: +3, F: −1;

(b) Mn: +7, O: −2. **4.6** (a) Hydrogen displacement reaction, (b) combination reaction, (c) disproportionation reaction, (d) metal displacement reaction. **4.7** 0.452 M. **4.8** 494 mL. **4.9** Dilute 34.2 mL of the stock solution to 200 mL. **4.10** 92.02%. **4.11** 0.3822 g. **4.12** 1.27 M. **4.13** 204 mL.

CHEMICAL *MYSTERY*

Who Killed Napoleon?

After his defeat at Waterloo in 1815, Napoleon was exiled to St. Helena, a small island in the Atlantic Ocean, where he spent the last 6 years of his life. In the 1960s, samples of his hair were analyzed and found to contain a high level of arsenic, suggesting that he might have been poisoned. The prime suspects are the governor of St. Helena, with whom Napoleon did not get along, and the French royal family, who wanted to prevent his return to France.

Elemental arsenic is not that harmful. The commonly used poison is actually arsenic(III) oxide, As_2O_3, a white compound that dissolves in water, is tasteless, and if administered over a period of time, is hard to detect. It was once known as the "inheritance powder" because it could be added to grandfather's wine to hasten his demise so that his grandson could inherit the estate!

In 1832 the English chemist James Marsh devised a procedure for detecting arsenic. This test, which now bears Marsh's name, combines hydrogen formed by the reaction between zinc and sulfuric acid with a sample of the suspected poison. If As_2O_3 is present, it reacts with hydrogen to form a toxic gas, arsine (AsH_3). When arsine gas is heated, it decomposes to form arsenic, which is recognized by its metallic luster. The Marsh test is an effective deterrent to murder by As_2O_3, but it was invented too late to do Napoleon any good, if, in fact, he was a victim of deliberate arsenic poisoning.

Apparatus for Marsh's test. Sulfuric acid is added to zinc metal and a solution containing arsenic(III) oxide. The hydrogen produced reacts with As_2O_3 to yield arsine (AsH_3). On heating, arsine decomposes to elemental arsenic, which has a metallic appearance, and hydrogen gas.

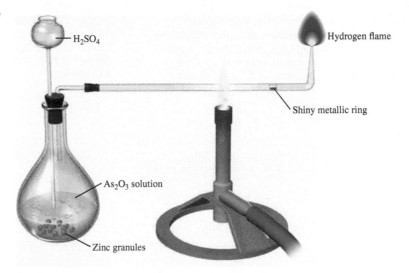

H_2SO_4

Hydrogen flame

Shiny metallic ring

As_2O_3 solution

Zinc granules

Doubts about the conspiracy theory of Napoleon's death developed in the early 1990s, when a sample of the wallpaper from his drawing room was found to contain copper arsenate ($CuHAsO_4$), a green pigment that was commonly used at the time Napoleon lived. It has been suggested that the damp climate on St. Helena promoted the growth of molds on the wallpaper. To rid themselves of arsenic, the molds could have converted it to trimethyl arsine [$(CH_3)_3As$], which is a volatile and highly poisonous compound. Prolonged exposure to these vapors would have ruined Napoleon's health and would also account for the presence of arsenic in his body, though it may not have been the primary cause of his death. This provocative theory is supported by the fact that Napoleon's regular guests suffered from gastrointestinal disturbances and other symptoms of arsenic poisoning and that their health all seemed to improve whenever they spent hours working outdoors in the garden, their main hobby on the island.

We will probably never know whether Napoleon died from arsenic poisoning, intentional or accidental, but this exercise in historical sleuthing provides a fascinating example of the use of chemical analysis. Not only is chemical analysis used in forensic science, but it also plays an essential part in endeavors ranging from pure research to practical applications, such as quality control of commercial products and medical diagnosis.

A lock of Napoleon's hair.

Chemical Clues

1. The arsenic in Napoleon's hair was detected using a technique called *neutron activation*. When As-75 is bombarded with high-energy neutrons, it is converted to the radioactive As-76 isotope. The energy of the γ rays emitted by the radioactive isotope is characteristic of arsenic, and the intensity of the rays establishes how much arsenic is present in a sample. With this technique, as little as 5 ng (5×10^{-9} g) of arsenic can be detected in 1 g of material. (a) Write symbols for the two isotopes of As, showing mass number and atomic number. (b) Name two advantages of analyzing the arsenic content by neutron activation instead of a chemical analysis.

2. Arsenic is not an essential element for the human body. (a) Based on its position in the periodic table, suggest a reason for its toxicity. (b) In addition to hair, where else might one look for the accumulation of the element if arsenic poisoning is suspected?

3. The Marsh test for arsenic involves the following steps: (a) The generation of hydrogen gas when sulfuric acid is added to zinc. (b) The reaction of hydrogen with As(III) oxide to produce arsine. (c) Conversion of arsine to arsenic by heating. Write equations representing these steps and identify the type of the reaction in each step.

CHAPTER

5

Gases

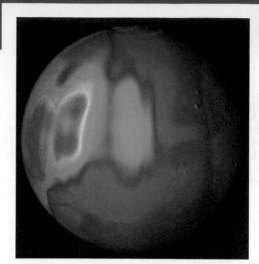

Water vapor and methane have recently been detected in significant amounts in the Martian atmosphere. (The concentration increases from purple to red.) The methane could be released by geothermal activity, or it could be produced by bacteria, fueling speculation that there may be life on Mars.

CHAPTER OUTLINE

A LOOK AHEAD

▶ We begin by examining the substances that exist as gases and their general properties. (5.1)

▶ We learn units for expressing gas pressure and the characteristics of atmospheric pressure. (5.2)

▶ Next, we study the relationship among pressure, volume, temperature, and amount of a gas in terms of various gas laws. We will see that these laws can be summarized by the ideal gas equation, which can be used to calculate the density or molar mass of a gas. (5.3 and 5.4)

▶ We will see that the ideal gas equation can be used to study the stoichiometry involving gases. (5.5)

▶ We learn that the behavior of a mixture of gases can be understood by Dalton's law of partial pressures, which is an extension of the ideal gas equation. (5.6)

▶ We will see how the kinetic molecular theory of gases, which is based on the properties of individual molecules, can be used to describe macroscopic properties such as the pressure and temperature of a gas. We learn that this theory enables us to obtain an expression for the speed of molecules at a given temperature, and understand phenomena such as gas diffusion and effusion. (5.7)

▶ Finally, we will study the correction for the nonideal behavior of gases using the van der Waals equation. (5.8)

Under certain conditions of pressure and temperature, most substances can exist in any one of three states of matter: solid, liquid, or gas. Water, for example, can be solid ice, liquid water, steam, or water vapor. The physical properties of a substance often depend on its state.

Gases, the subject of this chapter, are simpler than liquids and solids in many ways. Molecular motion in gases is totally random, and the forces of attraction between gas molecules are so small that each molecule moves freely and essentially independently of other molecules. Subjected to changes in temperature and pressure, it is easier to predict the behavior of gases. The laws that govern this behavior have played an important role in the development of the atomic theory of matter and the kinetic molecular theory of gases.

5.1 Substances That Exist as Gases

We live at the bottom of an ocean of air whose composition by volume is roughly 78 percent N_2, 21 percent O_2, and 1 percent other gases, including CO_2. Today, the chemistry of this vital mixture of gases has become a source of great interest because of the detrimental effects of environmental pollution. The chemistry of the atmosphere and polluting gases is discussed in Chapter 20. Here we will focus generally on the behavior of substances that exist as gases under normal atmospheric conditions, which are defined as 25°C and 1 atmosphere (atm) pressure.

Figure 5.1 shows the elements that are gases under normal atmospheric conditions. Note that hydrogen, nitrogen, oxygen, fluorine, and chlorine exist as gaseous diatomic molecules: H_2, N_2, O_2, F_2, and Cl_2. An allotrope of oxygen, ozone (O_3), is also a gas at room temperature. All the elements in Group 8A, the noble gases, are monatomic gases: He, Ne, Ar, Kr, Xe, and Rn.

Ionic compounds do not exist as gases at 25°C and 1 atm, because cations and anions in an ionic solid are held together by very strong electrostatic forces; that is, forces between positive and negative charges. To overcome these attractions we must apply a large amount of energy, which in practice means strongly heating the solid. Under normal conditions, all we can do is melt the solid; for example, NaCl melts at the rather high temperature of 801°C. In order to boil it, we would have to raise the temperature to well above 1000°C.

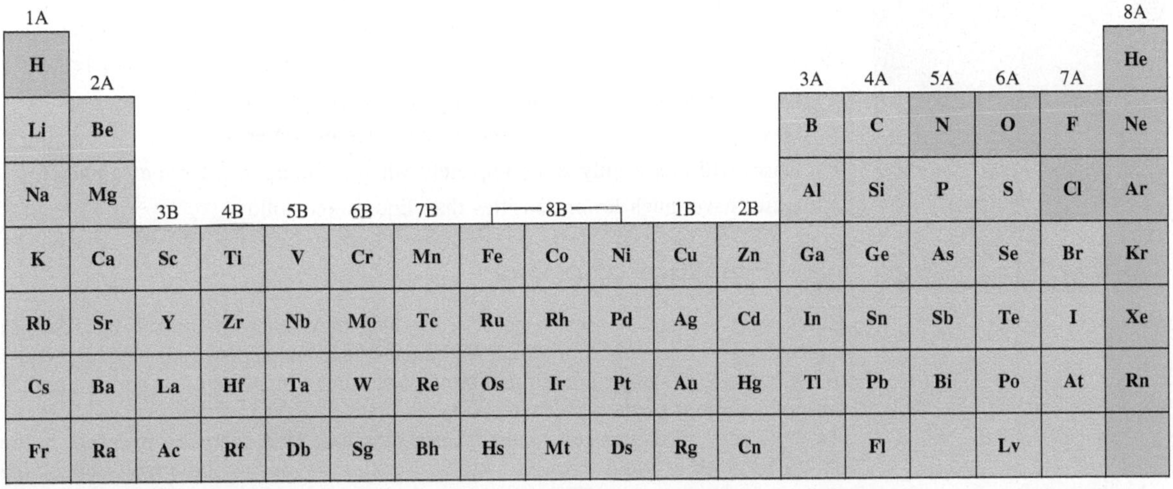

Figure 5.1 *Elements that exist as gases at 25°C and 1 atm. The noble gases (the Group 8A elements) are monatomic species; the other elements exist as diatomic molecules. Ozone (O_3) is also a gas.*

Table 5.1	Some Substances Found as Gases at 1 atm and 25°C
Elements	
H₂ (molecular hydrogen)	N₂ (molecular nitrogen)
O₂ (molecular oxygen)	O₃ (ozone)
F₂ (molecular fluorine)	Cl₂ (molecular chlorine)
He (helium)	Ne (neon)
Ar (argon)	Kr (krypton)
Xe (xenon)	Rn (radon)
Compounds	
HF (hydrogen fluoride)	HCl (hydrogen chloride)
HBr (hydrogen bromide)	HI (hydrogen iodide)
CO (carbon monoxide)	CO₂ (carbon dioxide)
CH₄ (methane)	C₂H₂ (acetylene)
NH₃ (ammonia)	NO (nitric oxide)
NO₂ (nitrogen dioxide)	N₂O (nitrous oxide)
SO₂ (sulfur dioxide)	SF₆ (sulfur hexafluoride)
H₂S (hydrogen sulfide)	HCN (hydrogen cyanide)*

*The boiling point of HCN is 26°C, but it is close enough to qualify as a gas at ordinary atmospheric conditions.

Although "gas" and "vapor" are often used interchangeably, there is a difference. A gas is a substance that is normally in the gaseous state at ordinary temperatures and pressures; a vapor is the gaseous form of any substance that is a liquid or a solid at normal temperatures and pressures. Thus, at 25°C and 1 atm pressure, we speak of water vapor and oxygen gas.

The behavior of molecular compounds is more varied. Some—for example, CO, CO_2, HCl, NH_3, and CH_4 (methane)—are gases, but the majority of molecular compounds are liquids or solids at room temperature. However, on heating they are converted to gases much more easily than ionic compounds. In other words, molecular compounds usually boil at much lower temperatures than ionic compounds do. There is no simple rule to help us determine whether a certain molecular compound is a gas under normal atmospheric conditions. To make such a determination we need to understand the nature and magnitude of the attractive forces among the molecules, called *intermolecular forces* (discussed in Chapter 11). In general, the stronger these attractions, the less likely a compound can exist as a gas at ordinary temperatures.

Of the gases listed in Table 5.1, only O_2 is essential for our survival. Hydrogen sulfide (H_2S) and hydrogen cyanide (HCN) are deadly poisons. Several others, such as CO, NO_2, O_3, and SO_2, are somewhat less toxic. The gases He, Ne, and Ar are chemically inert; that is, they do not react with any other substance. Most gases are colorless. Exceptions are F_2, Cl_2, and NO_2. The dark-brown color of NO_2 is sometimes visible in polluted air. All gases have the following physical characteristics:

• Gases assume the volume and shape of their containers.

• Gases are the most compressible of the states of matter.

• Gases will mix evenly and completely when confined to the same container.

• Gases have much lower densities than liquids and solids.

5.2 Pressure of a Gas

NO₂ gas.

Gases exert pressure on any surface with which they come in contact, because gas molecules are constantly in motion. We humans have adapted so well physiologically to the pressure of the air around us that we are usually unaware of it, perhaps as fish are not conscious of the water's pressure on them.

It is easy to demonstrate atmospheric pressure. One everyday example is the ability to drink a liquid through a straw. Sucking air out of the straw reduces the pressure inside the straw. The greater atmospheric pressure on the liquid pushes it up into the straw to replace the air that has been sucked out.

SI Units of Pressure

Pressure is one of the most readily measurable properties of a gas. In order to under-stand how we measure the pressure of a gas, it is helpful to know how the units of measurement are derived. We begin with velocity and acceleration.

Velocity is defined as the change in distance with elapsed time; that is,

$$\text{velocity} = \frac{\text{distance moved}}{\text{elapsed time}}$$

The SI unit for velocity is m/s, although we also use cm/s.

Acceleration is the change in velocity with time, or

$$\text{acceleration} = \frac{\text{change in velocity}}{\text{elapsed time}}$$

Acceleration is measured in m/s^2 (or cm/s^2).

The second law of motion, formulated by Sir Isaac Newton[†] in the late seven-teenth century, defines another term, from which the units of pressure are derived, namely, *force*. According to this law,

$$\text{force} = \text{mass} \times \text{acceleration}$$

In this context, the *SI unit of force* is the **newton (N),** where

$$1 \text{ N} = 1 \text{ kg m/s}^2$$

1 N is roughly equivalent to the force exerted by Earth's gravity on an apple.

Finally, we define **pressure** as *force applied per unit area:*

$$\text{pressure} = \frac{\text{force}}{\text{area}}$$

The SI unit of pressure is the **pascal (Pa),**[‡] defined as *one newton per square meter:*

$$1 \text{ Pa} = 1 \text{ N/m}^2$$

Atmospheric Pressure

The atoms and molecules of the gases in the atmosphere, like those of all other matter, are subject to Earth's gravitational pull. As a consequence, the atmosphere is much denser near the surface of Earth than at high altitudes. (The air outside the pressurized cabin of an airplane at 9 km is too thin to breathe.) In fact, the density of air decreases very rapidly with increasing distance from Earth. Measurements show that about 50 percent of the atmosphere lies within 6.4 km of Earth's surface, 90 percent within 16 km, and 99 percent within 32 km. Not surprisingly, the denser the air is, the greater the pressure it exerts. The force experienced by any area exposed to Earth's atmosphere is equal to *the weight of the column of air above it.* **Atmospheric pressure** is *the pressure exerted by Earth's atmosphere* (Figure 5.2). The actual value of atmospheric pressure depends on location, temperature, and weather conditions.

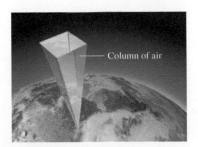

Figure 5.2 *A column of air extending from sea level to the upper atmosphere.*

[†]Sir Isaac Newton (1642–1726). English mathematician, physicist, and astronomer. Newton is regarded by many as one of the two greatest physicists the world has known (the other is Albert Einstein). There was hardly a branch of physics to which Newton did not make a significant contribution. His book *Principia*, published in 1687, marks a milestone in the history of science.

[‡]Blaise Pascal (1623–1662). French mathematician and physicist. Pascal's work ranged widely in mathemat-ics and physics, but his specialty was in the area of hydrodynamics (the study of the motion of fluids). He also invented a calculating machine.

176   **Chapter 5 ▪ Gases**

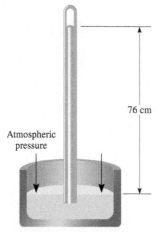

76 cm

Atmospheric
pressure

Figure 5.3 *A barometer for measuring atmospheric pressure. Above the mercury in the tube is a vacuum. The column of mercury is supported by the atmospheric pressure.*

Does atmospheric pressure act only downward, as you might infer from its definition? Imagine what would happen, then, if you were to hold a piece of paper tight (with both hands) above your head. You might expect the paper to bend due to the pressure of air acting on it, but this does not happen. The reason is that air, like water, is a fluid. The pressure exerted on an object in a fluid comes from all directions—downward and upward, as well as from the left and from the right. At the molecular level, air pressure results from collisions between the air molecules and any surface with which they come in contact. The magnitude of pressure depends on how often and how strongly the molecules impact the surface. It turns out that there are just as many molecules hitting the paper from the top as there are from underneath, so the paper stays flat.

How is atmospheric pressure measured? The **barometer** is probably the most familiar *instrument for measuring atmospheric pressure*. A simple barometer consists of a long glass tube, closed at one end and filled with mercury. If the tube is carefully inverted in a dish of mercury so that no air enters the tube, some mercury will flow out of the tube into the dish, creating a vacuum at the top (Figure 5.3). The weight of the mercury remaining in the tube is supported by atmospheric pressure acting on the surface of the mercury in the dish. **Standard atmospheric pressure (1 atm)** is equal to *the pressure that supports a column of mercury exactly 760 mm (or 76 cm) high at 0°C at sea level*. In other words, the standard atmosphere equals a pressure of 760 mmHg, where mmHg represents the pressure exerted by a column of mercury 1 mm high. The mmHg unit is also called the *torr*, after the Italian scientist Evangelista Torricelli,[†] who invented the barometer. Thus,

$$1 \text{ torr} = 1 \text{ mmHg}$$

and

$$1 \text{ atm} = 760 \text{ mmHg} \quad (\text{exactly})$$

The relation between atmospheres and pascals (see Appendix 2) is

$$1 \text{ atm} = 101{,}325 \text{ Pa}$$
$$= 1.01325 \times 10^5 \text{ Pa}$$

and because 1000 Pa = 1 kPa (kilopascal)

$$1 \text{ atm} = 1.01325 \times 10^2 \text{ kPa}$$

Examples 5.1 and 5.2 show the conversion from mmHg to atm and kPa.

Example 5.1

The pressure outside a jet plane flying at high altitude falls considerably below standard atmospheric pressure. Therefore, the air inside the cabin must be pressurized to protect the passengers. What is the pressure in atmospheres in the cabin if the barometer reading is 688 mmHg?

Strategy Because 1 atm = 760 mmHg, the following conversion factor is needed to obtain the pressure in atmospheres:

$$\frac{1 \text{ atm}}{760 \text{ mmHg}}$$

(Continued)

[†]Evangelista Torricelli (1608–1674). Italian mathematician. Torricelli was supposedly the first person to recognize the existence of atmospheric pressure.

Solution The pressure in the cabin is given by

$$\text{pressure} = 688 \; \cancel{\text{mmHg}} \times \frac{1 \; \text{atm}}{760 \; \cancel{\text{mmHg}}}$$

$$= 0.905 \; \text{atm}$$

Similar problem: 5.13.

Practice Exercise Convert 749 mmHg to atmospheres.

Example 5.2

Hurricane Sandy ("Superstorm Sandy") was one the most destructive hurricanes in recent years, affecting the Caribbean, Cuba, the Bahamas, and 24 states along U.S. east coast. The lowest pressure recorded for Hurricane Sandy was 705 mmHg. What was the pressure in kPa?

Strategy Here we are asked to convert mmHg to kPa. Because

$$1 \; \text{atm} = 1.01325 \times 10^5 \; \text{Pa} = 760 \; \text{mmHg}$$

the conversion factor we need is

$$\frac{1.01325 \times 10^5 \; \text{Pa}}{760 \; \text{mmHg}}$$

Solution The pressure in kPa is

$$\text{pressure} = 705 \; \cancel{\text{mmHg}} \times \frac{1.01325 \times 10^5 \; \text{Pa}}{760 \; \cancel{\text{mmHg}}}$$

$$= 9.40 \times 10^4 \; \text{Pa}$$

$$= 94.0 \; \text{kPa}$$

Similar problem: 5.14.

Practice Exercise Convert 295 mmHg to kilopascals.

Review of Concepts

Rank the following pressures from lowest to highest: (a) 736 mmHg, (b) 0.928 atm, (c) 728 torr, (d) 1.12×10^5 Pa.

A **manometer** is *a device used to measure the pressure of gases other than the atmosphere.* The principle of operation of a manometer is similar to that of a barometer. There are two types of manometers, shown in Figure 5.4. The *closed-tube manometer* is normally used to measure pressures below atmospheric pressure [Figure 5.4(a)], whereas the *open-tube manometer* is better suited for measuring pressures equal to or greater than atmospheric pressure [Figure 5.4(b)].

Nearly all barometers and many manometers use mercury as the working fluid, despite the fact that it is a toxic substance with a harmful vapor. The reason is that mercury has a very high density (13.6 g/mL) compared with most other liquids. Because the height of the liquid in a column is inversely proportional to the liquid's density, this property enables the construction of manageably small barometers and manometers.

Review of Concepts

Would it be easier to drink water with a straw on top or at the foot of Mt. Everest?

Figure 5.4 *Two types of manometers used to measure gas pressures. (a) Gas pressure may be less or greater than atmospheric pressure. (b) Gas pressure is greater than atmospheric pressure.*

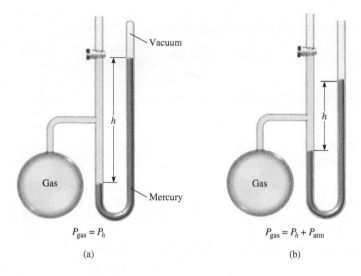

$$P_{gas} = P_h$$

(a)

$$P_{gas} = P_h + P_{atm}$$

(b)

5.3 The Gas Laws

The gas laws we will study in this chapter are the product of countless experiments on the physical properties of gases that were carried out over several centuries. Each of these generalizations regarding the macroscopic behavior of gaseous substances represents a milestone in the history of science. Together they have played a major role in the development of many ideas in chemistry.

The Pressure-Volume Relationship: Boyle's Law

Animation
The Gas Laws

In the seventeenth century, Robert Boyle[†] studied the behavior of gases systematically and quantitatively. In one series of studies, Boyle investigated the pressure-volume relationship of a gas sample. Typical data collected by Boyle are shown in Table 5.2. Note that as the pressure (P) is increased at constant temperature, the volume (V) occupied by a given amount of gas decreases. Compare the first data point with a pressure of 724 mmHg and a volume of 1.50 (in arbitrary unit) to the last data point with a pressure of 2250 mmHg and a volume of 0.58. Clearly there is an inverse relationship between pressure and volume of a gas at constant temperature. As the pressure is increased, the volume occupied by the gas decreases. Conversely, if the applied pressure is decreased, the volume the gas occupies increases. This relationship is now known as ***Boyle's law,*** which states that *the pressure of a fixed amount of gas at a constant temperature is inversely proportional to the volume of the gas.*

[†]Robert Boyle (1627–1691). British chemist and natural philosopher. Although Boyle is commonly associated with the gas law that bears his name, he made many other significant contributions in chemistry and physics. Despite the fact that Boyle was often at odds with scientists of his generation, his book *The Skeptical Chymist* (1661) influenced generations of chemists.

Table 5.2	Typical Pressure-Volume Relationship Obtained by Boyle						
P (mmHg)	724	869	951	998	1230	1893	2250
V (arbitrary units)	1.50	1.33	1.22	1.18	0.94	0.61	0.58
PV	1.09×10^3	1.16×10^3	1.16×10^3	1.18×10^3	1.2×10^3	1.2×10^3	1.3×10^3

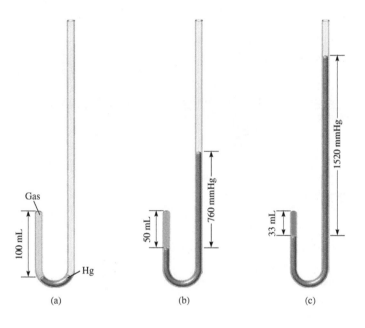

Figure 5.5 *Apparatus for studying the relationship between pressure and volume of a gas. (a) The levels of mercury are equal and the pressure of the gas is equal to the atmospheric pressure (760 mmHg). The gas volume is 100 mL. (b) Doubling the pressure by adding more mercury reduces the gas volume to 50 mL. (c) Tripling the pressure decreases the gas volume to one-third of the original value. The temperature and amount of gas are kept constant.*

The apparatus used by Boyle in this experiment was very simple (Figure 5.5). In Figure 5.5(a), the pressure exerted on the gas is equal to atmospheric pressure and the volume of the gas is 100 mL. (Note that the tube is open at the top and is therefore exposed to atmospheric pressure.) In Figure 5.5(b), more mercury has been added to double the pressure on the gas, and the gas volume decreases to 50 mL. Tripling the pressure on the gas decreases its volume to a third of the original value [Figure 5.5(c)].

The pressure applied to a gas is equal to the gas pressure.

We can write a mathematical expression showing the inverse relationship between pressure and volume:

$$P \propto \frac{1}{V}$$

where the symbol $\propto$ means *proportional to*. We can change $\propto$ to an equals sign and write

$$P = k_1 \times \frac{1}{V} \tag{5.1a}$$

where k_1 is a constant called the *proportionality constant*. Equation (5.1a) is the mathematical expression of Boyle's law. We can rearrange Equation (5.1a) and obtain

$$PV = k_1 \tag{5.1b}$$

This form of Boyle's law says that the product of the pressure and volume of a gas at constant temperature and amount of gas is a constant. The top diagram in Figure 5.6 is a schematic representation of Boyle's law. The quantity n is the number of moles of the gas and R is a constant to be defined in Section 5.4. We will see in Section 5.4 that the proportionality constant k_1 in Equations (5.1) is equal to nRT.

The concept of one quantity being proportional to another and the use of a proportionality constant can be clarified through the following analogy. The daily income of a movie theater depends on both the price of the tickets (in dollars per

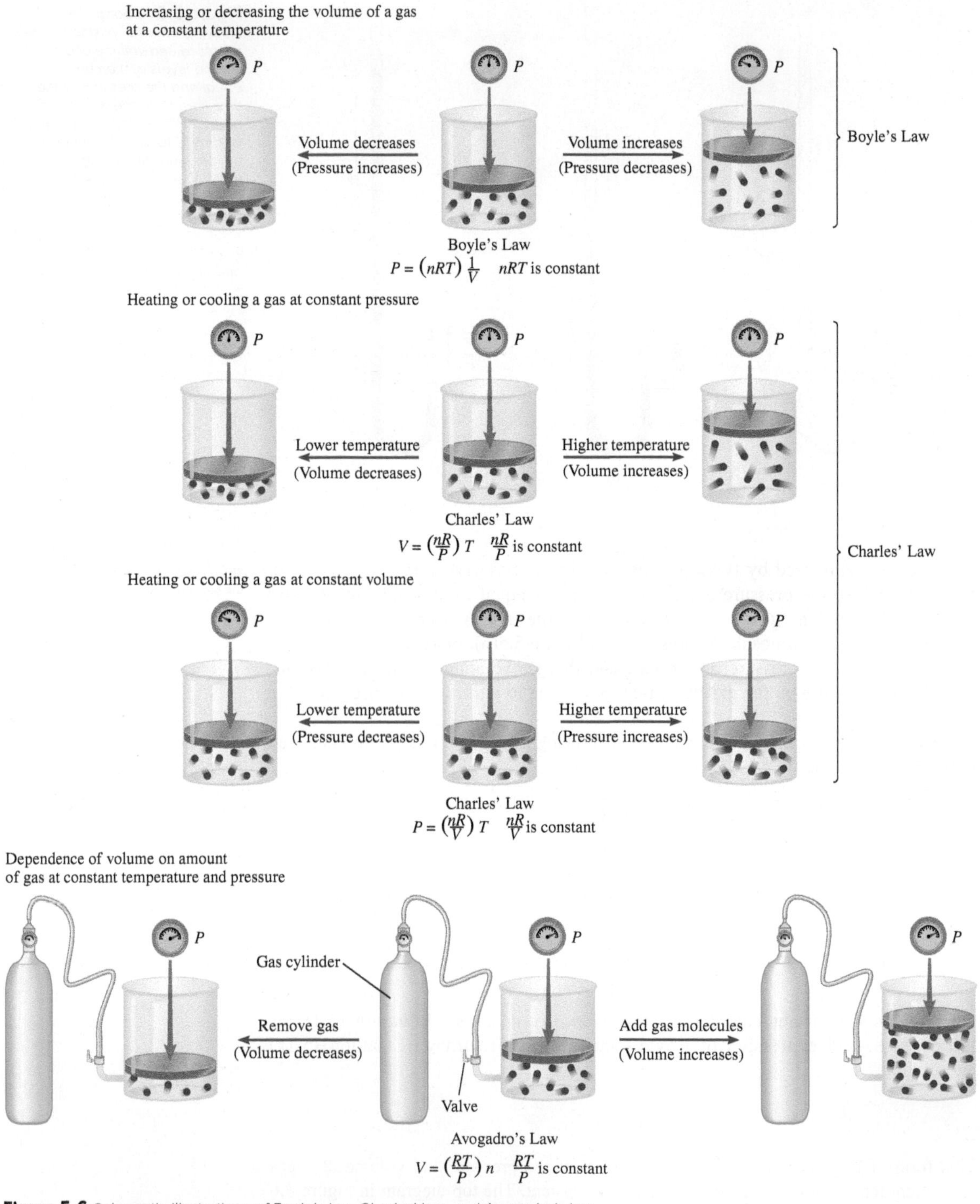
Increasing or decreasing the volume of a gas
at a constant temperature
P
Volume decreases
(Pressure increases)
Volume increases
(Pressure decreases)
Boyle's Law
Boyle's Law
$P = (nRT)\frac{1}{V}$ nRT is constant
Heating or cooling a gas at constant pressure
Lower temperature
(Volume decreases)
Higher temperature
(Volume increases)
Charles' Law
$V = (\frac{nR}{P})T$ $\frac{nR}{P}$ is constant
Charles' Law
Heating or cooling a gas at constant volume
Lower temperature
(Pressure decreases)
Higher temperature
(Pressure increases)
Charles' Law
$P = (\frac{nR}{V})T$ $\frac{nR}{V}$ is constant
Dependence of volume on amount
of gas at constant temperature and pressure
Gas cylinder
Remove gas
(Volume decreases)
Add gas molecules
(Volume increases)
Valve
Avogadro's Law
$V = (\frac{RT}{P})n$ $\frac{RT}{P}$ is constant

Figure 5.6 *Schematic illustrations of Boyle's law, Charles' law, and Avogadro's law.*

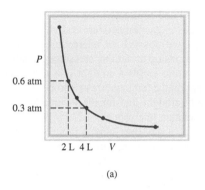

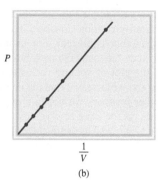

(a)   (b)

Figure 5.7 *Graphs showing variation of the volume of a gas with the pressure exerted on the gas, at constant temperature. (a) P versus V. Note that the volume of the gas doubles as the pressure is halved. (b) P versus 1/V. The slope of the line is equal to k_1.*

ticket) and the number of tickets sold. Assuming that the theater charges one price for all tickets, we write

$$income = (dollar/ticket) \times number\ of\ tickets\ sold$$

Because the number of tickets sold varies from day to day, the income on a given day is said to be proportional to the number of tickets sold:

$$income \propto number\ of\ tickets\ sold$$
$$= C \times number\ of\ tickets\ sold$$

where C, the proportionality constant, is the price per ticket.

Figure 5.7 shows two conventional ways of expressing Boyle's findings graphically. Figure 5.7(a) is a graph of the equation $PV = k_1$; Figure 5.7(b) is a graph of the equivalent equation $P = k_1 \times 1/V$. Note that the latter is a linear equation of the form $y = mx + b$, where $b = 0$ and $m = k_1$.

Although the individual values of pressure and volume can vary greatly for a given sample of gas, as long as the temperature is held constant and the amount of the gas does not change, P times V is always equal to the same constant. Therefore, for a given sample of gas under two different sets of conditions at constant temperature, we have

$$P_1V_1 = k_1 = P_2V_2$$

or $$P_1V_1 = P_2V_2 \qquad (5.2)$$

where V_1 and V_2 are the volumes at pressures P_1 and P_2, respectively.

The Temperature-Volume Relationship: Charles' and Gay-Lussac's Law

Boyle's law depends on the temperature of the system remaining constant. But suppose the temperature changes: How does a change in temperature affect the volume and pressure of a gas? Let us first look at the effect of temperature on the volume of a gas. The earliest investigators of this relationship were French scientists, Jacques Charles[†] and Joseph Gay-Lussac.[‡] Their studies showed that, at constant pressure, the

---

[†]Jacques Alexandre Cesar Charles (1746–1823). French physicist. He was a gifted lecturer, an inventor of scientific apparatus, and the first person to use hydrogen to inflate balloons.

[‡]Joseph Louis Gay-Lussac (1778–1850). French chemist and physicist. Like Charles, Gay-Lussac was a balloon enthusiast. Once he ascended to an altitude of 20,000 ft to collect air samples for analysis.

182   **Chapter 5** ▪ Gases

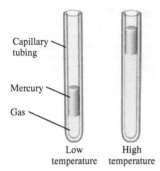

Capillary
tubing

Mercury

Gas

Low   High
temperature temperature

Figure 5.8 *Variation of the volume of a gas sample with temperature, at constant pressure. The pressure exerted on the gas is the sum of the atmospheric pressure and the pressure due to the weight of the mercury.*

Under special experimental conditions, scientists have succeeded in approaching absolute zero to within a small fraction of a kelvin.

volume of a gas sample expands when heated and contracts when cooled (Figure 5.8). The quantitative relations involved in changes in gas temperature and volume turn out to be remarkably consistent. For example, we observe an interesting phenomenon when we study the temperature-volume relationship at various pressures. At any given pressure, the plot of volume versus temperature yields a straight line. By extending the line to zero volume, we find the intercept on the temperature axis to be −273.15°C. At any other pressure, we obtain a different straight line for the volume-temperature plot, but we get the *same* zero-volume temperature intercept at −273.15°C (Figure 5.9). (In practice, we can measure the volume of a gas over only a limited temperature range, because all gases condense at low temperatures to form liquids.)

In 1848 Lord Kelvin[†] realized the significance of this phenomenon. He identified −273.15°C as *absolute zero, theoretically the lowest attainable temperature.* Then he set up an *absolute temperature scale,* now called the *Kelvin temperature scale,* with *absolute zero as the starting point* (see Section 1.7). On the Kelvin scale, one kelvin (K) is equal *in magnitude* to one degree Celsius. The only difference between the absolute temperature scale and the Celsius scale is that the zero position is shifted. Important points on the two scales match up as follows:

	Kelvin Scale	Celsius Scale
Absolute zero	0 K	−273.15°C
Freezing point of water	273.15 K	0°C
Boiling point of water	373.15 K	100°C

The conversion between °C and K is given on p. 16. In most calculations we will use 273 instead of 273.15 as the term relating K and °C. By convention, we use T to denote absolute (kelvin) temperature and t to indicate temperature on the Celsius scale.

The dependence of the volume of a gas on temperature is given by

$$V \propto T$$
$$V = k_2 T$$

Remember that temperature must be in kelvins in gas law calculations.

or

$$\frac{V}{T} = k_2 \qquad (5.3)$$

where k_2 is the proportionality constant. Equation (5.3) is known as *Charles' and Gay-Lussac's law,* or simply *Charles' law,* which states that *the volume of a fixed amount of gas maintained at constant pressure is directly proportional to the absolute*

[†]William Thomson, Lord Kelvin (1824–1907). Scottish mathematician and physicist. Kelvin did important work in many branches of physics.

Figure 5.9 *Variation of the volume of a gas sample with temperature, at constant pressure. Each line represents the variation at a certain pressure. The pressures increase from P_1 to P_4. All gases ultimately condense (become liquids) if they are cooled to sufficiently low temperatures; the solid portions of the lines represent the temperature region above the condensation point. When these lines are extrapolated, or extended (the dashed portions), they all intersect at the point representing zero volume and a temperature of −273.15°C.*

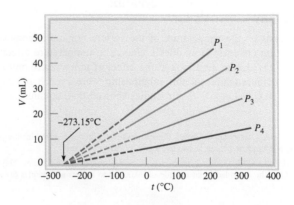

temperature of the gas. Charles' law is also illustrated in Figure 5.6. We see that the proportionality constant k_2 in Equation (5.3) is equal to nR/P.

Just as we did for pressure-volume relationships at constant temperature, we can compare two sets of volume-temperature conditions for a given sample of gas at constant pressure. From Equation (5.3) we can write

$$\frac{V_1}{T_1} = k_2 = \frac{V_2}{T_2}$$

or

$$\frac{V_1}{T_1} = \frac{V_2}{T_2} \tag{5.4}$$

where V_1 and V_2 are the volumes of the gas at temperatures T_1 and T_2 (both in kelvins), respectively.

Another form of Charles' law shows that at constant amount of gas and volume, the pressure of a gas is proportional to temperature

$$P \propto T$$
$$P = k_3 T$$

or

$$\frac{P}{T} = k_3 \tag{5.5}$$

From Figure 5.6 we see that $k_3 = nR/V$. Starting with Equation (5.5), we have

$$\frac{P_1}{T_1} = k_3 = \frac{P_2}{T_2}$$

or

$$\frac{P_1}{T_1} = \frac{P_2}{T_2} \tag{5.6}$$

where P_1 and P_2 are the pressures of the gas at temperatures T_1 and T_2, respectively.

Review of Concepts

Compare the changes in volume when the temperature of a gas is increased at constant pressure from (a) 200 K to 400 K and (b) 200°C to 400°C.

The Volume-Amount Relationship: Avogadro's Law

The work of the Italian scientist Amedeo Avogadro complemented the studies of Boyle, Charles, and Gay-Lussac. In 1811 he published a hypothesis stating that at the same temperature and pressure, equal volumes of different gases contain the same number of molecules (or atoms if the gas is monatomic). It follows that the volume of any given gas must be proportional to the number of moles of molecules present; that is,

Avogadro's name first appeared in Section 3.2.

$$V \propto n$$

$$V = k_4 n \tag{5.7}$$

where n represents the number of moles and k_4 is the proportionality constant. Equation (5.7) is the mathematical expression of **Avogadro's law,** which states that *at constant*

184   **Chapter 5** ▪ Gases

Figure 5.10 *Volume relationship of gases in a chemical reaction. The ratio of the volumes of molecular hydrogen to molecular nitrogen is 3:1, and that of ammonia (the product) to molecular hydrogen and molecular nitrogen combined (the reactants) is 2:4, or 1:2.*

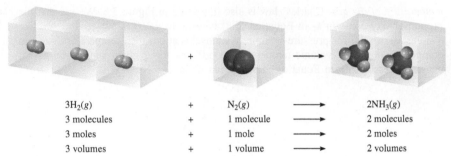

$3H_2(g)$	+	$N_2(g)$	$\longrightarrow$	$2NH_3(g)$
3 molecules	+	1 molecule	$\longrightarrow$	2 molecules
3 moles	+	1 mole	$\longrightarrow$	2 moles
3 volumes	+	1 volume	$\longrightarrow$	2 volumes

pressure and temperature, the volume of a gas is directly proportional to the number of moles of the gas present. From Figure 5.6 we see that $k_4 = RT/P$.

According to Avogadro's law we see that when two gases react with each other, their reacting volumes have a simple ratio to each other. If the product is a gas, its volume is related to the volume of the reactants by a simple ratio (a fact demonstrated earlier by Gay-Lussac). For example, consider the synthesis of ammonia from molecular hydrogen and molecular nitrogen:

$$3H_2(g) + N_2(g) \longrightarrow 2NH_3(g)$$
3 mol   1 mol   2 mol

Because, at the same temperature and pressure, the volumes of gases are directly proportional to the number of moles of the gases present, we can now write

$$3H_2(g) + N_2(g) \longrightarrow 2NH_3(g)$$
3 volumes 1 volume   2 volumes

The volume ratio of molecular hydrogen to molecular nitrogen is 3:1, and that of ammonia (the product) to the sum of the volumes of molecular hydrogen and molecular nitrogen (the reactants) is 2:4 or 1:2 (Figure 5.10).

Worked examples illustrating the gas laws are presented in Section 5.4.

5.4 The Ideal Gas Equation

Let us summarize the gas laws we have discussed so far:

Boyle's law: $V \propto \dfrac{1}{P}$ (at constant n and T)

Charles' law: $V \propto T$ (at constant n and P)

Avogadro's law: $V \propto n$ (at constant P and T)

We can combine all three expressions to form a single master equation for the behavior of gases:

$$V \propto \frac{nT}{P}$$

$$V = R\frac{nT}{P}$$

or

$$PV = nRT \tag{5.8}$$

Keep in mind that the ideal gas equation, unlike the gas laws discussed in Section 5.3, applies to systems that do not undergo changes in pressure, volume, temperature, and amount of a gas.

where **R,** *the proportionality constant,* is called the **gas constant.** Equation (5.8), which is called the **ideal gas equation,** *describes the relationship among the four*

Figure 5.11 *A comparison of the molar volume at STP (which is approximately 22.4 L) with a basketball.*

variables *P, V, T, and n.* An **ideal gas** is *a hypothetical gas whose pressure-volume-temperature behavior can be completely accounted for by the ideal gas equation.* The molecules of an ideal gas do not attract or repel one another, and their volume is negligible compared with the volume of the container. Although there is no such thing in nature as an ideal gas, the ideal gas approximation works rather well for most reasonable temperature and pressure ranges. Thus, we can safely use the ideal gas equation to solve many gas problems.

Before we can apply the ideal gas equation to a real system, we must evaluate the gas constant *R.* At 0°C (273.15 K) and 1 atm pressure, many real gases behave like an ideal gas. Experiments show that under these conditions, 1 mole of an ideal gas occupies 22.414 L, which is somewhat greater than the volume of a basketball, as shown in Figure 5.11. *The conditions 0°C and 1 atm are called* **standard temperature and pressure,** often abbreviated **STP.** From Equation (5.8) we can write

$$
\begin{aligned}
R &= \frac{PV}{nT} \\
&= \frac{(1\ \text{atm})(22.414\ \text{L})}{(1\ \text{mol})(273.15\ \text{K})} \\
&= 0.082057\ \frac{\text{L} \cdot \text{atm}}{\text{K} \cdot \text{mol}} \\
&= 0.082057\ \text{L} \cdot \text{atm}/\text{K} \cdot \text{mol}
\end{aligned}
$$

The gas constant can be expressed in different units (see Appendix 2).

The dots between L and atm and between K and mol remind us that both L and atm are in the numerator and both K and mol are in the denominator. For most calculations, we will round off the value of *R* to three significant figures (0.0821 L · atm/K · mol) and use 22.41 L for the molar volume of a gas at STP.

Example 5.3 shows that if we know the quantity, volume, and temperature of a gas, we can calculate its pressure using the ideal gas equation. Unless otherwise stated, we assume that the temperatures given in °C in calculations are exact so that they do not affect the number of significant figures.

Example 5.3

Sulfur hexafluoride (SF_6) is a colorless and odorless gas. Due to its lack of chemical reactivity, it is used as an insulator in electronic equipment. Calculate the pressure (in atm) exerted by 1.82 moles of the gas in a steel vessel of volume 5.43 L at 69.5°C.

(Continued)

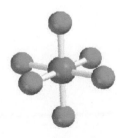

SF_6

186   **Chapter 5** ▪ Gases

Strategy The problem gives the amount of the gas and its volume and temperature. Is the gas undergoing a change in any of its properties? What equation should we use to solve for the pressure? What temperature unit should we use?

Solution Because no changes in gas properties occur, we can use the ideal gas equation to calculate the pressure. Rearranging Equation (5.8), we write

$$P = \frac{nRT}{V}$$

$$= \frac{(1.82 \text{ mol})(0.0821 \text{ L} \cdot \text{atm/K} \cdot \text{mol})(69.5 + 273) \text{ K}}{5.43 \text{ L}}$$

$$= 9.42 \text{ atm}$$

Similar problem: 5.32.

Practice Exercise Calculate the volume (in liters) occupied by 2.12 moles of nitric oxide (NO) at 6.54 atm and 76°C.

By using the fact that the molar volume of a gas occupies 22.41 L at STP, we can calculate the volume of a gas at STP without using the ideal gas equation.

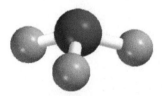

NH_3

Industrial ammonia refrigeration system.

Similar problem: 5.40.

Example 5.4

Ammonia gas is used as a refrigerant in food processing and storage industries. Calculate the volume (in liters) occupied by 7.40 g of NH_3 at STP.

Strategy What is the volume of one mole of an ideal gas at STP? How many moles are there in 7.40 g of NH_3?

Solution Recognizing that 1 mole of an ideal gas occupies 22.41 L at STP and using the molar mass of NH_3 (17.03 g), we write the sequence of conversions as

$$\text{grams of } NH_3 \longrightarrow \text{moles of } NH_3 \longrightarrow \text{liters of } NH_3 \text{ at STP}$$

so the volume of NH_3 is given by

$$V = 7.40 \text{ g } NH_3 \times \frac{1 \text{ mol } NH_3}{17.03 \text{ g } NH_3} \times \frac{22.41 \text{ L}}{1 \text{ mol } NH_3}$$

$$= 9.74 \text{ L}$$

It is often true in chemistry, particularly in gas-law calculations, that a problem can be solved in more than one way. Here the problem can also be solved by first converting 7.40 g of NH_3 to number of moles of NH_3, and then applying the ideal gas equation ($V = nRT/P$). Try it.

Check Because 7.40 g of NH_3 is smaller than its molar mass, its volume at STP should be smaller than 22.41 L. Therefore, the answer is reasonable.

Practice Exercise What is the volume (in liters) occupied by 49.8 g of HCl at STP?

Review of Concepts

Assuming ideal behavior, which of the following gases will have the greatest volume at STP? (a) 0.82 mole of He. (b) 24 g of N_2. (c) 5.0×10^{23} molecules of Cl_2. Which gas will have the greatest density?

The ideal gas equation is useful for problems that do not involve changes in P, V, T, and n for a gas sample. Thus, if we know any three of the variables we can calculate the fourth one using the equation. At times, however, we need to deal with changes in pressure, volume, and temperature, or even in the amount of gas. When conditions change, we must employ a modified form of the ideal gas equation that takes into account the initial and final conditions. We derive the modified equation as follows. From Equation (5.8),

$$R = \frac{P_1 V_1}{n_1 T_1} \text{ (before change)} \quad \text{and} \quad R = \frac{P_2 V_2}{n_2 T_2} \text{ (after change)}$$

The subscripts 1 and 2 denote the initial and final states of the gas, respectively.

Therefore,

$$\frac{P_1 V_1}{n_1 T_1} = \frac{P_2 V_2}{n_2 T_2} \tag{5.9}$$

It is interesting to note that all the gas laws discussed in Section 5.3 can be derived from Equation (5.9). If $n_1 = n_2$, as is usually the case because the amount of gas normally does not change, the equation then becomes

$$\frac{P_1 V_1}{T_1} = \frac{P_2 V_2}{T_2} \tag{5.10}$$

Applications of Equation (5.9) are shown in Examples 5.5, 5.6, and 5.7.

Example 5.5

An inflated helium balloon with a volume of 0.55 L at sea level (1.0 atm) is allowed to rise to a height of 6.5 km, where the pressure is about 0.40 atm. Assuming that the temperature remains constant, what is the final volume of the balloon?

Strategy The amount of gas inside the balloon and its temperature remain constant, but both the pressure and the volume change. What gas law do you need?

Solution We start with Equation (5.9)

$$\frac{P_1 V_1}{n_1 T_1} = \frac{P_2 V_2}{n_2 T_2}$$

Because $n_1 = n_2$ and $T_1 = T_2$,

$$P_1 V_1 = P_2 V_2$$

which is Boyle's law [see Equation (5.2)]. The given information is tabulated:

Initial Conditions	Final Conditions
P_1 = 1.0 atm	P_2 = 0.40 atm
V_1 = 0.55 L	V_2 = ?

Therefore,

$$V_2 = V_1 \times \frac{P_1}{P_2}$$

$$= 0.55 \text{ L} \times \frac{1.0 \text{ atm}}{0.40 \text{ atm}}$$

$$= 1.4 \text{ L}$$

(Continued)

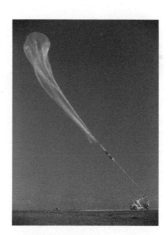

A scientific research helium balloon.

188   **Chapter 5** ▪ Gases

Check When pressure applied on the balloon is reduced (at constant temperature), the helium gas expands and the balloon's volume increases. The final volume is greater than the initial volume, so the answer is reasonable.

Practice Exercise A sample of chlorine gas occupies a volume of 946 mL at a pressure of 726 mmHg. Calculate the pressure of the gas (in mmHg) if the volume is reduced at constant temperature to 154 mL.

Electric lightbulbs are usually filled with argon.

Example 5.6

Argon is an inert gas used in lightbulbs to retard the vaporization of the tungsten filament. A certain lightbulb containing argon at 1.20 atm and 18°C is heated to 85°C at constant volume. Calculate its final pressure (in atm).

Strategy The temperature and pressure of argon change but the amount and volume of gas remain the same. What equation would you use to solve for the final pressure? What temperature unit should you use?

Solution Because $n_1 = n_2$ and $V_1 = V_2$, Equation (5.9) becomes

$$\frac{P_1}{T_1} = \frac{P_2}{T_2}$$

which is Charles' law [see Equation (5.6)]. Next we write

Initial Conditions	Final Conditions
$P_1 = 1.20$ atm	$P_2 = ?$
$T_1 = (18 + 273)$ K $= 291$ K	$T_2 = (85 + 273)$ K $= 358$ K

The final pressure is given by

$$P_2 = P_1 \times \frac{T_2}{T_1}$$
$$= 1.20 \text{ atm} \times \frac{358 \text{ K}}{291 \text{ K}}$$
$$= 1.48 \text{ atm}$$

Check At constant volume, the pressure of a given amount of gas is directly proportional to its absolute temperature. Therefore the increase in pressure is reasonable.

Practice Exercise A sample of oxygen gas initially at 0.97 atm is cooled from 21°C to −68°C at constant volume. What is its final pressure (in atm)?

Example 5.7

A small bubble rises from the bottom of a lake, where the temperature and pressure are 8°C and 6.4 atm, to the water's surface, where the temperature is 25°C and the pressure is 1.0 atm. Calculate the final volume (in mL) of the bubble if its initial volume was 2.1 mL.

(Continued)

Strategy In solving this kind of problem, where a lot of information is given, it is sometimes helpful to make a sketch of the situation, as shown here:

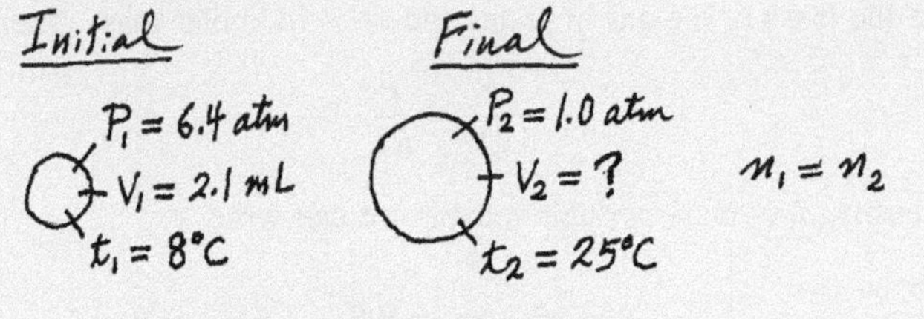

What temperature unit should be used in the calculation?

Solution According to Equation (5.9)

$$\frac{P_1 V_1}{n_1 T_1} = \frac{P_2 V_2}{n_2 T_2}$$

We assume that the amount of air in the bubble remains constant, that is, $n_1 = n_2$ so that

$$\frac{P_1 V_1}{T_1} = \frac{P_2 V_2}{T_2}$$

which is Equation (5.10). The given information is summarized:

Initial Conditions	Final Conditions
$P_1 = 6.4$ atm	$P_2 = 1.0$ atm
$V_1 = 2.1$ mL	$V_2 = ?$
$T_1 = (8 + 273)$ K $= 281$ K	$T_2 = (25 + 273)$ K $= 298$ K

Rearranging Equation (5.10) gives

$$V_2 = V_1 \times \frac{P_1}{P_2} \times \frac{T_2}{T_1}$$

$$= 2.1 \text{ mL} \times \frac{6.4 \text{ atm}}{1.0 \text{ atm}} \times \frac{298 \text{ K}}{281 \text{ K}}$$

$$= 14 \text{ mL}$$

We can use any appropriate units for volume (or pressure) as long as we use the same units on both sides of the equation.

Check We see that the final volume involves multiplying the initial volume by a ratio of pressures (P_1/P_2) and a ratio of temperatures (T_2/T_1). Recall that volume is inversely proportional to pressure, and volume is directly proportional to temperature. Because the pressure decreases and temperature increases as the bubble rises, we expect the bubble's volume to increase. In fact, here the change in pressure plays a greater role in the volume change.

Similar problem: 5.35.

Practice Exercise A gas initially at 4.0 L, 1.2 atm, and 66°C undergoes a change so that its final volume and temperature are 1.7 L and 42°C. What is its final pressure? Assume the number of moles remains unchanged.

Density Calculations

If we rearrange the ideal gas equation, we can calculate the density of a gas:

$$\frac{n}{V} = \frac{P}{RT}$$

The number of moles of the gas, n, is given by

$$n = \frac{m}{\mathcal{M}}$$

where m is the mass of the gas in grams and $\mathcal{M}$ is its molar mass. Therefore

$$\frac{m}{\mathcal{M}V} = \frac{P}{RT}$$

Because density, d, is mass per unit volume, we can write

$$d = \frac{m}{V} = \frac{P\mathcal{M}}{RT} \tag{5.11}$$

Unlike molecules in condensed matter (that is, in liquids and solids), gaseous molecules are separated by distances that are large compared with their size. Consequently, the density of gases is very low under atmospheric conditions. For this reason, gas densities are usually expressed in grams per liter (g/L) rather than grams per milliliter (g/mL), as Example 5.8 shows.

CO_2

Example 5.8

Calculate the density of carbon dioxide (CO_2) in grams per liter (g/L) at 0.990 atm and 55°C.

Strategy We need Equation (5.11) to calculate gas density. Is sufficient information provided in the problem? What temperature unit should be used?

Solution To use Equation (5.11), we convert temperature to kelvins ($T = 273 + 55 = 328$ K) and use 44.01 g for the molar mass of CO_2:

$$d = \frac{P\mathcal{M}}{RT}$$

$$= \frac{(0.990 \text{ atm})(44.01 \text{ g/mol})}{(0.0821 \text{ L} \cdot \text{atm/K} \cdot \text{mol})(328 \text{ K})} = 1.62 \text{ g/L}$$

Alternatively, we can solve for the density by writing

$$\text{density} = \frac{\text{mass}}{\text{volume}}$$

Being an intensive property, density is independent of the amount of substance. Therefore, we can use any convenient amount to help us solve the problem.

Assuming that we have 1 mole of CO_2, the mass is 44.01 g. The volume of the gas can be obtained from the ideal gas equation

$$V = \frac{nRT}{P}$$

$$= \frac{(1 \text{ mol})(0.0821 \text{ L} \cdot \text{atm/K} \cdot \text{mol})(328 \text{ K})}{0.990 \text{ atm}}$$

$$= 27.2 \text{ L}$$

Therefore, the density of CO_2 is given by

$$d = \frac{44.01 \text{ g}}{27.2 \text{ L}} = 1.62 \text{ g/L}$$

(Continued)

Comment In units of grams per milliliter, the gas density is 1.62×10^{-3} g/mL, which is a very small number. In comparison, the density of water is 1.0 g/mL and that of gold is 19.3 g/cm^3.

Practice Exercise What is the density (in g/L) of uranium hexafluoride (UF$_6$) at 779 mmHg and 62°C?

Similar problem: 5.48.

The Molar Mass of a Gaseous Substance

From what we have seen so far, you may have the impression that the molar mass of a substance is found by examining its formula and summing the molar masses of its component atoms. However, this procedure works only if the actual formula of the substance is known. In practice, chemists often deal with substances of unknown or only partially defined composition. If the unknown substance is gaseous, its molar mass can nevertheless be found thanks to the ideal gas equation. All that is needed is an experimentally determined density value (or mass and volume data) for the gas at a known temperature and pressure. By rearranging Equation (5.11) we get

$$\mathcal{M} = \frac{dRT}{P} \qquad (5.12)$$

Figure 5.12 *An apparatus for measuring the density of a gas. A bulb of known volume is filled with the gas under study at a certain temperature and pressure. First the bulb is weighed, and then it is emptied (evacuated) and weighed again. The difference in masses gives the mass of the gas. Knowing the volume of the bulb, we can calculate the density of the gas. Under atmospheric conditions, 100 mL of air weigh about 0.12 g, an easily measured quantity.*

In a typical experiment, a bulb of known volume is filled with the gaseous substance under study. The temperature and pressure of the gas sample are recorded, and the total mass of the bulb plus gas sample is determined (Figure 5.12). The bulb is then evacuated (emptied) and weighed again. The difference in mass is the mass of the gas. The density of the gas is equal to its mass divided by the volume of the bulb. Once we know the density of a gas, we can calculate the molar mass of the substance using Equation (5.12).

The mass spectrometer has become the dominant instrument for determining molar mass, but the determination of molar mass by the density method is still useful, as illustrated by Example 5.9.

Example 5.9

A chemist has synthesized a greenish-yellow gaseous compound of chlorine and oxygen and finds that its density is 7.71 g/L at 36°C and 2.88 atm. Calculate the molar mass of the compound and determine its molecular formula.

Strategy Because Equations (5.11) and (5.12) are rearrangements of each other, we can calculate the molar mass of a gas if we know its density, temperature, and pressure. The molecular formula of the compound must be consistent with its molar mass. What temperature unit should we use?

Solution From Equation (5.12)

$$
\begin{aligned}
\mathcal{M} &= \frac{dRT}{P} \\
&= \frac{(7.71\ \text{g/L})(0.0821\ \text{L} \cdot \text{atm/K} \cdot \text{mol})(36 + 273)\ \text{K}}{2.88\ \text{atm}} \\
&= 67.9\ \text{g/mol}
\end{aligned}
$$

Note that we can determine the molar mass of a gaseous compound by this procedure without knowing its chemical formula.

(Continued)

192   **Chapter 5** ▪ Gases

Alternatively, we can solve for the molar mass by writing

$$\text{molar mass of compound} = \frac{\text{mass of compound}}{\text{moles of compound}}$$

From the given density we know there are 7.71 g of the gas in 1 L. The number of moles of the gas in this volume can be obtained from the ideal gas equation

$$n = \frac{PV}{RT}$$

$$= \frac{(2.88 \text{ atm})(1.00 \text{ L})}{(0.0821 \text{ L} \cdot \text{atm/K} \cdot \text{mol})(309 \text{ K})}$$

$$= 0.1135 \text{ mol}$$

Therefore, the molar mass is given by

$$\mathcal{M} = \frac{\text{mass}}{\text{number of moles}} = \frac{7.71 \text{ g}}{0.1135 \text{ mol}} = 67.9 \text{ g/mol}$$

ClO₂

We can determine the molecular formula of the compound by trial and error, using only the knowledge of the molar masses of chlorine (35.45 g) and oxygen (16.00 g). We know that a compound containing one Cl atom and one O atom would have a molar mass of 51.45 g, which is too low, while the molar mass of a compound made up of two Cl atoms and one O atom is 86.90 g, which is too high. Thus, the compound must contain one Cl atom and two O atoms and have the formula ClO₂, which has a molar mass of 67.45 g.

Practice Exercise The density of a gaseous organic compound is 3.38 g/L at 40°C and 1.97 atm. What is its molar mass?

Similar problems: 5.43, 5.47.

Because Equation (5.12) is derived from the ideal gas equation, we can also calculate the molar mass of a gaseous substance using the ideal gas equation, as shown in Example 5.10.

Example 5.10

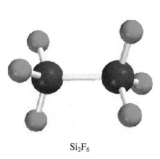

Si₂F₆

Chemical analysis of a gaseous compound showed that it contained 33.0 percent silicon (Si) and 67.0 percent fluorine (F) by mass. At 35°C, 0.210 L of the compound exerted a pressure of 1.70 atm. If the mass of 0.210 L of the compound was 2.38 g, calculate the molecular formula of the compound.

Strategy This problem can be divided into two parts. First, it asks for the empirical formula of the compound from the percent by mass of Si and F. Second, the information provided enables us to calculate the molar mass of the compound and hence determine its molecular formula. What is the relationship between empirical molar mass and molar mass calculated from the molecular formula?

Solution We follow the procedure in Example 3.9 (p. 86) to calculate the empirical formula by assuming that we have 100 g of the compound, so the percentages are converted to grams. The number of moles of Si and F are given by

$$n_{\text{Si}} = 33.0 \text{ g Si} \times \frac{1 \text{ mol Si}}{28.09 \text{ g Si}} = 1.17 \text{ mol Si}$$

$$n_{\text{F}} = 67.0 \text{ g F} \times \frac{1 \text{ mol F}}{19.00 \text{ g F}} = 3.53 \text{ mol F}$$

(Continued)

Therefore, the empirical formula is $Si_{1.17}F_{3.53}$, or, dividing by the smaller subscript (1.17), we obtain SiF_3.

To calculate the molar mass of the compound, we need first to calculate the number of moles contained in 2.38 g of the compound. From the ideal gas equation

$$n = \frac{PV}{RT}$$

$$= \frac{(1.70 \text{ atm})(0.210 \text{ L})}{(0.0821 \text{ L} \cdot \text{atm/K} \cdot \text{mol})(308 \text{ K})} = 0.0141 \text{ mol}$$

Because there are 2.38 g in 0.0141 mole of the compound, the mass in 1 mole, or the molar mass, is given by

$$\mathcal{M} = \frac{2.38 \text{ g}}{0.0141 \text{ mol}} = 169 \text{ g/mol}$$

The molar mass of the empirical formula SiF_3 is 85.09 g. Recall that the ratio (molar mass/empirical molar mass) is always an integer ($169/85.09 \approx 2$). Therefore, the molecular formula of the compound must be $(SiF_3)_2$ or Si_2F_6.

Similar problem: 5.49.

Practice Exercise A gaseous compound is 78.14 percent boron and 21.86 percent hydrogen. At 27°C, 74.3 mL of the gas exerted a pressure of 1.12 atm. If the mass of the gas was 0.0934 g, what is its molecular formula?

5.5 Gas Stoichiometry

In Chapter 3 we used relationships between amounts (in moles) and masses (in grams) of reactants and products to solve stoichiometry problems. When the reactants and/or products are gases, we can also use the relationships between amounts (moles, n) and volume (V) to solve such problems (Figure 5.13). Examples 5.11, 5.12, and 5.13 show how the gas laws are used in these calculations.

The key to solving stoichiometry problems is mole ratio, regardless of the physical state of the reactants and products.

Example 5.11

The combustion of acetylene with pure oxygen produces a very high-temperature flame used for welding and cutting metals. Calculate the volume of O_2 (in liters) required for the complete combustion of 7.64 L of acetylene (C_2H_2) measured at the same temperature and pressure.

$$2C_2H_2(g) + 5O_2(g) \longrightarrow 4CO_2(g) + 2H_2O(l)$$

Strategy Note that the temperature and pressure of O_2 and C_2H_2 are the same. Which gas law do we need to relate the volume of the gases to the moles of gases?

Solution According to Avogadro's law, at the same temperature and pressure, the number of moles of gases are directly related to their volumes. From the equation, we have 5 mol $O_2 \simeq 2$ mol C_2H_2; therefore, we can also write 5 L $O_2 \simeq 2$ L C_2H_2. The volume of O_2 that will react with 7.64 L C_2H_2 is given by

$$\text{volume of } O_2 = 7.64 \text{ L } C_2H_2 \times \frac{5 \text{ L } O_2}{2 \text{ L } C_2H_2}$$

$$= 19.1 \text{ L}$$

The reaction of calcium carbide (CaC_2) with water produces acetylene (C_2H_2), a flammable gas.

Similar problem: 5.26.

Practice Exercise Assuming no change in temperature and pressure, calculate the volume of O_2 (in liters) required for the complete combustion of 14.9 L of butane (C_4H_{10}):

$$2C_4H_{10}(g) + 13O_2(g) \longrightarrow 8CO_2(g) + 10H_2O(l)$$

194 **Chapter 5** ▪ Gases

Figure 5.13 *Stoichiometric calculations involving gases.*

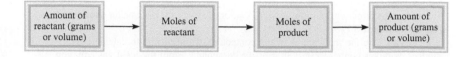

| Amount of reactant (grams or volume) | → | Moles of reactant | → | Moles of product | → | Amount of product (grams or volume) |

An air bag can protect the driver in an automobile collision.

Example 5.12

Sodium azide (NaN_3) is used in some automobile air bags. The impact of a collision triggers the decomposition of NaN_3 as follows:

$$2NaN_3(s) \longrightarrow 2Na(s) + 3N_2(g)$$

The nitrogen gas produced quickly inflates the bag between the driver and the windshield and dashboard. Calculate the volume of N_2 generated at 80°C and 823 mmHg by the decomposition of 60.0 g of NaN_3.

Strategy From the balanced equation we see that 2 mol NaN_3 ≏ 3 mol N_2 so the conversion factor between NaN_3 and N_2 is

$$\frac{3 \text{ mol } N_2}{2 \text{ mol } NaN_3}$$

Because the mass of NaN_3 is given, we can calculate the number of moles of NaN_3 and hence the number of moles of N_2 produced. Finally, we can calculate the volume of N_2 using the ideal gas equation.

Solution First we calculate number of moles of N_2 produced by 60.0 g NaN_3 using the following sequence of conversions

$$\text{grams of } NaN_3 \longrightarrow \text{moles of } NaN_3 \longrightarrow \text{moles of } N_2$$

so that

$$\text{moles of } N_2 = 60.0 \text{ g } NaN_3 \times \frac{1 \text{ mol } NaN_3}{65.02 \text{ g } NaN_3} \times \frac{3 \text{ mol } N_2}{2 \text{ mol } NaN_3}$$

$$= 1.38 \text{ mol } N_2$$

The volume of 1.38 moles of N_2 can be obtained by using the ideal gas equation:

$$V = \frac{nRT}{P} = \frac{(1.38 \text{ mol})(0.0821 \text{ L} \cdot \text{atm/K} \cdot \text{mol})(80 + 273 \text{ K})}{(823/760) \text{ atm}}$$

$$= 36.9 \text{ L}$$

Similar problem: 5.62.

Practice Exercise The equation for the metabolic breakdown of glucose ($C_6H_{12}O_6$) is the same as the equation for the combustion of glucose in air:

$$C_6H_{12}O_6(s) + 6O_2(g) \longrightarrow 6CO_2(g) + 6H_2O(l)$$

Calculate the volume of CO_2 produced at 37°C and 1.00 atm when 5.60 g of glucose is used up in the reaction.

Example 5.13

Aqueous lithium hydroxide solution is used to purify air in spacecrafts and submarines because it absorbs carbon dioxide, which is an end product of metabolism, according to the equation

$$2LiOH(aq) + CO_2(g) \longrightarrow Li_2CO_3(aq) + H_2O(l)$$

(Continued)

The pressure of carbon dioxide inside the cabin of a submarine having a volume of 2.4×10^5 L is 7.9×10^{-3} atm at 312 K. A solution of lithium hydroxide (LiOH) of negligible volume is introduced into the cabin. Eventually the pressure of CO_2 falls to 1.2×10^{-4} atm. How many grams of lithium carbonate are formed by this process?

Strategy How do we calculate the number of moles of CO_2 reacted from the drop in CO_2 pressure? From the ideal gas equation we write

$$n = P \times \left(\frac{V}{RT}\right)$$

At constant T and V, the change in pressure of CO_2, ΔP, corresponds to the change in the number of moles of CO_2, Δn. Thus,

$$\Delta n = \Delta P \times \left(\frac{V}{RT}\right)$$

What is the conversion factor between CO_2 and Li_2CO_3?

Solution The drop in CO_2 pressure is $(7.9 \times 10^{-3}$ atm$) - (1.2 \times 10^{-4}$ atm$)$ or 7.8×10^{-3} atm. Therefore, the number of moles of CO_2 reacted is given by

$$\Delta n = 7.8 \times 10^{-3} \text{ atm} \times \frac{2.4 \times 10^5 \text{ L}}{(0.0821 \text{ L} \cdot \text{atm/K} \cdot \text{mol})(312 \text{ K})}$$
$$= 73 \text{ mol}$$

From the chemical equation we see that 1 mol $CO_2 \simeq$ 1 mol Li_2CO_3, so the amount of Li_2CO_3 formed is also 73 moles. Then, with the molar mass of Li_2CO_3 (73.89 g), we calculate its mass:

$$\text{mass of } Li_2CO_3 \text{ formed} = 73 \text{ mol } \cancel{Li_2CO_3} \times \frac{73.89 \text{ g } Li_2CO_3}{1 \text{ mol } \cancel{Li_2CO_3}}$$
$$= 5.4 \times 10^3 \text{ g } Li_2CO_3$$

Practice Exercise A 2.14-L sample of hydrogen chloride (HCl) gas at 2.61 atm and 28°C is completely dissolved in 668 mL of water to form hydrochloric acid solution. Calculate the molarity of the acid solution. Assume no change in volume.

The air in submerged submarines and space vehicles needs to be purified continuously.

Similar problem: 5.100.

Review of Concepts

Alkanes (C_nH_{2n+2}) are discussed in Section 2.8. For which alkanes, if any, does the number of moles of gas remain constant as the gas-phase combustion reaction

$$\text{alkane}(g) + \text{oxygen}(g) \rightarrow \text{carbon dioxide}(g) + \text{water vapor}(g)$$

proceeds from reactants to products?

5.6 Dalton's Law of Partial Pressures

Thus far we have concentrated on the behavior of pure gaseous substances, but experimental studies very often involve mixtures of gases. For example, for a study of air pollution, we may be interested in the pressure-volume-temperature

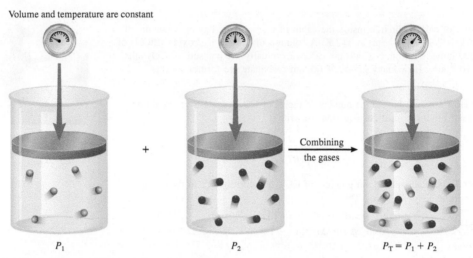

Figure 5.14 *Schematic illustration of Dalton's law of partial pressures.*

relationship of a sample of air, which contains several gases. In this case, and all cases involving mixtures of gases, the total gas pressure is related to ***partial pressures,*** that is, *the pressures of individual gas components in the mixture.* In 1801 Dalton formulated a law, now known as ***Dalton's law of partial pressures,*** which states that *the total pressure of a mixture of gases is just the sum of the pressures that each gas would exert if it were present alone.* Figure 5.14 illustrates Dalton's law.

Consider a case in which two gases, A and B, are in a container of volume *V.* The pressure exerted by gas A, according to the ideal gas equation, is

$$P_A = \frac{n_A RT}{V}$$

where n_A is the number of moles of A present. Similarly, the pressure exerted by gas B is

$$P_B = \frac{n_B RT}{V}$$

In a mixture of gases A and B, the total pressure P_T is the result of the collisions of both types of molecules, A and B, with the walls of the container. Thus, according to Dalton's law,

$$
\begin{aligned}
P_T &= P_A + P_B \\
&= \frac{n_A RT}{V} + \frac{n_B RT}{V} \\
&= \frac{RT}{V}(n_A + n_B) \\
&= \frac{nRT}{V}
\end{aligned}
$$

where *n*, the total number of moles of gases present, is given by $n = n_A + n_B$, and P_A and P_B are the partial pressures of gases A and B, respectively. For a mixture of gases, then, P_T depends only on the total number of moles of gas present, not on the nature of the gas molecules.

In general, the total pressure of a mixture of gases is given by

$$P_T = P_1 + P_2 + P_3 + \cdots$$

where P_1, P_2, P_3, . . . are the partial pressures of components 1, 2, 3, ... To see how each partial pressure is related to the total pressure, consider again the case of a mixture of two gases A and B. Dividing P_A by P_T, we obtain

$$\frac{P_A}{P_T} = \frac{n_A RT/V}{(n_A + n_B)RT/V}$$
$$= \frac{n_A}{n_A + n_B}$$
$$= X_A$$

where X_A is called the mole fraction of A. The **_mole fraction_** is _a dimensionless quantity that expresses the ratio of the number of moles of one component to the number of moles of all components present._ In general, the mole fraction of component i in a mixture is given by

$$X_i = \frac{n_i}{n_T} \qquad (5.13)$$

where n_i and n_T are the number of moles of component i and the total number of moles present, respectively. The mole fraction is always smaller than 1. We can now express the partial pressure of A as

$$P_A = X_A P_T$$

Similarly,

$$P_B = X_B P_T$$

Note that the sum of the mole fractions for a mixture of gases must be unity. If only two components are present, then

$$X_A + X_B = \frac{n_A}{n_A + n_B} + \frac{n_B}{n_A + n_B} = 1$$

If a system contains more than two gases, then the partial pressure of the ith component is related to the total pressure by

For gas mixtures, the sum of partial pressures must equal the total pressure and the sum of mole fractions must equal 1.

$$P_i = X_i P_T \qquad (5.14)$$

How are partial pressures determined? A manometer can measure only the total pressure of a gaseous mixture. To obtain the partial pressures, we need to know the mole fractions of the components, which would involve elaborate chemical analyses. The most direct method of measuring partial pressures is using a mass spectrometer. The relative intensities of the peaks in a mass spectrum are directly proportional to the amounts, and hence to the mole fractions, of the gases present.

From mole fractions and total pressure, we can calculate the partial pressures of individual components, as Example 5.14 shows. A direct application of Dalton's law of partial pressures to scuba diving is discussed in the Chemistry in Action essay on p. 200.

Example 5.14

A mixture of gases contains 4.46 moles of neon (Ne), 0.74 mole of argon (Ar), and 2.15 moles of xenon (Xe). Calculate the partial pressures of the gases if the total pressure is 2.00 atm at a certain temperature.

Strategy What is the relationship between the partial pressure of a gas and the total gas pressure? How do we calculate the mole fraction of a gas?

Solution According to Equation (5.14), the partial pressure of Ne (P_{Ne}) is equal to the product of its mole fraction (X_{Ne}) and the total pressure (P_T)

$$\underset{\text{want to calculate}}{P_{Ne}} = \underset{\text{need to find}}{X_{Ne}} \underset{\text{given}}{P_T}$$

Using Equation (5.13), we calculate the mole fraction of Ne as follows:

$$X_{Ne} = \frac{n_{Ne}}{n_{Ne} + n_{Ar} + n_{Xe}} = \frac{4.46 \text{ mol}}{4.46 \text{ mol} + 0.74 \text{ mol} + 2.15 \text{ mol}}$$
$$= 0.607$$

Therefore,

$$P_{Ne} = X_{Ne}P_T$$
$$= 0.607 \times 2.00 \text{ atm}$$
$$= 1.21 \text{ atm}$$

Similarly,

$$P_{Ar} = X_{Ar}P_T$$
$$= 0.10 \times 2.00 \text{ atm}$$
$$= 0.20 \text{ atm}$$

and

$$P_{Xe} = X_{Xe}P_T$$
$$= 0.293 \times 2.00 \text{ atm}$$
$$= 0.586 \text{ atm}$$

Check Make sure that the sum of the partial pressures is equal to the given total pressure; that is, $(1.21 + 0.20 + 0.586)$ atm $= 2.00$ atm.

Similar problem: 5.67.

Practice Exercise A sample of natural gas contains 8.24 moles of methane (CH_4), 0.421 mole of ethane (C_2H_6), and 0.116 mole of propane (C_3H_8). If the total pressure of the gases is 1.37 atm, what are the partial pressures of the gases?

▶▶ Animation
Collecting a Gas over Water

An important application of Dalton's law of partial pressures involves calculating the amount of a gas collected over water. Gases that are commonly used in the laboratory are generally obtained from pressurized gas cylinders, but if there is an occasional need for a small amount of a certain gas, it may be more convenient to prepare it chemically. For example, when potassium chlorate ($KClO_3$) is heated, it decomposes to KCl and O_2:

$$2KClO_3(s) \longrightarrow 2KCl(s) + 3O_2(g)$$

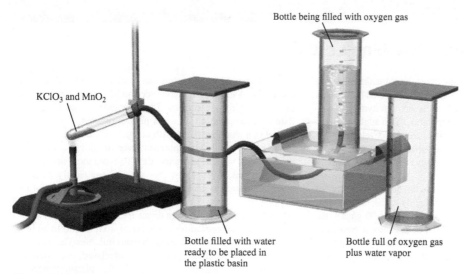

Bottle being filled with oxygen gas

KClO$_3$ and MnO$_2$

Bottle filled with water
ready to be placed in
the plastic basin

Bottle full of oxygen gas
plus water vapor

Figure 5.15 *An apparatus for collecting gas over water. The oxygen generated by heating potassium chlorate (KClO$_3$) in the presence of a small amount of manganese dioxide (MnO$_2$), which speeds up the reaction, is bubbled through water and collected in a bottle as shown. Water originally present in the bottle is pushed into the trough by the oxygen gas.*

When collecting a gas over water, the total pressure (gas plus water vapor) is equal to the atmospheric pressure.

The oxygen gas can be collected over water, as shown in Figure 5.15. Initially, the inverted bottle is completely filled with water. As oxygen gas is generated, the gas bubbles rise to the top and displace water from the bottle. This method of collecting a gas is based on the assumptions that the gas does not react with water and that it is not appreciably soluble in it. These assumptions are valid for oxygen gas, but not for gases such as NH$_3$, which dissolves readily in water. The oxygen gas collected in this way is not pure, however, because water vapor is also present in the bottle. The total gas pressure is equal to the sum of the pressures exerted by the oxygen gas and the water vapor:

$$P_T = P_{O_2} + P_{H_2O}$$

Consequently, we must allow for the pressure caused by the presence of water vapor when we calculate the amount of O$_2$ generated. Table 5.3 shows the pressure of water vapor at various temperatures. These data are plotted in Figure 5.16.

Example 5.15 shows how to use Dalton's law to calculate the amount of a gas collected over water.

Table 5.3

Pressure of Water Vapor at Various Temperatures

Temperature (°C)	Water Vapor Pressure (mmHg)
0	4.58
5	6.54
10	9.21
15	12.79
20	17.54
25	23.76
30	31.82
35	42.18
40	55.32
45	71.88
50	92.51
55	118.04
60	149.38
65	187.54
70	233.7
75	289.1
80	355.1
85	433.6
90	525.76
95	633.90
100	760.00

Example 5.15

Oxygen gas generated by the decomposition of potassium chlorate is collected as shown in Figure 5.15. The volume of oxygen collected at 24°C and atmospheric pressure of 762 mmHg is 128 mL. Calculate the mass (in grams) of oxygen gas obtained. The pressure of the water vapor at 24°C is 22.4 mmHg.

Strategy To solve for the mass of O$_2$ generated, we must first calculate the partial pressure of O$_2$ in the mixture. What gas law do we need? How do we convert pressure of O$_2$ gas to mass of O$_2$ in grams?

(Continued)

CHEMISTRY *in Action*

Scuba Diving and the Gas Laws

Scuba diving is an exhilarating sport, and, thanks in part to the gas laws, it is also a safe activity for trained individuals who are in good health. ("Scuba" is an acronym for self-contained underwater breathing apparatus.) Two applications of the gas laws to this popular pastime are the development of guidelines for returning safely to the surface after a dive and the determination of the proper mix of gases to prevent a potentially fatal condition during a dive.

A typical dive might be 40 to 65 ft, but dives to 90 ft are not uncommon. Because seawater has a slightly higher density than fresh water—about 1.03 g/mL, compared with 1.00 g/mL—the pressure exerted by a column of 33 ft of seawater is equivalent to 1 atm pressure. Pressure increases with increasing depth, so at a depth of 66 ft the pressure of the water will be 2 atm, and so on.

What would happen if a diver rose to the surface from a depth of, say, 20 ft rather quickly without breathing? The total decrease in pressure for this change in depth would be (20 ft/33 ft) × 1 atm, or 0.6 atm. When the diver reached the surface, the volume of air trapped in the lungs would have increased by a factor of (1 + 0.6) atm/1 atm, or 1.6 times. This sudden expansion of air can fatally rupture the membranes of the lungs. Another serious possibility is that an *air embolism* might develop. As air expands in the lungs, it is forced into tiny blood vessels called capillaries. The presence

of air bubbles in these vessels can block normal blood flow to the brain. As a result, the diver might lose consciousness before reaching the surface. The only cure for an air embolism is recompression. For this painful process, the victim is placed in a chamber filled with compressed air. Here bubbles in the blood are slowly squeezed down to harmless size over the course of several hours to a day. To avoid these unpleasant complications, divers know they must ascend slowly, pausing at certain points to give their bodies time to adjust to the falling pressure.

Our second example is a direct application of Dalton's law. Oxygen gas is essential for our survival, so it is hard to believe that an excess of oxygen could be harmful. Nevertheless, the toxicity of too much oxygen is well established. For example, newborn infants placed in oxygen tents often sustain damage to the retinal tissue, which can cause partial or total blindness.

Our bodies function best when oxygen gas has a partial pressure of about 0.20 atm, as it does in the air we breathe. The oxygen partial pressure is given by

$$P_{O_2} = X_{O_2}P_T = \frac{n_{O_2}}{n_{O_2} + n_{N_2}}P_T$$

where P_T is the total pressure. However, because volume is directly proportional to the number of moles of gas present (at

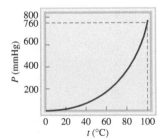

Figure 5.16 *The pressure of water vapor as a function of temperature. Note that at the boiling point of water (100°C) the pressure is 760 mmHg, which is exactly equal to 1 atm.*

Solution From Dalton's law of partial pressures we know that

$$P_T = P_{O_2} + P_{H_2O}$$

Therefore,

$$P_{O_2} = P_T - P_{H_2O}$$
$$= 762 \text{ mmHg} - 22.4 \text{ mmHg}$$
$$= 740 \text{ mmHg}$$

From the ideal gas equation we write

$$PV = nRT = \frac{m}{\mathcal{M}}RT$$

(Continued)

constant temperature and pressure), we can now write

$$P_{O_2} = \frac{V_{O_2}}{V_{O_2} + V_{N_2}} P_T$$

Thus, the composition of air is 20 percent oxygen gas and 80 percent nitrogen gas by volume. When a diver is submerged, the pressure of the water on the diver is greater than atmospheric pressure. The air pressure inside the body cavities (for example, lungs, sinuses) must be the same as the pressure of the surrounding water; otherwise they would collapse. A special valve automatically adjusts the pressure of the air breathed from a scuba tank to ensure that the air pressure equals the water pressure at all times. For example, at a depth where the total pressure is 2.0 atm, the oxygen content in air should be reduced to 10 percent by volume to maintain the same partial pressure of 0.20 atm; that is,

$$P_{O_2} = 0.20 \text{ atm} = \frac{V_{O_2}}{V_{O_2} + V_{N_2}} \times 2.0 \text{ atm}$$

$$\frac{V_{O_2}}{V_{O_2} + V_{N_2}} = \frac{0.20 \text{ atm}}{2.0 \text{ atm}} = 0.10 \text{ or } 10\%$$

Scuba divers.

Although nitrogen gas may seem to be the obvious choice to mix with oxygen gas, there is a serious problem with it. When the partial pressure of nitrogen gas exceeds 1 atm, enough of the gas dissolves in the blood to cause a condition known as *nitrogen narcosis*. The effects on the diver resemble those associated with alcohol intoxication. Divers suffering from nitrogen narcosis have been known to do strange things, such as dancing on the seafloor and chasing sharks. For this reason, helium is often used to dilute oxygen gas. An inert gas, helium is much less soluble in blood than nitrogen and produces no narcotic effects.

where m and $\mathcal{M}$ are the mass of O_2 collected and the molar mass of O_2, respectively. Rearranging the equation we obtain

$$m = \frac{PV\mathcal{M}}{RT} = \frac{(740/760)\text{atm}(0.128 \text{ L})(32.00 \text{ g/mol})}{(0.0821 \text{ L} \cdot \text{atm/K} \cdot \text{mol})(273 + 24) \text{ K}}$$

$$= 0.164 \text{ g}$$

Check The density of the oxygen gas is (0.164 g/0.128 L), or 1.28 g/L, which is a reasonable value for gases under atmospheric conditions (see Example 5.8).

Similar problem: 5.72.

Practice Exercise Hydrogen gas generated when calcium metal reacts with water is collected as shown in Figure 5.15. The volume of gas collected at 30°C and pressure of 988 mmHg is 641 mL. What is the mass (in grams) of the hydrogen gas obtained? The pressure of water vapor at 30°C is 31.82 mmHg.

202   **Chapter 5** ▪ Gases

Review of Concepts

Each of the color spheres represents a different gas molecule. Calculate the partial pressures of the gases if the total pressure is 2.6 atm.

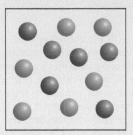

5.7 The Kinetic Molecular Theory of Gases

The gas laws help us to predict the behavior of gases, but they do not explain what happens at the molecular level to cause the changes we observe in the macroscopic world. For example, why does a gas expand on heating?

In the nineteenth century, a number of physicists, notably Ludwig Boltzmann[†] and James Clerk Maxwell,[‡] found that the physical properties of gases can be explained in terms of the motion of individual molecules. This molecular movement is a form of *energy*, which we define as the capacity to do work or to produce change. In mechanics, *work* is defined as force times distance. Because energy can be measured as work, we can write

$$\text{energy} = \text{work done}$$
$$= \text{force} \times \text{distance}$$

The *joule (J)*[§] is *the SI unit of energy*

$$1 \text{ J} = 1 \text{ kg m}^2/\text{s}^2$$
$$= 1 \text{ N m}$$

Alternatively, energy can be expressed in kilojoules (kJ):

$$1 \text{ kJ} = 1000 \text{ J}$$

As we will see in Chapter 6, there are many different kinds of energy. *Kinetic energy (KE)* is the type of energy expended by a moving object, or *energy of motion*.

The findings of Maxwell, Boltzmann, and others resulted in *a number of generalizations about gas behavior* that have since been known as the **kinetic molecular**

[†]Ludwig Eduard Boltzmann (1844–1906). Austrian physicist. Although Boltzmann was one of the greatest theoretical physicists of all time, his work was not recognized by other scientists in his own lifetime. Suffering from poor health and great depression, he committed suicide in 1906.

[‡]James Clerk Maxwell (1831–1879). Scottish physicist. Maxwell was one of the great theoretical physicists of the nineteenth century; his work covered many areas in physics, including kinetic theory of gases, thermodynamics, and electricity and magnetism.

[§]James Prescott Joule (1818–1889). English physicist. As a young man, Joule was tutored by John Dalton. He is most famous for determining the mechanical equivalent of heat, the conversion between mechanical energy and thermal energy.

theory of gases, or simply the *kinetic theory of gases.* Central to the kinetic theory are the following assumptions:

1. A gas is composed of molecules that are separated from each other by distances far greater than their own dimensions. The molecules can be considered to be "points"; that is, they possess mass but have negligible volume.

   The kinetic theory of gases treats molecules as hard spheres without internal structure.

2. Gas molecules are in constant motion in random directions, and they frequently collide with one another. Collisions among molecules are perfectly elastic. In other words, energy can be transferred from one molecule to another as a result of a collision. Nevertheless, the total energy of all the molecules in a system remains the same.

3. Gas molecules exert neither attractive nor repulsive forces on one another.

4. The average kinetic energy of the molecules is proportional to the temperature of the gas in kelvins. Any two gases at the same temperature will have the same average kinetic energy. The average kinetic energy of a molecule is given by

$$\overline{KE} = \tfrac{1}{2}m\overline{u^2}$$

where m is the mass of the molecule and u is its speed. The horizontal bar denotes an average value. The quantity $\overline{u^2}$ is called mean square speed; it is the average of the square of the speeds of all the molecules:

$$\overline{u^2} = \frac{u_1^2 + u_2^2 + \cdots + u_N^2}{N}$$

where N is the number of molecules.

Assumption 4 enables us to write

$$\overline{KE} \propto T$$
$$\tfrac{1}{2}m\overline{u^2} \propto T$$

Hence, $$\overline{KE} = \tfrac{1}{2}m\overline{u^2} = CT \qquad (5.15)$$

where C is the proportionality constant and T is the absolute temperature.

According to the kinetic molecular theory, gas pressure is the result of collisions between molecules and the walls of their container. It depends on the frequency of collision per unit area and on how "hard" the molecules strike the wall. The theory also provides a molecular interpretation of temperature. According to Equation (5.15), the absolute temperature of a gas is a measure of the average kinetic energy of the molecules. In other words, the absolute temperature is an indication of the random motion of the molecules—the higher the temperature, the more energetic the molecules. Because it is related to the temperature of the gas sample, random molecular motion is sometimes referred to as thermal motion.

Application to the Gas Laws

Although the kinetic theory of gases is based on a rather simple model, the mathematical details involved are very complex. However, on a qualitative basis, it is possible to use the theory to account for the general properties of substances in the gaseous state. The following examples illustrate the range of its utility.

- **Compressibility of Gases.** Because molecules in the gas phase are separated by large distances (assumption 1), gases can be compressed easily to occupy less volume.

- **Boyle's Law.** The pressure exerted by a gas results from the impact of its molecules on the walls of the container. The collision rate, or the number of molecular collisions with the walls per second, is proportional to the number density (that is, number of molecules per unit volume) of the gas. Decreasing the volume of a given amount of gas increases its number density and hence its collision rate. For this reason, the pressure of a gas is inversely proportional to the volume it occupies; as volume decreases, pressure increases and vice versa.

- **Charles' Law.** Because the average kinetic energy of gas molecules is proportional to the sample's absolute temperature (assumption 4), raising the temperature increases the average kinetic energy. Consequently, molecules will collide with the walls of the container more frequently and with greater impact if the gas is heated, and thus the pressure increases. The volume of gas will expand until the gas pressure is balanced by the constant external pressure (see Figure 5.8).

Another way of stating Avogadro's law is that at the same pressure and temperature, equal volumes of gases, whether they are the same or different gases, contain equal numbers of molecules.

- **Avogadro's Law.** We have shown that the pressure of a gas is directly proportional to both the density and the temperature of the gas. Because the mass of the gas is directly proportional to the number of moles (n) of the gas, we can represent density by n/V. Therefore

$$P \propto \frac{n}{V}T$$

For two gases, 1 and 2, we write

$$P_1 \propto \frac{n_1 T_1}{V_1} = C\frac{n_1 T_1}{V_1}$$

$$P_2 \propto \frac{n_2 T_2}{V_2} = C\frac{n_2 T_2}{V_2}$$

where C is the proportionality constant. Thus, for two gases under the same conditions of pressure, volume, and temperature (that is, when $P_1 = P_2$, $T_1 = T_2$, and $V_1 = V_2$), it follows that $n_1 = n_2$, which is a mathematical expression of Avogadro's law.

- **Dalton's Law of Partial Pressures.** If molecules do not attract or repel one another (assumption 3), then the pressure exerted by one type of molecule is unaffected by the presence of another gas. Consequently, the total pressure is given by the sum of individual gas pressures.

Distribution of Molecular Speeds

The kinetic theory of gases enables us to investigate molecular motion in more detail. Suppose we have a large number of gas molecules, say, 1 mole, in a container. As long as we hold the temperature constant, the average kinetic energy and the mean-square speed will remain unchanged as time passes. As you might expect, the motion of the molecules is totally random and unpredictable. At a given instant, how many molecules are moving at a particular speed? To answer this question Maxwell analyzed the behavior of gas molecules at different temperatures.

Figure 5.17(a) shows typical *Maxwell speed distribution curves* for nitrogen gas at three different temperatures. At a given temperature, the distribution curve tells us the number of molecules moving at a certain speed. The peak of each curve represents the *most probable speed,* that is, the speed of the largest number of molecules. Note that the most probable speed increases as temperature increases

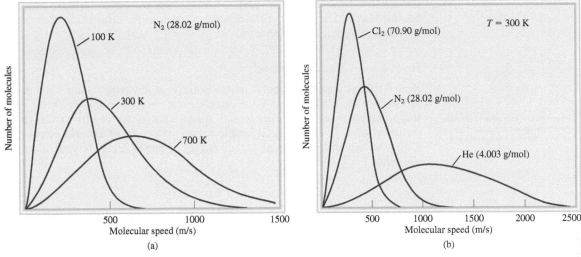

Figure 5.17 *(a) The distribution of speeds for nitrogen gas at three different temperatures. At the higher temperatures, more molecules are moving at faster speeds. (b) The distribution of speeds for three gases at 300 K. At a given temperature, the lighter molecules are moving faster, on the average.*

(the peak shifts toward the right). Furthermore, the curve also begins to flatten out with increasing temperature, indicating that larger numbers of molecules are moving at greater speed. Figure 5.17(b) shows the speed distributions of three gases at the *same* temperature. The difference in the curves can be explained by noting that lighter molecules move faster, on average, than heavier ones.

The distribution of molecular speeds can be demonstrated with the apparatus shown in Figure 5.18. A beam of atoms (or molecules) exits from an oven at a known temperature and passes through a pinhole (to collimate the beam). Two circular plates mounted on the same shaft are rotated by a motor. The first plate is called the "chopper" and the second is the detector. The purpose of the chopper is to allow small bursts of atoms (or molecules) to pass through it whenever the slit is aligned with the beam. Within each burst, the faster-moving molecules will reach the detector earlier than the slower-moving ones. Eventually, a layer of deposit will accumulate on the detector. Because the two plates are rotating at the same speed, molecules in the next burst will hit the detector plate at approximately the same place as molecules from

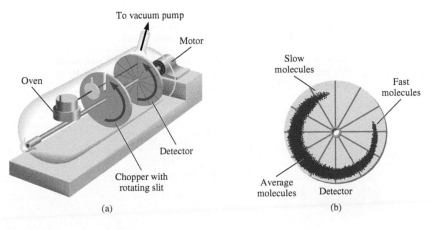

Figure 5.18 *(a) Apparatus for studying molecular speed distribution at a certain temperature. The vacuum pump causes the molecules to travel from left to right as shown. (b) The spread of the deposit on the detector gives the range of molecular speeds, and the density of the deposit is proportional to the fraction of molecules moving at different speeds.*

the previous burst having the same speed. In time, the molecular deposition will become visible. The density of the deposition indicates the distribution of molecular speeds at that particular temperature.

Root-Mean-Square Speed

How fast does a molecule move, on the average, at any temperature T? One way to estimate molecular speed is to calculate the *root-mean-square (rms) speed* (u_{rms}), which is *an average molecular speed*. One of the results of the kinetic theory of gases is that the total kinetic energy of a mole of any gas equals $\frac{3}{2}RT$. Earlier we saw that the average kinetic energy of one molecule is $\frac{1}{2}m\overline{u^2}$ and so we can write

$$\overline{KE} = \tfrac{3}{2}RT$$
$$N_A(\tfrac{1}{2}m\overline{u^2}) = \tfrac{3}{2}RT$$

where N_A is Avogadro's number and m is the mass of a single molecule. Because $N_A m = \mathcal{M}$, the above equation can be rearranged to give

$$\overline{u^2} = \frac{3RT}{\mathcal{M}}$$

Taking the square root of both sides gives

$$\sqrt{\overline{u^2}} = u_{rms} = \sqrt{\frac{3RT}{\mathcal{M}}} \tag{5.16}$$

Equation (5.16) shows that the root-mean-square speed of a gas increases with the square root of its temperature (in kelvins). Because $\mathcal{M}$ appears in the denominator, it follows that the heavier the gas, the more slowly its molecules move. If we substitute 8.314 J/K · mol for R (see Appendix 2) and convert the molar mass to kg/mol, then u_{rms} will be calculated in meters per second (m/s). This procedure is illustrated in Example 5.16.

> There are comparable ways to estimate the "average" speed of molecules, of which root-mean-square speed is one.

Example 5.16

Calculate the root-mean-square speeds of helium atoms and nitrogen molecules in m/s at 25°C.

Strategy To calculate the root-mean-square speed we need Equation (5.16). What units should we use for R and $\mathcal{M}$ so that u_{rms} will be expressed in m/s?

Solution To calculate u_{rms}, the units of R should be 8.314 J/K · mol and, because 1 J = 1 kg m²/s², the molar mass must be in kg/mol. The molar mass of He is 4.003 g/mol, or 4.003×10^{-3} kg/mol. From Equation (5.16),

$$u_{rms} = \sqrt{\frac{3RT}{\mathcal{M}}}$$
$$= \sqrt{\frac{3(8.314 \text{ J/K} \cdot \text{mol})(298 \text{ K})}{4.003 \times 10^{-3} \text{ kg/mol}}}$$
$$= \sqrt{1.86 \times 10^6 \text{ J/kg}}$$

(Continued)

Using the conversion factor $1 \text{ J} = 1 \text{ kg m}^2/\text{s}^2$ we get

$$u_{rms} = \sqrt{1.86 \times 10^6 \text{ kg m}^2/\text{kg} \cdot \text{s}^2}$$
$$= \sqrt{1.86 \times 10^6 \text{ m}^2/\text{s}^2}$$
$$= 1.36 \times 10^3 \text{ m/s}$$

The procedure is the same for N_2, the molar mass of which is 28.02 g/mol, or 2.802×10^{-2} kg/mol so that we write

$$u_{rms} = \sqrt{\frac{3(8.314 \text{ J/K} \cdot \text{mole})(298 \text{ K})}{2.802 \times 10^{-2} \text{ kg/mol}}}$$
$$= \sqrt{2.65 \times 10^5 \text{ m}^2/\text{s}^2}$$
$$= 515 \text{ m/s}$$

Check Because He is a lighter gas, we expect it to move faster, on average, than N_2. A quick way to check the answers is to note that the ratio of the two u_{rms} values $(1.36 \times 10^3/515 \approx 2.6)$ should be equal to the square root of the ratios of the molar masses of N_2 to He, that is, $\sqrt{28/4} \approx 2.6$.

Practice Exercise Calculate the root-mean-square speed of molecular chlorine in m/s at 20°C.

Figure 5.19 *The path traveled by a single gas molecule. Each change in direction represents a collision with another molecule.*

Similar problems: 5.81, 5.82.

The calculation in Example 5.16 has an interesting relationship to the composition of Earth's atmosphere. Unlike Jupiter, Earth does not have appreciable amounts of hydrogen or helium in its atmosphere. Why is this the case? A smaller planet than Jupiter, Earth has a weaker gravitational attraction for these lighter molecules. A fairly straightforward calculation shows that to escape Earth's gravitational field, a molecule must possess an escape velocity equal to or greater than 1.1×10^4 m/s. Because the average speed of helium is considerably greater than that of molecular nitrogen or molecular oxygen, more helium atoms escape from Earth's atmosphere into outer space. Consequently, only a trace amount of helium is present in our atmosphere. On the other hand, Jupiter, with a mass about 320 times greater than that of Earth, retains both heavy and light gases in its atmosphere.

The Chemistry in Action essay on p. 208 describes a fascinating phenomenon involving gases at extremely low temperatures.

Jupiter. The interior of this massive planet consists mainly of hydrogen.

Gas Diffusion and Effusion

We will now discuss two phenomena based on gaseous motion.

Gas Diffusion

A direct demonstration of gaseous random motion is provided by *diffusion, the gradual mixing of molecules of one gas with molecules of another by virtue of their kinetic properties.* Despite the fact that molecular speeds are very great, the diffusion process takes a relatively long time to complete. For example, when a bottle of concentrated ammonia solution is opened at one end of a lab bench, it takes some time before a person at the other end of the bench can smell it. The reason is that a molecule experiences numerous collisions while moving from one end of the bench to the other, as shown in Figure 5.19. Thus, diffusion of gases always happens gradually, and not instantly as molecular speeds seem to suggest. Furthermore, because the root-mean-square speed of a light gas is greater than that of a heavier gas (see Example 5.16),

Diffusion always proceeds from a region of higher concentration to one where the concentration is lower.

▶▶▶ Animation
Diffusion of Gases

CHEMISTRY *in Action*

Super Cold Atoms

What happens to a gas when cooled to nearly absolute zero? More than 85 years ago, Albert Einstein, extending work by the Indian physicist Satyendra Nath Bose, predicted that at extremely low temperatures gaseous atoms of certain elements would "merge" or "condense" to form a single entity and a new form of matter. Unlike ordinary gases, liquids, and solids, this supercooled substance, which was named the *Bose-Einstein condensate (BEC)*, would contain no individual atoms because the original atoms would overlap one another, leaving no space in between.

Einstein's hypothesis inspired an international effort to produce the BEC. But, as sometimes happens in science, the necessary technology was not available until fairly recently, and so early investigations were fruitless. Lasers, which use a process based on another of Einstein's ideas, were not designed specifically for BEC research, but they became a critical tool for this work.

Finally, in 1995, physicists found the evidence they had sought for so long. A team at the University of Colorado was the first to report success. They created a BEC by cooling a sample of gaseous rubidium (Rb) atoms to about 5.0×10^{-8} K using a technique called "laser cooling," a process in which a laser light is directed at a beam of atoms, hitting them head on and dramatically slowing them down. The Rb atoms were further cooled in an "optical molasses" produced by the intersection of six lasers. The slowest, coolest atoms were trapped in a magnetic field while the faster-moving, "hotter" atoms escaped, thereby removing more energy from the gas. Under these conditions, the kinetic energy of the trapped atoms was virtually zero, which accounts for the extremely low temperature of the gas. At this point the Rb atoms formed the condensate, just as Einstein had predicted. Although this BEC was invisible to the naked eye (it measured only 5×10^{-3} cm across), the scientists were able to capture its image on a computer screen by focusing another laser beam on it. The laser caused the BEC to break up after about 15 seconds, but that was long enough to record its existence.

The figure shows the Maxwell velocity distribution[†] of the Rb atoms at this temperature. The colors indicate the number of atoms having velocity specified by the two horizontal axes. The blue and white portions represent atoms that have merged to form the BEC.

Within weeks of the Colorado team's discovery, a group of scientists at Rice University, using similar techniques, succeeded in producing a BEC with lithium atoms and in 1998 scientists at the Massachusetts Institute of Technology were able to produce a BEC with hydrogen atoms. Since then, many advances have been made in understanding the properties of the BEC in general and experiments are being extended to molecular systems. It is expected that studies of the BEC will shed light on atomic properties that are still not fully understood (see Chapter 7) and on the mechanism of superconductivity (see the Chemistry in Action essay on this topic in Chapter 11). An additional benefit might be the development of better lasers. Other applications will depend on further study of the BEC itself. Nevertheless, the discovery of a new form of matter has to be one of the foremost scientific achievements of the twentieth century.

[†]Velocity distribution differs from speed distribution in that velocity has both magnitude and direction. Thus, velocity can have both positive and negative values but speed can have only zero or positive values.

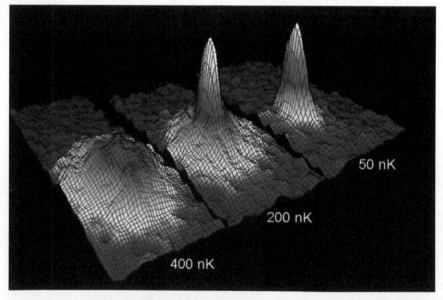

Maxwell velocity distribution of Rb atoms at three different temperatures during the formation of Bose-Einstein condensate. In each case, the velocity increases from the center (zero) outward along the two axes. The red color represents the lower number of Rb atoms and the white color the highest.

Figure 5.20 *A demonstration of gas diffusion. NH_3 gas (from a bottle containing aqueous ammonia) combines with HCl gas (from a bottle containing hydrochloric acid) to form solid NH_4Cl. Because NH_3 is lighter and therefore diffuses faster, solid NH_4Cl first appears nearer the HCl bottle (on the right).*

a lighter gas will diffuse through a certain space more quickly than will a heavier gas. Figure 5.20 illustrates gaseous diffusion.

In 1832 the Scottish chemist Thomas Graham[†] found that *under the same conditions of temperature and pressure, rates of diffusion for gases are inversely proportional to the square roots of their molar masses.* This statement, now known as ***Graham's law of diffusion,*** is expressed mathematically as

$$\frac{r_1}{r_2} = \sqrt{\frac{\mathcal{M}_2}{\mathcal{M}_1}} \tag{5.17}$$

where r_1 and r_2 are the diffusion rates of gases 1 and 2, and $\mathcal{M}_1$ and $\mathcal{M}_2$ are their molar masses, respectively.

Gas Effusion

Whereas diffusion is a process by which one gas gradually mixes with another, ***effusion*** is *the process by which a gas under pressure escapes from one compartment of a container to another by passing through a small opening.* Figure 5.21 shows the effusion of a gas into a vacuum. Although effusion differs from diffusion in nature, the rate of effusion of a gas has the same form as Graham's law of diffusion [see Equation (5.17)]. A helium-filled rubber balloon deflates faster than an air-filled one because the rate of effusion through the pores of the rubber is faster for the lighter helium atoms than for the air molecules. Industrially, gas effusion is used to separate uranium isotopes in the forms of gaseous $^{235}UF_6$ and $^{238}UF_6$. By subjecting the gases to many stages of effusion, scientists were able to obtain highly enriched ^{235}U isotope, which was used in the construction of atomic bombs during World War II.

Example 5.17 shows an application of Graham's law.

Gas   Vacuum

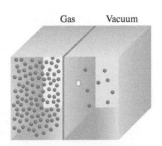

Example 5.17

A flammable gas made up only of carbon and hydrogen is found to effuse through a porous barrier in 1.50 min. Under the same conditions of temperature and pressure, it takes an equal volume of bromine vapor 4.73 min to effuse through the same barrier. Calculate the molar mass of the unknown gas, and suggest what this gas might be.

(Continued)

Figure 5.21 *Gas effusion. Gas molecules move from a high-pressure region (left) to a low-pressure one through a pinhole.*

[†]Thomas Graham (1805–1869). Scottish chemist. Graham did important work on osmosis and characterized a number of phosphoric acids.

Strategy The rate of diffusion is the number of molecules passing through a porous barrier in a given time. The longer the time it takes, the slower is the rate. Therefore, the rate is *inversely* proportional to the time required for diffusion. Equation (5.17) can now be written as $r_1/r_2 = t_2/t_1 = \sqrt{\mathcal{M}_2/\mathcal{M}_1}$, where t_1 and t_2 are the times for effusion for gases 1 and 2, respectively.

Solution From the molar mass of Br_2, we write

$$\frac{1.50 \text{ min}}{4.73 \text{ min}} = \sqrt{\frac{\mathcal{M}}{159.8 \text{ g/mol}}}$$

where $\mathcal{M}$ is the molar mass of the unknown gas. Solving for $\mathcal{M}$, we obtain

$$\mathcal{M} = \left(\frac{1.50 \text{ min}}{4.73 \text{ min}}\right)^2 \times 159.8 \text{ g/mol}$$

$$= 16.1 \text{ g/mol}$$

Because the molar mass of carbon is 12.01 g and that of hydrogen is 1.008 g, the gas is methane (CH_4).

Similar problems: 5.87, 5.88.

Practice Exercise It takes 192 s for an unknown gas to effuse through a porous wall and 84 s for the same volume of N_2 gas to effuse at the same temperature and pressure. What is the molar mass of the unknown gas?

Review of Concepts

If one mole each of He and Cl_2 gases are compared at STP, which of the following quantities will be equal to each other? (a) Root-mean-square speed, (b) effusion rate, (c) average kinetic energy, (d) volume.

5.8 Deviation from Ideal Behavior

The gas laws and the kinetic molecular theory assume that molecules in the gaseous state do not exert any force, either attractive or repulsive, on one another. The other assumption is that the volume of the molecules is negligibly small compared with that of the container. A gas that satisfies these two conditions is said to exhibit *ideal behavior.*

Although we can assume that real gases behave like an ideal gas, we cannot expect them to do so under all conditions. For example, without intermolecular forces, gases could not condense to form liquids. The important question is: Under what conditions will gases most likely exhibit nonideal behavior?

Figure 5.22 shows PV/RT plotted against P for three real gases and an ideal gas at a given temperature. This graph provides a test of ideal gas behavior. According to the ideal gas equation (for 1 mole of gas), PV/RT equals 1, regardless of the actual gas pressure. (When $n = 1$, $PV = nRT$ becomes $PV = RT$, or $PV/RT = 1$.) For real gases, this is true only at moderately low pressures (≤ 5 atm); significant deviations occur as pressure increases. Attractive forces operate among molecules at relatively short distances. At atmospheric pressure, the molecules in a gas are far apart and the attractive forces are negligible. At high pressures, the density of the gas increases; the molecules are much closer to one another. Intermolecular forces can then be significant enough to affect the motion of the molecules, and the gas will not behave ideally.

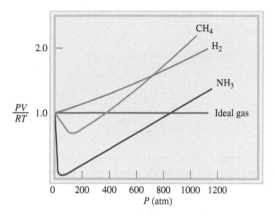

Figure 5.22 *Plot of PV/RT versus P of 1 mole of a gas at 0°C. For 1 mole of an ideal gas, PV/RT is equal to 1, no matter what the pressure of the gas is. For real gases, we observe various deviations from ideality at high pressures. At very low pressures, all gases exhibit ideal behavior; that is, their PV/RT values all converge to 1 as P approaches zero.*

Another way to observe the nonideal behavior of gases is to lower the temperature. Cooling a gas decreases the molecules' average kinetic energy, which in a sense deprives molecules of the drive they need to break from their mutual attraction.

To study real gases accurately, then, we need to modify the ideal gas equation, taking into account intermolecular forces and finite molecular volumes. Such an analysis was first made by the Dutch physicist J. D. van der Waals[†] in 1873. Besides being mathematically simple, van der Waals' treatment provides us with an interpretation of real gas behavior at the molecular level.

Consider the approach of a particular molecule toward the wall of a container (Figure 5.23). The intermolecular attractions exerted by its neighbors tend to soften the impact made by this molecule against the wall. The overall effect is a lower gas pressure than we would expect for an ideal gas. Van der Waals suggested that the pressure exerted by an ideal gas, P_{ideal}, is related to the experimentally measured pressure, P_{real}, by the equation

$$P_{\text{ideal}} = \underset{\substack{\uparrow \\ \text{observed} \\ \text{pressure}}}{P_{\text{real}}} + \underset{\substack{\uparrow \\ \text{correction} \\ \text{term}}}{\frac{an^2}{V^2}}$$

where a is a constant and n and V are the number of moles and volume of the container, respectively. The correction term for pressure (an^2/V^2) can be understood as follows. The intermolecular interaction that gives rise to nonideal behavior depends on how frequently any two molecules approach each other closely. The frequency of such "encounters" increases with the square of the number of molecules per unit volume (n^2/V^2), because the probability of finding each of the two molecules in a particular region is proportional to n/V. Thus, a is just a proportionality constant.

Another correction concerns the volume occupied by the gas molecules. In the ideal gas equation, V represents the volume of the container. However, each molecule does occupy a finite, although small, intrinsic volume, so the effective volume of the gas becomes ($V - nb$), where n is the number of moles of the gas and b is a constant. The term nb represents the volume occupied by n moles of the gas.

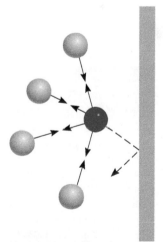

Figure 5.23 *Effect of intermolecular forces on the pressure exerted by a gas. The speed of a molecule that is moving toward the container wall (red sphere) is reduced by the attractive forces exerted by its neighbors (gray spheres). Consequently, the impact this molecule makes with the wall is not as great as it would be if no intermolecular forces were present. In general, the measured gas pressure is lower than the pressure the gas would exert if it behaved ideally.*

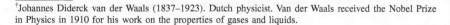

[†]Johannes Diderck van der Waals (1837–1923). Dutch physicist. Van der Waals received the Nobel Prize in Physics in 1910 for his work on the properties of gases and liquids.

Having taken into account the corrections for pressure and volume, we can rewrite the ideal gas equation as follows:

Keep in mind that in Equation (5.18), P is the experimentally measured gas pressure and V is the volume of the gas container.

$$\underbrace{\left(P + \frac{an^2}{V^2}\right)}_{\substack{\text{corrected} \\ \text{pressure}}} \underbrace{(V - nb)}_{\substack{\text{corrected} \\ \text{volume}}} = nRT \qquad (5.18)$$

Equation (5.18), *relating P, V, T, and n for a nonideal gas,* is known as the **van der Waals equation.** The van der Waals constants a and b are selected to give the best possible agreement between Equation (5.18) and observed behavior of a particular gas.

Table 5.4 lists the values of a and b for a number of gases. The value of a indicates how strongly molecules of a given type of gas attract one another. We see that helium atoms have the weakest attraction for one another, because helium has the smallest a value. There is also a rough correlation between molecular size and b. Generally, the larger the molecule (or atom), the greater b is, but the relationship between b and molecular (or atomic) size is not a simple one.

Example 5.18 compares the pressure of a gas calculated using the ideal gas equation and the van der Waals equation.

Example 5.18

Given that 3.50 moles of NH_3 occupy 5.20 L at 47°C, calculate the pressure of the gas (in atm) using (a) the ideal gas equation and (b) the van der Waals equation.

Strategy To calculate the pressure of NH_3 using the ideal gas equation, we proceed as in Example 5.3. What corrections are made to the pressure and volume terms in the van der Waals equation?

Solution (a) We have the following data:

$$V = 5.20 \text{ L}$$
$$T = (47 + 273) \text{ K} = 320 \text{ K}$$
$$n = 3.50 \text{ mol}$$
$$R = 0.0821 \text{ L} \cdot \text{atm/K} \cdot \text{mol}$$

Substituting these values in the ideal gas equation, we write

$$P = \frac{nRT}{V}$$
$$= \frac{(3.50 \text{ mol})(0.0821 \text{ L} \cdot \text{atm/K} \cdot \text{mol})(320 \text{ K})}{5.20 \text{ L}}$$
$$= 17.7 \text{ atm}$$

(b) We need Equation (5.18). It is convenient to first calculate the correction terms in Equation (5.18) separately. From Table 5.4, we have

$$a = 4.17 \text{ atm} \cdot \text{L}^2/\text{mol}^2$$
$$b = 0.0371 \text{ L/mol}$$

(Continued)

Table 5.4

van der Waals Constants of Some Common Gases

Gas	a $\left(\dfrac{\text{atm} \cdot \text{L}^2}{\text{mol}^2}\right)$	b $\left(\dfrac{\text{L}}{\text{mol}}\right)$
He	0.034	0.0237
Ne	0.211	0.0171
Ar	1.34	0.0322
Kr	2.32	0.0398
Xe	4.19	0.0266
H_2	0.244	0.0266
N_2	1.39	0.0391
O_2	1.36	0.0318
Cl_2	6.49	0.0562
CO_2	3.59	0.0427
CH_4	2.25	0.0428
CCl_4	20.4	0.138
NH_3	4.17	0.0371
H_2O	5.46	0.0305

so that the correction terms for pressure and volume are

$$\frac{an^2}{V^2} = \frac{(4.17 \text{ atm} \cdot \text{L}^2/\text{mol}^2)(3.50 \text{ mol})^2}{(5.20 \text{ L})^2} = 1.89 \text{ atm}$$

$$nb = (3.50 \text{ mol})(0.0371 \text{ L/mol}) = 0.130 \text{ L}$$

Finally, substituting these values in the van der Waals equation, we have

$$(P + 1.89 \text{ atm})(5.20 \text{ L} - 0.130 \text{ L}) = (3.50 \text{ mol})(0.0821 \text{ L} \cdot \text{atm/K} \cdot \text{mol})(320 \text{ K})$$

$$P = 16.2 \text{ atm}$$

Check Based on your understanding of nonideal gas behavior, is it reasonable that the pressure calculated using the van der Waals equation should be smaller than that using the ideal gas equation? Why?

Similar problem: 5.93.

Practice Exercise Using the data shown in Table 5.4, calculate the pressure exerted by 4.37 moles of molecular chlorine confined in a volume of 2.45 L at 38°C. Compare the pressure with that calculated using the ideal gas equation.

Review of Concepts

What pressure and temperature conditions cause the most deviation from ideal gas behavior?

Key Equations

$P_1V_1 = P_2V_2$ (5.2)	Boyle's law. For calculating pressure or volume changes.
$\dfrac{V_1}{T_1} = \dfrac{V_2}{T_2}$ (5.4)	Charles' law. For calculating temperature or volume changes.
$\dfrac{P_1}{T_1} = \dfrac{P_2}{T_2}$ (5.6)	Charles' law. For calculating temperature or pressure changes.
$V = k_4 n$ (5.7)	Avogadro's law. Constant P and T.
$PV = nRT$ (5.8)	Ideal gas equation.
$\dfrac{P_1V_1}{n_1T_1} = \dfrac{P_2V_2}{n_2T_2}$ (5.9)	For calculating changes in pressure, temperature, volume, or amount of gas.
$\dfrac{P_1V_1}{T_1} = \dfrac{P_2V_2}{T_2}$ (5.10)	For calculating changes in pressure, temperature, or volume when n is constant.
$d = \dfrac{P\mathcal{M}}{RT}$ (5.11)	For calculating density or molar mass.
$X_i = \dfrac{n_i}{n_T}$ (5.13)	Definition of mole fraction.
$P_i = X_i P_T$ (5.14)	Dalton's law of partial pressures. For calculating partial pressures.
$\overline{KE} = \tfrac{1}{2}m\overline{u^2} = CT$ (5.15)	Relating the average kinetic energy of a gas to its absolute temperature.

$$u_{rms} = \sqrt{\frac{3RT}{\mathcal{M}}} \quad (5.16)$$

For calculating the root-mean-square speed of gas molecules.

$$\frac{r_1}{r_2} = \sqrt{\frac{\mathcal{M}_2}{\mathcal{M}_1}} \quad (5.17)$$

Graham's law of diffusion and effusion.

$$\left(P + \frac{an^2}{V^2}\right)(V - nb) = nRT \quad (5.18)$$

van der Waals equation. For calculating the pressure of a nonideal gas.

Summary of Facts & Concepts

1. At 25°C and 1 atm, a number of elements and molecular compounds exist as gases. Ionic compounds are solids rather than gases under atmospheric conditions.

2. Gases exert pressure because their molecules move freely and collide with any surface with which they make contact. Units of gas pressure include millimeters of mercury (mmHg), torr, pascals, and atmospheres. One atmosphere equals 760 mmHg, or 760 torr.

3. The pressure-volume relationships of ideal gases are governed by Boyle's law: Volume is inversely proportional to pressure (at constant T and n).

4. The temperature-volume relationships of ideal gases are described by Charles' and Gay-Lussac's law: Volume is directly proportional to temperature (at constant P and n).

5. Absolute zero (-273.15°C) is the lowest theoretically attainable temperature. The Kelvin temperature scale takes 0 K as absolute zero. In all gas law calculations, temperature must be expressed in kelvins.

6. The amount-volume relationships of ideal gases are described by Avogadro's law: Equal volumes of gases contain equal numbers of molecules (at the same T and P).

7. The ideal gas equation, $PV = nRT$, combines the laws of Boyle, Charles, and Avogadro. This equation describes the behavior of an ideal gas.

8. Dalton's law of partial pressures states that each gas in a mixture of gases exerts the same pressure that it would if it were alone and occupied the same volume.

9. The kinetic molecular theory, a mathematical way of describing the behavior of gas molecules, is based on the following assumptions: Gas molecules are separated by distances far greater than their own dimensions, they possess mass but have negligible volume, they are in constant motion, and they frequently collide with one another. The molecules neither attract nor repel one another.

10. A Maxwell speed distribution curve shows how many gas molecules are moving at various speeds at a given temperature. As temperature increases, more molecules move at greater speeds.

11. In diffusion, two gases gradually mix with each other. In effusion, gas molecules move through a small opening under pressure. Both processes are governed by the same mathematical law—Graham's law of diffusion and effusion.

12. The van der Waals equation is a modification of the ideal gas equation that takes into account the nonideal behavior of real gases. It corrects for the fact that real gas molecules do exert forces on each other and that they do have volume. The van der Waals constants are determined experimentally for each gas.

Key Words

Questions & Problems

Substances That Exist as Gases

Review Questions

● 5.1   Name five elements and five compounds that exist as gases at room temperature.

5.2   List the physical characteristics of gases.

Pressure of a Gas

Review Questions

5.3   Define pressure and give the common units for pressure.

5.4   When you are in a plane flying at high altitudes, your ears often experience pain. This discomfort can be temporarily relieved by yawning or swallowing some water. Explain.

5.5   Why is mercury a more suitable substance to use in a barometer than water?

5.6   Explain why the height of mercury in a barometer is independent of the cross-sectional area of the tube. Would the barometer still work if the tubing were tilted at an angle, say 15° (see Figure 5.3)?

5.7   Explain how a unit of length (mmHg) can be used as a unit for pressure.

5.8   Describe what would happen to the column of mercury in the following manometers when the stopcock is opened.

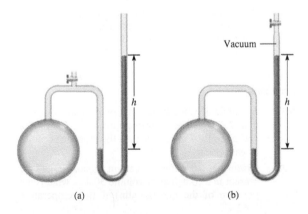

(a)   (b)

5.9   What is the difference between a gas and a vapor? At 25°C, which of the following substances in the gas phase should be properly called a gas and which should be called a vapor: molecular nitrogen (N_2), mercury?

5.10   If the maximum distance that water may be brought up a well by a suction pump is 34 ft (10.3 m), how is it possible to obtain water and oil from hundreds of feet below the surface of Earth?

5.11   Why is it that if the barometer reading falls in one part of the world, it must rise somewhere else?

5.12   Why do astronauts have to wear protective suits when they are on the surface of the moon?

Problems

5.13   Convert 562 mmHg to atm.

● 5.14   The atmospheric pressure at the summit of Mt. McKinley is 606 mmHg on a certain day. What is the pressure in atm and in kPa?

The Gas Laws

Review Questions

5.15   State the following gas laws in words and also in the form of an equation: Boyle's law, Charles' law, Avogadro's law. In each case, indicate the conditions under which the law is applicable, and give the units for each quantity in the equation.

5.16   A certain amount of gas is contained in a closed mercury manometer as shown here. Assuming no other parameters change, would h increase, decrease, or remain the same if (a) the amount of the gas were increased; (b) the molar mass of the gas were doubled; (c) the temperature of the gas was increased; (d) the atmospheric pressure in the room was increased; (e) the mercury in the tube were replaced with a less dense fluid; (f) some gas was added to the vacuum at the top of the right-side tube; (g) a hole was drilled in the top of the right-side tube?

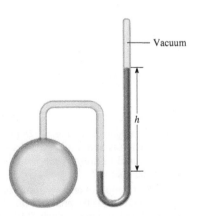

Problems

● 5.17   A gaseous sample of a substance is cooled at constant pressure. Which of the following diagrams best represents the situation if the final temperature is

216   **Chapter 5** ▪ Gases

(a) above the boiling point of the substance and (b) below the boiling point but above the freezing point of the substance?

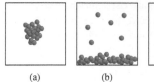 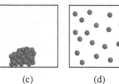

(a)   (b)   (c)   (d)

● **5.18** Consider the following gaseous sample in a cylinder fitted with a movable piston. Initially there are n moles of the gas at temperature T, pressure P, and volume V.

Choose the cylinder that correctly represents the gas after each of the following changes. (1) The pressure on the piston is tripled at constant n and T. (2) The temperature is doubled at constant n and P. (3) n moles of another gas are added at constant T and P. (4) T is halved and pressure on the piston is reduced to a quarter of its original value.

(a)   (b)   (c)

● **5.19** A gas occupying a volume of 725 mL at a pressure of 0.970 atm is allowed to expand at constant temperature until its pressure reaches 0.541 atm. What is its final volume?

● **5.20** At 46°C a sample of ammonia gas exerts a pressure of 5.3 atm. What is the pressure when the volume of the gas is reduced to one-tenth (0.10) of the original value at the same temperature?

● **5.21** The volume of a gas is 5.80 L, measured at 1.00 atm. What is the pressure of the gas in mmHg if the volume is changed to 9.65 L? (The temperature remains constant.)

● **5.22** A sample of air occupies 3.8 L when the pressure is 1.2 atm. (a) What volume does it occupy at 6.6 atm? (b) What pressure is required in order to compress it to 0.075 L? (The temperature is kept constant.)

● **5.23** A 36.4-L volume of methane gas is heated from 25°C to 88°C at constant pressure. What is the final volume of the gas?

● **5.24** Under constant-pressure conditions a sample of hydrogen gas initially at 88°C and 9.6 L is cooled until its final volume is 3.4 L. What is its final temperature?

● **5.25** Ammonia burns in oxygen gas to form nitric oxide (NO) and water vapor. How many volumes of NO are obtained from one volume of ammonia at the same temperature and pressure?

● **5.26** Molecular chlorine and molecular fluorine combine to form a gaseous product. Under the same conditions of temperature and pressure it is found that one volume of Cl_2 reacts with three volumes of F_2 to yield two volumes of the product. What is the formula of the product?

The Ideal Gas Equation
Review Questions

5.27 List the characteristics of an ideal gas. Write the ideal gas equation and also state it in words. Give the units for each term in the equation.

5.28 Use Equation (5.9) to derive all the gas laws.

5.29 What are standard temperature and pressure (STP)? What is the significance of STP in relation to the volume of 1 mole of an ideal gas?

5.30 Why is the density of a gas much lower than that of a liquid or solid under atmospheric conditions? What units are normally used to express the density of gases?

Problems

● **5.31** A sample of nitrogen gas kept in a container of volume 2.3 L and at a temperature of 32°C exerts a pressure of 4.7 atm. Calculate the number of moles of gas present.

● **5.32** Given that 6.9 moles of carbon monoxide gas are present in a container of volume 30.4 L, what is the pressure of the gas (in atm) if the temperature is 62°C?

● **5.33** What volume will 5.6 moles of sulfur hexafluoride (SF_6) gas occupy if the temperature and pressure of the gas are 128°C and 9.4 atm?

● **5.34** A certain amount of gas at 25°C and at a pressure of 0.800 atm is contained in a glass vessel. Suppose that the vessel can withstand a pressure of 2.00 atm. How high can you raise the temperature of the gas without bursting the vessel?

5.35 A gas-filled balloon having a volume of 2.50 L at 1.2 atm and 25°C is allowed to rise to the stratosphere (about 30 km above the surface of Earth), where the temperature and pressure are −23°C and 3.00×10^{-3} atm, respectively. Calculate the final volume of the balloon.

5.36 The temperature of 2.5 L of a gas initially at STP is raised to 250°C at constant volume. Calculate the final pressure of the gas in atm.

5.37 The pressure of 6.0 L of an ideal gas in a flexible container is decreased to one-third of its original pressure, and its absolute temperature is decreased by one-half. What is the final volume of the gas?

5.38 A gas evolved during the fermentation of glucose (wine making) has a volume of 0.78 L at 20.1°C and 1.00 atm. What was the volume of this gas at the fermentation temperature of 36.5°C and 1.00 atm pressure?

5.39 An ideal gas originally at 0.85 atm and 66°C was allowed to expand until its final volume, pressure, and temperature were 94 mL, 0.60 atm, and 45°C, respectively. What was its initial volume?

5.40 Calculate its volume (in liters) of 88.4 g of CO_2 at STP.

5.41 A gas at 772 mmHg and 35.0°C occupies a volume of 6.85 L. Calculate its volume at STP.

5.42 Dry ice is solid carbon dioxide. A 0.050-g sample of dry ice is placed in an evacuated 4.6-L vessel at 30°C. Calculate the pressure inside the vessel after all the dry ice has been converted to CO_2 gas.

5.43 At STP, 0.280 L of a gas weighs 0.400 g. Calculate the molar mass of the gas.

5.44 At 741 torr and 44°C, 7.10 g of a gas occupy a volume of 5.40 L. What is the molar mass of the gas?

5.45 Ozone molecules in the stratosphere absorb much of the harmful radiation from the sun. Typically, the temperature and pressure of ozone in the stratosphere are 250 K and 1.0×10^{-3} atm, respectively. How many ozone molecules are present in 1.0 L of air under these conditions?

5.46 Assuming that air contains 78 percent N_2, 21 percent O_2, and 1 percent Ar, all by volume, how many molecules of each type of gas are present in 1.0 L of air at STP?

5.47 A 2.10-L vessel contains 4.65 g of a gas at 1.00 atm and 27.0°C. (a) Calculate the density of the gas in grams per liter. (b) What is the molar mass of the gas?

5.48 Calculate the density of hydrogen bromide (HBr) gas in grams per liter at 733 mmHg and 46°C.

5.49 A certain anesthetic contains 64.9 percent C, 13.5 percent H, and 21.6 percent O by mass. At 120°C and 750 mmHg, 1.00 L of the gaseous compound weighs 2.30 g. What is the molecular formula of the compound?

5.50 A compound has the empirical formula SF_4. At 20°C, 0.100 g of the gaseous compound occupies a volume of 22.1 mL and exerts a pressure of 1.02 atm. What is the molecular formula of the gas?

5.51 What pressure will be required for neon at 30°C to have the same density as nitrogen at 20°C and 1.0 atm?

5.52 The density of a mixture of fluorine and chlorine gases is 1.77 g/L at 14°C and 0.893 atm. Calculate the mass percent of the gases.

Gas Stoichiometry
Problems

5.53 Consider the formation of nitrogen dioxide from nitric oxide and oxygen:

$$2NO(g) + O_2(g) \longrightarrow 2NO_2(g)$$

If 9.0 L of NO are reacted with excess O_2 at STP, what is the volume in liters of the NO_2 produced?

5.54 Methane, the principal component of natural gas, is used for heating and cooking. The combustion process is

$$CH_4(g) + 2O_2(g) \longrightarrow CO_2(g) + 2H_2O(l)$$

If 15.0 moles of CH_4 are reacted, what is the volume of CO_2 (in liters) produced at 23.0°C and 0.985 atm?

5.55 When coal is burned, the sulfur present in coal is converted to sulfur dioxide (SO_2), which is responsible for the acid rain phenomenon.

$$S(s) + O_2(g) \longrightarrow SO_2(g)$$

If 2.54 kg of S are reacted with oxygen, calculate the volume of SO_2 gas (in mL) formed at 30.5°C and 1.12 atm.

5.56 In alcohol fermentation, yeast converts glucose to ethanol and carbon dioxide:

$$C_6H_{12}O_6(s) \longrightarrow 2C_2H_5OH(l) + 2CO_2(g)$$

If 5.97 g of glucose are reacted and 1.44 L of CO_2 gas are collected at 293 K and 0.984 atm, what is the percent yield of the reaction?

5.57 A compound of P and F was analyzed as follows: Heating 0.2324 g of the compound in a 378-cm^3 container turned all of it to gas, which had a pressure of 97.3 mmHg at 77°C. Then the gas was mixed with calcium chloride solution, which turned all of the F to 0.2631 g of CaF_2. Determine the molecular formula of the compound.

5.58 A quantity of 0.225 g of a metal M (molar mass = 27.0 g/mol) liberated 0.303 L of molecular hydrogen (measured at 17°C and 741 mmHg) from an excess of hydrochloric acid. Deduce from these data the corresponding equation and write formulas for the oxide and sulfate of M.

5.59 What is the mass of the solid NH_4Cl formed when 73.0 g of NH_3 are mixed with an equal mass of HCl? What is the volume of the gas remaining, measured at 14.0°C and 752 mmHg? What gas is it?

5.60 Dissolving 3.00 g of an impure sample of calcium carbonate in hydrochloric acid produced 0.656 L of carbon dioxide (measured at 20.0°C and 792 mmHg). Calculate the percent by mass of calcium carbonate in the sample. State any assumptions.

5.61 Calculate the mass in grams of hydrogen chloride produced when 5.6 L of molecular hydrogen measured at STP react with an excess of molecular chlorine gas.

5.62 Ethanol (C_2H_5OH) burns in air:

$$C_2H_5OH(l) + O_2(g) \longrightarrow CO_2(g) + H_2O(l)$$

Balance the equation and determine the volume of air in liters at 35.0°C and 790 mmHg required to burn 227 g of ethanol. Assume that air is 21.0 percent O_2 by volume.

5.63 (a) What volumes (in liters) of ammonia and oxygen must react to form 12.8 L of nitric oxide according to the equation at the same temperature and pressure?

$$4NH_3(g) + 5O_2(g) \longrightarrow 4NO(g) + 6H_2O(g)$$

(b) What volumes (in liters) of propane and water vapor must react to form 8.96 L of hydrogen according to the equation at the same temperature and pressure?

$$C_3H_8(g) + 3H_2O(g) \longrightarrow 3CO(g) + 7H_2(g)$$

5.64 A 4.00-g sample of FeS containing nonsulfide impurities reacted with HCl to give 896 mL of H_2S at 14°C and 782 mmHg. Calculate mass percent purity of the sample.

Dalton's Law of Partial Pressures

Review Questions

5.65 State Dalton's law of partial pressures and explain what mole fraction is. Does mole fraction have units?

5.66 A sample of air contains only nitrogen and oxygen gases whose partial pressures are 0.80 atm and 0.20 atm, respectively. Calculate the total pressure and the mole fractions of the gases.

Problems

5.67 A mixture of gases contains 0.31 mol CH_4, 0.25 mol C_2H_6, and 0.29 mol C_3H_8. The total pressure is 1.50 atm. Calculate the partial pressures of the gases.

5.68 A 2.5-L flask at 15°C contains a mixture of N_2, He, and Ne at partial pressures of 0.32 atm for N_2, 0.15 atm for He, and 0.42 atm for Ne. (a) Calculate the total

pressure of the mixture. (b) Calculate the volume in liters at STP occupied by He and Ne if the N_2 is removed selectively.

5.69 Dry air near sea level has the following composition by volume: N_2, 78.08 percent; O_2, 20.94 percent; Ar, 0.93 percent; CO_2, 0.05 percent. The atmospheric pressure is 1.00 atm. Calculate (a) the partial pressure of each gas in atm and (b) the concentration of each gas in moles per liter at 0°C. (*Hint:* Because volume is proportional to the number of moles present, mole fractions of gases can be expressed as ratios of volumes at the same temperature and pressure.)

5.70 A mixture of helium and neon gases is collected over water at 28.0°C and 745 mmHg. If the partial pressure of helium is 368 mmHg, what is the partial pressure of neon? (Vapor pressure of water at 28°C = 28.3 mmHg.)

5.71 A piece of sodium metal reacts completely with water as follows:

$$2Na(s) + 2H_2O(l) \longrightarrow 2NaOH(aq) + H_2(g)$$

The hydrogen gas generated is collected over water at 25.0°C. The volume of the gas is 246 mL measured at 1.00 atm. Calculate the number of grams of sodium used in the reaction. (Vapor pressure of water at 25°C = 0.0313 atm.)

5.72 A sample of zinc metal reacts completely with an excess of hydrochloric acid:

$$Zn(s) + 2HCl(aq) \longrightarrow ZnCl_2(aq) + H_2(g)$$

The hydrogen gas produced is collected over water at 25.0°C using an arrangement similar to that shown in Figure 5.15. The volume of the gas is 7.80 L, and the pressure is 0.980 atm. Calculate the amount of zinc metal in grams consumed in the reaction. (Vapor pressure of water at 25°C = 23.8 mmHg.)

5.73 Helium is mixed with oxygen gas for deep-sea divers. Calculate the percent by volume of oxygen gas in the mixture if the diver has to submerge to a depth where the total pressure is 4.2 atm. The partial pressure of oxygen is maintained at 0.20 atm at this depth.

5.74 A sample of ammonia (NH_3) gas is completely decomposed to nitrogen and hydrogen gases over heated iron wool. If the total pressure is 866 mmHg, calculate the partial pressures of N_2 and H_2.

5.75 Consider the three gas containers shown here. All of them have the same volume and are at the same temperature. (a) Which container has the smallest mole fraction of gas A (blue sphere)? (b) Which container has the highest partial pressure of gas B (green sphere)?

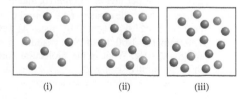

(i)   (ii)   (iii)

5.76 The volume of the box on the right is twice that of the box on the left. The boxes contain helium atoms (red) and hydrogen molecules (green) at the same temperature. (a) Which box has a higher total pressure? (b) Which box has a lower partial pressure of helium?

 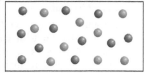

Kinetic Molecular Theory of Gases
Review Questions

5.77 What are the basic assumptions of the kinetic molecular theory of gases? How does the kinetic molecular theory explain Boyle's law, Charles' law, Avogadro's law, and Dalton's law of partial pressures?

5.78 What does the Maxwell speed distribution curve tell us? Does Maxwell's theory work for a sample of 200 molecules? Explain.

5.79 Which of the following statements is correct? (a) Heat is produced by the collision of gas molecules against one another. (b) When a gas is heated, the molecules collide with one another more often.

5.80 What is the difference between gas diffusion and effusion? State Graham's law and define the terms in Equation (5.17).

Problems

5.81 Compare the root-mean-square speeds of O_2 and UF_6 at 65°C.

5.82 The temperature in the stratosphere is −23°C. Calculate the root-mean-square speeds of N_2, O_2, and O_3 molecules in this region.

5.83 The average distance traveled by a molecule between successive collisions is called *mean free path*. For a given amount of a gas, how does the mean free path of a gas depend on (a) density, (b) temperature at constant volume, (c) pressure at constant temperature, (d) volume at constant temperature, and (e) size of the atoms?

5.84 At a certain temperature the speeds of six gaseous molecules in a container are 2.0 m/s, 2.2 m/s, 2.6 m/s, 2.7 m/s, 3.3 m/s, and 3.5 m/s. Calculate the root-mean-square speed and the average speed of the molecules. These two average values are close to each other, but the root-mean-square value is always the larger of the two. Why?

5.85 Based on your knowledge of the kinetic theory of gases, derive Graham's law [Equation (5.17)].

5.86 The ^{235}U isotope undergoes fission when bombarded with neutrons. However, its natural abundance is only 0.72 percent. To separate it from the more abundant ^{238}U isotope, uranium is first converted to UF_6, which is easily vaporized above room temperature. The mixture of the $^{235}UF_6$ and $^{238}UF_6$ gases is then subjected to many stages of effusion. Calculate the separation factor, that is, the enrichment of ^{235}U relative to ^{238}U after one stage of effusion.

5.87 A gas evolved from the fermentation of glucose is found to effuse through a porous barrier in 15.0 min. Under the same conditions of temperature and pressure, it takes an equal volume of N_2 12.0 min to effuse through the same barrier. Calculate the molar mass of the gas and suggest what the gas might be.

5.88 Nickel forms a gaseous compound of the formula $Ni(CO)_x$. What is the value of x given the fact that under the same conditions of temperature and pressure, methane (CH_4) effuses 3.3 times faster than the compound?

Deviation from Ideal Behavior
Review Questions

5.89 Cite two pieces of evidence to show that gases do not behave ideally under all conditions.

5.90 Under what set of conditions would a gas be expected to behave most ideally? (a) High temperature and low pressure, (b) high temperature and high pressure, (c) low temperature and high pressure, (d) low temperature and low pressure.

5.91 Shown here are plots of PV/RT against P for one mole of a nonideal gas at two different temperatures. Which curve is at the higher temperature?

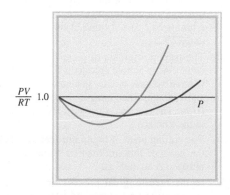

5.92 (a) A real gas is introduced into a flask of volume V. Is the corrected volume of the gas greater or less than V? (b) Ammonia has a larger a value than neon does (see Table 5.4). What can you conclude about the relative strength of the attractive forces between molecules of ammonia and between atoms of neon?

Problems

● 5.93   Using the data shown in Table 5.4, calculate the pressure exerted by 2.50 moles of CO_2 confined in a volume of 5.00 L at 450 K. Compare the pressure with that predicted by the ideal gas equation.

5.94   At 27°C, 10.0 moles of a gas in a 1.50-L container exert a pressure of 130 atm. Is this an ideal gas?

Additional Problems

5.95   Discuss the following phenomena in terms of the gas laws: (a) the pressure increase in an automobile tire on a hot day, (b) the "popping" of a paper bag, (c) the expansion of a weather balloon as it rises in the air, (d) the loud noise heard when a lightbulb shatters.

5.96   Under the same conditions of temperature and pressure, which of the following gases would behave most ideally: Ne, N_2, or CH_4? Explain.

● 5.97   Nitroglycerin, an explosive compound, decomposes according to the equation

$$4C_3H_5(NO_3)_3(s) \longrightarrow$$
$$12CO_2(g) + 10H_2O(g) + 6N_2(g) + O_2(g)$$

Calculate the total volume of gases when collected at 1.2 atm and 25°C from 2.6×10^2 g of nitroglycerin. What are the partial pressures of the gases under these conditions?

● **5.98**   The empirical formula of a compound is CH. At 200°C, 0.145 g of this compound occupies 97.2 mL at a pressure of 0.74 atm. What is the molecular formula of the compound?

● **5.99**   When ammonium nitrite (NH_4NO_2) is heated, it decomposes to give nitrogen gas. This property is used to inflate some tennis balls. (a) Write a balanced equation for the reaction. (b) Calculate the quantity (in grams) of NH_4NO_2 needed to inflate a tennis ball to a volume of 86.2 mL at 1.20 atm and 22°C.

● **5.100**   The percent by mass of bicarbonate (HCO_3^-) in a certain Alka-Seltzer product is 32.5 percent. Calculate the volume of CO_2 generated (in mL) at 37°C and 1.00 atm when a person ingests a 3.29-g tablet. (*Hint:* The reaction is between HCO_3^- and HCl acid in the stomach.)

5.101   The boiling point of liquid nitrogen is −196°C. On the basis of this information alone, do you think nitrogen is an ideal gas?

● **5.102**   In the metallurgical process of refining nickel, the metal is first combined with carbon monoxide to form tetracarbonylnickel, which is a gas at 43°C:

$$Ni(s) + 4CO(g) \longrightarrow Ni(CO)_4(g)$$

This reaction separates nickel from other solid impurities. (a) Starting with 86.4 g of Ni, calculate the pressure of $Ni(CO)_4$ in a container of volume 4.00 L. (Assume the above reaction goes to completion.) (b) At temperatures above 43°C, the pressure of the gas is observed to increase much more rapidly than predicted by the ideal gas equation. Explain.

5.103   The partial pressure of carbon dioxide varies with seasons. Would you expect the partial pressure in the Northern Hemisphere to be higher in the summer or winter? Explain.

5.104   A healthy adult exhales about 5.0×10^2 mL of a gaseous mixture with each breath. Calculate the number of molecules present in this volume at 37°C and 1.1 atm. List the major components of this gaseous mixture.

● 5.105   Sodium bicarbonate ($NaHCO_3$) is called baking soda because when heated, it releases carbon dioxide gas, which is responsible for the rising of cookies, doughnuts, and bread. (a) Calculate the volume (in liters) of CO_2 produced by heating 5.0 g of $NaHCO_3$ at 180°C and 1.3 atm. (b) Ammonium bicarbonate (NH_4HCO_3) has also been used for the same purpose. Suggest one advantage and one disadvantage of using NH_4HCO_3 instead of $NaHCO_3$ for baking.

5.106   A barometer having a cross-sectional area of 1.00 cm^2 at sea level measures a pressure of 76.0 cm of mercury. The pressure exerted by this column of mercury is equal to the pressure exerted by all the air on 1 cm^2 of Earth's surface. Given that the density of mercury is 13.6 g/mL and the average radius of Earth is 6371 km, calculate the total mass of Earth's atmosphere in kilograms. (*Hint:* The surface area of a sphere is $4\pi r^2$ where r is the radius of the sphere.)

● 5.107   Some commercial drain cleaners contain a mixture of sodium hydroxide and aluminum powder. When the mixture is poured down a clogged drain, the following reaction occurs:

$$2NaOH(aq) + 2Al(s) + 6H_2O(l) \longrightarrow$$
$$2NaAl(OH)_4(aq) + 3H_2(g)$$

The heat generated in this reaction helps melt away obstructions such as grease, and the hydrogen gas released stirs up the solids clogging the drain. Calculate the volume of H_2 formed at 23°C and 1.00 atm if 3.12 g of Al are treated with an excess of NaOH.

● **5.108**   The volume of a sample of pure HCl gas was 189 mL at 25°C and 108 mmHg. It was completely dissolved in about 60 mL of water and titrated with an NaOH solution; 15.7 mL of the NaOH solution were required to neutralize the HCl. Calculate the molarity of the NaOH solution.

● 5.109   Propane (C_3H_8) burns in oxygen to produce carbon dioxide gas and water vapor. (a) Write a balanced equation for this reaction. (b) Calculate the number of liters of carbon dioxide measured at STP that could be produced from 7.45 g of propane.

5.110 Consider the following apparatus. Calculate the partial pressures of helium and neon after the stopcock is open. The temperature remains constant at 16°C.

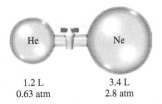

1.2 L
0.63 atm

3.4 L
2.8 atm

5.111 Nitric oxide (NO) reacts with molecular oxygen as follows:

$$2NO(g) + O_2(g) \longrightarrow 2NO_2(g)$$

Initially NO and O_2 are separated as shown here. When the valve is opened, the reaction quickly goes to completion. Determine what gases remain at the end and calculate their partial pressures. Assume that the temperature remains constant at 25°C.

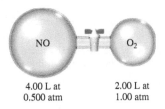

4.00 L at
0.500 atm

2.00 L at
1.00 atm

5.112 Consider the apparatus shown here. When a small amount of water is introduced into the flask by squeezing the bulb of the medicine dropper, water is squirted upward out of the long glass tubing. Explain this observation. (*Hint:* Hydrogen chloride gas is soluble in water.)

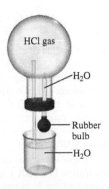

HCl gas

—H$_2$O

—Rubber bulb

—H$_2$O

5.113 Describe how you would measure, by either chemical or physical means, the partial pressures of a mixture of gases of the following composition: (a) CO_2 and H_2, (b) He and N_2.

5.114 A certain hydrate has the formula $MgSO_4 \cdot xH_2O$. A quantity of 54.2 g of the compound is heated in an oven to drive off the water. If the steam generated exerts a pressure of 24.8 atm in a 2.00-L container at 120°C, calculate x.

5.115 A mixture of Na_2CO_3 and $MgCO_3$ of mass 7.63 g is reacted with an excess of hydrochloric acid. The CO_2 gas generated occupies a volume of 1.67 L at 1.24 atm and 26°C. From these data, calculate the percent composition by mass of Na_2CO_3 in the mixture.

5.116 The following apparatus can be used to measure atomic and molecular speed. Suppose that a beam of metal atoms is directed at a rotating cylinder in a vacuum. A small opening in the cylinder allows the atoms to strike a target area. Because the cylinder is rotating, atoms traveling at different speeds will strike the target at different positions. In time, a layer of the metal will deposit on the target area, and the variation in its thickness is found to correspond to Maxwell's speed distribution. In one experiment it is found that at 850°C some bismuth (Bi) atoms struck the target at a point 2.80 cm from the spot directly opposite the slit. The diameter of the cylinder is 15.0 cm and it is rotating at 130 revolutions per second. (a) Calculate the speed (m/s) at which the target is moving. (*Hint:* The circumference of a circle is given by $2\pi r$, where r is the radius.) (b) Calculate the time (in seconds) it takes for the target to travel 2.80 cm. (c) Determine the speed of the Bi atoms. Compare your result in (c) with the u_{rms} of Bi at 850°C. Comment on the difference.

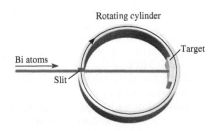

Rotating cylinder

Bi atoms

Slit

Target

5.117 If 10.00 g of water are introduced into an evacuated flask of volume 2.500 L at 65°C, calculate the mass of water vaporized. (*Hint:* Assume that the volume of the remaining liquid water is negligible; the vapor pressure of water at 65°C is 187.5 mmHg.)

5.118 Commercially, compressed oxygen is sold in metal cylinders. If a 120-L cylinder is filled with oxygen to a pressure of 132 atm at 22°C, what is the mass (in grams) of O_2 present? How many liters of O_2 gas at 1.00 atm and 22°C could the cylinder produce? (Assume ideal behavior.)

● 5.119 The shells of hard-boiled eggs sometimes crack due to the rapid thermal expansion of the shells at high temperatures. Suggest another reason why the shells may crack.

5.120 Ethylene gas (C_2H_4) is emitted by fruits and is known to be responsible for their ripening. Based on this information, explain why a bunch of bananas ripens faster in a closed paper bag than in a bowl.

● 5.121 About 8.0×10^6 tons of urea [$(NH_2)_2CO$] are used annually as a fertilizer. The urea is prepared at 200°C and under high-pressure conditions from carbon dioxide and ammonia (the products are urea and steam). Calculate the volume of ammonia (in liters) measured at 150 atm needed to prepare 1.0 ton of urea.

5.122 Some ballpoint pens have a small hole in the main body of the pen. What is the purpose of this hole?

5.123 The gas laws are vitally important to scuba divers. The pressure exerted by 33 ft of seawater is equivalent to 1 atm pressure. (a) A diver ascends quickly to the surface of the water from a depth of 36 ft without exhaling gas from his lungs. By what factor will the volume of his lungs increase by the time he reaches the surface? Assume that the temperature is constant. (b) The partial pressure of oxygen in air is about 0.20 atm. (Air is 20 percent oxygen by volume.) In deep-sea diving, the composition of air the diver breathes must be changed to maintain this partial pressure. What must the oxygen content (in percent by volume) be when the total pressure exerted on the diver is 4.0 atm? (At constant temperature and pressure, the volume of a gas is directly proportional to the number of moles of gases.) (*Hint:* See the Chemistry in Action essay on p. 200.)

5.124 Nitrous oxide (N_2O) can be obtained by the thermal decomposition of ammonium nitrate (NH_4NO_3). (a) Write a balanced equation for the reaction. (b) In a certain experiment, a student obtains 0.340 L of the gas at 718 mmHg and 24°C. If the gas weighs 0.580 g, calculate the value of the gas constant.

● 5.125 Two vessels are labeled A and B. Vessel A contains NH_3 gas at 70°C, and vessel B contains Ne gas at the same temperature. If the average kinetic energy of NH_3 is 7.1×10^{-21} J/molecule, calculate the mean-square speed of Ne atoms in m^2/s^2.

5.126 Which of the following molecules has the largest a value: CH_4, F_2, C_6H_6, Ne?

5.127 The following procedure is a simple though somewhat crude way to measure the molar mass of a gas. A liquid of mass 0.0184 g is introduced into a syringe like the one shown here by injection through the rubber tip using a hypodermic needle. The syringe is then transferred to a temperature bath heated to 45°C, and the liquid vaporizes. The final volume of the vapor (measured by the outward movement of the plunger) is 5.58 mL and the atmospheric pressure is 760 mmHg. Given that the compound's empirical formula is CH_2, determine the molar mass of the compound.

5.128 In 1995 a man suffocated as he walked by an abandoned mine in England. At that moment there was a sharp drop in atmospheric pressure due to a change in the weather. Suggest what might have caused the man's death.

● 5.129 Acidic oxides such as carbon dioxide react with basic oxides like calcium oxide (CaO) and barium oxide (BaO) to form salts (metal carbonates). (a) Write equations representing these two reactions. (b) A student placed a mixture of BaO and CaO of combined mass 4.88 g in a 1.46-L flask containing carbon dioxide gas at 35°C and 746 mmHg. After the reactions were complete, she found that the CO_2 pressure had dropped to 252 mmHg. Calculate the percent composition by mass of the mixture. Assume volumes of the solids are negligible.

5.130 Identify the Maxwell speed distribution curves shown here with the following gases: Br_2, CH_4, N_2, SO_3.

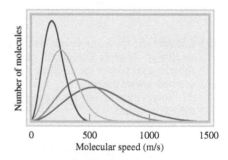

● 5.131 The running engine of an automobile produces carbon monoxide (CO), a toxic gas, at the rate of about 188 g CO per hour. A car is left idling in a poorly ventilated garage that is 6.0 m long, 4.0 m wide, and 2.2 m high at 20°C. (a) Calculate the rate of CO production in moles per minute. (b) How long would it take to build up a lethal concentration of CO of 1000 ppmv (parts per million by volume)?

5.132 Interstellar space contains mostly hydrogen atoms at a concentration of about 1 atom/cm^3. (a) Calculate the pressure of the H atoms. (b) Calculate the volume (in liters) that contains 1.0 g of H atoms. The temperature is 3 K.

5.133   Atop Mt. Everest, the atmospheric pressure is 210 mmHg and the air density is 0.426 kg/m³. (a) Calculate the air temperature, given that the molar mass of air is 29.0 g/mol. (b) Assuming no change in air composition, calculate the percent decrease in oxygen gas from sea level to the top of Mt. Everest.

5.134   Relative humidity is defined as the ratio (expressed as a percentage) of the partial pressure of water vapor in the air to the equilibrium vapor pressure (see Table 5.3) at a given temperature. On a certain summer day in North Carolina the partial pressure of water vapor in the air is 3.9×10^3 Pa at 30°C. Calculate the relative humidity.

5.135   Under the same conditions of temperature and pressure, why does one liter of moist air weigh less than one liter of dry air? In weather forecasts, an oncoming low-pressure front usually means imminent rainfall. Explain.

● 5.136   Air entering the lungs ends up in tiny sacs called alveoli. It is from the alveoli that oxygen diffuses into the blood. The average radius of the alveoli is 0.0050 cm and the air inside contains 14 percent oxygen. Assuming that the pressure in the alveoli is 1.0 atm and the temperature is 37°C, calculate the number of oxygen molecules in one of the alveoli. (*Hint:* The volume of a sphere of radius r is $\frac{4}{3}\pi r^3$.)

5.137   A student breaks a thermometer and spills most of the mercury (Hg) onto the floor of a laboratory that measures 15.2 m long, 6.6 m wide, and 2.4 m high. (a) Calculate the mass of mercury vapor (in grams) in the room at 20°C. The vapor pressure of mercury at 20°C is 1.7×10^{-6} atm. (b) Does the concentration of mercury vapor exceed the air quality regulation of 0.050 mg Hg/m³ of air? (c) One way to treat small quantities of spilled mercury is to spray sulfur powder over the metal. Suggest a physical and a chemical reason for this action.

5.138   Consider two bulbs containing argon (left) and oxygen (right) gases. After the stopcock is opened, the pressure of the combined gases is 1.08 atm. Calculate the volume of the right bulb. The temperature is kept at 20°C. Assume ideal behavior.

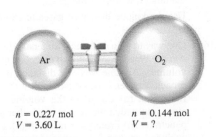

$n = 0.227$ mol $n = 0.144$ mol
$V = 3.60$ L $V = ?$

● 5.139   Nitrogen dioxide (NO_2) cannot be obtained in a pure form in the gas phase because it exists as a mixture of NO_2 and N_2O_4. At 25°C and 0.98 atm, the density of this gas mixture is 2.7 g/L. What is the partial pressure of each gas?

5.140   The Chemistry in Action essay on p. 208 describes the cooling of rubidium vapor to 5.0×10^{-8} K. Calculate the root-mean-square speed and average kinetic energy of a Rb atom at this temperature.

● 5.141   Lithium hydride reacts with water as follows:

$$LiH(s) + H_2O(l) \longrightarrow LiOH(aq) + H_2(g)$$

During World War II, U.S. pilots carried LiH tablets. In the event of a crash landing at sea, the LiH would react with the seawater and fill their life belts and lifeboats with hydrogen gas. How many grams of LiH are needed to fill a 4.1-L life belt at 0.97 atm and 12°C?

5.142   The atmosphere on Mars is composed mainly of carbon dioxide. The surface temperature is 220 K and the atmospheric pressure is about 6.0 mmHg. Taking these values as Martian "STP," calculate the molar volume in liters of an ideal gas on Mars.

5.143   Venus's atmosphere is composed of 96.5 percent CO_2, 3.5 percent N_2, and 0.015 percent SO_2 by volume. Its standard atmospheric pressure is 9.0×10^6 Pa. Calculate the partial pressures of the gases in pascals.

5.144   A student tries to determine the volume of a bulb like the one shown on p. 191. These are her results: Mass of the bulb filled with dry air at 23°C and 744 mmHg = 91.6843 g; mass of evacuated bulb = 91.4715 g. Assume the composition of air is 78 percent N_2, 21 percent O_2, and 1 percent argon. What is the volume (in milliliters) of the bulb? (*Hint:* First calculate the average molar mass of air, as shown in Problem 3.152.)

5.145   Apply your knowledge of the kinetic theory of gases to the following situations. (a) Two flasks of volumes V_1 and V_2 ($V_2 > V_1$) contain the same number of helium atoms at the same temperature. (i) Compare the root-mean-square (rms) speeds and average kinetic energies of the helium (He) atoms in the flasks. (ii) Compare the frequency and the force with which the He atoms collide with the walls of their containers. (b) Equal numbers of He atoms are placed in two flasks of the same volume at temperatures T_1 and T_2 ($T_2 > T_1$). (i) Compare the rms speeds of the atoms in the two flasks. (ii) Compare the frequency and the force with which the He atoms collide with the walls of their containers. (c) Equal numbers of He and neon (Ne) atoms are placed in two flasks of the same volume, and the temperature of both gases is 74°C. Comment on the validity of the following statements: (i) The rms speed of He is equal to that of Ne. (ii) The average kinetic energies of the two gases are equal. (iii) The rms speed of each He atom is 1.47×10^3 m/s.

224 **Chapter 5** ▪ Gases

• **5.146** It has been said that every breath we take, on average, contains molecules that were once exhaled by Wolfgang Amadeus Mozart (1756–1791). The following calculations demonstrate the validity of this statement. (a) Calculate the total number of molecules in the atmosphere. (*Hint:* Use the result in Problem 5.106 and 29.0 g/mol as the molar mass of air.) (b) Assuming the volume of every breath (inhale or exhale) is 500 mL, calculate the number of molecules exhaled in each breath at 37°C, which is the body temperature. (c) If Mozart's life span was exactly 35 years, what is the number of molecules he exhaled in that period? (Given that an average person breathes 12 times per minute.) (d) Calculate the fraction of molecules in the atmosphere that was exhaled by Mozart. How many of Mozart's molecules do we breathe in with every inhalation of air? Round off your answer to one significant figure. (e) List three important assumptions in these calculations.

5.147 At what temperature will He atoms have the same u_{rms} value as N_2 molecules at 25°C?

5.148 Estimate the distance (in nanometers) between molecules of water vapor at 100°C and 1.0 atm. Assume ideal behavior. Repeat the calculation for liquid water at 100°C, given that the density of water is 0.96 g/cm^3 at that temperature. Comment on your results. (Assume water molecule to be a sphere with a diameter of 0.3 nm.) (*Hint:* First calculate the number density of water molecules. Next, convert the number density to linear density, that is, number of molecules in one direction.)

5.149 Which of the noble gases would not behave ideally under any circumstance? Why?

• **5.150** A relation known as the barometric formula is useful for estimating the change in atmospheric pressure with altitude. The formula is given by $P = P_0e^{-gMh/RT}$, where P and P_0 are the pressures at height h and sea level, respectively, g is the acceleration due to gravity (9.8 m/s^2), M is the average molar mass of air (29.0 g/mol), and R is the gas constant. Calculate the atmospheric pressure in atm at a height of 5.0 km, assuming the temperature is constant at 5°C and $P_0 = 1.0$ atm.

• **5.151** A 5.72-g sample of graphite was heated with 68.4 g of O_2 in a 8.00-L flask. The reaction that took place was

$$C(graphite) + O_2(g) \longrightarrow CO_2(g)$$

After the reaction was complete, the temperature in the flask was 182°C. What was the total pressure inside the flask?

5.152 An equimolar mixture of H_2 and D_2 effuses through an orifice (small hole) at a certain temperature. Calculate the composition (in mole fractions) of the gases that pass through the orifice. The molar mass of D_2 is 2.014 g/mol.

5.153 A mixture of calcium carbonate ($CaCO_3$) and magnesium carbonate ($MgCO_3$) of mass 6.26 g reacts completely with hydrochloric acid (HCl) to generate 1.73 L of CO_2 at 48°C and 1.12 atm. Calculate the mass percentages of $CaCO_3$ and $MgCO_3$ in the mixture.

5.154 A 6.11-g sample of a Cu-Zn alloy reacts with HCl acid to produce hydrogen gas. If the hydrogen gas has a volume of 1.26 L at 22°C and 728 mmHg, what is the percent of Zn in the alloy? (*Hint:* Cu does not react with HCl.)

• **5.155** A stockroom supervisor measured the contents of a partially filled 25.0-gallon acetone drum on a day when the temperature was 18.0°C and atmospheric pressure was 750 mmHg, and found that 15.4 gallons of the solvent remained. After tightly sealing the drum, an assistant dropped the drum while carrying it upstairs to the organic laboratory. The drum was dented and its internal volume was decreased to 20.4 gallons. What is the total pressure inside the drum after the accident? The vapor pressure of acetone at 18.0°C is 400 mmHg. (*Hint:* At the time the drum was sealed, the pressure inside the drum, which is equal to the sum of the pressures of air and acetone, was equal to the atmospheric pressure.)

• **5.156** In 2.00 min, 29.7 mL of He effuse through a small hole. Under the same conditions of pressure and temperature, 10.0 mL of a mixture of CO and CO_2 effuse through the hole in the same amount of time. Calculate the percent composition by volume of the mixture.

5.157 Referring to Figure 5.22, explain the following: (a) Why do the curves dip below the horizontal line labeled ideal gas at low pressures and then why do they arise above the horizontal line at high pressures? (b) Why do the curves all converge to 1 at very low pressures? (c) Each curve intercepts the horizontal line labeled ideal gas. Does it mean that at that point the gas behaves ideally?

• **5.158** A mixture of methane (CH_4) and ethane (C_2H_6) is stored in a container at 294 mmHg. The gases are burned in air to form CO_2 and H_2O. If the pressure of CO_2 is 356 mmHg measured at the same temperature and volume as the original mixture, calculate the mole fractions of the gases.

5.159 Use the kinetic theory of gases to explain why hot air rises.

5.160 One way to gain a physical understanding of b in the van der Waals equation is to calculate the "excluded volume." Assume that the distance of closest approach between two similar atoms is the sum of their radii ($2r$). (a) Calculate the volume around each atom into which the center of another atom cannot penetrate. (b) From your result in (a), calculate the excluded volume for 1 mole of the atoms, which is the constant b. How does this volume compare with the sum of the volumes of 1 mole of the atoms?

5.161 Use the van der Waals constants in Table 5.4 to estimate the radius of argon in picometers. (*Hint:* See Problem 5.160.)

5.162 Identify the gas whose root-mean-square speed is 2.82 times that of hydrogen iodide (HI) at the same temperature.

5.163 A 5.00-mole sample of NH_3 gas is kept in a 1.92-L container at 300 K. If the van der Waals equation is assumed to give the correct answer for the pressure of the gas, calculate the percent error made in using the ideal gas equation to calculate the pressure.

5.164 The root-mean-square speed of a certain gaseous oxide is 493 m/s at 20°C. What is the molecular formula of the compound?

5.165 Referring to Figure 5.17, we see that the maximum of each speed distribution plot is called the most probable speed (u_{mp}) because it is the speed possessed by the largest number of molecules. It is given by $u_{mp} = \sqrt{2RT/\mathscr{M}}$. (a) Compare u_{mp} with u_{rms} for nitrogen at 25°C. (b) The following diagram shows the Maxwell speed distribution curves for an ideal gas at two different temperatures T_1 and T_2. Calculate the value of T_2.

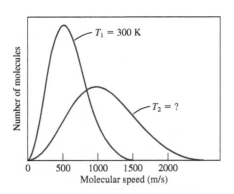

5.166 A gaseous reaction takes place at constant volume and constant pressure in a cylinder shown here. Which of the following equations best describes the reaction? The initial temperature (T_1) is twice that of the final temperature (T_2).

(a) $A + B \longrightarrow C$
(b) $AB \longrightarrow C + D$
(c) $A + B \longrightarrow C + D$
(d) $A + B \longrightarrow 2C + D$

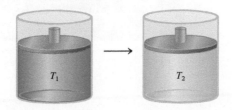

5.167 A gaseous hydrocarbon (containing C and H atoms) in a container of volume 20.2 L at 350 K and 6.63 atm reacts with an excess of oxygen to form 205.1 g of CO_2 and 168.0 g of H_2O. What is the molecular formula of the hydrocarbon?

5.168 Three flasks containing gases A (red) and B (green) are shown here. (i) If the pressure in (a) is 4.0 atm, what are the pressures in (b) and (c)? (ii) Calculate the total pressure and partial pressure of each gas after the valves are opened. The volumes of (a) and (c) are 4.0 L each and that of (b) is 2.0 L. The temperature is the same throughout.

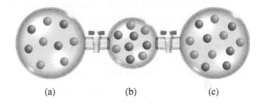

(a)   (b)   (c)

5.169 (a) Show that the pressure exerted by a fluid P (in pascals) is given by $P = hdg$, where h is the column of the fluid in meters, d is the density in kg/m³, and g is the acceleration due to gravity (9.81 m/s²). (*Hint:* See Appendix 2.) (b) The volume of an air bubble that starts at the bottom of a lake at 5.24°C increases by a factor of 6 as it rises to the surface of water where the temperature is 18.73°C and the air pressure is 0.973 atm. The density of the lake water is 1.02 g/cm³. Use the equation in (a) to determine the depth of the lake in meters.

5.170 A student first measured the total pressure of a mixture of gases methane (CH_4), ethane (C_2H_6), and propane (C_3H_8) at a certain temperature, which turned out to be 4.50 atm. She then recorded the mass spectra of the gases shown here. Calculate the partial pressure of the gases.

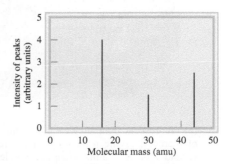

5.171 In 2012, Felix Baumgartner jumped from a balloon roughly 24 mi above Earth, breaking the record for the highest skydive. He reached speeds of more than 700 miles per hour and became the first skydiver to exceed the speed of sound during free

226   **Chapter 5** ▪ Gases

fall. The helium-filled plastic balloon used to carry Baumgartner to the edge of space was designed to expand to 8.5×10^8 L in order to accommodate the low pressures at the altitude required to break the record. (a) Calculate the mass of helium in the balloon from the conditions at the time of the jump (8.5×10^8 L, $-67.8°C$, 0.027 mmHg). (b) Determine the volume of the helium in the balloon just before it was released, assuming a pressure of 1.0 atm and a temperature of 23°C.

Interpreting, Modeling & Estimating

5.172   Which of the following has a greater mass: a sample of air of volume V at a certain temperature T and pressure P or a sample of air plus water vapor having the same volume and at the same temperature and pressure?

5.173   A flask with a volume of 14.5 L contains 1.25 moles of helium gas. Estimate the average distance between He atoms in nanometers.

5.174   Hyperbaric oxygen therapy (HBOT) is very effective in treating burns, crush injuries that impede blood flow, and tissue-damaging infections, as well as carbon monoxide poisoning. However, it has generated some controversy in its application to other maladies (for example, autism, multiple sclerosis). A typical oxygen hyperbaric chamber is shown here. HBOT can be administered using pressure up to six atmospheres, but lower pressures are more common. (a) If this chamber was pressurized to 3.0 atm with pure oxygen, how many moles of O_2 would be contained in an empty chamber? (b) Given that a full tank of oxygen contains about 2500 moles of the gas, how many times could the chamber be filled with a single tank of oxygen?

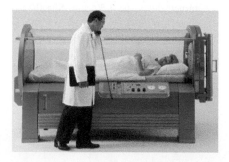

5.175   (a) Fluorescent lightbulbs contain a small amount of mercury, giving a mercury vapor pressure of around 1×10^{-5} atm. When excited electrically, the Hg atoms emit UV light, which excites the phosphor coating of the inner tube, which then emits visible (white) light. Estimate the mass of Hg vapor present in the type of long, thin fluorescent tubes used in offices. (b) Ordinary tungsten incandescent lightbulbs used in households are filled with argon gas at about 0.5 atm to retard the sublimation of the tungsten filament. Estimate the number of moles of Ar in a typical lightbulb.

5.176   (a) Estimate the volume of air at 1.0 atm and 22°C needed to fill a bicycle tire to a pressure of 5.0 atm at the same temperature. (Note that the 5.0 atm is the gauge pressure, which is the difference between the pressure in the tire and atmospheric pressure.) (b) The tire is pumped by filling the cylinder of a hand pump with air at 1.0 atm and then, by compressing the gas in the cylinder, adding all the air in the pump to the air in the tire. If the volume of the pump is 33 percent of the tire's volume, what is the gauge pressure in the tire after three full strokes of the pump?

5.177   On October 15, 2009, a homemade helium balloon was released, and for a while authorities were led to believe that a 6-year-old boy had been carried away in the balloon. (The incident was later revealed to be a hoax.) The balloon traveled more than 50 mi and reached a height of 7000 ft. The shape and span of the balloon are shown in the figure. How much weight could this balloon lift? (A helium balloon can lift a mass equal to the difference in the mass of air and the mass of helium that would be contained in the balloon.) Could it actually lift a 6-year-old boy?

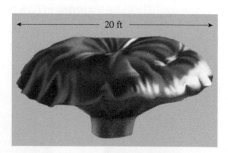

20 ft

Answers to Practice Exercises

5.1 0.986 atm. **5.2** 39.3 kPa. **5.3** 9.29 L. **5.4** 30.6 L.
5.5 4.46×10^3 mmHg. **5.6** 0.68 atm. **5.7** 2.6 atm.
5.8 13.1 g/L. **5.9** 44.1 g/mol. **5.10** B_2H_6. **5.11** 96.9 L.
5.12 4.75 L. **5.13** 0.338 M. **5.14** CH_4: 1.29 atm; C_2H_6:
0.0657 atm; C_3H_8: 0.0181 atm. **5.15** 0.0653 g.
5.16 321 m/s. **5.17** 146 g/mol. **5.18** 30.0 atm;
45.5 atm using the ideal gas equation.

CHEMICAL *MYSTERY*

Out of Oxygen[†]

In September 1991 four men and four women entered the world's largest glass bubble, known as Biosphere II, to test the idea that humans could design and build a totally self-contained ecosystem, a model for some future colony on another planet. Biosphere II (Earth is considered Biosphere I) was a 3-acre mini-world, complete with a tropical rain forest, savanna, marsh, desert, and working farm that was intended to be fully self-sufficient. This unique experiment was to continue for 2 to 3 years, but almost immediately there were signs that the project could be in jeopardy.

Soon after the bubble had been sealed, sensors inside the facility showed that the concentration of oxygen in Biosphere II's atmosphere had fallen from its initial level of 21 percent (by volume), while the amount of carbon dioxide had risen from a level of 0.035 percent (by volume), or 350 ppm (parts per million). Alarmingly, the oxygen level continued to fall at a rate of about 0.5 percent a month and the level of carbon dioxide kept rising, forcing the crew to turn on electrically powered chemical scrubbers, similar to those on submarines, to remove some of the excess CO_2. Gradually the CO_2 level stabilized around 4000 ppm, which is high but not dangerous. The loss of oxygen did not stop, though. By January 1993—16 months into the experiment—the oxygen concentration had dropped to 14 percent, which is equivalent to the O_2 concentration in air at an elevation of 4360 m (14,300 ft). The crew began having trouble performing normal tasks. For their safety it was necessary to pump pure oxygen into Biosphere II.

With all the plants present in Biosphere II, the production of oxygen should have been greater as a consequence of photosynthesis. Why had the oxygen concentration declined to such a low level? A small part of the loss was blamed on unusually cloudy weather, which had slowed down plant growth. The possibility that iron in the soil was reacting with oxygen to form iron(III) oxide or rust was ruled out along with several other explanations for lack of evidence. The most plausible hypothesis was that microbes (microorganisms) were using oxygen to metabolize the excess organic matter that had been added to the soils to promote plant growth. This turned out to be the case.

Identifying the cause of oxygen depletion raised another question. Metabolism produces carbon dioxide. Based on the amount of oxygen consumed by the microbes, the CO_2 level should have been at 40,000 ppm, 10 times what was measured. What happened to the excess gas? After ruling out leakage to the outside world and reactions between CO_2 with compounds in the soils and in water, scientists found that the concrete inside Biosphere II was consuming large amounts of CO_2!

Concrete is a mixture of sand and gravel held together by a binding agent that is a mixture of calcium silicate hydrates and calcium hydroxide. The calcium hydroxide is the key ingredient in the CO_2 mystery. Carbon dioxide diffuses into the porous structure of concrete, then reacts with calcium hydroxide to form calcium carbonate and water:

$$Ca(OH)_2(s) + CO_2(g) \longrightarrow CaCO_3(s) + H_2O(l)$$

Under normal conditions, this reaction goes on slowly. But CO_2 concentrations in Biosphere II were much higher than normal, so the reaction proceeded much faster. In

[†]Adapted with permission from "Biosphere II: Out of Oxygen," by Joe Alper, CHEM MATTERS, February, 1995, p. 8. Copyright 1995 American Chemical Society.

Vegetations in Biosphere II.

fact, in just over 2 years, $CaCO_3$ had accumulated to a depth of more than 2 cm in Biosphere II's concrete. Some 10,000 m^2 of exposed concrete was hiding 500,000 to 1,500,000 moles of CO_2.

The water produced in the reaction between $Ca(OH)_2$ and CO_2 created another problem: CO_2 also reacts with water to form carbonic acid (H_2CO_3), and hydrogen ions produced by the acid promote the corrosion of the reinforcing iron bars in the concrete, thereby weakening its structure. This situation was dealt with effectively by painting all concrete surfaces with an impermeable coating.

In the meantime, the decline in oxygen (and hence also the rise in carbon dioxide) slowed, perhaps because there was now less organic matter in the soils and also because new lights in the agricultural areas may have boosted photosynthesis. The project was terminated prematurely and in 1996, the facility was transformed into a science education and research center. As of 2011, the Biosphere is under the management of the University of Arizona.

The Biosphere II experiment is an interesting project from which we can learn a lot about Earth and its inhabitants. If nothing else, it has shown us how complex Earth's ecosystems are and how difficult it is to mimic nature, even on a small scale.

Chemical Clues

1. What solution would you use in a chemical scrubber to remove carbon dioxide?

2. Photosynthesis converts carbon dioxide and water to carbohydrates and oxygen gas, while metabolism is the process by which carbohydrates react with oxygen to form carbon dioxide and water. Using glucose ($C_6H_{12}O_6$) to represent carbohydrates, write equations for these two processes.

3. Why was diffusion of O_2 from Biosphere II to the outside world not considered a possible cause for the depletion in oxygen?

4. Carbonic acid is a diprotic acid. Write equations for the stepwise ionization of the acid in water.

5. What are the factors to consider in choosing a planet on which to build a structure like Biosphere II?

CHAPTER

6

Thermochemistry

The analysis of particles formed from burning methane in a flame is performed with a visible laser.

A LOOK AHEAD

▶   We begin by studying the nature and different types of energy, which, in principle, are interconvertible. (6.1)

▶   Next, we build up our vocabulary in learning thermochemistry, which is the study of heat change in chemical reactions. We see that the vast majority of reactions are either endothermic (absorbing heat) or exothermic (releasing heat). (6.2)

▶   We learn that thermochemistry is part of a broader subject called the first law of thermodynamics, which is based on the law of conservation of energy. We see that the change in internal energy can be expressed in terms of the changes in heat and work done of a system. (6.3)

▶   We then become acquainted with a new term for energy, called enthalpy, whose change applies to processes carried out under constant-pressure conditions. (6.4)

▶   We learn ways to measure the heats of reaction or calorimetry, and the meaning of specific heat and heat capacity, quantities used in experimental work. (6.5)

▶   Knowing the standard enthalpies of formation of reactants and products enables us to calculate the enthalpy of a reaction. We will discuss ways to determine these quantities either by the direct method from the elements or by the indirect method, which is based on Hess's law of heat summation. (6.6)

▶   Finally, we will study the heat changes when a solute dissolves in a solvent (heat of solution) and when a solution is diluted (heat of dilution). (6.7)

Every chemical reaction obeys two fundamental laws: the law of conservation of mass and the law of conservation of energy. We discussed the mass relationship between reactants and products in Chapter 3; here we will look at the energy changes that accompany chemical reactions.

6.1 The Nature of Energy and Types of Energy

"Energy" is a much-used term that represents a rather abstract concept. For instance, when we feel tired, we might say we haven't any *energy;* and we read about the need to find alternatives to nonrenewable *energy* sources. Unlike matter, energy is known and recognized by its effects. It cannot be seen, touched, smelled, or weighed.

Energy is usually defined as *the capacity to do work.* In Chapter 5 we defined work as "force × distance," but we will soon see that there are other kinds of work. All forms of energy are capable of doing work (that is, of exerting a force over a distance), but not all of them are equally relevant to chemistry. The energy contained in tidal waves, for example, can be harnessed to perform useful work, but the relationship between tidal waves and chemistry is minimal. Chemists define **work** as *directed energy change resulting from a process.* Kinetic energy—the energy produced by a moving object—is one form of energy that is of particular interest to chemists. Others include radiant energy, thermal energy, chemical energy, and potential energy.

Kinetic energy was introduced in Chapter 5 (p. 202).

Radiant energy, or *solar energy, comes from the sun* and is Earth's primary energy source. Solar energy heats the atmosphere and Earth's surface, stimulates the growth of vegetation through the process known as photosynthesis, and influences global climate patterns.

Thermal energy is *the energy associated with the random motion of atoms and molecules.* In general, thermal energy can be calculated from temperature measurements. The more vigorous the motion of the atoms and molecules in a sample of matter, the hotter the sample is and the greater its thermal energy. However, we need to distinguish carefully between thermal energy and temperature. A cup of coffee at 70°C has a higher temperature than a bathtub filled with warm water at 40°C, but much more thermal energy is stored in the bathtub water because it has a much larger volume and greater mass than the coffee and therefore more water molecules and more molecular motion.

Chemical energy is *stored within the structural units of chemical substances;* its quantity is determined by the type and arrangement of constituent atoms. When substances participate in chemical reactions, chemical energy is released, stored, or converted to other forms of energy.

Potential energy is *energy available by virtue of an object's position.* For instance, because of its altitude, a rock at the top of a cliff has more potential energy and will make a bigger splash if it falls into the water below than a similar rock located partway down the cliff. Chemical energy can be considered a form of potential energy because it is associated with the relative positions and arrangements of atoms within a given substance.

As the water falls over the dam, its potential energy is converted to kinetic energy. Use of this energy to generate electricity is called hydroelectric power.

All forms of energy can be converted (at least in principle) from one form to another. We feel warm when we stand in sunlight because radiant energy is converted to thermal energy on our skin. When we exercise, chemical energy stored in our bodies is used to produce kinetic energy. When a ball starts to roll downhill, its potential energy is converted to kinetic energy. You can undoubtedly think of many other examples. Although energy can assume many different forms that are interconvertible, scientists have concluded that energy can be neither destroyed nor created. When one form of energy disappears, some other form of energy (of equal magnitude) must appear, and vice versa. This principle is summarized by the **law of conservation of energy:** *the total quantity of energy in the universe is assumed constant.*

232   **Chapter 6** ▪ Thermochemistry

This infrared photo shows where energy (heat) leaks through the house. The more red the color, the more energy is lost to the outside.

▶▶ **Animation**
Heat Flow

When heat is absorbed or released during a process, energy is conserved, but it is transferred between system and surroundings.

6.2 Energy Changes in Chemical Reactions

Often the energy changes that take place during chemical reactions are of as much practical interest as the mass relationships we discussed in Chapter 3. For example, combustion reactions involving fuels such as natural gas and oil are carried out in daily life more for the thermal energy they release than for their products, which are water and carbon dioxide.

Almost all chemical reactions absorb or produce (release) energy, generally in the form of heat. It is important to understand the distinction between thermal energy and heat. ***Heat*** is *the transfer of thermal energy between two bodies that are at different temperatures.* Thus, we often speak of the "heat flow" from a hot object to a cold one. Although the term "heat" by itself implies the transfer of energy, we customarily talk of "heat absorbed" or "heat released" when describing the energy changes that occur during a process. ***Thermochemistry*** is *the study of heat change in chemical reactions.*

To analyze energy changes associated with chemical reactions we must first define the ***system,*** or *the specific part of the universe that is of interest to us.* For chemists, systems usually include substances involved in chemical and physical changes. For example, in an acid-base neutralization experiment, the system may be a beaker containing 50 mL of HCl to which 50 mL of NaOH is added. The ***surroundings*** are *the rest of the universe outside the system.*

There are three types of systems. An ***open system*** *can exchange mass and energy, usually in the form of heat with its surroundings.* For example, an open system may consist of a quantity of water in an open container, as shown in Figure 6.1(a). If we close the flask, as in Figure 6.1(b), so that no water vapor can escape from or condense into the container, we create a ***closed system,*** which *allows the transfer of energy (heat) but not mass.* By placing the water in a totally insulated container, we can construct an ***isolated system,*** which *does not allow the transfer of either mass or energy,* as shown in Figure 6.1(c).

The combustion of hydrogen gas in oxygen is one of many chemical reactions that release considerable quantities of energy (Figure 6.2):

$$2H_2(g) + O_2(g) \longrightarrow 2H_2O(l) + \text{energy}$$

In this case, we label the reacting mixture (hydrogen, oxygen, and water molecules) the *system* and the rest of the universe the *surroundings*. Because energy cannot be

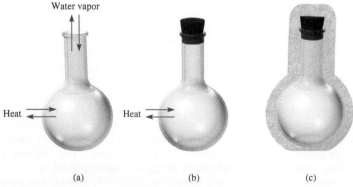

Water vapor

Heat

Heat

(a)   (b)   (c)

Figure 6.1 *Three systems represented by water in a flask: (a) an open system, which allows the exchange of both energy and mass with surroundings; (b) a closed system, which allows the exchange of energy but not mass; and (c) an isolated system, which allows neither energy nor mass to be exchanged (here the flask is enclosed by a vacuum jacket).*

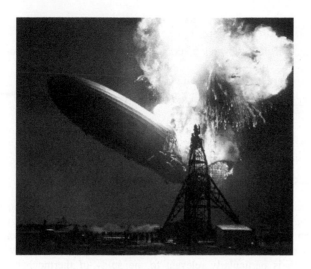

Figure 6.2 *The Hindenburg disaster. The Hindenburg, a German airship filled with hydrogen gas, was destroyed in a spectacular fire at Lakehurst, New Jersey, in 1937.*

created or destroyed, any energy lost by the system must be gained by the surroundings. Thus, the heat generated by the combustion process is transferred from the system to its surroundings. This reaction is an example of an ***exothermic process,*** which is *any process that gives off heat—that is, transfers thermal energy to the surroundings.* Figure 6.3(a) shows the energy change for the combustion of hydrogen gas.

Exo- comes from the Greek word meaning "outside"; endo- means "within."

Now consider another reaction, the decomposition of mercury(II) oxide (HgO) at high temperatures:

$$\text{energy} + 2\text{HgO}(s) \longrightarrow 2\text{Hg}(l) + \text{O}_2(g)$$

This reaction is an ***endothermic process,*** *in which heat has to be supplied to the system* (that is, to HgO) *by the surroundings* [Figure 6.3(b)].

From Figure 6.3 you can see that in exothermic reactions, the total energy of the products is less than the total energy of the reactants. The difference is the heat supplied by the system to the surroundings. Just the opposite happens in endothermic reactions. Here, the difference between the energy of the products and the energy of the reactants is equal to the heat supplied to the system by the surroundings.

On heating, HgO decomposes to give Hg and O_2.

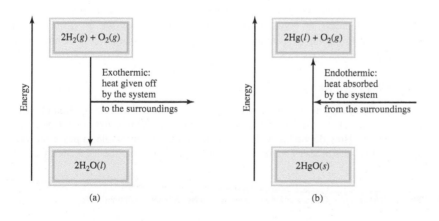

(a)   (b)

Figure 6.3 *(a) An exothermic process. (b) An endothermic process. Parts (a) and (b) are not drawn to the same scale; that is, the heat released in the formation of H_2O from H_2 and O_2 is not equal to the heat absorbed in the decomposition of HgO.*

> **Review of Concepts**
>
> Classify each of the following as an open system, a closed system, or an isolated system.
>   (a) Milk kept in a closed thermo flask.
>   (b) A student reading in her dorm room.
>   (c) Air inside a tennis ball.

6.3 Introduction to Thermodynamics

Thermochemistry is part of a broader subject called **thermodynamics**, which is *the scientific study of the interconversion of heat and other kinds of energy*. The laws of thermodynamics provide useful guidelines for understanding the energetics and directions of processes. In this section we will concentrate on the first law of thermodynamics, which is particularly relevant to the study of thermochemistry. We will continue our discussion of thermodynamics in Chapter 17.

In thermodynamics, we study changes in the **state of a system**, which is defined by *the values of all relevant macroscopic properties, for example, composition, energy, temperature, pressure, and volume*. Energy, pressure, volume, and temperature are said to be **state functions**—*properties that are determined by the state of the system, regardless of how that condition was achieved*. In other words, when the state of a system changes, the magnitude of change in any state function depends only on the initial and final states of the system and not on how the change is accomplished.

Changes in state functions do not depend on the pathway, but only on the initial and final state.

The state of a given amount of a gas is specified by its volume, pressure, and temperature. Consider a gas at 2 atm, 300 K, and 1 L (the initial state). Suppose a process is carried out at constant temperature such that the gas pressure decreases to 1 atm. According to Boyle's law, its volume must increase to 2 L. The final state then corresponds to 1 atm, 300 K, and 2 L. The change in volume (ΔV) is

The Greek letter delta, Δ, symbolizes change. We use Δ in this text to mean final − initial; that is, final "minus" initial.

$$\begin{aligned} \Delta V &= V_{\mathrm{f}} - V_{\mathrm{i}} \\ &= 2\,\mathrm{L} - 1\,\mathrm{L} \\ &= 1\,\mathrm{L} \end{aligned}$$

where V_{i} and V_{f} denote the initial and final volume, respectively. No matter how we arrive at the final state (for example, the pressure of the gas can be increased first and then decreased to 1 atm), the change in volume is always 1 L. Thus, the volume of a gas is a state function. In a similar manner, we can show that pressure and temperature are also state functions.

Recall that an object possesses potential energy by virtue of its position or chemical composition.

Energy is another state function. Using potential energy as an example, we find that the net increase in gravitational potential energy when we go from the same starting point to the top of a mountain is always the same, regardless of how we get there (Figure 6.4).

The First Law of Thermodynamics

The **first law of thermodynamics,** which is based on the law of conservation of energy, states that *energy can be converted from one form to another, but cannot be created or destroyed.*[†] How do we know this is so? It would be impossible to prove the validity of the first law of thermodynamics if we had to determine the total energy content

---

[†]See footnote on p. 40 (Chapter 2) for a discussion of mass and energy relationship in chemical reactions.

Figure 6.4 *The gain in gravitational potential energy that occurs when a person climbs from the base to the top of a mountain is independent of the path taken.*

of the universe. Even determining the total energy content of 1 g of iron, say, would be extremely difficult. Fortunately, we can test the validity of the first law by measuring only the *change* in the internal energy of a system between its *initial state* and its *final state* in a process. The change in internal energy ΔU is given by

$$\Delta U = U_f - U_i$$

where U_i and U_f are the internal energies of the system in the initial and final states, respectively.

The internal energy of a system has two components: kinetic energy and potential energy. The kinetic energy component consists of various types of molecular motion and the movement of electrons within molecules. Potential energy is determined by the attractive interactions between electrons and nuclei and by repulsive interactions between electrons and between nuclei in individual molecules, as well as by interaction between molecules. It is impossible to measure all these contributions accurately, so we cannot calculate the total energy of a system with any certainty. Changes in energy, on the other hand, can be determined experimentally.

Consider the reaction between 1 mole of sulfur and 1 mole of oxygen gas to produce 1 mole of sulfur dioxide:

$$S(s) + O_2(g) \longrightarrow SO_2(g)$$

In this case, our system is composed of the reactant molecules S and O_2 (the initial state) and the product molecules SO_2 (the final state). We do not know the internal energy content of either the reactant molecules or the product molecules, but we can accurately measure the *change* in energy content, ΔU, given by

$\Delta U = U(\text{product}) - U(\text{reactants})$
    $= $ energy content of 1 mol $SO_2(g)$ − energy content of [1 mol $S(s)$ + 1 mol $O_2(g)$]

We find that this reaction gives off heat. Therefore, the energy of the product is less than that of the reactants, and ΔU is negative.

Interpreting the release of heat in this reaction to mean that some of the chemical energy contained in the molecules has been converted to thermal energy, we conclude that the transfer of energy from the system to the surroundings does not change the total energy of the universe. That is, the sum of the energy changes must be zero:

$$\Delta U_{sys} + \Delta U_{surr} = 0$$

or

$$\Delta U_{sys} = -\Delta U_{surr}$$

where the subscripts "sys" and "surr" denote system and surroundings, respectively. Thus, if one system undergoes an energy change ΔU_{sys}, the rest of the universe, or

Sulfur burning in air to form SO_2.

the surroundings, must undergo a change in energy that is equal in magnitude but opposite in sign ($-\Delta U_{\text{surr}}$); energy gained in one place must have been lost somewhere else. Furthermore, because energy can be changed from one form to another, the energy lost by one system can be gained by another system in a different form. For example, the energy lost by burning oil in a power plant may ultimately turn up in our homes as electrical energy, heat, light, and so on.

In chemistry, we are normally interested in the energy changes associated with the system (which may be a flask containing reactants and products), not with its surroundings. Therefore, a more useful form of the first law is

$$\Delta U = q + w \qquad (6.1)$$

We use lowercase letters (such as *w* and *q*) to represent thermodynamic quantities that are not state functions.

(We drop the subscript "sys" for simplicity.) Equation (6.1) says that the change in the internal energy, ΔU, of a system is the sum of the heat exchange q between the system and the surroundings and the work done w on (or by) the system. The sign conventions for q and w are as follows: q is positive for an endothermic process and negative for an exothermic process and w is positive for work done on the system by the surroundings and negative for work done by the system on the surroundings. We can think of the first law of thermodynamics as an energy balance sheet, much like a money balance sheet kept in a bank that does currency exchange. You can withdraw or deposit money in either of two different currencies (like energy change due to heat exchange and work done). However, the value of your bank account depends only on the net amount of money left in it after these transactions, not on which currency you used.

For convenience, we sometimes omit the word "internal" when discussing the energy of a system.

Equation (6.1) may seem abstract, but it is actually quite logical. If a system loses heat to the surroundings or does work on the surroundings, we would expect its internal energy to decrease because those are energy-depleting processes. For this reason, both q and w are negative. Conversely, if heat is added to the system or if work is done on the system, then the internal energy of the system would increase. In this case, both q and w are positive. Table 6.1 summarizes the sign conventions for q and w.

Work and Heat

We will now look at the nature of work and heat in more detail.

Work

We have seen that work can be defined as force F multiplied by distance d:

$$w = F \times d \qquad (6.2)$$

In thermodynamics, work has a broader meaning that includes mechanical work (for example, a crane lifting a steel beam), electrical work (a battery supplying electrons

Table 6.1	Sign Conventions for Work and Heat	
Process		**Sign**
Work done by the system on the surroundings		−
Work done on the system by the surroundings		+
Heat absorbed by the system from the surroundings (endothermic process)		+
Heat absorbed by the surroundings from the system (exothermic process)		−

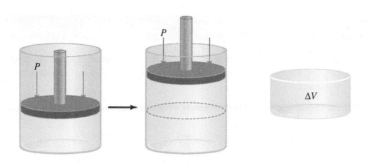

Figure 6.5 *The expansion of a gas against a constant external pressure (such as atmospheric pressure). The gas is in a cylinder fitted with a weightless movable piston. The work done is given by −PΔV. Because ΔV > 0, the work done is a negative quantity.*

to light the bulb of a flashlight), and surface work (blowing up a soap bubble). In this section we will concentrate on mechanical work; in Chapter 18 we will discuss the nature of electrical work.

One way to illustrate mechanical work is to study the expansion or compression of a gas. Many chemical and biological processes involve gas volume changes. Breathing and exhaling air involves the expansion and contraction of the tiny sacs called alveoli in the lungs. Another example is the internal combustion engine of the automobile. The successive expansion and compression of the cylinders due to the combustion of the gasoline-air mixture provide power to the vehicle. Figure 6.5 shows a gas in a cylinder fitted with a weightless, frictionless movable piston at a certain temperature, pressure, and volume. As it expands, the gas pushes the piston upward against a constant opposing external atmospheric pressure P. The work done by the gas on the surroundings is

$$w = -P\Delta V \tag{6.3}$$

where ΔV, the change in volume, is given by $V_f - V_i$. The minus sign in Equation (6.3) takes care of the sign convention for w. For gas expansion (work done *by* the system), $\Delta V > 0$, so $-P\Delta V$ is a negative quantity. For gas compression (work done *on* the system), $\Delta V < 0$, and $-P\Delta V$ is a positive quantity.

Equation (6.3) derives from the fact that pressure × volume can be expressed as (force/area) × volume; that is,

$$P \times V = \underset{\text{pressure}}{\frac{F}{d^2}} \times \underset{\text{volume}}{d^3} = F \times d = w$$

where F is the opposing force and d has the dimension of length, d^2 has the dimensions of area, and d^3 has the dimensions of volume. Thus, the product of pressure and volume is equal to force times distance, or work. You can see that for a given increase in volume (that is, for a certain value of ΔV), the work done depends on the magnitude of the external, opposing pressure P. If P is zero (that is, if the gas is expanding against a vacuum), the work done must also be zero. If P is some positive, nonzero value, then the work done is given by $-P\Delta V$.

According to Equation (6.3), the units for work done by or on a gas are liter atmospheres. To express the work done in the more familiar unit of joules, we use the conversion factor (see Appendix 2).

$$1 \text{ L} \cdot \text{atm} = 101.3 \text{ J}$$

Example 6.1

A certain gas expands in volume from 2.0 L to 6.0 L at constant temperature. Calculate the work done by the gas if it expands (a) against a vacuum and (b) against a constant pressure of 1.2 atm.

Strategy A simple sketch of the situation is helpful here:

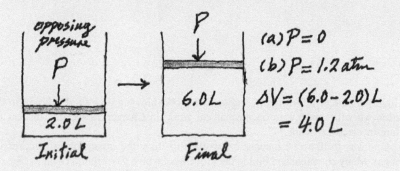

The work done in gas expansion is equal to the product of the external, opposing pressure and the change in volume. What is the conversion factor between L · atm and J?

Solution

(a) Because the external pressure is zero, no work is done in the expansion.

$$w = -P\Delta V$$
$$= -(0)(6.0 - 2.0)\,\text{L}$$
$$= 0$$

(b) The external, opposing pressure is 1.2 atm, so

$$w = -P\Delta V$$
$$= -(1.2\,\text{atm})(6.0 - 2.0)\,\text{L}$$
$$= -4.8\,\text{L} \cdot \text{atm}$$

To convert the answer to joules, we write

$$w = -4.8\,\text{L} \cdot \text{atm} \times \frac{101.3\,\text{J}}{1\,\text{L} \cdot \text{atm}}$$
$$= -4.9 \times 10^2\,\text{J}$$

Check Because this is gas expansion (work is done by the system on the surroundings), the work done has a negative sign.

Similar problems: 6.15, 6.16.

Practice Exercise A gas expands from 264 mL to 971 mL at constant temperature. Calculate the work done (in joules) by the gas if it expands (a) against a vacuum and (b) against a constant pressure of 4.00 atm.

Because temperature is kept constant, you can use Boyle's law to show that the final pressure is the same in (a) and (b).

Example 6.1 shows that work is not a state function. Although the initial and final states are the same in (a) and (b), the amount of work done is different because the external, opposing pressures are different. We *cannot* write $\Delta w = w_f - w_i$ for a change. Work done depends not only on the initial state and final state, but also on how the process is carried out, that is, on the path.

Heat

The other component of internal energy is heat, q. Like work, heat is not a state function. For example, it takes 4184 J of energy to raise the temperature of 100 g of water from 20°C to 30°C. This energy can be gained (a) directly as heat energy from a Bunsen burner, without doing any work on the water; (b) by doing work on the water without adding heat energy (for example, by stirring the water with a magnetic stir bar); or (c) by some combination of the procedures described in (a) and (b). This simple illustration shows that heat associated with a given process, like work, depends on how the process is carried out. It is important to note that regardless of which procedure is taken, the change in internal energy of the system, ΔU, depends on the sum of $(q + w)$. If changing the path from the initial state to the final state increases the value of q, then it will decrease the value of w by the same amount and vice versa, so that ΔU remains unchanged.

In summary, heat and work are not state functions because they are not properties of a system. They manifest themselves only during a process (during a change). Thus, their values depend on the path of the process and vary accordingly.

Example 6.2

The work done when a gas is compressed in a cylinder like that shown in Figure 6.5 is 462 J. During this process, there is a heat transfer of 128 J from the gas to the surroundings. Calculate the energy change for this process.

Strategy Compression is work done on the gas, so what is the sign for w? Heat is released by the gas to the surroundings. Is this an endothermic or exothermic process? What is the sign for q?

Solution To calculate the energy change of the gas, we need Equation (6.1). Work of compression is positive and because heat is released by the gas, q is negative. Therefore, we have

$$\Delta U = q + w$$
$$= -128 \text{ J} + 462 \text{ J}$$
$$= 334 \text{ J}$$

As a result, the energy of the gas increases by 334 J.

Similar problems: 6.17, 6.18.

Practice Exercise A gas expands and does *P-V* work on the surroundings equal to 279 J. At the same time, it absorbs 216 J of heat from the surroundings. What is the change in energy of the system?

Review of Concepts

Two ideal gases at the same temperature and pressure are placed in two equal-volume containers. One container has a fixed volume, while the other is a cylinder fitted with a weightless movable piston like that shown in Figure 6.5. Initially, the gas pressures are equal to the external atmospheric pressure. The gases are then heated with a Bunsen burner. What are the signs of q and w for the gases under these conditions?

CHEMISTRY *in Action*

Making Snow and Inflating a Bicycle Tire

Many phenomena in everyday life can be explained by the first law of thermodynamics. Here we will discuss two examples of interest to lovers of the outdoors.

Making Snow

If you are an avid downhill skier, you have probably skied on artificial snow. How is this stuff made in quantities large enough to meet the needs of skiers on snowless days? The secret of snowmaking is in the equation $\Delta U = q + w$. A snowmaking machine contains a mixture of compressed air and water vapor at about 20 atm. Because of the large difference in pressure between the tank and the outside atmosphere, when the mixture is sprayed into the atmosphere it expands so rapidly that, as a good approximation, no heat exchange occurs between the system (air and water) and its surroundings; that is, $q = 0$. (In thermodynamics, such a process is called an *adiabatic process*.) Thus, we write

$$\Delta U = q + w = w$$

Because the system does work on the surroundings, w is a negative quantity, and there is a decrease in the system's energy.

Kinetic energy is part of the total energy of the system. In Section 5.7 we saw that the average kinetic energy of a gas is directly proportional to the absolute temperature [Equation (5.15)]. It follows, therefore, that the change in energy ΔU is given by

$$\Delta U = C\Delta T$$

where C is the proportionality constant. Because ΔU is negative, ΔT must also be negative, and it is this cooling effect (or the decrease in the kinetic energy of the water molecules) that is responsible for the formation of snow. Although we need only water to form snow, the presence of air, which also

cools on expansion, helps to lower the temperature of the water vapor.

Inflating a Bicycle Tire

If you have ever pumped air into a bicycle tire, you probably noticed a warming effect at the valve stem. This phenomenon, too, can be explained by the first law of thermodynamics. The action of the pump compresses the air inside the pump and the tire. The process is rapid enough to be treated as approximately adiabatic, so that $q = 0$ and $\Delta U = w$. Because work is done on the gas in this case (it is being compressed), w is positive, and there is an increase in energy. Hence, the temperature of the system increases also, according to the equation

$$\Delta U = C\Delta T$$

A snowmaking machine in operation.

6.4 Enthalpy of Chemical Reactions

Our next step is to see how the first law of thermodynamics can be applied to processes carried out under different conditions. Specifically, we will consider two situations most commonly encountered in the laboratory; one in which the volume of the system is kept constant and one in which the pressure applied on the system is kept constant.

If a chemical reaction is run at constant volume, then $\Delta V = 0$ and no $P\text{-}V$ work will result from this change. From Equation (6.1) it follows that

Recall that $w = -P\Delta V$.

$$\Delta U = q - P\Delta V$$
$$= q_v \qquad (6.4)$$

We add the subscript "v" to remind us that this is a constant-volume process. This equality may seem strange at first, for we showed earlier that q is not a state function. The process is carried out under constant-volume conditions, however, so that the heat change can have only a specific value, which is equal to ΔU.

Enthalpy

Constant-volume conditions are often inconvenient and sometimes impossible to achieve. Most reactions occur under conditions of constant pressure (usually atmospheric pressure). If such a reaction results in a net increase in the number of moles of a gas, then the system does work on the surroundings (expansion). This result follows from the fact that for the gas formed to enter the atmosphere, it must push the surrounding air back. Conversely, if more gas molecules are consumed than are produced, work is done on the system by the surroundings (compression). Finally, no work is done if there is no net change in the number of moles of gases from reactants to products.

In general, for a constant-pressure process we write

$$\Delta U = q + w$$
$$= q_p - P\Delta V$$

or
$$q_p = \Delta U + P\Delta V \qquad (6.5)$$

where the subscript "p" denotes constant-pressure condition.

We now introduce a new thermodynamic function of a system called ***enthalpy (H),*** which is defined by the equation

$$H = U + PV \qquad (6.6)$$

where U is the internal energy of the system and P and V are the pressure and volume of the system, respectively. Because U and PV have energy units, enthalpy also has energy units. Furthermore, U, P, and V are all state functions, that is, the changes in $(U + PV)$ depend only on the initial and final states. It follows, therefore, that the change in H, or ΔH, also depends only on the initial and final states. Thus, H is a state function.

For any process, the change in enthalpy according to Equation (6.6) is given by

$$\Delta H = \Delta U + \Delta(PV) \qquad (6.7)$$

If the pressure is held constant, then

$$\Delta H = \Delta U + P\Delta V \qquad (6.8)$$

Comparing Equation (6.8) with Equation (6.5), we see that for a constant-pressure process, $q_p = \Delta H$. Again, although q is not a state function, the heat change at constant pressure is equal to ΔH because the "path" is defined and therefore it can have only a specific value.

242   **Chapter 6** ▪ Thermochemistry

In Section 6.5 we will discuss ways to measure heat changes at constant volume and constant pressure.

We now have two quantities—ΔU and ΔH—that can be associated with a reaction. If the reaction occurs under constant-volume conditions, then the heat change, q_v, is equal to ΔU. On the other hand, when the reaction is carried out at constant pressure, the heat change, q_p, is equal to ΔH.

Enthalpy of Reactions

Because most reactions are constant-pressure processes, we can equate the heat change in these cases to the change in enthalpy. For any reaction of the type

$$\text{reactants} \longrightarrow \text{products}$$

we define the change in enthalpy, called the ***enthalpy of reaction, ΔH_{rxn}***, as *the difference between the enthalpies of the products and the enthalpies of the reactants:*

$$\Delta H = H(\text{products}) - H(\text{reactants}) \tag{6.9}$$

We often omit the subscript "rxn" and simply write ΔH for enthalpy changes of reactions.

The enthalpy of reaction can be positive or negative, depending on the process. For an endothermic process (heat absorbed by the system from the surroundings), ΔH is positive (that is, $\Delta H > 0$). For an exothermic process (heat released by the system to the surroundings), ΔH is negative (that is, $\Delta H < 0$).

This analogy assumes that you will not overdraw your bank account. The enthalpy of a substance *cannot* be negative.

An analogy for enthalpy change is a change in the balance in your bank account. Suppose your initial balance is $100. After a transaction (deposit or withdrawal), the change in your bank balance, ΔX, is given by

$$\Delta X = X_{\text{final}} - X_{\text{initial}}$$

where X represents the bank balance. If you deposit $80 into your account, then $\Delta X = \$180 - \$100 = \$80$. This corresponds to an endothermic reaction. (The balance increases and so does the enthalpy of the system.) On the other hand, a withdrawal of $60 means $\Delta X = \$40 - \$100 = -\$60$. The negative sign of ΔX means your balance has decreased. Similarly, a negative value of ΔH reflects a decrease in enthalpy of the system as a result of an exothermic process. The difference between this analogy and Equation (6.9) is that while you always know your exact bank balance, there is no way to know the enthalpies of individual products and reactants. In practice, we can only measure the *difference* in their values.

Now let us apply the idea of enthalpy changes to two common processes, the first involving a physical change, the second a chemical change.

Thermochemical Equations

At 0°C and a pressure of 1 atm, ice melts to form liquid water. Measurements show that for every mole of ice converted to liquid water under these conditions, 6.01 kilojoules (kJ) of heat energy are absorbed by the system (ice). Because the pressure is constant, the heat change is equal to the enthalpy change, ΔH. Furthermore, this is an endothermic process, as expected for the energy-absorbing change of melting ice [Figure 6.6(a)]. Therefore, ΔH is a positive quantity. The equation for this physical change is

$$\text{H}_2\text{O}(s) \longrightarrow \text{H}_2\text{O}(l) \qquad\qquad \Delta H = 6.01 \text{ kJ/mol}$$

For simplicity, we use "per mole" rather than "per mole of reaction" for ΔH in thermochemical equations.

The "per mole" in the unit for ΔH means that this is the enthalpy change *per mole of the reaction (or process) as it is written;* that is, when 1 mole of ice is converted to 1 mole of liquid water.

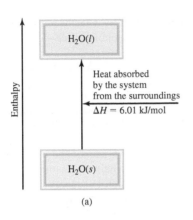

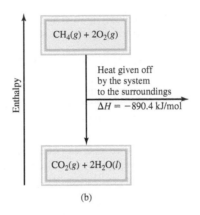

(a)   (b)

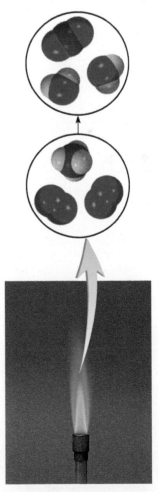

Figure 6.6 *(a) Melting 1 mole of ice at 0°C (an endothermic process) results in an enthalpy increase in the system of 6.01 kJ. (b) Burning 1 mole of methane in oxygen gas (an exothermic process) results in an enthalpy decrease in the system of 890.4 kJ. Parts (a) and (b) are not drawn to the same scale.*

As another example, consider the combustion of methane (CH_4), the principal component of natural gas:

$$CH_4(g) + 2O_2(g) \longrightarrow CO_2(g) + 2H_2O(l) \quad \Delta H = -890.4 \text{ kJ/mol}$$

From experience we know that burning natural gas releases heat to the surroundings, so it is an exothermic process. Under constant-pressure condition this heat change is equal to enthalpy change and ΔH must have a negative sign [Figure 6.6(b)]. Again, the per mole of reaction unit for ΔH means that when 1 mole of CH_4 reacts with 2 moles of O_2 to produce 1 mole of CO_2 and 2 moles of liquid H_2O, 890.4 kJ of heat energy are released to the surroundings. It is important to keep in mind that the ΔH value does not refer to a particular reactant or product. It simply means that the quoted ΔH value refers to all the reacting species in molar quantities. Thus, the following conversion factors can be created:

$$\frac{-890.4 \text{ kJ}}{1 \text{ mol CH}_4} \qquad \frac{-890.4 \text{ kJ}}{2 \text{ mol O}_2} \qquad \frac{-890.4 \text{ kJ}}{1 \text{ mol CO}_2} \qquad \frac{-890.4 \text{ kJ}}{2 \text{ mol H}_2\text{O}}$$

Expressing ΔH in units of kJ/mol (rather than just kJ) conforms to the standard convention; its merit will become apparent when we continue our study of thermodynamics in Chapter 17.

The equations for the melting of ice and the combustion of methane are examples of ***thermochemical equations,*** which *show the enthalpy changes as well as the mass relationships.* It is essential to specify a balanced equation when quoting the enthalpy change of a reaction. The following guidelines are helpful in writing and interpreting thermochemical equations.

1. When writing thermochemical equations, we must always specify the physical states of all reactants and products, because they help determine the actual enthalpy changes. For example, in the equation for the combustion of methane, if we show water vapor rather than liquid water as a product,

$$CH_4(g) + 2O_2(g) \longrightarrow CO_2(g) + 2H_2O(g) \quad \Delta H = -802.4 \text{ kJ/mol}$$

the enthalpy change is −802.4 kJ rather than −890.4 kJ because 88.0 kJ are needed to convert 2 moles of liquid water to water vapor; that is,

$$2H_2O(l) \longrightarrow 2H_2O(g) \quad \Delta H = 88.0 \text{ kJ/mol}$$

Methane gas burning from a Bunsen burner.

2. If we multiply both sides of a thermochemical equation by a factor n, then ΔH must also change by the same factor. Returning to the melting of ice

$$H_2O(s) \longrightarrow H_2O(l) \qquad \Delta H = 6.01 \text{ kJ/mol}$$

If we multiply the equation throughout by 2; that is, if we set $n = 2$, then

$$2H_2O(s) \longrightarrow 2H_2O(l) \qquad \Delta H = 2(6.01 \text{ kJ/mol}) = 12.0 \text{ kJ/mol}$$

3. When we reverse an equation, we change the roles of reactants and products. Consequently, the magnitude of ΔH for the equation remains the same, but its sign changes. For example, if a reaction consumes thermal energy from its surroundings (that is, if it is endothermic), then the reverse reaction must release thermal energy back to its surroundings (that is, it must be exothermic) and the enthalpy change expression must also change its sign. Thus, reversing the melting of ice and the combustion of methane, the thermochemical equations become

$$H_2O(l) \longrightarrow H_2O(s) \qquad \Delta H = -6.01 \text{ kJ/mol}$$
$$CO_2(g) + 2H_2O(l) \longrightarrow CH_4(g) + 2O_2(g) \qquad \Delta H = 890.4 \text{ kJ/mol}$$

and what was an endothermic process becomes exothermic, and vice versa.

Example 6.3

Given the thermochemical equation

$$2SO_2(g) + O_2(g) \longrightarrow 2SO_3(g) \qquad \Delta H = -198.2 \text{ kJ/mol}$$

calculate the heat evolved when 87.9 g of SO_2 (molar mass = 64.07 g/mol) is converted to SO_3.

Strategy The thermochemical equation shows that for every 2 moles of SO_2 reacted, 198.2 kJ of heat are given off (note the negative sign). Therefore, the conversion factor is

$$\frac{-198.2 \text{ kJ}}{2 \text{ mol SO}_2}$$

How many moles of SO_2 are in 87.9 g of SO_2? What is the conversion factor between grams and moles?

Solution We need to first calculate the number of moles of SO_2 in 87.9 g of the compound and then find the number of kilojoules produced from the exothermic reaction. The sequence of conversions is as follows:

$$\text{grams of } SO_2 \longrightarrow \text{moles of } SO_2 \longrightarrow \text{kilojoules of heat generated}$$

Therefore, the enthalpy change for this reaction is given by

$$\Delta H = 87.9 \text{ g SO}_2 \times \frac{1 \text{ mol SO}_2}{64.07 \text{ g SO}_2} \times \frac{-198.2 \text{ kJ}}{2 \text{ mol SO}_2} = -136 \text{ kJ}$$

and the heat released to the surroundings is 136 kJ.

Keep in mind that the ΔH for a reaction can be positive or negative, but the heat released or absorbed is *always* a positive quantity. The words "released" and "absorbed" give the direction of heat transfer, so no sign is needed.

(Continued)

Check Because 87.9 g is less than twice the molar mass of SO_2 (2×64.07 g) as shown in the preceding thermochemical equation, we expect the heat released to be smaller than 198.2 kJ.

Similar problem: 6.26.

Practice Exercise Calculate the heat evolved when 266 g of white phosphorus (P_4) burns in air according to the equation

$$P_4(s) + 5O_2(g) \longrightarrow P_4O_{10}(s) \qquad \Delta H = -3013 \text{ kJ/mol}$$

A Comparison of ΔH and ΔU

What is the relationship between ΔH and ΔU for a process? To find out, let us consider the reaction between sodium metal and water:

$$2Na(s) + 2H_2O(l) \longrightarrow 2NaOH(aq) + H_2(g) \quad \Delta H = -367.5 \text{ kJ/mol}$$

This thermochemical equation says that when two moles of sodium react with an excess of water, 367.5 kJ of heat are given off. Note that one of the products is hydrogen gas, which must push back air to enter the atmosphere. Consequently, some of the energy produced by the reaction is used to do work of pushing back a volume of air (ΔV) against atmospheric pressure (P) (Figure 6.7). To calculate the change in internal energy, we rearrange Equation (6.8) as follows:

$$\Delta U = \Delta H - P\Delta V$$

Sodium reacting with water to form hydrogen gas.

If we assume the temperature to be 25°C and ignore the small change in the volume of the solution, we can show that the volume of 1 mole of H_2 gas at 1.0 atm and 298 K is 24.5 L, so that $-P\Delta V = -24.5$ L · atm or -2.5 kJ. Finally,

Recall that 1 L · atm = 101.3 J.

$$\begin{aligned} \Delta U &= -367.5 \text{ kJ/mol} - 2.5 \text{ kJ/mol} \\ &= -370.0 \text{ kJ/mol} \end{aligned}$$

This calculation shows that ΔU and ΔH are approximately the same. The reason ΔH is smaller than ΔU in magnitude is that some of the internal energy released is used to do gas expansion work, so less heat is evolved. For reactions that do not involve gases, ΔV is usually very small and so ΔU is practically the same as ΔH.

For reactions that do not result in a change in the number of moles of gases from reactants to products [for example, $H_2(g) + F_2(g) \longrightarrow 2HF(g)$], $\Delta U = \Delta H$.

Another way to calculate the internal energy change of a gaseous reaction is to assume ideal gas behavior and constant temperature. In this case,

$$\begin{aligned} \Delta U &= \Delta H - \Delta(PV) \\ &= \Delta H - \Delta(nRT) \\ &= \Delta H - RT\Delta n \end{aligned} \qquad (6.10)$$

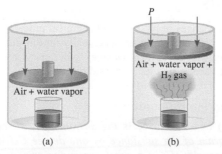

(a)   (b)

Figure 6.7 *(a) A beaker of water inside a cylinder fitted with a movable piston. The pressure inside is equal to the atmospheric pressure. (b) As the sodium metal reacts with water, the hydrogen gas generated pushes the piston upward (doing work on the surroundings) until the pressure inside is again equal to that of outside.*

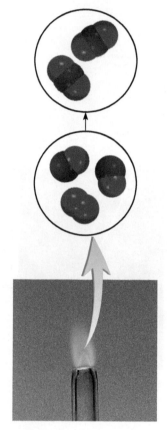

Carbon monoxide burns in air to form carbon dioxide.

Similar problem: 6.27.

where Δn is defined as

$$\Delta n = \text{number of moles of product gases} - \text{number of moles of reactant gases}$$

Example 6.4

Calculate the change in internal energy when 2 moles of CO are converted to 2 moles of CO_2 at 1 atm and 25°C:

$$2CO(g) + O_2(g) \longrightarrow 2CO_2(g) \qquad \Delta H = -566.0 \text{ kJ/mol}$$

Strategy We are given the enthalpy change, ΔH, for the reaction and are asked to calculate the change in internal energy, ΔU. Therefore, we need Equation (6.10). What is the change in the number of moles of gases? ΔH is given in kilojoules, so what units should we use for R?

Solution From the chemical equation we see that 3 moles of gases are converted to 2 moles of gases so that

$$\begin{aligned}\Delta n &= \text{number of moles of product gas} - \text{number of moles of reactant gases} \\ &= 2 - 3 \\ &= -1\end{aligned}$$

Using 8.314 J/K · mol for R and $T = 298$ K in Equation (6.10), we write

$$\begin{aligned}\Delta U &= \Delta H - RT\Delta n \\ &= -566.0 \text{ kJ/mol} - (8.314 \text{ J/K} \cdot \text{mol})\left(\frac{1 \text{ kJ}}{1000 \text{ J}}\right)(298 \text{ K})(-1) \\ &= -563.5 \text{ kJ/mol}\end{aligned}$$

Check Knowing that the reacting gaseous system undergoes a compression (3 moles to 2 moles), is it reasonable to have $\Delta H > \Delta U$ in magnitude?

Practice Exercise What is ΔU for the formation of 1 mole of CO at 1 atm and 25°C?

$$C(\text{graphite}) + \tfrac{1}{2}O_2(g) \longrightarrow CO(g) \qquad \Delta H = -110.5 \text{ kJ/mol}$$

Review of Concepts

Which of the constant-pressure processes shown here has the smallest difference between ΔU and ΔH?
(a) water $\longrightarrow$ water vapor
(b) water $\longrightarrow$ ice
(c) ice $\longrightarrow$ water vapor

6.5 Calorimetry

In the laboratory, heat changes in physical and chemical processes are measured with a *calorimeter,* a closed container designed specifically for this purpose. Our discussion of **calorimetry,** *the measurement of heat changes,* will depend on an understanding of specific heat and heat capacity, so let us consider them first.

Specific Heat and Heat Capacity

The **specific heat (s)** of a substance is *the amount of heat required to raise the temperature of one gram of the substance by one degree Celsius.* It has the units J/g · °C. The **heat capacity (C)** of a substance is *the amount of heat required to* raise the temperature of a given quantity of the substance by one degree Celsius. Its units are J/°C. Specific heat is an intensive property, whereas heat capacity is an extensive property. The relationship between the heat capacity and specific heat of a substance is

$$C = ms \qquad (6.11)$$

where m is the mass of the substance in grams. For example, the specific heat of water is 4.184 J/g · °C, and the heat capacity of 60.0 g of water is

$$(60.0 \text{ g})(4.184 \text{ J/g} \cdot \text{°C}) = 251 \text{ J/°C}$$

Table 6.2 shows the specific heat of some common substances.

If we know the specific heat and the amount of a substance, then the change in the sample's temperature (Δt) will tell us the amount of heat (q) that has been absorbed or released in a particular process. The equations for calculating the heat change are given by

$$q = ms\Delta t \qquad (6.12)$$

$$q = C\Delta t \qquad (6.13)$$

where Δt is the temperature change:

$$\Delta t = t_{\text{final}} - t_{\text{initial}}$$

The sign convention for q is the same as that for enthalpy change; q is positive for endothermic processes and negative for exothermic processes.

Table 6.2	
The Specific Heats of Some Common Substances	
Substance	**Specific Heat (J/g · °C)**
Al	0.900
Au	0.129
C (graphite)	0.720
C (diamond)	0.502
Cu	0.385
Fe	0.444
Hg	0.139
Pb	0.158
H_2O	4.184
C_2H_5OH (ethanol)	2.46

Example 6.5

A 466-g sample of water is heated from 8.50°C to 74.60°C. Calculate the amount of heat absorbed (in kilojoules) by the water.

Strategy We know the quantity of water and the specific heat of water. With this information and the temperature rise, we can calculate the amount of heat absorbed (q).

Solution Using Equation (6.12), we write

$$\begin{aligned} q &= ms\Delta t \\ &= (466 \text{ g})(4.184 \text{ J/g} \cdot \text{°C})(74.60\text{°C} - 8.50\text{°C}) \\ &= 1.29 \times 10^5 \text{ J} \times \frac{1 \text{ kJ}}{1000 \text{ J}} \\ &= 129 \text{ kJ} \end{aligned}$$

Check The units g and °C cancel, and we are left with the desired unit kJ. Because heat is absorbed by the water from the surroundings, it has a positive sign.

Practice Exercise An iron bar of mass 869 g cools from 94°C to 5°C. Calculate the heat released (in kilojoules) by the metal.

Similar problem: 6.33.

Constant-Volume Calorimetry

Heat of combustion is usually measured by placing a known mass of a compound in a steel container called a *constant-volume bomb calorimeter*, which is filled with oxygen at about 30 atm of pressure. The closed bomb is immersed in a known amount

"Constant volume" refers to the volume of the container, which does not change during the reaction. Note that the container remains intact after the measurement. The term "bomb calorimeter" connotes the explosive nature of the reaction (on a small scale) in the presence of excess oxygen gas.

248 **Chapter 6** ▪ Thermochemistry

Figure 6.8 *A constant-volume bomb calorimeter. The calorimeter is filled with oxygen gas before it is placed in the bucket. The sample is ignited electrically, and the heat produced by the reaction can be accurately determined by measuring the temperature increase in the known amount of surrounding water.*

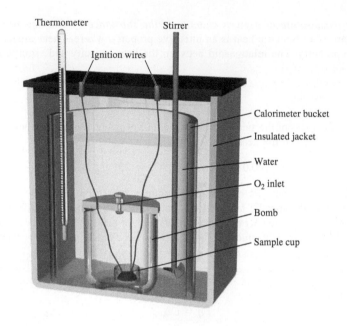

of water, as shown in Figure 6.8. The sample is ignited electrically, and the heat produced by the combustion reaction can be calculated accurately by recording the rise in temperature of the water. The heat given off by the sample is absorbed by the water and the bomb. The special design of the calorimeter enables us to assume that no heat (or mass) is lost to the surroundings during the time it takes to make measurements. Therefore, we can call the bomb and the water in which it is submerged an isolated system. Because no heat enters or leaves the system throughout the process, the heat change of the system (q_{system}) must be zero and we can write

$$q_{system} = q_{cal} + q_{rxn}$$
$$= 0 \qquad (6.14)$$

where q_{cal} and q_{rxn} are the heat changes for the calorimeter and the reaction, respectively. Thus,

$$q_{rxn} = -q_{cal} \qquad (6.15)$$

Note that C_{cal} comprises both the bomb and the surrounding water.

To calculate q_{cal}, we need to know the heat capacity of the calorimeter (C_{cal}) and the temperature rise, that is,

$$q_{cal} = C_{cal}\Delta t \qquad (6.16)$$

The quantity C_{cal} is calibrated by burning a substance with an accurately known heat of combustion. For example, it is known that the combustion of 1 g of benzoic acid (C_6H_5COOH) releases 26.42 kJ of heat. If the temperature rise is 4.673°C, then the heat capacity of the calorimeter is given by

Note that although the combustion reaction is exothermic, q_{cal} is a positive quantity because it represents the heat absorbed by the calorimeter.

$$C_{cal} = \frac{q_{cal}}{\Delta t}$$
$$= \frac{26.42 \text{ kJ}}{4.673°C} = 5.654 \text{ kJ/°C}$$

Once C_{cal} has been determined, the calorimeter can be used to measure the heat of combustion of other substances.

Note that because reactions in a bomb calorimeter occur under constant-volume rather than constant-pressure conditions, the heat changes correspond to ΔU, *not* the enthalpy change ΔH (see Section 6.4). Equation (6.10) can be used to correct the measured heat changes so that they correspond to ΔH values, but the corrections usually are quite small so we will not concern ourselves with the details here. Finally, it is interesting to note that the energy contents of food and fuel (usually expressed in calories where 1 cal = 4.184 J) are measured with constant-volume calorimeters.

Example 6.6

A quantity of 1.435 g of naphthalene ($C_{10}H_8$), a pungent-smelling substance used in moth repellents, was burned in a constant-volume bomb calorimeter. Consequently, the temperature of the water rose from 20.28°C to 25.95°C. If the heat capacity of the bomb plus water was 10.17 kJ/°C, calculate the heat of combustion of naphthalene on a molar basis; that is, find the molar heat of combustion.

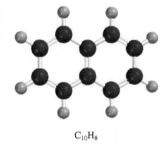

$C_{10}H_8$

Strategy Knowing the heat capacity and the temperature rise, how do we calculate the heat absorbed by the calorimeter? What is the heat generated by the combustion of 1.435 g of naphthalene? What is the conversion factor between grams and moles of naphthalene?

Solution The heat absorbed by the bomb and water is equal to the product of the heat capacity and the temperature change. From Equation (6.16), assuming no heat is lost to the surroundings, we write

$$\begin{aligned} q_{cal} &= C_{cal}\Delta t \\ &= (10.17 \text{ kJ/°C})(25.95°C - 20.28°C) \\ &= 57.66 \text{ kJ} \end{aligned}$$

Because $q_{sys} = q_{cal} + q_{rxn} = 0$, $q_{cal} = -q_{rxn}$. The heat change of the reaction is -57.66 kJ. This is the heat released by the combustion of 1.435 g of $C_{10}H_8$; therefore, we can write the conversion factor as

$$\frac{-57.66 \text{ kJ}}{1.435 \text{ g } C_{10}H_8}$$

The molar mass of naphthalene is 128.2 g, so the heat of combustion of 1 mole of naphthalene is

$$\text{molar heat of combustion} = \frac{-57.66 \text{ kJ}}{1.435 \text{ g } C_{10}H_8} \times \frac{128.2 \text{ g } C_{10}H_8}{1 \text{ mol } C_{10}H_8}$$
$$= -5.151 \times 10^3 \text{ kJ/mol}$$

Check Knowing that the combustion reaction is exothermic and that the molar mass of naphthalene is much greater than 1.4 g, is the answer reasonable? Under the reaction conditions, can the heat change (-57.66 kJ) be equated to the enthalpy change of the reaction?

Similar problem: 6.37.

Practice Exercise A quantity of 1.922 g of methanol (CH_3OH) was burned in a constant-volume bomb calorimeter. Consequently, the temperature of the water rose by 4.20°C. If the heat capacity of the bomb plus water was 10.4 kJ/°C, calculate the molar heat of combustion of methanol.

Constant-Pressure Calorimetry

A simpler device than the constant-volume calorimeter is the constant-pressure calorimeter, which is used to determine the heat changes for noncombustion reactions. A crude constant-pressure calorimeter can be constructed from two Styrofoam coffee

CHEMISTRY *in Action*

White Fat Cells, Brown Fat Cells, and a Potential Cure for Obesity

The food we eat is broken down, or metabolized, in stages by a group of complex biological molecules called enzymes. Most of the energy released at each stage is captured for function and growth. One interesting aspect of metabolism is that the overall change in energy is the same as it is in combustion. For example, the total enthalpy change for the conversion of glucose ($C_6H_{12}O_6$) to carbon dioxide and water is the same whether we burn the substance in air or digest it in our bodies:

$$C_6H_{12}O_6(s) + 6CO_2(g) \longrightarrow 6CO_2(g) + 6H_2O(l)$$
$$\Delta H = -2801 \text{ kJ/mol}$$

The energy content of food is generally measured in calories. The *calorie (cal)* is a non-SI unit of energy that is equivalent to 4.184 J:

$$1 \text{ cal} = 4.184 \text{ J}$$

In the context of nutrition, however, the calorie we speak of (sometimes called a "big calorie") is actually equal to a kilocalorie; that is,

$$1 \text{ Cal} = 1000 \text{ cal} = 4184 \text{ J}$$

The bomb calorimeter described in Section 6.5 is ideally suited for measuring the energy content, or "fuel values," of foods (see table).

The excess energy from food is stored in the body in the form of fats. Fats are a group of organic compounds (triesters of glycerol and fatty acids) that are soluble in organic solvents but insoluble in water. There are two types of fat cells called the white fat cells (WFC) and brown fat cells (BFC). The WFC are designed to store energy for use in time of need for body function. They accumulate under the skin and around

internal organs and they cushion and insulate the body. Obese people have a high content of WFC in their bodies. BFC, on the other hand, contain a high concentration of mitochondria, which are specialized subunits within a cell. The main role of BFC is to burn fat molecules and generate heat. Its name is derived from the fact that mitochondria contain iron, giving the tissue a reddish brown color. In general, women have more BFC than men.

We lose our brown fat as we age, but several studies carried out in 2009 showed that adults possess metabolically active BFC. In one experiment, PET/CT (positron emission tomography and computerized tomography) scans of 24 men exposed to cold and room temperature show that the chilly temperature activates the BFC as they burn off fat molecules to generate heat (see figure). Furthermore, it was found that lean people have more active BFC than obese people.

Mice have the same type of fat cells as humans. In 2013 it was demonstrated by genetically labeling the fat cells of mice that WFC could be converted into BFC by exposure to cold (8°C) for one week. Unfortunately, BFC were converted back to WFC a few weeks after the mice were returned to normal room temperature. A separate study suggested that a different type of BFC can be formed from WFC by exercise.

Obesity is a major health hazard in the United States. Treatments for obesity so far are focused on diet to lower the amount of energy consumed, or exercise to increase the amount of energy the body needs. Most current antiobesity drugs work on the diet half of treatment. If scientists can find a way to convert WFC to BFC by biological means, and signs are encouraging, drugs will one day be developed that would fight obesity based on energy expenditure rather than appetite. And one can accomplish this goal without having to exercise in a cold environment.

Fuel Values of Foods

Substance	$\Delta H_{\text{combustion}}$ (kJ/g)
Apple	−2
Beef	−8
Beer	−1.5
Bread	−11
Butter	−34
Cheese	−18
Eggs	−6
Milk	−3
Potatoes	−3

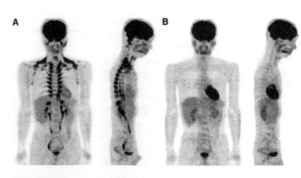

PET/CT scans of a person exposed to cold temperature (A) and room temperature (B).

Table 6.3	Heats of Some Typical Reactions Measured at Constant Pressure	
Type of Reaction	Example	ΔH (kJ/mol)
Heat of neutralization	$HCl(aq) + NaOH(aq) \longrightarrow NaCl(aq) + H_2O(l)$	-56.2
Heat of ionization	$H_2O(l) \longrightarrow H^+(aq) + OH^-(aq)$	56.2
Heat of fusion	$H_2O(s) \longrightarrow H_2O(l)$	6.01
Heat of vaporization	$H_2O(l) \longrightarrow H_2O(g)$	44.0^*
Heat of reaction	$MgCl_2(s) + 2Na(l) \longrightarrow 2NaCl(s) + Mg(s)$	-180.2

*Measured at 25°C. At 100°C, the value is 40.79 kJ.

cups, as shown in Figure 6.9. This device measures the heat effects of a variety of reactions, such as acid-base neutralization, as well as the heat of solution and heat of dilution. Because the pressure is constant, the heat change for the process (q_{rxn}) is equal to the enthalpy change (ΔH). As in the case of a constant-volume calorimeter, we treat the calorimeter as an isolated system. Furthermore, we neglect the small heat capacity of the coffee cups in our calculations. Table 6.3 lists some reactions that have been studied with the constant-pressure calorimeter.

Thermometer

Stirrer

Styrofoam cups

Reaction mixture

Figure 6.9 *A constant-pressure calorimeter made of two Styrofoam coffee cups. The outer cup helps to insulate the reacting mixture from the surroundings. Two solutions of known volume containing the reactants at the same temperature are carefully mixed in the calorimeter. The heat produced or absorbed by the reaction can be determined by measuring the temperature change.*

Example 6.7

A lead (Pb) pellet having a mass of 26.47 g at 89.98°C was placed in a constant-pressure calorimeter of negligible heat capacity containing 100.0 mL of water. The water temperature rose from 22.50°C to 23.17°C. What is the specific heat of the lead pellet?

Strategy A sketch of the initial and final situation is as follows:

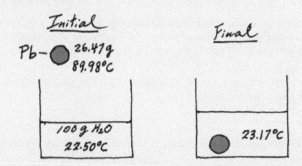

We know the masses of water and the lead pellet as well as the initial and final temperatures. Assuming no heat is lost to the surroundings, we can equate the heat lost by the lead pellet to the heat gained by the water. Knowing the specific heat of water, we can then calculate the specific heat of lead.

Solution Treating the calorimeter as an isolated system (no heat lost to the surroundings), we write

$$q_{Pb} + q_{H_2O} = 0$$

or

$$q_{Pb} = -q_{H_2O}$$

The heat gained by the water is given by

$$q_{H_2O} = ms\Delta t$$

(Continued)

where m and s are the mass and specific heat and $\Delta t = t_{final} - t_{initial}$. Therefore,

$$q_{H_2O} = (100.0 \text{ g})(4.184 \text{ J/g} \cdot °C)(23.17°C - 22.50°C)$$
$$= 280.3 \text{ J}$$

Because the heat lost by the lead pellet is equal to the heat gained by the water, $q_{Pb} = -280.3$ J. Solving for the specific heat of Pb, we write

$$q_{Pb} = ms\Delta t$$
$$-280.3 \text{ J} = (26.47 \text{ g})(s)(23.17°C - 89.98°C)$$
$$s = 0.158 \text{ J/g} \cdot °C$$

Similar problem: 6.88.

Practice Exercise A 30.14-g stainless steel ball bearing at 117.82°C is placed in a constant-pressure calorimeter containing 120.0 mL of water at 18.44°C. If the specific heat of the ball bearing is 0.474 J/g · °C, calculate the final temperature of the water. Assume the calorimeter to have negligible heat capacity.

Example 6.8

A quantity of 1.00×10^2 mL of 0.500 M HCl was mixed with 1.00×10^2 mL of 0.500 M NaOH in a constant-pressure calorimeter of negligible heat capacity. The initial temperature of the HCl and NaOH solutions was the same, 22.50°C, and the final temperature of the mixed solution was 25.86°C. Calculate the heat change for the neutralization reaction on a molar basis:

$$NaOH(aq) + HCl(aq) \longrightarrow NaCl(aq) + H_2O(l)$$

Assume that the densities and specific heats of the solutions are the same as for water (1.00 g/mL and 4.184 J/g · °C, respectively).

Strategy Because the temperature rose, the neutralization reaction is exothermic. How do we calculate the heat absorbed by the combined solution? What is the heat of the reaction? What is the conversion factor for expressing the heat of reaction on a molar basis?

Solution Assuming no heat is lost to the surroundings, $q_{sys} = q_{soln} + q_{rxn} = 0$, so $q_{rxn} = -q_{soln}$, where q_{soln} is the heat absorbed by the combined solution. Because the density of the solution is 1.00 g/mL, the mass of a 100-mL solution is 100 g. Thus,

$$q_{soln} = ms\Delta t$$
$$= (1.00 \times 10^2 \text{ g} + 1.00 \times 10^2 \text{ g})(4.184 \text{ J/g} \cdot °C)(25.86°C - 22.50°C)$$
$$= 2.81 \times 10^3 \text{ J}$$
$$= 2.81 \text{ kJ}$$

Because $q_{rxn} = -q_{soln}$, $q_{rxn} = -2.81$ kJ.

From the molarities given, the number of moles of both HCl and NaOH in 1.00×10^2 mL solution is

$$\frac{0.500 \text{ mol}}{1 \text{ L}} \times 0.100 \text{ L} = 0.0500 \text{ mol}$$

Therefore, the heat of neutralization when 1.00 mole of HCl reacts with 1.00 mole of NaOH is

$$\text{heat of neutralization} = \frac{-2.81 \text{ kJ}}{0.0500 \text{ mol}} = -56.2 \text{ kJ/mol}$$

Check Is the sign consistent with the nature of the reaction? Under the reaction condition, can the heat change be equated to the enthalpy change?

Similar problem: 6.38.

Practice Exercise A quantity of 4.00×10^2 mL of 0.600 M HNO$_3$ is mixed with 4.00×10^2 mL of 0.300 M Ba(OH)$_2$ in a constant-pressure calorimeter of negligible heat capacity. The initial temperature of both solutions is the same at 18.46°C. What is the final temperature of the solution? (Use the result in Example 6.8 for your calculation.)

6.6 Standard Enthalpy of Formation and Reaction

So far we have learned that we can determine the enthalpy change that accompanies a reaction by measuring the heat absorbed or released (at constant pressure). From Equation (6.9) we see that ΔH can also be calculated if we know the actual enthalpies of all reactants and products. However, as mentioned earlier, there is no way to measure the *absolute* value of the enthalpy of a substance. Only values *relative* to an arbitrary reference can be determined. This problem is similar to the one geographers face in expressing the elevations of specific mountains or valleys. Rather than trying to devise some type of "absolute" elevation scale (perhaps based on distance from the center of Earth?), by common agreement all geographic heights and depths are expressed relative to sea level, an arbitrary reference with a defined elevation of "zero" meters or feet. Similarly, chemists have agreed on an arbitrary reference point for enthalpy.

The "sea level" reference point for all enthalpy expressions is called the *standard enthalpy of formation* (ΔH_f°). Substances are said to be in the *standard state* at 1 atm,[†] hence the term "standard enthalpy." The superscript "°" represents standard-state conditions (1 atm), and the subscript "f" stands for formation. By convention, *the standard enthalpy of formation of any element in its most stable form is zero.* Take the element oxygen as an example. Molecular oxygen (O_2) is more stable than the other allotropic form of oxygen, ozone (O_3), at 1 atm and 25°C. Thus, we can write $\Delta H_f^\circ(O_2) = 0$, but $\Delta H_f^\circ(O_3) = 142.2$ kJ/mol. Similarly, graphite is a more stable allotropic form of carbon than diamond at 1 atm and 25°C, so we have $\Delta H_f^\circ(C, \text{graphite}) = 0$ and $\Delta H_f^\circ(C, \text{diamond}) = 1.90$ kJ/mol. Based on this reference for elements, we can now define the standard enthalpy of formation of a compound as *the heat change that results when 1 mole of the compound is formed from its elements at a pressure of 1 atm.* Table 6.4 lists the standard enthalpies of formation for a number of elements and compounds. (For a more complete list of ΔH_f° values, see Appendix 3.) Note that although the standard state does not specify a temperature, we will always use ΔH_f° values measured at 25°C for our discussion because most of the thermodynamic data are collected at this temperature.

Graphite (top) and diamond (bottom).

The importance of the standard enthalpies of formation is that once we know their values, we can readily calculate the *standard enthalpy of reaction,* ΔH_{rxn}°, defined as *the enthalpy of a reaction carried out at 1 atm.* For example, consider the hypothetical reaction

$$a\text{A} + b\text{B} \longrightarrow c\text{C} + d\text{D}$$

where a, b, c, and d are stoichiometric coefficients. For this reaction, ΔH_{rxn}° is given by

$$\Delta H_{rxn}^\circ = [c\Delta H_f^\circ(\text{C}) + d\Delta H_f^\circ(\text{D})] - [a\Delta H_f^\circ(\text{A}) + b\Delta H_f^\circ(\text{B})] \qquad (6.17)$$

[†]In thermodynamics, the standard pressure is defined as 1 bar, where 1 bar = 10^5 Pa = 0.987 atm. Because 1 bar differs from 1 atm by only 1.3 percent, we will continue to use 1 atm as the standard pressure. Note that the normal melting point and boiling point of a substance are defined in terms of 1 atm.

Table 6.4	Standard Enthalpies of Formation of Some Inorganic Substances at 25°C		
Substance	**ΔH_f°(kJ/mol)**	**Substance**	**ΔH_f°(kJ/mol)**
Ag(s)	0	$H_2O_2(l)$	−187.6
AgCl(s)	−127.0	Hg(l)	0
Al(s)	0	$I_2(s)$	0
$Al_2O_3(s)$	−1669.8	HI(g)	25.9
$Br_2(l)$	0	Mg(s)	0
HBr(g)	−36.2	MgO(s)	−601.8
C(graphite)	0	$MgCO_3(s)$	−1112.9
C(diamond)	1.90	$N_2(g)$	0
CO(g)	−110.5	$NH_3(g)$	−46.3
$CO_2(g)$	−393.5	NO(g)	90.4
Ca(s)	0	$NO_2(g)$	33.85
CaO(s)	−635.6	$N_2O(g)$	81.56
$CaCO_3(s)$	−1206.9	$N_2O_4(g)$	9.66
$Cl_2(g)$	0	O(g)	249.4
HCl(g)	−92.3	$O_2(g)$	0
Cu(s)	0	$O_3(g)$	142.2
CuO(s)	−155.2	S(rhombic)	0
$F_2(g)$	0	S(monoclinic)	0.30
HF(g)	−271.6	$SO_2(g)$	−296.1
H(g)	218.2	$SO_3(g)$	−395.2
$H_2(g)$	0	$H_2S(g)$	−20.15
$H_2O(g)$	−241.8	Zn(s)	0
$H_2O(l)$	−285.8	ZnO(s)	−348.0

We can generalize Equation (6.17) as

$$\Delta H_{rxn}^\circ = \Sigma n\Delta H_f^\circ(\text{products}) - \Sigma m\Delta H_f^\circ(\text{reactants}) \qquad (6.18)$$

where m and n denote the stoichiometric coefficients for the reactants and products, and Σ (sigma) means "the sum of." Note that in calculations, the stoichiometric coefficients are just numbers without units.

To use Equation (6.18) to calculate ΔH_{rxn}°, we must know the ΔH_f° values of the compounds that take part in the reaction. These values can be determined by applying the direct method or the indirect method.

The Direct Method

This method of measuring ΔH_f° works for compounds that can be readily synthesized from their elements. Suppose we want to know the enthalpy of formation of carbon dioxide. We must measure the enthalpy of the reaction when carbon (graphite) and molecular oxygen in their standard states are converted to carbon dioxide in its standard state:

$$C(\text{graphite}) + O_2(g) \longrightarrow CO_2(g) \quad \Delta H_{rxn}^\circ = -393.5 \text{ kJ/mol}$$

We know from experience that this combustion easily goes to completion. Thus, from Equation (6.18) we can write

$$\Delta H_{rxn}^\circ = \Delta H_f^\circ(CO_2, g) - [\Delta H_f^\circ(C, \text{graphite}) + \Delta H_f^\circ(O_2, g)]$$
$$= -393.5 \text{ kJ/mol}$$

Because both graphite and O_2 are stable allotropic forms of the elements, it follows that ΔH_f°(C, graphite) and ΔH_f°(O_2, g) are zero. Therefore,

$$\Delta H_{rxn}^\circ = \Delta H_f^\circ(CO_2, g) = -393.5 \text{ kJ/mol}$$

or
$$\Delta H_f^\circ(CO_2, g) = -393.5 \text{ kJ/mol}$$

Note that arbitrarily assigning zero ΔH_f° for each element in its most stable form at the standard state does not affect our calculations in any way. Remember, in thermochemistry we are interested only in enthalpy *changes* because they can be determined experimentally whereas the absolute enthalpy values cannot. The choice of a zero "reference level" for enthalpy makes calculations easier to handle. Again referring to the terrestrial altitude analogy, we find that Mt. Everest is 8708 ft higher than Mt. McKinley. This difference in altitude is unaffected by the decision to set sea level at 0 ft or at 1000 ft.

Other compounds that can be studied by the direct method are SF_6, P_4O_{10}, and CS_2. The equations representing their syntheses are

$$S(\text{rhombic}) + 3F_2(g) \longrightarrow SF_6(g)$$
$$P_4(\text{white}) + 5O_2(g) \longrightarrow P_4O_{10}(s)$$
$$C(\text{graphite}) + 2S(\text{rhombic}) \longrightarrow CS_2(l)$$

Note that S(rhombic) and P(white) are the most stable allotropes of sulfur and phosphorus, respectively, at 1 atm and 25°C, so their ΔH_f° values are zero.

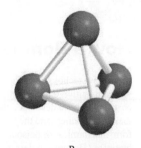

P_4

White phosphorus burns in air to form P_4O_{10}.

The Indirect Method

Many compounds cannot be directly synthesized from their elements. In some cases, the reaction proceeds too slowly, or side reactions produce substances other than the desired compound. In these cases, ΔH_f° can be determined by an indirect approach, which is based on Hess's law of heat summation, or simply Hess's law, named after the Swiss-Russian chemist Germain Hess.[†] **Hess's law** can be stated as follows: *When reactants are converted to products, the change in enthalpy is the same whether the reaction takes place in one step or in a series of steps.* In other words, if we can break down the reaction of interest into a series of reactions for which ΔH_{rxn}° can be measured, we can calculate ΔH_{rxn}° for the overall reaction. Hess's law is based on the fact that because H is a state function, ΔH depends only on the initial and final state (that is, only on the nature of reactants and products). The enthalpy change would be the same whether the overall reaction takes place in one step or many steps.

An analogy for Hess's law is as follows. Suppose you go from the first floor to the sixth floor of a building by elevator. The gain in your gravitational potential energy (which corresponds to the enthalpy change for the overall process) is the same whether you go directly there or stop at each floor on your way up (breaking the trip into a series of steps).

Let's say we are interested in the standard enthalpy of formation of carbon monoxide (CO). We might represent the reaction as

$$C(\text{graphite}) + \tfrac{1}{2}O_2(g) \longrightarrow CO(g)$$

However, burning graphite also produces some carbon dioxide (CO_2), so we cannot measure the enthalpy change for CO directly as shown. Instead, we must employ an indirect route, based on Hess's law. It is possible to carry out the following two separate reactions, which do go to completion:

(a) $C(\text{graphite}) + O_2(g) \longrightarrow CO_2(g) \quad \Delta H_{rxn}^\circ = -393.5 \text{ kJ/mol}$

(b) $CO(g) + \tfrac{1}{2}O_2(g) \longrightarrow CO_2(g) \quad \Delta H_{rxn}^\circ = -283.0 \text{ kJ/mol}$

[†]Germain Henri Hess (1802–1850). Swiss-Russian chemist. Hess was born in Switzerland but spent most of his life in Russia. For formulating Hess's law, he is called the father of thermochemistry.

CHEMISTRY *in Action*

How a Bombardier Beetle Defends Itself

Survival techniques of insects and small animals in a fiercely competitive environment take many forms. For example, chameleons have developed the ability to change color to match their surroundings and the butterfly *Limenitis* has evolved into a form that mimics the poisonous and unpleasant-tasting monarch butterfly (*Danaus*). A less passive defense mechanism is employed by bombardier beetles (*Brachinus*), which repel predators with a "chemical spray."

The bombardier beetle has a pair of glands at the tip of its abdomen. Each gland consists of two compartments. The inner compartment contains an aqueous solution of hydroquinone and hydrogen peroxide, and the outer compartment holds a mixture of enzymes. (Enzymes are biological molecules that can speed up a reaction.) When threatened, the beetle squeezes some fluid from the inner compartment into the outer compartment, where, in the presence of the enzymes, an exothermic reaction takes place:

(a) $\quad C_6H_4(OH)_2(aq) + H_2O_2(aq) \longrightarrow$
$\quad$ hydroquinone

$$C_6H_4O_2(aq) + 2H_2O(l)$$
$$\text{quinone}$$

To estimate the heat of reaction, let us consider the following steps:

(b) $\quad C_6H_4(OH)_2(aq) \longrightarrow C_6H_4O_2(aq) + H_2(g)$
$$\Delta H° = 177 \text{ kJ/mol}$$
(c) $\quad H_2O_2(aq) \longrightarrow H_2O(l) + \frac{1}{2}O_2(g)$
$$\Delta H° = -94.6 \text{ kJ/mol}$$
(d) $\quad H_2(g) + \frac{1}{2}O_2(g) \longrightarrow H_2O(l) \quad \Delta H° = -286 \text{ kJ/mol}$

Recalling Hess's law, we find that the heat of reaction for (a) is simply the *sum* of those for (b), (c), and (d).

A bombardier beetle discharging a chemical spray.

Therefore, we write

$$\Delta H_a° = \Delta H_b° + \Delta H_c° + \Delta H_d°$$
$$= (177 - 94.6 - 286) \text{ kJ/mol}$$
$$= -204 \text{ kJ/mol}$$

The large amount of heat generated is sufficient to bring the mixture to its boiling point. By rotating the tip of its abdomen, the beetle can quickly discharge the vapor in the form of a fine mist toward an unsuspecting predator. In addition to the thermal effect, the quinones also act as a repellent to other insects and animals. One bombardier beetle carries enough reagents to produce 20 to 30 discharges in quick succession, each with an audible detonation.

Remember to reverse the sign of ΔH when you reverse a chemical equation.

First, we reverse Equation (b) to get

(c) $\qquad\qquad CO_2(g) \longrightarrow CO(g) + \frac{1}{2}O_2(g) \quad \Delta H°_{rxn} = +283.0 \text{ kJ/mol}$

Because chemical equations can be added and subtracted just like algebraic equations, we carry out the operation (a) + (c) and obtain

(a) $\qquad C(\text{graphite}) + O_2(g) \longrightarrow CO_2(g)$ $\qquad\qquad \Delta H°_{rxn} = -393.5 \text{ kJ/mol}$
(c) $\qquad\qquad CO_2(g) \longrightarrow CO(g) + \frac{1}{2}O_2(g)$ $\qquad \Delta H°_{rxn} = +283.0 \text{ kJ/mol}$
(d) $\qquad \overline{C(\text{graphite}) + \frac{1}{2}O_2(g) \longrightarrow CO(g)}$ $\qquad\qquad \Delta H°_{rxn} = -110.5 \text{ kJ/mol}$

Thus, $\Delta H_f^\circ(CO) = -110.5$ kJ/mol. Looking back, we see that the overall reaction is the formation of CO_2 [Equation (a)], which can be broken down into two parts [Equations (d) and (b)]. Figure 6.10 shows the overall scheme of our procedure.

The general rule in applying Hess's law is to arrange a series of chemical equations (corresponding to a series of steps) in such a way that, when added together, all species will cancel except for the reactants and products that appear in the overall reaction. This means that we want the elements on the left and the compound of interest on the right of the arrow. Further, we often need to multiply some or all of the equations representing the individual steps by the appropriate coefficients.

Example 6.9

Calculate the standard enthalpy of formation of acetylene (C_2H_2) from its elements:

$$2C(graphite) + H_2(g) \longrightarrow C_2H_2(g)$$

The equations for each step and the corresponding enthalpy changes are

(a) $C(graphite) + O_2(g) \longrightarrow CO_2(g)$ $\Delta H_{rxn}^\circ = -393.5$ kJ/mol
(b) $H_2(g) + \frac{1}{2}O_2(g) \longrightarrow H_2O(l)$ $\Delta H_{rxn}^\circ = -285.8$ kJ/mol
(c) $2C_2H_2(g) + 5O_2(g) \longrightarrow 4CO_2(g) + 2H_2O(l)$ $\Delta H_{rxn}^\circ = -2598.8$ kJ/mol

Strategy Our goal here is to calculate the enthalpy change for the formation of C_2H_2 from its elements C and H_2. The reaction does not occur directly, however, so we must use an indirect route using the information given by Equations (a), (b), and (c).

Solution Looking at the synthesis of C_2H_2, we need 2 moles of graphite as reactant. So we multiply Equation (a) by 2 to get

(d) $2C(graphite) + 2O_2(g) \longrightarrow 2CO_2(g)$ $\Delta H_{rxn}^\circ = 2(-393.5 \text{ kJ/mol})$
                                                                $= -787.0$ kJ/mol

Next, we need 1 mole of H_2 as a reactant and this is provided by Equation (b). Last, we need 1 mole of C_2H_2 as a product. Equation (c) has 2 moles of C_2H_2 as a reactant so we need to reverse the equation and divide it by 2:

(e) $2CO_2(g) + H_2O(l) \longrightarrow C_2H_2(g) + \frac{5}{2}O_2(g)$ $\Delta H_{rxn}^\circ = \frac{1}{2}(2598.8 \text{ kJ/mol})$
                                                                $= 1299.4$ kJ/mol

Adding Equations (d), (b), and (e) together, we get

$2C(graphite) + 2O_2(g) \longrightarrow 2CO_2(g)$	$\Delta H_{rxn}^\circ = -787.0$ kJ/mol
$H_2(g) + \frac{1}{2}O_2(g) \longrightarrow H_2O(l)$	$\Delta H_{rxn}^\circ = -285.8$ kJ/mol
$2CO_2(g) + H_2O(l) \longrightarrow C_2H_2(g) + \frac{5}{2}O_2(g)$	$\Delta H_{rxn}^\circ = 1299.4$ kJ/mol
$2C(graphite) + H_2(g) \longrightarrow C_2H_2(g)$	$\Delta H_{rxn}^\circ = 226.6$ kJ/mol

Therefore, $\Delta H_f^\circ = \Delta H_{rxn}^\circ = 226.6$ kJ/mol. The ΔH_f° value means that when 1 mole of C_2H_2 is synthesized from 2 moles of C(graphite) and 1 mole of H_2, 226.6 kJ of heat are absorbed by the reacting system from the surroundings. Thus, this is an endothermic process.

Practice Exercise Calculate the standard enthalpy of formation of carbon disulfide (CS_2) from its elements, given that

$C(graphite) + O_2(g) \longrightarrow CO_2(g)$	$\Delta H_{rxn}^\circ = -393.5$ kJ/mol
$S(rhombic) + O_2(g) \longrightarrow SO_2(g)$	$\Delta H_{rxn}^\circ = -296.4$ kJ/mol
$CS_2(l) + 3O_2(g) \longrightarrow CO_2(g) + 2SO_2(g)$	$\Delta H_{rxn}^\circ = -1073.6$ kJ/mol

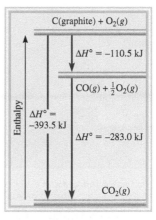

Figure 6.10 *The enthalpy change for the formation of 1 mole of CO_2 from graphite and O_2 can be broken down into two steps according to Hess's law.*

In the figure: C(graphite) + $O_2(g)$; $\Delta H^\circ = -110.5$ kJ; $CO(g) + \frac{1}{2}O_2(g)$; $\Delta H^\circ = -393.5$ kJ; $\Delta H^\circ = -283.0$ kJ; $CO_2(g)$; Enthalpy

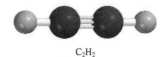

C_2H_2

An oxyacetylene torch has a high flame temperature (3000°C) and is used to weld metals.

Similar problems: 6.62, 6.63.

We can calculate the enthalpy of reactions from the values of ΔH_f°, as shown in Example 6.10.

258   **Chapter 6** ▪ Thermochemistry

Example 6.10

The thermite reaction involves aluminum and iron(III) oxide

$$2Al(s) + Fe_2O_3(s) \longrightarrow Al_2O_3(s) + 2Fe(l)$$

This reaction is highly exothermic and the liquid iron formed is used to weld metals. Calculate the heat released in kilojoules per gram of Al reacted with Fe_2O_3. The ΔH_f° for Fe(l) is 12.40 kJ/mol.

Strategy The enthalpy of a reaction is the difference between the sum of the enthalpies of the products and the sum of the enthalpies of the reactants. The enthalpy of each species (reactant or product) is given by its stoichiometric coefficient times the standard enthalpy of formation of the species.

Solution Using the given ΔH_f° value for Fe(l) and other ΔH_f° values in Appendix 3 and Equation (6.18), we write

$$\Delta H_{rxn}^\circ = [\Delta H_f^\circ(Al_2O_3) + 2\Delta H_f^\circ(Fe)] - [2\Delta H_f^\circ(Al) + \Delta H_f^\circ(Fe_2O_3)]$$
$$= [(-1669.8 \text{ kJ/mol}) + 2(12.40 \text{ kJ/mol})] - [2(0) + (-822.2 \text{ kJ/mol})]$$
$$= -822.8 \text{ kJ/mol}$$

This is the amount of heat released for two moles of Al reacted. We use the following ratio

$$\frac{-822.8 \text{ kJ}}{2 \text{ mol Al}}$$

to convert to kJ/g Al. The molar mass of Al is 26.98 g, so

$$\text{heat released per gram of Al} = \frac{-822.8 \text{ kJ}}{2 \text{ mol Al}} \times \frac{1 \text{ mol Al}}{26.98 \text{ g Al}}$$
$$= -15.25 \text{ kJ/g}$$

Check Is the negative sign consistent with the exothermic nature of the reaction? As a quick check, we see that 2 moles of Al weigh about 54 g and give off about 823 kJ of heat when reacted with Fe_2O_3. Therefore, the heat given off per gram of Al reacted is approximately -830 kJ/54 g or -15.4 kJ/g.

Practice Exercise Benzene (C_6H_6) burns in air to produce carbon dioxide and liquid water. Calculate the heat released (in kilojoules) per gram of the compound reacted with oxygen. The standard enthalpy of formation of benzene is 49.04 kJ/mol.

The molten iron formed in a thermite reaction is run down into a mold between the ends of two railroad rails. On cooling, the rails are welded together.

Similar problems: 6.54, 6.57.

Review of Concepts

Explain why reactions involving reactant compounds with positive ΔH_f° values are generally more exothermic than those with negative ΔH_f° values.

6.7 Heat of Solution and Dilution

Although we have focused so far on the thermal energy effects resulting from chemical reactions, many physical processes, such as the melting of ice or the condensation of a vapor, also involve the absorption or release of heat. Enthalpy changes occur as well when a solute dissolves in a solvent or when a solution is diluted. Let us look at these two related physical processes, involving heat of solution and heat of dilution.

Heat of Solution

In the vast majority of cases, dissolving a solute in a solvent produces measurable heat change. At constant pressure, the heat change is equal to the enthalpy change. The **heat of solution,** or **enthalpy of solution, ΔH_{soln},** is *the heat generated or absorbed when a certain amount of solute dissolves in a certain amount of solvent.* The quantity ΔH_{soln} represents the difference between the enthalpy of the final solution and the enthalpies of its original components (that is, solute and solvent) before they are mixed. Thus,

$$\Delta H_{soln} = H_{soln} - H_{components} \qquad (6.19)$$

Neither H_{soln} nor $H_{components}$ can be measured, but their difference, ΔH_{soln}, can be readily determined in a constant-pressure calorimeter. Like other enthalpy changes, ΔH_{soln} is positive for endothermic (heat-absorbing) processes and negative for exothermic (heat-generating) processes.

Consider the heat of solution of a process in which an ionic compound is the solute and water is the solvent. For example, what happens when solid NaCl dissolves in water? In solid NaCl, the Na^+ and Cl^- ions are held together by strong positive-negative (electrostatic) forces, but when a small crystal of NaCl dissolves in water, the three-dimensional network of ions breaks into its individual units. (The structure of solid NaCl is shown in Figure 2.13.) The separated Na^+ and Cl^- ions are stabilized in solution by their interaction with water molecules (see Figure 4.2). These ions are said to be *hydrated.* In this case water plays a role similar to that of a good electrical insulator. Water molecules shield the ions (Na^+ and Cl^-) from each other and effectively reduce the electrostatic attraction that held them together in the solid state. The heat of solution is defined by the following process:

$$NaCl(s) \xrightarrow{H_2O} Na^+(aq) + Cl^-(aq) \qquad \Delta H_{soln} = ?$$

Dissolving an ionic compound such as NaCl in water involves complex interactions among the solute and solvent species. However, for the sake of analysis we can imagine that the solution process takes place in two separate steps, illustrated in Figure 6.11. First, the Na^+ and Cl^- ions in the solid crystal are separated from each other and converted to the gaseous state:

$$energy + NaCl(s) \longrightarrow Na^+(g) + Cl^-(g)$$

The energy required to completely separate one mole of a solid ionic compound into gaseous ions is called **lattice energy (U).** The lattice energy of NaCl is 788 kJ/mol. In other words, we would need to supply 788 kJ of energy to break 1 mole of solid NaCl into 1 mole of Na^+ ions and 1 mole of Cl^- ions.

Next, the "gaseous" Na^+ and Cl^- ions enter the water and become hydrated:

$$Na^+(g) + Cl^-(g) \xrightarrow{H_2O} Na^+(aq) + Cl^-(aq) + energy$$

*The enthalpy change associated with the hydration process is called the **heat of hydration, ΔH_{hydr}** (heat of hydration is a negative quantity for cations and anions). Applying Hess's law, it is possible to consider ΔH_{soln} as the sum of two related quantities, lattice energy (U) and heat of hydration (ΔH_{hydr}), as shown in Figure 6.11:

$$\Delta H_{soln} = U + \Delta H_{hydr} \qquad (6.20)$$

The word "lattice" describes arrangement in space of isolated points (occupied by ions) in a regular pattern. Lattice energy is a positive quantity. Beware that lattice energy and internal energy share the same symbol.

260   **Chapter 6** ▪ Thermochemistry

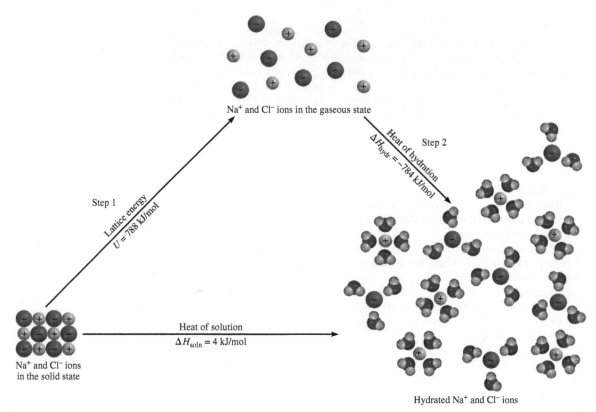

Na⁺ and Cl⁻ ions in the gaseous state

Step 1
Lattice energy
$U = 788$ kJ/mol

Step 2
Heat of hydration
$\Delta H_{hydr} = -784$ kJ/mol

Heat of solution
$\Delta H_{soln} = 4$ kJ/mol

Na⁺ and Cl⁻ ions
in the solid state

Hydrated Na⁺ and Cl⁻ ions

Figure 6.11 *The solution process for NaCl. The process can be considered to occur in two separate steps: (1) separation of ions from the crystal state to the gaseous state and (2) hydration of the gaseous ions. The heat of solution is equal to the energy changes for these two steps, $\Delta H_{soln} = U + \Delta H_{hydr}$.*

Therefore,

$$
\begin{array}{ll}
\text{NaCl}(s) \longrightarrow \text{Na}^+(g) + \text{Cl}^-(g) & U = 788 \text{ kJ/mol} \\
\text{Na}^+(g) + \text{Cl}^-(g) \xrightarrow{\text{H}_2\text{O}} \text{Na}^+(aq) + \text{Cl}^-(aq) & \Delta H_{\text{hydr}} = -784 \text{ kJ/mol} \\
\hline
\text{NaCl}(s) \xrightarrow{\text{H}_2\text{O}} \text{Na}^+(aq) + \text{Cl}^-(aq) & \Delta H_{\text{soln}} = 4 \text{ kJ/mol}
\end{array}
$$

Thus, when 1 mole of NaCl dissolves in water, 4 kJ of heat will be absorbed from the surroundings. We would observe this effect by noting that the beaker containing the solution becomes slightly colder. Table 6.5 lists the ΔH_{soln} of several ionic compounds. Depending on the nature of the cation and anion involved, ΔH_{soln} for an ionic compound may be either negative (exothermic) or positive (endothermic).

Table 6.5

Heats of Solution of Some Ionic Compounds

Compound	ΔH_{soln} (kJ/mol)
LiCl	−37.1
CaCl₂	−82.8
NaCl	4.0
KCl	17.2
NH₄Cl	15.2
NH₄NO₃	26.6

Review of Concepts

Use the data in Appendix 3 to calculate the heat of solution for the following process:

$$\text{KNO}_3(s) \longrightarrow \text{K}^+(aq) + \text{NO}_3^-(aq)$$

Heat of Dilution

When a previously prepared solution is *diluted,* that is, when more solvent is added to lower the overall concentration of the solute, additional heat is usually given off or absorbed. The **heat of dilution** is *the heat change associated with the dilution* *process.* If a certain solution process is endothermic and the solution is subsequently diluted, *more* heat will be absorbed by the same solution from the surroundings. The converse holds true for an exothermic solution process—more heat will be liberated if additional solvent is added to dilute the solution. Therefore, always be cautious when working on a dilution procedure in the laboratory. Because of its highly exothermic heat of dilution, concentrated sulfuric acid (H_2SO_4) poses a particularly hazardous problem if its concentration must be reduced by mixing it with additional water. Concentrated H_2SO_4 is composed of 98 percent acid and 2 percent water by mass. Diluting it with water releases considerable amount of heat to the surroundings. This process is so exothermic that you must *never* attempt to dilute the concentrated acid by adding water to it. The heat generated could cause the acid solution to boil and splatter. The recommended procedure is to add the concentrated acid slowly to the water (while constantly stirring).

Generations of chemistry students have been reminded of the safe procedure for diluting acids by the venerable saying, "Do as you oughter, add acid to water."

Key Equations

$\Delta U = q + w$ (6.1)	Mathematical statement of the first law of thermodynamics.
$w = -P\Delta V$ (6.3)	Calculating work done in gas expansion or gas compression.
$H = U + PV$ (6.6)	Definition of enthalpy.
$\Delta H = \Delta U + P\Delta V$ (6.8)	Calculating enthalpy (or energy) change for a constant-pressure process.
$C = ms$ (6.11)	Definition of heat capacity.
$q = ms\Delta t$ (6.12)	Calculating heat change in terms of specific heat.
$q = C\Delta t$ (6.13)	Calculating heat change in terms of heat capacity.
$\Delta H^{\circ}_{rxn} = \Sigma n \Delta H^{\circ}_{f}$ (products) $- \Sigma m \Delta H^{\circ}_{f}$ (reactants) (6.18)	Calculating standard enthalpy of reaction.
$\Delta H_{soln} = U + \Delta H_{hydr}$ (6.20)	Lattice energy and hydration contributions to heat of solution.

Summary of Facts & Concepts

1. Energy is the capacity to do work. There are many forms of energy and they are interconvertible. The law of conservation of energy states that the total amount of energy in the universe is constant.

2. A process that gives off heat to the surroundings is exothermic; a process that absorbs heat from the surroundings is endothermic.

3. The state of a system is defined by properties such as composition, volume, temperature, and pressure. These properties are called state functions.

4. The change in a state function for a system depends only on the initial and final states of the system, and not on the path by which the change is accomplished. Energy is a state function; work and heat are not.

5. Energy can be converted from one form to another, but it cannot be created or destroyed (first law of thermodynamics). In chemistry we are concerned mainly with thermal energy, electrical energy, and mechanical energy, which is usually associated with pressure-volume work.

6. Enthalpy is a state function. A change in enthalpy ΔH is equal to $\Delta U + P\Delta V$ for a constant-pressure process.

7. The change in enthalpy (ΔH, usually given in kilojoules) is a measure of the heat of reaction (or any other process) at constant pressure.

8. Constant-volume and constant-pressure calorimeters are used to measure heat changes that occur in physical and chemical processes.

9. Hess's law states that the overall enthalpy change in a reaction is equal to the sum of enthalpy changes for individual steps in the overall reaction.

10. The standard enthalpy of a reaction can be calculated from the standard enthalpies of formation of reactants and products.

11. The heat of solution of an ionic compound in water is the sum of the lattice energy of the compound and the heat of hydration. The relative magnitudes of these two quantities determine whether the solution process is endothermic or exothermic. The heat of dilution is the heat absorbed or evolved when a solution is diluted.

262   **Chapter 6** ▪ Thermochemistry

Key Words

Calorimetry, p. 246
Chemical energy, p. 231
Closed system, p. 232
Endothermic process, p. 233
Energy, p. 231
Enthalpy (H), p. 241
Enthalpy of reaction
   (ΔH_{rxn}), p. 242
Enthalpy of solution
   (ΔH_{soln}), p. 259
Exothermic process, p. 233

First law of
   thermodynamics, p. 234
Heat, p. 232
Heat capacity (C), p. 246
Heat of dilution, p. 260
Heat of hydration
   (ΔH_{hydr}), p. 259
Heat of solution
   (ΔH_{soln}), p. 259
Hess's law, p. 255
Isolated system, p. 232

Lattice energy (U), p. 259
Law of conservation of
   energy, p. 231
Open system, p. 232
Potential energy, p. 231
Radiant energy, p. 231
Specific heat (s), p. 246
Standard enthalpy of
   formation (ΔH_f°), p. 253
Standard enthalpy of reaction
   (ΔH_{rxn}°), p. 253

Standard state, p. 253
State function, p. 234
State of a system, p. 234
Surroundings, p. 232
System, p. 232
Thermal energy, p. 231
Thermochemical
   equation, p. 243
Thermochemistry, p. 232
Thermodynamics, p. 234
Work, p. 231

Questions & Problems

● *Problems available in Connect Plus*
Red numbered problems solved in Student Solutions Manual

Definitions
Review Questions

● 6.1   Define these terms: system, surroundings, open system, closed system, isolated system, thermal energy, chemical energy, potential energy, kinetic energy, law of conservation of energy.

6.2   What is heat? How does heat differ from thermal energy? Under what condition is heat transferred from one system to another?

6.3   What are the units for energy commonly employed in chemistry?

6.4   A truck initially traveling at 60 km per hour is brought to a complete stop at a traffic light. Does this change violate the law of conservation of energy? Explain.

6.5   These are various forms of energy: chemical, heat, light, mechanical, and electrical. Suggest ways of interconverting these forms of energy.

6.6   Describe the interconversions of forms of energy occurring in these processes: (a) You throw a softball up into the air and catch it. (b) You switch on a flashlight. (c) You ride the ski lift to the top of the hill and then ski down. (d) You strike a match and let it burn down.

Energy Changes in Chemical Reactions
Review Questions

● 6.7   Define these terms: thermochemistry, exothermic process, endothermic process.

6.8   Stoichiometry is based on the law of conservation of mass. On what law is thermochemistry based?

6.9   Describe two exothermic processes and two endothermic processes.

6.10   Decomposition reactions are usually endothermic, whereas combination reactions are usually exothermic. Give a qualitative explanation for these trends.

First Law of Thermodynamics
Review Questions

6.11   On what law is the first law of thermodynamics based? Explain the sign conventions in the equation $\Delta U = q + w$.

6.12   Explain what is meant by a state function. Give two examples of quantities that are state functions and two that are not.

6.13   The internal energy of an ideal gas depends only on its temperature. Do a first-law analysis of this process. A sample of an ideal gas is allowed to expand at constant temperature against atmospheric pressure. (a) Does the gas do work on its surroundings? (b) Is there heat exchange between the system and the surroundings? If so, in which direction? (c) What is ΔU for the gas for this process?

● 6.14   Consider these changes.

(a) $Hg(l) \longrightarrow Hg(g)$
(b) $3O_2(g) \longrightarrow 2O_3(g)$
(c) $CuSO_4 \cdot 5H_2O(s) \longrightarrow CuSO_4(s) + 5H_2O(g)$
(d) $H_2(g) + F_2(g) \longrightarrow 2HF(g)$

At constant pressure, in which of the reactions is work done by the system on the surroundings? By the surroundings on the system? In which of them is no work done?

Problems

● 6.15   A sample of nitrogen gas expands in volume from 1.6 L to 5.4 L at constant temperature. Calculate the work done in joules if the gas expands (a) against a vacuum, (b) against a constant pressure of 0.80 atm, and (c) against a constant pressure of 3.7 atm.

● **6.16**   A gas expands in volume from 26.7 mL to 89.3 mL at constant temperature. Calculate the work done (in joules) if the gas expands (a) against a vacuum, (b) against a constant pressure of 1.5 atm, and (c) against a constant pressure of 2.8 atm.

6.17 A gas expands and does P-V work on the surroundings equal to 325 J. At the same time, it absorbs 127 J of heat from the surroundings. Calculate the change in energy of the gas.

6.18 The work done to compress a gas is 74 J. As a result, 26 J of heat is given off to the surroundings. Calculate the change in energy of the gas.

6.19 Calculate the work done when 50.0 g of tin dissolves in excess acid at 1.00 atm and 25°C:

$$Sn(s) + 2H^+(aq) \longrightarrow Sn^{2+}(aq) + H_2(g)$$

Assume ideal gas behavior.

6.20 Calculate the work done in joules when 1.0 mole of water vaporizes at 1.0 atm and 100°C. Assume that the volume of liquid water is negligible compared with that of steam at 100°C, and ideal gas behavior.

Enthalpy of Chemical Reactions
Review Questions

6.21 Define these terms: enthalpy, enthalpy of reaction. Under what condition is the heat of a reaction equal to the enthalpy change of the same reaction?

6.22 In writing thermochemical equations, why is it important to indicate the physical state (that is, gaseous, liquid, solid, or aqueous) of each substance?

6.23 Explain the meaning of this thermochemical equation:

$$4NH_3(g) + 5O_2(g) \longrightarrow 4NO(g) + 6H_2O(g)$$
$$\Delta H = -904 \text{ kJ/mol}$$

6.24 Consider this reaction:

$$2CH_3OH(l) + 3O_2(g) \longrightarrow 4H_2O(l) + 2CO_2(g)$$
$$\Delta H = -1452.8 \text{ kJ/mol}$$

What is the value of ΔH if (a) the equation is multiplied throughout by 2, (b) the direction of the reaction is reversed so that the products become the reactants and vice versa, (c) water vapor instead of liquid water is formed as the product?

Problems

6.25 The first step in the industrial recovery of zinc from the zinc sulfide ore is roasting, that is, the conversion of ZnS to ZnO by heating:

$$2ZnS(s) + 3O_2(g) \longrightarrow 2ZnO(s) + 2SO_2(g)$$
$$\Delta H = -879 \text{ kJ/mol}$$

Calculate the heat evolved (in kJ) per gram of ZnS roasted.

6.26 Determine the amount of heat (in kJ) given off when 1.26×10^4 g of NO_2 are produced according to the equation

$$2NO(g) + O_2(g) \longrightarrow 2NO_2(g)$$
$$\Delta H = -114.6 \text{ kJ/mol}$$

6.27 Consider the reaction

$$2H_2O(g) \longrightarrow 2H_2(g) + O_2(g)$$
$$\Delta H = 483.6 \text{ kJ/mol}$$

If 2.0 moles of $H_2O(g)$ are converted to $H_2(g)$ and $O_2(g)$ against a pressure of 1.0 atm at 125°C, what is ΔU for this reaction?

6.28 Consider the reaction

$$H_2(g) + Cl_2(g) \longrightarrow 2HCl(g)$$
$$\Delta H = -184.6 \text{ kJ/mol}$$

If 3 moles of H_2 react with 3 moles of Cl_2 to form HCl, calculate the work done (in joules) against a pressure of 1.0 atm at 25°C. What is ΔU for this reaction? Assume the reaction goes to completion.

Calorimetry
Review Questions

6.29 What is the difference between specific heat and heat capacity? What are the units for these two quantities? Which is the intensive property and which is the extensive property?

6.30 Define calorimetry and describe two commonly used calorimeters. In a calorimetric measurement, why is it important that we know the heat capacity of the calorimeter? How is this value determined?

Problems

6.31 Consider the following data:

Metal	Al	Cu
Mass (g)	10	30
Specific heat (J/g · °C)	0.900	0.385
Temperature (°C)	40	60

When these two metals are placed in contact, which of the following will take place?

(a) Heat will flow from Al to Cu because Al has a larger specific heat.

(b) Heat will flow from Cu to Al because Cu has a larger mass.

(c) Heat will flow from Cu to Al because Cu has a larger heat capacity.

(d) Heat will flow from Cu to Al because Cu is at a higher temperature.

(e) No heat will flow in either direction.

6.32 A piece of silver of mass 362 g has a heat capacity of 85.7 J/°C. What is the specific heat of silver?

6.33 A 6.22-kg piece of copper metal is heated from 20.5°C to 324.3°C. Calculate the heat absorbed (in kJ) by the metal.

6.34 Calculate the amount of heat liberated (in kJ) from 366 g of mercury when it cools from 77.0°C to 12.0°C.

6.35 A sheet of gold weighing 10.0 g and at a temperature of 18.0°C is placed flat on a sheet of iron weighing 20.0 g and at a temperature of 55.6°C. What is the final temperature of the combined metals? Assume that no heat is lost to the surroundings. (*Hint:* The heat gained by the gold must be equal to the heat lost by the iron. The specific heats of the metals are given in Table 6.2.)

6.36 To a sample of water at 23.4°C in a constant-pressure calorimeter of negligible heat capacity is added a 12.1-g piece of aluminum whose temperature is 81.7°C. If the final temperature of water is 24.9°C, calculate the mass of the water in the calorimeter. (*Hint:* See Table 6.2.)

6.37 A 0.1375-g sample of solid magnesium is burned in a constant-volume bomb calorimeter that has a heat capacity of 3024 J/°C. The temperature increases by 1.126°C. Calculate the heat given off by the burning Mg, in kJ/g and in kJ/mol.

6.38 A quantity of 85.0 mL of 0.900 *M* HCl is mixed with 85.0 mL of 0.900 *M* KOH in a constant-pressure calorimeter that has a heat capacity of 325 J/°C. If the initial temperatures of both solutions are the same at 18.24°C, what is the final temperature of the mixed solution? The heat of neutralization is −56.2 kJ/mol. Assume the density and specific heat of the solutions are the same as those for water.

Standard Enthalpy of Formation and Reaction
Review Questions

6.39 What is meant by the standard-state condition?

6.40 How are the standard enthalpies of an element and of a compound determined?

6.41 What is meant by the standard enthalpy of a reaction?

6.42 Write the equation for calculating the enthalpy of a reaction. Define all the terms.

6.43 State Hess's law. Explain, with one example, the usefulness of Hess's law in thermochemistry.

6.44 Describe how chemists use Hess's law to determine the ΔH_f° of a compound by measuring its heat (enthalpy) of combustion.

Problems

6.45 Which of the following standard enthalpy of formation values is not zero at 25°C? $Na(s)$, $Ne(g)$, $CH_4(g)$, $S_8(s)$, $Hg(l)$, $H(g)$.

6.46 The ΔH_f° values of the two allotropes of oxygen, O_2 and O_3, are 0 and 142.2 kJ/mol, respectively, at 25°C. Which is the more stable form at this temperature?

6.47 Which is the more negative quantity at 25°C: ΔH_f° for $H_2O(l)$ or ΔH_f° for $H_2O(g)$?

6.48 Predict the value of ΔH_f° (greater than, less than, or equal to zero) for these elements at 25°C: (a) $Br_2(g)$; $Br_2(l)$. (b) $I_2(g)$; $I_2(s)$.

6.49 In general, compounds with negative ΔH_f° values are more stable than those with positive ΔH_f° values. $H_2O_2(l)$ has a negative ΔH_f° (see Table 6.4). Why, then, does $H_2O_2(l)$ have a tendency to decompose to $H_2O(l)$ and $O_2(g)$?

6.50 Suggest ways (with appropriate equations) that would enable you to measure the ΔH_f° values of $Ag_2O(s)$ and $CaCl_2(s)$ from their elements. No calculations are necessary.

6.51 Calculate the heat of decomposition for this process at constant pressure and 25°C:

$$CaCO_3(s) \longrightarrow CaO(s) + CO_2(g)$$

(Look up the standard enthalpy of formation of the reactant and products in Table 6.4.)

6.52 The standard enthalpies of formation of ions in aqueous solutions are obtained by arbitrarily assigning a value of zero to H^+ ions; that is, $\Delta H_f^\circ[H^+(aq)] = 0$.
(a) For the following reaction

$$HCl(g) \xrightarrow{H_2O} H^+(aq) + Cl^-(aq)$$
$$\Delta H^\circ = -74.9 \text{ kJ/mol}$$

calculate ΔH_f° for the Cl^- ions.
(b) Given that ΔH_f° for OH^- ions is −229.6 kJ/mol, calculate the enthalpy of neutralization when 1 mole of a strong monoprotic acid (such as HCl) is titrated by 1 mole of a strong base (such as KOH) at 25°C.

6.53 Calculate the heats of combustion for the following reactions from the standard enthalpies of formation listed in Appendix 3:
(a) $2H_2(g) + O_2(g) \longrightarrow 2H_2O(l)$
(b) $2C_2H_2(g) + 5O_2(g) \longrightarrow 4CO_2(g) + 2H_2O(l)$

6.54 Calculate the heats of combustion for the following reactions from the standard enthalpies of formation listed in Appendix 3:
(a) $C_2H_4(g) + 3O_2(g) \longrightarrow 2CO_2(g) + 2H_2O(l)$
(b) $2H_2S(g) + 3O_2(g) \longrightarrow 2H_2O(l) + 2SO_2(g)$

6.55 Methanol, ethanol, and *n*-propanol are three common alcohols. When 1.00 g of each of these alcohols is burned in air, heat is liberated as shown by the following data: (a) methanol (CH_3OH), −22.6 kJ; (b) ethanol (C_2H_5OH), −29.7 kJ; (c) *n*-propanol (C_3H_7OH), −33.4 kJ. Calculate the heats of combustion of these alcohols in kJ/mol.

6.56 The standard enthalpy change for the following reaction is 436.4 kJ/mol:

$$H_2(g) \longrightarrow H(g) + H(g)$$

Calculate the standard enthalpy of formation of atomic hydrogen (H).

6.57 From the standard enthalpies of formation, calculate ΔH_{rxn}° for the reaction

$$C_6H_{12}(l) + 9O_2(g) \longrightarrow 6CO_2(g) + 6H_2O(l)$$

For $C_6H_{12}(l)$, $\Delta H_f^\circ = -151.9$ kJ/mol.

6.58 Pentaborane-9, B_5H_9, is a colorless, highly reactive liquid that will burst into flame when exposed to oxygen. The reaction is

$$2B_5H_9(l) + 12O_2(g) \longrightarrow 5B_2O_3(s) + 9H_2O(l)$$

Calculate the kilojoules of heat released per gram of the compound reacted with oxygen. The standard enthalpy of formation of B_5H_9 is 73.2 kJ/mol.

● 6.59 Determine the amount of heat (in kJ) given off when 1.26×10^4 g of ammonia are produced according to the equation

$$N_2(g) + 3H_2(g) \longrightarrow 2NH_3(g)$$
$$\Delta H^\circ_{rxn} = -92.6 \text{ kJ/mol}$$

Assume that the reaction takes place under standard-state conditions at 25°C.

● 6.60 At 850°C, $CaCO_3$ undergoes substantial decomposition to yield CaO and CO_2. Assuming that the ΔH°_f values of the reactant and products are the same at 850°C as they are at 25°C, calculate the enthalpy change (in kJ) if 66.8 g of CO_2 are produced in one reaction.

● 6.61 From these data,

$$S\text{(rhombic)} + O_2(g) \longrightarrow SO_2(g)$$
$$\Delta H^\circ_{rxn} = -296.06 \text{ kJ/mol}$$

$$S\text{(monoclinic)} + O_2(g) \longrightarrow SO_2(g)$$
$$\Delta H^\circ_{rxn} = -296.36 \text{ kJ/mol}$$

calculate the enthalpy change for the transformation

$$S\text{(rhombic)} \longrightarrow S\text{(monoclinic)}$$

(Monoclinic and rhombic are different allotropic forms of elemental sulfur.)

● 6.62 From the following data,

$$C\text{(graphite)} + O_2(g) \longrightarrow CO_2(g)$$
$$\Delta H^\circ_{rxn} = -393.5 \text{ kJ/mol}$$

$$H_2(g) + \tfrac{1}{2}O_2(g) \longrightarrow H_2O(l)$$
$$\Delta H^\circ_{rxn} = -285.8 \text{ kJ/mol}$$

$$2C_2H_6(g) + 7O_2(g) \longrightarrow 4CO_2(g) + 6H_2O(l)$$
$$\Delta H^\circ_{rxn} = -3119.6 \text{ kJ/mol}$$

calculate the enthalpy change for the reaction

$$2C\text{(graphite)} + 3H_2(g) \longrightarrow C_2H_6(g)$$

● 6.63 From the following heats of combustion,

$$CH_3OH(l) + \tfrac{3}{2}O_2(g) \longrightarrow CO_2(g) + 2H_2O(l)$$
$$\Delta H^\circ_{rxn} = -726.4 \text{ kJ/mol}$$

$$C\text{(graphite)} + O_2(g) \longrightarrow CO_2(g)$$
$$\Delta H^\circ_{rxn} = -393.5 \text{ kJ/mol}$$

$$H_2(g) + \tfrac{1}{2}O_2(g) \longrightarrow H_2O(l)$$
$$\Delta H^\circ_{rxn} = -285.8 \text{ kJ/mol}$$

calculate the enthalpy of formation of methanol (CH_3OH) from its elements:

$$C\text{(graphite)} + 2H_2(g) + \tfrac{1}{2}O_2(g) \longrightarrow CH_3OH(l)$$

● 6.64 Calculate the standard enthalpy change for the reaction

$$2Al(s) + Fe_2O_3(s) \longrightarrow 2Fe(s) + Al_2O_3(s)$$

given that

$$2Al(s) + \tfrac{3}{2}O_2(g) \longrightarrow Al_2O_3(s)$$
$$\Delta H^\circ_{rxn} = -1669.8 \text{ kJ/mol}$$

$$2Fe(s) + \tfrac{3}{2}O_2(g) \longrightarrow Fe_2O_3(s)$$
$$\Delta H^\circ_{rxn} = -822.2 \text{ kJ/mol}$$

Heat of Solution and Dilution
Review Questions

6.65 Define the following terms: enthalpy of solution, heat of hydration, lattice energy, heat of dilution.

6.66 Why is the lattice energy of a solid always a positive quantity? Why is the hydration of ions always a negative quantity?

6.67 Consider two ionic compounds A and B. A has a larger lattice energy than B. Which of the two compounds is more stable?

6.68 Mg^{2+} is a smaller cation than Na^+ and also carries more positive charge. Which of the two species has a larger hydration energy (in kJ/mol)? Explain.

6.69 Consider the dissolution of an ionic compound such as potassium fluoride in water. Break the process into the following steps: separation of the cations and anions in the vapor phase and the hydration of the ions in the aqueous medium. Discuss the energy changes associated with each step. How does the heat of solution of KF depend on the relative magnitudes of these two quantities? On what law is the relationship based?

6.70 Why is it dangerous to add water to a concentrated acid such as sulfuric acid in a dilution process?

Additional Problems

6.71 Which of the following does not have $\Delta H^\circ_f = 0$ at 25°C?

$$He(g) \quad Fe(s) \quad Cl(g) \quad S_8(s) \quad O_2(g) \quad Br_2(l)$$

6.72 Calculate the expansion work done when 3.70 moles of ethanol are converted to vapor at its boiling point (78.3°C) and 1.0 atm.

6.73 The convention of arbitrarily assigning a zero enthalpy value for the most stable form of each element in the standard state at 25°C is a convenient way of dealing with enthalpies of reactions. Explain why this convention cannot be applied to nuclear reactions.

6.74 Given the thermochemical equations:

$$Br_2(l) + F_2(g) \longrightarrow 2BrF(g)$$
$$\Delta H^\circ = -188 \text{ kJ/mol}$$

$$Br_2(l) + 3F_2(g) \longrightarrow 2BrF_3(g)$$
$$\Delta H^\circ = -768 \text{ kJ/mol}$$

calculate the ΔH°_{rxn} for the reaction

$$BrF(g) + F_2(g) \longrightarrow BrF_3(g)$$

● 6.75 The standard enthalpy change ΔH° for the thermal decomposition of silver nitrate according to the following equation is +78.67 kJ:

$$AgNO_3(s) \longrightarrow AgNO_2(s) + \tfrac{1}{2}O_2(g)$$

The standard enthalpy of formation of $AgNO_3(s)$ is −123.02 kJ/mol. Calculate the standard enthalpy of formation of $AgNO_2(s)$.

6.76 Hydrazine, N_2H_4, decomposes according to the following reaction:

$$3N_2H_4(l) \longrightarrow 4NH_3(g) + N_2(g)$$

(a) Given that the standard enthalpy of formation of hydrazine is 50.42 kJ/mol, calculate $\Delta H°$ for its decomposition. (b) Both hydrazine and ammonia burn in oxygen to produce $H_2O(l)$ and $N_2(g)$. Write balanced equations for each of these processes and calculate $\Delta H°$ for each of them. On a mass basis (per kg), would hydrazine or ammonia be the better fuel?

6.77   A quantity of 2.00×10^2 mL of 0.862 M HCl is mixed with an equal volume of 0.431 M Ba(OH)$_2$ in a constant-pressure calorimeter of negligible heat capacity. The initial temperature of the HCl and Ba(OH)$_2$ solutions is the same at 20.48°C, For the process

$$H^+(aq) + OH^-(aq) \longrightarrow H_2O(l)$$

the heat of neutralization is -56.2 kJ/mol. What is the final temperature of the mixed solution?

6.78   A 3.53-g sample of ammonium nitrate (NH$_4$NO$_3$) was added to 80.0 mL of water in a constant-pressure calorimeter of negligible heat capacity. As a result, the temperature of the water decreased from 21.6°C to 18.1°C. Calculate the heat of solution (ΔH_{soln}) of ammonium nitrate.

• 6.79   Consider the reaction

$$N_2(g) + 3H_2(g) \longrightarrow 2NH_3(g)$$
$$\Delta H°_{rxn} = -92.6 \text{ kJ/mol}$$

If 2.0 moles of N$_2$ react with 6.0 moles of H$_2$ to form NH$_3$, calculate the work done (in joules) against a pressure of 1.0 atm at 25°C. What is ΔU for this reaction? Assume the reaction goes to completion.

• 6.80   Calculate the heat released when 2.00 L of Cl$_2(g)$ with a density of 1.88 g/L react with an excess of sodium metal at 25°C and 1 atm to form sodium chloride.

• 6.81   Photosynthesis produces glucose, C$_6$H$_{12}$O$_6$, and oxygen from carbon dioxide and water:

$$6CO_2 + 6H_2O \longrightarrow C_6H_{12}O_6 + 6O_2$$

(a) How would you determine experimentally the $\Delta H°_{rxn}$ value for this reaction? (b) Solar radiation produces about 7.0×10^{14} kg glucose a year on Earth. What is the corresponding $\Delta H°$ change?

6.82   A 2.10-mole sample of crystalline acetic acid, initially at 17.0°C, is allowed to melt at 17.0°C and is then heated to 118.1°C (its normal boiling point) at 1.00 atm. The sample is allowed to vaporize at 118.1°C and is then rapidly quenched to 17.0°C, so that it recrystallizes. Calculate $\Delta H°$ for the total process as described.

• 6.83   Calculate the work done in joules by the reaction

$$2Na(s) + 2H_2O(l) \longrightarrow 2NaOH(aq) + H_2(g)$$

when 0.34 g of Na reacts with water to form hydrogen gas at 0°C and 1.0 atm.

• 6.84   You are given the following data:

$$H_2(g) \longrightarrow 2H(g) \quad \Delta H° = 436.4 \text{ kJ/mol}$$
$$Br_2(g) \longrightarrow 2Br(g) \quad \Delta H° = 192.5 \text{ kJ/mol}$$
$$H_2(g) + Br_2(g) \longrightarrow 2HBr(g)$$
$$\Delta H° = -72.4 \text{ kJ/mol}$$

Calculate $\Delta H°$ for the reaction

$$H(g) + Br(g) \longrightarrow HBr(g)$$

6.85   A gaseous mixture consists of 28.4 mole percent of hydrogen and 71.6 mole percent of methane. A 15.6-L gas sample, measured at 19.4°C and 2.23 atm, is burned in air. Calculate the heat released.

6.86   When 2.740 g of Ba reacts with O$_2$ at 298 K and 1 atm to form BaO, 11.14 kJ of heat are released. What is $\Delta H°_f$ for BaO?

• 6.87   Methanol (CH$_3$OH) is an organic solvent and is also used as a fuel in some automobile engines. From the following data, calculate the standard enthalpy of formation of methanol:

$$2CH_3OH(l) + 3O_2(g) \longrightarrow 2CO_2(g) + 4H_2O(l)$$
$$\Delta H°_{rxn} = -1452.8 \text{ kJ/mol}$$

• 6.88   A 44.0-g sample of an unknown metal at 99.0°C was placed in a constant-pressure calorimeter containing 80.0 g of water at 24.0°C. The final temperature of the system was found to be 28.4°C. Calculate the specific heat of the metal. (The heat capacity of the calorimeter is 12.4 J/°C.)

• 6.89   Using the data in Appendix 3, calculate the enthalpy change for the gaseous reaction shown here. (*Hint:* First determine the limiting reagent.)

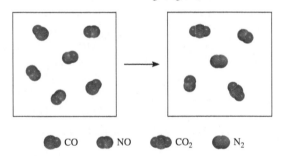

● CO	● NO	● CO$_2$	● N$_2$

6.90   Producer gas (carbon monoxide) is prepared by passing air over red-hot coke:

$$C(s) + \tfrac{1}{2}O_2(g) \longrightarrow CO(g)$$

Water gas (mixture of carbon monoxide and hydrogen) is prepared by passing steam over red-hot coke:

$$C(s) + H_2O(g) \longrightarrow CO(g) + H_2(g)$$

For many years, both producer gas and water gas were used as fuels in industry and for domestic cooking. The large-scale preparation of these gases was carried out alternately, that is, first producer gas, then water gas, and so on. Using thermochemical reasoning, explain why this procedure was chosen.

• 6.91   Compare the heat produced by the complete combustion of 1 mole of methane (CH$_4$) with a mole of water gas (0.50 mole H$_2$ and 0.50 mole CO) under the same conditions. On the basis of your answer, would you prefer methane over water gas as a fuel? Can you suggest two other reasons why methane is preferable to water gas as a fuel?

6.92 The so-called hydrogen economy is based on hydrogen produced from water using solar energy. The gas may be burned as a fuel:

$$2H_2(g) + O_2(g) \longrightarrow 2H_2O(l)$$

A primary advantage of hydrogen as a fuel is that it is nonpolluting. A major disadvantage is that it is a gas and therefore is harder to store than liquids or solids. Calculate the volume of hydrogen gas at 25°C and 1.00 atm required to produce an amount of energy equivalent to that produced by the combustion of a gallon of octane (C_8H_{18}). The density of octane is 2.66 kg/gal, and its standard enthalpy of formation is −249.9 kJ/mol.

6.93 Ethanol (C_2H_5OH) and gasoline (assumed to be all octane, C_8H_{18}) are both used as automobile fuel. If gasoline is selling for $4.50/gal, what would the price of ethanol have to be in order to provide the same amount of heat per dollar? The density and ΔH_f° of octane are 0.7025 g/mL and −249.9 kJ/mol and of ethanol are 0.7894 g/mL and −277.0 kJ/mol, respectively. 1 gal = 3.785 L.

6.94 The combustion of what volume of ethane (C_2H_6), measured at 23.0°C and 752 mmHg, would be required to heat 855 g of water from 25.0°C to 98.0°C?

6.95 If energy is conserved, how can there be an energy crisis?

6.96 The heat of vaporization of a liquid (ΔH_{vap}) is the energy required to vaporize 1.00 g of the liquid at its boiling point. In one experiment, 60.0 g of liquid nitrogen (boiling point −196°C) are poured into a Styrofoam cup containing 2.00×10^2 g of water at 55.3°C. Calculate the molar heat of vaporization of liquid nitrogen if the final temperature of the water is 41.0°C.

6.97 Explain the cooling effect experienced when ethanol is rubbed on your skin, given that

$$C_2H_5OH(l) \longrightarrow C_2H_5OH(g) \quad \Delta H^\circ = 42.2 \text{ kJ/mol}$$

6.98 For which of the following reactions does $\Delta H_{rxn}^\circ = \Delta H_f^\circ$?
(a) $H_2(g) + S(\text{rhombic}) \longrightarrow H_2S(g)$
(b) $C(\text{diamond}) + O_2(g) \longrightarrow CO_2(g)$
(c) $H_2(g) + CuO(s) \longrightarrow H_2O(l) + Cu(s)$
(d) $O(g) + O_2(g) \longrightarrow O_3(g)$

6.99 Calculate the work done (in joules) when 1.0 mole of water is frozen at 0°C and 1.0 atm. The volumes of one mole of water and ice at 0°C are 0.0180 L and 0.0196 L, respectively.

6.100 A quantity of 0.020 mole of a gas initially at 0.050 L and 20°C undergoes a constant-temperature expansion until its volume is 0.50 L. Calculate the work done (in joules) by the gas if it expands (a) against a vacuum and (b) against a constant pressure of 0.20 atm. (c) If the gas in (b) is allowed to expand unchecked until its pressure is equal to the external pressure, what would its final volume be before it stopped expanding, and what would be the work done?

6.101 Calculate the standard enthalpy of formation for diamond, given that

$$C(\text{graphite}) + O_2(g) \longrightarrow CO_2(g)$$
$$\Delta H^\circ = -393.5 \text{ kJ/mol}$$
$$C(\text{diamond}) + O_2(g) \longrightarrow CO_2(g)$$
$$\Delta H^\circ = -395.4 \text{ kJ/mol}$$

6.102 (a) For most efficient use, refrigerator freezer compartments should be fully packed with food. What is the thermochemical basis for this recommendation? (b) Starting at the same temperature, tea and coffee remain hot longer in a thermal flask than chicken noodle soup. Explain.

6.103 Calculate the standard enthalpy change for the fermentation process. (See Problem 3.72.)

6.104 Portable hot packs are available for skiers and people engaged in other outdoor activities in a cold climate. The air-permeable paper packet contains a mixture of powdered iron, sodium chloride, and other components, all moistened by a little water. The exothermic reaction that produces the heat is a very common one—the rusting of iron:

$$4Fe(s) + 3O_2(g) \longrightarrow 2Fe_2O_3(s)$$

When the outside plastic envelope is removed, O_2 molecules penetrate the paper, causing the reaction to begin. A typical packet contains 250 g of iron to warm your hands or feet for up to 4 hours. How much heat (in kJ) is produced by this reaction? (Hint: See Appendix 3 for ΔH_f° values.)

6.105 A person ate 0.50 pound of cheese (an energy intake of 4000 kJ). Suppose that none of the energy was stored in his body. What mass (in grams) of water would he need to perspire in order to maintain his original temperature? (It takes 44.0 kJ to vaporize 1 mole of water.)

6.106 The total volume of the Pacific Ocean is estimated to be 7.2×10^8 km^3. A medium-sized atomic bomb produces 1.0×10^{15} J of energy upon explosion. Calculate the number of atomic bombs needed to release enough energy to raise the temperature of the water in the Pacific Ocean by 1°C.

6.107 A 19.2-g quantity of dry ice (solid carbon dioxide) is allowed to sublime (evaporate) in an apparatus like the one shown in Figure 6.5. Calculate the expansion work done against a constant external pressure of 0.995 atm and at a constant temperature of 22°C. Assume that the initial volume of dry ice is negligible and that CO_2 behaves like an ideal gas.

6.108 The enthalpy of combustion of benzoic acid (C_6H_5COOH) is commonly used as the standard for calibrating constant-volume bomb calorimeters; its value has been accurately determined to be −3226.7 kJ/mol. When 1.9862 g of benzoic acid are burned in a calorimeter, the temperature rises from 21.84°C to 25.67°C. What is the heat capacity of the bomb? (Assume that the quantity of water surrounding the bomb is exactly 2000 g.)

268   **Chapter 6** ▪ Thermochemistry

● 6.109   The combustion of a 25.0-g gaseous mixture of H_2 and CH_4 releases 2354 kJ of heat. Calculate the amounts of the gases in grams.

● **6.110**   Calcium oxide (CaO) is used to remove sulfur dioxide generated by coal-burning power stations:

$$2CaO(s) + 2SO_2(g) + O_2(g) \longrightarrow 2CaSO_4(s)$$

Calculate the enthalpy change for this process if 6.6×10^5 g of SO_2 are removed by this process every day.

● 6.111   Glauber's salt, sodium sulfate decahydrate ($Na_2SO_4 \cdot 10H_2O$), undergoes a phase transition (that is, melting or freezing) at a convenient temperature of about 32°C:

$$Na_2SO_4 \cdot 10H_2O(s) \longrightarrow Na_2SO_4 \cdot 10H_2O(l)$$
$$\Delta H° = 74.4 \text{ kJ/mol}$$

As a result, this compound is used to regulate the temperature in homes. It is placed in plastic bags in the ceiling of a room. During the day, the endothermic melting process absorbs heat from the surroundings, cooling the room. At night, it gives off heat as it freezes. Calculate the mass of Glauber's salt in kilograms needed to lower the temperature of air in a room by 8.2°C at 1.0 atm. The dimensions of the room are 2.80 m × 10.6 m × 17.2 m, the specific heat of air is 1.2 J/g · °C, and the molar mass of air may be taken as 29.0 g/mol.

● 6.112   A balloon 16 m in diameter is inflated with helium at 18°C. (a) Calculate the mass of He in the balloon, assuming ideal behavior. (b) Calculate the work done (in joules) during the inflation process if the atmospheric pressure is 98.7 kPa.

6.113   Acetylene (C_2H_2) can be hydrogenated (reacting with hydrogen) first to ethylene (C_2H_4) and then to ethane (C_2H_6). Starting with one mole of C_2H_2, label the diagram shown here analogous to Figure 6.10. Use the data in Appendix 3.

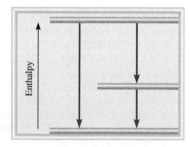

6.114   Calculate the $\Delta H°$ for the reaction

$$Fe^{3+}(aq) + 3OH^-(aq) \longrightarrow Fe(OH)_3(s)$$

6.115   An excess of zinc metal is added to 50.0 mL of a 0.100 M $AgNO_3$ solution in a constant-pressure calorimeter like the one pictured in Figure 6.9. As a result of the reaction

$$Zn(s) + 2Ag^+(aq) \longrightarrow Zn^{2+}(aq) + 2Ag(s)$$

the temperature rises from 19.25°C to 22.17°C. If the heat capacity of the calorimeter is 98.6 J/°C, calculate the enthalpy change for the above reaction on a molar basis. Assume that the density and specific heat of the solution are the same as those for water, and ignore the specific heats of the metals.

6.116   (a) A person drinks four glasses of cold water (3.0°C) every day. The volume of each glass is 2.5×10^2 mL. How much heat (in kJ) does the body have to supply to raise the temperature of the water to 37°C, the body temperature? (b) How much heat would your body lose if you were to ingest 8.0×10^2 g of snow at 0°C to quench thirst? (The amount of heat necessary to melt snow is 6.01 kJ/mol.)

6.117   A driver's manual states that the stopping distance quadruples as the speed doubles; that is, if it takes 30 ft to stop a car moving at 25 mph then it would take 120 ft to stop a car moving at 50 mph. Justify this statement by using mechanics and the first law of thermodynamics. [Assume that when a car is stopped, its kinetic energy ($\frac{1}{2}mu^2$) is totally converted to heat.]

● 6.118   At 25°C, the standard enthalpy of formation of HF(aq) is given by -320.1 kJ/mol; of OH^-(aq), it is -229.6 kJ/mol; of F^-(aq), it is -329.1 kJ/mol; and of $H_2O(l)$, it is -285.8 kJ/mol.

(a) Calculate the standard enthalpy of neutralization of HF(aq):

$$HF(aq) + OH^-(aq) \longrightarrow F^-(aq) + H_2O(l)$$

(b) Using the value of -56.2 kJ as the standard enthalpy change for the reaction

$$H^+(aq) + OH^-(aq) \longrightarrow H_2O(l)$$

calculate the standard enthalpy change for the reaction

$$HF(aq) \longrightarrow H^+(aq) + F^-(aq)$$

6.119   Why are cold, damp air and hot, humid air more uncomfortable than dry air at the same temperatures? (The specific heats of water vapor and air are approximately 1.9 J/g · °C and 1.0 J/g · °C, respectively.)

6.120   From the enthalpy of formation for CO_2 and the following information, calculate the standard enthalpy of formation for carbon monoxide (CO).

$$CO(g) + \frac{1}{2}O_2(g) \longrightarrow CO_2(g)$$
$$\Delta H° = -283.0 \text{ kJ/mol}$$

Why can't we obtain it directly by measuring the enthalpy of the following reaction?

$$C(graphite) + \frac{1}{2}O_2(g) \longrightarrow CO(g)$$

● 6.121   A 46-kg person drinks 500 g of milk, which has a "caloric" value of approximately 3.0 kJ/g. If only 17 percent of the energy in milk is converted to mechanical work, how high (in meters) can the person climb based on this energy intake? [Hint: The work done in ascending is given by mgh, where m is the mass (in kilograms), g the gravitational acceleration (9.8 m/s²), and h the height (in meters).]

6.122 The height of Niagara Falls on the American side is 51 m. (a) Calculate the potential energy of 1.0 g of water at the top of the falls relative to the ground level. (b) What is the speed of the falling water if all of the potential energy is converted to kinetic energy? (c) What would be the increase in temperature of the water if all the kinetic energy were converted to heat? (See Problem 6.121 for suggestions.)

6.123 In the nineteenth century two scientists named Dulong and Petit noticed that for a solid element, the product of its molar mass and its specific heat is approximately 25 J/°C. This observation, now called Dulong and Petit's law, was used to estimate the specific heat of metals. Verify the law for the metals listed in Table 6.2. The law does not apply to one of the metals. Which one is it? Why?

6.124 Determine the standard enthalpy of formation of ethanol (C_2H_5OH) from its standard enthalpy of combustion (-1367.4 kJ/mol).

6.125 Acetylene (C_2H_2) and benzene (C_6H_6) have the same empirical formula. In fact, benzene can be made from acetylene as follows:

$$3C_2H_2(g) \longrightarrow C_6H_6(l)$$

The enthalpies of combustion for C_2H_2 and C_6H_6 are -1299.4 kJ/mol and -3267.4 kJ/mol, respectively. Calculate the standard enthalpies of formation of C_2H_2 and C_6H_6 and hence the enthalpy change for the formation of C_6H_6 from C_2H_2.

6.126 Ice at 0°C is placed in a Styrofoam cup containing 361 g of a soft drink at 23°C. The specific heat of the drink is about the same as that of water. Some ice remains after the ice and soft drink reach an equilibrium temperature of 0°C. Determine the mass of ice that has melted. Ignore the heat capacity of the cup. (*Hint:* It takes 334 J to melt 1 g of ice at 0°C.)

6.127 After a dinner party, the host performed the following trick. First, he blew out one of the burning candles. He then quickly brought a lighted match to about 1 in above the wick. To everyone's surprise, the candle was relighted. Explain how the host was able to accomplish the task without touching the wick.

6.128 How much heat is required to decompose 89.7 g of NH_4Cl? (*Hint:* You may use the enthalpy of formation values at 25°C for the calculation.)

6.129 A gas company in Massachusetts charges $1.30 for 15 ft³ of natural gas (CH_4) measured at 20°C and 1.0 atm. Calculate the cost of heating 200 mL of water (enough to make a cup of coffee or tea) from 20°C to 100°C. Assume that only 50 percent of the heat generated by the combustion is used to heat the water; the rest of the heat is lost to the surroundings.

6.130 Calculate the internal energy of a Goodyear blimp filled with helium gas at 1.2×10^5 Pa. The volume of the blimp is 5.5×10^3 m³. If all the energy were used to heat 10.0 tons of copper at 21°C, calculate the final temperature of the metal. (*Hint:* See Section 5.7 for help in calculating the internal energy of a gas. 1 ton = 9.072×10^5 g.)

6.131 Decomposition reactions are usually endothermic, whereas combination reactions are usually exothermic. Give a qualitative explanation for these trends.

6.132 Acetylene (C_2H_2) can be made by reacting calcium carbide (CaC_2) with water. (a) Write an equation for the reaction. (b) What is the maximum amount of heat (in joules) that can be obtained from the combustion of acetylene, starting with 74.6 g of CaC_2?

6.133 The average temperature in deserts is high during the day but quite cool at night, whereas that in regions along the coastline is more moderate. Explain.

6.134 When 1.034 g of naphthalene ($C_{10}H_8$) are burned in a constant-volume bomb calorimeter at 298 K, 41.56 kJ of heat are evolved. Calculate ΔU and ΔH for the reaction on a molar basis.

6.135 From a thermochemical point of view, explain why a carbon dioxide fire extinguisher or water should not be used on a magnesium fire.

6.136 Calculate the ΔU for the following reaction at 298 K:

$$2H_2(g) + O_2(g) \longrightarrow 2H_2O(l)$$

6.137 Lime is a term that includes calcium oxide (CaO, also called quicklime) and calcium hydroxide [Ca(OH)$_2$, also called slaked lime]. It is used in the steel industry to remove acidic impurities, in air-pollution control to remove acidic oxides such as SO_2, and in water treatment. Quicklime is made industrially by heating limestone ($CaCO_3$) above 2000°C:

$$CaCO_3(s) \longrightarrow CaO(s) + CO_2(g)$$
$$\Delta H° = 177.8 \text{ kJ/mol}$$

Slaked lime is produced by treating quicklime with water:

$$CaO(s) + H_2O(l) \longrightarrow Ca(OH)_2(s)$$
$$\Delta H° = -65.2 \text{ kJ/mol}$$

The exothermic reaction of quicklime with water and the rather small specific heats of both quicklime (0.946 J/g · °C) and slaked lime (1.20 J/g · °C) make it hazardous to store and transport lime in vessels made of wood. Wooden sailing ships carrying lime would occasionally catch fire when water leaked into the hold. (a) If a 500-g sample of water reacts with an

270   **Chapter 6** ▪ Thermochemistry

equimolar amount of CaO (both at an initial temperature of 25°C), what is the final temperature of the product, $Ca(OH)_2$? Assume that the product absorbs all of the heat released in the reaction. (b) Given that the standard enthalpies of formation of CaO and H_2O are −635.6 kJ/mol and −285.8 kJ/mol, respectively, calculate the standard enthalpy of formation of $Ca(OH)_2$.

6.138 A 4.117-g impure sample of glucose ($C_6H_{12}O_6$) was burned in a constant-volume calorimeter having a heat capacity of 19.65 kJ/°C. If the rise in temperature is 3.134°C, calculate the percent by mass of the glucose in the sample. Assume that the impurities are unaffected by the combustion process. See Appendix 3 for thermodynamic data.

6.139   Construct a table with the headings q, w, ΔU, and ΔH. For each of the following processes, deduce whether each of the quantities listed is positive (+), negative (−), or zero (0). (a) Freezing of benzene. (b) Compression of an ideal gas at constant temperature. (c) Reaction of sodium with water. (d) Boiling liquid ammonia. (e) Heating a gas at constant volume. (f) Melting of ice.

6.140 The combustion of 0.4196 g of a hydrocarbon releases 17.55 kJ of heat. The masses of the products are CO_2 = 1.419 g and H_2O = 0.290 g. (a) What is the empirical formula of the compound? (b) If the approximate molar mass of the compound is 76 g, calculate its standard enthalpy of formation.

6.141   Metabolic activity in the human body releases approximately 1.0×10^4 kJ of heat per day. Assuming the body is 50 kg of water, how much would the body temperature rise if it were an isolated system? How much water must the body eliminate as perspiration to maintain the normal body temperature (98.6°F)? Comment on your results. The heat of vaporization of water may be taken as 2.41 kJ/g.

6.142 Give an example for each of the following situations: (a) Adding heat to a system raises its temperature, (b) adding heat to a system does not change (raise) its temperature, and (c) a system's temperature is changed even though no heat is added or removed from it.

6.143   From the following data, calculate the heat of solution for KI:

	NaCl	NaI	KCl	KI
Lattice energy (kJ/mol)	788	686	699	632
Heat of solution (kJ/mol)	4.0	−5.1	17.2	?

6.144 Starting at A, an ideal gas undergoes a cyclic process involving expansion and compression, as shown here. Calculate the total work done. Does your result support the notion that work is not a state function?

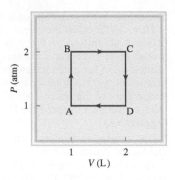

* 6.145 For reactions in condensed phases (liquids and solids), the difference between ΔH and ΔU is usually quite small. This statement holds for reactions carried out under atmospheric conditions. For certain geochemical processes, however, the external pressure may be so great that ΔH and ΔU can differ by a significant amount. A well-known example is the slow conversion of graphite to diamond under Earth's surface. Calculate ($\Delta H - \Delta U$) for the conversion of 1 mole of graphite to 1 mole of diamond at a pressure of 50,000 atm. The densities of graphite and diamond are 2.25 g/cm³ and 3.52 g/cm³, respectively.

6.146   The diagrams shown here represent various physical and chemical processes. (a) $2A(g) \longrightarrow A_2(g)$. (b) $MX(s) \longrightarrow M^+(aq) + X^-(aq)$. (c) $AB(g) + C(g) \longrightarrow AC(g) + B(g)$. (d) $B(l) \longrightarrow B(g)$. Predict whether the situations shown are endothermic or exothermic. Explain why in some cases no clear conclusions can be made.

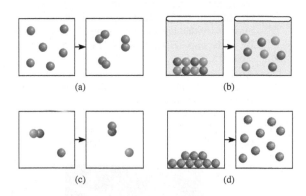

6.147   A 20.3-g sample of an unknown metal and a 28.5-g sample of copper, both at 80.6°C, are added to 100 g of water at 11.2°C in a constant-pressure calorimeter of negligible heat capacity. If the final temperature of the metals and water is 13.7°C, determine the specific heat of the unknown metal.

Interpreting, Modeling & Estimating

6.148 For most biological processes, $\Delta H \approx \Delta U$. Explain.

6.149 Estimate the potential energy expended by an average adult male in going from the ground to the top floor of the Empire State Building using the staircase.

6.150 The fastest serve in tennis is about 150 mph. Can the kinetic energy of a tennis ball traveling at this speed be sufficient to heat 1 mL of water by 30°C?

6.151 Can the total energy output of the sun in one second be sufficient to heat all of the ocean water on Earth to its boiling point?

6.152 It has been estimated that 3 trillion standard cubic feet of methane is released into the atmosphere every year. Capturing that methane would provide a source of energy, and it would also remove a potent greenhouse gas from the atmosphere (methane is 25 times more effective at trapping heat than an equal number of molecules of carbon dioxide). Standard cubic feet is measured at 60°F and 1 atm. Determine the amount of energy that could be obtained by combustion of the methane that escapes each year.

6.153 Biomass plants generate electricity from waste material such as wood chips. Some of these plants convert the feedstock to ethanol (C_2H_5OH) for later use as a fuel. (a) How many grams of ethanol can be produced from 1.0 ton of wood chips, if 85 percent of the carbon is converted to C_2H_5OH? (b) How much energy would be released by burning the ethanol obtained from 1.0 ton of wood chips? (*Hint:* Treat the wood chips as cellulose.)

6.154 Suppose an automobile carried hydrogen gas in its fuel tank instead of gasoline. At what pressure would the hydrogen gas need to be kept for the tank to contain an equivalent amount of chemical energy as a tank of gasoline?

6.155 A press release announcing a new fuel-cell car to the public stated that hydrogen is "relatively cheap" and "some stations in California sell hydrogen for $5 a kilogram. A kg has the same energy as a gallon of gasoline, so it's like paying $5 a gallon. But you go two to three times as far on the hydrogen." Analyze this claim.

6.156 We hear a lot about how the burning of hydrocarbons produces the greenhouse gas CO_2, but what about the effect of increasing energy consumption on the amount of oxygen in the atmosphere required to sustain life. The figure shows past and projected energy world consumption. (a) How many moles of oxygen would be required to generate the additional energy expenditure for the next decade? (b) What would be the resulting decrease in atmospheric oxygen?

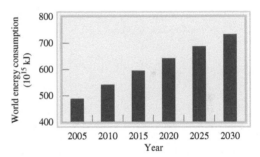

Answers to Practice Exercises

6.1 (a) 0, (b) −286 J. **6.2** −63 J. **6.3** −6.47 × 10³ kJ.
6.4 −111.7 kJ/mol. **6.5** −34.3 kJ. **6.6** −728 kJ/mol.
6.7 21.19°C. **6.8** 22.49°C. **6.9** 87.3 kJ/mol.
6.10 −41.83 kJ/g.

CHEMICAL *MYSTERY*

The Exploding Tire[†]

It was supposed to be a routine job: Fix the flat tire on Harvey Smith's car. The owner of Tom's Garage, Tom Lee, gave the tire to Jerry to work on, while he went outside to pump gas. A few minutes later, Tom heard a loud bang. He rushed inside to find the tire blown to pieces, a wall collapsed, equipment damaged, and Jerry lying on the floor, unconscious and bleeding. Luckily Jerry's injury was not serious. As he lay in the hospital recovering, the mystery of the exploding tire unfolded.

The tire had gone flat when Harvey drove over a nail. Being a cautious driver, Harvey carried a can of instant tire repair in the car, so he was able to reinflate the tire and drive safely home. The can of tire repair Harvey used contained latex (natural rubber) dissolved in a liquid propellant, which is a mixture of propane (C_3H_8) and butane (C_4H_{10}). Propane and butane are gases under atmospheric conditions but exist as liquids under compression in the can. When the valve on the top of the can is pressed, it opens, releasing the pressure inside. The mixture boils, forming a latex foam which is propelled by the gases into the tire to seal the puncture while the gas reinflates the tire.

The pressure in a flat tire is approximately one atmosphere, or roughly 15 pounds per square inch (psi). Using the aerosol tire repair, Harvey reinflated his damaged tire to a pressure of 35 psi. This is called the gauge pressure, which is the pressure of the tire *above* the atmospheric pressure. Thus, the total pressure in the tire was actually (15 + 35) psi, or 50 psi. One problem with using natural gases like propane and butane as propellants is that they are highly flammable. In fact, these gases can react explosively when mixed with air at a concentration of 2 percent to 9 percent by volume. Jerry was aware of the hazards of repairing Harvey's tire and took precautions to avoid an accident. First he let out the excess gas in the tire. Next he reinflated the tire to 35 psi with air. And he repeated the procedure once. Clearly, this is a dilution process intended to gradually decrease the concentrations of propane and butane. The fact that the tire exploded means that Jerry had not diluted the gases enough. But what was the source of ignition?

When Jerry found the nail hole in the tire, he used a tire reamer, a metal file-like instrument, to clean dirt and loose rubber from the hole before applying a rubber plug and liquid sealant. The last thing Jerry remembered was pulling the reamer out of the hole. The next thing he knew he was lying in the hospital, hurting all over. To solve this mystery, make use of the following clues.

[†]Adapted from "The Exploding Tire," by Jay A. Young, CHEM MATTERS, April, 1988, p. 12. Copyright 1995 American Chemical Society.

Chemical Clues

1. Write balanced equations for the combustion of propane and butane. The products are carbon dioxide and water.

2. When Harvey inflated his flat tire to 35 psi, the composition by volume of the propane and butane gases is given by (35 psi/50 psi) $\times$ 100%, or 70 percent. When Jerry deflated the tire the first time, the pressure fell to 15 psi but the composition remained at 70 percent. Based on these facts, calculate the percent composition of propane and butane at the end of two deflation-inflation steps. Does it fall within the explosive range?

3. Given that Harvey's flat tire is a steel-belted tire, explain how the ignition of the gas mixture might have been triggered. (A steel-belted tire has two belts of steel wire for outer reinforcement and two belts of polyester cord for inner reinforcement.)

Instant flat tire repair.

Quantum Theory and the Electronic Structure of Atoms

"Neon light" is a generic term for atomic emission involving various noble gases, mercury, and phosphor. The UV light from excited mercury atoms causes phosphor-coated tubes to fluoresce white light and other colors.

A LOOK AHEAD

▶ We begin by discussing the transition from classical physics to quantum theory. In particular, we become familiar with properties of waves and electromagnetic radiation and Planck's formulation of the quantum theory. (7.1)

▶ Einstein's explanation of the photoelectric effect is another step toward the development of the quantum theory. To explain experimental observations, Einstein suggested that light behaves like a bundle of particles called photons. (7.2)

▶ We then study Bohr's theory for the emission spectrum of the hydrogen atom. In particular, Bohr postulated that the energies of an electron in the atom are quantized and transitions from higher levels to lower ones account for the emission lines. (7.3)

▶ Some of the mysteries of Bohr's theory are explained by de Broglie who suggested that electrons can behave like waves. (7.4)

▶ We see that the early ideas of quantum theory led to a new era in physics called quantum mechanics. The Heisenberg uncertainty principle sets the limits for measurement of quantum mechanical systems. The Schrödinger wave equation describes the behavior of electrons in atoms and molecules. (7.5)

▶ We learn that there are four quantum numbers to describe an electron in an atom and the characteristics of orbitals in which the electrons reside. (7.6 and 7.7)

▶ Electron configuration enables us to keep track of the distribution of electrons in an atom and understand its magnetic properties. (7.8)

▶ Finally, we apply the rules in writing electron configurations to the entire periodic table. In particular, we group elements according to their valence electron configurations. (7.9)

Quantum theory enables us to predict and understand the critical role that electrons play in chemistry. In one sense, studying atoms amounts to asking the following questions:

1. How many electrons are present in a particular atom?
2. What energies do individual electrons possess?
3. Where in the atom can electrons be found?

The answers to these questions have a direct relationship to the behavior of all substances in chemical reactions, and the story of the search for answers provides a fascinating backdrop for our discussion.

7.1 From Classical Physics to Quantum Theory

Early attempts by nineteenth-century physicists to understand atoms and molecules met with only limited success. By assuming that molecules behave like rebounding balls, physicists were able to predict and explain some macroscopic phenomena, such as the pressure exerted by a gas. However, this model did not account for the stability of molecules; that is, it could not explain the forces that hold atoms together. It took a long time to realize—and an even longer time to accept—that the properties of atoms and molecules are *not* governed by the same physical laws as larger objects.

The new era in physics started in 1900 with a young German physicist named Max Planck.[†] While analyzing the data on radiation emitted by solids heated to various temperatures, Planck discovered that atoms and molecules emit energy only in certain discrete quantities, or *quanta*. Physicists had always assumed that energy is continuous and that any amount of energy could be released in a radiation process. Planck's *quantum theory* turned physics upside down. Indeed, the flurry of research that ensued altered our concept of nature forever.

Properties of Waves

To understand Planck's quantum theory, we must first know something about the nature of waves. A *wave* can be thought of as *a vibrating disturbance by which energy is transmitted*. The fundamental properties of a wave are illustrated by a familiar type—water waves (Figure 7.1). The regular variation of the peaks and troughs enable us to sense the propagation of the waves.

Waves are characterized by their length and height and by the number of waves that pass through a certain point in one second (Figure 7.2). *Wavelength* λ (lambda) is *the distance between identical points on successive waves*. The *frequency* ν (nu) is *the number of waves that pass through a particular point in 1 second*. *Amplitude* is *the vertical distance from the midline of a wave to the peak or trough*.

Another important property of waves is their speed, which depends on the type of wave and the nature of the medium through which the wave is traveling (for example, air, water, or a vacuum). The speed (u) of a wave is the product of its wavelength and its frequency:

$$u = \lambda \nu \qquad (7.1)$$

The inherent "sensibility" of Equation (7.1) becomes apparent if we analyze the physical dimensions involved in the three terms. The wavelength (λ) expresses the length

Figure 7.1 *Ocean water waves.*

[†]Max Karl Ernst Ludwig Planck (1858–1947). German physicist. Planck received the Nobel Prize in Physics in 1918 for his quantum theory. He also made significant contributions in thermodynamics and other areas of physics.

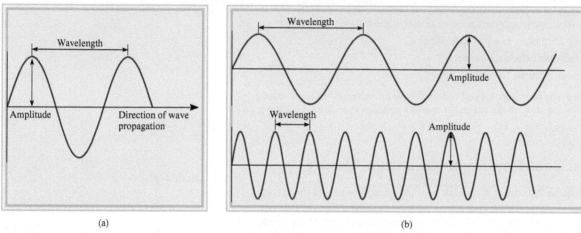

(a)   (b)

Figure 7.2 *(a) Wavelength and amplitude. (b) Two waves having different wavelengths and frequencies. The wavelength of the top wave is three times that of the lower wave, but its frequency is only one-third that of the lower wave. Both waves have the same speed and amplitude.*

of a wave, or distance/wave. The frequency (ν) indicates the number of these waves that pass any reference point per unit of time, or waves/time. Thus, the product of these terms results in dimensions of distance/time, which is speed:

$$\frac{\text{distance}}{\text{time}} = \frac{\text{distance}}{\text{wave}} \times \frac{\text{waves}}{\text{time}}$$

Wavelength is usually expressed in units of meters, centimeters, or nanometers, and frequency is measured in hertz (Hz), where

$$1\ \text{Hz} = 1\ \text{cycle/s}$$

The word "cycle" may be left out and the frequency expressed as, for example, 25/s or 25 s^{-1} (read as "25 per second").

> ### *Review of Concepts*
> Which of the waves shown here has (a) the highest frequency, (b) the longest wavelength, (c) the greatest amplitude?
>
> (a)   (b)   (c)

Electromagnetic Radiation

There are many kinds of waves, such as water waves, sound waves, and light waves. In 1873 James Clerk Maxwell proposed that visible light consists of electromagnetic waves. According to Maxwell's theory, an ***electromagnetic wave*** *has an electric*

Sound waves and water waves are not electromagnetic waves, but X rays and radio waves are.

field component and a magnetic field component. These two components have the same wavelength and frequency, and hence the same speed, but they travel in mutually perpendicular planes (Figure 7.3). The significance of Maxwell's theory is that it provides a mathematical description of the general behavior of light. In particular, his model accurately describes how energy in the form of radiation can be propagated through space as vibrating electric and magnetic fields. **Electromagnetic radiation** is *the emission and transmission of energy in the form of electromagnetic waves.*

Electromagnetic waves travel 3.00×10^8 meters per second (rounded off), or 186,000 miles per second in a vacuum. This speed differs from one medium to another, but not enough to distort our calculations significantly. By convention, we use the symbol c for the speed of electromagnetic waves, or as it is more commonly called, the *speed of light.* The wavelength of electromagnetic waves is usually given in nanometers (nm).

A more accurate value for the speed of light is given on the inside back cover of the book.

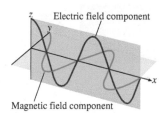

Figure 7.3 *The electric field and magnetic field components of an electromagnetic wave. These two components have the same wavelength, frequency, and amplitude, but they oscillate in two mutually perpendicular planes.*

Example 7.1

The wavelength of the green light from a traffic signal is centered at 522 nm. What is the frequency of this radiation?

Strategy We are given the wavelength of an electromagnetic wave and asked to calculate its frequency. Rearranging Equation (7.1) and replacing u with c (the speed of light) gives

$$\nu = \frac{c}{\lambda}$$

Solution Because the speed of light is given in meters per second, it is convenient to first convert wavelength to meters. Recall that 1 nm $= 1 \times 10^{-9}$ m (see Table 1.3). We write

$$\lambda = 522 \text{ nm} \times \frac{1 \times 10^{-9} \text{ m}}{1 \text{ nm}} = 522 \times 10^{-9} \text{ m}$$
$$= 5.22 \times 10^{-7} \text{ m}$$

Substituting in the wavelength and the speed of light (3.00×10^8 m/s), the frequency is

$$\nu = \frac{3.00 \times 10^8 \text{ m/s}}{5.22 \times 10^{-7} \text{ m}}$$
$$= 5.75 \times 10^{14}/\text{s, or } 5.75 \times 10^{14} \text{ Hz}$$

Check The answer shows that 5.75×10^{14} waves pass a fixed point every second. This very high frequency is in accordance with the very high speed of light.

Similar problem: 7.7.

Practice Exercise What is the wavelength (in meters) of an electromagnetic wave whose frequency is 3.64×10^7 Hz?

Figure 7.4 shows various types of electromagnetic radiation, which differ from one another in wavelength and frequency. The long radio waves are emitted by large antennas, such as those used by broadcasting stations. The shorter, visible light waves are produced by the motions of electrons within atoms and molecules. The shortest waves, which also have the highest frequency, are associated with γ (gamma) rays, which result from changes within the nucleus of the atom (see Chapter 2). As we will see shortly, the higher the frequency, the more energetic the radiation. Thus, ultraviolet radiation, X rays, and γ rays are high-energy radiation.

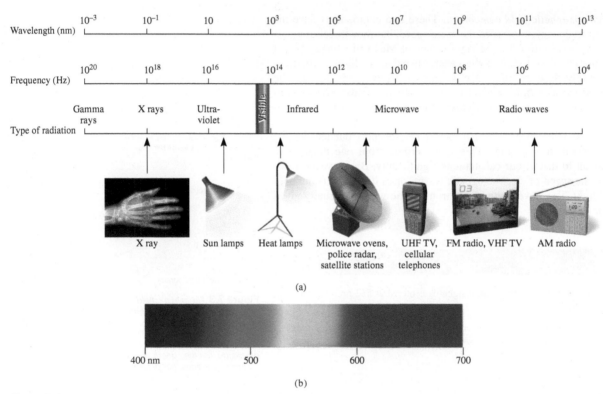

(a)

(b)

Figure 7.4 *(a) Types of electromagnetic radiation. Gamma rays have the shortest wavelength and highest frequency; radio waves have the longest wavelength and the lowest frequency. Each type of radiation is spread over a specific range of wavelengths (and frequencies). (b) Visible light ranges from a wavelength of 400 nm (violet) to 700 nm (red).*

Planck's Quantum Theory

When solids are heated, they emit electromagnetic radiation over a wide range of wavelengths. The dull red glow of an electric heater and the bright white light of a tungsten lightbulb are examples of radiation from heated solids.

Measurements taken in the latter part of the nineteenth century showed that the amount of radiant energy emitted by an object at a certain temperature depends on its wavelength. The amount of radiant energy emitted by an object depends on its wavelength, and if the intensity of radiation versus the wavelength emitted is measured at different temperatures, a series of curves similar to the ones shown in Figure 7.4a is obtained. If the object is in thermal equilibrium with its surroundings, then the radiation versus wavelength curve will

Figure 7.4a *Blackbody radiation curves at various temperatures.*

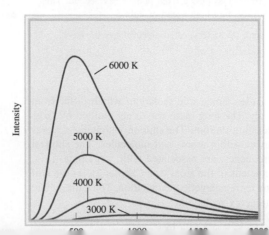

depend only on temperature. Such a body would be a perfect absorber; therefore, it would absorb all of the radiation that strikes it, including visible light, and would appear black at low temperatures. Because the object is in thermal equilibrium with its surroundings, a blackbody is also a perfect emitter of radiation. For this reason, plots like the ones shown in Figure 7.4a are commonly referred to as blackbody radiation curves.

Attempts to account for the temperature dependence of radiation versus wavelength curves in terms of established wave theory and thermodynamic laws were only partially successful. One theory explained short-wavelength dependence but failed to account for the longer wavelengths. Another theory accounted for the longer wavelengths but failed for short wavelengths. It seemed that something fundamental was missing from the laws of classical physics.

Planck solved the problem with an assumption that departed drastically from accepted concepts. Classical physics assumed that atoms and molecules could emit (or absorb) any arbitrary amount of radiant energy. Planck said that atoms and molecules could emit (or absorb) energy only in discrete quantities, like small packages or bundles. Planck gave the name **quantum** to *the smallest quantity of energy that can be emitted (or absorbed) in the form of electromagnetic radiation.* The energy E of a single quantum of energy is given by

$$E = h\nu \tag{7.2}$$

where h is called *Planck's constant* and ν is the frequency of radiation. The value of Planck's constant is 6.63×10^{-34} J · s. Because $\nu = c/\lambda$, Equation (7.2) can also be expressed as

$$E = h\frac{c}{\lambda} \tag{7.3}$$

> The failure in the short wavelength region is called the *ultraviolet catastrophe.*

According to quantum theory, energy is always emitted in integral multiples of $h\nu$; for example, $h\nu$, $2h\nu$, $3h\nu$, . . . , but never, for example, $1.67h\nu$ or $4.98h\nu$. At the time Planck presented his theory, he could not explain why energies should be fixed or quantized in this manner. Starting with this hypothesis, however, he had no trouble correlating the experimental data for emission by solids over the *entire* range of wavelengths; they all supported the quantum theory.

The idea that energy should be quantized or "bundled" may seem strange, but the concept of quantization has many analogies. For example, an electric charge is also quantized; there can be only whole-number multiples of e, the charge of one electron. Matter itself is quantized, for the numbers of electrons, protons, and neutrons and the numbers of atoms in a sample of matter must also be integers. Our money system is based on a "quantum" of value called a penny. Even processes in living systems involve quantized phenomena. The eggs laid by hens are quantized, and a pregnant cat gives birth to an integral number of kittens, not to one-half or three-quarters of a kitten.

Review of Concepts

Why is radiation only in the UV but not the visible or infrared region responsible for sun tanning?

7.2 The Photoelectric Effect

In 1905, only five years after Planck presented his quantum theory, Albert Einstein[†] used the theory to solve another mystery in physics, the **photoelectric effect,** a phenomenon in which *electrons are ejected from the surface of certain metals exposed to light of at least a certain minimum frequency,* called *the threshold frequency* (Figure 7.5). The number of electrons ejected was proportional to the intensity (or

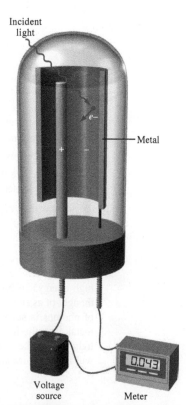

Figure 7.5 *An apparatus for studying the photoelectric effect. Light of a certain frequency falls on a clean metal surface. Ejected electrons are attracted toward the positive electrode. The flow of electrons is registered by a*

[†]Albert Einstein (1879–1955). German-born American physicist. Regarded by many as one of the two greatest physicists the world has known (the other is Isaac Newton). The three papers (on special relativity, Brownian motion, and the photoelectric effect) that he published in 1905 while employed as a technical

brightness) of the light, but the energies of the ejected electrons were not. Below the threshold frequency no electrons were ejected no matter how intense the light.

The photoelectric effect could not be explained by the wave theory of light. Einstein, however, made an extraordinary assumption. He suggested that a beam of light is really a stream of particles. These *particles of light* are now called ***photons.*** Using Planck's quantum theory of radiation as a starting point, Einstein deduced that each photon must possess energy E, given by the equation

> This equation has the same form as Equation (7.2) because, as we will see shortly, electromagnetic radiation is emitted as well as absorbed in the form of photons.

$$E = h\nu$$

where ν is the frequency of light.

Example 7.2

Calculate the energy (in joules) of (a) a photon with a wavelength of 5.00×10^4 nm (infrared region) and (b) a photon with a wavelength of 5.00×10^{-2} nm (X-ray region).

Strategy In both (a) and (b) we are given the wavelength of a photon and asked to calculate its energy. We need to use Equation (7.3) to calculate the energy. Planck's constant is given in the text and also on the back inside cover.

Solution

(a) From Equation (7.3),

$$E = h\frac{c}{\lambda}$$

$$= \frac{(6.63 \times 10^{-34}\,\text{J} \cdot \text{s})(3.00 \times 10^8\,\text{m/s})}{(5.00 \times 10^4\,\text{nm})\dfrac{1 \times 10^{-9}\,\text{m}}{1\,\text{nm}}}$$

$$= 3.98 \times 10^{-21}\,\text{J}$$

This is the energy of a single photon with a 5.00×10^4 nm wavelength.

(b) Following the same procedure as in (a), we can show that the energy of the photon that has a wavelength of 5.00×10^{-2} nm is 3.98×10^{-15} J .

Check Because the energy of a photon increases with decreasing wavelength, we see that an "X-ray" photon is 1×10^6, or a million times, more energetic than an "infrared" photon.

Similar problem: 7.15.

Practice Exercise The energy of a photon is 5.87×10^{-20} J. What is its wavelength (in nanometers)?

Electrons are held in a metal by attractive forces, and so removing them from the metal requires light of a sufficiently high frequency (which corresponds to sufficiently high energy) to break them free. Shining a beam of light onto a metal surface can be thought of as shooting a beam of particles—photons—at the metal atoms. If the frequency of photons is such that $h\nu$ is exactly equal to the energy that binds the electrons in the metal, then the light will have just enough energy to knock the electrons loose. If we use light of a higher frequency, then not only will the electrons be knocked loose, but they will also acquire some kinetic energy. This situation is summarized by the equation

$$h\nu = \text{KE} + W \tag{7.4}$$

where KE is the kinetic energy of the ejected electron and W is the work function, which is a measure of how strongly the electrons are held in the metal. Rewriting Equation (7.4) as

$$\text{KE} = h\nu - W$$

shows that the more energetic the photon (that is, the higher the frequency), the greater

Now consider two beams of light having the same frequency (which is greater than the threshold frequency) but different intensities. The more intense beam of light consists of a larger number of photons; consequently, it ejects more electrons from the metal's surface than the weaker beam of light. Thus, the more intense the light, the greater the number of electrons emitted by the target metal; the higher the frequency of the light, the greater the kinetic energy of the ejected electrons.

Example 7.3

The work function of cesium metal is 3.42×10^{-19} J. (a) Calculate the minimum frequency of light required to release electrons from the metal. (b) Calculate the kinetic energy of the ejected electron if light of frequency 1.00×10^{15} s^{-1} is used for irradiating the metal.

Strategy (a) The relationship between the work function of an element and the frequency of light is given by Equation (7.4). The minimum frequency of light needed to dislodge an electron is the point where the kinetic energy of the ejected electron is zero. (b) Knowing both the work function and the frequency of light, we can solve for the kinetic energy of the ejected electron.

Solution

(a) Setting KE = 0 in Equation (7.4), we write

$$h\nu = W$$

Thus,

$$\nu = \frac{W}{h} = \frac{3.42 \times 10^{-19} \text{ J}}{6.63 \times 10^{-34} \text{ J} \cdot \text{s}}$$
$$= 5.16 \times 10^{14} \text{ s}^{-1}$$

(b) Rearranging Equation (7.4) gives

$$KE = h\nu - W$$
$$= (6.63 \times 10^{-34} \text{ J} \cdot \text{s})(1.00 \times 10^{15} \text{ s}^{-1}) - 3.42 \times 10^{-19} \text{ J}$$
$$= 3.21 \times 10^{-19} \text{ J}$$

Check The kinetic energy of the ejected electron (3.21×10^{-19} J) is smaller than the energy of the photon (6.63×10^{-19} J). Therefore, the answer is reasonable.

Similar problems: 7.21, 7.22.

Practice Exercise The work function of titanium metal is 6.93×10^{-19} J. Calculate the kinetic energy of the ejected electrons if light of frequency 2.50×10^{15} s^{-1} is used to irradiate the metal.

Einstein's theory of light posed a dilemma for scientists. On the one hand, it explains the photoelectric effect satisfactorily. On the other hand, the particle theory of light is not consistent with the known wave behavior of light. The only way to resolve the dilemma is to accept the idea that light possesses *both* particlelike and wavelike properties. Depending on the experiment, light behaves either as a wave or as a stream of particles. This concept, called particle-wave duality, was totally alien to the way physicists had thought about matter and radiation, and it took a long time for them to accept it. We will see in Section 7.4 that a dual nature (particles and waves) is not unique to light but is also characteristic of all matter, including electrons.

Review of Concepts

A clean metal surface is irradiated with light of three different wavelengths λ_1, λ_2, and λ_3. The kinetic energies of the ejected electrons are as follows: λ_1: 2.9×10^{-20} J; λ_2: approximately zero; λ_3: 4.2×10^{-19} J. Which light has the shortest wavelength and which has the longest wavelength?

7.3 Bohr's Theory of the Hydrogen Atom

Einstein's work paved the way for the solution of yet another nineteenth-century "mystery" in physics: the emission spectra of atoms.

Emission Spectra

 Animation
Emission Spectra

 Animation
Line Spectra

Ever since the seventeenth century, when Newton showed that sunlight is composed of various color components that can be recombined to produce white light, chemists and physicists have studied the characteristics of *emission spectra,* that is, *either continuous or line spectra of radiation emitted by substances.* The emission spectrum of a substance can be seen by energizing a sample of material either with thermal energy or with some other form of energy (such as a high-voltage electrical discharge). A "red-hot" or "white-hot" iron bar freshly removed from a high-temperature source produces a characteristic glow. This visible glow is the portion of its emission spectrum that is sensed by eye. The warmth of the same iron bar represents another portion of its emission spectrum—the infrared region. A feature common to the emission spectra of the sun and of a heated solid is that both are continuous; that is, all wavelengths of visible light are represented in the spectra (see the visible region in Figure 7.4).

The emission spectra of atoms in the gas phase, on the other hand, do not show a continuous spread of wavelengths from red to violet; rather, the atoms produce bright lines in different parts of the visible spectrum. These *line spectra* are *the light emission only at specific wavelengths.* Figure 7.6 is a schematic diagram of a discharge tube that is used to study emission spectra, and Figure 7.7 shows the color emitted by hydrogen atoms in a discharge tube.

Every element has a unique emission spectrum. The characteristic lines in atomic spectra can be used in chemical analysis to identify unknown atoms, much as fingerprints are used to identify people. When the lines of the emission spectrum of a known element exactly match the lines of the emission spectrum of an unknown sample, the identity of the sample is established. Although the utility of this procedure was recognized some time ago in chemical analysis, the origin of these lines was unknown until early in the twentieth century. Figure 7.8 shows the emission spectra of several elements.

When a high voltage is applied between the forks, some of the sodium ions in the pickle are converted to sodium atoms in an excited state. These atoms emit the characteristic yellow light as they relax to the ground state.

Emission Spectrum of the Hydrogen Atom

Animation
Atomic Line Spectra

In 1913, not too long after Planck's and Einstein's discoveries, a theoretical explanation of the emission spectrum of the hydrogen atom was presented by the Danish physicist Niels Bohr.[†] Bohr's treatment is very complex and is no longer considered to be correct in all its details. Thus, we will concentrate only on his important assumptions and final results, which do account for the spectral lines.

When Bohr first tackled this problem, physicists already knew that the atom contains electrons and protons. They thought of an atom as an entity in which electrons whirled around the nucleus in circular orbits at high velocities. This was an appealing model because it resembled the motions of the planets around the sun. In the hydrogen atom, it was believed that the electrostatic attraction between the positive "solar" proton and the negative "planetary" electron pulls the electron inward and that this force is balanced exactly by the outward acceleration due to the circular motion of the electron.

[†]Niels Henrik David Bohr (1885–1962). Danish physicist. One of the founders of modern physics, he received the Nobel Prize in Physics in 1922 for his theory explaining the spectrum of the hydrogen atom.

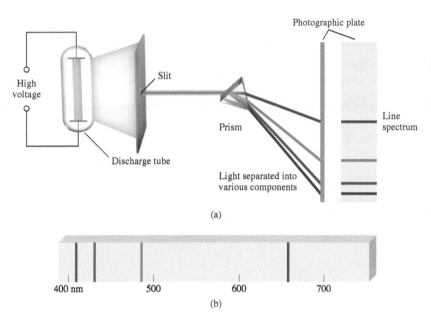

Figure 7.7 *Color emitted by hydrogen atoms in a discharge tube. The color observed results from the combination of the colors emitted in the visible spectrum.*

Figure 7.6 *(a) An experimental arrangement for studying the emission spectra of atoms and molecules. The gas under study is in a discharge tube containing two electrodes. As electrons flow from the negative electrode to the positive electrode, they collide with the gas. This collision process eventually leads to the emission of light by the atoms (or molecules). The emitted light is separated into its components by a prism. Each component color is focused at a definite position, according to its wavelength, and forms a colored image of the slit on the photographic plate. The colored images are called spectral lines. (b) The line emission spectrum of hydrogen atoms.*

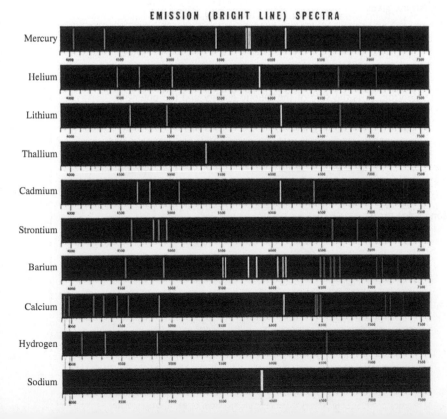

Figure 7.8 *The emission spectra of various elements. The units for the spectral lines are angstroms (Å), where 1 Å = 1 × 10⁻¹⁰ m.*

Chapter 7 ▪ Quantum Theory and the Electronic Structure of Atoms

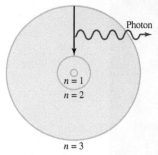

Figure 7.9 *The emission process in an excited hydrogen atom, according to Bohr's theory. An electron originally in a higher-energy orbit (n = 3) falls back to a lower-energy orbit (n = 2). As a result, a photon with energy hν is given off. The value of hν is equal to the difference in energies of the two orbits occupied by the electron in the emission process. For simplicity, only three orbits are shown.*

According to the laws of classical physics, however, an electron moving in an orbit of a hydrogen atom would experience an acceleration toward the nucleus by radiating away energy in the form of electromagnetic waves. Thus, such an electron would quickly spiral into the nucleus and annihilate itself with the proton. To explain why this does not happen, Bohr postulated that the electron is allowed to occupy only certain orbits of specific energies. In other words, the energies of the electron are quantized. An electron in any of the allowed orbits will not spiral into the nucleus and therefore will not radiate energy. Bohr attributed the emission of radiation by an energized hydrogen atom to the electron dropping from a higher-energy allowed orbit to a lower one and emitting a quantum of energy (a photon) in the form of light (Figure 7.9). Bohr's model retained the notion that electrons move in circular orbits around the nucleus and that the electron is held in orbit by the coulombic force of attraction between the nucleus and the electron, as expressed by Coulomb's law,

$$f = \frac{Ze^2}{4\pi\varepsilon_0 r^2} \tag{7.4a}$$

where Z is the charge of the nucleus, e is the electronic charge of an electron, ε_0 is the permittivity of free space, and r is the radius of the orbit. The coulombic force is balanced by the centrifugal "force" (an apparent force that opposes the force of attraction):

$$f = \frac{m_e u^2}{r} \tag{7.4b}$$

where m_e is the mass of the electron and u is the velocity of the electron. Equating the opposing force equations gives

$$\frac{Ze^2}{4\pi\varepsilon_0 r^2} = \frac{m_e u^2}{r} \tag{7.4c}$$

The total energy of the electron, E, is the sum of the kinetic energy and the potential energy, where the potential-energy term is negative because the interaction between the electron and the nucleus is attractive, as given by

$$E = \frac{1}{2}m_e u^2 - \frac{Ze^2}{4\pi\varepsilon_0 r} \tag{7.4d}$$

Rearranging Equation (7.4c) gives

$$m_e u^2 = \frac{Ze^2}{4\pi\varepsilon_0 r} \tag{7.4e}$$

Substitution of Equation (7.4e) into Equation (7.4d) yields

$$E = \frac{1}{2}m_e u^2 - m_e u^2 \tag{7.4f}$$

$$= -\frac{1}{2}m_e u^2$$

In order to accommodate quantum theory, Bohr restricted the angular momentum of the electron ($m_e u r$) to certain values using

$$m_e u r = n\frac{h}{2\pi} \qquad n = 1, 2, 3, \ldots \tag{7.4g}$$

where n is limited to being a positive integer; hence, n is a *quantum number*. Dividing Equation (7.4e) by Equation (7.4g) yields

$$u = \frac{Ze^2}{2nh\varepsilon_0} \tag{7.4h}$$

which is then substituted into Equation (7.4f) to give

$$E_n = -\frac{m_e Z^2 e^4}{8h^2 \varepsilon_0^2}\frac{1}{n^2} \qquad n = 1, 2, 3, \ldots \tag{7.4i}$$

Note that the symbol for energy now carries a subscript because different values of n will give different values for E_n.

Plugging in the appropriate constants and using $Z = 1$ for the hydrogen nucleus, Equation (7.4i) simplifies to

$$E_n = -R_{\mathrm{H}}\left(\frac{1}{n^2}\right) \tag{7.5}$$

where R_{H}, the Rydberg[†] constant for the hydrogen atom, has the value 2.18×10^{-18} J.

The negative sign in Equation (7.5) is an arbitrary convention, signifying that the energy of the electron in the atom is *lower* than the energy of a *free electron,* which is an electron that is infinitely far from the nucleus. The energy of a free electron is arbitrarily assigned a value of zero. Mathematically, this corresponds to setting n equal to infinity in Equation (7.5), so that $E_\infty = 0$. As the electron gets closer to the nucleus (as n decreases), E_n becomes larger in absolute value, but also more negative. The most negative value, then, is reached when $n = 1$, which corresponds to the most stable energy state. We call this the **ground state,** or the **ground level,** which refers to *the lowest energy state of a system* (which is an atom in our discussion). The stability of the electron diminishes for $n = 2, 3, \ldots$. Each of these levels is called an **excited state,** or **excited level,** which is *higher in energy than the ground state.* A hydrogen electron for which n is greater than 1 is said to be in an excited state. Bohr's model of the atom can also be used to derive an expression for the radius of the electron's orbit. Rearranging Equation (7.4g) to isolate r and substituting for u with Equation (7.4h) gives

$$r_n = \frac{nh}{2\pi m_e u} \tag{7.5a}$$

$$= \frac{nh}{2\pi m_e} \times \frac{2nh\varepsilon_0}{Ze^2}$$

$$= \frac{n^2 h^2 \varepsilon_0}{Z\pi m_e e^2}$$

[†]Johannes Robert Rydberg (1854–1919). Swedish physicist. Rydberg's major contribution to physics was his study of the line spectra of many elements.

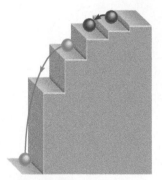

Figure 7.10 *A mechanical analogy for the emission processes. The ball can rest on any step but not between steps.*

where r_n is the radius of the nth orbit. Note that the radius of each circular orbit in Bohr's model depends on n^2. For the H atom, $r = 529$ pm for $n = 1$, and this value is called the Bohr radius. As n increases from 1 to 2 to 3, the orbit radius increases very rapidly. The higher the excited state, the farther away the electron is from the nucleus (and the less tightly it is held by the nucleus). An understanding of why the electron would be limited to certain orbits required a revolutionary insight as to the nature of the electron, as we will see in the next section.

Bohr's theory enables us to explain the line spectrum of the hydrogen atom. Radiant energy absorbed by the atom causes the electron to move from a lower-energy state (characterized by a smaller n value) to a higher-energy state (characterized by a larger n value). Conversely, radiant energy (in the form of a photon) is emitted when the electron moves from a higher-energy state to a lower-energy state. The quantized movement of the electron from one energy state to another is analogous to the movement of a tennis ball either up or down a set of stairs (Figure 7.10). The ball can be on any of several steps but never between steps. The journey from a lower step to a higher one is an energy-requiring process, whereas movement from a higher step to a lower step is an energy-releasing process. The quantity of energy involved in either type of change is determined by the distance between the beginning and ending steps. Similarly, the amount of energy needed to move an electron in the Bohr atom depends on the difference in energy levels between the initial and final states.

To apply Equation (7.5) to the emission process in a hydrogen atom, let us suppose that the electron is initially in an excited state characterized by the principal quantum number n_i. During emission, the electron drops to a lower energy state characterized by the principal quantum number n_f (the subscripts i and f denote the initial and final states, respectively). This lower energy state may be either a less excited state or the ground state. The difference between the energies of the initial and final states is

$$\Delta E = E_f - E_i$$

From Equation (7.5),

$$E_f = -R_H\left(\frac{1}{n_f^2}\right)$$

and

$$E_i = -R_H\left(\frac{1}{n_i^2}\right)$$

Therefore,

$$\Delta E = \left(\frac{-R_H}{n_f^2}\right) - \left(\frac{-R_H}{n_i^2}\right)$$

$$= R_H\left(\frac{1}{n_i^2} - \frac{1}{n_f^2}\right)$$

Because this transition results in the emission of a photon of frequency ν and energy $h\nu$, we can write

$$\Delta E = h\nu = R_H\left(\frac{1}{n_i^2} - \frac{1}{n_f^2}\right) \tag{7.6}$$

Table 7.1	The Various Series in Atomic Hydrogen Emission Spectrum		
Series	n_f	n_i	**Spectrum Region**
Lyman	1	2, 3, 4, . . .	Ultraviolet
Balmer	2	3, 4, 5, . . .	Visible and ultraviolet
Paschen	3	4, 5, 6, . . .	Infrared
Brackett	4	5, 6, 7, . . .	Infrared

When a photon is emitted, $n_i > n_f$. Consequently the term in parentheses is negative and ΔE is negative (energy is lost to the surroundings). When energy is absorbed, $n_i < n_f$ and the term in parentheses is positive, so ΔE is positive. Each spectral line in the emission spectrum corresponds to a particular transition in a hydrogen atom. When we study a large number of hydrogen atoms, we observe all possible transitions and hence the corresponding spectral lines. The brightness of a spectral line depends on how many photons of the same wavelength are emitted.

The emission spectrum of hydrogen includes a wide range of wavelengths from the infrared to the ultraviolet. Table 7.1 lists the series of transitions in the hydrogen spectrum; they are named after their discoverers. The Balmer series was particularly easy to study because a number of its lines fall in the visible range.

Figure 7.9 shows a single transition. However, it is more informative to express transitions as shown in Figure 7.11. Each horizontal line represents an allowed energy level for the electron in a hydrogen atom. The energy levels are labeled with their principal quantum numbers.

Example 7.4 illustrates the use of Equation (7.6).

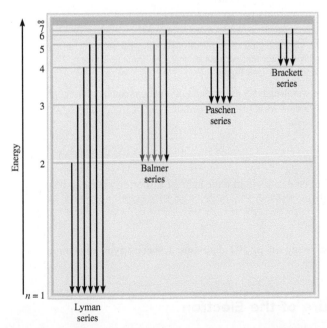

Figure 7.11 *The energy levels in the hydrogen atom and the various emission series. Each energy level corresponds to the energy associated with an allowed energy state for an orbit, as postulated by Bohr and shown in Figure 7.9. The emission lines are labeled according to the scheme in Table 7.1.*

Example 7.4

What is the wavelength of a photon (in nanometers) emitted during a transition from the $n_i = 5$ state to the $n_f = 2$ state in the hydrogen atom?

Strategy We are given the initial and final states in the emission process. We can calculate the energy of the emitted photon using Equation (7.6). Then from Equations (7.2) and (7.1) we can solve for the wavelength of the photon. The value of Rydberg's constant is given in the text.

Solution From Equation (7.6) we write

$$\Delta E = R_H\left(\frac{1}{n_i^2} - \frac{1}{n_f^2}\right)$$
$$= 2.18 \times 10^{-18}\,\text{J}\left(\frac{1}{5^2} - \frac{1}{2^2}\right)$$
$$= -4.58 \times 10^{-19}\,\text{J}$$

The negative sign is in accord with our convention that energy is given off to the surroundings.

The negative sign indicates that this is energy associated with an emission process. To calculate the wavelength, we will omit the minus sign for ΔE because the wavelength of the photon must be positive. Because $\Delta E = h\nu$ or $\nu = \Delta E/h$, we can calculate the wavelength of the photon by writing

$$\lambda = \frac{c}{\nu}$$
$$= \frac{ch}{\Delta E}$$
$$= \frac{(3.00 \times 10^8\,\text{m/s})(6.63 \times 10^{-34}\,\text{J} \cdot \text{s})}{4.58 \times 10^{-19}\,\text{J}}$$
$$= 4.34 \times 10^{-7}\,\text{m}$$
$$= 4.34 \times 10^{-7}\,\text{m} \times \left(\frac{1\,\text{nm}}{1 \times 10^{-9}\,\text{m}}\right) = 434\,\text{nm}$$

Similar problems: 7.31, 7.32.

Check The wavelength is in the visible region of the electromagnetic region (see Figure 7.4). This is consistent with the fact that because $n_f = 2$, this transition gives rise to a spectral line in the Balmer series (see Figure 7.6).

Practice Exercise What is the wavelength (in nanometers) of a photon emitted during a transition from $n_i = 6$ to $n_f = 4$ state in the H atom?

Review of Concepts

Which transition in the hydrogen atom would emit light of a shorter wavelength?
(a) $n_i = 5 \longrightarrow n_f = 3$ or (b) $n_i = 4 \longrightarrow n_f = 2$.

The Chemistry in Action essay on p. 290 discusses a special type of atomic emission—lasers.

7.4 The Dual Nature of the Electron

Physicists were both mystified and intrigued by Bohr's theory. They questioned why the energies of the hydrogen electron are quantized. Or, phrasing the question in a more concrete way, Why is the electron in a Bohr atom restricted to orbiting the

7.4 The Dual Nature of the Electron   289

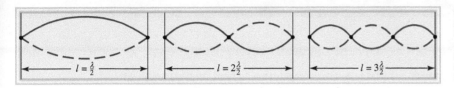

Figure 7.12 *The standing waves generated by plucking a guitar string. Each dot represents a node. The length of the string (l) must be equal to a whole number times one-half the wavelength (λ/2).*

nucleus at certain fixed distances? For a decade no one, not even Bohr himself, had a logical explanation. In 1924 Louis de Broglie[†] provided a solution to this puzzle. De Broglie reasoned that if light waves can behave like a stream of particles (photons), then perhaps particles such as electrons can possess wave properties. According to de Broglie, an electron bound to the nucleus behaves like a *standing wave*. Standing waves can be generated by plucking, say, a guitar string (Figure 7.12). The waves are described as standing, or stationary, because they do not travel along the string. Some points on the string, called **nodes,** do not move at all; that is, *the amplitude of the wave at these points is zero*. There is a node at each end, and there may be nodes between the ends. The greater the frequency of vibration, the shorter the wavelength of the standing wave and the greater the number of nodes. As Figure 7.12 shows, there can be only certain wavelengths in any of the allowed motions of the string.

De Broglie argued that if an electron does behave like a standing wave in the hydrogen atom, the length of the wave must fit the circumference of the orbit exactly (Figure 7.13). Otherwise the wave would partially cancel itself on each successive orbit. Eventually the amplitude of the wave would be reduced to zero, and the wave would not exist.

The relation between the circumference of an allowed orbit ($2\pi r$) and the wavelength (λ) of the electron is given by

$$2\pi r = n\lambda \qquad (7.7)$$

where r is the radius of the orbit, λ is the wavelength of the electron wave, and $n = 1, 2, 3, \ldots$. Because n is an integer, it follows that r can have only certain values as n increases from 1 to 2 to 3 and so on. And because the energy of the electron depends on the size of the orbit (or the value of r), its value must be quantized.

De Broglie's reasoning led to the conclusion that waves can behave like particles and particles can exhibit wavelike properties. De Broglie deduced that the particle and wave properties are related by the expression

$$\lambda = \frac{h}{mu} \qquad (7.8)$$

where λ, m, and u are the wavelengths associated with a moving particle, its mass, and its velocity, respectively. Equation (7.8) implies that a particle in motion can be treated as a wave, and a wave can exhibit the properties of a particle. Note that the left side of Equation (7.8) involves the wavelike property of wavelength, whereas the right side makes references to mass, a distinctly particlelike property.

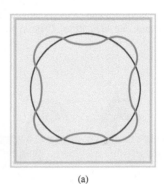

(a)

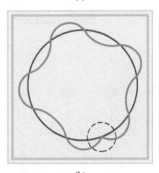

(b)

Figure 7.13 *(a) The circumference of the orbit is equal to an integral number of wavelengths. This is an allowed orbit. (b) The circumference of the orbit is not equal to an integral number of wavelengths. As a result, the electron wave does not close in on itself. This is a nonallowed orbit.*

In using Equation (7.8), *m* must be in kilograms and *u* must be in m/s.

[†]Louis Victor Pierre Raymond Duc de Broglie (1892–1977). French physicist. Member of an old and noble family in France, he held the title of a prince. In his doctoral dissertation, he proposed that matter and radiation have the properties of both wave and particle. For this work, de Broglie was awarded the Nobel Prize in Physics in 1929.

CHEMISTRY *in Action*

Laser—The Splendid Light

Laser is an acronym for light amplification by stimulated emission of radiation. It is a special type of emission that involves either atoms or molecules. Since the discovery of laser in 1960, it has been used in numerous systems designed to operate in the gas, liquid, and solid states. These systems emit radiation with wavelengths ranging from infrared through visible and ultraviolet. The advent of laser has truly revolutionized science, medicine, and technology.

Ruby laser was the first known laser. Ruby is a deep-red mineral containing corundum, Al_2O_3, in which some of the Al^{3+}

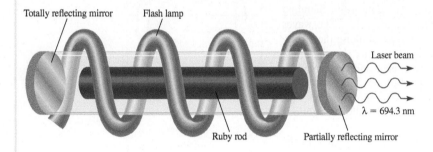

The emission of laser light from a ruby laser.

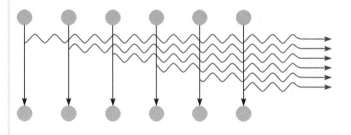

The stimulated emission of one photon by another photon in a cascade event that leads to the emission of laser light. The synchronization of the light waves produces an intensely penetrating laser beam.

Example 7.5

Calculate the wavelength of the "particle" in the following two cases: (a) The fastest serve in tennis is about 150 miles per hour, or 68 m/s. Calculate the wavelength associated with a 6.0×10^{-2}-kg tennis ball traveling at this speed. (b) Calculate the wavelength associated with an electron (9.1094×10^{-31} kg) moving at 68 m/s.

Strategy We are given the mass and the speed of the particle in (a) and (b) and asked to calculate the wavelength so we need Equation (7.8). Note that because the units of Planck's constants are J · s, m and u must be in kg and m/s (1 J = 1 kg m^2/s^2), respectively.

Solution

(a) Using Equation (7.8) we write

$$\lambda = \frac{h}{mu}$$

$$= \frac{6.63 \times 10^{-34} \text{ J} \cdot \text{s}}{(6.0 \times 10^{-2} \text{ kg}) \times 68 \text{ m/s}}$$

$$= 1.6 \times 10^{-34} \text{ m}$$

ions have been replaced by Cr^{3+} ions. A flashlamp is used to excite the chromium atoms to a higher energy level. The excited atoms are unstable, so at a given instant some of them will return to the ground state by emitting a photon in the red region of the spectrum. The photon bounces back and forth many times between mirrors at opposite ends of the laser tube. This photon can stimulate the emission of photons of exactly the same wavelength from other excited chromium atoms; these photons in turn can stimulate the emission of more photons, and so on. Because the light waves are *in phase*—that is, their maxima and minima coincide—the photons enhance one another, increasing their power with each passage between the mirrors. One of the mirrors is only partially reflecting, so that when the light reaches a certain intensity it emerges from the mirror as a laser beam. Depending on the mode of operation, the laser light may be emitted in pulses (as in the ruby laser case) or in continuous waves.

Laser light is characterized by three properties: It is intense, it has precisely known wavelength and hence energy, and it is coherent. By *coherent* we mean that the light waves are all in phase. The applications of lasers are quite numerous. Their high intensity and ease of focus make them suitable for doing eye surgery, for drilling holes in metals and welding, and for carrying out nuclear fusion. The fact that they are highly directional and have precisely known wavelengths makes them very useful for telecommunications. Lasers are also used in isotope separation, in holography (three-dimensional photography), in compact disc players, and in supermarket scanners. Lasers have played an important role in the spectroscopic investigation of molecular properties and of many chemical and biological processes.

State-of-the-art lasers used in the research laboratory of Dr. A. H. Zewail at the California Institute of Technology.

Comment This is an exceedingly small wavelength considering that the size of an atom itself is on the order of 1×10^{-10} m. For this reason, the wave properties of a tennis ball cannot be detected by any existing measuring device.

(b) In this case,

$$\lambda = \frac{h}{mu}$$

$$= \frac{6.63 \times 10^{-34} \, \text{J} \cdot \text{s}}{(9.1094 \times 10^{-31} \, \text{kg}) \times 68 \, \text{m/s}}$$

$$= 1.1 \times 10^{-5} \, \text{m}$$

Comment This wavelength (1.1×10^{-5} m or 1.1×10^4 nm) is in the infrared region. This calculation shows that only electrons (and other submicroscopic particles) have measurable wavelengths.

Similar problems: 7.40, 7.41.

Practice Exercise Calculate the wavelength (in nanometers) of a H atom (mass = 1.674×10^{-27} kg) moving at 7.00×10^2 cm/s.

Figure 7.14 *(a) X-ray diffraction pattern of aluminum foil. (b) Electron diffraction of aluminum foil. The similarity of these two patterns shows that electrons can behave like X rays and display wave properties.*

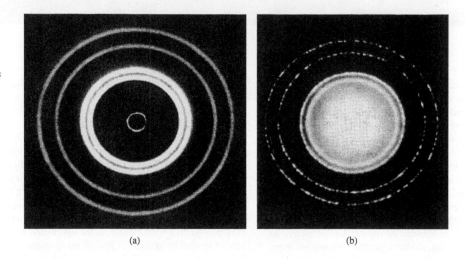

(a)   (b)

Review of Concepts

Which quantity in Equation (7.8) is responsible for the fact that macroscopic objects do not show observable wave properties?

Example 7.5 shows that although de Broglie's equation can be applied to diverse systems, the wave properties become observable only for submicroscopic objects.

Shortly after de Broglie introduced his equation, Clinton Davisson[†] and Lester Germer[‡] in the United States and G. P. Thomson[§] in England demonstrated that electrons do indeed possess wavelike properties. By directing a beam of electrons through a thin piece of gold foil, Thomson obtained a set of concentric rings on a screen, similar to the pattern observed when X rays (which are waves) were used. Figure 7.14 shows such a pattern for aluminum.

The Chemistry in Action essay on p. 293 describes electron microscopy.

7.5 Quantum Mechanics

In reality, Bohr's theory accounted for the observed emission spectra of He[+] and Li[2+] ions, as well as that of hydrogen. However, all three systems have one feature in common—each contains a single electron. Thus, the Bohr model worked successfully only for the hydrogen atom and for "hydrogenlike ions."

The spectacular success of Bohr's theory was followed by a series of disappointments. Bohr's approach did not account for the emission spectra of atoms containing more than one electron, such as atoms of helium and lithium. Nor did it explain why extra lines appear in the hydrogen emission spectrum when a magnetic field is applied. Another problem arose with the discovery that electrons are wavelike: How can the "position" of a wave be specified? We cannot define the precise location of a wave because a wave extends in space.

[†]Clinton Joseph Davisson (1881–1958). American physicist. He and G. P. Thomson shared the Nobel Prize in Physics in 1937 for demonstrating wave properties of electrons.

[‡]Lester Halbert Germer (1896–1972). American physicist. Discoverer (with Davisson) of the wave properties of electrons.

[§]George Paget Thomson (1892–1975). English physicist. Son of J. J. Thomson, he received the Nobel Prize in Physics in 1937, along with Clinton Davisson, for demonstrating wave properties of electrons.

CHEMISTRY *in Action*

Electron Microscopy

The electron microscope is an extremely valuable application of the wavelike properties of electrons because it produces images of objects that cannot be seen with the naked eye or with light microscopes. According to the laws of optics, it is impossible to form an image of an object that is smaller than half the wavelength of the light used for the observation. Because the range of visible light wavelengths starts at around 400 nm, or 4×10^{-5} cm, we cannot see anything smaller than 2×10^{-5} cm. In principle, we can see objects on the atomic and molecular scale by using X rays, whose wavelengths range from about 0.01 nm to 10 nm. However, X rays cannot be focused, so they do not produce well-formed images. Electrons, on the other hand, are charged particles, which can be focused in the same way the image on a TV screen is focused, that is, by applying an electric field or a magnetic field. According to Equation (7.8), the wavelength of an electron is inversely proportional to its velocity. By accelerating electrons to very high velocities, we can obtain wavelengths as short as 0.004 nm.

A different type of electron microscope, called the *scanning tunneling microscope* (*STM*), makes use of another quantum mechanical property of the electron to produce an image of the atoms on the surface of a sample. Because of its extremely small mass, an electron is able to move or "tunnel" through an energy barrier (instead of going over it). The STM consists of a tungsten metal needle with a very fine point, the source of the tunneling electrons. A voltage is

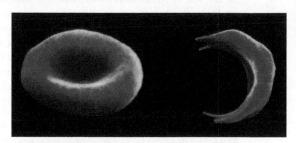

An electron micrograph showing a normal red blood cell and a sickled red blood cell from the same person.

maintained between the needle and the surface of the sample to induce electrons to tunnel through space to the sample. As the needle moves over the sample, at a distance of a few atomic diameters from the surface, the tunneling current is measured. This current decreases with increasing distance from the sample. By using a feedback loop, the vertical position of the tip can be adjusted to a constant distance from the surface. The extent of these adjustments, which profile the sample, is recorded and displayed as a three-dimensional false-colored image.

Both the electron microscope and the STM are among the most powerful tools in chemical and biological research.

To describe the problem of trying to locate a subatomic particle that behaves like a wave, Werner Heisenberg[†] formulated what is now known as the **Heisenberg uncertainty principle:** *it is impossible to know simultaneously both the momentum p* (defined as mass times velocity) *and the position of a particle with certainty.* Stated mathematically,

$$\Delta x \Delta p \geq \frac{h}{4\pi} \tag{7.9}$$

The ≥ sign means that the product $\Delta x \Delta p$ can be greater than or equal to $h/4\pi$, but it can never be smaller than $h/4\pi$. Also, in using Equation (7.9), m must be in kilograms and u must be in m/s.

where Δx and Δp are the uncertainties in measuring the position and momentum of the particle, respectively. The ≥ signs have the following meaning. If the measured uncertainties of position and momentum are large (say, in a crude experiment), their product can be substantially greater than $h/4\pi$ (hence the > sign). The significance of Equation 7.9 is that even in the most favorable conditions for measuring position and momentum,

---

[†]Werner Karl Heisenberg (1901–1976). German physicist. One of the founders of modern quantum theory, Heisenberg received the Nobel Prize in Physics in 1932.

the product of the uncertainties can never be less than $h/4\pi$ (hence the = sign). Thus, making measurement of the momentum of a particle *more* precise (that is, making Δp a *small* quantity) means that the position must become correspondingly *less* precise (that is, Δx will become *larger*). Similarly, if the position of the particle is known *more* precisely, its momentum measurement must become less precise.

Applying the Heisenberg uncertainty principle to the hydrogen atom, we see that in reality the electron does not orbit the nucleus in a well-defined path, as Bohr thought. If it did, we could determine precisely both the position of the electron (from its location on a particular orbit) and its momentum (from its kinetic energy) at the same time, a violation of the uncertainty principle.

Example 7.6

(a) An electron is moving at a speed of 8.0×10^6 m/s. If the uncertainty in measuring the speed is 1.0 percent of the speed, calculate the uncertainty in the electron's position. The mass of the electron is 9.1094×10^{-31} kg. (b) A baseball of mass 0.15 kg thrown at 100 mph has a momentum of 6.7 kg · m/s. If the uncertainty in measuring this momentum is 1.0×10^{-7} of the momentum, calculate the uncertainty in the baseball's position.

Strategy To calculate the *minimum* uncertainty in both (a) and (b), we use an equal sign in Equation (7.9).

Solution

(a) The uncertainty in the electron's speed u is

$$\Delta u = 0.010 \times 8.0 \times 10^6 \text{ m/s}$$
$$= 8.0 \times 10^4 \text{ m/s}$$

Momentum (p) is $p = mu$, so that

$$\Delta p = m\Delta u$$
$$= 9.1094 \times 10^{-31} \text{ kg} \times 8.0 \times 10^4 \text{ m/s}$$
$$= 7.3 \times 10^{-26} \text{ kg · m/s}$$

From Equation (7.9), the uncertainty in the electron's position is

$$\Delta x = \frac{h}{4\pi \Delta p}$$
$$= \frac{6.63 \times 10^{-34} \text{ J · s}}{4\pi (7.3 \times 10^{-26} \text{ kg · m/s})}$$
$$= 7.2 \times 10^{-10} \text{ m}$$

This uncertainty corresponds to about 4 atomic diameters.

(b) The uncertainty in the position of the baseball is

$$\Delta x = \frac{h}{4\pi \Delta p}$$
$$= \frac{6.63 \times 10^{-34} \text{ J · s}}{4\pi \times 1.0 \times 10^{-7} \times 6.7 \text{ kg · m/s}}$$
$$= 7.9 \times 10^{-29} \text{ m}$$

This is such a small number as to be of no consequence; that is, there is practically no uncertainty in determining the position of the baseball in the macroscopic world.

Practice Exercise Estimate the uncertainty in the speed of an oxygen molecule if its position is known to be ± 3 nm. The mass of an oxygen molecule is 5.31×10^{-26} kg.

To be sure, Bohr made a significant contribution to our understanding of atoms, and his suggestion that the energy of an electron in an atom is quantized remains unchallenged. But his theory did not provide a complete description of electronic behavior in atoms. In 1926 the Austrian physicist Erwin Schrödinger,[†] using a complicated mathematical technique, formulated an equation that describes the behavior and energies of submicroscopic particles in general, an equation analogous to Newton's laws of motion for macroscopic objects. The *Schrödinger equation* requires advanced calculus to solve, and we will not discuss it here. It is important to know, however, that the equation incorporates both particle behavior, in terms of mass m, and wave behavior, in terms of a *wave function* Ψ (psi), which depends on the location in space of the system (such as an electron in an atom).

The wave function itself has no direct physical meaning. However, the probability of finding the electron in a certain region in space is proportional to the square of the wave function, Ψ^2. The idea of relating Ψ^2 to probability stemmed from a wave theory analogy. According to wave theory, the intensity of light is proportional to the square of the amplitude of the wave, or Ψ^2. The most likely place to find a photon is where the intensity is greatest, that is, where the value of Ψ^2 is greatest. A similar argument associates Ψ^2 with the likelihood of finding an electron in regions surrounding the nucleus.

Schrödinger's equation began a new era in physics and chemistry, for it launched a new field, *quantum mechanics* (also called *wave mechanics*). We now refer to the developments in quantum theory from 1913—the time Bohr presented his analysis for the hydrogen atom—to 1926 as "old quantum theory."

The Quantum Mechanical Description of the Hydrogen Atom

The Schrödinger equation specifies the possible energy states the electron can occupy in a hydrogen atom and identifies the corresponding wave functions (Ψ). These energy states and wave functions are characterized by a set of quantum numbers (to be discussed shortly), with which we can construct a comprehensive model of the hydrogen atom.

Although quantum mechanics tells us that we cannot pinpoint an electron in an atom, it does define the region where the electron might be at a given time. The concept of **electron density** *gives the probability that an electron will be found in a particular region of an atom.* The square of the wave function, Ψ^2, defines the distribution of electron density in three-dimensional space around the nucleus. Regions of high electron density represent a high probability of locating the electron, whereas the opposite holds for regions of low electron density (Figure 7.15).

To distinguish the quantum mechanical description of an atom from Bohr's model, we speak of an atomic orbital, rather than an orbit. An **atomic orbital** can be thought of as *the wave function of an electron in an atom.* When we say that an electron is in a certain orbital, we mean that the distribution of the electron density or the probability of locating the electron in space is described by the square of the wave function associated with that orbital. An atomic orbital, therefore, has a characteristic energy, as well as a characteristic distribution of electron density.

The Schrödinger equation works nicely for the simple hydrogen atom with its one proton and one electron, but it turns out that it cannot be solved exactly for any atom containing more than one electron! Fortunately, chemists and physicists have

Figure 7.15 *A representation of the electron density distribution surrounding the nucleus in the hydrogen atom. It shows a high probability of finding the electron closer to the nucleus.*

[†]Erwin Schrödinger (1887–1961). Austrian physicist. Schrödinger formulated wave mechanics, which laid the foundation for modern quantum theory. He received the Nobel Prize in Physics in 1933.

learned to get around this kind of difficulty by approximation. For example, although the behavior of electrons in **many-electron atoms** (that is, *atoms containing two or more electrons*) is not the same as in the hydrogen atom, we assume that the difference is probably not too great. Thus, we can use the energies and wave functions obtained from the hydrogen atom as good approximations of the behavior of electrons in more complex atoms. In fact, this approach provides fairly reliable descriptions of electronic behavior in many-electron atoms.

> Although the helium atom has only two electrons, in quantum mechanics it is regarded as a many-electron atom.

Review of Concepts

What is the difference between Ψ and Ψ^2 for the electron in a hydrogen atom?

The Particle in a One-Dimensional Box Model for Quantum Mechanical Systems

The complex quantum mechanical behavior of atoms and molecules can be greatly simplified by considering a particle in a one-dimensional box. Of course, we cannot realistically study anything in just one dimension, but the solution to this simple problem provides us with some useful insights into more complex quantum mechanical systems.

Figure 7.15a illustrates a particle contained in a one-dimensional box, along the x axis. To visualize this construct, imagine a ball rolling along a line. The walls on either side of the box are high enough to keep the particle in the box. To simplify matters further, assume that the potential energy, V, of the particle is zero, but it does have kinetic energy. Because the kinetic energy is nonzero, the ball has velocity, so it bounces back and forth between the two walls. If the particle is small enough to exhibit quantum mechanical behavior, we are interested in the following questions: (1) What are the wave properties of the particle? and (2) What (kinetic) energies can the particle possess? Although this problem may be solved by using the Schrödinger wave equation, essentially the same results can be obtained by using Equation (7.8). Because the particle is confined between the points at $x = 0$ and $x = L$, the wave behavior associated with its motion closely resembles the "standing waves" generated by plucking a guitar string of length L, fixed at both ends (Figure 7.12). The least energetic motion corresponds to a wave whose length is twice that of the box. As the energy of the particle increases, its wavelength decreases, as shown in Figure 7.15b. The general expression for the wavelength is given by

$$\lambda = \frac{2L}{n}$$

where n is a quantum number, given by $n = 1, 2, 3, \ldots$. Thus, we have $n = 1$ for the first wave, $n = 2$ for the second wave, and so on. From de Broglie's relation, Equation (7.8), we can also express the wavelengths as

$$\lambda = \frac{h}{mu}$$

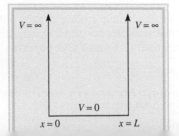

Figure 7.15a *A one-dimensional*

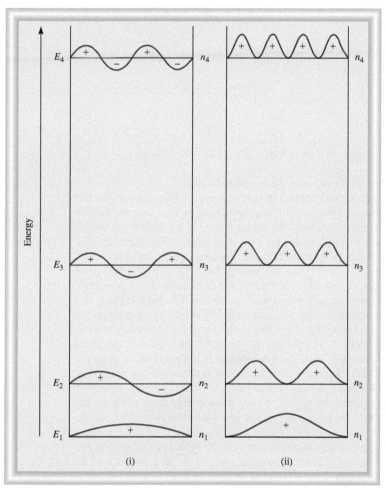

Figure 7.15b *(i) The first four energy levels and the corresponding plots of Ψ showing the wave properties for a particle in a one-dimensional box with infinite potential barriers. Note that the energies E_1, E_2, E_3, and E_4 vary with n^2, as required by Equation (7.9a). The + and − signs denote whether the wave is above or below the horizontal line. (ii) Plots of $Ψ^2$ showing the probabilities for the location of a particle in a one-dimensional box for the first four energy levels. Because the probability is given by the square of the wave function, all the signs are positive in this case. Note that the probability is a maximum in the middle of the box for the $n = 1$ state, but there are two maxima of probabilities for the $n = 2$ state and so on.*

Combining both equations, we obtain

$$\frac{h}{mu} = \frac{2L}{n}$$

or

$$u = \frac{nh}{2mL}$$

Because the kinetic energy of the particle is given by

$$E = \frac{1}{2}mu^2$$

we have

$$E = \frac{1}{2}m\left(\frac{nh}{2mL}\right)^2$$

or

$$E_n = \frac{n^2h^2}{8mL^2} \qquad (7.9a)$$

where the subscript n on E is the same as the quantum number n.

Equation 7.9a is interesting and unusual in several respects. First we see that the kinetic energy of the particle is quantized, its value governed by the quantum number n [see Figure 7.15b(i)]. More surprisingly, the lowest energy is not zero as we would expect, but rather it equals $h^2/8mL^2$, called the *zero-point* energy. The particle, once confined in the box, is constantly set in motion and can never be totally at rest! The Heisenberg uncertainty helps us understand this strange behavior. Since the box is of finite length L, the maximum uncertainty for locating the particle inside the box obviously cannot exceed L itself; that is, the maximum value Δx is L. Now suppose the particle does possess the lowest energy value of zero. Its velocity and momentum must then also be zero. In other words, it is sitting still. Consequently, we would have zero uncertainty in determining its momentum ($\Delta p = 0$). If this were true, the product $\Delta x \Delta p$ would be zero instead of $h/4\pi$. Such a behavior is *not* possible for quantum mechanical systems, and the dilemma is avoided by the existence of the zero-point energy described above. While there is no way to prove the validity of this statement for our one-dimension problem, the notion of zero-point energy does apply to the dynamics of molecules, such as electronic motion and molecular vibrations, as we shall see in later chapters.

Another interesting result of this equation concerns the probability of finding the particle inside the box. Figure 7.15b(ii) shows the plots of Ψ^2 as a function of x. According to classical mechanics, the likelihood of finding a particle is the same anywhere along the box. Obviously, this is not the case for a quantum mechanical particle. The probability of locating the particle not only varies along x, but also depends on the value of n. For the ground state ($n = 1$), the maximum probability occurs at $x = L/4$ and $x = 3L/4$, and the value of Ψ^2 is zero at $x = L/2$. In all cases, the probabilities are zero at the walls ($x = 0$ and $x = L$). These conditions are met as long as the walls are infinitely high.

The usefulness of the particle in a one-dimensional box problem is that it demonstrates a number of quantum mechanical concepts such as quantization of energy, the Heisenberg uncertainty principle, the wave behavior of particles, and the interpretation of the probability of locating a particle. It turns out that all of the results discussed in this section are, with some modifications, directly applicable to atoms and molecules. For example, as a first approximation we can treat the electron in a hydrogen atom as a particle in a three-dimensional box. Based on our discussion so far, we can make the following predictions: (1) the energies of the electron in an atom are quantized; (2) the lowest energy of the electron is not equal to zero, that is, it possesses a zero-point energy; and (3) the electron is characterized by three quantum numbers, one for each direction. Predictions 1 and 2 are obviously in accord with the Bohr model of the hydrogen atom, and in the next section we consider quantum numbers beyond n.

The Chemistry in Action at the end of this chapter describes quantum dots in which the color of light emitted depends on the size of the particle, and this behavior can be understood by considering the particle to be in a three-dimensional box.

7.6 Quantum Numbers

In quantum mechanics, three **quantum numbers** are required to *describe the distribution of electrons in hydrogen and other atoms*. These numbers are derived from the mathematical solution of the Schrödinger equation for the hydrogen atom. They are called the *principal quantum number,* the *angular momentum quantum number,* and the *magnetic quantum number.* These quantum numbers will be used to describe atomic orbitals and to label electrons that reside in them. A fourth quantum number— the *spin quantum number*—describes the behavior of a specific electron and completes the description of electrons in atoms.

The Principal Quantum Number (*n*)

The principal quantum number (*n*) can have integral values 1, 2, 3, and so forth; it corresponds to the quantum number in Equation (7.5). In a hydrogen atom, the value of *n* determines the energy of an orbital. As we will see shortly, this is not the case for a many-electron atom. The principal quantum number also relates to the average distance of the electron from the nucleus in a particular orbital. The larger *n* is, the greater the average distance of an electron in the orbital from the nucleus and therefore the larger the orbital.

Equation (7.5) holds only for the hydrogen atom.

The Angular Momentum Quantum Number (ℓ)

The angular momentum quantum number (ℓ) tells us the "shape" of the orbitals (see Section 7.7). The values of ℓ depend on the value of the principal quantum number, *n*. For a given value of *n*, ℓ has possible integral values from 0 to $(n - 1)$. If $n = 1$, there is only one possible value of ℓ; that is, $\ell = n - 1 = 1 - 1 = 0$. If $n = 2$, there are two values of ℓ, given by 0 and 1. If $n = 3$, there are three values of ℓ, given by 0, 1, and 2. The value of ℓ is generally designated by the letters $s, p, d, \ldots$ as follows:

The value of ℓ is fixed based on the type of the orbital.

ℓ	0	1	2	3	4	5
Name of orbital	s	p	d	f	g	h

Thus, if $\ell = 0$, we have an s orbital; if $\ell = 1$, we have a p orbital; and so on.

The unusual sequence of letters (s, p, and d) has a historical origin. Physicists who studied atomic emission spectra tried to correlate the observed spectral lines with the particular energy states involved in the transitions. They noted that some of the lines were *s*harp; some were rather spread out, or *d*iffuse; and some were very strong and hence referred to as *p*rincipal lines. Subsequently, the initial letters of each adjective were assigned to those energy states. However, after the letter d and starting with the letter f (for *f*undamental), the orbital designations follow alphabetical order.

A collection of orbitals with the same value of *n* is frequently called a shell. One or more orbitals with the same *n* and ℓ values are referred to as a subshell. For example, the shell with $n = 2$ is composed of two subshells, $\ell = 0$ and 1 (the allowed values for $n = 2$). These subshells are called the 2s and 2p subshells where 2 denotes the value of *n*, and s and p denote the values of ℓ.

Remember that the "2" in 2s refers to the value of *n* and the "s" symbolizes the value of ℓ.

The Magnetic Quantum Number (m_ℓ)

The magnetic quantum number (m_ℓ) describes the orientation of the orbital in space (to be discussed in Section 7.7). Within a subshell, the value of m_ℓ depends on the value of the angular momentum quantum number, ℓ. For a certain value of ℓ, there are ($2\ell + 1$) integral values of m_ℓ as follows:

$$-\ell, (-\ell + 1), \ldots 0, \ldots (+\ell - 1), +\ell$$

If $\ell = 0$, then $m_\ell = 0$. If $\ell = 1$, then there are $[(2 \times 1) + 1]$, or three values of m_ℓ, namely, -1, 0, and 1. If $\ell = 2$, there are $[(2 \times 2) + 1]$, or five values of m_ℓ, namely,

−2, −1, 0, 1, and 2. The number of m_ℓ values indicates the number of orbitals in a subshell with a particular ℓ value.

To conclude our discussion of these three quantum numbers, let us consider a situation in which $n = 2$ and $\ell = 1$. The values of n and ℓ indicate that we have a 2p subshell, and in this subshell we have *three* 2p orbitals (because there are three values of m_ℓ, given by −1, 0, and 1).

The Electron Spin Quantum Number (m_s)

Experiments on the emission spectra of hydrogen and sodium atoms indicated that lines in the emission spectra could be split by the application of an external magnetic field. The only way physicists could explain these results was to assume that electrons act like tiny magnets. If electrons are thought of as spinning on their own axes, as Earth does, their magnetic properties can be accounted for. According to electromagnetic theory, a spinning charge generates a magnetic field, and it is this motion that causes an electron to behave like a magnet. Figure 7.16 shows the two possible spinning motions of an electron, one clockwise and the other counterclockwise. To take the electron spin into account, it is necessary to introduce a fourth quantum number, called the electron spin quantum number (m_s), which has a value of $+\frac{1}{2}$ or $-\frac{1}{2}$.

Conclusive proof of electron spin was provided by Otto Stern[†] and Walther Gerlach[‡] in 1924. Figure 7.17 shows the basic experimental arrangement. A beam of gaseous atoms generated in a hot furnace passes through a nonhomogeneous magnetic field. The interaction between an electron and the magnetic field causes the atom to be deflected from its straight-line path. Because the spinning motion is completely random, the electrons in half of the atoms will be spinning in one direction, and those atoms will be deflected in one way; the electrons in the other half of the atoms will be spinning in the opposite direction, and those atoms will be deflected in the other direction. Thus, two spots of equal intensity are observed on the detecting screen.

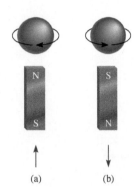

(a)   (b)

Figure 7.16 *The (a) clockwise and (b) counterclockwise spins of an electron. The magnetic fields generated by these two spinning motions are analogous to those from the two magnets. The upward and downward arrows are used to denote the direction of spin.*

In their experiment, Stern and Gerlach used silver atoms, which contain just one unpaired electron. To illustrate the principle, we can assume that hydrogen atoms are used in the study.

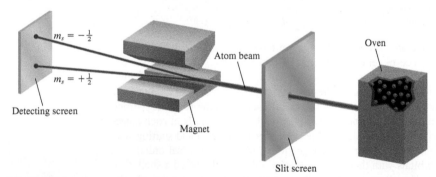

Figure 7.17 *Experimental arrangement for demonstrating the spinning motion of electrons. A beam of atoms is directed through a magnetic field. For example, when a hydrogen atom with a single electron passes through the field, it is deflected in one direction or the other, depending on the direction of the spin. In a stream consisting of many atoms, there will be equal distributions of the two kinds of spins, so that two spots of equal intensity are detected on the screen.*

Review of Concepts

Give the four quantum numbers for each of the two electrons in a 6s orbital.

[†]Otto Stern (1888–1969). German physicist. He made important contributions to the study of magnetic properties of atoms and the kinetic theory of gases. Stern was awarded the Nobel Prize in Physics in 1943.

[‡]Walther Gerlach (1889–1979). German physicist. Gerlach's main area of research was in quantum theory.

7.7 Atomic Orbitals

Table 7.2 shows the relation between quantum numbers and atomic orbitals. We see that when $\ell = 0$, $(2\ell + 1) = 1$ and there is only one value of m_ℓ, thus we have an s orbital. When $\ell = 1$, $(2\ell + 1) = 3$, so there are three values of m_ℓ or three p orbitals, labeled p_x, p_y, and p_z. When $\ell = 2$, $(2\ell + 1) = 5$ and there are five values of m_ℓ, and the corresponding five d orbitals are labeled with more elaborate subscripts. In the following sections we will consider the s, p, and d orbitals separately.

s **Orbitals.** One of the important questions we ask when studying the properties of atomic orbitals is, What are the shapes of the orbitals? Strictly speaking, an orbital does not have a well-defined shape because the wave function characterizing the orbital extends from the nucleus to infinity. In that sense, it is difficult to say what an orbital looks like. On the other hand, it is certainly convenient to think of orbitals as having specific shapes, particularly in discussing the formation of chemical bonds between atoms, as we will do in Chapters 9 and 10.

Although in principle an electron can be found anywhere, we know that most of the time it is quite close to the nucleus. Figure 7.18(a) shows the distribution

That the wave function for an orbital theoretically has no outer limit as one moves outward from the nucleus raises interesting philosophical questions regarding the sizes of atoms. Chemists have agreed on an operational definition of atomic size, as we will see in later chapters.

Table 7.2		Relation Between Quantum Numbers and Atomic Orbitals		
n	ℓ	m_ℓ	Number of Orbitals	Atomic Orbital Designations
1	0	0	1	$1s$
2	0	0	1	$2s$
	1	$-1, 0, 1$	3	$2p_x, 2p_y, 2p_z$
3	0	0	1	$3s$
	1	$-1, 0, 1$	3	$3p_x, 3p_y, 3p_z$
	2	$-2, -1, 0, 1, 2$	5	$3d_{xy}, 3d_{yz}, 3d_{xz},$ $3d_{x^2 - y^2}, 3d_{z^2}$
.	.	.	.	.
.	.	.	.	.
.	.	.	.	.

An s subshell has one orbital, a p subshell has three orbitals, and a d subshell has five orbitals.

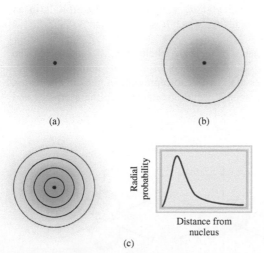

(a)   (b)

Radial probability

Distance from nucleus

(c)

Figure 7.18 *(a) Plot of electron density in the hydrogen 1s orbital as a function of the distance from the nucleus. The electron density falls off rapidly as the distance from the nucleus increases. (b) Boundary surface diagram of the hydrogen 1s orbital. (c) A more realistic way of viewing electron density distribution is to divide the 1s orbital into successive spherical thin shells. A plot of the probability of finding the electron in each shell, called radial probability, as a function of distance shows a maximum at 52.9 pm*

of electron density in a hydrogen 1s orbital moving outward from the nucleus. As you can see, the electron density falls off rapidly as the distance from the nucleus increases. Roughly speaking, there is about a 90 percent probability of finding the electron within a sphere of radius 100 pm (1 pm = 1×10^{-12} m) surrounding the nucleus. Thus, we can represent the 1s orbital by drawing a **boundary surface diagram** that *encloses about 90 percent of the total electron density in an orbital*, as shown in Figure 7.18(b). A 1s orbital represented in this manner is merely a sphere.

Figure 7.19 shows boundary surface diagrams for the 1s, 2s, and 3s hydrogen atomic orbitals. All s orbitals are spherical in shape but differ in size, which increases as the principal quantum number increases. Although the details of electron density variation within each boundary surface are lost, there is no serious disadvantage. For us the most important features of atomic orbitals are their shapes and *relative* sizes, which are adequately represented by boundary surface diagrams.

p **Orbitals.** It should be clear that the *p* orbitals start with the principal quantum number $n = 2$. If $n = 1$, then the angular momentum quantum number ℓ can assume only the value of zero; therefore, there is only a 1s orbital. As we saw earlier, when $\ell = 1$, the magnetic quantum number m_ℓ can have values of −1, 0, 1. Starting with $n = 2$ and $\ell = 1$, we therefore have three 2p orbitals: $2p_x$, $2p_y$, and $2p_z$ (Figure 7.20). The letter subscripts indicate the axes along which the orbitals are oriented. These three *p* orbitals are identical in size, shape, and energy; they differ from one another only in orientation. Note, however, that there is no simple relation between the values of m_ℓ and the *x*, *y*, and *z* directions. For our purpose, you need only remember that because there are three possible values of m_ℓ, there are three *p* orbitals with different orientations.

The boundary surface diagrams of *p* orbitals in Figure 7.20 show that each *p* orbital can be thought of as two lobes on opposite sides of the nucleus. Like *s* orbitals, *p* orbitals increase in size from 2p to 3p to 4p orbital and so on.

d **Orbitals and Other Higher-Energy Orbitals.** When $\ell = 2$, there are five values of m_ℓ, which correspond to five *d* orbitals. The lowest value of *n* for a *d* orbital is 3. Because ℓ can never be greater than $n - 1$, when $n = 3$ and $\ell = 2$, we have five 3d orbitals ($3d_{xy}$, $3d_{yz}$, $3d_{xz}$, $3d_{x^2-y^2}$, and $3d_{z^2}$), shown in Figure 7.21. As in the case of the *p* orbitals, the different orientations of the *d* orbitals correspond to the different values of m_ℓ, but again there is no direct correspondence between a given orientation and a particular m_ℓ value. All the 3d orbitals in an atom are identical in energy. The *d* orbitals for which *n* is greater than 3 (4d, 5d, . . .) have similar shapes.

Orbitals having higher energy than *d* orbitals are labeled *f*, *g*, . . . and so on. The *f* orbitals are important in accounting for the behavior of elements with atomic numbers greater than 57, but their shapes are difficult to represent. In general chemistry, we are not concerned with orbitals having ℓ values greater than 3 (the *g* orbitals and beyond).

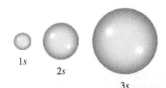

1s   2s

3s

Figure 7.19 *Boundary surface diagrams of the hydrogen 1s, 2s, and 3s orbitals. Each sphere contains about 90 percent of the total electron density. All s orbitals are spherical. Roughly speaking, the size of an orbital is proportional to n^2, where n is the principal quantum number.*

Orbitals that have the same energy are said to be degenerate orbitals.

Figure 7.20 *The boundary surface diagrams of the three 2p orbitals. These orbitals are identical in shape and energy, but their orientations are different. The p orbitals of higher principal quantum numbers have similar shapes.*

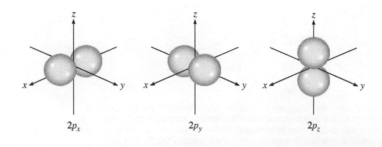

$2p_x$ $2p_y$ $2p_z$

7.7 Atomic Orbitals   303

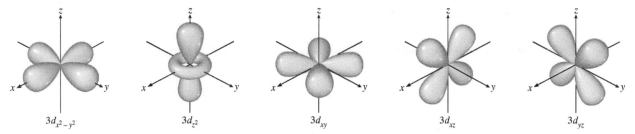

Figure 7.21 *Boundary surface diagrams of the five 3d orbitals. Although the $3d_{z^2}$ orbital looks different, it is equivalent to the other four orbitals in all other respects. The d orbitals of higher principal quantum numbers have similar shapes.*

Examples 7.7 and 7.8 illustrate the labeling of orbitals with quantum numbers and the calculation of total number of orbitals associated with a given principal quantum number.

Example 7.7

List the values of n, ℓ, and m_ℓ for orbitals in the $4d$ subshell.

Strategy What are the relationships among n, ℓ, and m_ℓ? What do "4" and "d" represent in $4d$?

Solution As we saw earlier, the number given in the designation of the subshell is the principal quantum number, so in this case $n = 4$. The letter designates the type of orbital. Because we are dealing with d orbitals, $\ell = 2$. The values of m_ℓ can vary from $-\ell$ to ℓ. Therefore, m_ℓ can be -2, -1, 0, 1, or 2.

Check The values of n and ℓ are fixed for $4d$, but m_ℓ can have any one of the five values, which correspond to the five d orbitals.

Similar problem: 7.57.

Practice Exercise Give the values of the quantum numbers associated with the orbitals in the $3p$ subshell.

Example 7.8

What is the total number of orbitals associated with the principal quantum number $n = 3$?

Strategy To calculate the total number of orbitals for a given n value, we need to first write the possible values of ℓ. We then determine how many m_ℓ values are associated with each value of ℓ. The total number of orbitals is equal to the sum of all the m_ℓ values.

Solution For $n = 3$, the possible values of ℓ are 0, 1, and 2. Thus, there is one $3s$ orbital ($n = 3$, $\ell = 0$, and $m_\ell = 0$); there are three $3p$ orbitals ($n = 3$, $\ell = 1$, and $m_\ell = -1, 0, 1$); there are five $3d$ orbitals ($n = 3$, $\ell = 2$, and $m_\ell = -2, -1, 0, 1, 2$). The total number of orbitals is $1 + 3 + 5 = 9$.

Check The total number of orbitals for a given value of n is n^2. So here we have $3^2 = 9$. Can you prove the validity of this relationship?

Similar problem: 7.62.

Practice Exercise What is the total number of orbitals associated with the principal quantum number $n = 4$?

Review of Concepts

Why is it not possible to have a $2d$ orbital but a $3d$ orbital is allowed?

304   **Chapter 7** ▪ Quantum Theory and the Electronic Structure of Atoms

The Energies of Orbitals

Now that we have some understanding of the shapes and sizes of atomic orbitals, we are ready to inquire into their relative energies and look at how energy levels affect the actual arrangement of electrons in atoms.

According to Equation (7.5), the energy of an electron in a hydrogen atom is determined solely by its principal quantum number. Thus, the energies of hydrogen orbitals increase as follows (Figure 7.22):

$$1s < 2s = 2p < 3s = 3p = 3d < 4s = 4p = 4d = 4f < \cdots$$

Although the electron density distributions are different in the $2s$ and $2p$ orbitals, hydrogen's electron has the same energy whether it is in the $2s$ orbital or a $2p$ orbital. The $1s$ orbital in a hydrogen atom corresponds to the most stable condition, the ground state. An electron residing in this orbital is most strongly held by the nucleus because it is closest to the nucleus. An electron in the $2s$, $2p$, or higher orbitals in a hydrogen atom is in an excited state.

The energy picture is more complex for many-electron atoms than for hydrogen. The energy of an electron in such an atom depends on its angular momentum quantum number as well as on its principal quantum number (Figure 7.23). For many-electron atoms, the $3d$ energy level is very close to the $4s$ energy level. The total energy of

Figure 7.22 *Orbital energy levels in the hydrogen atom. Each short horizontal line represents one orbital. Orbitals with the same principal quantum number (n) all have the same energy.*

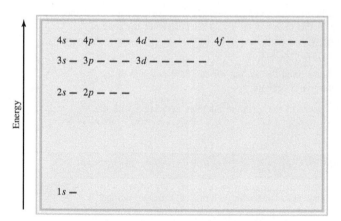

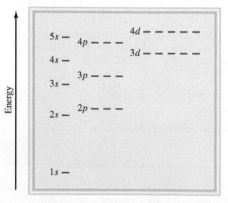

Figure 7.23 *Orbital energy levels in a many-electron atom. Note that the energy level depends on both n and ℓ values.*

an atom, however, depends not only on the sum of the orbital energies but also on the energy of repulsion between the electrons in these orbitals (each orbital can accommodate up to two electrons, as we will see in Section 7.8). It turns out that the total energy of an atom is lower when the $4s$ subshell is filled before a $3d$ subshell. Figure 7.24 depicts the order in which atomic orbitals are filled in a many-electron atom. We will consider specific examples in Section 7.8.

7.8 Electron Configuration

The four quantum numbers n, ℓ, m_ℓ, and m_s enable us to label completely an electron in any orbital in any atom. In a sense, we can regard the set of four quantum numbers as the "address" of an electron in an atom, somewhat in the same way that a street address, city, state, and postal ZIP code specify the address of an individual. For example, the four quantum numbers for a $2s$ orbital electron are $n = 2$, $\ell = 0$, $m_\ell = 0$, and $m_s = +\frac{1}{2}$ or $-\frac{1}{2}$. It is inconvenient to write out all the individual quantum numbers, and so we use the simplified notation (n, ℓ, m_ℓ, m_s). For the preceding example, the quantum numbers are either $(2, 0, 0, +\frac{1}{2})$ or $(2, 0, 0, -\frac{1}{2})$. The value of m_s has no effect on the energy, size, shape, or orientation of an orbital, but it determines how electrons are arranged in an orbital.

Example 7.9 shows how quantum numbers of an electron in an orbital are assigned.

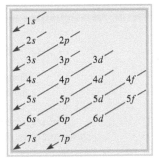

Figure 7.24 *The order in which atomic subshells are filled in a many-electron atom. Start with the 1s orbital and move downward, following the direction of the arrows. Thus, the order goes as follows: 1s < 2s < 2p < 3s < 3p < 4s < 3d < ....*

Example 7.9

Write the four quantum numbers for an electron in a $3p$ orbital.

Strategy What do the "3" and "p" designate in $3p$? How many orbitals (values of m_ℓ) are there in a $3p$ subshell? What are the possible values of electron spin quantum number?

Solution To start with, we know that the principal quantum number n is 3 and the angular momentum quantum number ℓ must be 1 (because we are dealing with a p orbital).

For $\ell = 1$, there are three values of m_ℓ given by -1, 0, and 1. Because the electron spin quantum number m_s can be either $+\frac{1}{2}$ or $-\frac{1}{2}$, we conclude that there are six possible ways to designate the electron using the (n, ℓ, m_ℓ, m_s) notation:

$$
\begin{array}{ll}
(3, 1, -1, +\tfrac{1}{2}) & (3, 1, -1, -\tfrac{1}{2}) \\
(3, 1, 0, +\tfrac{1}{2}) & (3, 1, 0, -\tfrac{1}{2}) \\
(3, 1, 1, +\tfrac{1}{2}) & (3, 1, 1, -\tfrac{1}{2})
\end{array}
$$

Check In these six designations we see that the values of n and ℓ are constant, but the values of m_ℓ and m_s can vary.

Practice Exercise Write the four quantum numbers for an electron in a $4d$ orbital.

Similar problem: 7.58.

The hydrogen atom is a particularly simple system because it contains only one electron. The electron may reside in the $1s$ orbital (the ground state), or it may be found in some higher-energy orbital (an excited state). For many-electron atoms, however, we must know the **electron configuration** of the atom, that is, *how the electrons are distributed among the various atomic orbitals,* in order to understand electronic behavior. We will use the first 10 elements (hydrogen to neon) to illustrate the rules for writing electron configurations for atoms in the *ground state.* (Section 7.9 will describe how these rules can be applied to the remainder of the elements in the periodic table.) For this discussion, recall that the number of electrons in an atom is equal to its atomic number Z.

▶▶ Animation
Electron Configurations

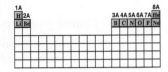

Figure 7.22 indicates that the electron in a ground-state hydrogen atom must be in the 1s orbital, so its electron configuration is $1s^1$:

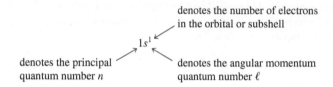

denotes the number of electrons
in the orbital or subshell

denotes the principal
quantum number n

$1s^1$

denotes the angular momentum
quantum number ℓ

The electron configuration can also be represented by an *orbital diagram* that shows the spin of the electron (see Figure 7.16):

H   ⬆
$1s^1$

The upward arrow denotes one of the two possible spinning motions of the electron. (Alternatively, we could have represented the electron with a downward arrow.) The box represents an atomic orbital.

The Pauli Exclusion Principle

For many-electron atoms we use the **Pauli[†] exclusion principle** to determine electron configurations. This principle states that *no two electrons in an atom can have the same set of four quantum numbers*. If two electrons in an atom should have the same n, ℓ, and m_ℓ values (that is, these two electrons are in the *same* atomic orbital), then they must have different values of m_s. In other words, only two electrons may occupy the same atomic orbital, and these electrons must have opposite spins. Consider the helium atom, which has two electrons. The three possible ways of placing two electrons in the 1s orbital are as follows:

He   ⬆⬆   ⬇⬇   ⬆⬇
      $1s^2$ $1s^2$ $1s^2$
      (a)   (b)   (c)

Diagrams (a) and (b) are ruled out by the Pauli exclusion principle. In (a), both electrons have the same upward spin and would have the quantum numbers $(1, 0, 0, +\frac{1}{2})$; in (b), both electrons have downward spins and would have the quantum numbers $(1, 0, 0, -\frac{1}{2})$. Only the configuration in (c) is physically acceptable, because one electron has the quantum numbers $(1, 0, 0, +\frac{1}{2})$ and the other has $(1, 0, 0, -\frac{1}{2})$. Thus, the helium atom has the following configuration:

He   ⬆⬇
$1s^2$

Note that $1s^2$ is read "one s two," not "one s squared."

Diamagnetism and Paramagnetism

The Pauli exclusion principle is one of the fundamental principles of quantum mechanics. It can be tested by a simple observation. If the two electrons in the 1s orbital of

---

[†]Wolfgang Pauli (1900–1958). Austrian physicist. One of the founders of quantum mechanics, Pauli was

7.8 Electron Configuration 307

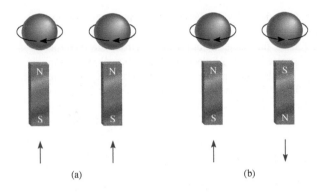

Figure 7.25 *The (a) parallel and (b) antiparallel spins of two electrons. In (a) the two magnetic fields reinforce each other. In (b) the two magnetic fields cancel each other.*

(a)   (b)

a helium atom had the same, or parallel, spins (↑↑ or ↓↓), their net magnetic fields would reinforce each other [Figure 7.25(a)]. Such an arrangement would make the helium gas paramagnetic. ***Paramagnetic*** substances are those that *contain net unpaired spins and are attracted by a magnet.* On the other hand, if the electron spins are paired, or antiparallel to each other (↑↓ or ↓↑), the magnetic effects cancel out [Figure 7.25(b)]. ***Diamagnetic*** substances *do not contain net unpaired spins and are slightly repelled by a magnet.*

Measurements of magnetic properties provide the most direct evidence for specific electron configurations of elements. Advances in instrument design during the last 30 years or so enable us to determine the number of unpaired electrons in an atom (Figure 7.26). By experiment we find that the helium atom in its ground state has no net magnetic field. Therefore, the two electrons in the $1s$ orbital must be paired in accord with the Pauli exclusion principle and the helium gas is diamagnetic. A useful rule to keep in mind is that any atom with an *odd* number of electrons will always contain one or more unpaired spins because we need an even number of electrons for complete pairing. On the other hand, atoms containing an even number of electrons may or may not contain unpaired spins. We will see the reason for this behavior shortly.

As another example, consider the lithium atom ($Z = 3$), which has three electrons. The third electron cannot go into the $1s$ orbital because it would inevitably have the same set of four quantum numbers as one of the first two electrons. Therefore, this electron "enters" the next (energetically) higher orbital, which is the $2s$ orbital (see Figure 7.23). The electron configuration of lithium is $1s^2 2s^1$, and its orbital diagram is

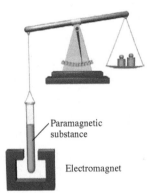

Paramagnetic substance

Electromagnet

Figure 7.26 *Initially the paramagnetic substance was weighed on a balance in the absence of a magnetic field. When the electromagnet is turned on, the balance is offset because the sample tube is drawn into the magnetic field. Knowing the concentration and the additional mass needed to reestablish balance, it is possible to calculate the number of unpaired electrons in the sample.*

Li ↑↓ ↑
   $1s^2$ $2s^1$

The lithium atom contains one unpaired electron and the lithium metal is therefore paramagnetic.

The Shielding Effect in Many-Electron Atoms

Experimentally we find that the $2s$ orbital lies at a lower energy level than the $2p$ orbital in a many-electron atom. Why? In comparing the electron configurations of $1s^2 2s^1$ and $1s^2 2p^1$, we note that, in both cases, the $1s$ orbital is filled with two electrons. Figure 7.27 shows the radial probability plots for the $1s$, $2s$, and $2p$ orbitals. Because the $2s$ and $2p$ orbitals are larger than the $1s$ orbital, an electron in either of these orbitals will spend more time away from the nucleus than an electron in the $1s$ orbital. Thus, we can speak of a $2s$ or $2p$ electron being partly "shielded" from the attractive force of the nucleus by the $1s$ electrons. The important consequence of the shielding effect is that it *reduces* the electrostatic attraction between the protons in the nucleus and the electron in the $2s$ or $2p$ orbital.

308   **Chapter 7** ▪ Quantum Theory and the Electronic Structure of Atoms

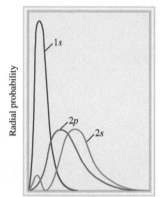

Radial probability

Distance from nucleus

Figure 7.27 *Radial probability plots (see Figure 7.18) for the 1s, 2s, and 2p orbitals. The 1s electrons effectively shield both the 2s and 2p electrons from the nucleus. The 2s orbital is more penetrating than the 2p orbital.*

The manner in which the electron density varies as we move from the nucleus outward depends on the type of orbital. Although a 2s electron spends most of its time (on average) slightly farther from the nucleus than a 2p electron, the electron density near the nucleus is actually greater for the 2s electron (see the small maximum for the 2s orbital in Figure 7.27). For this reason, the 2s orbital is said to be more "penetrating" than the 2p orbital. Therefore, a 2s electron is less shielded by the 1s electrons and is more strongly held by the nucleus. In fact, for the same principal quantum number n, the penetrating power decreases as the angular momentum quantum number ℓ increases, or

$$s > p > d > f > \cdots$$

Because the stability of an electron is determined by the strength of its attraction to the nucleus, it follows that a 2s electron will be lower in energy than a 2p electron. To put it another way, less energy is required to remove a 2p electron than a 2s electron because a 2p electron is not held quite as strongly by the nucleus. The hydrogen atom has only one electron and, therefore, is without such a shielding effect.

Continuing our discussion of atoms of the first 10 elements, we go next to beryllium ($Z = 4$). The ground-state electron configuration of beryllium is $1s^2 2s^2$, or

Be   ⇅   ⇅
      $1s^2$ $2s^2$

Beryllium is diamagnetic, as we would expect.

The electron configuration of boron ($Z = 5$) is $1s^2 2s^2 2p^1$, or

B   ⇅   ⇅   ↑
     $1s^2$ $2s^2$ $2p^1$

Note that the unpaired electron can be in the $2p_x$, $2p_y$, or $2p_z$ orbital. The choice is completely arbitrary because the three p orbitals are equivalent in energy. As the diagram shows, boron is paramagnetic.

Hund's Rule

The electron configuration of carbon ($Z = 6$) is $1s^2 2s^2 2p^2$. The following are different ways of distributing two electrons among three p orbitals:

⇅ | ↑ ↓ | ↑ ↑
$2p_x$ $2p_y$ $2p_z$ $2p_x$ $2p_y$ $2p_z$ $2p_x$ $2p_y$ $2p_z$
(a)   (b)   (c)

None of the three arrangements violates the Pauli exclusion principle, so we must determine which one will give the greatest stability. The answer is provided by **Hund's rule**,[†] which states that *the most stable arrangement of electrons in subshells is the one with the greatest number of parallel spins.* The arrangement shown in (c) satisfies this condition. In both (a) and (b) the two spins cancel each other. Thus, the orbital diagram for carbon is

C   ⇅   ⇅   ↑ ↑
     $1s^2$ $2s^2$ $2p^2$

[†]Frederick Hund (1896–1997). German physicist. Hund's work was mainly in quantum mechanics. He also helped to develop the molecular orbital theory of chemical bonding.

Qualitatively, we can understand why (c) is preferred to (a). In (a), the two electrons are in the same $2p_x$ orbital, and their proximity results in a greater mutual repulsion than when they occupy two separate orbitals, say $2p_x$ and $2p_y$. The choice of (c) over (b) is more subtle but can be justified on theoretical grounds. The fact that carbon atoms contain two unpaired electrons is in accord with Hund's rule.

The electron configuration of nitrogen ($Z = 7$) is $1s^2 2s^2 2p^3$:

N   [⇅]   [⇅]   [↑][↑][↑]
    $1s^2$ $2s^2$ $2p^3$

Again, Hund's rule dictates that all three $2p$ electrons have spins parallel to one another; the nitrogen atom contains three unpaired electrons.

The electron configuration of oxygen ($Z = 8$) is $1s^2 2s^2 2p^4$. An oxygen atom has two unpaired electrons:

O   [⇅]   [⇅]   [⇅][↑][↑]
    $1s^2$ $2s^2$ $2p^4$

The electron configuration of fluorine ($Z = 9$) is $1s^2 2s^2 2p^5$. The nine electrons are arranged as follows:

F   [⇅]   [⇅]   [⇅][⇅][↑]
    $1s^2$ $2s^2$ $2p^5$

The fluorine atom has one unpaired electron.

In neon ($Z = 10$), the $2p$ subshell is completely filled. The electron configuration of neon is $1s^2 2s^2 2p^6$, and *all* the electrons are paired, as follows:

Ne   [⇅]   [⇅]   [⇅][⇅][⇅]
     $1s^2$ $2s^2$ $2p^6$

The neon gas should be diamagnetic, and experimental observation bears out this prediction.

General Rules for Assigning Electrons to Atomic Orbitals

Based on the preceding examples we can formulate some general rules for determining the maximum number of electrons that can be assigned to the various subshells and orbitals for a given value of n:

1. Each shell or principal level of quantum number n contains n subshells. For example, if $n = 2$, then there are two subshells (two values of ℓ) of angular momentum quantum numbers 0 and 1.

2. Each subshell of quantum number ℓ contains $(2\ell + 1)$ orbitals. For example, if $\ell = 1$, then there are three p orbitals.

3. No more than two electrons can be placed in each orbital. Therefore, the maximum number of electrons is simply twice the number of orbitals that are employed.

4. A quick way to determine the maximum number of electrons that an atom can have in a principal level n is to use the formula $2n^2$.

Examples 7.10 and 7.11 illustrate the procedure for calculating the number of electrons in orbitals and labeling electrons with the four quantum numbers.

Example 7.10

What is the maximum number of electrons that can be present in the principal level for which $n = 3$?

Strategy We are given the principal quantum number (n) so we can determine all the possible values of the angular momentum quantum number (ℓ). The preceding rule shows that the number of orbitals for each value of ℓ is ($2\ell + 1$). Thus, we can determine the total number of orbitals. How many electrons can each orbital accommodate?

Solution When $n = 3$, $\ell = 0, 1,$ and 2. The number of orbitals for each value of ℓ is given by

Value of ℓ	Number of Orbitals ($2\ell + 1$)
0	1
1	3
2	5

The total number of orbitals is nine. Because each orbital can accommodate two electrons, the maximum number of electrons that can reside in the orbitals is 2×9, or 18.

Check If we use the formula (n^2) in Example 7.8, we find that the total number of orbitals is 3^2 and the total number of electrons is $2(3^2)$ or 18. In general, the number of electrons in a given principal energy level n is $2n^2$.

Similar problems: 7.64, 7.65.

Practice Exercise Calculate the total number of electrons that can be present in the principal level for which $n = 4$.

Example 7.11

An oxygen atom has a total of eight electrons. Write the four quantum numbers for each of the eight electrons in the ground state.

Strategy We start with $n = 1$ and proceed to fill orbitals in the order shown in Figure 7.24. For each value of n we determine the possible values of ℓ. For each value of ℓ, we assign the possible values of m_ℓ. We can place electrons in the orbitals according to the Pauli exclusion principle and Hund's rule.

Solution We start with $n = 1$, so $\ell = 0$, a subshell corresponding to the $1s$ orbital. This orbital can accommodate a total of two electrons. Next, $n = 2$, and ℓ may be either 0 or 1. The $\ell = 0$ subshell contains one $2s$ orbital, which can accommodate two electrons. The remaining four electrons are placed in the $\ell = 1$ subshell, which contains three $2p$ orbitals. The orbital diagram is

$$\text{O} \quad \boxed{\uparrow\downarrow} \quad \boxed{\uparrow\downarrow} \quad \boxed{\uparrow\downarrow\,|\,\uparrow\,|\,\uparrow}$$
$$\phantom{\text{O} \quad} 1s^2 \qquad 2s^2 \qquad 2p^4$$

The results are summarized in the following table:

Electron	n	ℓ	m_ℓ	m_s	Orbital
1	1	0	0	$+\frac{1}{2}$	$1s$
2	1	0	0	$-\frac{1}{2}$	$1s$
3	2	0	0	$+\frac{1}{2}$	$2s$
4	2	0	0	$-\frac{1}{2}$	$2s$
5	2	1	-1	$+\frac{1}{2}$	
6	2	1	0	$+\frac{1}{2}$	$2p_x, 2p_y, 2p_z$
7	2	1	1	$+\frac{1}{2}$	
8	2	1	1	$-\frac{1}{2}$	

Of course, the placement of the eighth electron in the orbital labeled $m_\ell = 1$ is completely arbitrary. It would be equally correct to assign it to $m_\ell = 0$ or $m_\ell = -1$.

Similar problem: 7.91.

Practice Exercise Write a complete set of quantum numbers for each of the electrons

At this point let's summarize what our examination of the first 10 elements has revealed about ground-state electron configurations and the properties of electrons in atoms:

1. No two electrons in the same atom can have the same four quantum numbers. This is the Pauli exclusion principle.

2. Each orbital can be occupied by a maximum of two electrons. They must have opposite spins, or different electron spin quantum numbers.

3. The most stable arrangement of electrons in a subshell is the one that has the greatest number of parallel spins. This is Hund's rule.

4. Atoms in which one or more electrons are unpaired are paramagnetic. Atoms in which all the electron spins are paired are diamagnetic.

5. In a hydrogen atom, the energy of the electron depends only on its principal quantum number n. In a many-electron atom, the energy of an electron depends on both n and its angular momentum quantum number ℓ.

6. In a many-electron atom the subshells are filled in the order shown in Figure 7.24.

7. For electrons of the same principal quantum number, their penetrating power, or proximity to the nucleus, decreases in the order $s > p > d > f$. This means that, for example, more energy is required to separate a $3s$ electron from a many-electron atom than is required to remove a $3p$ electron.

Review of Concepts

The ground-state electron configuration of an atom is $1s^2 2s^2 2p^6 3s^2 3p^3$. Which of the four quantum numbers would be the same for the three $3p$ electrons?

7.9 The Building-Up Principle

Here we will extend the rules used in writing electron configurations for the first 10 elements to the rest of the elements. This process is based on the Aufbau principle. The **Aufbau principle** dictates that *as protons are added one by one to the nucleus to build up the elements, electrons are similarly added to the atomic orbitals.* Through this process we gain a detailed knowledge of the ground-state electron configurations of the elements. As we will see later, knowledge of electron configurations helps us to understand and predict the properties of the elements; it also explains why the periodic table works so well.

The German word "Aufbau" means "building up."

Table 7.3 gives the ground-state electron configurations of elements from H ($Z = 1$) through the named elements up to Lv ($Z = 116$). The electron configurations of all elements except hydrogen and helium are represented by a **noble gas core**, which *shows in brackets the noble gas element that most nearly precedes the element being considered,* followed by the symbol for the highest filled subshells in the outermost shells. Notice that the electron configurations of the highest filled subshells in the outermost shells for the elements sodium ($Z = 11$) through argon ($Z = 18$) follow a pattern similar to those of lithium ($Z = 3$) through neon ($Z = 10$).

As mentioned in Section 7.7, the $4s$ subshell is filled before the $3d$ subshell in a many-electron atom (see Figure 7.24). Thus, the electron configuration of potassium ($Z = 19$) is $1s^2 2s^2 2p^6 3s^2 3p^6 4s^1$. Because $1s^2 2s^2 2p^6 3s^2 3p^6$ is the electron configuration of argon, we can simplify the electron configuration of potassium by writing [Ar]$4s^1$, where [Ar] denotes the "argon core." Similarly, we can write the electron configuration of calcium ($Z = 20$) as [Ar]$4s^2$. The placement of the outermost

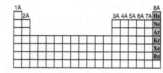

The noble gases.

312   **Chapter 7** ▪ Quantum Theory and the Electronic Structure of Atoms

| Table 7.3 | The Ground-State Electron Configurations of the Elements* | | | | | | | |

Atomic Number	Symbol	Electron Configuration	Atomic Number	Symbol	Electron Configuration	Atomic Number	Symbol	Electron Configuration
1	H	$1s^1$	39	Y	$[Kr]5s^24d^1$	77	Ir	$[Xe]6s^24f^{14}5d^7$
2	He	$1s^2$	40	Zr	$[Kr]5s^24d^2$	78	Pt	$[Xe]6s^14f^{14}5d^9$
3	Li	$[He]2s^1$	41	Nb	$[Kr]5s^14d^4$	79	Au	$[Xe]6s^14f^{14}5d^{10}$
4	Be	$[He]2s^2$	42	Mo	$[Kr]5s^14d^5$	80	Hg	$[Xe]6s^24f^{14}5d^{10}$
5	B	$[He]2s^22p^1$	43	Tc	$[Kr]5s^24d^5$	81	Tl	$[Xe]6s^24f^{14}5d^{10}6p^1$
6	C	$[He]2s^22p^2$	44	Ru	$[Kr]5s^14d^7$	82	Pb	$[Xe]6s^24f^{14}5d^{10}6p^2$
7	N	$[He]2s^22p^3$	45	Rh	$[Kr]5s^14d^8$	83	Bi	$[Xe]6s^24f^{14}5d^{10}6p^3$
8	O	$[He]2s^22p^4$	46	Pd	$[Kr]4d^{10}$	84	Po	$[Xe]6s^24f^{14}5d^{10}6p^4$
9	F	$[He]2s^22p^5$	47	Ag	$[Kr]5s^14d^{10}$	85	At	$[Xe]6s^24f^{14}5d^{10}6p^5$
10	Ne	$[He]2s^22p^6$	48	Cd	$[Kr]5s^24d^{10}$	86	Rn	$[Xe]6s^24f^{14}5d^{10}6p^6$
11	Na	$[Ne]3s^1$	49	In	$[Kr]5s^24d^{10}5p^1$	87	Fr	$[Rn]7s^1$
12	Mg	$[Ne]3s^2$	50	Sn	$[Kr]5s^24d^{10}5p^2$	88	Ra	$[Rn]7s^2$
13	Al	$[Ne]3s^23p^1$	51	Sb	$[Kr]5s^24d^{10}5p^3$	89	Ac	$[Rn]7s^26d^1$
14	Si	$[Ne]3s^23p^2$	52	Te	$[Kr]5s^24d^{10}5p^4$	90	Th	$[Rn]7s^26d^2$
15	P	$[Ne]3s^23p^3$	53	I	$[Kr]5s^24d^{10}5p^5$	91	Pa	$[Rn]7s^25f^26d^1$
16	S	$[Ne]3s^23p^4$	54	Xe	$[Kr]5s^24d^{10}5p^6$	92	U	$[Rn]7s^25f^36d^1$
17	Cl	$[Ne]3s^23p^5$	55	Cs	$[Xe]6s^1$	93	Np	$[Rn]7s^25f^46d^1$
18	Ar	$[Ne]3s^23p^6$	56	Ba	$[Xe]6s^2$	94	Pu	$[Rn]7s^25f^6$
19	K	$[Ar]4s^1$	57	La	$[Xe]6s^25d^1$	95	Am	$[Rn]7s^25f^7$
20	Ca	$[Ar]4s^2$	58	Ce	$[Xe]6s^24f^15d^1$	96	Cm	$[Rn]7s^25f^76d^1$
21	Sc	$[Ar]4s^23d^1$	59	Pr	$[Xe]6s^24f^3$	97	Bk	$[Rn]7s^25f^9$
22	Ti	$[Ar]4s^23d^2$	60	Nd	$[Xe]6s^24f^4$	98	Cf	$[Rn]7s^25f^{10}$
23	V	$[Ar]4s^23d^3$	61	Pm	$[Xe]6s^24f^5$	99	Es	$[Rn]7s^25f^{11}$
24	Cr	$[Ar]4s^13d^5$	62	Sm	$[Xe]6s^24f^6$	100	Fm	$[Rn]7s^25f^{12}$
25	Mn	$[Ar]4s^23d^5$	63	Eu	$[Xe]6s^24f^7$	101	Md	$[Rn]7s^25f^{13}$
26	Fe	$[Ar]4s^23d^6$	64	Gd	$[Xe]6s^24f^75d^1$	102	No	$[Rn]7s^25f^{14}$
27	Co	$[Ar]4s^23d^7$	65	Tb	$[Xe]6s^24f^9$	103	Lr	$[Rn]7s^25f^{14}6d^1$
28	Ni	$[Ar]4s^23d^8$	66	Dy	$[Xe]6s^24f^{10}$	104	Rf	$[Rn]7s^25f^{14}6d^2$
29	Cu	$[Ar]4s^13d^{10}$	67	Ho	$[Xe]6s^24f^{11}$	105	Db	$[Rn]7s^25f^{14}6d^3$
30	Zn	$[Ar]4s^23d^{10}$	68	Er	$[Xe]6s^24f^{12}$	106	Sg	$[Rn]7s^25f^{14}6d^4$
31	Ga	$[Ar]4s^23d^{10}4p^1$	69	Tm	$[Xe]6s^24f^{13}$	107	Bh	$[Rn]7s^25f^{14}6d^5$
32	Ge	$[Ar]4s^23d^{10}4p^2$	70	Yb	$[Xe]6s^24f^{14}$	108	Hs	$[Rn]7s^25f^{14}6d^6$
33	As	$[Ar]4s^23d^{10}4p^3$	71	Lu	$[Xe]6s^24f^{14}5d^1$	109	Mt	$[Rn]7s^25f^{14}6d^7$
34	Se	$[Ar]4s^23d^{10}4p^4$	72	Hf	$[Xe]6s^24f^{14}5d^2$	110	Ds	$[Rn]7s^25f^{14}6d^8$
35	Br	$[Ar]4s^23d^{10}4p^5$	73	Ta	$[Xe]6s^24f^{14}5d^3$	111	Rg	$[Rn]7s^25f^{14}6d^9$
36	Kr	$[Ar]4s^23d^{10}4p^6$	74	W	$[Xe]6s^24f^{14}5d^4$	112	Cn	$[Rn]7s^25f^{14}6d^{10}$
37	Rb	$[Kr]5s^1$	75	Re	$[Xe]6s^24f^{14}5d^5$	114	Fl	$[Rn]7s^25f^{14}6d^{10}7p^2$
38	Sr	$[Kr]5s^2$	76	Os	$[Xe]6s^24f^{14}5d^6$	116	Lv	$[Rn]7s^25f^{14}6d^{10}7p^4$

*The symbol [He] is called the helium core and represents $1s^2$. [Ne] is called the neon core and represents $1s^22s^22p^6$. [Ar] is called the argon core and represents [Ne]$3s^23p^6$. [Kr] is called the krypton core and represents [Ar]$4s^23d^{10}4p^6$. [Xe] is called the xenon core and represents [Kr]$5s^24d^{10}5p^6$. [Rn] is called the radon core and represents [Xe]$6s^24f^{14}5d^{10}6p^6$.

electron in the 4s orbital (rather than in the 3d orbital) of potassium is strongly supported by experimental evidence. The following comparison also suggests that this is the correct configuration. The chemistry of potassium is very similar to that of lithium and sodium, the first two alkali metals. The outermost electron of both lithium and sodium is in an s orbital (there is no ambiguity in assigning their electron configurations); therefore, we expect the last electron in potassium to occupy the 4s rather than the 3d orbital.

The elements from scandium ($Z = 21$) to copper ($Z = 29$) are transition metals. **Transition metals** either *have incompletely filled d subshells or readily give rise to cations that have incompletely filled d subshells.* Consider the first transition metal series, from scandium through copper. In this series additional electrons are placed in the 3d orbitals, according to Hund's rule. However, there are two irregularities. The electron configuration of chromium ($Z = 24$) is $[Ar]4s^1 3d^5$ and not $[Ar]4s^2 3d^4$, as we might expect. A similar break in the pattern is observed for copper, whose electron configuration is $[Ar]4s^1 3d^{10}$ rather than $[Ar]4s^2 3d^9$. The reason for these irregularities is that a slightly greater stability is associated with the half-filled ($3d^5$) and completely filled ($3d^{10}$) subshells. Electrons in the same subshell (in this case, the d orbitals) have equal energy but different spatial distributions. Consequently, their shielding of one another is relatively small, and the electrons are more strongly attracted by the nucleus when they have the $3d^5$ configuration. According to Hund's rule, the orbital diagram for Cr is

The transition metals.

Thus, Cr has a total of six unpaired electrons. The orbital diagram for copper is

Cu [Ar]   ↑   ↑↓ ↑↓ ↑↓ ↑↓ ↑↓
          $4s^1$ $3d^{10}$

Again, extra stability is gained in this case by having the 3d subshell completely filled. In general, half-filled and completely filled subshells have extra stability.

For elements Zn ($Z = 30$) through Kr ($Z = 36$), the 4s and 4p subshells fill in a straightforward manner. With rubidium ($Z = 37$), electrons begin to enter the $n = 5$ energy level.

The electron configurations in the second transition metal series [yttrium ($Z = 39$) to silver ($Z = 47$)] are also irregular, but we will not be concerned with the details here.

The sixth period of the periodic table begins with cesium ($Z = 55$) and barium ($Z = 56$), whose electron configurations are $[Xe]6s^1$ and $[Xe]6s^2$, respectively. Next we come to lanthanum ($Z = 57$). From Figure 7.24 we would expect that after filling the 6s orbital we would place the additional electrons in 4f orbitals. In reality, the energies of the 5d and 4f orbitals are very close; in fact, for lanthanum 4f is slightly higher in energy than 5d. Thus, lanthanum's electron configuration is $[Xe]6s^2 5d^1$ and not $[Xe]6s^2 4f^1$.

Following lanthanum are the 14 elements known as the **lanthanides,** or *rare earth series* [cerium ($Z = 58$) to lutetium ($Z = 71$)]. The rare earth metals *have incompletely filled 4f subshells or readily give rise to cations that have incompletely filled 4f subshells.* In this series, the added electrons are placed in 4f orbitals. After the 4f subshell is completely filled, the next electron enters the 5d subshell of lutetium. Note that the electron configuration of gadolinium ($Z = 64$) is $[Xe]6s^2 4f^7 5d^1$ rather than $[Xe]6s^2 4f^8$. Like chromium, gadolinium gains extra stability by having a half-filled subshell ($4f^7$).

CHEMISTRY *in Action*

Quantum Dots

We normally consider the color of a chemical substance to be an intensive property (p. 11) because the color does not depend on the amount of that substance that is being considered. As we are learning in this chapter, however, the "normal" behavior of matter is much harder to define as we enter the quantum world of the very small.

Quantum dots are tiny pieces of matter, typically on the order of a few nanometers in diameter, composed of a metal or a semiconductor (see Section 21.3 for a description of semiconductors). By confining the electrons to such a small volume, the allowed energies of these electrons are quantized. Therefore, if quantum dots are excited to higher energy, only certain wavelengths of light are emitted when the electrons go back to their ground states, just as in the case of the emission spectra of atoms. But unlike atoms, the energy of light omitted from a quantum dot can be "tuned"

Emission from dispersed solutions of CdSe quantum dots arranged from left to right in order of increasing diameter (2 nm to 7 nm).

The third transition metal series, including lanthanum and hafnium ($Z = 72$) and extending through gold ($Z = 79$), is characterized by the filling of the $5d$ subshell. With Hg ($Z = 80$), both the $6s$ and $5d$ orbitals are now filled. The $6p$ subshell is filled next, which takes us to radon ($Z = 86$).

The *last row of elements* is the ***actinide series,*** which starts at thorium ($Z = 90$). *Most of these elements are not found in nature but have been synthesized.*

With few exceptions, you should be able to write the electron configuration of any element, using Figure 7.24 as a guide. Elements that require particular care are the transition metals, the lanthanides, and the actinides. As we noted earlier, at larger values of the principal quantum number n, the order of subshell filling may reverse from one element to the next. Figure 7.28 groups the elements according to the type of subshell in which the outermost electrons are placed.

by varying the size of the quantum dot because that changes the volume within which the electrons are confined. This phenomenon is due to the wavelike behavior of electrons and is analogous to changing the pitch (frequency) of the sound made by plucking a guitar string (see Figure 7.12) by pressing against the neck of the instrument, effectively shortening the string. The ability to regulate the energy of light emitted by a quantum dot is quite remarkable, enabling one to generate the visible spectrum using a single chemical substance by simply varying the diameter of the quantum dots over a range of a few nanometers.

Besides illustrating the quantum behavior of matter and enabling that behavior to be studied on the nanometer scale (as opposed to on a picometer scale at the atomic level), quantum dots offer great promise for yielding important applications in the fields of technology and medicine. Like bulk semiconducting materials, quantum dots can be made to function as LEDs (light emitting diodes), but unlike these bulk materials, quantum dots emit light symmetrically in very narrow ranges. By combining three quantum dots that emit light of appropriate colors, it is possible to create devices that produce white light at much lower energy costs than required for incandescent bulbs or even fluorescent bulbs, which carry an additional environmental concern because they contain mercury. Quantum dots can also be used to label biological tissue. Besides offering the advantage of greater stability over traditional biological dyes, the surface of quantum dots can be chemically modified to target certain cells such as cancer cells. In addition to enabling tumors to be imaged, these modified quantum dots have the

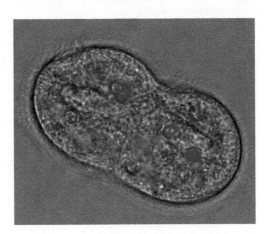

A light micrograph showing the fluorescence of quantum dots in a protozoan, used to study the movement of nanoparticles through the food chain and their potential for accumulation by way of bioconcentration.

added potential to act therapeutically, either by being incorporated into the more permeable cancer cells and destroying those cells, or by attaching a known antitumor agent to the quantum dot. Other potential applications for quantum dots include quantum computing and photovoltaic cells for harvesting solar energy.

1s			
2s			2p
3s			3p
4s	3d		4p
5s	4d		5p
6s	5d		6p
7s	6d		7p

4f
5f

Figure 7.28 *Classification of groups of elements in the periodic table according to the type of subshell being filled with electrons.*

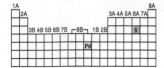

Example 7.12

Write the ground-state electron configurations for (a) sulfur (S) and (b) palladium (Pd), which is diamagnetic.

(a) Strategy How many electrons are in the S ($Z = 16$) atom? We start with $n = 1$ and proceed to fill orbitals in the order shown in Figure 7.24. For each value of ℓ, we assign the possible values of m_ℓ. We can place electrons in the orbitals according to the Pauli exclusion principle and Hund's rule and then write the electron configuration. The task is simplified if we use the noble gas core preceding S for the inner electrons.

Solution Sulfur has 16 electrons. The noble gas core in this case is [Ne]. (Ne is the noble gas in the period preceding sulfur.) [Ne] represents $1s^2 2s^2 2p^6$. This leaves us 6 electrons to fill the $3s$ subshell and partially fill the $3p$ subshell. Thus, the electron configuration of S is $1s^2 2s^2 2p^6 3s^2 3p^4$ or $[Ne]3s^2 3p^4$.

(b) Strategy We use the same approach as that in (a). What does it mean to say that Pd is a diamagnetic element?

Solution Palladium has 46 electrons. The noble gas core in this case is [Kr]. (Kr is the noble gas in the period preceding palladium.) [Kr] represents

$$1s^2 2s^2 2p^6 3s^2 3p^6 4s^2 3d^{10} 4p^6$$

The remaining 10 electrons are distributed among the $4d$ and $5s$ orbitals. The three choices are (1) $4d^{10}$, (2) $4d^9 5s^1$, and (3) $4d^8 5s^2$. Because palladium is diamagnetic, all the electrons are paired and its electron configuration must be

$$1s^2 2s^2 2p^6 3s^2 3p^6 4s^2 3d^{10} 4p^6 4d^{10}$$

or simply $[Kr]4d^{10}$. The configurations in (2) and (3) both represent paramagnetic elements.

Check To confirm the answer, write the orbital diagrams for (1), (2), and (3).

Practice Exercise Write the ground-state electron configuration for phosphorus (P).

Similar problems: 7.87, 7.88.

Review of Concepts

Identify the atom that has the following ground-state electron configuration: $[Ar]4s^2 3d^6$

Key Equations

$u = \lambda\nu$ (7.1)	Relating speed of a wave to its wavelength and frequency.
$E = h\nu$ (7.2)	Relating energy of a quantum (and of a photon) to the frequency.
$E = h\dfrac{c}{\lambda}$ (7.3)	Relating energy of a quantum (and of a photon) to the wavelength.
$h\nu = KE + W$ (7.4)	The photoelectric effect.
$E_n = -R_H\left(\dfrac{1}{n^2}\right)$ (7.5)	Energy of an electron in the nth state in a hydrogen atom.
$\Delta E = h\nu = R_H\left(\dfrac{1}{n_i^2} - \dfrac{1}{n_f^2}\right)$ (7.6)	Energy of a photon absorbed or emitted as the electron undergoes a transition from the n_i level to the n_f level.
$\lambda = \dfrac{h}{mu}$ (7.8)	Relating wavelength of a particle to its mass m and velocity u.
$\Delta x\Delta p \geq \dfrac{h}{4\pi}$ (7.9)	Calculating the uncertainty in the position or in the momentum of a particle.

Summary of Facts & Concepts

1. The quantum theory developed by Planck successfully explains the emission of radiation by heated solids. The quantum theory states that radiant energy is emitted by atoms and molecules in small discrete amounts (quanta), rather than over a continuous range. This behavior is governed by the relationship $E = h\nu$, where E is the energy of the radiation, h is Planck's constant, and ν is the frequency of the radiation. Energy is always emitted in whole-number multiples of $h\nu$ ($1\ h\nu$, $2\ h\nu$, $3\ h\nu$, . . .).

2. Using quantum theory, Einstein solved another mystery of physics—the photoelectric effect. Einstein proposed that light can behave like a stream of particles (photons).

3. The line spectrum of hydrogen, yet another mystery to nineteenth-century physicists, was also explained by applying the quantum theory. Bohr developed a model of the hydrogen atom in which the energy of its single electron is quantized—limited to certain energy values determined by an integer, the principal quantum number.

4. An electron in its most stable energy state is said to be in the ground state, and an electron at an energy level higher than its most stable state is said to be in an excited state. In the Bohr model, an electron emits a photon when it drops from a higher-energy state (an excited state) to a lower-energy state (the ground state or another, less excited state). The release of specific amounts of energy in the form of photons accounts for the lines in the hydrogen emission spectrum.

5. De Broglie extended Einstein's wave-particle description of light to all matter in motion. The wavelength of a moving particle of mass m and velocity u is given by the de Broglie equation $\lambda = h/mu$.

6. The Schrödinger equation describes the motions and energies of submicroscopic particles. This equation launched quantum mechanics and a new era in physics.

7. The Schrödinger equation tells us the possible energy states of the electron in a hydrogen atom and the probability of its location in a particular region surrounding the nucleus. These results can be applied with reasonable accuracy to many-electron atoms.

8. An atomic orbital is a function (Ψ) that defines the distribution of electron density (Ψ^2) in space. Orbitals are represented by electron density diagrams or boundary surface diagrams.

9. Four quantum numbers characterize each electron in an atom: the principal quantum number n identifies the main energy level, or shell, of the orbital; the angular momentum quantum number ℓ indicates the shape of the orbital; the magnetic quantum number m_ℓ specifies the orientation of the orbital in space; and the electron spin quantum number m_s indicates the direction of the electron's spin on its own axis.

10. The single s orbital for each energy level is spherical and centered on the nucleus. The three p orbitals present at $n = 2$ and higher; each has two lobes, and the pairs of lobes are arranged at right angles to one another. Starting with $n = 3$, there are five d orbitals, with more complex shapes and orientations.

11. The energy of the electron in a hydrogen atom is determined solely by its principal quantum number. In many-electron atoms, the principal quantum number and the angular momentum quantum number together determine the energy of an electron.

12. No two electrons in the same atom can have the same four quantum numbers (the Pauli exclusion principle).

13. The most stable arrangement of electrons in a subshell is the one that has the greatest number of parallel spins (Hund's rule). Atoms with one or more unpaired electron spins are paramagnetic. Atoms in which all electrons are paired are diamagnetic.

14. The Aufbau principle provides the guideline for building up the elements. The periodic table classifies the elements according to their atomic numbers and thus also by the electronic configurations of their atoms.

Key Words

318   Chapter 7 ▪ Quantum Theory and the Electronic Structure of Atoms

Questions & Problems

Quantum Theory and Electromagnetic Radiation
Review Questions

7.1   What is a wave? Explain the following terms associated with waves: wavelength, frequency, amplitude.

7.2   What are the units for wavelength and frequency of electromagnetic waves? What is the speed of light in meters per second and miles per hour?

7.3   List the types of electromagnetic radiation, starting with the radiation having the longest wavelength and ending with the radiation having the shortest wavelength.

7.4   Give the high and low wavelength values that define the visible region of the electromagnetic spectrum.

7.5   Briefly explain Planck's quantum theory and explain what a quantum is. What are the units for Planck's constant?

7.6   Give two everyday examples that illustrate the concept of quantization.

Problems

● 7.7   (a) What is the wavelength (in nanometers) of light having a frequency of 8.6×10^{13} Hz? (b) What is the frequency (in Hz) of light having a wavelength of 566 nm?

● **7.8**   (a) What is the frequency of light having a wavelength of 456 nm? (b) What is the wavelength (in nanometers) of radiation having a frequency of 2.45×10^{9} Hz? (This is the type of radiation used in microwave ovens.)

● 7.9   The average distance between Mars and Earth is about 1.3×10^{8} miles. How long would it take TV pictures transmitted from the *Viking* space vehicle on Mars' surface to reach Earth? (1 mile = 1.61 km.)

7.10   How many minutes would it take a radio wave to travel from the planet Venus to Earth? (Average distance from Venus to Earth is 28 million miles.)

● 7.11   The SI unit of time is the second, which is defined as 9,192,631,770 cycles of radiation associated with a certain emission process in the cesium atom. Calculate the wavelength of this radiation (to three significant figures). In which region of the electromagnetic spectrum is this wavelength found?

7.12   The SI unit of length is the meter, which is defined as the length equal to 1,650,763.73 wavelengths of the light emitted by a particular energy transition in krypton atoms. Calculate the frequency of the light to three significant figures.

The Photoelectric Effect
Review Questions

7.13   What are photons? What role did Einstein's explanation of the photoelectric effect play in the development of the particle-wave interpretation of the nature of electromagnetic radiation?

7.14   Consider the plots shown here for the photoelectric effect of two different metals A (green line) and B (red line). (a) Which metal has a greater work function? (b) What does the slope of the lines tell us?

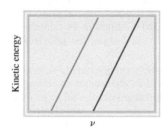

Problems

● 7.15   A photon has a wavelength of 624 nm. Calculate the energy of the photon in joules.

● **7.16**   The blue color of the sky results from the scattering of sunlight by air molecules. The blue light has a frequency of about 7.5×10^{14} Hz. (a) Calculate the wavelength, in nm, associated with this radiation, and (b) calculate the energy, in joules, of a single photon associated with this frequency.

● 7.17   A photon has a frequency of 6.0×10^{4} Hz. (a) Convert this frequency into wavelength (nm). Does this frequency fall in the visible region? (b) Calculate the energy (in joules) of this photon. (c) Calculate the energy (in joules) of 1 mole of photons all with this frequency.

7.18   What is the wavelength, in nm, of radiation that has an energy content of 1.0×10^{3} kJ/mol? In which region of the electromagnetic spectrum is this radiation found?

● 7.19   When copper is bombarded with high-energy electrons, X rays are emitted. Calculate the energy (in joules) associated with the photons if the wavelength of the X rays is 0.154 nm.

7.20 A particular form of electromagnetic radiation has a frequency of 8.11×10^{14} Hz. (a) What is its wavelength in nanometers? In meters? (b) To what region of the electromagnetic spectrum would you assign it? (c) What is the energy (in joules) of one quantum of this radiation?

7.21 The work function of potassium is 3.68×10^{-19} J. (a) What is the minimum frequency of light needed to eject electrons from the metal? (b) Calculate the kinetic energy of the ejected electrons when light of frequency equal to 8.62×10^{14} s^{-1} is used for irradiation.

7.22 When light of frequency equal to 2.11×10^{15} s^{-1} shines on the surface of gold metal, the kinetic energy of ejected electrons is found to be 5.83×10^{-19} J. What is the work function of gold?

Bohr's Theory of the Hydrogen Atom
Review Questions

7.23 (a) What is an energy level? Explain the difference between ground state and excited state. (b) What are emission spectra? How do line spectra differ from continuous spectra?

7.24 (a) Briefly describe Bohr's theory of the hydrogen atom and how it explains the appearance of an emission spectrum. How does Bohr's theory differ from concepts of classical physics? (b) Explain the meaning of the negative sign in Equation (7.5).

Problems

7.25 Explain why elements produce their own characteristic colors when they emit photons?

7.26 Some copper compounds emit green light when they are heated in a flame. How would you determine whether the light is of one wavelength or a mixture of two or more wavelengths?

7.27 Is it possible for a fluorescent material to emit radiation in the ultraviolet region after absorbing visible light? Explain your answer.

7.28 Explain how astronomers are able to tell which elements are present in distant stars by analyzing the electromagnetic radiation emitted by the stars.

7.29 Consider the following energy levels of a hypothetical atom:

E_4 _____ -1.0×10^{-19} J
E_3 _____ -5.0×10^{-19} J
E_2 _____ -10×10^{-19} J
E_1 _____ -15×10^{-19} J

(a) What is the wavelength of the photon needed to excite an electron from E_1 to E_4? (b) What is the energy (in joules) a photon must have in order to excite an electron from E_2 to E_3? (c) When an electron drops from the E_3 level to the E_1 level, the atom is said to undergo emission. Calculate the wavelength of the photon emitted in this process.

7.30 The first line of the Balmer series occurs at a wavelength of 656.3 nm. What is the energy difference between the two energy levels involved in the emission that results in this spectral line?

7.31 Calculate the wavelength (in nanometers) of a photon emitted by a hydrogen atom when its electron drops from the $n = 5$ state to the $n = 3$ state.

7.32 Calculate the frequency (Hz) and wavelength (nm) of the emitted photon when an electron drops from the $n = 4$ to the $n = 2$ level in a hydrogen atom.

7.33 Careful spectral analysis shows that the familiar yellow light of sodium lamps (such as street lamps) is made up of photons of two wavelengths, 589.0 nm and 589.6 nm. What is the difference in energy (in joules) between photons with these wavelengths?

7.34 An electron in the hydrogen atom makes a transition from an energy state of principal quantum numbers n_i to the $n = 2$ state. If the photon emitted has a wavelength of 434 nm, what is the value of n_i?

Particle-Wave Duality
Review Questions

7.35 Explain the statement, Matter and radiation have a "dual nature."

7.36 How does de Broglie's hypothesis account for the fact that the energies of the electron in a hydrogen atom are quantized?

7.37 Why is Equation (7.8) meaningful only for submicroscopic particles, such as electrons and atoms, and not for macroscopic objects?

7.38 (a) If a H atom and a He atom are traveling at the same speed, what will be the relative wavelengths of the two atoms? (b) If a H atom and a He atom have the same kinetic energy, what will be the relative wavelengths of the two atoms?

Problems

7.39 Thermal neutrons are neutrons that move at speeds comparable to those of air molecules at room temperature. These neutrons are most effective in initiating a nuclear chain reaction among ^{235}U isotopes. Calculate the wavelength (in nm) associated with a beam of neutrons moving at 7.00×10^2 m/s. (Mass of a neutron = 1.675×10^{-27} kg.)

7.40 Protons can be accelerated to speeds near that of light in particle accelerators. Estimate the wavelength (in nm) of such a proton moving at 2.90×10^8 m/s. (Mass of a proton = 1.673×10^{-27} kg.)

● 7.41 What is the de Broglie wavelength, in cm, of a 12.4-g hummingbird flying at 1.20×10^2 mph? (1 mile = 1.61 km.)

● 7.42 What is the de Broglie wavelength (in nm) associated with a 2.5-g Ping-Pong ball traveling 35 mph?

Quantum Mechanics
Review Questions

7.43 What are the inadequacies of Bohr's theory?

7.44 What is the Heisenberg uncertainty principle? What is the Schrödinger equation?

7.45 What is the physical significance of the wave function?

7.46 How is the concept of electron density used to describe the position of an electron in the quantum mechanical treatment of an atom?

Atomic Orbitals
Review Questions

7.47 What is an atomic orbital? How does an atomic orbital differ from an orbit?

7.48 Describe the shapes of s, p, and d orbitals. How are these orbitals related to the quantum numbers n, ℓ, and m_ℓ?

7.49 List the hydrogen orbitals in increasing order of energy.

7.50 Describe the characteristics of an s orbital, a p orbital, and a d orbital. Which of the following orbitals do not exist: $1p$, $2s$, $2d$, $3p$, $3d$, $3f$, $4g$?

7.51 Why is a boundary surface diagram useful in representing an atomic orbital?

7.52 Describe the four quantum numbers used to characterize an electron in an atom.

7.53 Which quantum number defines a shell? Which quantum numbers define a subshell?

● 7.54 Which of the four quantum numbers (n, ℓ, m_ℓ, m_s) determine (a) the energy of an electron in a hydrogen atom and in a many-electron atom, (b) the size of an orbital, (c) the shape of an orbital, (d) the orientation of an orbital in space?

Problems

● 7.55 An electron in a certain atom is in the $n = 2$ quantum level. List the possible values of ℓ and m_ℓ that it can have.

● 7.56 An electron in an atom is in the $n = 3$ quantum level. List the possible values of ℓ and m_ℓ that it can have.

● 7.57 Give the values of the quantum numbers associated with the following orbitals: (a) $2p$, (b) $3s$, (c) $5d$.

● 7.58 Give the values of the four quantum numbers of an electron in the following orbitals: (a) $3s$, (b) $4p$, (c) $3d$.

7.59 Discuss the similarities and differences between a $1s$ and a $2s$ orbital.

7.60 What is the difference between a $2p_x$ and a $2p_y$ orbital?

● 7.61 List all the possible subshells and orbitals associated with the principal quantum number n, if $n = 5$.

● 7.62 List all the possible subshells and orbitals associated with the principal quantum number n, if $n = 6$.

● 7.63 Calculate the total number of electrons that can occupy (a) one s orbital, (b) three p orbitals, (c) five d orbitals, (d) seven f orbitals.

7.64 What is the total number of electrons that can be held in all orbitals having the same principal quantum number n?

● 7.65 Determine the maximum number of electrons that can be found in each of the following subshells: $3s$, $3d$, $4p$, $4f$, $5f$.

● 7.66 Indicate the total number of (a) p electrons in N ($Z = 7$); (b) s electrons in Si ($Z = 14$); and (c) $3d$ electrons in S ($Z = 16$).

7.67 Make a chart of all allowable orbitals in the first four principal energy levels of the hydrogen atom. Designate each by type (for example, s, p) and indicate how many orbitals of each type there are.

7.68 Why do the $3s$, $3p$, and $3d$ orbitals have the same energy in a hydrogen atom but different energies in a many-electron atom?

● 7.69 For each of the following pairs of hydrogen orbitals, indicate which is higher in energy: (a) $1s$, $2s$; (b) $2p$, $3p$; (c) $3d_{xy}$, $3d_{yz}$; (d) $3s$, $3d$; (e) $4f$, $5s$.

● 7.70 Which orbital in each of the following pairs is lower in energy in a many-electron atom? (a) $2s$, $2p$; (b) $3p$, $3d$; (c) $3s$, $4s$; (d) $4d$, $5f$.

Electron Configuration
Review Questions

7.71 What is electron configuration? Describe the roles that the Pauli exclusion principle and Hund's rule play in writing the electron configuration of elements.

● 7.72 Explain the meaning of the symbol $4d^6$.

7.73 Explain the meaning of diamagnetic and paramagnetic. Give an example of an element that is diamagnetic and one that is paramagnetic. What does it mean when we say that electrons are paired?

7.74 What is meant by the term "shielding of electrons" in an atom? Using the Li atom as an example, describe the effect of shielding on the energy of electrons in an atom.

Problems

7.75 Indicate which of the following sets of quantum numbers in an atom are unacceptable and explain why: (a) $(1, 0, \frac{1}{2}, \frac{1}{2})$, (b) $(3, 0, 0, +\frac{1}{2})$, (c) $(2, 2, 1, +\frac{1}{2})$, (d) $(4, 3, -2, +\frac{1}{2})$, (e) $(3, 2, 1, 1)$.

7.76 The ground-state electron configurations listed here are incorrect. Explain what mistakes have been made in each and write the correct electron configurations.

Al: $1s^2 2s^2 2p^4 3s^2 3p^3$

B: $1s^2 2s^2 2p^5$

F: $1s^2 2s^2 2p^6$

7.77 The atomic number of an element is 73. Is this element diamagnetic or paramagnetic?

7.78 Indicate the number of unpaired electrons present in each of the following atoms: B, Ne, P, Sc, Mn, Se, Kr, Fe, Cd, I, Pb.

The Building-Up Principle

Review Questions

7.79 State the Aufbau principle and explain the role it plays in classifying the elements in the periodic table.

7.80 Describe the characteristics of the following groups of elements: transition metals, lanthanides, actinides.

7.81 What is the noble gas core? How does it simplify the writing of electron configurations?

7.82 What are the group and period of the element osmium?

7.83 Define the following terms and give an example of each: transition metals, lanthanides, actinides.

7.84 Explain why the ground-state electron configurations of Cr and Cu are different from what we might expect.

7.85 Explain what is meant by a noble gas core. Write the electron configuration of a xenon core.

7.86 Comment on the correctness of the following statement: The probability of finding two electrons with the same four quantum numbers in an atom is zero.

Problems

7.87 Use the Aufbau principle to obtain the ground-state electron configuration of selenium.

7.88 Use the Aufbau principle to obtain the ground-state electron configuration of technetium.

7.89 Write the ground-state electron configurations for the following elements: B, V, Ni, As, I, Au.

7.90 Write the ground-state electron configurations for the following elements: Ge, Fe, Zn, Ni, W, Tl.

7.91 The electron configuration of a neutral atom is $1s^2 2s^2 2p^6 3s^2$. Write a complete set of quantum numbers for each of the electrons. Name the element.

7.92 Which of the following species has the most unpaired electrons? S^+, S, or S^-. Explain how you arrive at your answer.

Additional Problems

7.93 A sample tube consisted of atomic hydrogens in their ground state. A student illuminated the atoms with monochromatic light, that is, light of a single wavelength. If only two spectral emission lines in the visible region are observed, what is the wavelength (or wavelengths) of the incident radiation?

7.94 A laser produces a beam of light with a wavelength of 532 nm. If the power output is 25.0 mW, how many photons does the laser emit per second? (1 W = 1 J/s.)

7.95 When a compound containing cesium ion is heated in a Bunsen burner flame, photons with an energy of 4.30×10^{-19} J are emitted. What color is the cesium flame?

7.96 Discuss the current view of the correctness of the following statements. (a) The electron in the hydrogen atom is in an orbit that never brings it closer than 100 pm to the nucleus. (b) Atomic absorption spectra result from transitions of electrons from lower to higher energy levels. (c) A many-electron atom behaves somewhat like a solar system that has a number of planets.

7.97 What is the basis for thinking that atoms are spherical in shape even though the atomic orbitals $p, d, \ldots$ have distinctly nonspherical shapes?

7.98 What is the maximum number of electrons in an atom that can have the following quantum numbers? Specify the orbitals in which the electrons would be found. (a) $n = 2$, $m_s = +\frac{1}{2}$; (b) $n = 4$, $m_\ell = +1$; (c) $n = 3$, $\ell = 2$; (d) $n = 2$, $\ell = 0$, $m_s = -\frac{1}{2}$; (e) $n = 4$, $\ell = 3$, $m_\ell = -2$.

7.99 Identify the following individuals and their contributions to the development of quantum theory: Bohr, de Broglie, Einstein, Planck, Heisenberg, Schrödinger.

7.100 What properties of electrons are used in the operation of an electron microscope?

7.101 In a photoelectric experiment a student uses a light source whose frequency is greater than that needed to eject electrons from a certain metal. However, after continuously shining the light on the same area of the metal for a long period of time the student notices that the maximum kinetic energy of ejected electrons begins to decrease, even though the frequency of the light is held constant. How would you account for this behavior?

7.102 A certain pitcher's fastballs have been clocked at about 100 mph. (a) Calculate the wavelength of a 0.141-kg baseball (in nm) at this speed. (b) What is the wavelength of a hydrogen atom at the same speed? (1 mile = 1609 m.)

7.103 A student carried out a photoelectric experiment by shining visible light on a clean piece of cesium metal. The table here shows the kinetic energies (KE) of the ejected electrons as a function of wavelengths (λ). Determine graphically the work function and the Planck constant.

λ (nm)	405	435.8	480	520	577.7
KE (J)	2.360×10^{-19}	2.029×10^{-19}	1.643×10^{-19}	1.417×10^{-19}	1.067×10^{-19}

7.104 (a) What is the lowest possible value of the principal quantum number (n) when the angular momentum quantum number (ℓ) is 1? (b) What are the possible values of the angular momentum quantum number (ℓ) when the magnetic quantum number (m_ℓ) is 0, given than $n \leq 4$?

7.105 Considering only the ground-state electron configuration, are there more diamagnetic or paramagnetic elements? Explain.

7.106 A ruby laser produces radiation of wavelength 633 nm in pulses whose duration is 1.00×10^{-9} s. (a) If the laser produces 0.376 J of energy per pulse, how many photons are produced in each pulse? (b) Calculate the power (in watts) delivered by the laser per pulse. (1 W = 1 J/s.)

7.107 A 368-g sample of water absorbs infrared radiation at 1.06×10^4 nm from a carbon dioxide laser. Suppose all the absorbed radiation is converted to heat. Calculate the number of photons at this wavelength required to raise the temperature of the water by 5.00°C.

7.108 Photodissociation of water

$$H_2O(l) + h\nu \longrightarrow H_2(g) + \tfrac{1}{2}O_2(g)$$

has been suggested as a source of hydrogen. The ΔH°_{rxn} for the reaction, calculated from thermochemical data, is 285.8 kJ per mole of water decomposed. Calculate the maximum wavelength (in nm) that would provide the necessary energy. In principle, is it feasible to use sunlight as a source of energy for this process?

7.109 Spectral lines of the Lyman and Balmer series do not overlap. Verify this statement by calculating the longest wavelength associated with the Lyman series and the shortest wavelength associated with the Balmer series (in nm).

7.110 An atom moving at its root-mean-square speed at 20°C has a wavelength of 3.28×10^{-11} m. Identify the atom.

7.111 Certain sunglasses have small crystals of silver chloride (AgCl) incorporated in the lenses. When the lenses are exposed to light of the appropriate wavelength, the following reaction occurs:

$$AgCl \longrightarrow Ag + Cl$$

The Ag atoms formed produce a uniform gray color that reduces the glare. If ΔH for the preceding reaction is 248 kJ/mol, calculate the maximum wavelength of light that can induce this process.

7.112 The He$^+$ ion contains only one electron and is therefore a hydrogenlike ion. Calculate the wavelengths, in increasing order, of the first four transitions in the Balmer series of the He$^+$ ion. Compare these wavelengths with the same transitions in a H atom. Comment on the differences. (The Rydberg constant for He$^+$ is 8.72×10^{-18} J.)

7.113 Ozone (O_3) in the stratosphere absorbs the harmful radiation from the sun by undergoing decomposition: $O_3 \longrightarrow O + O_2$. (a) Referring to Table 6.4, calculate the ΔH° for this process. (b) Calculate the maximum wavelength of photons (in nm) that possess this energy to cause the decomposition of ozone photochemically.

7.114 The retina of a human eye can detect light when radiant energy incident on it is at least 4.0×10^{-17} J. For light of 600-nm wavelength, how many photons does this correspond to?

7.115 A helium atom and a xenon atom have the same kinetic energy. Calculate the ratio of the de Broglie wavelength of the helium atom to that of the xenon atom.

7.116 A laser is used in treating retina detachment. The wavelength of the laser beam is 514 nm and the power is 1.6 W. If the laser is turned on for 0.060 s during surgery, calculate the number of photons emitted by the laser. (1 W = 1 J/s.)

7.117 An electron in an excited state in a hydrogen atom can return to the ground state in two different ways: (a) via a direct transition in which a photon of wavelength λ_1 is emitted and (b) via an intermediate excited state reached by the emission of a photon of wavelength λ_2. This intermediate excited state then decays to the ground state by emitting another photon of wavelength λ_3. Derive an equation that relates λ_1 to λ_2 and λ_3.

7.118 A photoelectric experiment was performed by separately shining a laser at 450 nm (blue light) and a laser at 560 nm (yellow light) on a clean metal surface and measuring the number and kinetic energy of the ejected electrons. Which light would generate more electrons? Which light would eject electrons with greater kinetic energy? Assume that the same amount of energy is delivered to the metal surface by each laser and that the frequencies of the laser lights exceed the threshold frequency.

7.119 Draw the shapes (boundary surfaces) of the following orbitals: (a) $2p_y$, (b) $3d_{z^2}$, (c) $3d_{x^2-y^2}$. (Show coordinate axes in your sketches.)

• 7.120 The electron configurations described in this chapter all refer to gaseous atoms in their ground states. An atom may absorb a quantum of energy and promote one of its electrons to a higher-energy orbital. When this happens, we say that the atom is in an excited state. The electron configurations of some excited atoms are given. Identify these atoms and write their ground-state configurations:

(a) $1s^1 2s^1$

(b) $1s^2 2s^2 2p^2 3d^1$

(c) $1s^2 2s^2 2p^6 4s^1$

(d) $[Ar]4s^1 3d^{10} 4p^4$

(e) $[Ne]3s^2 3p^4 3d^1$

• 7.121 Draw orbital diagrams for atoms with the following electron configurations:

(a) $1s^2 2s^2 2p^5$

(b) $1s^2 2s^2 2p^6 3s^2 3p^3$

(c) $1s^2 2s^2 2p^6 3s^2 3p^6 4s^2 3d^7$

7.122 If Rutherford and his coworkers had used electrons instead of alpha particles to probe the structure of the nucleus as described in Section 2.2, what might they have discovered?

• 7.123 Scientists have found interstellar hydrogen atoms with quantum number n in the hundreds. Calculate the wavelength of light emitted when a hydrogen atom undergoes a transition from $n = 236$ to $n = 235$. In what region of the electromagnetic spectrum does this wavelength fall?

7.124 Calculate the wavelength of a helium atom whose speed is equal to the root-mean-square speed at 20°C.

7.125 Ionization energy is the minimum energy required to remove an electron from an atom. It is usually expressed in units of kJ/mol, that is, the energy in kilojoules required to remove one mole of electrons from one mole of atoms. (a) Calculate the ionization energy for the hydrogen atom. (b) Repeat the calculation, assuming in this second case that the electrons are removed from the $n = 2$ state.

• 7.126 An electron in a hydrogen atom is excited from the ground state to the $n = 4$ state. Comment on the correctness of the following statements (true or false).

(a) $n = 4$ is the first excited state.

(b) It takes more energy to ionize (remove) the electron from $n = 4$ than from the ground state.

(c) The electron is farther from the nucleus (on average) in $n = 4$ than in the ground state.

(d) The wavelength of light emitted when the electron drops from $n = 4$ to $n = 1$ is longer than that from $n = 4$ to $n = 2$.

(e) The wavelength the atom absorbs in going from $n = 1$ to $n = 4$ is the same as that emitted as it goes from $n = 4$ to $n = 1$.

• 7.127 The ionization energy of a certain element is 412 kJ/mol (see Problem 7.125). However, when the atoms of this element are in the first excited state, the ionization energy is only 126 kJ/mol. Based on this information, calculate the wavelength of light emitted in a transition from the first excited state to the ground state.

• 7.128 Alveoli are the tiny sacs of air in the lungs (see Problem 5.136) whose average diameter is 5.0×10^{-5} m. Consider an oxygen molecule (5.3×10^{-26} kg) trapped within a sac. Calculate the uncertainty in the velocity of the oxygen molecule. (*Hint:* The maximum uncertainty in the position of the molecule is given by the diameter of the sac.)

• 7.129 How many photons at 660 nm must be absorbed to melt 5.0×10^2 g of ice? On average, how many H_2O molecules does one photon convert from ice to water? (*Hint:* It takes 334 J to melt 1 g of ice at 0°C.)

• 7.130 Shown are portions of orbital diagrams representing the ground-state electron configurations of certain elements. Which of them violate the Pauli exclusion principle? Hund's rule?

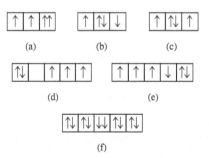

• 7.131 The UV light that is responsible for tanning the skin falls in the 320- to 400-nm region. Calculate the total energy (in joules) absorbed by a person exposed to this radiation for 2.0 h, given that there are 2.0×10^{16} photons hitting Earth's surface per square centimeter per second over a 80-nm (320 nm to 400 nm) range and that the exposed body area is 0.45 m^2. Assume that only half of the radiation is absorbed and the other half is reflected by the body. (*Hint:* Use an average wavelength of 360 nm in calculating the energy of a photon.)

7.132 The sun is surrounded by a white circle of gaseous material called the corona, which becomes visible during a total eclipse of the sun. The temperature of the corona is in the millions of degrees Celsius, which is high enough to break up molecules and remove some or all of the electrons from atoms. One way astronomers have been able to estimate the temperature of the corona is by studying the emission lines of ions of certain elements. For example, the emission spectrum of Fe^{14+} ions has been recorded and analyzed. Knowing that it takes 3.5×10^4 kJ/mol to convert Fe^{13+} to Fe^{14+}, estimate the temperature of the sun's corona. (*Hint:* The average kinetic energy of one mole of a gas is $\frac{3}{2}RT$.)

7.133 In 1996 physicists created an anti-atom of hydrogen. In such an atom, which is the antimatter equivalent of an ordinary atom, the electrical charges of all the component particles are reversed. Thus, the nucleus of an anti-atom is made of an anti-proton, which has the same mass as a proton but bears a negative charge, while the electron is replaced by an anti-electron (also called positron) with the same mass as an electron, but bearing a positive charge. Would you expect the energy levels, emission spectra, and atomic orbitals of an antihydrogen atom to be different from those of a hydrogen atom? What would happen if an anti-atom of hydrogen collided with a hydrogen atom?

7.134 Use Equation (5.16) to calculate the de Broglie wavelength of a N_2 molecule at 300 K.

7.135 When an electron makes a transition between energy levels of a hydrogen atom, there are no restrictions on the initial and final values of the principal quantum number n. However, there is a quantum mechanical rule that restricts the initial and final values of the orbital angular momentum ℓ. This is the *selection rule*, which states that $\Delta \ell = \pm 1$; that is, in a transition, the value of ℓ can only increase or decrease by one. According to this rule, which of the following transitions are allowed: (a) $2s \longrightarrow 1s$, (b) $3p \longrightarrow 1s$, (c) $3d \longrightarrow 4f$, (d) $4d \longrightarrow 3s$? In view of this selection rule, explain why it is possible to observe the various emission series shown in Figure 7.11.

7.136 In an electron microscope, electrons are accelerated by passing them through a voltage difference. The kinetic energy thus acquired by the electrons is equal to the voltage times the charge on the electron. Thus, a voltage difference of 1 V imparts a kinetic energy of 1.602×10^{-19} C × V or 1.602×10^{-19} J. Calculate the wavelength associated with electrons accelerated by 5.00×10^3 V.

7.137 A microwave oven operating at 1.22×10^8 nm is used to heat 150 mL of water (roughly the volume of a tea cup) from 20°C to 100°C. Calculate the number of photons needed if 92.0 percent of microwave energy is converted to the thermal energy of water.

7.138 The radioactive Co-60 isotope is used in nuclear medicine to treat certain types of cancer. Calculate the wavelength and frequency of an emitted gamma photon having the energy of 1.29×10^{11} J/mol.

7.139 (a) An electron in the ground state of the hydrogen atom moves at an average speed of 5×10^6 m/s. If the speed is known to an uncertainty of 1 percent, what is the uncertainty in knowing its position? Given that the radius of the hydrogen atom in the ground state is 5.29×10^{-11} m, comment on your result. The mass of an electron is 9.1094×10^{-31} kg. (b) A 3.2-g Ping-Pong ball moving at 50 mph has a momentum of 0.073 kg · m/s. If the uncertainty in measuring the momentum is 1.0×10^{-7} of the momentum, calculate the uncertainty in the Ping-Pong ball's position.

7.140 One wavelength in the hydrogen emission spectrum is 1280 nm. What are the initial and final states of the transition responsible for this emission?

7.141 Owls have good night vision because their eyes can detect a light intensity as low as 5.0×10^{-13} W/m². Calculate the number of photons per second that an owl's eye can detect if its pupil has a diameter of 9.0 mm and the light has a wavelength of 500 nm. (1 W = 1 J/s.)

7.142 For hydrogenlike ions, that is, ions containing only one electron, Equation (7.5) is modified as follows: $E_n = -R_H Z^2(1/n^2)$, where Z is the atomic number of the parent atom. The figure here represents the emission spectrum of such a hydrogenlike ion in the gas phase. All the lines result from the electronic transitions from the excited states to the $n = 2$ state. (a) What electronic transitions correspond to lines B and C? (b) If the wavelength of line C is 27.1 nm, calculate the wavelengths of lines A and B. (c) Calculate the energy needed to remove the electron from the ion in the $n = 4$ state. (d) What is the physical significance of the continuum?

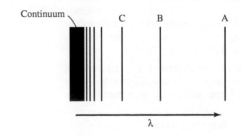

7.143 When two atoms collide, some of their kinetic energy may be converted into electronic energy in one or both atoms. If the average kinetic energy is about equal to the energy for some allowed electronic transition, an appreciable number of atoms can absorb enough energy through an inelastic collision to be raised to an excited electronic state. (a) Calculate the average kinetic energy per atom in a gas sample at 298 K. (b) Calculate the energy difference between the $n = 1$ and $n = 2$ levels in hydrogen. (c) At what temperature is it possible to excite a hydrogen atom from the $n = 1$ level to $n = 2$ level by collision? [The average kinetic energy of 1 mole of an ideal gas is $(\frac{3}{2})RT$.]

7.144 Calculate the energies needed to remove an electron from the $n = 1$ state and the $n = 5$ state in the Li^{2+} ion. What is the wavelength (in nm) of the emitted photon in a transition from $n = 5$ to $n = 1$? The Rydberg constant for hydrogenlike ions is $(2.18 \times 10^{-18} \text{ J})Z^2$, where Z is the atomic number.

7.145 The de Broglie wavelength of an accelerating proton in the Large Hadron Collider is 2.5×10^{-14} m. What is the kinetic energy (in joules) of the proton?

7.146 The minimum uncertainty in the position of a certain moving particle is equal to its de Broglie wavelength. If the speed of the particle is 1.2×10^5 m/s, what is the minimum uncertainty in its speed?

• 7.147 According to Einstein's special theory of relativity, the mass of a moving particle, m_{moving}, is related to its mass at rest, m_{rest}, by the following equation

$$m_{\text{moving}} = \frac{m_{\text{rest}}}{\sqrt{1 - \left(\dfrac{u}{c}\right)^2}}$$

where u and c are the speeds of the particle and light, respectively. (a) In particle accelerators, protons, electrons, and other charged particles are often accelerated to speeds close to the speed of light. Calculate the wavelength (in nm) of a proton moving at 50.0 percent the speed of light. The mass of a proton is 1.673×10^{-27} kg. (b) Calculate the mass of a 6.0×10^{-2} kg tennis ball moving at 63 m/s. Comment on your results.

• **7.148** The mathematical equation for studying the photoelectric effect is

$$h\nu = W + \tfrac{1}{2}m_e u^2$$

where ν is the frequency of light shining on the metal, W is the work function, and m_e and u are the mass and speed of the ejected electron. In an experiment, a student found that a maximum wavelength of 351 nm is needed to just dislodge electrons from a zinc metal surface. Calculate the speed (in m/s) of an ejected electron when she employed light with a wavelength of 313 nm.

7.149 In the beginning of the twentieth century, some scientists thought that a nucleus may contain both electrons and protons. Use the Heisenberg uncertainty principle to show that an electron cannot be confined within a nucleus. Repeat the calculation for a proton. Comment on your results. Assume the radius of a nucleus to be 1.0×10^{-15} m. The masses of an electron and a proton are 9.109×10^{-31} kg and 1.673×10^{-27} kg, respectively. (*Hint:* Treat the diameter of the nucleus as the uncertainty in position.)

7.150 Blackbody radiation is the term used to describe the dependence of the radiation energy emitted by an object on wavelength at a certain temperature. Planck proposed the quantum theory to account for this dependence. Shown in the figure is a plot of the radiation energy emitted by our sun versus wavelength. This curve is characteristic of the temperature at the surface of the sun. At a higher temperature, the curve has a similar shape but the maximum will shift to a shorter wavelength. What does this curve reveal about two consequences of great biological significance on Earth?

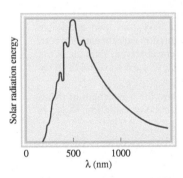

7.151 All molecules undergo vibrational motions. Quantum mechanical treatment shows that the vibrational energy, E_{vib}, of a diatomic molecule like HCl is given by

$$E_{\text{vib}} = \left(n + \frac{1}{2}\right)h\nu$$

where n is a quantum number given by $n = 0, 1, 2, 3, \dots$ and ν is the fundamental frequency of vibration. (a) Sketch the first three vibrational energy levels for HCl. (b) Calculate the energy required to excite a HCl molecule from the ground level to the first excited level. The fundamental frequency of vibration for HCl is 8.66×10^{13} s^{-1}. (c) The fact that the lowest vibrational energy in the ground level is not zero but equal to $\frac{1}{2}h\nu$ means that molecules will vibrate at all temperatures, including the absolute zero. Use the Heisenberg uncertainty principle to justify this prediction. (*Hint:* Consider a nonvibrating molecule and predict the uncertainty in the momentum and hence the uncertainty in the position.)

7.152 The wave function for the 2s orbital in the hydrogen atom is

$$\Psi_{2s} = \frac{1}{\sqrt{2a_0^3}}\left(1 - \frac{\rho}{2}\right)e^{-\rho/2}$$

where a_0 is the value of the radius of the first Bohr orbit, equal to 0.529 nm, ρ is $Z(r/a_0)$, and r is the distance from the nucleus in meters. Calculate the location of the node of the 2s wave function from the nucleus.

7.153 A student placed a large unwrapped chocolate bar in a microwave oven without a rotating glass plate. After turning the oven on for less than a minute, she noticed there were evenly spaced dents (due to melting) about 6 cm apart. Based on her observations, calculate the speed of light given that the microwave frequency is 2.45 GHz. (*Hint:* The energy of a wave is proportional to the square of its amplitude.)

7.154 The wave properties of matter can generally be ignored for macroscopic objects such as tennis balls; however, wave properties have been measured at the fringe of detection for some very large molecules. For example, wave patterns were detected for $C_{60}(C_{12}F_{25})_8$ molecules moving at a velocity of 63 m/s. (a) Calculate the wavelength of a $C_{60}(C_{12}F_{25})_8$ molecule moving at this velocity. (b) How does the wavelength compare to the size of the molecule given that its diameter is roughly 3000 pm?

Interpreting, Modeling & Estimating

7.155 Atoms of an element have only two accessible excited states. In an emission experiment, however, three spectral lines were observed. Explain. Write an equation relating the shortest wavelength to the other two wavelengths.

7.156 According to Wien's law, the wavelength of maximum intensity in blackbody radiation, λ_{max}, is given by

$$\lambda_{max} = \frac{b}{T}$$

where b is a constant (2.898×10^6 nm · K) and T is the temperature of the radiating body in kelvins. (a) Estimate the temperature at the surface of the sun. (b) How are astronomers able to determine the temperature of stars in general? (See Problem 7.150 for a definition of blackbody radiation.)

7.157 Only a fraction of the electrical energy supplied to an incandescent-tungsten lightbulb is converted to visible light. The rest of the energy shows up as infrared radiation (that is, heat). A 60-W lightbulb converts about 15.0 percent of the energy supplied to it into visible light. Roughly how many photons are emitted by the lightbulb per second? (1 W = 1 J/s.)

7.158 Photosynthesis makes use of photons of visible light to bring about chemical changes. Explain why heat energy in the form of infrared photons is ineffective for photosynthesis. (*Hint:* Typical chemical bond energies are 200 kJ/mol or greater.)

7.159 A typical red laser pointer has a power of 5 mW. How long would it take a red laser pointer to emit the same number of photons emitted by a 1-W blue laser in 1 s? (1 W = 1 J/s.)

7.160 Referring to the Chemistry in Action essay on p. 314, estimate the wavelength of light that would be emitted by a cadmium selenide (CdSe) quantum dot with a diameter of 10 nm. Would the emitted light be visible to the human eye? The diameter and emission wavelength for a series of quantum dots are given here.

Diameter (nm)	2.2	2.5	3.3	4.2	4.9	6.3
Wavelength (nm)	462	503	528	560	583	626

Advanced Problems

Bohr's Theory of the Atom

7.161 Show that Equation (7.4i) is dimensionally correct. The permittivity of free space, ε_0, is $8.8542 \times 10^{-12} \, C^2 \cdot N^{-1} \cdot m^{-2}$.

7.162 Calculate the ground-state energy of the He^+ ion.

Quantum Mechanics

7.163 According to Equation (7.9a), the energy of the particle is inversely proportional to the square of the length of the box. How would you account for this dependence in terms of the Heisenberg uncertainty principle?

7.164 Referring to Figure 7.15b(ii), energy is supplied to the particle to induce an $n = 1 \longrightarrow 2$ transition. Suggest where along the bottom of the box the transition would most likely take place. Explain your choice.

7.165 Consider the situation in which an electron is placed in a one-dimensional box of length L. Calculate the difference in energy for the $n = 1$ and $n = 2$ states of (a) $L = 100$ pm and (b) $L = 10$ cm.

Answers to Practice Exercises

7.1 8.24 m. **7.2** 3.39×10^3 nm. **7.3** 9.65×10^{-19} J. **7.4** 2.63×10^3 nm. **7.5** 56.6 nm. **7.6** 0.2 m/s. **7.7** $n = 3$, $\ell = 1$, $m_\ell = -1, 0, 1$. **7.8** 16. **7.9** $(4, 2, -2, +\frac{1}{2})$, $(4, 2, -1, +\frac{1}{2})$, $(4, 2, 0, +\frac{1}{2})$, $(4, 2, 1, +\frac{1}{2})$, $(4, 2, 2, +\frac{1}{2})$, $(4, 2, -2, -\frac{1}{2})$, $(4, 2, -1, -\frac{1}{2})$, $(4, 2, 0, -\frac{1}{2})$, $(4, 2, 1, -\frac{1}{2})$, $(4, 2, 2, -\frac{1}{2})$. **7.10** 32. **7.11** $(1, 0, 0, +\frac{1}{2})$, $(1, 0, 0, -\frac{1}{2})$, $(2, 0, 0, +\frac{1}{2})$, $(2, 0, 0, -\frac{1}{2})$, $(2, 1, -1, -\frac{1}{2})$. There are five other acceptable ways to write the quantum numbers for the last electron (in the $2p$ orbital). **7.12** $[Ne]3s^2 3p^3$.

CHEMICAL *MYSTERY*

Discovery of Helium and the Rise and Fall of Coronium

Scientists know that our sun and other stars contain certain elements. How was this information obtained?

In the early nineteenth century, the German physicist Josef Fraunhofer studied the emission spectrum of the sun and noticed certain dark lines at specific wavelengths. We interpret the appearance of these lines by supposing that originally a continuous band of color was radiated and that, as the emitted light moves outward from the sun, some of the radiation is reabsorbed at those wavelengths by the atoms in space. These dark lines are therefore absorption lines. For atoms, the emission and absorption of light occur at the same wavelengths. By matching the absorption lines in the emission spectra of a star with the emission spectra of known elements in the laboratory, scientists have been able to deduce the types of elements present in the star.

Another way to study the sun spectroscopically is during its eclipse. In 1868 the French physicist Pierre Janssen observed a bright yellow line (see Figure 7.8) in the emission spectrum of the sun's corona during the totality of the eclipse. (The corona is the pearly white crown of light visible around the sun during a total eclipse.) This line did not match the emission lines of known elements, but did match one of the dark lines in the spectrum sketched by Fraunhofer. The name helium (from Helios, the sun god in

Fraunhofer's original drawing, in 1814, showing the dark absorption lines in the sun's emission spectrum. The top of the diagram shows the overall brightness of the sun at different colors.

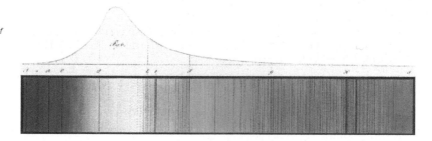

Greek mythology) was given to the element responsible for the emission line. Twenty-seven years later, helium was discovered on Earth by the British chemist William Ramsay in a mineral of uranium. On Earth, the only source of helium is through radioactive decay processes—α particles emitted during nuclear decay are eventually converted to helium atoms.

The search for new elements from the sun did not end with helium. Around the time of Janssen's work, scientists also detected a bright green line in the spectrum from the corona. They did not know the identity of the element giving rise to the line, so they called it coronium because it was only found in the corona. Over the following years, additional mystery coronal emission lines were found. The coronium problem proved much harder to solve than the helium case because no matchings were found with the emission lines of known elements. It was not until the late 1930s that the Swedish physicist Bengt Edlén identified these lines as coming from partially ionized atoms of iron, calcium, and nickel. At very high temperatures (over a million degrees Celsius), many atoms become ionized by losing one or more electrons. Therefore, the mystery emission lines come from the resulting ions of the metals and not from a new element. So, after some 80 years the coronium problem was finally solved. There is no such element as coronium after all!

During the total eclipse of the sun, which lasts for only a few minutes, the corona becomes visible.

Chemical Clues

1. Sketch a two-energy-level system (E_1 and E_2) to illustrate the absorption and emission processes.

2. Explain why the sun's spectrum provides only absorption lines (the dark lines), whereas the corona spectrum provides only emission lines.

3. Why is it difficult to detect helium on Earth?

4. How are scientists able to determine the abundances of elements in stars?

5. Knowing the identity of an ion of an element giving rise to a coronal emission line, describe in qualitative terms how you can estimate the temperature of the corona.

CHAPTER

8

Periodic Relationships Among the Elements

While the recurring or "periodic" trends in the properties of elements are most commonly illustrated in tabular form, alternative geometric arrangements are possible.

CHAPTER OUTLINE

A LOOK AHEAD

▶ We start with the development of the periodic table and the contributions made by nineteenth-century scientists, in particular by Mendeleev. (8.1)

▶ We see that electron configuration is the logical way to build up the periodic table, which explains some of the early anomalies. We also learn the rules for writing the electron configurations of cations and anions. (8.2)

▶ Next, we examine the periodic trends in physical properties such as the size of atoms and ions in terms of effective nuclear charge. (8.3)

▶ We continue our study of periodic trends by examining chemical properties like ionization energy and electron affinity. (8.4 and 8.5)

▶ We then apply the knowledge acquired in the chapter to systematically study the properties of the representative elements as individual groups and also across a given period. (8.6)

Many of the chemical properties of the elements can be understood in terms of their electron configurations. Because electrons fill atomic orbitals in a fairly regular fashion, it is not surprising that elements with similar electron configurations, such as sodium and potassium, behave similarly in many respects and that, in general, the properties of the elements exhibit observable trends. Chemists in the nineteenth century recognized periodic trends in the physical and chemical properties of the elements, long before quantum theory came onto the scene. Although these chemists were not aware of the existence of electrons and protons, their efforts to systematize the chemistry of the elements were remarkably successful. Their main sources of information were the atomic masses of the elements and other known physical and chemical properties.

8.1 Development of the Periodic Table

In the nineteenth century, when chemists had only a vague idea of atoms and molecules and did not know of the existence of electrons and protons, they devised the periodic table using their knowledge of atomic masses. Accurate measurements of the atomic masses of many elements had already been made. Arranging elements according to their atomic masses in a periodic table seemed logical to those chemists, who felt that chemical behavior should somehow be related to atomic mass.

In 1864 the English chemist John Newlands[†] noticed that when the elements were arranged in order of atomic mass, every eighth element had similar properties. Newlands referred to this peculiar relationship as the *law of octaves*. However, this "law" turned out to be inadequate for elements beyond calcium, and Newlands's work was not accepted by the scientific community.

In 1869 the Russian chemist Dmitri Mendeleev[‡] and the German chemist Lothar Meyer[§] independently proposed a much more extensive tabulation of the elements based on the regular, periodic recurrence of properties. Mendeleev's classification system was a great improvement over Newlands's for two reasons. First, it grouped the elements together more accurately, according to their properties. Equally important, it made possible the prediction of the properties of several elements that had not yet been discovered. For example, Mendeleev proposed the existence of an unknown element that he called eka-aluminum and predicted a number of its properties. (*Eka* is a Sanskrit word meaning "first"; thus eka-aluminum would be the first element under aluminum in the same group.) When gallium was discovered four years later, its properties matched the predicted properties of eka-aluminum remarkably well:

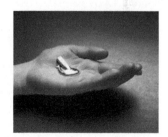

	Eka-Aluminum (Ea)	**Gallium (Ga)**
Atomic mass	68 amu	69.9 amu
Melting point	Low	29.78°C
Density	5.9 g/cm^3	5.94 g/cm^3
Formula of oxide	Ea_2O_3	Ga_2O_3

Gallium melts in a person's hand (body temperature is about 37°C).

Mendeleev's periodic table included 66 known elements. By 1900, some 30 more had been added to the list, filling in some of the empty spaces. Figure 8.1 charts the discovery of the elements chronologically.

Appendix 1 explains the names and symbols of the elements.

[†]John Alexander Reina Newlands (1838–1898). English chemist. Newlands's work was a step in the right direction in the classification of the elements. Unfortunately, because of its shortcomings, he was subjected to much criticism, and even ridicule. At one meeting he was asked if he had ever examined the elements according to the order of their initial letters! Nevertheless, in 1887 Newlands was honored by the Royal Society of London for his contribution.

[‡]Dmitri Ivanovich Mendeleev (1836–1907). Russian chemist. His work on the periodic classification of elements is regarded by many as the most significant achievement in chemistry in the nineteenth century.

[§]Julius Lothar Meyer (1830–1895). German chemist. In addition to his contribution to the periodic table, Meyer also discovered the chemical affinity of hemoglobin for oxygen.

328   **Chapter 8** ▪ Periodic Relationships Among the Elements

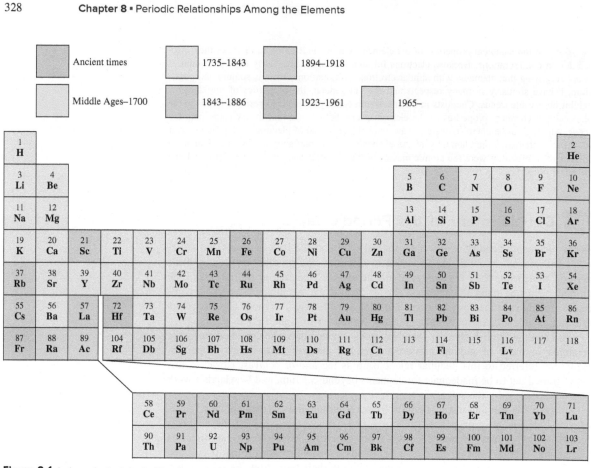

Figure 8.1 *A chronological chart of the discovery of the elements. To date, 118 elements have been identified.*

Although this periodic table was a celebrated success, the early versions had some glaring inconsistencies. For example, the atomic mass of argon (39.95 amu) is greater than that of potassium (39.10 amu). If elements were arranged solely according to increasing atomic mass, argon would appear in the position occupied by potassium in our modern periodic table (see the inside front cover). But no chemist would place argon, an inert gas, in the same group as lithium and sodium, two very reactive metals. This and other discrepancies suggested that some fundamental property other than atomic mass must be the basis of periodicity. This property turned out to be associated with atomic number, a concept unknown to Mendeleev and his contemporaries.

Using data from α-particle scattering experiments (see Section 2.2), Rutherford estimated the number of positive charges in the nucleus of a few elements, but the significance of these numbers was overlooked for several more years. In 1913 a young English physicist, Henry Moseley,[†] discovered a correlation between what he called *atomic number* and the frequency of X rays generated by bombarding an element with high-energy electrons. Moseley noticed that the frequencies of X rays emitted from the elements could be correlated by the equation

$$\sqrt{\nu} = a(Z - b) \tag{8.1}$$

[†]Henry Gwyn-Jeffreys Moseley (1887–1915). English physicist. Moseley discovered the relationship between X-ray spectra and atomic number. A lieutenant in the Royal Engineers, he was killed in action at the age of 28 during the British campaign in Gallipoli, Turkey.

where v is the frequency of the emitted X rays and a and b are constants that are the same for all the elements. Thus, from the square root of the measured frequency of the X rays emitted, we can determine the atomic number of the element.

With a few exceptions, Moseley found that atomic number increases in the same order as atomic mass. For example, calcium is the twentieth element in order of increasing atomic mass, and it has an atomic number of 20. The discrepancies that had puzzled earlier scientists now made sense. The atomic number of argon is 18 and that of potassium is 19, so potassium should follow argon in the periodic table.

A modern periodic table usually shows the atomic number along with the element symbol. As you already know, the atomic number also indicates the number of electrons in the atoms of an element. Electron configurations of elements help to explain the recurrence of physical and chemical properties. The importance and usefulness of the periodic table lie in the fact that we can use our understanding of the general properties and trends within a group or a period to predict with considerable accuracy the properties of any element, even though that element may be unfamiliar to us.

8.2 Periodic Classification of the Elements

Figure 8.2 shows the periodic table together with the outermost ground-state electron configurations of the elements. (The electron configurations of the elements are also given in Table 7.3.) Starting with hydrogen, we see that subshells are filled in the order shown in Figure 7.24. According to the type of subshell being filled, the elements can be divided into categories—the representative elements, the noble gases,

1 1A	2 2A	3 3B	4 4B	5 5B	6 6B	7 7B	8	9 8B	10	11 1B	12 2B	13 3A	14 4A	15 5A	16 6A	17 7A	18 8A
1 H $1s^1$																	2 He $1s^2$
3 Li $2s^1$	4 Be $2s^2$											5 B $2s^22p^1$	6 C $2s^22p^2$	7 N $2s^22p^3$	8 O $2s^22p^4$	9 F $2s^22p^5$	10 Ne $2s^22p^6$
11 Na $3s^1$	12 Mg $3s^2$											13 Al $3s^23p^1$	14 Si $3s^23p^2$	15 P $3s^23p^3$	16 S $3s^23p^4$	17 Cl $3s^23p^5$	18 Ar $3s^23p^6$
19 K $4s^1$	20 Ca $4s^2$	21 Sc $4s^23d^1$	22 Ti $4s^23d^2$	23 V $4s^23d^3$	24 Cr $4s^13d^5$	25 Mn $4s^23d^5$	26 Fe $4s^23d^6$	27 Co $4s^23d^7$	28 Ni $4s^23d^8$	29 Cu $4s^13d^{10}$	30 Zn $4s^23d^{10}$	31 Ga $4s^24p^1$	32 Ge $4s^24p^2$	33 As $4s^24p^3$	34 Se $4s^24p^4$	35 Br $4s^24p^5$	36 Kr $4s^24p^6$
37 Rb $5s^1$	38 Sr $5s^2$	39 Y $5s^24d^1$	40 Zr $5s^24d^2$	41 Nb $5s^14d^4$	42 Mo $5s^14d^5$	43 Tc $5s^24d^5$	44 Ru $5s^14d^7$	45 Rh $5s^14d^8$	46 Pd $4d^{10}$	47 Ag $5s^14d^{10}$	48 Cd $5s^24d^{10}$	49 In $5s^25p^1$	50 Sn $5s^25p^2$	51 Sb $5s^25p^3$	52 Te $5s^25p^4$	53 I $5s^25p^5$	54 Xe $5s^25p^6$
55 Cs $6s^1$	56 Ba $6s^2$	57 La $6s^25d^1$	72 Hf $6s^25d^2$	73 Ta $6s^25d^3$	74 W $6s^25d^4$	75 Re $6s^25d^5$	76 Os $6s^25d^6$	77 Ir $6s^25d^7$	78 Pt $6s^15d^9$	79 Au $6s^15d^{10}$	80 Hg $6s^25d^{10}$	81 Tl $6s^26p^1$	82 Pb $6s^26p^2$	83 Bi $6s^26p^3$	84 Po $6s^26p^4$	85 At $6s^26p^5$	86 Rn $6s^26p^6$
87 Fr $7s^1$	88 Ra $7s^2$	89 Ac $7s^26d^1$	104 Rf $7s^26d^2$	105 Db $7s^26d^3$	106 Sg $7s^26d^4$	107 Bh $7s^26d^5$	108 Hs $7s^26d^6$	109 Mt $7s^26d^7$	110 Ds $7s^26d^8$	111 Rg $7s^26d^9$	112 Cn $7s^26d^{10}$	113 $7s^27p^1$	114 Fl $7s^27p^2$	115 $7s^27p^3$	116 Lv $7s^27p^4$	117 $7s^27p^5$	118 $7s^27p^6$

58 Ce $6s^24f^15d^1$	59 Pr $6s^24f^3$	60 Nd $6s^24f^4$	61 Pm $6s^24f^5$	62 Sm $6s^24f^6$	63 Eu $6s^24f^7$	64 Gd $6s^24f^75d^1$	65 Tb $6s^24f^9$	66 Dy $6s^24f^{10}$	67 Ho $6s^24f^{11}$	68 Er $6s^24f^{12}$	69 Tm $6s^24f^{13}$	70 Yb $6s^24f^{14}$	71 Lu $6s^24f^{14}5d^1$
90 Th $7s^26d^2$	91 Pa $7s^25f^26d^1$	92 U $7s^25f^36d^1$	93 Np $7s^25f^46d^1$	94 Pu $7s^25f^6$	95 Am $7s^25f^7$	96 Cm $7s^25f^76d^1$	97 Bk $7s^25f^9$	98 Cf $7s^25f^{10}$	99 Es $7s^25f^{11}$	100 Fm $7s^25f^{12}$	101 Md $7s^25f^{13}$	102 No $7s^25f^{14}$	103 Lr $7s^25f^{14}6d^1$

Figure 8.2 *The ground-state electron configurations of the elements. For simplicity, only the configurations of the outer electrons are shown.*

the transition elements (or transition metals), the lanthanides, and the actinides. The **representative elements** (also called *main group elements*) are *the elements in Groups 1A through 7A, all of which have incompletely filled s or p subshells of the highest principal quantum number*. With the exception of helium, the *noble gases* (the Group 8A elements) all have a completely filled *p* subshell. (The electron configurations are $1s^2$ for helium and ns^2np^6 for the other noble gases, where *n* is the principal quantum number for the outermost shell.)

The transition metals are the elements in Groups 1B and 3B through 8B, which have incompletely filled *d* subshells, or readily produce cations with incompletely filled *d* subshells. (These metals are sometimes referred to as the *d*-block transition elements.) The nonsequential numbering of the transition metals in the periodic table (that is, 3B–8B, followed by 1B–2B) acknowledges a correspondence between the outer electron configurations of these elements and those of the representative elements. For example, scandium and gallium both have three outer electrons. However, because they are in different types of atomic orbitals, they are placed in different groups (3B and 3A). The metals iron (Fe), cobalt (Co), and nickel (Ni) do not fit this classification and are all placed in Group 8B. The Group 2B elements, Zn, Cd, and Hg, are neither representative elements nor transition metals. There is no special name for this group of metals. It should be noted that the designation of A and B groups is not universal. In Europe the practice is to use B for representative elements and A for transition metals, which is just the opposite of the American convention. The International Union of Pure and Applied Chemistry (IUPAC) has recommended numbering the columns sequentially with Arabic numerals 1 through 18 (see Figure 8.2). The proposal has sparked much controversy in the international chemistry community, and its merits and drawbacks will be deliberated for some time to come. In this text we will adhere to the American designation.

The lanthanides and actinides are sometimes called *f*-block transition elements because they have incompletely filled *f* subshells. Figure 8.3 distinguishes the groups of elements discussed here.

The chemical reactivity of the elements is largely determined by their **valence electrons,** which are *the outermost electrons*. For the representative elements, the valence electrons are those in the highest occupied *n* shell. *All nonvalence electrons in an atom* are referred to as **core electrons.** Looking at the electron configurations of the representative elements once again, a clear pattern emerges: all the elements in a given group have the same number and type of valence electrons. The similarity of the valence electron configurations is what makes the elements in the same group resemble one another in chemical behavior. Thus, for instance, the alkali metals (the Group 1A elements) all have the valence electron configuration of ns^1 (Table 8.1) and they all tend to lose one electron to form the unipositive cations. Similarly, the alkaline earth metals (the Group 2A elements) all have the valence electron configuration of ns^2, and they all tend to lose two electrons to form the dipositive cations. We must be careful, however, in predicting element properties based solely on "group membership." For example, the elements in Group 4A all have the same valence electron configuration ns^2np^2, but there is a notable variation in chemical properties among the elements: carbon is a nonmetal, silicon and germanium are metalloids, and tin and lead are metals.

As a group, the noble gases behave very similarly. Helium and neon are chemically inert, and there are few examples of compounds formed by the other noble gases. This lack of chemical reactivity is due to the completely filled *ns* and *np* subshells, a condition that often correlates with great stability. Although the valence electron configuration of the transition metals is not always the same within a group and there is no regular pattern in the change of the electron configuration from one metal to the next in the same period, all transition metals share many characteristics that set them apart from other elements. The reason is

For the representative elements, the valence electrons are simply those electrons at the highest principal energy level *n*.

Table 8.1

Electron Configurations of Group 1A and Group 2A Elements

Group 1A	Group 2A
Li [He]$2s^1$	Be [He]$2s^2$
Na [Ne]$3s^1$	Mg [Ne]$3s^2$
K [Ar]$4s^1$	Ca [Ar]$4s^2$
Rb [Kr]$5s^1$	Sr [Kr]$5s^2$
Cs [Xe]$6s^1$	Ba [Xe]$6s^2$
Fr [Rn]$7s^1$	Ra [Rn]$7s^2$

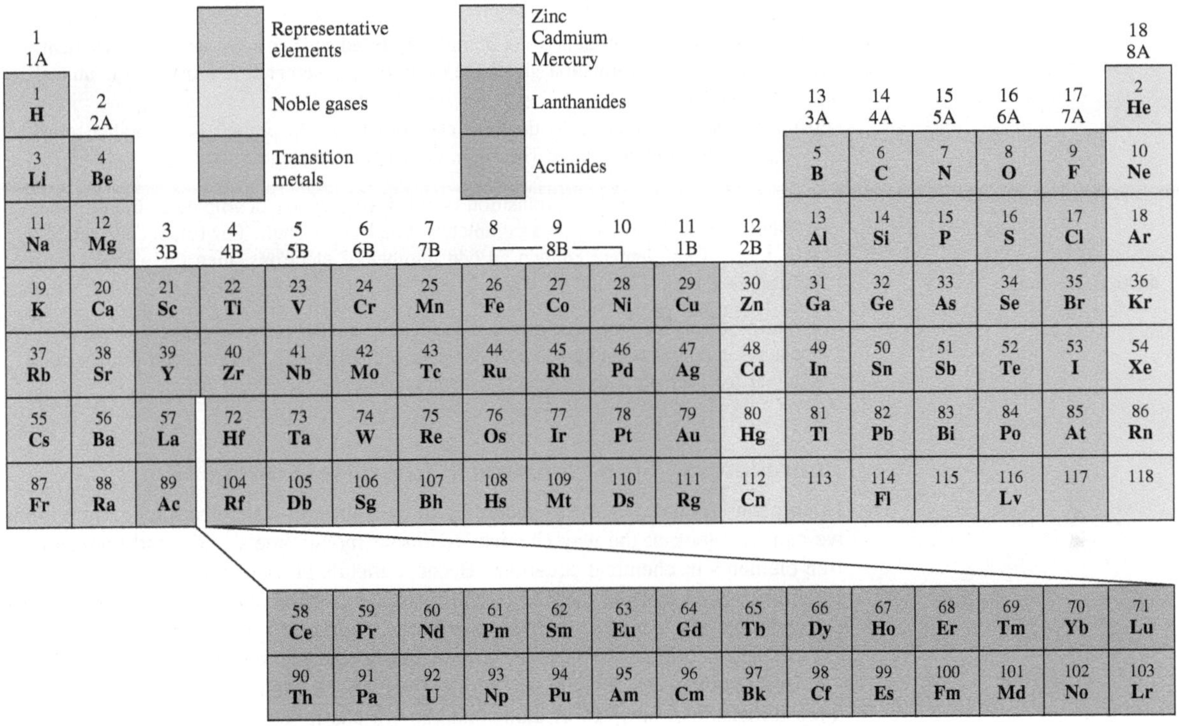

Figure 8.3 *Classification of the elements. Note that the Group 2B elements are often classified as transition metals even though they do not exhibit the characteristics of the transition metals.*

that these metals all have an incompletely filled *d* subshell. Likewise, the lanthanide (and the actinide) elements resemble one another because they have incompletely filled *f* subshells.

Example 8.1

An atom of a certain element has 15 electrons. Without consulting a periodic table, answer the following questions: (a) What is the ground-state electron configuration of the element? (b) How should the element be classified? (c) Is the element diamagnetic or paramagnetic?

Strategy (a) We refer to the building-up principle discussed in Section 7.9 and start writing the electron configuration with principal quantum number $n = 1$ and continuing upward until all the electrons are accounted for. (b) What are the electron configuration characteristics of representative elements? transition elements? noble gases? (c) Examine the pairing scheme of the electrons in the outermost shell. What determines whether an element is diamagnetic or paramagnetic?

Solution

(a) We know that for $n = 1$ we have a $1s$ orbital (2 electrons); for $n = 2$ we have a $2s$ orbital (2 electrons) and three $2p$ orbitals (6 electrons); for $n = 3$ we have a $3s$ orbital (2 electrons). The number of electrons left is $15 - 12 = 3$ and these three electrons are placed in the $3p$ orbitals. The electron configuration is $1s^2 2s^2 2p^6 3s^2 3p^3$.

(Continued)

(b) Because the 3p subshell is not completely filled, this is a representative element. Based on the information given, we cannot say whether it is a metal, a nonmetal, or a metalloid.

(c) According to Hund's rule, the three electrons in the 3p orbitals have parallel spins (three unpaired electrons). Therefore, the element is paramagnetic.

Check For (b), note that a transition metal possesses an incompletely filled d subshell and a noble gas has a completely filled outer shell. For (c), recall that if the atoms of an element contain an odd number of electrons, then the element must be paramagnetic.

Similar problem: 8.20.

Practice Exercise An atom of a certain element has 20 electrons. (a) Write the ground-state electron configuration of the element, (b) classify the element, (c) determine whether the element is diamagnetic or paramagnetic.

Representing Free Elements in Chemical Equations

Having classified the elements according to their ground-state electron configurations, we can now look at the way chemists represent metals, metalloids, and nonmetals as free elements in chemical equations. Because metals do not exist in discrete molecular units, we always use their empirical formulas in chemical equations. The empirical formulas are the same as the symbols that represent the elements. For example, the empirical formula for iron is Fe, the same as the symbol for the element.

For nonmetals there is no single rule. Carbon, for example, exists as an extensive three-dimensional network of atoms, and so we use its empirical formula (C) to represent elemental carbon in chemical equations. But hydrogen, nitrogen, oxygen, and the halogens exist as diatomic molecules, and so we use their molecular formulas (H_2, N_2, O_2, F_2, Cl_2, Br_2, I_2) in equations. The stable form of phosphorus is molecular (P_4), and so we use P_4. For sulfur, chemists often use the empirical formula (S) in chemical equations, rather than S_8, which is the stable form. Thus, instead of writing the equation for the combustion of sulfur as

$$S_8(s) + 8O_2(g) \longrightarrow 8SO_2(g)$$

Note that these two equations for the combustion of sulfur have identical stoichiometry. This correspondence should not be surprising, because both equations describe the same chemical system. In both cases, a number of sulfur atoms react with twice as many oxygen atoms.

we usually write

$$S(s) + O_2(g) \longrightarrow SO_2(g)$$

All the noble gases are monatomic species; thus we use their symbols: He, Ne, Ar, Kr, Xe, and Rn. The metalloids, like the metals, all have complex three-dimensional networks, and we represent them, too, with their empirical formulas, that is, their symbols: B, Si, Ge, and so on.

Electron Configurations of Cations and Anions

Because many ionic compounds are made up of monatomic anions and cations, it is helpful to know how to write the electron configurations of these ionic species. Just as for neutral atoms, we use the Pauli exclusion principle and Hund's rule in writing the ground-state electron configurations of cations and anions. We will group the ions in two categories for discussion.

Ions Derived from Representative Elements

Ions formed from atoms of most representative elements have the noble-gas outer-electron configuration of ns^2np^6. In the formation of a cation from the atom of a representative element, one or more electrons are removed from the highest occupied

n shell. The electron configurations of some atoms and their corresponding cations are as follows:

Na: $[Ne]3s^1$ Na$^+$: $[Ne]$
Ca: $[Ar]4s^2$ Ca^{2+}: $[Ar]$
Al: $[Ne]3s^23p^1$ Al^{3+}: $[Ne]$

Note that each ion has a stable noble gas configuration.

In the formation of an anion, one or more electrons are added to the highest partially filled n shell. Consider the following examples:

H: $1s^1$ H$^-$: $1s^2$ or $[He]$
F: $1s^22s^22p^5$ F$^-$: $1s^22s^22p^6$ or $[Ne]$
O: $1s^22s^22p^4$ O^{2-}: $1s^22s^22p^6$ or $[Ne]$
N: $1s^22s^22p^3$ N^{3-}: $1s^22s^22p^6$ or $[Ne]$

All of these anions also have stable noble gas configurations. Notice that F$^-$, Na$^+$, and Ne (and Al^{3+}, O^{2-}, and N^{3-}) have the same electron configuration. They are said to be *isoelectronic* because they *have the same number of electrons, and hence the same ground-state electron configuration*. Thus, H$^-$ and He are also isoelectronic.

Cations Derived from Transition Metals

In Section 7.9 we saw that in the first-row transition metals (Sc to Cu), the $4s$ orbital is always filled before the $3d$ orbitals. Consider manganese, whose electron configuration is $[Ar]4s^23d^5$. When the Mn^{2+} ion is formed, we might expect the two electrons to be removed from the $3d$ orbitals to yield $[Ar]4s^23d^3$. In fact, the electron configuration of Mn^{2+} is $[Ar]3d^5$! The reason is that the electron-electron and electron-nucleus interactions in a neutral atom can be quite different from those in its ion. Thus, whereas the $4s$ orbital is always filled before the $3d$ orbital in Mn, electrons are removed from the $4s$ orbital in forming Mn^{2+} because the $3d$ orbital is more stable than the $4s$ orbital in transition metal ions. Therefore, when a cation is formed from an atom of a transition metal, electrons are always removed first from the ns orbital and then from the $(n-1)d$ orbitals.

Keep in mind that most transition metals can form more than one cation and that frequently the cations are not isoelectronic with the preceding noble gases.

Bear in mind that the order of electron filling does not determine or predict the order of electron removal for transition metals. For these metals, the ns electrons are lost before the $(n-1)d$ electrons.

Review of Concepts

Identify the elements that fit the following descriptions: (a) An alkaline earth metal ion that is isoelectronic with Kr. (b) An anion with a -3 charge that is isoelectronic with K$^+$. (c) An ion with a $+2$ charge that is isoelectronic with Co^{3+}.

8.3 Periodic Variation in Physical Properties

As we have seen, the electron configurations of the elements show a periodic variation with increasing atomic number. Consequently, there are also periodic variations in physical and chemical behavior. In this section and the next two, we will examine some physical properties of elements that are in the same group or period and additional properties that influence the chemical behavior of the elements. First, let's look at the concept of effective nuclear charge, which has a direct bearing on many atomic properties.

334   **Chapter 8** ▪ Periodic Relationships Among the Elements

Effective Nuclear Charge

In Chapter 7 we discussed the shielding effect that electrons close to the nucleus have on outer-shell electrons in many-electron atoms. The presence of other electrons in an atom reduces the electrostatic attraction between a given electron and the positively charged protons in the nucleus. The ***effective nuclear charge*** (Z_{eff}) is *the nuclear charge felt by an electron when both the actual nuclear charge (Z) and the repulsive effects (shielding) of the other electrons are taken into account.* In general, Z_{eff} is given by

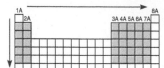

The increase in effective nuclear charge from left to right across a period and from top to bottom in a group for representative elements.

$$Z_{eff} = Z - \sigma \qquad (8.2)$$

where σ (sigma) is called the *shielding constant* (also called the *screening constant*). The shielding constant is greater than zero but smaller than Z.

One way to illustrate how electrons in an atom shield one another is to consider the amounts of energy required to remove the two electrons from a helium atom. Experiments show that it takes 3.94×10^{-18} J to remove the first electron and 8.72×10^{-18} J to remove the second electron. There is no shielding once the first electron is removed, so the second electron feels the full effect of the +2 nuclear charge.

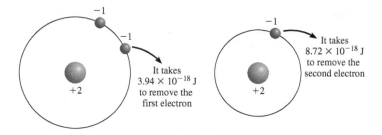

See Figure 7.27 for radial probability plots of 1s and 2s orbitals.

Because the core electrons are, on average, closer to the nucleus than valence electrons, core electrons shield valence electrons much more than valence electrons shield one another. Consider the second-period elements from Li to Ne. Moving from left to right, we find the number of core electrons ($1s^2$) remains constant while the nuclear charge increases. However, because the added electron is a valence electron and valence electrons do not shield each other well, the net effect of moving across the period is a greater effective nuclear charge felt by the valence electrons, as shown here.

	Li	Be	B	C	N	O	F	Ne
Z	3	4	5	6	7	8	9	10
Z_{eff}	1.28	1.91	2.42	3.14	3.83	4.45	5.10	5.76

The attractive force between the nucleus and a particular electron is directly proportional to the effective nuclear charge and inversely proportional to the square of the distance of separation.

The effective nuclear charge also increases as we go down a particular periodic group. However, because the valence electrons are now added to increasingly large shells as *n* increases, the electrostatic attraction between the nucleus and the valence electrons actually decreases.

	Li	Na	K	Rb	Cs
Z	3	11	19	37	55
Z_{eff}	1.28	2.51	3.50	4.98	6.36

Atomic Radius

A number of physical properties, including density, melting point, and boiling point, are related to the sizes of atoms, but atomic size is difficult to define. As we saw in Chapter 7, the electron density in an atom extends far beyond the nucleus, but we normally think of atomic size as the volume containing about 90 percent of the total electron density around the nucleus. When we must be even more specific, we define the size of an atom in terms of its ***atomic radius,*** which is *one-half the distance between the two nuclei in two adjacent metal atoms or in a diatomic molecule.*

For atoms linked together to form an extensive three-dimensional network, atomic radius is simply one-half the distance between the nuclei in two neighboring atoms [Figure 8.4(a)]. For elements that exist as simple diatomic molecules, the atomic radius is one-half the distance between the nuclei of the two atoms in a particular molecule [Figure 8.4(b)].

Figure 8.5 shows the atomic radius of many elements according to their positions in the periodic table, and Figure 8.6 plots the atomic radii of these elements against their atomic numbers. Periodic trends are clearly evident. Consider the second-period elements. Because the effective nuclear charge increases from left to right, the added valence electron at each step is more strongly attracted by the nucleus than the one before. Therefore, we expect and indeed find the atomic radius

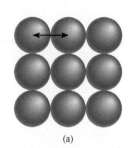

▶▶▶ **Animation**
Atomic and Ionic Radius

(a)

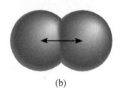

(b)

Figure 8.4 *(a) In metals such as polonium, the atomic radius is defined as one-half the distance between the centers of two adjacent atoms. (b) For elements that exist as diatomic molecules, such as iodine, the radius of the atom is defined as one-half the distance between the centers of the atoms in the molecule.*

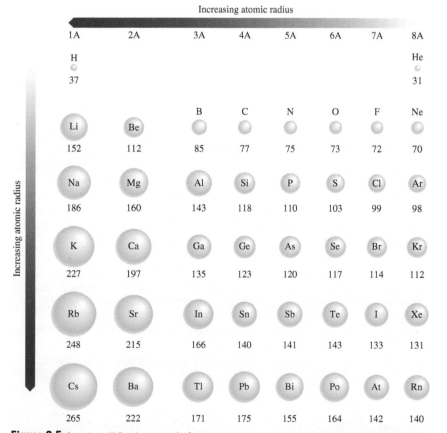

Figure 8.5 *Atomic radii (in picometers) of representative elements according to their positions in the periodic table. Note that there is no general agreement on the size of atomic radii. We focus only on the trends in atomic radii, not on their precise values.*

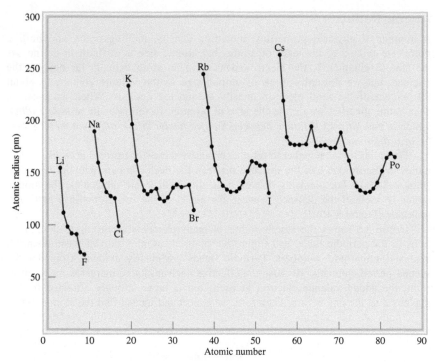

Figure 8.6 *Plot of atomic radii (in picometers) of elements against their atomic numbers.*

decreases from Li to Ne. Within a group we find that atomic radius increases with atomic number. For the alkali metals in Group 1A, the valence electron resides in the *ns* orbital. Because orbital size increases with the increasing principal quantum number *n*, the size of the atomic radius increases even though the effective nuclear charge also increases from Li to Cs.

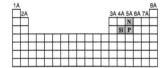

Example 8.2

Referring to a periodic table, arrange the following atoms in order of increasing atomic radius: P, Si, N.

Strategy What are the trends in atomic radii in a periodic group and in a particular period? Which of the preceding elements are in the same group? in the same period?

Solution From Figure 8.1 we see that N and P are in the same group (Group 5A). Therefore, the radius of N is smaller than that of P (atomic radius increases as we go down a group). Both Si and P are in the third period, and Si is to the left of P. Therefore, the radius of P is smaller than that of Si (atomic radius decreases as we move from left to right across a period). Thus, the order of increasing radius is N < P < Si .

Practice Exercise Arrange the following atoms in order of decreasing radius: C, Li, Be.

Similar problems: 8.37, 8.38.

Review of Concepts

Compare the size of each pair of atoms listed here: (a) Be, Ba; (b) Al, S; (c) ^{12}C, ^{13}C.

Ionic Radius

Ionic radius is *the radius of a cation or an anion*. It can be measured by X-ray diffraction (see Chapter 11). Ionic radius affects the physical and chemical properties of an ionic compound. For example, the three-dimensional structure of an ionic compound depends on the relative sizes of its cations and anions.

When a neutral atom is converted to an ion, we expect a change in size. If the atom forms an anion, its size (or radius) increases, because the nuclear charge remains the same but the repulsion resulting from the additional electron(s) enlarges the domain of the electron cloud. On the other hand, removing one or more electrons from an atom reduces electron-electron repulsion but the nuclear charge remains the same, so the electron cloud shrinks, and the cation is smaller than the atom. Figure 8.7 shows the changes in size that result when alkali metals are converted to cations and halogens are converted to anions; Figure 8.8 shows the changes in size that occur when a lithium atom reacts with a fluorine atom to form a LiF unit.

Figure 8.9 shows the radii of ions derived from the familiar elements, arranged according to the elements' positions in the periodic table. We can see parallel trends between atomic radii and ionic radii. For example, from top to bottom both the atomic radius and the ionic radius increase within a group. For ions derived from elements in different groups, a size comparison is meaningful only if the ions are isoelectronic. If we examine isoelectronic ions, we find that cations are smaller than anions. For example, Na^+ is smaller than F^-. Both ions have the same number of electrons, but Na ($Z = 11$) has more protons than F ($Z = 9$). The larger effective nuclear charge of Na^+ results in a smaller radius.

For isoelectronic ions, the size of the ion is based on the size of the electron cloud, not on the number of protons in the nucleus.

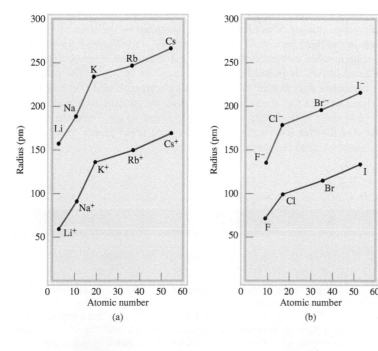

Figure 8.7 *Comparison of atomic radii with ionic radii. (a) Alkali metals and alkali metal cations. (b) Halogens and halide ions.*

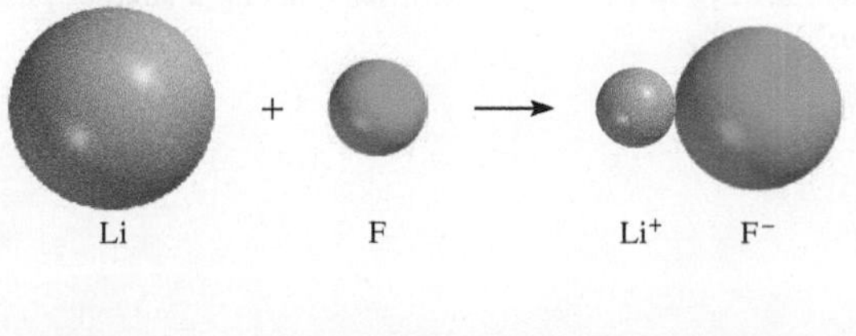

Figure 8.8 *Changes in the sizes of Li and F when they react to form LiF.*

338   **Chapter 8** ▪ Periodic Relationships Among the Elements

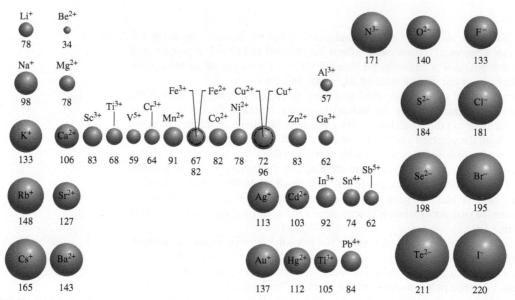

Figure 8.9 *The radii (in picometers) of ions of familiar elements arranged according to the elements' positions in the periodic table.*

Focusing on isoelectronic cations, we see that the radii of *tripositive ions* (ions that bear three positive charges) are smaller than those of *dipositive ions* (ions that bear two positive charges), which in turn are smaller than *unipositive ions* (ions that bear one positive charge). This trend is nicely illustrated by the sizes of three isoelectronic ions in the third period: Al^{3+}, Mg^{2+}, and Na^+ (see Figure 8.9). The Al^{3+} ion has the same number of electrons as Mg^{2+}, but it has one more proton. Thus, the electron cloud in Al^{3+} is pulled inward more than that in Mg^{2+}. The smaller radius of Mg^{2+} compared with that of Na^+ can be similarly explained. Turning to isoelectronic anions, we find that the radius increases as we go from ions with uninegative charge ($-$) to those with dinegative charge ($2-$), and so on. Thus, the oxide ion is larger than the fluoride ion because oxygen has one fewer proton than fluorine; the electron cloud is spread out more in O^{2-}.

Example 8.3

For each of the following pairs, indicate which one of the two species is larger: (a) N^{3-} or F^-; (b) Mg^{2+} or Ca^{2+}; (c) Fe^{2+} or Fe^{3+}.

Strategy In comparing ionic radii, it is useful to classify the ions into three categories: (1) isoelectronic ions, (2) ions that carry the same charges and are generated from atoms of the same periodic group, and (3) ions that carry different charges but are generated from the same atom. In case (1), ions that carry a greater negative charge are always larger; in case (2), ions from atoms having a greater atomic number are always larger; in case (3), ions having a smaller positive charge are always larger.

(Continued)

Solution

(a) N^{3-} and F^- are isoelectronic anions, both containing 10 electrons. Because N^{3-} has only seven protons and F^- has nine, the smaller attraction exerted by the nucleus on the electrons results in a larger N^{3-} ion.

(b) Both Mg and Ca belong to Group 2A (the alkaline earth metals). Thus, Ca^{2+} ion is larger than Mg^{2+} because Ca's valence electrons are in a larger shell ($n = 4$) than are Mg's ($n = 3$).

(c) Both ions have the same nuclear charge, but Fe^{2+} has one more electron (24 electrons compared to 23 electrons for Fe^{3+}) and hence greater electron-electron repulsion. The radius of Fe^{2+} is larger.

Similar problems: 8.43, 8.45.

Practice Exercise Select the smaller ion in each of the following pairs: (a) K^+, Li^+; (b) Au^+, Au^{3+}; (c) P^{3-}, N^{3-}.

Review of Concepts

Identify the spheres shown here with each of the following: S^{2-}, Mg^{2+}, F^-, Na^+.

Variation of Physical Properties Across a Period and Within a Group

From left to right across a period there is a transition from metals to metalloids to nonmetals. Consider the third-period elements from sodium to argon (Figure 8.10). Sodium, the first element in the third period, is a very reactive metal, whereas chlorine, the second-to-last element of that period, is a very reactive nonmetal. In between, the elements show a gradual transition from metallic properties to nonmetallic properties. Sodium, magnesium, and aluminum all have extensive three-dimensional atomic networks, which are held together by forces characteristic of the metallic state. Silicon is a metalloid; it has a giant three-dimensional structure in which the Si atoms are held together very strongly. Starting with phosphorus, the elements exist in simple, discrete molecular units (P_4, S_8, Cl_2, and Ar) that have low melting points and boiling points.

Within a periodic group the physical properties vary more predictably, especially if the elements are in the same physical state. For example, the melting points of argon and xenon are $-189.2°C$ and $-111.9°C$, respectively. We can estimate the melting point of the intermediate element krypton by taking the average of these two values as follows:

$$\text{melting point of Kr} = \frac{[(-189.2°C) + (-111.9°C)]}{2} = -150.6°C$$

This value is quite close to the actual melting point of $-156.6°C$.

The Chemistry in Action essay on p. 341 illustrates one interesting application of periodic group properties.

340   **Chapter 8** ▪ Periodic Relationships Among the Elements

Figure 8.10 *The third-period elements. The photograph of argon, which is a colorless, odorless gas, shows the color emitted by the gas from a discharge tube.*

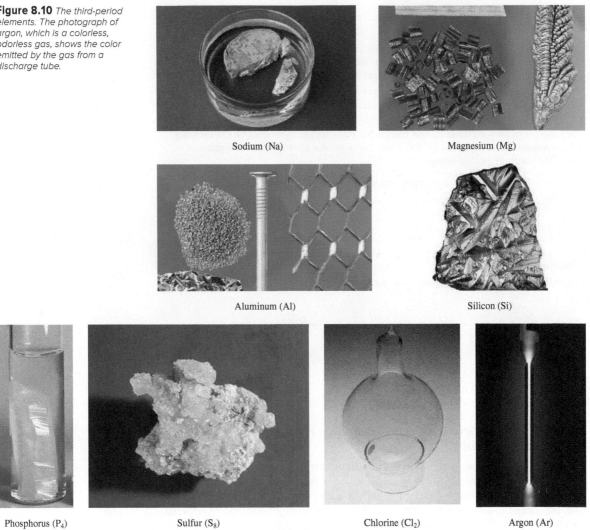

Sodium (Na)   Magnesium (Mg)

Aluminum (Al)   Silicon (Si)

Phosphorus (P_4)   Sulfur (S_8)   Chlorine (Cl_2)   Argon (Ar)

8.4 Ionization Energy

Not only is there a correlation between electron configuration and physical properties, but a close correlation also exists between electron configuration (a microscopic property) and chemical behavior (a macroscopic property). As we will see throughout this book, the chemical properties of any atom are determined by the configuration of the atom's valence electrons. The stability of these outermost electrons is reflected directly in the atom's ionization energies. *Ionization energy (IE)* is *the minimum energy (in kJ/mol) required to remove an electron from a gaseous atom in its ground state*. In other words, ionization energy is the amount of energy in kilojoules needed to strip 1 mole of electrons from 1 mole of gaseous atoms. Gaseous atoms are specified in this definition because an atom in the gas phase is virtually uninfluenced by its neighbors and so there are no intermolecular forces (that is, forces between molecules) to take into account when measuring ionization energy.

CHEMISTRY *in Action*

The Third Liquid Element?

Of the 118 known elements, 11 are gases under atmospheric conditions. Six of these are the Group 8A elements (the noble gases He, Ne, Ar, Kr, Xe, and Rn), and the other five are hydrogen (H_2), nitrogen (N_2), oxygen (O_2), fluorine (F_2), and chlorine (Cl_2). Curiously, only two elements are liquids at 25°C: mercury (Hg) and bromine (Br_2).

We do not know the properties of all the known elements because some of them have never been prepared in quantities large enough for investigation. In these cases, we must rely on periodic trends to predict their properties. What are the chances, then, of discovering a third liquid element?

Let us look at francium (Fr), the last member of Group 1A, to see if it might be a liquid at 25°C. All of francium's isotopes are radioactive. The most stable isotope is francium-223, which has a half-life of 21 minutes. (*Half-life* is the time it takes for one-half of the nuclei in any given amount of a radioactive substance to disintegrate.) This short half-life means that only very small traces of francium could possibly exist on Earth. And although it is feasible to prepare francium in the laboratory, no weighable quantity of the element has been prepared or isolated. Thus, we know very little about francium's physical and chemical properties. Yet we can use the group periodic trends to predict some of those properties.

Take francium's melting point as an example. The plot shows how the melting points of the alkali metals vary with atomic number. From lithium to sodium, the melting point

drops 81.4°; from sodium to potassium, 34.6°; from potassium to rubidium, 24°; from rubidium to cesium, 11°. On the basis of this trend, we can predict that the change from cesium to francium would be about 5°. If so, the melting point of francium would be about 23°C, which would make it a liquid under atmospheric conditions.

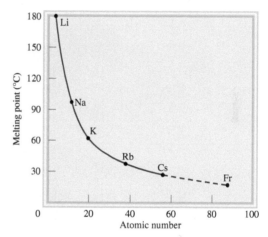

A plot of the melting points of the alkali metals versus their atomic numbers. By extrapolation, the melting point of francium should be 23°C.

The magnitude of ionization energy is a measure of how "tightly" the electron is held in the atom. The higher the ionization energy, the more difficult it is to remove the electron. For a many-electron atom, the amount of energy required to remove the first electron from the atom in its ground state,

$$\text{energy} + X(g) \longrightarrow X^+(g) + e^- \tag{8.3}$$

is called the *first ionization energy* (IE_1). In Equation (8.3), X represents an atom of any element and e^- is an electron. The second ionization energy (IE_2) and the third ionization energy (IE_3) are shown in the following equations:

$$\text{energy} + X^+(g) \longrightarrow X^{2+}(g) + e^- \quad \text{second ionization}$$
$$\text{energy} + X^{2+}(g) \longrightarrow X^{3+}(g) + e^- \quad \text{third ionization}$$

The pattern continues for the removal of subsequent electrons.

When an electron is removed from an atom, the repulsion among the remaining electrons decreases. Because the nuclear charge remains constant, more energy is

Note that while valence electrons are relatively easy to remove from the atom, core electrons are much harder to remove. Thus, there is a large jump in ionization energy between the last valence electron and the first core electron.

342   **Chapter 8** ▪ Periodic Relationships Among the Elements

Table 8.2	The Ionization Energies (kJ/mol) of the First 20 Elements						
Z	Element	First	Second	Third	Fourth	Fifth	Sixth
1	H	1,312					
2	He	2,373	5,251				
3	Li	520	7,300	11,815			
4	Be	899	1,757	14,850	21,005		
5	B	801	2,430	3,660	25,000	32,820	
6	C	1,086	2,350	4,620	6,220	38,000	47,261
7	N	1,400	2,860	4,580	7,500	9,400	53,000
8	O	1,314	3,390	5,300	7,470	11,000	13,000
9	F	1,680	3,370	6,050	8,400	11,000	15,200
10	Ne	2,080	3,950	6,120	9,370	12,200	15,000
11	Na	495.9	4,560	6,900	9,540	13,400	16,600
12	Mg	738.1	1,450	7,730	10,500	13,600	18,000
13	Al	577.9	1,820	2,750	11,600	14,800	18,400
14	Si	786.3	1,580	3,230	4,360	16,000	20,000
15	P	1,012	1,904	2,910	4,960	6,240	21,000
16	S	999.5	2,250	3,360	4,660	6,990	8,500
17	Cl	1,251	2,297	3,820	5,160	6,540	9,300
18	Ar	1,521	2,666	3,900	5,770	7,240	8,800
19	K	418.7	3,052	4,410	5,900	8,000	9,600
20	Ca	589.5	1,145	4,900	6,500	8,100	11,000

The increase in first ionization energy from left to right across a period and from bottom to top in a group for representative elements.

needed to remove another electron from the positively charged ion. Thus, ionization energies always increase in the following order:

$$IE_1 < IE_2 < IE_3 < \cdots$$

Table 8.2 lists the ionization energies of the first 20 elements. Ionization is always an endothermic process. By convention, energy absorbed by atoms (or ions) in the ionization process has a positive value. Thus, ionization energies are all positive quantities. Figure 8.11 shows the variation of the first ionization energy with atomic number. The plot clearly exhibits the periodicity in the stability of the most loosely held electron. Note that, apart from small irregularities, the first ionization energies of elements in a period increase with increasing atomic number. This trend is due to the increase in effective nuclear charge from left to right (as in the case of atomic radii variation). A larger effective nuclear charge means a more tightly held valence electron, and hence a higher first ionization energy. A notable feature of Figure 8.11 is the peaks, which correspond to the noble gases. We tend to associate full valence-shell electron configurations with an inherent degree of chemical stability. The high ionization energies of the noble gases, stemming from their large effective nuclear charge, comprise one of the reasons for this stability. In fact, helium ($1s^2$) has the highest first ionization energy of all the elements.

At the bottom of the graph in Figure 8.11 are the Group 1A elements (the alkali metals), which have the lowest first ionization energies. Each of these metals has one valence electron (the outermost electron configuration is ns^1), which is effectively shielded by the completely filled inner shells. Consequently, it is energetically easy to remove an electron from the atom of an alkali metal to form a

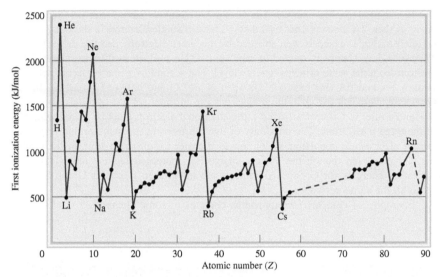

Figure 8.11 *Variation of the first ionization energy with atomic number. Note that the noble gases have high ionization energies, whereas the alkali metals and alkaline earth metals have low ionization energies.*

unipositive ion (Li^+, Na^+, K^+, ...). Significantly, the electron configurations of these cations are isoelectronic with those noble gases just preceding them in the periodic table.

The Group 2A elements (the alkaline earth metals) have higher first ionization energies than the alkali metals do. The alkaline earth metals have two valence electrons (the outermost electron configuration is ns^2). Because these two s electrons do not shield each other well, the effective nuclear charge for an alkaline earth metal atom is larger than that for the preceding alkali metal. Most alkaline earth compounds contain dipositive ions (Mg^{2+}, Ca^{2+}, Sr^{2+}, Ba^{2+}). The Be^{2+} ion is isoelectronic with Li^+ and with He, Mg^{2+} is isoelectronic with Na^+ and with Ne, and so on.

As Figure 8.11 shows, metals have relatively low ionization energies compared to nonmetals. The ionization energies of the metalloids generally fall between those of metals and nonmetals. The difference in ionization energies suggests why metals always form cations and nonmetals form anions in ionic compounds. (The only important nonmetallic cation is the ammonium ion, NH_4^+.) For a given group, ionization energy decreases with increasing atomic number (that is, as we move down the group). Elements in the same group have similar outer electron configurations. However, as the principal quantum number n increases, so does the average distance of a valence electron from the nucleus. A greater separation between the electron and the nucleus means a weaker attraction, so that it becomes easier to remove the first electron as we go from element to element down a group even though the effective nuclear charge also increases in the same direction. Thus, the metallic character of the elements within a group increases from top to bottom. This trend is particularly noticeable for elements in Groups 3A to 7A. For example, in Group 4A, carbon is a nonmetal, silicon and germanium are metalloids, and tin and lead are metals.

Although the general trend in the periodic table is for first ionization energies to increase from left to right, some irregularities do exist. The first exception occurs between Group 2A and 3A elements in the same period (for example, between Be and B and between Mg and Al). The Group 3A elements have lower first ionization energies than 2A elements because they all have a single electron in the outermost p subshell (ns^2np^1), which is well shielded by the inner electrons and the ns^2 electrons. Therefore, less energy is needed to remove a single p electron than to remove an s electron from the same principal energy level. The second irregularity occurs between Groups 5A and 6A (for example, between N and O and between P and S). In the Group 5A elements (ns^2np^3), the p electrons are in three separate orbitals according to Hund's rule. In Group 6A (ns^2np^4), the additional electron must be paired with one of the three p electrons. The proximity of two electrons in the same orbital results in greater electrostatic repulsion, which makes it easier to ionize an atom of the Group 6A element, even though the nuclear charge has increased by one unit. Thus, the ionization energies for Group 6A elements are lower than those for Group 5A elements in the same period.

Example 8.4 compares the ionization energies of some elements.

Example 8.4

(a) Which atom should have a lower first ionization energy: oxygen or sulfur? (b) Which atom should have a higher second ionization energy: lithium or beryllium?

Strategy (a) First ionization energy decreases as we go down a group because the outermost electron is farther away from the nucleus and feels less attraction. (b) Removal of the outermost electron requires less energy if it is shielded by a filled inner shell.

Solution

(a) Oxygen and sulfur are members of Group 6A. They have the same valence electron configuration (ns^2np^4), but the $3p$ electron in sulfur is farther from the nucleus and experiences less nuclear attraction than the $2p$ electron in oxygen. Thus, we predict that sulfur should have a smaller first ionization energy.

(b) The electron configurations of Li and Be are $1s^22s^1$ and $1s^22s^2$, respectively. The second ionization energy is the minimum energy required to remove an electron from a gaseous unipositive ion in its ground state. For the second ionization process, we write

$$\begin{array}{ll} \text{Li}^+(g) \longrightarrow \text{Li}^{2+}(g) + e^- \\ 1s^2 \qquad\qquad 1s^1 \\ \text{Be}^+(g) \longrightarrow \text{Be}^{2+}(g) + e^- \\ 1s^22s^1 \qquad\quad 1s^2 \end{array}$$

Because $1s$ electrons shield $2s$ electrons much more effectively than they shield each other, we predict that it should be easier to remove a $2s$ electron from Be$^+$ than to remove a $1s$ electron from Li$^+$.

Check Compare your result with the data shown in Table 8.2. In (a), is your prediction consistent with the fact that the metallic character of the elements increases as we move down a periodic group? In (b), does your prediction account for the fact that alkali metals form +1 ions while alkaline earth metals form +2 ions?

Similar problem: 8.55.

Practice Exercise (a) Which of the following atoms should have a larger first ionization energy: N or P? (b) Which of the following atoms should have a smaller second ionization energy: Na or Mg?

Review of Concepts

Label the plots shown here for the first, second, and third ionization energies for Mg, Al, and K.

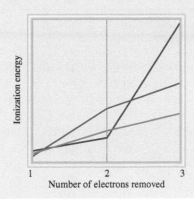

8.5 Electron Affinity

Another property that greatly influences the chemical behavior of atoms is their ability to accept one or more electrons. This property is called ***electron affinity (EA),*** which is *the negative of the energy change that occurs when an electron is accepted by an atom in the gaseous state to form an anion.*

$$X(g) + e^- \longrightarrow X^-(g) \tag{8.4}$$

Consider the process in which a gaseous fluorine atom accepts an electron:

$$F(g) + e^- \longrightarrow F^-(g) \qquad \Delta H = -328 \text{ kJ/mol}$$

The electron affinity of fluorine is therefore assigned a value of $+328$ kJ/mol. The more positive is the electron affinity of an element, the greater is the affinity of an atom of the element to accept an electron. Another way of viewing electron affinity is to think of it as the energy that must be supplied to remove an electron from the anion. For fluorine, we write

$$F^-(g) \longrightarrow F(g) + e^- \qquad \Delta H = +328 \text{ kJ/mol}$$

Electron affinity is positive if the reaction is exothermic and negative if the reaction is endothermic. This convention is used in inorganic and physical chemistry texts.

Thus, a large positive electron affinity means that the negative ion is very stable (that is, the atom has a great tendency to accept an electron), just as a high ionization energy of an atom means that the electron in the atom is very stable.

Experimentally, electron affinity is determined by removing the additional electron from an anion. In contrast to ionization energies, however, electron affinities are difficult to measure because the anions of many elements are unstable. Table 8.3 shows the electron affinities of some representative elements and the noble gases, and Figure 8.12 plots the electron affinities of the first 56 elements versus atomic number. The overall trend is an increase in the tendency to accept electrons (electron affinity values become more positive) from left to right across a period. The electron affinities of metals are generally lower than those of nonmetals. The values vary little within a given group. The halogens (Group 7A) have the highest electron affinity values.

346   **Chapter 8** ▪ Periodic Relationships Among the Elements

Table 8.3	Electron Affinities (kJ/mol) of Some Representative Elements and the Noble Gases*						
1A	**2A**	**3A**	**4A**	**5A**	**6A**	**7A**	**8A**
H							He
73							< 0
Li	Be	B	C	N	O	F	Ne
60	≤ 0	27	122	0	141	328	< 0
Na	Mg	Al	Si	P	S	Cl	Ar
53	≤ 0	44	134	72	200	349	< 0
K	Ca	Ga	Ge	As	Se	Br	Kr
48	2.4	29	118	77	195	325	< 0
Rb	Sr	In	Sn	Sb	Te	I	Xe
47	4.7	29	121	101	190	295	< 0
Cs	Ba	Tl	Pb	Bi	Po	At	Rn
45	14	30	110	110	?	?	< 0

*The electron affinities of the noble gases, Be, and Mg have not been determined experimentally, but are believed to be close to zero or negative.

There is a general correlation between electron affinity and effective nuclear charge, which also increases from left to right in a given period (see p. 334). However, as in the case of ionization energies, there are some irregularities. For example, the electron affinity of a Group 2A element is lower than that for the corresponding Group 1A element, and the electron affinity of a Group 5A element is lower than that for the corresponding Group 4A element. These exceptions are due to the valence electron configurations of the elements involved. An electron added to a

Figure 8.12 *A plot of electron affinity against atomic number from hydrogen to barium.*

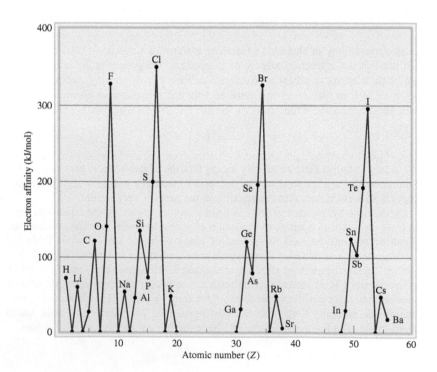

Group 2A element must end up in a higher-energy np orbital, where it is effectively shielded by the ns^2 electrons and therefore experiences a weaker attraction to the nucleus. Therefore, it has a lower electron affinity than the corresponding Group 1A element. Likewise, it is harder to add an electron to a Group 5A element (ns^2np^3) than to the corresponding Group 4A element (ns^2np^2) because the electron added to the Group 5A element must be placed in a np orbital that already contains an electron and will therefore experience a greater electrostatic repulsion. Finally, in spite of the fact that noble gases have high effective nuclear charge, they have extremely low electron affinities (zero or negative values). The reason is that an electron added to an atom with an ns^2np^6 configuration has to enter an $(n + 1)s$ orbital, where it is well shielded by the core electrons and will only be very weakly attracted by the nucleus. This analysis also explains why species with complete valence shells tend to be chemically stable.

The variation in electron affinities from top to bottom within a group is much less regular (see Table 8.3).

Example 8.5 shows why the alkaline earth metals do not have a great tendency to accept electrons.

Example 8.5

Why are the electron affinities of the alkaline earth metals, shown in Table 8.3, either negative or small positive values?

Strategy What are the electron configurations of alkaline earth metals? Would the added electron to such an atom be held strongly by the nucleus?

Solution The valence electron configuration of the alkaline earth metals is ns^2, where n is the highest principal quantum number. For the process

$$\underset{ns^2}{M(g)} + e^- \longrightarrow \underset{ns^2np^1}{M^-(g)}$$

where M denotes a member of the Group 2A family, the extra electron must enter the np subshell, which is effectively shielded by the two ns electrons (the ns electrons are more penetrating than the np electrons) and the inner electrons. Consequently, alkaline earth metals have little tendency to pick up an extra electron.

Practice Exercise Is it likely that Ar will form the anion Ar^-?

Similar problem: 8.63.

Review of Concepts

Why is it possible to measure the successive ionization energies of an atom until all the electrons are removed, but it becomes increasingly difficult and often impossible to measure the electron affinity of an atom beyond the first stage?

8.6 Variation in Chemical Properties of the Representative Elements

Ionization energy and electron affinity help chemists understand the types of reactions that elements undergo and the nature of the elements' compounds. On a conceptual level, these two measures are related in a simple way: Ionization energy measures the attraction of an atom for its own electrons, whereas electron affinity expresses the

348   **Chapter 8** ▪ Periodic Relationships Among the Elements

attraction of an atom for an additional electron from some other source. Together they give us insight into the general attraction of an atom for electrons. With these concepts we can survey the chemical behavior of the elements systematically, paying particular attention to the relationship between their chemical properties and their electron configurations.

We have seen that the metallic character of the elements *decreases* from left to right across a period and *increases* from top to bottom within a group. On the basis of these trends and the knowledge that metals usually have low ionization energies while nonmetals usually have high electron affinities, we can frequently predict the outcome of a reaction involving some of these elements.

General Trends in Chemical Properties

Before we study the elements in individual groups, let us look at some overall trends. We have said that elements in the same group resemble one another in chemical behavior because they have similar valence electron configurations. This statement, although correct in the general sense, must be applied with caution. Chemists have long known that the first member of each group (the element in the second period from lithium to fluorine) differs from the rest of the members of the same group. Lithium, for example, exhibits many, but not all, of the properties characteristic of the alkali metals. Similarly, beryllium is a somewhat atypical member of Group 2A, and so on. The difference can be attributed to the unusually small size of the first element in each group (see Figure 8.5).

Another trend in the chemical behavior of the representative elements is the diagonal relationship. *Diagonal relationships* are *similarities between pairs of elements in different groups and periods of the periodic table*. Specifically, the first three members of the second period (Li, Be, and B) exhibit many similarities to those elements located diagonally below them in the periodic table (Figure 8.13). The reason for this phenomenon is the closeness of the charge densities of their cations. (*Charge density* is the charge of an ion divided by its volume.) Cations with comparable charge densities react similarly with anions and therefore form the same type of compounds. Thus, the chemistry of lithium resembles that of magnesium in some ways; the same holds for beryllium and aluminum and for boron and silicon. Each of these pairs is said to exhibit a diagonal relationship. We will see a number of examples of this relationship later.

Bear in mind that a comparison of the properties of elements in the same group is most valid if we are dealing with elements of the same type with respect to their metallic character. This guideline applies to the elements in Groups 1A and 2A, which are all metals, and to the elements in Groups 7A and 8A, which are all nonmetals. In Groups 3A through 6A, where the elements change either from nonmetals to metals or from nonmetals to metalloids, it is natural to expect greater variation in chemical properties even though the members of the same group have similar outer electron configurations.

Now let us take a closer look at the chemical properties of the representative elements and the noble gases. (We will consider the chemistry of the transition metals in Chapter 23.)

Hydrogen ($1s^1$)

There is no totally suitable position for hydrogen in the periodic table. Traditionally hydrogen is shown in Group 1A, but it really could be a class by itself. Like the alkali metals, it has a single s valence electron and forms a unipositive ion (H^+), which is hydrated in solution. On the other hand, hydrogen also forms the hydride ion (H^-) in ionic compounds such as NaH and CaH$_2$. In this respect, hydrogen resembles the halogens, all of which form uninegative ions (F^-, Cl^-, Br^-, and I^-)

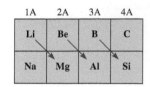

Figure 8.13 *Diagonal relationships in the periodic table.*

in ionic compounds. Ionic hydrides react with water to produce hydrogen gas and the corresponding metal hydroxides:

$$2NaH(s) + 2H_2O(l) \longrightarrow 2NaOH(aq) + H_2(g)$$
$$CaH_2(s) + 2H_2O(l) \longrightarrow Ca(OH)_2(s) + 2H_2(g)$$

Of course, the most important compound of hydrogen is water, which forms when hydrogen burns in air:

$$2H_2(g) + O_2(g) \longrightarrow 2H_2O(l)$$

Group 1A Elements (ns^1, $n \geq 2$)

Figure 8.14 shows the Group 1A elements, the alkali metals. All of these elements have low ionization energies and therefore a great tendency to lose the single valence electron. In fact, in the vast majority of their compounds they are uni-positive ions. These metals are so reactive that they are never found in the pure state in nature. They react with water to produce hydrogen gas and the corresponding metal hydroxide:

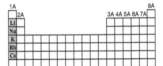

$$2M(s) + 2H_2O(l) \longrightarrow 2MOH(aq) + H_2(g)$$

where M denotes an alkali metal. When exposed to air, they gradually lose their shiny appearance as they combine with oxygen gas to form oxides. Lithium forms lithium oxide (containing the O^{2-} ion):

$$4Li(s) + O_2(g) \longrightarrow 2Li_2O(s)$$

The other alkali metals all form oxides and *peroxides* (containing the O_2^{2-} ion). For example,

$$2Na(s) + O_2(g) \longrightarrow Na_2O_2(s)$$

Lithium (Li)

Sodium (Na)

Figure 8.14 *The Group 1A elements: the alkali metals. Francium (not shown) is radioactive.*

Potassium (K)

Rubidium (Rb)

Cesium (Cs)

Potassium, rubidium, and cesium also form *superoxides* (containing the O_2^- ion):

$$K(s) + O_2(g) \longrightarrow KO_2(s)$$

The reason that different types of oxides are formed when alkali metals react with oxygen has to do with the stability of the oxides in the solid state. Because these oxides are all ionic compounds, their stability depends on how strongly the cations and anions attract one another. Lithium tends to form predominantly lithium oxide because this compound is more stable than lithium peroxide. The formation of other alkali metal oxides can be explained similarly.

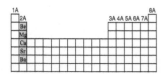

Group 2A Elements (ns^2, $n \geq 2$)

Figure 8.15 shows the Group 2A elements. As a group, the alkaline earth metals are somewhat less reactive than the alkali metals. Both the first and the second ionization energies decrease from beryllium to barium. Thus, the tendency is to form M^{2+} ions (where M denotes an alkaline earth metal atom), and hence the metallic character increases from top to bottom. Most beryllium compounds (BeH_2 and beryllium halides, such as $BeCl_2$) and some magnesium compounds (MgH_2, for example) are molecular rather than ionic in nature.

The reactivities of alkaline earth metals with water vary quite markedly. Beryllium does not react with water; magnesium reacts slowly with steam; calcium, strontium, and barium are reactive enough to attack cold water:

$$Ba(s) + 2H_2O(l) \longrightarrow Ba(OH)_2(aq) + H_2(g)$$

The reactivities of the alkaline earth metals toward oxygen also increase from Be to Ba. Beryllium and magnesium form oxides (BeO and MgO) only at elevated temperatures, whereas CaO, SrO, and BaO form at room temperature.

Magnesium reacts with acids in aqueous solution, liberating hydrogen gas:

$$Mg(s) + 2H^+(aq) \longrightarrow Mg^{2+}(aq) + H_2(g)$$

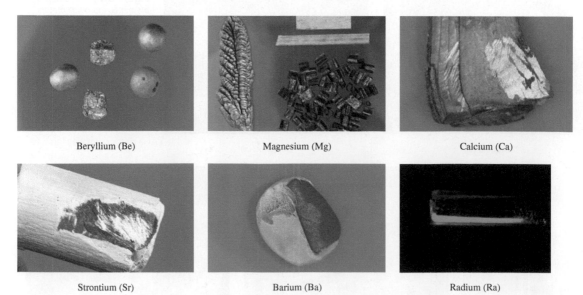

| Beryllium (Be) | Magnesium (Mg) | Calcium (Ca) |
| Strontium (Sr) | Barium (Ba) | Radium (Ra) |

Figure 8.15 *The Group 2A elements: the alkaline earth metals.*

Calcium, strontium, and barium also react with aqueous acid solutions to produce hydrogen gas. However, because these metals also attack water, two different reactions will occur simultaneously.

The chemical properties of calcium and strontium provide an interesting example of periodic group similarity. Strontium-90, a radioactive isotope, is a major product of an atomic bomb explosion. If an atomic bomb is exploded in the atmosphere, the strontium-90 formed will eventually settle on land and water, and it will reach our bodies via a relatively short food chain. For example, if cows eat contaminated grass and drink contaminated water, they will pass along strontium-90 in their milk. Because calcium and strontium are chemically similar, Sr^{2+} ions can replace Ca^{2+} ions in our bones. Constant exposure of the body to the high-energy radiation emitted by the strontium-90 isotopes can lead to anemia, leukemia, and other chronic illnesses.

Group 3A Elements (ns^2np^1, $n \geq 2$)

The first member of Group 3A, boron, is a metalloid; the rest are metals (Figure 8.16). Boron does not form binary ionic compounds and is unreactive toward oxygen gas and water. The next element, aluminum, readily forms aluminum oxide when exposed to air:

$$4Al(s) + 3O_2(g) \longrightarrow 2Al_2O_3(s)$$

Aluminum that has a protective coating of aluminum oxide is less reactive than elemental aluminum. Aluminum forms only tripositive ions. It reacts with hydrochloric acid as follows:

$$2Al(s) + 6H^+(aq) \longrightarrow 2Al^{3+}(aq) + 3H_2(g)$$

The other Group 3A metallic elements form both unipositive and tripositive ions. Moving down the group, we find that the unipositive ion becomes more stable than the tripositive ion.

Boron (B)

Aluminum (Al)

Figure 8.16 *The Group 3A elements. The low melting point of gallium (29.8°C) causes it to melt when held in hand.*

Gallium (Ga)

Indium (In)

Figure 8.17 *The Group 4A elements.*

Carbon (graphite)   Carbon (diamond)   Silicon (Si)

Germanium (Ge)   Tin (Sn)   Lead (Pb)

The metallic elements in Group 3A also form many molecular compounds. For example, aluminum reacts with hydrogen to form AlH_3, which resembles BeH_2 in its properties. (Here is an example of the diagonal relationship.) Thus, from left to right across the periodic table, we are seeing a gradual shift from metallic to nonmetallic character in the representative elements.

Group 4A Elements (ns^2np^2, $n \geq 2$)

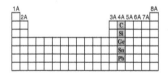

The first member of Group 4A, carbon, is a nonmetal, and the next two members, silicon and germanium, are metalloids (Figure 8.17). The metallic elements of this group, tin and lead, do not react with water, but they do react with acids (hydrochloric acid, for example) to liberate hydrogen gas:

$$Sn(s) + 2H^+(aq) \longrightarrow Sn^{2+}(aq) + H_2(g)$$
$$Pb(s) + 2H^+(aq) \longrightarrow Pb^{2+}(aq) + H_2(g)$$

The Group 4A elements form compounds in both the +2 and +4 oxidation states. For carbon and silicon, the +4 oxidation state is the more stable one. For example, CO_2 is more stable than CO, and SiO_2 is a stable compound, but SiO does not exist under normal conditions. As we move down the group, however, the trend in stability is reversed. In tin compounds the +4 oxidation state is only slightly more stable than the +2 oxidation state. In lead compounds the +2 oxidation state is unquestionably the more stable one. The outer electron configuration of lead is $6s^26p^2$, and lead tends to lose only the $6p$ electrons (to form Pb^{2+}) rather than both the $6p$ and $6s$ electrons (to form Pb^{4+}).

Group 5A Elements (ns^2np^3, $n \geq 2$)

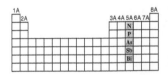

In Group 5A, nitrogen and phosphorus are nonmetals, arsenic and antimony are metalloids, and bismuth is a metal (Figure 8.18). Thus, we expect a greater variation in properties within the group.

Liquid nitrogen (N_2)

White and red phosphorus (P)

Figure 8.18 *The Group 5A elements. Molecular nitrogen is a colorless, odorless gas.*

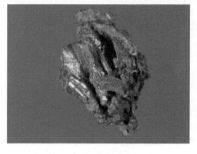

Arsenic (As)

Antimony (Sb)

Bismuth (Bi)

Elemental nitrogen is a diatomic gas (N_2). It forms a number of oxides (NO, N_2O, NO_2, N_2O_4, and N_2O_5), of which only N_2O_5 is a solid; the others are gases. Nitrogen has a tendency to accept three electrons to form the nitride ion, N^{3-} (thus achieving the electron configuration $1s^2 2s^2 2p^6$, which is isoelectronic with neon). Most metallic nitrides (Li_3N and Mg_3N_2, for example) are ionic compounds. Phosphorus exists as P_4 molecules. It forms two solid oxides with the formulas P_4O_6 and P_4O_{10}. The important oxoacids HNO_3 and H_3PO_4 are formed when the following oxides react with water:

$$N_2O_5(s) + H_2O(l) \longrightarrow 2HNO_3(aq)$$
$$P_4O_{10}(s) + 6H_2O(l) \longrightarrow 4H_3PO_4(aq)$$

Arsenic, antimony, and bismuth have extensive three-dimensional structures. Bismuth is a far less reactive metal than those in the preceding groups.

Group 6A Elements (ns^2np^4, $n \geq 2$)

The first three members of Group 6A (oxygen, sulfur, and selenium) are nonmetals, and the last two (tellurium and polonium) are metalloids (Figure 8.19). Oxygen is a diatomic gas; elemental sulfur and selenium have the molecular formulas S_8 and Se_8, respectively; tellurium and polonium have more extensive three-dimensional structures. (Polonium, the last member, is a radioactive element that is difficult to study in the laboratory.) Oxygen has a tendency to accept two electrons to form the oxide ion (O^{2-}) in many ionic compounds. Sulfur, selenium, and tellurium also

354   **Chapter 8 ▪** Periodic Relationships Among the Elements

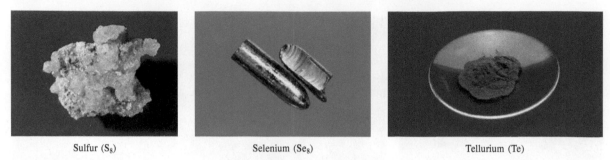

Sulfur (S₈)   Selenium (Se₈)   Tellurium (Te)

Figure 8.19 *The Group 6A elements sulfur, selenium, and tellurium. Molecular oxygen is a colorless, odorless gas. Polonium (not shown) is radioactive.*

form dinegative anions (S^{2-}, Se^{2-}, and Te^{2-}). The elements in this group (especially oxygen) form a large number of molecular compounds with nonmetals. The important compounds of sulfur are SO_2, SO_3, and H_2S. The most important commercial sulfur compound is sulfuric acid, which is formed when sulfur trioxide reacts with water:

$$SO_3(g) + H_2O(l) \longrightarrow H_2SO_4(aq)$$

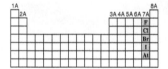

Group 7A Elements (ns^2np^5, $n \geq 2$)

All the halogens are nonmetals with the general formula X_2, where X denotes a halogen element (Figure 8.20). Because of their great reactivity, the halogens are never found in the elemental form in nature. (The last member of Group 7A, astatine, is a radioactive element. Little is known about its properties.) Fluorine is so reactive that it attacks water to generate oxygen:

$$2F_2(g) + 2H_2O(l) \longrightarrow 4HF(aq) + O_2(g)$$

Actually the reaction between molecular fluorine and water is quite complex; the products formed depend on reaction conditions. The reaction shown above is one of several possible chemical changes.

The halogens have high ionization energies and large positive electron affinities. Anions derived from the halogens (F^-, Cl^-, Br^-, and I^-) are called *halides*. They are isoelectronic with the noble gases immediately to their right in

Figure 8.20 *The Group 7A elements chlorine, bromine, and iodine. Fluorine is a greenish-yellow gas that attacks ordinary glassware. Astatine is radioactive.*

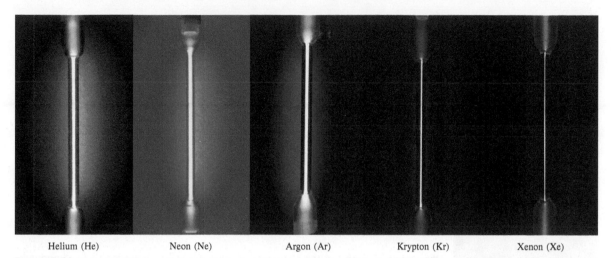

| Helium (He) | Neon (Ne) | Argon (Ar) | Krypton (Kr) | Xenon (Xe) |

Figure 8.21 *All noble gases are colorless and odorless. These pictures show the colors emitted by the gases from a discharge tube.*

the periodic table. For example, F^- is isoelectronic with Ne, Cl^- with Ar, and so on. The vast majority of the alkali metal halides and alkaline earth metal halides are ionic compounds. The halogens also form many molecular compounds among themselves (such as ICl and BrF_3) and with nonmetallic elements in other groups (such as NF_3, PCl_5, and SF_6). The halogens react with hydrogen to form hydrogen halides:

$$H_2(g) + X_2(g) \longrightarrow 2HX(g)$$

When this reaction involves fluorine, it is explosive, but it becomes less and less violent as we substitute chlorine, bromine, and iodine. The hydrogen halides dissolve in water to form hydrohalic acids. Hydrofluoric acid (HF) is a weak acid (that is, it is a weak electrolyte), but the other hydrohalic acids (HCl, HBr, and HI) are all strong acids (strong electrolytes).

Group 8A Elements (ns^2np^6, $n \geq 2$)

All noble gases exist as monatomic species (Figure 8.21). Their atoms have completely filled outer ns and np subshells, which give them great stability. (Helium is $1s^2$.) The Group 8A ionization energies are among the highest of all elements, and these gases have no tendency to accept extra electrons. For years these elements were called inert gases, and rightly so. Until 1963 no one had been able to prepare a compound containing any of these elements. The British chemist Neil Bartlett[†] shattered chemists' long-held views of these elements when he exposed xenon to platinum hexafluoride, a strong oxidizing agent, and brought about the following reaction (Figure 8.22):

$$Xe(g) + 2PtF_6(g) \longrightarrow XeF^+Pt_2F_{11}^-(s)$$

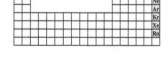

Since then, a number of xenon compounds (XeF_4, XeO_3, XeO_4, $XeOF_4$) and a few krypton compounds (KrF_2, for example) have been prepared (Figure 8.23). Despite

In 2000, chemists prepared a compound containing argon (HArF) that is stable only at very low temperatures.

[†]Neil Bartlett (1932–2008). English chemist. Bartlett's work was mainly in the preparation and study of compounds with unusual oxidation states and in solid-state chemistry.

356   **Chapter 8** ▪ Periodic Relationships Among the Elements

Figure 8.22 *(a) Xenon gas (colorless) and PtF$_6$ (red gas) separated from each other. (b) When the two gases are allowed to mix, a yellow-orange solid compound is formed. Note that the product was initially given the incorrect formula XePtF$_6$.*

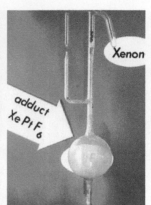

In 2013 astronomers reported finding the emission of HAr$^+$ in the Crab Nebula, making it the first molecular noble gas species to be detected in space.

the immense interest in the chemistry of the noble gases, however, their compounds do not have any major commercial applications, and they are not involved in natural biological processes. No compounds of helium and neon are known.

Comparison of Group 1A and Group 1B Elements

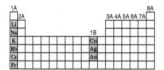

When we compare the Group 1A elements (alkali metals) and the Group 1B elements (copper, silver, and gold), we arrive at an interesting conclusion. Although the metals in these two groups have similar outer electron configurations, with one electron in the outermost *s* orbital, their chemical properties are quite different.

The first ionization energies of Cu, Ag, and Au are 745 kJ/mol, 731 kJ/mol, and 890 kJ/mol, respectively. Because these values are considerably larger than those of the alkali metals (see Table 8.2), the Group 1B elements are much less reactive. The higher ionization energies of the Group 1B elements result from incomplete shielding of the nucleus by the inner *d* electrons (compared with the more effective shielding of the completely filled noble gas cores). Consequently the outer *s* electrons of these elements are more strongly attracted by the nucleus. In fact, copper, silver, and gold are so unreactive that they are usually found in the uncombined state in nature. The inertness and rarity of these metals make them valuable in the manufacture of coins and in jewelry. For this reason, these metals are also called "coinage metals." The difference in chemical properties between the Group 2A elements (the alkaline earth metals) and the Group 2B metals (zinc, cadmium, and mercury) can be explained in a similar way.

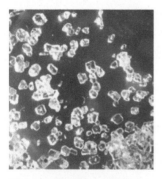

Figure 8.23 *Crystals of xenon tetrafluoride (XeF$_4$).*

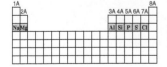

Properties of Oxides Across a Period

One way to compare the properties of the representative elements across a period is to examine the properties of a series of similar compounds. Because oxygen combines with almost all elements, we will compare the properties of oxides of the third-period elements to see how metals differ from metalloids and nonmetals. Some elements in the third period (P, S, and Cl) form several types of oxides, but for simplicity we will consider only those oxides in which the elements have the highest oxidation number. Table 8.4 lists a few general characteristics of these oxides. We observed earlier that oxygen has a tendency to form the oxide ion. This tendency is greatly favored when oxygen combines with metals that have low ionization energies, namely, those in Groups 1A and 2A, plus aluminum. Thus, Na$_2$O, MgO, and Al$_2$O$_3$ are ionic compounds, as indicated by their high melting points and boiling points. They have extensive three-dimensional structures in which each cation is surrounded by a specific number of anions, and vice versa. As the ionization energies

Table 8.4	**Some Properties of Oxides of the Third-Period Elements**						
	Na₂O	**MgO**	**Al₂O₃**	**SiO₂**	**P₄O₁₀**	**SO₃**	**Cl₂O₇**
Type of compound	← Ionic →			← Molecular →			
Structure	← Extensive three-dimensional →			← Discrete molecular units →			
Melting point (°C)	1275	2800	2045	1610	580	16.8	−91.5
Boiling point (°C)	?	3600	2980	2230	?	44.8	82
Acid-base nature	Basic	Basic	Amphoteric	← Acidic →			

of the elements increase from left to right, so does the molecular nature of the oxides that are formed. Silicon is a metalloid; its oxide (SiO_2) also has a huge three-dimensional network, although no ions are present. The oxides of phosphorus, sulfur, and chlorine are molecular compounds composed of small discrete units. The weak attractions among these molecules result in relatively low melting points and boiling points.

Most oxides can be classified as acidic or basic depending on whether they produce acids or bases when dissolved in water or react as acids or bases in certain processes. Some oxides are **amphoteric,** which means that they *display both acidic and basic properties*. The first two oxides of the third period, Na_2O and MgO, are basic oxides. For example, Na_2O reacts with water to form the base sodium hydroxide:

$$Na_2O(s) + H_2O(l) \longrightarrow 2NaOH(aq)$$

Magnesium oxide is quite insoluble; it does not react with water to any appreciable extent. However, it does react with acids in a manner that resembles an acid-base reaction:

$$MgO(s) + 2HCl(aq) \longrightarrow MgCl_2(aq) + H_2O(l)$$

Note that the products of this reaction are a salt ($MgCl_2$) and water, the usual products of an acid-base neutralization.

Aluminum oxide is even less soluble than magnesium oxide; it too does not react with water. However, it shows basic properties by reacting with acids:

$$Al_2O_3(s) + 6HCl(aq) \longrightarrow 2AlCl_3(aq) + 3H_2O(l)$$

It also exhibits acidic properties by reacting with bases:

$$Al_2O_3(s) + 2NaOH(aq) + 3H_2O(l) \longrightarrow 2NaAl(OH)_4(aq)$$

Note that this acid-base neutralization produces a salt but no water.

Thus, Al_2O_3 is classified as an amphoteric oxide because it has properties of both acids and bases. Other amphoteric oxides are ZnO, BeO, and Bi_2O_3.

Silicon dioxide is insoluble and does not react with water. It has acidic properties, however, because it reacts with very concentrated bases:

$$SiO_2(s) + 2NaOH(aq) \longrightarrow Na_2SiO_3(aq) + H_2O(l)$$

For this reason, concentrated aqueous, strong bases such as NaOH(aq) should not be stored in Pyrex glassware, which is made of SiO_2.

CHEMISTRY *in Action*

Discovery of the Noble Gases

In the late 1800s John William Strutt, Third Baron of Rayleigh, who was a professor of physics at the Cavendish Laboratory in Cambridge, England, accurately determined the atomic masses of a number of elements, but he obtained a puzzling result with nitrogen. One of his methods of preparing nitrogen was by the thermal decomposition of ammonia:

$$2NH_3(g) \longrightarrow N_2(g) + 3H_2(g)$$

Another method was to start with air and remove from it oxygen, carbon dioxide, and water vapor. Invariably, the nitrogen from air was a little denser (by about 0.5 percent) than the nitrogen from ammonia.

Lord Rayleigh's work caught the attention of Sir William Ramsay, a professor of chemistry at the University College, London. In 1898 Ramsay passed nitrogen, which he had obtained from air by Rayleigh's procedure, over red-hot magnesium to convert it to magnesium nitride:

$$3Mg(s) + N_2(g) \longrightarrow Mg_3N_2(s)$$

After all of the nitrogen had reacted with magnesium, Ramsay was left with an unknown gas that would not combine with anything.

With the help of Sir William Crookes, the inventor of the discharge tube, Ramsay and Lord Rayleigh found that the emission spectrum of the gas did not match any of the known elements. The gas was a new element! They determined its atomic mass to be 39.95 amu and called it argon, which means "the lazy one" in Greek.

Once argon had been discovered, other noble gases were quickly identified. Also in 1898 Ramsay isolated helium from uranium ores (see the Chemical Mystery essay on p. 324). From the atomic masses of helium and argon, their lack of chemical reactivity, and what was then known about the periodic table, Ramsay was convinced that there were other unreactive gases and that they were all members of one periodic group. He and his student Morris Travers set out to find the unknown gases. They used a refrigeration machine to first produce liquid air. Applying a technique called *fractional distillation,* they then allowed the liquid air to warm up gradually and collected components that boiled off at different temperatures. In this manner, they analyzed and identified three new elements—neon, krypton, and xenon—in only three months. Three new elements in three months is a record that may never be broken!

The discovery of the noble gases helped to complete the periodic table. Their atomic masses suggested that these elements should be placed to the right of the halogens. The apparent discrepancy with the position of argon was resolved by Moseley, as discussed in the chapter.

Finally, the last member of the noble gases, radon, was discovered by the German chemist Frederick Dorn in 1900. A radioactive element and the heaviest elemental gas known, radon's discovery not only completed the Group 8A elements, but also advanced our understanding about the nature of radioactive decay and transmutation of elements.

Lord Rayleigh and Ramsay both won Nobel prizes in 1904 for the discovery of argon. Lord Rayleigh received the prize in physics and Ramsay's award was in chemistry.

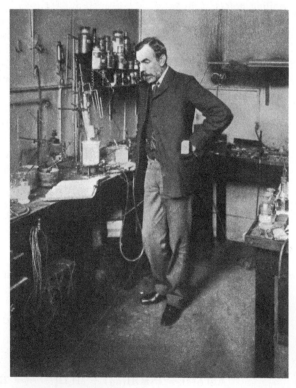

Sir William Ramsay (1852–1916).

The remaining third-period oxides are acidic. They react with water to form phosphoric acid (H_3PO_4), sulfuric acid (H_2SO_4), and perchloric acid ($HClO_4$):

$$P_4O_{10}(s) + 6H_2O(l) \longrightarrow 4H_3PO_4(aq)$$
$$SO_3(g) + H_2O(l) \longrightarrow H_2SO_4(aq)$$
$$Cl_2O_7(l) + H_2O(l) \longrightarrow 2HClO_4(aq)$$

Certain oxides such as CO and NO are neutral; that is, they do not react with water to produce an acidic or basic solution. In general, oxides containing nonmetallic elements are not basic.

This brief examination of oxides of the third-period elements shows that as the metallic character of the elements decreases from left to right across the period, their oxides change from basic to amphoteric to acidic. Metallic oxides are usually basic, and most oxides of nonmetals are acidic. The intermediate properties of the oxides (as shown by the amphoteric oxides) are exhibited by elements whose positions are intermediate within the period. Note also that because the metallic character of the elements increases from top to bottom within a group of representative elements, we would expect oxides of elements with higher atomic numbers to be more basic than the lighter elements. This is indeed the case.

Example 8.6

Classify the following oxides as acidic, basic, or amphoteric: (a) Rb_2O, (b) BeO, (c) As_2O_5.

Strategy What type of elements form acidic oxides? basic oxides? amphoteric oxides?

Solution

(a) Because rubidium is an alkali metal, we would expect Rb_2O to be a basic oxide.

(b) Beryllium is an alkaline earth metal. However, because it is the first member of Group 2A, we expect that it may differ somewhat from the other members of the group. In the text we saw that Al_2O_3 is amphoteric. Because beryllium and aluminum exhibit a diagonal relationship, BeO may resemble Al_2O_3 in properties. It turns out that BeO is also an amphoteric oxide.

(c) Because arsenic is a nonmetal, we expect As_2O_5 to be an acidic oxide.

Similar problem: 8.72.

Practice Exercise Classify the following oxides as acidic, basic, or amphoteric: (a) ZnO, (b) P_4O_{10}, (c) CaO.

Review of Concepts

An oxide of an element was determined to be basic. Which of the following could be that element? (a) Ba, (b) Al, and (c) Sb.

Key Equation

$Z_{eff} = Z - \sigma$ (8.2)   Definition of effective nuclear charge.

Summary of Facts & Concepts

1. Nineteenth-century chemists developed the periodic table by arranging elements in the increasing order of their atomic masses. Discrepancies in early versions of the periodic table were resolved by arranging the elements in order of their atomic numbers.

2. Electron configuration determines the properties of an element. The modern periodic table classifies the elements according to their atomic numbers, and thus also by their electron configurations. The configuration of the valence electrons directly affects the properties of the atoms of the representative elements.

360   **Chapter 8** ▪ Periodic Relationships Among the Elements

3. Periodic variations in the physical properties of the elements reflect differences in atomic structure. The metallic character of elements decreases across a period from metals through the metalloids to nonmetals and increases from top to bottom within a particular group of representative elements.

4. Atomic radius varies periodically with the arrangement of the elements in the periodic table. It decreases from left to right and increases from top to bottom.

5. Ionization energy is a measure of the tendency of an atom to resist the loss of an electron. The higher the ionization energy, the stronger the attraction between the nucleus and an electron. Electron affinity is a measure of the tendency of an atom to gain an electron. The

more positive the electron affinity, the greater the tendency for the atom to gain an electron. Metals usually have low ionization energies, and nonmetals usually have high electron affinities.

6. Noble gases are very stable because their outer ns and np subshells are completely filled. The metals among the representative elements (in Groups 1A, 2A, and 3A) tend to lose electrons until their cations become isoelectronic with the noble gases that precede them in the periodic table. The nonmetals in Groups 5A, 6A, and 7A tend to accept electrons until their anions become isoelectronic with the noble gases that follow them in the periodic table.

Key Words

Amphoteric oxide, p. 357	Effective nuclear charge	Ionic radius, p. 337	Representative elements,
Atomic radius, p. 335	(Z_{eff}), p. 334	Ionization energy	p. 330
Core electrons, p. 330	Electron affinity	(*IE*), p. 340	Valence electrons,
Diagonal relationship, p. 348	(*EA*), p. 345	Isoelectronic, p. 333	p. 330

Questions & Problems

● *Problems available in Connect Plus*
Red numbered problems solved in Student Solutions Manual

Development of the Periodic Table
Review Questions

8.1   Briefly describe the significance of Mendeleev's periodic table.

8.2   What is Moseley's contribution to the modern periodic table?

8.3   Describe the general layout of a modern periodic table.

8.4   What is the most important relationship among elements in the same group in the periodic table?

Periodic Classification of the Elements
Review Questions

● 8.5   Which of the following elements are metals, nonmetals, or metalloids? As, Xe, Fe, Li, B, Cl, Ba, P, I, Si.

8.6   Compare the physical and chemical properties of metals and nonmetals.

8.7   Draw a rough sketch of a periodic table (no details are required). Indicate regions where metals, nonmetals, and metalloids are located.

8.8   What is a representative element? Give names and symbols of four representative elements.

● 8.9   Without referring to a periodic table, write the name and give the symbol for an element in each of the following groups: 1A, 2A, 3A, 4A, 5A, 6A, 7A, 8A, transition metals.

● 8.10   Indicate whether the following elements exist as atomic species, molecular species, or extensive three-dimensional structures in their most stable states at 25°C and 1 atm and write the molecular or empirical formula for each one: phosphorus, iodine, magnesium, neon, carbon, sulfur, cesium, and oxygen.

8.11   You are given a dark shiny solid and asked to determine whether it is iodine or a metallic element. Suggest a nondestructive test that would enable you to arrive at the correct answer.

8.12   What are valence electrons? For representative elements, the number of valence electrons of an element is equal to its group number. Show that this is true for the following elements: Al, Sr, K, Br, P, S, C.

8.13   Write the outer electron configurations for the (a) alkali metals, (b) alkaline earth metals, (c) halogens, (d) noble gases.

8.14   Use the first-row transition metals (Sc to Cu) as an example to illustrate the characteristics of the electron configurations of transition metals.

8.15   The electron configurations of ions derived from representative elements follow a common pattern. What is the pattern, and how does it relate to the stability of these ions?

8.16   What do we mean when we say that two ions or an atom and an ion are isoelectronic?

8.17   What is wrong with the statement "The atoms of element X are isoelectronic with the atoms of element Y"?

8.18   Give three examples of first-row transition metal (Sc to Cu) ions whose electron configurations are represented by the argon core.

Problems

8.19   In the periodic table, the element hydrogen is sometimes grouped with the alkali metals (as in this book) and sometimes with the halogens. Explain why hydrogen can resemble the Group 1A and the Group 7A elements.

8.20   A neutral atom of a certain element has 17 electrons. Without consulting a periodic table, (a) write the ground-state electron configuration of the element, (b) classify the element, (c) determine whether this element is diamagnetic or paramagnetic.

8.21   Group the following electron configurations in pairs that would represent similar chemical properties of their atoms:
(a) $1s^2 2s^2 2p^6 3s^2$
(b) $1s^2 2s^2 2p^3$
(c) $1s^2 2s^2 2p^6 3s^2 3p^6 4s^2 3d^{10} 4p^6$
(d) $1s^2 2s^2$
(e) $1s^2 2s^2 2p^6$
(f) $1s^2 2s^2 2p^6 3s^2 3p^3$

8.22   Group the following electron configurations in pairs that would represent similar chemical properties of their atoms:
(a) $1s^2 2s^2 2p^5$
(b) $1s^2 2s^1$
(c) $1s^2 2s^2 2p^6$
(d) $1s^2 2s^2 2p^6 3s^2 3p^5$
(e) $1s^2 2s^2 2p^6 3s^2 3p^6 4s^1$
(f) $1s^2 2s^2 2p^6 3s^2 3p^6 4s^2 3d^{10} 4p^6$

8.23   Without referring to a periodic table, write the electron configuration of elements with the following atomic numbers: (a) 9, (b) 20, (c) 26, (d) 33. Classify the elements.

8.24   Specify the group of the periodic table in which each of the following elements is found: (a) $[Ne]3s^1$, (b) $[Ne]3s^2 3p^3$, (c) $[Ne]3s^2 3p^6$, (d) $[Ar]4s^2 3d^8$.

8.25   A M^{2+} ion derived from a metal in the first transition metal series has four electrons in the $3d$ subshell. What element might M be?

8.26   A metal ion with a net $+3$ charge has five electrons in the $3d$ subshell. Identify the metal.

8.27   Write the ground-state electron configurations of the following ions: (a) Li^+, (b) H^-, (c) N^{3-}, (d) F^-, (e) S^{2-}, (f) Al^{3+}, (g) Se^{2-}, (h) Br^-, (i) Rb^+, (j) Sr^{2+}, (k) Sn^{2+}, (l) Te^{2-}, (m) Ba^{2+}, (n) Pb^{2+}, (o) In^{3+}, (p) Tl^+, (q) Tl^{3+}.

8.28   Write the ground-state electron configurations of the following ions, which play important roles in biochemical processes in our bodies: (a) Na^+, (b) Mg^{2+}, (c) Cl^-, (d) K^+, (e) Ca^{2+}, (f) Fe^{2+}, (g) Cu^{2+}, (h) Zn^{2+}.

8.29   Write the ground-state electron configurations of the following transition metal ions: (a) Sc^{3+}, (b) Ti^{4+}, (c) V^{5+}, (d) Cr^{3+}, (e) Mn^{2+}, (f) Fe^{2+}, (g) Fe^{3+}, (h) Co^{2+}, (i) Ni^{2+}, (j) Cu^+, (k) Cu^{2+}, (l) Ag^+, (m) Au^+, (n) Au^{3+}, (o) Pt^{2+}.

8.30   Name the ions with $+3$ charges that have the following electron configurations: (a) $[Ar]3d^3$, (b) $[Ar]$, (c) $[Kr]4d^6$, (d) $[Xe]4f^{14}5d^6$.

8.31   Which of the following species are isoelectronic with each other? C, Cl^-, Mn^{2+}, B^-, Ar, Zn, Fe^{3+}, Ge^{2+}.

8.32   Group the species that are isoelectronic: Be^{2+}, F^-, Fe^{2+}, N^{3-}, He, S^{2-}, Co^{3+}, Ar.

Periodic Variation in Physical Properties
Review Questions

8.33   Define atomic radius. Does the size of an atom have a precise meaning?

8.34   How does atomic radius change (a) from left to right across a period and (b) from top to bottom in a group?

8.35   Define ionic radius. How does the size of an atom change when it is converted to (a) an anion and (b) a cation?

8.36   Explain why, for isoelectronic ions, the anions are larger than the cations.

Problems

8.37   On the basis of their positions in the periodic table, select the atom with the larger atomic radius in each of the following pairs: (a) Na, Cs; (b) Be, Ba; (c) N, Sb; (d) F, Br; (e) Ne, Xe.

8.38   Arrange the following atoms in order of decreasing atomic radius: Na, Al, P, Cl, Mg.

8.39   Which is the largest atom in Group 4A?

8.40   Which is the smallest atom in Group 7A?

8.41   Why is the radius of the lithium atom considerably larger than the radius of the hydrogen atom?

8.42   Use the second period of the periodic table as an example to show that the size of atoms decreases as we move from left to right. Explain the trend.

8.43   Indicate which one of the two species in each of the following pairs is smaller: (a) Cl or Cl^-; (b) Na or Na^+; (c) O^{2-} or S^{2-}; (d) Mg^{2+} or Al^{3+}; (e) Au^+ or Au^{3+}.

8.44   List the following ions in order of increasing ionic radius: N^{3-}, Na^+, F^-, Mg^{2+}, O^{2-}.

8.45   Explain which of the following cations is larger, and why: Cu^+ or Cu^{2+}.

362   Chapter 8 ▪ Periodic Relationships Among the Elements

● **8.46**   Explain which of the following anions is larger, and why: Se^{2-} or Te^{2-}.

8.47   Give the physical states (gas, liquid, or solid) of the representative elements in the fourth period (K, Ca, Ga, Ge, As, Se, Br) at 1 atm and 25°C.

8.48   Both H^- and He contain two $1s$ electrons. Which species is larger? Explain your choice.

Ionization Energy
Review Questions

8.49   Define ionization energy. Ionization energy measurements are usually made when atoms are in the gaseous state. Why? Why is the second ionization energy always greater than the first ionization energy for any element?

8.50   Sketch the outline of the periodic table and show group and period trends in the first ionization energy of the elements. What types of elements have the highest ionization energies and what types the lowest ionization energies?

Problems

● **8.51**   Arrange the following in order of increasing first ionization energy: Na, Cl, Al, S, and Cs.

8.52   Arrange the following in order of increasing first ionization energy: F, K, P, Ca, and Ne.

● **8.53**   Use the third period of the periodic table as an example to illustrate the change in first ionization energies of the elements as we move from left to right. Explain the trend.

8.54   In general, ionization energy increases from left to right across a given period. Aluminum, however, has a lower ionization energy than magnesium. Explain.

8.55   The first and second ionization energies of K are 419 kJ/mol and 3052 kJ/mol, and those of Ca are 590 kJ/mol and 1145 kJ/mol, respectively. Compare their values and comment on the differences.

8.56   Two atoms have the electron configurations $1s^2 2s^2 2p^6$ and $1s^2 2s^2 2p^6 3s^1$. The first ionization energy of one is 2080 kJ/mol, and that of the other is 496 kJ/mol. Match each ionization energy with one of the given electron configurations. Justify your choice.

● **8.57**   A hydrogenlike ion is an ion containing only one electron. The energies of the electron in a hydrogenlike ion are given by

$$E_n = -(2.18 \times 10^{-18} \text{ J}) Z^2 \left(\frac{1}{n^2} \right)$$

where n is the principal quantum number and Z is the atomic number of the element. Calculate the ionization energy (in kJ/mol) of the He^+ ion.

● **8.58**   Plasma is a state of matter consisting of positive gaseous ions and electrons. In the plasma state, a mercury

atom could be stripped of its 80 electrons and therefore would exist as Hg^{80+}. Use the equation in Problem 8.57 to calculate the energy required for the last ionization step, that is,

$$Hg^{79+}(g) \longrightarrow Hg^{80+}(g) + e^-$$

Electron Affinity
Review Questions

8.59   (a) Define electron affinity. (b) Electron affinity measurements are made with gaseous atoms. Why? (c) Ionization energy is always a positive quantity, whereas electron affinity may be either positive or negative. Explain.

8.60   Explain the trends in electron affinity from aluminum to chlorine (see Table 8.3).

Problems

● **8.61**   Arrange the elements in each of the following groups in increasing order of the most positive electron affinity: (a) Li, Na, K; (b) F, Cl, Br, I; (c) O, Si, P, Ca, Ba.

● **8.62**   Specify which of the following elements you would expect to have the greatest electron affinity and which would have the least: He, K, Co, S, Cl.

● **8.63**   Considering their electron affinities, do you think it is possible for the alkali metals to form an anion like M^-, where M represents an alkali metal?

8.64   Explain why alkali metals have a greater affinity for electrons than alkaline earth metals.

Variation in Chemical Properties of the Representative Elements
Review Questions

8.65   What is meant by the diagonal relationship? Name two pairs of elements that show this relationship.

8.66   Which elements are more likely to form acidic oxides? Basic oxides? Amphoteric oxides?

Problems

8.67   Use the alkali metals and alkaline earth metals as examples to show how we can predict the chemical properties of elements simply from their electron configurations.

8.68   Based on your knowledge of the chemistry of the alkali metals, predict some of the chemical properties of francium, the last member of the group.

8.69   As a group, the noble gases are very stable chemically (only Kr and Xe are known to form compounds). Use the concepts of shielding and the effective nuclear charge to explain why the noble gases tend to neither give up electrons nor accept additional electrons.

8.70 Why are Group 1B elements more stable than Group 1A elements even though they seem to have the same outer electron configuration, ns^1, where n is the principal quantum number of the outermost shell?

8.71 How do the chemical properties of oxides change from left to right across a period? From top to bottom within a particular group?

8.72 Write balanced equations for the reactions between each of the following oxides and water: (a) Li_2O, (b) CaO, (c) SO_3.

8.73 Write formulas for and name the binary hydrogen compounds of the second-period elements (Li to F). Describe how the physical and chemical properties of these compounds change from left to right across the period.

8.74 Which oxide is more basic, MgO or BaO? Why?

Additional Problems

8.75 State whether each of the following properties of the representative elements generally increases or decreases (a) from left to right across a period and (b) from top to bottom within a group: metallic character, atomic size, ionization energy, acidity of oxides.

8.76 With reference to the periodic table, name (a) a halogen element in the fourth period, (b) an element similar to phosphorus in chemical properties, (c) the most reactive metal in the fifth period, (d) an element that has an atomic number smaller than 20 and is similar to strontium.

8.77 Write equations representing the following processes:
(a) The electron affinity of S^-.
(b) The third ionization energy of titanium.
(c) The electron affinity of Mg^{2+}.
(d) The ionization energy of O^{2-}.

8.78 List all the common ions of representative elements and transition metals that are isoelectronic with Ar.

8.79 Write the empirical (or molecular) formulas of compounds that the elements in the third period (sodium to chlorine) should form with (a) molecular oxygen and (b) molecular chlorine. In each case indicate whether you would expect the compound to be ionic or molecular in character.

8.80 Element M is a shiny and highly reactive metal (melting point 63°C), and element X is a highly reactive nonmetal (melting point −7.2°C). They react to form a compound with the empirical formula MX, a colorless, brittle white solid that melts at 734°C. When dissolved in water or when in the molten state, the substance conducts electricity. When chlorine gas is bubbled through an aqueous solution containing MX, a reddish-brown liquid appears and Cl^- ions are formed. From these observations, identify M and X. (You may need to consult a handbook of chemistry for the melting-point values.)

8.81 Match each of the elements on the right with its description on the left:
(a) A dark-red liquid   Calcium (Ca)
(b) A colorless gas that burns   Gold (Au)
    in oxygen gas   Hydrogen (H_2)
(c) A reactive metal that attacks   Argon (Ar)
    water   Bromine (Br_2)
(d) A shiny metal that is used
    in jewelry
(e) An inert gas

8.82 Arrange the following species in isoelectronic pairs: O^+, Ar, S^{2-}, Ne, Zn, Cs^+, N^{3-}, As^{3+}, N, Xe.

8.83 In which of the following are the species written in decreasing order by size of radius? (a) Be, Mg, Ba, (b) N^{3-}, O^{2-}, F^-, (c) Tl^{3+}, Tl^{2+}, Tl^+.

8.84 Which of the following properties show a clear periodic variation? (a) first ionization energy, (b) molar mass of the elements, (c) number of isotopes of an element, (d) atomic radius.

8.85 When carbon dioxide is bubbled through a clear calcium hydroxide solution, the solution appears milky. Write an equation for the reaction and explain how this reaction illustrates that CO_2 is an acidic oxide.

8.86 You are given four substances: a fuming red liquid, a dark metallic-looking solid, a pale-yellow gas, and a yellow-green gas that attacks glass. You are told that these substances are the first four members of Group 7A, the halogens. Name each one.

8.87 Calculate the change in energy for the following processes:
(a) $Na(g) + Cl(g) \longrightarrow Na^+(g) + Cl^-(g)$
(b) $Ca(g) + 2Br(g) \longrightarrow Ca^{2+}(g) + 2Br^-(g)$

8.88 Calculate the change in energy for the following processes:
(a) $Mg(g) + 2F(g) \longrightarrow Mg^{2+}(g) + 2F^-(g)$
(b) $2Al(g) + 3O(g) \longrightarrow 2Al^{3+}(g) + 3O^{2-}(g)$
The electron affinity of O^- is −844 kJ/mol.

8.89 For each pair of elements listed, give three properties that show their chemical similarity: (a) sodium and potassium and (b) chlorine and bromine.

8.90 Name the element that forms compounds, under appropriate conditions, with every other element in the periodic table except He, Ne, and Ar.

8.91 Explain why the first electron affinity of sulfur is 200 kJ/mol but the second electron affinity is −649 kJ/mol.

8.92 The H^- ion and the He atom have two $1s$ electrons each. Which of the two species is larger? Explain.

8.93 Predict the products of the following oxides with water: Na_2O, BaO, CO_2, N_2O_5, P_4O_{10}, SO_3. Write an equation for each of the reactions. Specify whether the oxides are acidic, basic, or amphoteric.

8.94   Write the formulas and names of the oxides of the second-period elements (Li to N). Identify the oxides as acidic, basic, or amphoteric.

● 8.95   State whether each of the following elements is a gas, a liquid, or a solid under atmospheric conditions. Also state whether it exists in the elemental form as atoms, as molecules, or as a three-dimensional network: Mg, Cl, Si, Kr, O, I, Hg, Br.

8.96   What factors account for the unique nature of hydrogen?

● 8.97   The air in a manned spacecraft or submarine needs to be purified of exhaled carbon dioxide. Write equations for the reactions between carbon dioxide and (a) lithium oxide (Li_2O), (b) sodium peroxide (Na_2O_2), and (c) potassium superoxide (KO_2).

8.98   The formula for calculating the energies of an electron in a hydrogenlike ion is given in Problem 8.57. This equation cannot be applied to many-electron atoms. One way to modify it for the more complex atoms is to replace Z with $(Z - \sigma)$, where Z is the atomic number and σ is a positive dimensionless quantity called the shielding constant. Consider the helium atom as an example. The physical significance of σ is that it represents the extent of shielding that the two $1s$ electrons exert on each other. Thus, the quantity $(Z - \sigma)$ is appropriately called the "effective nuclear charge." Calculate the value of σ if the first ionization energy of helium is 3.94×10^{-18} J per atom. (Ignore the minus sign in the given equation in your calculation.)

8.99   Why do noble gases have negative electron affinity values?

● 8.100   The atomic radius of K is 227 pm and that of K^+ is 133 pm. Calculate the percent decrease in volume that occurs when $K(g)$ is converted to $K^+(g)$. [The volume of a sphere is $(\frac{4}{3})\pi r^3$, where r is the radius of the sphere.]

● 8.101   The atomic radius of F is 72 pm and that of F^- is 133 pm. Calculate the percent increase in volume that occurs when $F(g)$ is converted to $F^-(g)$. (See Problem 8.100 for the volume of a sphere.)

● 8.102   A technique called photoelectron spectroscopy is used to measure the ionization energy of atoms. A sample is irradiated with UV light, and electrons are ejected from the valence shell. The kinetic energies of the ejected electrons are measured. Because the energy of the UV photon and the kinetic energy of the ejected electron are known, we can write

$$h\nu = IE + \tfrac{1}{2}mu^2$$

where ν is the frequency of the UV light, and m and u are the mass and velocity of the electron, respectively. In one experiment the kinetic energy of the ejected electron from potassium is found to be 5.34×10^{-19} J using a UV source of wavelength

162 nm. Calculate the ionization energy of potassium. How can you be sure that this ionization energy corresponds to the electron in the valence shell (that is, the most loosely held electron)?

8.103   Referring to the Chemistry in Action essay on p. 358, answer the following questions. (a) Why did it take so long to discover the first noble gas (argon) on Earth? (b) Once argon had been discovered, why did it take relatively little time to discover the rest of the noble gases? (c) Why was helium not isolated by the fractional distillation of liquid air?

● 8.104   The energy needed for the following process is 1.96×10^4 kJ/mol:

$$Li(g) \longrightarrow Li^{3+}(g) + 3e^-$$

If the first ionization energy of lithium is 520 kJ/mol, calculate the second ionization energy of lithium, that is, the energy required for the process

$$Li^+(g) \longrightarrow Li^{2+}(g) + e^-$$

(*Hint:* You need the equation in Problem 8.57.)

● 8.105   An element X reacts with hydrogen gas at 200°C to form compound Y. When Y is heated to a higher temperature, it decomposes to the element X and hydrogen gas in the ratio of 559 mL of H_2 (measured at STP) for 1.00 g of X reacted. X also combines with chlorine to form a compound Z, which contains 63.89 percent by mass of chlorine. Deduce the identity of X.

● 8.106   A student is given samples of three elements, X, Y, and Z, which could be an alkali metal, a member of Group 4A, and a member of Group 5A. She makes the following observations: Element X has a metallic luster and conducts electricity. It reacts slowly with hydrochloric acid to produce hydrogen gas. Element Y is a light-yellow solid that does not conduct electricity. Element Z has a metallic luster and conducts electricity. When exposed to air, it slowly forms a white powder. A solution of the white powder in water is basic. What can you conclude about the elements from these observations?

8.107   Identify the ions whose orbital diagrams for the valence electrons are shown below. The charges of the ions are: (a) 1+, (b) 3+, (c) 4+, (d) 2+.

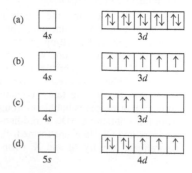

8.108   What is the electron affinity of the Na^+ ion?

8.109   The ionization energies of sodium (in kJ/mol), starting with the first and ending with the eleventh, are 495.9, 4560, 6900, 9540, 13,400, 16,600, 20,120, 25,490, 28,930, 141,360, 170,000. Plot the log of ionization energy (y axis) versus the number of ionization (x axis); for example, log 495.9 is plotted versus 1 (labeled IE_1, the first ionization energy), log 4560 is plotted versus 2 (labeled IE_2, the second ionization energy), and so on. (a) Label IE_1 through IE_{11} with the electrons in orbitals such as $1s$, $2s$, $2p$, and $3s$. (b) What can you deduce about electron shells from the breaks in the curve?

● 8.110   Experimentally, the electron affinity of an element can be determined by using a laser light to ionize the anion of the element in the gas phase:

$$X^-(g) + h\nu \longrightarrow X(g) + e^-$$

Referring to Table 8.3, calculate the photon wavelength (in nanometers) corresponding to the electron affinity for chlorine. In what region of the electromagnetic spectrum does this wavelength fall?

8.111   Explain, in terms of their electron configurations, why Fe^{2+} is more easily oxidized to Fe^{3+} than Mn^{2+} to Mn^{3+}.

● 8.112   The standard enthalpy of atomization of an element is the energy required to convert one mole of an element in its most stable form at 25°C to one mole of monatomic gas. Given that the standard enthalpy of atomization for sodium is 108.4 kJ/mol, calculate the energy in kilojoules required to convert one mole of sodium metal at 25°C to one mole of gaseous Na^+ ions.

8.113   Write the formulas and names of the hydrides of the following second-period elements: Li, C, N, O, F. Predict their reactions with water.

8.114   Based on knowledge of the electronic configuration of titanium, state which of the following compounds of titanium is unlikely to exist: K_3TiF_6, $K_2Ti_2O_5$, $TiCl_3$, K_2TiO_4, K_2TiF_6.

8.115   Name an element in Group 1A or Group 2A that is an important constituent of each of the following substances: (a) remedy for acid indigestion, (b) coolant in nuclear reactors, (c) Epsom salt, (d) baking powder, (e) gunpowder, (f) a light alloy, (g) fertilizer that also neutralizes acid rain, (h) cement, and (i) grit for icy roads. You may need to ask your instructor about some of the items.

● 8.116   In halogen displacement reactions a halogen element can be generated by oxidizing its anions with a halogen element that lies above it in the periodic table. This means that there is no way to prepare elemental fluorine, because it is the first member of Group 7A. Indeed, for years the only way to prepare elemental fluorine was to oxidize F^- ions by electrolytic means.

Then, in 1986, a chemist reported that by reacting potassium hexafluoromanganate(IV) (K_2MnF_6) with antimony pentafluoride (SbF_5) at 150°C, he had generated elemental fluorine. Balance the following equation representing the reaction:

$$K_2MnF_6 + SbF_5 \longrightarrow KSbF_6 + MnF_3 + F_2$$

8.117   Write a balanced equation for the preparation of (a) molecular oxygen, (b) ammonia, (c) carbon dioxide, (d) molecular hydrogen, (e) calcium oxide. Indicate the physical state of the reactants and products in each equation.

8.118   Write chemical formulas for oxides of nitrogen with the following oxidation numbers: +1, +2, +3, +4, +5. (*Hint:* There are *two* oxides of nitrogen with +4 oxidation number.)

8.119   Most transition metal ions are colored. For example, a solution of $CuSO_4$ is blue. How would you show that the blue color is due to the hydrated Cu^{2+} ions and not the SO_4^{2-} ions?

8.120   In general, atomic radius and ionization energy have opposite periodic trends. Why?

8.121   Explain why the electron affinity of nitrogen is approximately zero, while the elements on either side, carbon and oxygen, have substantial positive electron affinities.

● 8.122   Consider the halogens chlorine, bromine, and iodine. The melting point and boiling point of chlorine are −101.0°C and −34.6°C while those of iodine are 113.5°C and 184.4°C, respectively. Thus, chlorine is a gas and iodine is a solid under room conditions. Estimate the melting point and boiling point of bromine. Compare your values with those from a handbook of chemistry.

8.123   Write a balanced equation that predicts the reaction of rubidium (Rb) with (a) $H_2O(l)$, (b) $Cl_2(g)$, (c) $H_2(g)$.

8.124   The successive IE of the first four electrons of a representative element are 738.1 kJ/mol, 1450 kJ/mol, 7730 kJ/mol, and 10,500 kJ/mol. Characterize the element according to the periodic group.

● 8.125   Little is known of the chemistry of astatine, the last member of Group 7A. Describe the physical characteristics that you would expect this halogen to have. Predict the products of the reaction between sodium astatide (NaAt) and sulfuric acid. (*Hint:* Sulfuric acid is an oxidizing agent.)

8.126   As discussed in the chapter, the atomic mass of argon is greater than that of potassium. This observation created a problem in the early development of the periodic table because it meant that argon should be placed after potassium. (a) How was this difficulty resolved? (b) From the following data, calculate the average atomic masses of argon and potassium: Ar-36 (35.9675 amu; 0.337 percent), Ar-38 (37.9627 amu; 0.063 percent), Ar-40 (39.9624 amu; 99.60 percent); K-39 (38.9637 amu; 93.258 percent), K-40 (39.9640 amu; 0.0117 percent), K-41 (40.9618 amu; 6.730 percent).

8.127 Calculate the maximum wavelength of light (in nanometers) required to ionize a single sodium atom.

8.128 Predict the atomic number and ground-state electron configuration of the next member of the alkali metals after francium.

8.129 Why do elements that have high ionization energies also have more positive electron affinities? Which group of elements would be an exception to this generalization?

8.130 The first four ionization energies of an element are approximately 579 kJ/mol, 1980 kJ/mol, 2963 kJ/mol, and 6180 kJ/mol. To which periodic group does this element belong?

8.131 Some chemists think that helium should properly be called "helon." Why? What does the ending in helium (-ium) suggest?

8.132 (a) The formula of the simplest hydrocarbon is CH_4 (methane). Predict the formulas of the simplest compounds formed between hydrogen and the following elements: silicon, germanium, tin, and lead. (b) Sodium hydride (NaH) is an ionic compound. Would you expect rubidium hydride (RbH) to be more or less ionic than NaH? (c) Predict the reaction between radium (Ra) and water. (d) When exposed to air, aluminum forms a tenacious oxide (Al_2O_3) coating that protects the metal from corrosion. Which metal in Group 2A would you expect to exhibit similar properties? Why?

8.133 Give equations to show that molecular hydrogen can act both as a reducing agent and an oxidizing agent.

8.134 Both Mg^{2+} and Ca^{2+} are important biological ions. One of their functions is to bind to the phosphate groups of ATP molecules or amino acids of proteins. For Group 2A metals in general, the tendency for binding to the anions increases in the order $Ba^{2+} < Sr^{2+} < Ca^{2+} < Mg^{2+}$. Explain the trend.

8.135 Match each of the elements on the right with its description on the left:

(a) A pale yellow gas that reacts with water.

(b) A soft metal that reacts with water to produce hydrogen.

(c) A metalloid that is hard and has a high melting point.

(d) A colorless, odorless gas.

(e) A metal that is more reactive than iron, but does not corrode in air.

Nitrogen (N_2)
Boron (B)
Aluminum (Al)
Fluorine (F_2)
Sodium (Na)

8.136 Write an account on the importance of the periodic table. Pay particular attention to the significance of the position of an element in the table and how the position relates to the chemical and physical properties of the element.

8.137 On the same graph, plot the effective nuclear charge (see p. 334) and atomic radius (see Figure 8.5) versus atomic number for the second period elements Li to Ne. Comment on the trends.

8.138 One allotropic form of an element X is a colorless crystalline solid. The reaction of X with an excess amount of oxygen produces a colorless gas. This gas dissolves in water to yield an acidic solution. Choose one of the following elements that matches X: (a) sulfur, (b) phosphorus, (c) carbon, (d) boron, and (e) silicon.

8.139 When magnesium metal is burned in air, it forms two products A and B. A reacts with water to form a basic solution. B reacts with water to form a similar solution as that of A plus a gas with a pungent odor. Identify A and B and write equations for the reactions. (*Hint:* See Chemistry in Action on p. 358.)

8.140 The ionization energy of a certain element is 412 kJ/mol. When the atoms of this element are in the first excited state, however, the ionization energy is only 126 kJ/mol. Based on this information, calculate the wavelength of light emitted in a transition from the first excited state to the ground state.

8.141 Use your knowledge of thermochemistry to calculate the ΔH for the following processes: (a) $Cl^-(g) \rightarrow Cl^+(g) + 2e^-$ and (b) $K^+(g) + 2e^- \rightarrow K^-(g)$.

8.142 Referring to Table 8.2, explain why the first ionization energy of helium is less than twice the ionization energy of hydrogen, but the second ionization energy of helium is greater than twice the ionization energy of hydrogen. [*Hint:* According to Coulomb's law, the energy between two charges Q_1 and Q_2 separated by distance r is proportional to (Q_1Q_2/r).]

8.143 As mentioned in Chapter 3 (p. 105), ammonium nitrate (NH_4NO_3) is the most important nitrogen-containing fertilizer in the world. Describe how you would prepare this compound, given only air and water as the starting materials. You may have any device at your disposal for this task.

8.144 One way to estimate the effective charge (Z_{eff}) of a many-electron atom is to use the equation $IE_1 = (1312 \text{ kJ/mol})(Z^2_{eff}/n^2)$, where IE_1 is the first ionization energy and n is the principal quantum number of the shell in which the electron resides. Use this equation to calculate the effective charges of Li, Na, and K. Also calculate Z_{eff}/n for each metal. Comment on your results.

8.145 To prevent the formation of oxides, peroxides, and superoxides, alkali metals are sometimes stored in an inert atmosphere. Which of the following gases should not be used for lithium: Ne, Ar, N_2, Kr? Explain. (*Hint:* As mentioned in the chapter, Li and Mg exhibit a diagonal relationship. Compare the common compounds of these two elements.)

8.146 Describe the biological role of the elements in the human body shown in the following periodic table.

(You may need to do research at websites such as www.webelements.com.)

H																	
												C	N	O			
Na	Mg												P	S	Cl		
K	Ca				Cr	Mn	Fe	Co		Cu	Zn				Br		
															I		

8.147 Recent theoretical calculations suggest that astatine may be a monoatomic metal rather than a diatomic molecule like the other halogens. (a) Rationalize this prediction based on astatine's position in the periodic table. (b) The energy required to remove an electron from one At atom was determined by laser ionization to be 9.3175 eV. Given that 1 eV = 1.602×10^{-19} J, calculate the first ionization energy of astatine in kJ/mol. (c) Comment on whether or not the following first ionization energies support your answer to part (a): Pb, 715.6 kJ/mol; Bi, 702.9 kJ/mol; Po, 811.8 kJ/mol; Rn, 1037 kJ/mol.

Interpreting, Modeling & Estimating

8.148 Consider the first 18 elements from hydrogen to argon. Would you expect the atoms of half of them to be diamagnetic and half of them to be paramagnetic? Explain.

8.149 Compare the work function for cesium (206 kJ/mol) with its first ionization energy (376 kJ/mol). Explain the difference.

8.150 The only confirmed compound of radon is radon difluoride, RnF_2. One reason that it is difficult to study the chemistry of radon is that all isotopes of radon are radioactive so it is dangerous to handle the substance. Can you suggest another reason why there are so few known radon compounds? (*Hint:* Radioactive decays are exothermic processes.)

8.151 Arsenic (As) is not an essential element for the human body. (a) Based on its position in the periodic table, suggest a reason for its toxicity. (b) When arsenic enters a person's body, it quickly shows up in the follicle of the growing hair. This action has enabled detectives to solve many murder mysteries by analyzing a victim's hair. Where else might one look for the accumulation of the element if arsenic poisoning is suspected?

8.152 The boiling points of neon and krypton are $-245.9°C$ and $-152.9°C$, respectively. Using these data, estimate the boiling point of argon.

8.153 Using the following boiling-point data, estimate the boiling point of francium:

Metal	Li	Na	K	Rb	Cs	Fr
B.pt.(°C)	1347	882.9	774	688	678.4	?

8.154 The energy gap between the 6s and 5d levels in gold is 4.32×10^{-19} J. Based on this information, predict the perceived color of gold vapor. (*Hint:* You need to be familiar with the notion of complementary color; see Figure 23.18.)

8.155 Calculate the volume of 1 mole of K atoms (see Figure 8.5) and compare the result by using the density of K (0.856 g/cm³). Account for the difference.

Answers to Practice Exercises

8.1 (a) $1s^2 2s^2 2p^6 3s^2 3p^6 4s^2$, (b) it is a representative element, (c) diamagnetic. **8.2** Li > Be > C.
8.3 (a) Li^+, (b) Au^{3+}, (c) N^{3-}. **8.4** (a) N, (b) Mg.
8.5 No. **8.6** (a) amphoteric, (b) acidic, (c) basic.

CHAPTER

9

Chemical Bonding I
Basic Concepts

Lewis developed many of the models we still use today
to understand chemical bonding.

A LOOK AHEAD

▶ Our study of chemical bonds begins with an introduction to Lewis dot symbols, which shows the valence electrons on an atom. (9.1)

▶ We then study the formation of ionic bonds and learn how to determine lattice energy, which is a measure of the stability of ionic compounds. (9.2 and 9.3)

▶ Next we turn our attention to the formation of covalent bonds. We learn to write Lewis structures, which are governed by the octet rule. (9.4)

▶ We see that electronegativity is an important concept in understanding the properties of molecules. (9.5)

▶ We continue to practice writing Lewis structures for molecules and ions and use formal charges to study the distribution of electrons in these species. (9.6 and 9.7)

▶ We learn further aspects of writing Lewis structures in terms of resonance structures, which are alternate Lewis structures for a molecule. We also see that there are exceptions to the octet rule. (9.8 and 9.9)

▶ The chapter ends with an examination of the strength of covalent bonds, which leads to the use of bond enthalpies to determine the enthalpy of a reaction. (9.10)

Why do atoms of different elements react? What are the forces that hold atoms together in molecules and ionic compounds? What shapes do they assume? These are some of the questions addressed in this chapter and in Chapter 10. We begin by looking at the two types of bonds—ionic and covalent—and the forces that stabilize them.

9.1 Lewis Dot Symbols

The development of the periodic table and concept of electron configuration gave chemists a rationale for molecule and compound formation. This explanation, formulated by Gilbert Lewis,[†] is that atoms combine in order to achieve a more stable electron configuration. Maximum stability results when an atom is isoelectronic with a noble gas.

When atoms interact to form a chemical bond, only their outer regions are in contact. For this reason, when we study chemical bonding, we are concerned primarily with the valence electrons of the atoms. To keep track of valence electrons in a chemical reaction, and to make sure that the total number of electrons does not change, chemists use a system of dots devised by Lewis called Lewis dot symbols. A **Lewis dot symbol** *consists of the symbol of an element and one dot for each valence electron in an atom of the element.* Figure 9.1 shows the Lewis dot symbols for the representative elements and the noble gases. Note that, except for helium, the number of valence electrons each atom has is the same as the group number of the element. For example, Li is a Group 1A element and has one dot for one valence electron; Be, a Group 2A element, has two valence electrons (two dots); and so on. Elements in the same group have similar outer electron configurations and hence similar Lewis dot symbols. The transition metals, lanthanides, and actinides all have incompletely filled inner shells, and in general, we cannot write simple Lewis dot symbols for them.

In this chapter, we will learn to use electron configurations and the periodic table to predict the type of bond atoms will form, as well as the number of bonds an atom of a particular element can form and the stability of the product.

[†]Gilbert Newton Lewis (1875–1946). American chemist. Lewis made many important contributions in the areas of chemical bonding, thermodynamics, acids and bases, and spectroscopy. Despite the significance of Lewis's work, he was never awarded a Nobel prize.

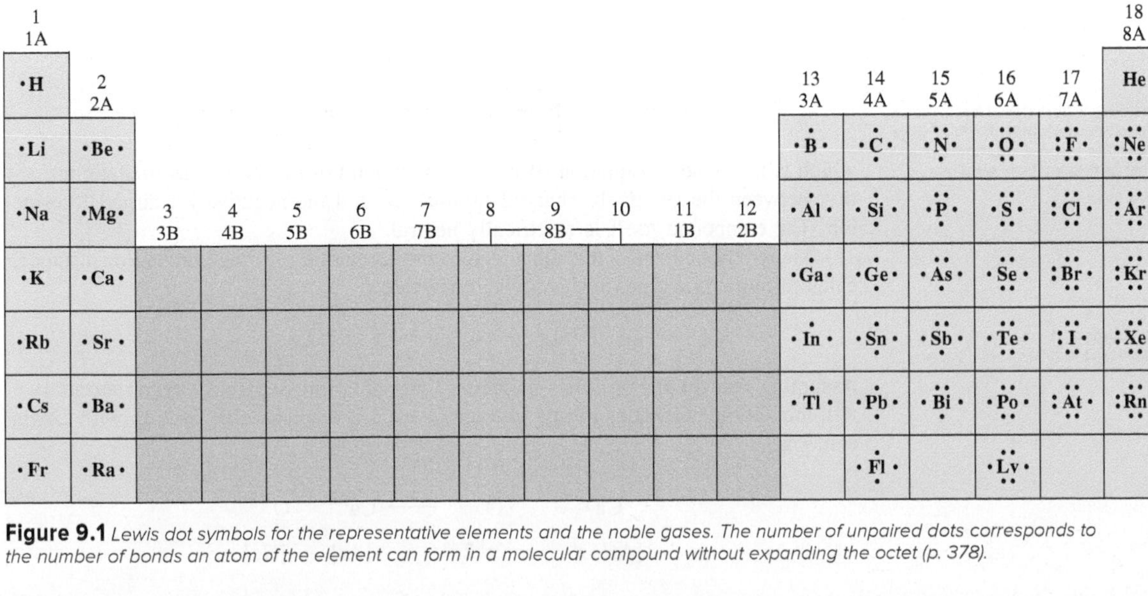

Figure 9.1 *Lewis dot symbols for the representative elements and the noble gases. The number of unpaired dots corresponds to the number of bonds an atom of the element can form in a molecular compound without expanding the octet (p. 378).*

> ### *Review of Concepts*
> What is the maximum number of dots that can be drawn around the atom of a representative element?

9.2 The Ionic Bond

In Chapter 8 we saw that atoms of elements with low ionization energies tend to form cations, while those with high electron affinities tend to form anions. As a rule, the elements most likely to form cations in ionic compounds are the alkali metals and alkaline earth metals, and the elements most likely to form anions are the halogens and oxygen. Consequently, a wide variety of ionic compounds combine a Group 1A or Group 2A metal with a halogen or oxygen. An ***ionic bond*** is *the electrostatic force that holds ions together in an ionic compound.* Consider, for example, the reaction between lithium and fluorine to form lithium fluoride, a poisonous white powder used in lowering the melting point of solders and in manufacturing ceramics. The electron configuration of lithium is $1s^2 2s^1$, and that of fluorine is $1s^2 2s^2 2p^5$. When lithium and fluorine atoms come in contact with each other, the outer $2s^1$ valence electron of lithium is transferred to the fluorine atom. Using Lewis dot symbols, we represent the reaction like this:

Lithium fluoride. Industrially, LiF (like most other ionic compounds) is obtained by purifying minerals containing the compound.

$$
\cdot \mathrm{Li} \; + \; :\!\overset{\cdot\cdot}{\underset{\cdot\cdot}{\mathrm{F}}}\!\cdot \; \longrightarrow \; \mathrm{Li}^+ \quad :\!\overset{\cdot\cdot}{\underset{\cdot\cdot}{\mathrm{F}}}\!:^- \quad (\text{or LiF}) \tag{9.1}
$$
$$
{\scriptstyle 1s^2 2s^1 \quad\; 1s^2 2s^2 2p^5 \qquad 1s^2 \;\; 1s^2 2s^2 2p^6}
$$

For convenience, imagine that this reaction occurs in separate steps—first the ionization of Li:

$$\cdot \mathrm{Li} \longrightarrow \mathrm{Li}^+ + e^-$$

and then the acceptance of an electron by F:

$$:\!\overset{\cdot\cdot}{\underset{\cdot\cdot}{\mathrm{F}}}\!\cdot \; + \; e^- \longrightarrow :\!\overset{\cdot\cdot}{\underset{\cdot\cdot}{\mathrm{F}}}\!:^-$$

Next, imagine the two separate ions joining to form a LiF unit:

$$\mathrm{Li}^+ + :\!\overset{\cdot\cdot}{\underset{\cdot\cdot}{\mathrm{F}}}\!:^- \longrightarrow \mathrm{Li}^+ :\!\overset{\cdot\cdot}{\underset{\cdot\cdot}{\mathrm{F}}}\!:^-$$

Note that the sum of these three equations is

$$\cdot \mathrm{Li} + :\!\overset{\cdot\cdot}{\underset{\cdot\cdot}{\mathrm{F}}}\!\cdot \longrightarrow \mathrm{Li}^+ :\!\overset{\cdot\cdot}{\underset{\cdot\cdot}{\mathrm{F}}}\!:^-$$

We normally write the empirical formulas of ionic compounds without showing the charges. The + and − are shown here to emphasize the transfer of electrons.

which is the same as Equation (9.1). The ionic bond in LiF is the electrostatic attraction between the positively charged lithium ion and the negatively charged fluoride ion. The compound itself is electrically neutral.

Many other common reactions lead to the formation of ionic bonds. For instance, calcium burns in oxygen to form calcium oxide:

$$2\mathrm{Ca}(s) + \mathrm{O}_2(g) \longrightarrow 2\mathrm{CaO}(s)$$

▶▶ Animation
Reactions of Magnesium and Oxygen

Assuming that the diatomic O_2 molecule first splits into separate oxygen atoms (we will look at the energetics of this step later), we can represent the reaction with Lewis symbols:

$$
\cdot \mathrm{Ca} \cdot \; + \; \cdot \overset{\cdot\cdot}{\mathrm{O}} \cdot \; \longrightarrow \; \mathrm{Ca}^{2+} \quad :\!\overset{\cdot\cdot}{\underset{\cdot\cdot}{\mathrm{O}}}\!:^{2-}
$$
$$
{\scriptstyle [\mathrm{Ar}]4s^2 \quad\; 1s^2 2s^2 2p^4 \qquad\; [\mathrm{Ar}] \qquad [\mathrm{Ne}]}
$$

There is a transfer of two electrons from the calcium atom to the oxygen atom. Note that the resulting calcium ion (Ca^{2+}) has the argon electron configuration, the oxide ion (O^{2-}) is isoelectronic with neon, and the compound (CaO) is electrically neutral.

In many cases, the cation and the anion in a compound do not carry the same charges. For instance, when lithium burns in air to form lithium oxide (Li_2O), the balanced equation is

$$4Li(s) + O_2(g) \longrightarrow 2Li_2O(s)$$

Using Lewis dot symbols, we write

$$2 \cdot Li + \cdot \overset{..}{\underset{..}{O}} \cdot \longrightarrow 2Li^+ \quad :\overset{..}{\underset{..}{O}}:^{2-} \text{ (or } Li_2O)$$
$$1s^2 2s^1 \quad 1s^2 2s^2 2p^4 \qquad [He] \quad [Ne]$$

In this process, the oxygen atom receives two electrons (one from each of the two lithium atoms) to form the oxide ion. The Li^+ ion is isoelectronic with helium.

When magnesium reacts with nitrogen at elevated temperatures, a white solid compound, magnesium nitride (Mg_3N_2), forms:

$$3Mg(s) + N_2(g) \longrightarrow Mg_3N_2(s)$$

or

$$3 \cdot Mg \cdot + 2 \cdot \overset{..}{N} \cdot \longrightarrow 3Mg^{2+} \quad 2 :\overset{..}{N}:^{3-} \text{ (or } Mg_3N_2)$$
$$[Ne]3s^2 \quad 1s^2 2s^2 2p^3 \qquad [Ne] \quad [Ne]$$

The reaction involves the transfer of six electrons (two from each Mg atom) to two nitrogen atoms. The resulting magnesium ion (Mg^{2+}) and the nitride ion (N^{3-}) are both isoelectronic with neon. Because there are three +2 ions and two −3 ions, the charges balance and the compound is electrically neutral.

In Example 9.1, we apply the Lewis dot symbols to study the formation of an ionic compound.

Example 9.1

Aluminum oxide, obtained from the mineral corundum, is used primarily for the production of aluminum metal. Use Lewis dot symbols to show the formation of aluminum oxide (Al_2O_3).

Strategy We use electroneutrality as our guide in writing formulas for ionic compounds; that is, the total positive charges on the cations must be equal to the total negative charges on the anions.

Solution According to Figure 9.1, the Lewis dot symbols of Al and O are

$$\cdot \overset{\cdot}{Al} \cdot \qquad \cdot \overset{..}{O} \cdot$$

Because aluminum tends to form the cation (Al^{3+}) and oxygen the anion (O^{2-}) in ionic compounds, the transfer of electrons is from Al to O. There are three valence electrons in each Al atom; each O atom needs two electrons to form the O^{2-} ion, which is isoelectronic with neon. Thus, the simplest neutralizing ratio of Al^{3+} to O^{2-} is 2:3; two Al^{3+} ions have a total charge of +6, and three O^{2-} ions have a total charge of −6. So the empirical formula of aluminum oxide is Al_2O_3, and the reaction is

$$2 \cdot \overset{\cdot}{Al} \cdot + 3 \cdot \overset{..}{O} \cdot \longrightarrow 2Al^{3+} \quad 3 :\overset{..}{\underset{..}{O}}:^{2-} \text{ (or } Al_2O_3)$$
$$[Ne]3s^2 3p^1 \quad 1s^2 2s^2 2p^4 \qquad [Ne] \quad [Ne]$$

(Continued)

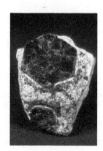

The mineral corundum (Al_2O_3).

Similar problems: 9.17, 9.18.

Check Make sure that the number of valence electrons (24) is the same on both sides of the equation. Are the subscripts in Al_2O_3 reduced to the smallest possible whole numbers?

Practice Exercise Use Lewis dot symbols to represent the formation of barium hydride.

Review of Concepts

Use Lewis dot symbols to represent the formation of rubidium sulfide.

9.3 Lattice Energy of Ionic Compounds

We can predict which elements are likely to form ionic compounds based on ionization energy and electron affinity, but how do we evaluate the stability of an ionic compound? Ionization energy and electron affinity are defined for processes occurring in the gas phase, but at 1 atm and 25°C all ionic compounds are solids. The solid state is a very different environment because each cation in a solid is surrounded by a specific number of anions, and vice versa. Thus, the overall stability of a solid ionic compound depends on the interactions of all these ions and not merely on the interaction of a single cation with a single anion. A quantitative measure of the stability of any ionic solid is its *lattice energy,* defined as the energy required to completely separate one mole of a solid ionic compound into gaseous ions (see Section 6.7).

Lattice energy is determined by the charge of the ions and the distance between the ions.

The Born-Haber Cycle for Determining Lattice Energies

Lattice energy cannot be measured directly. However, if we know the structure and composition of an ionic compound, we can calculate the compound's lattice energy by using **Coulomb's[†] law,** which states that *the potential energy (E) between two ions is directly proportional to the product of their charges and inversely proportional to the distance of separation between them.* For a single Li^+ ion and a single F^- ion separated by distance r, the potential energy of the system is given by

Because energy = force × distance, Coulomb's law can also be stated as

$$F = k\frac{Q_{Li^+}Q_{F^-}}{r^2}$$

where F is the force between the ions.

$$E \propto \frac{Q_{Li^+}Q_{F^-}}{r}$$
$$= k\frac{Q_{Li^+}Q_{F^-}}{r} \tag{9.2}$$

where Q_{Li^+} and Q_{F^-} are the charges on the Li^+ and F^- ions and k is the proportionality constant. Because Q_{Li^+} is positive and Q_{F^-} is negative, E is a negative quantity, and the formation of an ionic bond from Li^+ and F^- is an exothermic process. Consequently, energy must be supplied to reverse the process (in other words, the lattice energy of LiF is positive), and so a bonded pair of Li^+ and F^- ions is more stable than separate Li^+ and F^- ions.

We can also determine lattice energy indirectly, by assuming that the formation of an ionic compound takes place in a series of steps. This procedure, known as the **Born-Haber cycle,** *relates lattice energies of ionic compounds to ionization energies,*

[†]Charles Augustin de Coulomb (1736–1806). French physicist. Coulomb did research in electricity and magnetism and applied Newton's inverse square law to electricity. He also invented a torsion balance.

electron affinities, and other atomic and molecular properties. It is based on Hess's law (see Section 6.6). Developed by Max Born[†] and Fritz Haber,[‡] the Born-Haber cycle defines the various steps that precede the formation of an ionic solid. We will illustrate its use to find the lattice energy of lithium fluoride.

Consider the reaction between lithium and fluorine:

$$Li(s) + \tfrac{1}{2}F_2(g) \longrightarrow LiF(s)$$

The standard enthalpy change for this reaction is -594.1 kJ/mol. (Because the reactants and product are in their standard states, that is, at 1 atm, the enthalpy change is also the standard enthalpy of formation for LiF.) Keeping in mind that the sum of enthalpy changes for the steps is equal to the enthalpy change for the overall reaction (-594.1 kJ/mol), we can trace the formation of LiF from its elements through five separate steps. The process may not occur exactly this way, but this pathway enables us to analyze the energy changes of ionic compound formation, with the application of Hess's law.

1. Convert solid lithium to lithium vapor (the direct conversion of a solid to a gas is called sublimation):

$$Li(s) \longrightarrow Li(g) \qquad \Delta H_1^\circ = 155.2 \text{ kJ/mol}$$

   The energy of sublimation for lithium is 155.2 kJ/mol.

2. Dissociate $\tfrac{1}{2}$ mole of F_2 gas into separate gaseous F atoms:

$$\tfrac{1}{2}F_2(g) \longrightarrow F(g) \qquad \Delta H_2^\circ = 75.3 \text{ kJ/mol}$$

   The energy needed to break the bonds in 1 mole of F_2 molecules is 150.6 kJ. Here we are breaking the bonds in half a mole of F_2, so the enthalpy change is 150.6/2, or 75.3, kJ.

> The F atoms in a F_2 molecule are held together by a covalent bond. The energy required to break this bond is called the bond enthalpy (Section 9.10).

3. Ionize 1 mole of gaseous Li atoms (see Table 8.2):

$$Li(g) \longrightarrow Li^+(g) + e^- \qquad \Delta H_3^\circ = 520 \text{ kJ/mol}$$

   This process corresponds to the first ionization of lithium.

4. Add 1 mole of electrons to 1 mole of gaseous F atoms. As discussed on page 345, the energy change for this process is just the opposite of electron affinity (see Table 8.3):

$$F(g) + e^- \longrightarrow F^-(g) \qquad \Delta H_4^\circ = -328 \text{ kJ/mol}$$

5. Combine 1 mole of gaseous Li^+ and 1 mole of F^- to form 1 mole of solid LiF:

$$Li^+(g) + F^-(g) \longrightarrow LiF(s) \qquad \Delta H_5^\circ = ?$$

The reverse of step 5,

$$\text{energy} + LiF(s) \longrightarrow Li^+(g) + F^-(g)$$

[†]Max Born (1882–1970). German physicist. Born was one of the founders of modern physics. His work covered a wide range of topics. He received the Nobel Prize in Physics in 1954 for his interpretation of the wave function for particles.

[‡]Fritz Haber (1868–1934). German chemist. Haber's process for synthesizing ammonia from atmospheric nitrogen kept Germany supplied with nitrates for explosives during World War I. He also did work on gas warfare. In 1918 Haber received the Nobel Prize in Chemistry.

defines the lattice energy of LiF. Thus, the lattice energy must have the same magnitude as ΔH_5° but an opposite sign. Although we cannot determine ΔH_5° directly, we can calculate its value by the following procedure.

1.	$\text{Li}(s) \longrightarrow \text{Li}(g)$	$\Delta H_1^\circ = 155.2 \text{ kJ/mol}$
2.	$\frac{1}{2}\text{F}_2(g) \longrightarrow \text{F}(g)$	$\Delta H_2^\circ = 75.3 \text{ kJ/mol}$
3.	$\text{Li}(g) \longrightarrow \text{Li}^+(g) + e^-$	$\Delta H_3^\circ = 520 \text{ kJ/mol}$
4.	$\text{F}(g) + e^- \longrightarrow \text{F}^-(g)$	$\Delta H_4^\circ = -328 \text{ kJ/mol}$
5.	$\text{Li}^+(g) + \text{F}^-(g) \longrightarrow \text{LiF}(s)$	$\Delta H_5^\circ = ?$

$$\text{Li}(s) + \frac{1}{2}\text{F}_2(g) \longrightarrow \text{LiF}(s) \qquad \Delta H_{\text{overall}}^\circ = -594.1 \text{ kJ/mol}$$

According to Hess's law, we can write

$$\Delta H_{\text{overall}}^\circ = \Delta H_1^\circ + \Delta H_2^\circ + \Delta H_3^\circ + \Delta H_4^\circ + \Delta H_5^\circ$$

or

$$-594.1 \text{ kJ/mol} = 155.2 \text{ kJ/mol} + 75.3 \text{ kJ/mol} + 520 \text{ kJ/mol} - 328 \text{ kJ/mol} + \Delta H_5^\circ$$

Hence,

$$\Delta H_5^\circ = -1017 \text{ kJ/mol}$$

and the lattice energy of LiF is +1017 kJ/mol.

Figure 9.2 summarizes the Born-Haber cycle for LiF. Steps 1, 2, and 3 all require the input of energy. On the other hand, steps 4 and 5 release energy. Because ΔH_5° is a large negative quantity, the lattice energy of LiF is a large positive quantity, which accounts for the stability of solid LiF. The greater the lattice energy, the more stable the ionic compound. Keep in mind that lattice energy is *always* a positive quantity because the separation of ions in a solid into ions in the gas phase is, by Coulomb's law, an endothermic process.

Table 9.1 lists the lattice energies and the melting points of several common ionic compounds. There is a rough correlation between lattice energy and melting point. The larger the lattice energy, the more stable the solid and the more tightly held the ions. It takes more energy to melt such a solid, and so the solid has a higher melting point than one with a smaller lattice energy. Note that $MgCl_2$, Na_2O, and MgO have

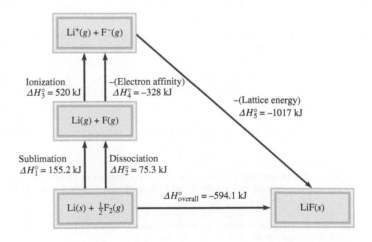

Figure 9.2 *The Born-Haber cycle for the formation of 1 mole of solid LiF.*

Table 9.1	Lattice Energies and Melting Points of Some Alkali Metal and Alkaline Earth Metal Halides and Oxides	
Compound	Lattice Energy (kJ/mol)	Melting Point (°C)
LiF	1017	845
LiCl	828	610
LiBr	787	550
LiI	732	450
NaCl	788	801
NaBr	736	750
NaI	686	662
KCl	699	772
KBr	689	735
KI	632	680
$MgCl_2$	2527	714
Na_2O	2570	Sub*
MgO	3890	2800

*Na_2O sublimes at 1275°C.

unusually high lattice energies. The first of these ionic compounds has a doubly charged cation (Mg^{2+}) and the second a doubly charged anion (O^{2-}); in the third compound there is an interaction between two doubly charged species (Mg^{2+} and O^{2-}). The coulombic attractions between two doubly charged species, or between a doubly charged ion and a singly charged ion, are much stronger than those between singly charged anions and cations.

Lattice Energy and the Formulas of Ionic Compounds

Because lattice energy is a measure of the stability of ionic compounds, its value can help us explain the formulas of these compounds. Consider magnesium chloride as an example. We have seen that the ionization energy of an element increases rapidly as successive electrons are removed from its atom. For example, the first ionization energy of magnesium is 738 kJ/mol, and the second ionization energy is 1450 kJ/mol, almost twice the first. We might ask why, from the standpoint of energy, magnesium does not prefer to form unipositive ions in its compounds. Why doesn't magnesium chloride have the formula MgCl (containing the Mg^+ ion) rather than $MgCl_2$ (containing the Mg^{2+} ion)? Admittedly, the Mg^{2+} ion has the noble gas configuration [Ne], which represents stability because of its completely filled shells. But the stability gained through the filled shells does not, in fact, outweigh the energy input needed to remove an electron from the Mg^+ ion. The reason the formula is $MgCl_2$ lies in the extra stability gained by the formation of solid magnesium chloride. The lattice energy of $MgCl_2$ is 2527 kJ/mol, which is more than enough to compensate for the energy needed to remove the first two electrons from a Mg atom (738 kJ/mol + 1450 kJ/mol = 2188 kJ/mol).

What about sodium chloride? Why is the formula for sodium chloride NaCl and not $NaCl_2$ (containing the Na^{2+} ion)? Although Na^{2+} does not have the noble gas electron configuration, we might expect the compound to be $NaCl_2$ because Na^{2+} has a higher charge and therefore the hypothetical $NaCl_2$ should have a greater lattice energy. Again, the answer lies in the balance between energy input (that is, ionization

CHEMISTRY *in Action*

Sodium Chloride—A Common and Important Ionic Compound

We are all familiar with sodium chloride as table salt. It is a typical ionic compound, a brittle solid with a high melting point (801°C) that conducts electricity in the molten state and in aqueous solution. The structure of solid NaCl is shown in Figure 2.13.

One source of sodium chloride is rock salt, which is found in subterranean deposits often hundreds of meters thick. It is also obtained from seawater or brine (a concentrated NaCl solution) by solar evaporation. Sodium chloride also occurs in nature as the mineral *halite*.

Sodium chloride is used more often than any other material in the manufacture of inorganic chemicals. World consumption of this substance is about 200 million tons per year. The major use of sodium chloride is in the production of other essential inorganic chemicals such as chlorine gas, sodium hydroxide, sodium metal, hydrogen gas, and sodium carbonate. It is also used to melt ice and snow on highways and roads. However, because sodium chloride is harmful to plant life and promotes corrosion of cars, its use for this purpose is of considerable environmental concern.

Solar evaporation process for obtaining sodium chloride.

Underground rock salt mining.

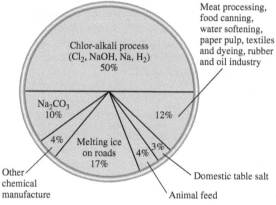

Uses of sodium chloride.

energies) and the stability gained from the formation of the solid. The sum of the first two ionization energies of sodium is

$$496 \text{ kJ/mol} + 4560 \text{ kJ/mol} = 5056 \text{ kJ/mol}$$

The compound $NaCl_2$ does not exist, but if we assume a value of 2527 kJ/mol as its lattice energy (same as that for $MgCl_2$), we see that the energy yield would be far too small to compensate for the energy required to produce the Na^{2+} ion.

What has been said about the cations applies also to the anions. In Section 8.5 we observed that the electron affinity of oxygen is 141 kJ/mol, meaning that the following process releases energy (and is therefore favorable):

$$O(g) + e^- \longrightarrow O^-(g)$$

As we would expect, adding another electron to the O^- ion

$$O^-(g) + e^- \longrightarrow O^{2-}(g)$$

would be unfavorable in the gas phase because of the increase in electrostatic repulsion. Indeed, the electron affinity of O^- is negative (-844 kJ/mol). Yet compounds containing the oxide ion (O^{2-}) do exist and are very stable, whereas compounds containing the O^- ion are not known. Again, the high lattice energy resulting from the O^{2-} ions in compounds such as Na_2O and MgO far outweighs the energy needed to produce the O^{2-} ion.

Review of Concepts

Which of the following compounds has a larger lattice energy, LiCl or CsBr?

9.4 The Covalent Bond

Although the concept of molecules goes back to the seventeenth century, it was not until early in the twentieth century that chemists began to understand how and why molecules form. The first major breakthrough was Gilbert Lewis's suggestion that a chemical bond involves electron sharing by atoms. He depicted the formation of a chemical bond in H_2 as

$$H \cdot + \cdot H \longrightarrow H : H$$

This type of electron pairing is an example of a ***covalent bond,*** *a bond in which two electrons are shared by two atoms.* ***Covalent compounds*** *are compounds that contain only covalent bonds.* For the sake of simplicity, the shared pair of electrons is often represented by a single line. Thus, the covalent bond in the hydrogen molecule can be written as H—H. In a covalent bond, each electron in a shared pair is attracted to the nuclei of both atoms. This attraction holds the two atoms in H_2 together and is responsible for the formation of covalent bonds in other molecules.

Covalent bonding between many-electron atoms involves only the valence electrons. Consider the fluorine molecule, F_2. The electron configuration of F is $1s^2 2s^2 2p^5$. The $1s$ electrons are low in energy and stay near the nucleus most of the time. For this reason they do not participate in bond formation. Thus, each F atom has seven valence electrons (the $2s$ and $2p$ electrons). According to Figure 9.1, there is only one unpaired electron on F, so the formation of the F_2 molecule can be represented as follows:

$$:\!\overset{..}{F}\!\cdot \; + \; \cdot\overset{..}{\underset{..}{F}}\!: \; \longrightarrow \; :\!\overset{..}{\underset{..}{F}}\!:\!\overset{..}{\underset{..}{F}}\!: \quad \text{or} \quad :\!\overset{..}{\underset{..}{F}}\!-\!\overset{..}{\underset{..}{F}}\!:$$

Note that only two valence electrons participate in the formation of F_2. The other, nonbonding electrons, are called ***lone pairs***—*pairs of valence electrons that are*

> ▶▶ Animation
> Formation of a Covalent Bond

> This discussion applies only to representative elements. Remember that for these elements, the number of valence electrons is equal to the group number (Groups 1A–7A).

not involved in covalent bond formation. Thus, each F in F_2 has three lone pairs of electrons:

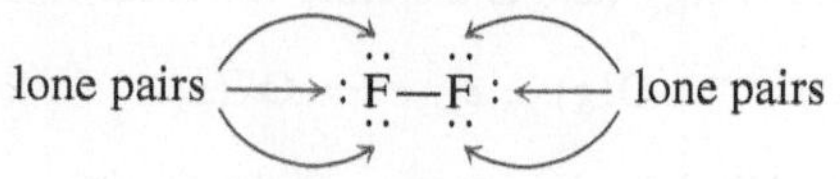

lone pairs $\longrightarrow$ $:\ddot{F}-\ddot{F}:$ $\longleftarrow$ lone pairs

The structures we use to represent covalent compounds, such as H_2 and F_2, are called Lewis structures. A **Lewis structure** is *a representation of covalent bonding in which shared electron pairs are shown either as lines or as pairs of dots between two atoms, and lone pairs are shown as pairs of dots on individual atoms.* Only valence electrons are shown in a Lewis structure.

Let us consider the Lewis structure of the water molecule. Figure 9.1 shows the Lewis dot symbol for oxygen with two unpaired dots or two unpaired electrons, so we expect that O might form two covalent bonds. Because hydrogen has only one electron, it can form only one covalent bond. Thus, the Lewis structure for water is

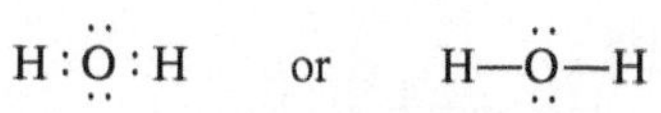

$$H:\ddot{O}:H \quad \text{or} \quad H-\ddot{O}-H$$

In this case, the O atom has two lone pairs. The hydrogen atom has no lone pairs because its only electron is used to form a covalent bond.

In the F_2 and H_2O molecules, the F and O atoms achieve a noble gas configuration by sharing electrons:

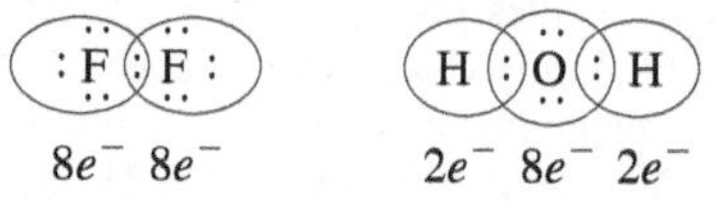

$8e^-$ $8e^-$ $2e^-$ $8e^-$ $2e^-$

The formation of these molecules illustrates the **octet rule,** formulated by Lewis: *An atom other than hydrogen tends to form bonds until it is surrounded by eight valence electrons.* In other words, a covalent bond forms when there are not enough electrons for each individual atom to have a complete octet. By sharing electrons in a covalent bond, the individual atoms can complete their octets. The requirement for hydrogen is that it attain the electron configuration of helium, or a total of two electrons.

The octet rule works mainly for elements in the second period of the periodic table. These elements have only $2s$ and $2p$ subshells, which can hold a total of eight electrons. When an atom of one of these elements forms a covalent compound, it can attain the noble gas electron configuration [Ne] by sharing electrons with other atoms in the same compound. Later, we will discuss a number of important exceptions to the octet rule that give us further insight into the nature of chemical bonding.

Atoms can form different types of covalent bonds. In a **single bond,** *two atoms are held together by one electron pair.* Many compounds are held together by **multiple bonds,** that is, bonds formed when *two atoms share two or more pairs of electrons.* If *two atoms share two pairs of electrons,* the covalent bond is called a **double bond.** Double bonds are found in molecules of carbon dioxide (CO_2) and ethylene (C_2H_4):

Shortly you will be introduced to the rules for writing proper Lewis structures. Here we simply want to become familiar with the language associated with them.

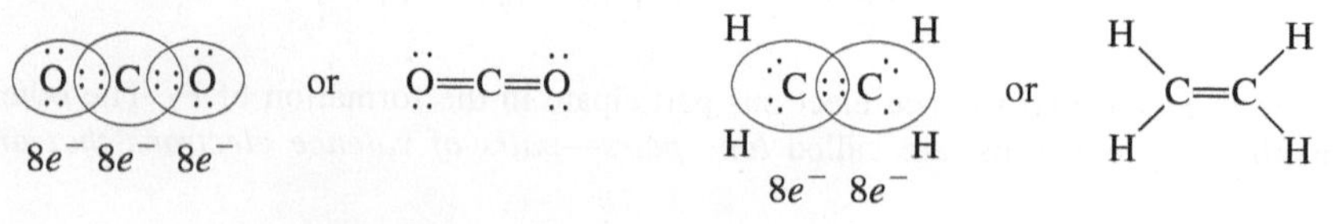

$8e^-$ $8e^-$ $8e^-$

$8e^-$ $8e^-$

A *triple bond* arises when *two atoms share three pairs of electrons,* as in the nitrogen molecule (N_2):

$$8e^-\quad 8e^-\qquad\qquad\qquad\text{or}\qquad : N\equiv N :$$

Figure 9.3 *Bond length (in pm) in* H_2 *and HI.*

The acetylene molecule (C_2H_2) also contains a triple bond, in this case between two carbon atoms:

$$H : C \text{ ⋮ } C : H\qquad\qquad\text{or}\qquad\qquad H-C\equiv C-H$$
$$8e^-\quad 8e^-$$

Note that in ethylene and acetylene all the valence electrons are used in bonding; there are no lone pairs on the carbon atoms. In fact, with the exception of carbon monoxide, stable molecules containing carbon do not have lone pairs on the carbon atoms.

Multiple bonds are shorter than single covalent bonds. **Bond length** is defined as the *distance between the nuclei of two covalently bonded atoms in a molecule* (Figure 9.3). Table 9.2 shows some experimentally determined bond lengths. For a given pair of atoms, such as carbon and nitrogen, triple bonds are shorter than double bonds, which, in turn, are shorter than single bonds. The shorter multiple bonds are also more stable than single bonds, as we will see later.

Comparison of the Properties of Covalent and Ionic Compounds

Ionic and covalent compounds differ markedly in their general physical properties because of differences in the nature of their bonds. There are two types of attractive forces in covalent compounds. The first type is the force that holds the atoms together in a molecule. A quantitative measure of this attraction is given by bond enthalpy, to be discussed in Section 9.10. The second type of attractive force operates *between* molecules and is called an *intermolecular force.* Because intermolecular forces are usually quite weak compared with the forces holding atoms together within a molecule, molecules of a covalent compound are not held together tightly. Consequently covalent compounds are usually gases, liquids, or low-melting solids. On the other hand, the electrostatic forces holding ions together in an ionic compound are usually very strong, so ionic compounds are solids at room temperature and have high melting points. Many ionic compounds are soluble in water, and the resulting aqueous solutions conduct electricity, because the compounds are strong electrolytes. Most covalent compounds are insoluble in water, or if they do dissolve, their aqueous solutions generally do not conduct electricity, because the compounds are nonelectrolytes. Molten ionic compounds conduct electricity because they contain mobile cations and anions; liquid or molten covalent compounds do not conduct electricity because no ions are present. Table 9.3 compares some of the general properties of a typical ionic compound, sodium chloride, with those of a covalent compound, carbon tetrachloride (CCl_4).

▶▶ Animation
Ionic vs. Covalent Bonding

▶▶ Animation
Ionic and Covalent Bonding

If intermolecular forces are weak, it is relatively easy to break up aggregates of molecules to form liquids (from solids) and gases (from liquids).

Review of Concepts

Why is it not possible for hydrogen to form double or triple bonds in covalent compounds?

380   Chapter 9 ▪ Chemical Bonding I: Basic Concepts

Table 9.2

Average Bond Lengths of Some Common Single, Double, and Triple Bonds

Bond Type	Bond Length (pm)
C—H	107
C—O	143
C=O	121
C—C	154
C=C	133
C≡C	120
C—N	143
C=N	138
C≡N	116
N—O	136
N=O	122
O—H	96

Table 9.3   **Comparison of Some General Properties of an Ionic Compound and a Covalent Compound**

Property	NaCl	CCl₄
Appearance	White solid	Colorless liquid
Melting point (°C)	801	−23
Molar heat of fusion* (kJ/mol)	30.2	2.5
Boiling point (°C)	1413	76.5
Molar heat of vaporization* (kJ/mol)	600	30
Density (g/cm³)	2.17	1.59
Solubility in water	High	Very low
Electrical conductivity		
Solid	Poor	Poor
Liquid	Good	Poor

*Molar heat of fusion and molar heat of vaporization are the amounts of heat needed to melt 1 mole of the solid and to vaporize 1 mole of the liquid, respectively.

9.5 Electronegativity

A covalent bond, as we have said, is the sharing of an electron pair by two atoms. In a molecule like H_2, in which the atoms are identical, we expect the electrons to be equally shared—that is, the electrons spend the same amount of time in the vicinity of each atom. However, in the covalently bonded HF molecule, the H and F atoms do not share the bonding electrons equally because H and F are different atoms:

$$H—\overset{..}{\underset{..}{F}}:$$

The bond in HF is called a ***polar covalent bond,*** or simply a *polar bond,* because *the electrons spend more time in the vicinity of one atom than the other.* Experimental evidence indicates that in the HF molecule the electrons spend more time near the F atom. We can think of this unequal sharing of electrons as a partial electron transfer or a shift in electron density, as it is more commonly described, from H to F (Figure 9.4). This "unequal sharing" of the bonding electron pair results in a relatively greater electron density near the fluorine atom and a correspondingly lower electron density near hydrogen. The HF bond and other polar bonds can be thought of as being intermediate between a (nonpolar) covalent bond, in which the sharing of electrons is exactly equal, and an ionic bond, in which the *transfer of the electron(s) is nearly complete.*

A property that helps us distinguish a nonpolar covalent bond from a polar covalent bond is ***electronegativity,*** *the ability of an atom to attract toward itself the electrons in a chemical bond.* Elements with high electronegativity have a greater tendency to attract electrons than do elements with low electronegativity. As we might expect, electronegativity is related to electron affinity and ionization energy. Thus, an atom such as fluorine, which has a high electron affinity (tends to pick up electrons easily) and a high ionization energy (does not lose electrons easily), has a high electronegativity. On the other hand, sodium has a low electron affinity, a low ionization energy, and a low electronegativity.

Hydrogen fluoride is a clear, fuming liquid that boils at 19.8°C. It is used to make refrigerants and to prepare hydrofluoric acid.

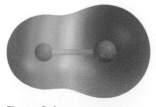

Figure 9.4 *Electrostatic potential map of the HF molecule. The distribution varies according to the colors of the rainbow. The most electron-rich region is red; the most electron-poor region is blue.*

Increasing electronegativity →

↑ Increasing electronegativity

1A	2A	3B	4B	5B	6B	7B	8B	8B	8B	1B	2B	3A	4A	5A	6A	7A	8A
H 2.1																	
Li 1.0	**Be** 1.5											**B** 2.0	**C** 2.5	**N** 3.0	**O** 3.5	**F** 4.0	
Na 0.9	**Mg** 1.2											**Al** 1.5	**Si** 1.8	**P** 2.1	**S** 2.5	**Cl** 3.0	
K 0.8	**Ca** 1.0	**Sc** 1.3	**Ti** 1.5	**V** 1.6	**Cr** 1.6	**Mn** 1.5	**Fe** 1.8	**Co** 1.9	**Ni** 1.9	**Cu** 1.9	**Zn** 1.6	**Ga** 1.6	**Ge** 1.8	**As** 2.0	**Se** 2.4	**Br** 2.8	**Kr** 3.0
Rb 0.8	**Sr** 1.0	**Y** 1.2	**Zr** 1.4	**Nb** 1.6	**Mo** 1.8	**Tc** 1.9	**Ru** 2.2	**Rh** 2.2	**Pd** 2.2	**Ag** 1.9	**Cd** 1.7	**In** 1.7	**Sn** 1.8	**Sb** 1.9	**Te** 2.1	**I** 2.5	**Xe** 2.6
Cs 0.7	**Ba** 0.9	**La-Lu** 1.0-1.2	**Hf** 1.3	**Ta** 1.5	**W** 1.7	**Re** 1.9	**Os** 2.2	**Ir** 2.2	**Pt** 2.2	**Au** 2.4	**Hg** 1.9	**Tl** 1.8	**Pb** 1.9	**Bi** 1.9	**Po** 2.0	**At** 2.2	
Fr 0.7	**Ra** 0.9																

Figure 9.5 *The electronegativities of common elements.*

Electronegativity values have no units.

Electronegativity is a relative concept, meaning that an element's electronegativity can be measured only in relation to the electronegativity of other elements. Linus Pauling[†] devised a method for calculating *relative* electronegativities of most elements. These values are shown in Figure 9.5. A careful examination of this chart reveals trends and relationships among electronegativity values of different elements. In general, electronegativity increases from left to right across a period in the periodic table, as the metallic character of the elements decreases. Within each group, electronegativity decreases with increasing atomic number, and increasing metallic character. Note that the transition metals do not follow these trends. The most electronegative elements—the halogens, oxygen, nitrogen, and sulfur—are found in the upper right-hand corner of the periodic table, and the least electronegative elements (the alkali and alkaline earth metals) are clustered near the lower left-hand corner. These trends are readily apparent on a graph, as shown in Figure 9.6.

Atoms of elements with widely different electronegativities tend to form ionic bonds (such as those that exist in NaCl and CaO compounds) with each other because the atom of the less electronegative element gives up its electron(s) to the atom of the more electronegative element. An ionic bond generally joins an atom of a metallic element and an atom of a nonmetallic element. Atoms of elements with comparable electronegativities tend to form polar covalent bonds with each other because the shift in electron density is usually small. Most covalent bonds involve atoms of nonmetallic elements. Only atoms of the same element, which have the same electronegativity, can be joined by a pure covalent bond. These trends and characteristics are what we would expect, given our knowledge of ionization energies and electron affinities.

[†]Linus Carl Pauling (1901–1994). American chemist. Regarded by many as the most influential chemist of the twentieth century, Pauling did research in a remarkably broad range of subjects, from chemical physics to molecular biology. Pauling received the Nobel Prize in Chemistry in 1954 for his work on protein structure, and the Nobel Peace Prize in 1962. He is the only person to be the sole recipient of two Nobel prizes.

382   **Chapter 9** ▪ Chemical Bonding I: Basic Concepts

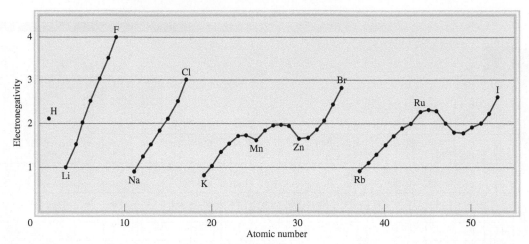

Figure 9.6 *Variation of electronegativity with atomic number. The halogens have the highest electronegativities, and the alkali metals the lowest.*

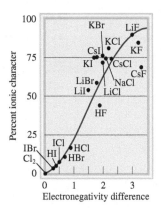

Figure 9.7 *Relation between percent ionic character and electronegativity difference.*

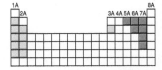

The most electronegative elements are the nonmetals (Groups 5A–7A) and the least electronegative elements are the alkali and alkaline earth metals (Groups 1A–2A) and aluminum. Beryllium, the first member of Group 2A, forms mostly covalent compounds.

There is no sharp distinction between a polar bond and an ionic bond, but the following general rule is helpful in distinguishing between them. An ionic bond forms when the electronegativity difference between the two bonding atoms is 2.0 or more. This rule applies to most but not all ionic compounds. Sometimes chemists use the quantity *percent ionic character* to describe the nature of a bond. A purely ionic bond would have 100 percent ionic character, although no such bond is known, whereas a nonpolar or purely covalent bond has 0 percent ionic character. As Figure 9.7 shows, there is a correlation between the percent ionic character of a bond and the electronegativity difference between the bonding atoms.

Electronegativity and electron affinity are related but different concepts. Both indicate the tendency of an atom to attract electrons. However, electron affinity refers to an isolated atom's attraction for an additional electron, whereas electronegativity signifies the ability of an atom in a chemical bond (with another atom) to attract the shared electrons. Furthermore, electron affinity is an experimentally measurable quantity, whereas electronegativity is an estimated number that cannot be measured.

Example 9.2 shows how a knowledge of electronegativity can help us determine whether a chemical bond is covalent or ionic.

Example 9.2

Classify the following bonds as ionic, polar covalent, or covalent: (a) the bond in HCl, (b) the bond in KF, and (c) the CC bond in H_3CCH_3.

Strategy We follow the 2.0 rule of electronegativity difference and look up the values in Figure 9.5.

Solution

(a) The electronegativity difference between H and Cl is 0.9, which is appreciable but not large enough (by the 2.0 rule) to qualify HCl as an ionic compound. Therefore, the bond between H and Cl is polar covalent.

(Continued)

(b) The electronegativity difference between K and F is 3.2, which is well above the 2.0 mark; therefore, the bond between K and F is ionic.

(c) The two C atoms are identical in every respect—they are bonded to each other and each is bonded to three other H atoms. Therefore, the bond between them is purely covalent.

Similar problems: 9.39, 9.40.

Practice Exercise Which of the following bonds is covalent, which is polar covalent, and which is ionic? (a) the bond in CsCl, (b) the bond in H_2S, (c) the NN bond in H_2NNH_2.

Electronegativity and Oxidation Number

In Chapter 4 we introduced the rules for assigning oxidation numbers of elements in their compounds. The concept of electronegativity is the basis for these rules. In essence, oxidation number refers to the number of charges an atom would have if electrons were transferred completely to the more electronegative of the bonded atoms in a molecule.

Consider the NH_3 molecule, in which the N atom forms three single bonds with the H atoms. Because N is more electronegative than H, electron density will be shifted from H to N. If the transfer were complete, each H would donate an electron to N, which would have a total charge of -3 while each H would have a charge of $+1$. Thus, we assign an oxidation number of -3 to N and an oxidation number of $+1$ to H in NH_3.

Oxygen usually has an oxidation number of -2 in its compounds, except in hydrogen peroxide (H_2O_2), whose Lewis structure is

$$H\text{—}\overset{\cdot\cdot}{\underset{\cdot\cdot}{O}}\text{—}\overset{\cdot\cdot}{\underset{\cdot\cdot}{O}}\text{—}H$$

A bond between identical atoms makes no contribution to the oxidation number of those atoms because the electron pair of that bond is *equally* shared. Because H has an oxidation number of $+1$, each O atom has an oxidation number of -1.

Can you see now why fluorine always has an oxidation number of -1? It is the most electronegative element known, and it *always* forms a single bond in its compounds. Therefore, it would bear a -1 charge if electron transfer were complete.

Review of Concepts

Identify the electrostatic potential maps shown here with HCl and LiH. In both diagrams, the H atom is on the left.

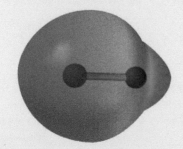 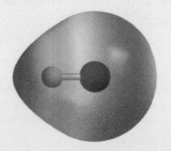

9.6 Writing Lewis Structures

Although the octet rule and Lewis structures do not present a complete picture of covalent bonding, they do help to explain the bonding scheme in many compounds and account for the properties and reactions of molecules. For this reason, you should practice writing Lewis structures of compounds. The basic steps are as follows:

1. Write the skeletal structure of the compound, using chemical symbols and placing bonded atoms next to one another. For simple compounds, this task is fairly easy. For more complex compounds, we must either be given the information or make an intelligent guess about it. In general, the least electronegative atom occupies the central position. Hydrogen and fluorine usually occupy the terminal (end) positions in the Lewis structure.

2. Count the total number of valence electrons present, referring, if necessary, to Figure 9.1. For polyatomic anions, add the number of negative charges to that total. (For example, for the CO_3^{2-} ion we add two electrons because the $2-$ charge indicates that there are two more electrons than are provided by the atoms.) For polyatomic cations, we subtract the number of positive charges from this total. (Thus, for NH_4^+ we subtract one electron because the $1+$ charge indicates a loss of one electron from the group of atoms.)

3. Draw a single covalent bond between the central atom and each of the surrounding atoms. Complete the octets of the atoms bonded to the central atom. (Remember that the valence shell of a hydrogen atom is complete with only two electrons.) Electrons belonging to the central or surrounding atoms must be shown as lone pairs if they are not involved in bonding. The total number of electrons to be used is that determined in step 2.

Hydrogen follows a "duet rule" when drawing Lewis structures.

4. After completing steps 1–3, if the central atom has fewer than eight electrons, try adding double or triple bonds between the surrounding atoms and the central atom, using lone pairs from the surrounding atoms to complete the octet of the central atom.

Examples 9.3, 9.4, and 9.5 illustrate the four-step procedure for writing Lewis structures of compounds and an ion.

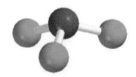

NF$_3$ is a colorless, odorless, unreactive gas.

Example 9.3

Write the Lewis structure for nitrogen trifluoride (NF_3) in which all three F atoms are bonded to the N atom.

Solution We follow the preceding procedure for writing Lewis structures.

Step 1: The N atom is less electronegative than F, so the skeletal structure of NF_3 is

$$F \quad N \quad F$$
$$F$$

Step 2: The outer-shell electron configurations of N and F are $2s^2 2p^3$ and $2s^2 2p^5$, respectively. Thus, there are $5 + (3 \times 7)$, or 26, valence electrons to account for in NF_3.

(Continued)

Step 3: We draw a single covalent bond between N and each F, and complete the octets for the F atoms. We place the remaining two electrons on N:

$$:\ddot{F}-\underset{\underset{\textstyle :\ddot{F}:}{|}}{N}-\ddot{F}:$$

Because this structure satisfies the octet rule for all the atoms, step 4 is not required.

Check Count the valence electrons in NF_3 (in bonds and in lone pairs). The result is 26, the same as the total number of valence electrons on three F atoms ($3 \times 7 = 21$) and one N atom (5).

Similar problem: 9.45.

Practice Exercise Write the Lewis structure for carbon disulfide (CS_2).

Example 9.4

Write the Lewis structure for nitric acid (HNO_3) in which the three O atoms are bonded to the central N atom and the ionizable H atom is bonded to one of the O atoms.

Solution We follow the procedure already outlined for writing Lewis structures.

Step 1: The skeletal structure of HNO_3 is

O N O H

O

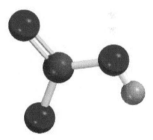

HNO₃ is a strong electrolyte.

Step 2: The outer-shell electron configurations of N, O, and H are $2s^2 2p^3$, $2s^2 2p^4$, and $1s^1$, respectively. Thus, there are $5 + (3 \times 6) + 1$, or 24, valence electrons to account for in HNO_3.

Step 3: We draw a single covalent bond between N and each of the three O atoms and between one O atom and the H atom. Then we fill in electrons to comply with the octet rule for the O atoms:

$$:\ddot{O}-\underset{\underset{\textstyle :\ddot{O}:}{|}}{N}-\ddot{O}-H$$

Step 4: We see that this structure satisfies the octet rule for all the O atoms but not for the N atom. The N atom has only six electrons. Therefore, we move a lone pair from one of the end O atoms to form another bond with N. Now the octet rule is also satisfied for the N atom:

$$\ddot{O}=\underset{\underset{\textstyle :\ddot{O}:}{|}}{N}-\ddot{O}-H$$

Check Make sure that all the atoms (except H) satisfy the octet rule. Count the valence electrons in HNO_3 (in bonds and in lone pairs). The result is 24, the same as the total number of valence electrons on three O atoms ($3 \times 6 = 18$), one N atom (5), and one H atom (1).

Similar problem: 9.45.

Practice Exercise Write the Lewis structure for formic acid (HCOOH).

386   **Chapter 9** ▪ Chemical Bonding I: Basic Concepts

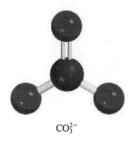

CO_3^{2-}

Example 9.5

Write the Lewis structure for the carbonate ion (CO_3^{2-}).

Solution We follow the preceding procedure for writing Lewis structures and note that this is an anion with two negative charges.

Step 1: We can deduce the skeletal structure of the carbonate ion by recognizing that C is less electronegative than O. Therefore, it is most likely to occupy a central position as follows:

$$O$$
$$O \quad C \quad O$$

Step 2: The outer-shell electron configurations of C and O are $2s^2 2p^2$ and $2s^2 2p^4$, respectively, and the ion itself has two negative charges. Thus, the total number of electrons is $4 + (3 \times 6) + 2$, or 24.

Step 3: We draw a single covalent bond between C and each O and comply with the octet rule for the O atoms:

$$:\ddot{O}:$$
$$\overset{|}{:\ddot{O}-C-\ddot{O}:}$$

This structure shows all 24 electrons.

Step 4: Although the octet rule is satisfied for the O atoms, it is not for the C atom. Therefore, we move a lone pair from one of the O atoms to form another bond with C. Now the octet rule is also satisfied for the C atom:

$$\left[\begin{array}{c} :\ddot{O}: \\ \| \\ :\ddot{O}-C-\ddot{O}: \end{array} \right]^{2-}$$

We use the square brackets to indicate that the −2 charge is on the whole ion.

Check Make sure that all the atoms satisfy the octet rule. Count the valence electrons in CO_3^{2-} (in chemical bonds and in lone pairs). The result is 24, the same as the total number of valence electrons on three O atoms ($3 \times 6 = 18$), one C atom (4), and two negative charges (2).

Similar problem: 9.44.

Practice Exercise Write the Lewis structure for the nitrite ion (NO_2^-).

Review of Concepts

The molecular model shown here represents guanine, a component of a DNA molecule. Only the connections between the atoms are shown in this model. Draw a complete Lewis structure of the molecule, showing all the multiple bonds and lone pairs. (For color code, see inside back endpaper.)

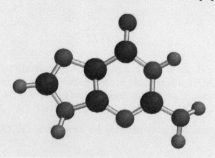

9.7 Formal Charge and Lewis Structure

By comparing the number of electrons in an isolated atom with the number of electrons that are associated with the same atom in a Lewis structure, we can determine the distribution of electrons in the molecule and draw the most plausible Lewis structure. The bookkeeping procedure is as follows: In an isolated atom, the number of electrons associated with the atom is simply the number of valence electrons. (As usual, we need not be concerned with the inner electrons.) In a molecule, electrons associated with the atom are the nonbonding electrons plus the electrons in the bonding pair(s) between the atom and other atom(s). However, because electrons are shared in a bond, we must divide the electrons in a bonding pair equally between the atoms forming the bond. An atom's *formal charge* is *the electrical charge difference between the valence electrons in an isolated atom and the number of electrons assigned to that atom in a Lewis structure.*

To assign the number of electrons on an atom in a Lewis structure, we proceed as follows:

- All the atom's nonbonding electrons are assigned to the atom.
- We break the bond(s) between the atom and other atom(s) and assign half of the bonding electrons to the atom.

Let us illustrate the concept of formal charge using the ozone molecule (O_3). Proceeding by steps, as we did in Examples 9.3 and 9.4, we draw the skeletal structure of O_3 and then add bonds and electrons to satisfy the octet rule for the two end atoms:

$$: \overset{..}{\underset{..}{O}} - \overset{..}{\underset{..}{O}} - \overset{..}{\underset{..}{O}} :$$

You can see that although all available electrons are used, the octet rule is not satisfied for the central atom. To remedy this, we convert a lone pair on one of the end atoms to a second bond between that end atom and the central atom, as follows:

$$\overset{..}{\underset{..}{O}} = \overset{..}{\underset{..}{O}} - \overset{..}{\underset{..}{O}} :$$

The formal charge on each atom in O_3 can now be calculated according to the following scheme:

Valence e^-	6	6	6
e^- assigned to atom	6	5	7
Difference (formal charge)	0	+1	−1

where the wavy red lines denote the breaking of the bonds. Note that the breaking of a single bond results in the transfer of an electron, the breaking of a double bond results in a transfer of two electrons to each of the bonding atoms, and so on. Thus, the formal charges of the atoms in O_3 are

$$\overset{..}{\underset{..}{O}} = \overset{..}{\underset{}{\overset{+}{O}}} - \overset{..}{\underset{..}{O}} : {}^-$$

For single positive and negative charges, we normally omit the numeral 1.

When you write formal charges, these rules are helpful:

1. For molecules, the sum of the charges must add up to zero because molecules are electrically neutral species. (This rule applies, for example, to the O_3 molecule.)
2. For cations, the sum of formal charges must equal the positive charge. For anions, the sum of formal charges must equal the negative charge.

Liquid ozone below its boiling point (−111.3°C). Ozone is a toxic, light-blue gas with a pungent odor.

Assign half of the bonding electrons to each atom.

In determining formal charges, does the atom in the molecule (or ion) have more electrons than its valence electrons (negative formal charge), or does the atom have fewer electrons than its valence electrons (positive formal charge)?

Note that formal charges help us keep track of valence electrons and gain a qualitative picture of charge distribution in a molecule. We should not interpret formal charges as actual, complete transfer of electrons. In the O_3 molecule, for example, experimental studies do show that the central O atom bears a partial positive charge while the end O atoms bear a partial negative charge, but there is no evidence that there is a complete transfer of electrons from one atom to another.

Example 9.6

Write formal charges for the carbonate ion.

Strategy The Lewis structure for the carbonate ion was developed in Example 9.5:

$$\left[\begin{array}{c} :\!\overset{..}{O}\!: \\ \overset{\curvearrowright}{} \\ :\!\overset{..}{O}\!\lessgtr C\lessgtr\overset{..}{O}\!: \end{array} \right]^{2-}$$

The formal charges on the atoms can be calculated using the given procedure.

Solution We subtract the number of nonbonding electrons and half of the bonding electrons from the valence electrons of each atom.

The C atom: The C atom has four valence electrons and there are no nonbonding electrons on the atom in the Lewis structure. The breaking of the double bond and two single bonds results in the transfer of four electrons to the C atom. Therefore, the formal charge is $4 - 4 = 0$.

The O atom in C═O: The O atom has six valence electrons and there are four nonbonding electrons on the atom. The breaking of the double bond results in the transfer of two electrons to the O atom. Here the formal charge is $6 - 4 - 2 = 0$.

The O atom in C─O: This atom has six nonbonding electrons and the breaking of the single bond transfers another electron to it. Therefore, the formal charge is $6 - 6 - 1 = -1$.

Thus, the Lewis structure for CO_3^{2-} with formal charges is

$$\overset{\displaystyle :\overset{..}{O}:}{\underset{}{\overset{\|}{}}}$$
$$^-:\overset{..}{\underset{..}{O}}\!-\!C\!-\!\overset{..}{\underset{..}{O}}:^-$$

Check Note that the sum of the formal charges is -2, the same as the charge on the carbonate ion.

Similar problem: 9.46.

Practice Exercise Write formal charges for the nitrite ion (NO_2^-).

Sometimes there is more than one acceptable Lewis structure for a given species. In such cases, we can often select the most plausible Lewis structure by using formal charges and the following guidelines:

• For molecules, a Lewis structure in which there are no formal charges is preferable to one in which formal charges are present.

• Lewis structures with large formal charges ($+2$, $+3$, and/or -2, -3, and so on) are less plausible than those with small formal charges.

• Among Lewis structures having similar distributions of formal charges, the most plausible structure is the one in which negative formal charges are placed on the more electronegative atoms.

Example 9.7 shows how formal charges facilitate the choice of the correct Lewis structure for a molecule.

Example 9.7

Formaldehyde (CH_2O), a liquid with a disagreeable odor, traditionally has been used to preserve laboratory specimens. Draw the most likely Lewis structure for the compound.

Strategy A plausible Lewis structure should satisfy the octet rule for all the elements, except H, and have the formal charges (if any) distributed according to electronegativity guidelines.

Solution The two possible skeletal structures are

H C O H
(a)

H
C O
H
(b)

First we draw the Lewis structures for each of these possibilities

H—C̈=Ö—H
(a)

H
  C=Ö
H
(b)

To show the formal charges, we follow the procedure given in Example 9.6. In (a) the C atom has a total of five electrons (one lone pair plus three electrons from the breaking of a single and a double bond). Because C has four valence electrons, the formal charge on the atom is $4 - 5 = -1$. The O atom has a total of five electrons (one lone pair and three electrons from the breaking of a single and a double bond). Because O has six valence electrons, the formal charge on the atom is $6 - 5 = +1$. In (b) the C atom has a total of four electrons from the breaking of two single bonds and a double bond, so its formal charge is $4 - 4 = 0$. The O atom has a total of six electrons (two lone pairs and two electrons from the breaking of the double bond). Therefore, the formal charge on the atom is $6 - 6 = 0$. Although both structures satisfy the octet rule, (b) is the more likely structure because it carries no formal charges.

Check In each case make sure that the total number of valence electrons is 12. Can you suggest two other reasons why (a) is less plausible?

Practice Exercise Draw the most reasonable Lewis structure of a molecule that contains a N atom, a C atom, and a H atom.

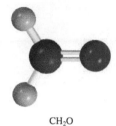

CH_2O

Similar problem: 9.47.

Review of Concepts

Consider three possible atomic arrangements for cyanamide (CH_2N_2): (a) H_2CNN, (b) H_2NCN, (c) HNNCH. Using formal charges as a guide, determine which is the most plausible arrangement.

9.8 The Concept of Resonance

Electrostatic potential map of O_3. The electron density is evenly distributed between the two end O atoms.

▶▶▶ Animation
Resonance

Our drawing of the Lewis structure for ozone (O_3) satisfied the octet rule for the central atom because we placed a double bond between it and one of the two end O atoms. In fact, we can put the double bond at either end of the molecule, as shown by these two equivalent Lewis structures:

$$\ddot{O}{=}\overset{..}{\underset{}{\overset{+}{O}}}{-}\ddot{\underset{..}{O}}{:}^{-} \qquad {}^{-}{:}\ddot{\underset{..}{O}}{-}\overset{..}{\overset{+}{O}}{=}\ddot{O}$$

However, neither one of these two Lewis structures accounts for the known bond lengths in O_3.

We would expect the O—O bond in O_3 to be longer than the O=O bond because double bonds are known to be shorter than single bonds. Yet experimental evidence shows that both oxygen-to-oxygen bonds are equal in length (128 pm). We resolve this discrepancy by using *both* Lewis structures to represent the ozone molecule:

$$\ddot{O}{=}\overset{..}{\overset{+}{O}}{-}\ddot{\underset{..}{O}}{:}^{-} \longleftrightarrow {}^{-}{:}\ddot{\underset{..}{O}}{-}\overset{..}{\overset{+}{O}}{=}\ddot{O}$$

Each of these structures is called a resonance structure. A ***resonance structure,*** then, is *one of two or more Lewis structures for a single molecule that cannot be represented accurately by only one Lewis structure.* The double-headed arrow indicates that the structures shown are resonance structures.

The term ***resonance*** itself means *the use of two or more Lewis structures to represent a particular molecule.* Like the medieval European traveler to Africa who described a rhinoceros as a cross between a griffin and a unicorn, two familiar but imaginary animals, we describe ozone, a real molecule, in terms of two familiar but nonexistent structures.

A common misconception about resonance is the notion that a molecule such as ozone somehow shifts quickly back and forth from one resonance structure to the other. Keep in mind that *neither* resonance structure adequately represents the actual molecule, which has its own unique, stable structure. "Resonance" is a human invention, designed to address the limitations in these simple bonding models. To extend the animal analogy, a rhinoceros is a distinct creature, not some oscillation between mythical griffin and unicorn!

The carbonate ion provides another example of resonance:

$$
{}^{-}{:}\ddot{\underset{..}{O}}{-}\overset{\displaystyle {:}\overset{..}{O}{:}}{\underset{}{C}}{-}\ddot{\underset{..}{O}}{:}^{-} \longleftrightarrow \overset{\displaystyle {:}\overset{..}{O}{:}^{-}}{\underset{}{\ddot{O}{=}C}}{-}\ddot{\underset{..}{O}}{:}^{-} \longleftrightarrow {}^{-}{:}\ddot{\underset{..}{O}}{-}\overset{\displaystyle {:}\overset{..}{O}{:}^{-}}{\underset{}{C}}{=}\ddot{O}
$$

According to experimental evidence, all carbon-to-oxygen bonds in CO_3^{2-} are equivalent. Therefore, the properties of the carbonate ion are best explained by considering its resonance structures together.

The concept of resonance applies equally well to organic systems. A good example is the benzene molecule (C_6H_6):

(benzene resonance structures)

If one of these resonance structures corresponded to the actual structure of benzene, there would be two different bond lengths between adjacent C atoms, one characteristic of the single bond and the other of the double bond. In fact, the distance between all adjacent C atoms in benzene is 140 pm, which is shorter than a C—C bond (154 pm) and longer than a C=C bond (133 pm).

A simpler way of drawing the structure of the benzene molecule and other compounds containing the "benzene ring" is to show only the skeleton and not the carbon and hydrogen atoms. By this convention the resonance structures are represented by

Note that the C atoms at the corners of the hexagon and the H atoms are all omitted, although they are understood to exist. Only the bonds between the C atoms are shown.

Remember this important rule for drawing resonance structures: The positions of electrons, but not those of atoms, can be rearranged in different resonance structures. In other words, the same atoms must be bonded to one another in all the resonance structures for a given species.

So far, the resonance structures shown in the examples all contribute equally to the real structure of the molecules and ion. This is not always the case, as we will see in Example 9.8.

Example 9.8

Draw three resonance structures for the molecule nitrous oxide, N_2O (the atomic arrangement is NNO). Indicate formal charges. Rank the structures in their relative importance to the overall properties of the molecule.

Strategy The skeletal structure for N_2O is

$$N \quad N \quad O$$

We follow the procedure used for drawing Lewis structures and calculating formal charges in Examples 9.5 and 9.6.

Solution The three resonance structures are

We see that all three structures show formal charges. Structure (b) is the most important one because the negative charge is on the more electronegative oxygen atom. Structure (c) is the least important one because it has a larger separation of formal charges. Also, the positive charge is on the more electronegative oxygen atom.

Check Make sure there is no change in the positions of the atoms in the structures. Because N has five valence electrons and O has six valence electrons, the total number of valence electrons is $5 \times 2 + 6 = 16$. The sum of formal charges is zero in each structure.

Practice Exercise Draw three resonance structures for the thiocyanate ion, SCN^-. Rank the structures in decreasing order of importance.

Resonance structures with formal charges greater than +2 or −2 are usually considered highly implausible and can be discarded.

Similar problems: 9.51, 9.56.

Review of Concepts

The molecular model shown here represents acetamide, which is used as an organic solvent. Only the connections between the atoms are shown in this model. Draw two resonance structures for the molecule, showing the positions of multiple bonds and formal charges. (For color code, see inside back endpaper.)

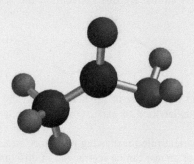

9.9 Exceptions to the Octet Rule

As mentioned earlier, the octet rule applies mainly to the second-period elements. Exceptions to the octet rule fall into three categories characterized by an incomplete octet, an odd number of electrons, or more than eight valence electrons around the central atom.

The Incomplete Octet

Beryllium, unlike the other Group 2A elements, forms mostly covalent compounds of which BeH₂ is an example.

In some compounds, the number of electrons surrounding the central atom in a stable molecule is fewer than eight. Consider, for example, beryllium, which is a Group 2A (and a second-period) element. The electron configuration of beryllium is $1s^2 2s^2$; it has two valence electrons in the $2s$ orbital. In the gas phase, beryllium hydride (BeH_2) exists as discrete molecules. The Lewis structure of BeH_2 is

$$\text{H—Be—H}$$

As you can see, only four electrons surround the Be atom, and there is no way to satisfy the octet rule for beryllium in this molecule.

Elements in Group 3A, particularly boron and aluminum, also tend to form compounds in which they are surrounded by fewer than eight electrons. Take boron as an example. Because its electron configuration is $1s^2 2s^2 2p^1$, it has a total of three valence electrons. Boron reacts with the halogens to form a class of compounds having the general formula BX_3, where X is a halogen atom. Thus, in boron trifluoride there are only six electrons around the boron atom:

$$: \overset{\displaystyle ..}{\underset{\displaystyle ..}{F}} \text{—} \overset{\displaystyle ..}{\underset{\displaystyle ..}{B}} \text{—} \overset{\displaystyle :\overset{..}{F}:}{\underset{\displaystyle :\overset{..}{F}:}{}}$$

The following resonance structures all contain a double bond between B and F and satisfy the octet rule for boron:

$$
{}^+F{=}B^- \longleftrightarrow \ :F{-}B^- \longleftrightarrow \ :F{-}B^-
$$

The fact that the B—F bond length in BF_3 (130.9 pm) is shorter than a single bond (137.3 pm) lends support to the resonance structures even though in each case the negative formal charge is placed on the B atom and the positive formal charge on the more electronegative F atom.

Although boron trifluoride is stable, it readily reacts with ammonia. This reaction is better represented by using the Lewis structure in which boron has only six valence electrons around it:

$$
:F{-}B \ + \ :N{-}H \longrightarrow \ :F{-}B^-{-}N^+{-}H
$$

It seems that the properties of BF_3 are best explained by all four resonance structures.

The B—N bond in the above compound is different from the covalent bonds discussed so far in the sense that both electrons are contributed by the N atom. This type of bond is called a **coordinate covalent bond** (also referred to as a *dative bond*), defined as *a covalent bond in which one of the atoms donates both electrons*. Although the properties of a coordinate covalent bond do not differ from those of a normal covalent bond (because all electrons are alike no matter what their source), the distinction is useful for keeping track of valence electrons and assigning formal charges.

Odd-Electron Molecules

Some molecules contain an *odd* number of electrons. Among them are nitric oxide (NO) and nitrogen dioxide (NO_2):

$$
\ddot{N}{=}\ddot{O} \qquad \ddot{O}{=}N^+{-}\ddot{O}:^-
$$

Because we need an even number of electrons for complete pairing (to reach eight), the octet rule clearly cannot be satisfied for all the atoms in any of these molecules.

Odd-electron molecules are sometimes called *radicals*. Many radicals are highly reactive. The reason is that there is a tendency for the unpaired electron to form a covalent bond with an unpaired electron on another molecule. For example, when two nitrogen dioxide molecules collide, they form dinitrogen tetroxide in which the octet rule is satisfied for both the N and O atoms:

$$
\overset{.}{O}{=}N{-}\overset{.}{O} \ + \ \overset{.}{N}{=}\overset{.}{O} \longrightarrow \ \overset{.}{O}{=}N{-}N{=}\overset{.}{O}
$$

The Expanded Octet

Atoms of the second-period elements cannot have more than eight valence electrons around the central atom, but atoms of elements in and beyond the third period of the periodic table form some compounds in which more than eight

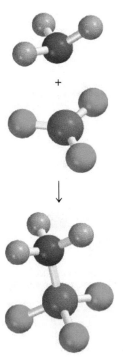

$NH_3 + BF_3 \longrightarrow H_3N{-}BF_3$

Yellow: second-period elements cannot have an expanded octet. Blue: third-period elements and beyond can have an expanded octet. Green: the noble gases usually only have an expanded octet.

394   **Chapter 9** ▪ Chemical Bonding I: Basic Concepts

electrons surround the central atom. In addition to the $3s$ and $3p$ orbitals, elements in the third period also have $3d$ orbitals that can be used in bonding. These orbitals enable an atom to form an *expanded octet*. One compound in which there is an expanded octet is sulfur hexafluoride, a very stable compound. The electron configuration of sulfur is $[\text{Ne}]3s^2 3p^4$. In SF_6, each of sulfur's six valence electrons forms a covalent bond with a fluorine atom, so there are 12 electrons around the central sulfur atom:

$$\ddot{\text{F}} \quad :\ddot{\text{F}}: \quad \ddot{\text{F}}:$$
$$\text{S}$$
$$:\ddot{\text{F}} \quad :\ddot{\text{F}}: \quad \ddot{\text{F}}:$$

In Chapter 10 we will see that these 12 electrons, or six bonding pairs, are accommodated in six orbitals that originate from the one $3s$, the three $3p$, and two of the five $3d$ orbitals. Sulfur also forms many compounds in which it obeys the octet rule. In sulfur dichloride, for instance, S is surrounded by only eight electrons:

$$:\ddot{\text{Cl}}\text{—}\ddot{\text{S}}\text{—}\ddot{\text{Cl}}:$$

Sulfur dichloride is a toxic, foul-smelling cherry-red liquid (boiling point: 59°C).

Examples 9.9–9.11 concern compounds that do not obey the octet rule.

Example 9.9

AlI₃ has a tendency to dimerize or combine two units to form Al₂I₆.

At high temperatures aluminum iodide (Al_2I_6) dissociates into AlI_3 molecules. Draw the Lewis structure for AlI_3.

Strategy We follow the procedures used in Examples 9.5 and 9.6 to draw the Lewis structure and calculate formal charges.

Solution The outer-shell electron configurations of Al and I are $3s^2 3p^1$ and $5s^2 5p^5$, respectively. The total number of valence electrons is $3 + 3 \times 7$ or 24. Because Al is less electronegative than I, it occupies a central position and forms three bonds with the I atoms:

$$:\ddot{\text{I}}:$$
$$|$$
$$:\ddot{\text{I}}\text{—Al}$$
$$|$$
$$:\ddot{\text{I}}:$$

Note that there are no formal charges on the Al and I atoms.

Similar problem: 9.62.

Check Although the octet rule is satisfied for the I atoms, there are only six valence electrons around the Al atom. Thus, AlI_3 is an example of the incomplete octet.

Practice Exercise Draw the Lewis structure for BeF_2.

Example 9.10

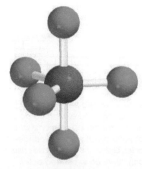

PF₅ is a reactive gaseous compound.

Draw the Lewis structure for phosphorus pentafluoride (PF_5), in which all five F atoms are bonded to the central P atom.

Strategy Note that P is a third-period element. We follow the procedures given in Examples 9.5 and 9.6 to draw the Lewis structure and calculate formal charges.

(Continued)

Solution The outer-shell electron configurations for P and F are $3s^2 3p^3$ and $2s^2 2p^5$, respectively, and so the total number of valence electrons is $5 + (5 \times 7)$, or 40. Phosphorus, like sulfur, is a third-period element, and therefore it can have an expanded octet. The Lewis structure of PF_5 is

:F̈⟍   :F̈:
    P—F̈:
:F̈⟋   :F̈:

Note that there are no formal charges on the P and F atoms.

Check Although the octet rule is satisfied for the F atoms, there are 10 valence electrons around the P atom, giving it an expanded octet.

Similar problem: 9.64.

Practice Exercise Draw the Lewis structure for arsenic pentafluoride (AsF_5).

Example 9.11

Draw a Lewis structure for the sulfate ion (SO_4^{2-}) in which all four O atoms are bonded to the central S atom.

Strategy Note that S is a third-period element. We follow the procedures given in Examples 9.5 and 9.6 to draw the Lewis structure and calculate formal charges.

Solution The outer-shell electron configurations of S and O are $3s^2 3p^4$ and $2s^2 2p^4$, respectively.

Step 1: The skeletal structure of (SO_4^{2-}) is

O
O S O
O

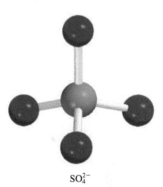

SO_4^{2-}

Step 2: Both O and S are Group 6A elements and so have six valence electrons each. Including the two negative charges, we must therefore account for a total of $6 + (4 \times 6) + 2$, or 32, valence electrons in SO_4^{2-}.

Step 3: We draw a single covalent bond between all the bonding atoms:

:Ö:
  |
:Ö—S—Ö:
  |
:Ö:

Next we show formal charges on the S and O atoms:

:Ö:⁻
  |
⁻:Ö—S²⁺—Ö:⁻
  |
:Ö:⁻

(Continued)

396   **Chapter 9** ▪ Chemical Bonding I: Basic Concepts

Note that we can eliminate some of the formal charges for SO_4^{2-} by expanding the S atom's octet as follows:

Note that this structure is only one of the six equivalent structures for SO_4^{2-}.

$$:\overset{\displaystyle :O:}{\underset{\displaystyle :O:}{\overset{\displaystyle \|}{\underset{\displaystyle \|}{-\!:\ddot{O}\!-\!S\!-\!\ddot{O}\!:^-}}}}$$

The question of which of these two structures is more important, that is, the one in which the S atom obeys the octet rule but bears more formal charges or the one in which the S atom expands its octet, has been the subject of some debate among chemists. In many cases, only elaborate quantum mechanical calculations can provide a clearer answer. At this stage of learning, you should realize that both representations are valid Lewis structures and you should be able to draw both types of structures. One helpful rule is that in trying to minimize formal charges by expanding the central atom's octet, only add enough double bonds to make the formal charge on the central atom zero. Thus, the following structure would give formal charges on S(-2) and O(0) that are inconsistent with the electronegativities of these elements and should therefore not be included to represent the SO_4^{2-} ion.

Similar problem: 9.85.

$$\overset{\displaystyle :O:}{\underset{\displaystyle :O:}{\overset{\displaystyle \|}{\underset{\displaystyle \|}{\ddot{O}\!=\!\overset{2-}{S}\!\overset{..}{=}\!\ddot{O}}}}}$$

Practice Exercise Draw reasonable Lewis structures of sulfuric acid (H_2SO_4).

A final note about the expanded octet: In drawing Lewis structures of compounds containing a central atom from the third period and beyond, sometimes we find that the octet rule is satisfied for all the atoms but there are still valence electrons left to place. In such cases, the extra electrons should be placed as lone pairs on the central atom. Example 9.12 shows this approach.

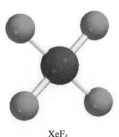

XeF₄

Example 9.12

Draw a Lewis structure of the noble gas compound xenon tetrafluoride (XeF_4) in which all F atoms are bonded to the central Xe atom.

Strategy Note that Xe is a fifth-period element. We follow the procedures in Examples 9.5 and 9.6 for drawing the Lewis structure and calculating formal charges.

Solution Step 1: The skeletal structure of XeF_4 is

$$\begin{array}{ccc} F & & F \\ & Xe & \\ F & & F \end{array}$$

Step 2: The outer-shell electron configurations of Xe and F are $5s^25p^6$ and $2s^22p^5$, respectively, and so the total number of valence electrons is $8 + (4 \times 7)$ or 36.

(Continued)

CHEMISTRY *in Action*

Just Say NO

Nitric oxide (NO), the simplest nitrogen oxide, is an odd-electron molecule, and therefore it is paramagnetic. A colorless gas (boiling point: $-152°C$), NO can be prepared in the laboratory by reacting sodium nitrite ($NaNO_2$) with a reducing agent such as Fe^{2+} in an acidic medium.

$$NO_2^-(aq) + Fe^{2+}(aq) + 2H^+(aq) \longrightarrow$$
$$NO(g) + Fe^{3+}(aq) + H_2O(l)$$

Environmental sources of nitric oxide include the burning of fossil fuels containing nitrogen compounds and the reaction between nitrogen and oxygen inside the automobile engine at high temperatures

$$N_2(g) + O_2(g) \longrightarrow 2NO(g)$$

Lightning also contributes to the atmospheric concentration of NO. Exposed to air, nitric oxide quickly forms brown nitrogen dioxide gas:

$$2NO(g) + O_2(g) \longrightarrow 2NO_2(g)$$

Nitrogen dioxide is a major component of smog.

About 40 years ago scientists studying muscle relaxation discovered that our bodies produce nitric oxide for use as a neurotransmitter. (A *neurotransmitter* is a small molecule that serves to facilitate cell-to-cell communications.) Since then, it has been detected in at least a dozen cell types in various parts of the body. Cells in the brain, the liver, the pancreas, the gastrointestinal tract, and the blood vessels can synthesize nitric oxide. This molecule also functions as a cellular toxin to kill harmful bacteria. And that's not all: In 1996 it was reported that NO binds to hemoglobin, the oxygen-carrying protein in the blood. No doubt it helps to regulate blood pressure.

The discovery of the biological role of nitric oxide has shed light on how nitroglycerin ($C_3H_5N_3O_9$) works as a drug. For many years, nitroglycerin tablets have been prescribed for heart patients to relieve pain (*angina pectoris*) caused by a brief interference in the flow of blood to the heart, although how it worked was not understood. We now know that nitroglycerin produces nitric oxide, which causes

muscles to relax and allows the arteries to dilate. In this respect, it is interesting to note that Alfred Nobel, the inventor of dynamite (a mixture of nitroglycerin and clay that stabilizes the explosive before use), who established the prizes bearing his name, had heart trouble. But he refused his doctor's recommendation to ingest a small amount of nitroglycerin to ease the pain.

That NO evolved as a messenger molecule is entirely appropriate. Nitric oxide is small and so can diffuse quickly from cell to cell. It is a stable molecule, but under certain circumstances it is highly reactive, which accounts for its protective function. The enzyme that brings about muscle relaxation contains iron for which nitric oxide has a high affinity. It is the binding of NO to the iron that activates the enzyme. Nevertheless, in the cell, where biological effectors are typically very large molecules, the pervasive effects of one of the smallest known molecules are unprecedented.

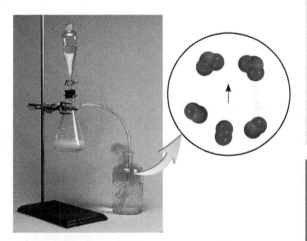

Colorless nitric oxide gas is produced by the action of Fe^{2+} on an acidic sodium nitrite solution. The gas is bubbled through water and immediately reacts with oxygen to form the brown NO_2 gas when exposed to air.

Step 3: We draw a single covalent bond between all the bonding atoms. The octet rule is satisfied for the F atoms, each of which has three lone pairs. The sum of the lone pair electrons on the four F atoms (4×6) and the four bonding pairs (4×2) is 32. Therefore, the remaining four electrons are shown as two lone pairs on the Xe atom:

$$
\begin{array}{ccc}
:\ddot{F} & & \ddot{F}: \\
 \diagdown & :\!: & \diagup \\
 & \text{Xe} & \\
 \diagup & :\!: & \diagdown \\
:\ddot{F} & & \ddot{F}:
\end{array}
$$

We see that the Xe atom has an expanded octet. There are no formal charges on the Xe and F atoms.

Similar problem: 9.63.

Practice Exercise Write the Lewis structure of sulfur tetrafluoride (SF_4).

Review of Concepts

Both boron and aluminum tend to form compounds in which they are surrounded with fewer than eight electrons. However, aluminum is able to form compounds and polyatomic ions where it is surrounded by more than eight electrons (e.g., AlF_6^-). Why is it possible for aluminum, but not boron, to expand the octet?

9.10 Bond Enthalpy

Remember that it takes energy to break a bond so that energy is released when a bond is formed.

A measure of the stability of a molecule is its **bond enthalpy,** which is *the enthalpy change required to break a particular bond in 1 mole of gaseous molecules.* (Bond enthalpies in solids and liquids are affected by neighboring molecules.) The experimentally determined bond enthalpy of the diatomic hydrogen molecule, for example, is

$$H_2(g) \longrightarrow H(g) + H(g) \qquad \Delta H° = 436.4 \text{ kJ/mol}$$

This equation tells us that breaking the covalent bonds in 1 mole of gaseous H_2 molecules requires 436.4 kJ of energy. For the less stable chlorine molecule,

$$Cl_2(g) \longrightarrow Cl(g) + Cl(g) \qquad \Delta H° = 242.7 \text{ kJ/mol}$$

Bond enthalpies can also be directly measured for diatomic molecules containing unlike elements, such as HCl,

$$HCl(g) \longrightarrow H(g) + Cl(g) \qquad \Delta H° = 431.9 \text{ kJ/mol}$$

as well as for molecules containing double and triple bonds:

The Lewis structure of O_2 is $\ddot{O}{=}\ddot{O}$ and that for N_2 is $:N{\equiv}N:$.

$$O_2(g) \longrightarrow O(g) + O(g) \qquad \Delta H° = 498.7 \text{ kJ/mol}$$
$$N_2(g) \longrightarrow N(g) + N(g) \qquad \Delta H° = 941.4 \text{ kJ/mol}$$

Measuring the strength of covalent bonds in polyatomic molecules is more complicated. For example, measurements show that the energy needed to break

Table 9.4	Some Bond Enthalpies of Diatomic Molecules* and Average Bond Enthalpies for Bonds in Polyatomic Molecules		
Bond	**Bond Enthalpy (kJ/mol)**	**Bond**	**Bond Enthalpy (kJ/mol)**
H—H	436.4	C—I	240
H—N	393	C—P	263
H—O	460	C—S	255
H—S	368	C=S	477
H—P	326	N—N	193
H—F	568.2	N=N	418
H—Cl	431.9	N≡N	941.4
H—Br	366.1	N—O	176
H—I	298.3	N=O	607
C—H	414	O—O	142
C—C	347	O=O	498.7
C=C	620	O—P	502
C≡C	812	O=S	469
C—N	276	P—P	197
C=N	615	P=P	489
C≡N	891	S—S	268
C—O	351	S=S	352
C=O†	745	F—F	156.9
C≡O	1076.5	Cl—Cl	242.7
C—F	450	Br—Br	192.5
C—Cl	338	I—I	151.0
C—Br	276		

*Bond enthalpies for diatomic molecules (in color) have more significant figures than bond enthalpies for bonds in polyatomic molecules because the bond enthalpies of diatomic molecules are directly measurable quantities and not averaged over many compounds.
†The C=O bond enthalpy in CO_2 is 799 kJ/mol.

the first O—H bond in H_2O is different from that needed to break the second O—H bond:

$$H_2O(g) \longrightarrow H(g) + OH(g) \qquad \Delta H° = 502 \text{ kJ/mol}$$
$$OH(g) \longrightarrow H(g) + O(g) \qquad \Delta H° = 427 \text{ kJ/mol}$$

In each case, an O—H bond is broken, but the first step is more endothermic than the second. The difference between the two $\Delta H°$ values suggests that the second O—H bond itself has undergone change, because of the changes in the chemical environment.

Now we can understand why the bond enthalpy of the same O—H bond in two different molecules such as methanol (CH_3OH) and water (H_2O) will not be the same: Their environments are different. Thus, for polyatomic molecules we speak of the *average* bond enthalpy of a particular bond. For example, we can measure the energy of the O—H bond in 10 different polyatomic molecules and obtain the average O—H bond enthalpy by dividing the sum of the bond enthalpies by 10. Table 9.4 lists the average bond enthalpies of a number of diatomic and polyatomic molecules. As stated earlier, triple bonds are stronger than double bonds, which, in turn, are stronger than single bonds.

Use of Bond Enthalpies in Thermochemistry

A comparison of the thermochemical changes that take place during a number of reactions (Chapter 6) reveals a strikingly wide variation in the enthalpies of different reactions. For example, the combustion of hydrogen gas in oxygen gas is fairly exothermic:

$$H_2(g) + \tfrac{1}{2}O_2(g) \longrightarrow H_2O(l) \qquad \Delta H° = -285.8 \text{ kJ/mol}$$

On the other hand, the formation of glucose ($C_6H_{12}O_6$) from water and carbon dioxide, best achieved by photosynthesis, is highly endothermic:

$$6CO_2(g) + 6H_2O(l) \longrightarrow C_6H_{12}O_6(s) + 6O_2(g) \qquad \Delta H° = 2801 \text{ kJ/mol}$$

We can account for such variations by looking at the stability of individual reactant and product molecules. After all, most chemical reactions involve the making and breaking of bonds. Therefore, knowing the bond enthalpies and hence the stability of molecules tells us something about the thermochemical nature of reactions that molecules undergo.

In many cases, it is possible to predict the approximate enthalpy of reaction by using the average bond enthalpies. Because energy is always required to break chemical bonds and chemical bond formation is always accompanied by a release of energy, we can estimate the enthalpy of a reaction by counting the total number of bonds broken and formed in the reaction and recording all the corresponding energy changes. The enthalpy of reaction in the *gas phase* is given by

$$\Delta H° = \Sigma BE(\text{reactants}) - \Sigma BE(\text{products}) \\ = \text{total energy input} - \text{total energy released} \qquad (9.3)$$

where BE stands for average bond enthalpy and Σ is the summation sign. As written, Equation (9.3) takes care of the sign convention for $\Delta H°$. Thus, if the total energy input is greater than the total energy released, $\Delta H°$ is positive and the reaction is endothermic. On the other hand, if more energy is released than absorbed, $\Delta H°$ is negative and the reaction is exothermic (Figure 9.8). If reactants and products are all

Figure 9.8 *Bond enthalpy changes in (a) an endothermic reaction and (b) an exothermic reaction.*

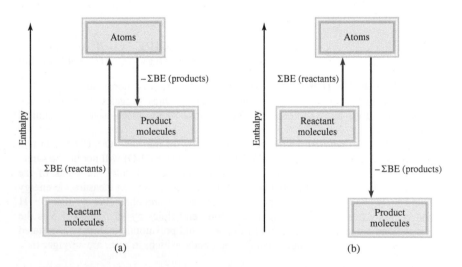

diatomic molecules, then Equation (9.3) will yield accurate results because the bond enthalpies of diatomic molecules are accurately known. If some or all of the reactants and products are polyatomic molecules, Equation (9.3) will yield only approximate results because the bond enthalpies used will be averages.

For diatomic molecules, Equation (9.3) is equivalent to Equation (6.18), so the results obtained from these two equations should correspond, as Example 9.13 illustrates.

Example 9.13

Use Equation (9.3) to calculate the enthalpy of reaction for the process

$$H_2(g) + Cl_2(g) \longrightarrow 2HCl(g)$$

Compare your result with that obtained using Equation (6.18).

Strategy Keep in mind that bond breaking is an energy absorbing (endothermic) process and bond making is an energy releasing (exothermic) process. Therefore, the overall energy change is the difference between these two opposing processes, as described by Equation (9.3).

Solution We start by counting the number of bonds broken and the number of bonds formed and the corresponding energy changes. This is best done by creating a table:

Type of bonds broken	Number of bonds broken	Bond enthalpy (kJ/mol)	Energy change (kJ/mol)
H—H (H_2)	1	436.4	436.4
Cl—Cl (Cl_2)	1	242.7	242.7

Type of bonds formed	Number of bonds formed	Bond enthalpy (kJ/mol)	Energy change (kJ/mol)
H—Cl (HCl)	2	431.9	863.8

Next, we obtain the total energy input and total energy released:

total energy input = 436.4 kJ/mol + 242.7 kJ/mol = 679.1 kJ/mol
total energy released = 863.8 kJ/mol

Using Equation (9.3), we write

$$\Delta H° = 679.1 \text{ kJ/mol} - 863.8 \text{ kJ/mol} = -184.7 \text{ kJ/mol}$$

Alternatively, we can use Equation (6.18) and the data in Appendix 3 to calculate the enthalpy of reaction:

$$\Delta H° = 2\Delta H_f°(\text{HCl}) - [\Delta H_f°(\text{H}_2) + \Delta H_f°(\text{Cl}_2)]$$
$$= (2)(-92.3 \text{ kJ/mol}) - 0 - 0$$
$$= -184.6 \text{ kJ/mol}$$

Check Because the reactants and products are all diatomic molecules, we expect the results of Equations (9.3) and (6.18) to be the same. The small discrepancy here is due to different ways of rounding off.

Practice Exercise Calculate the enthalpy of the reaction

$$H_2(g) + F_2(g) \longrightarrow 2HF(g)$$

using (a) Equation (9.3) and (b) Equation (6.18).

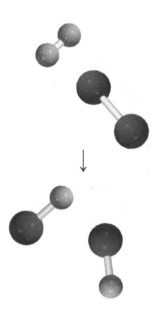

Refer to Table 9.4 for bond enthalpies of these diatomic molecules.

Similar problem: 9.104.

Example 9.14 uses Equation (9.3) to estimate the enthalpy of a reaction involving a polyatomic molecule.

Example 9.14

Estimate the enthalpy change for the combustion of hydrogen gas:

$$2H_2(g) + O_2(g) \longrightarrow 2H_2O(g)$$

Strategy We basically follow the same procedure as that in Example 9.13. Note, however, that H_2O is a polyatomic molecule, and so we need to use the average bond enthalpy value for the O—H bond.

Solution We construct the following table:

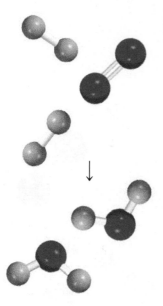

Type of bonds broken	Number of bonds broken	Bond enthalpy (kJ/mol)	Energy change (kJ/mol)
H—H (H_2)	2	436.4	872.8
O=O (O_2)	1	498.7	498.7

Type of bonds formed	Number of bonds formed	Bond enthalpy (kJ/mol)	Energy change (kJ/mol)
O—H (H_2O)	4	460	1840

Next, we obtain the total energy input and total energy released:

$$\text{total energy input} = 872.8 \text{ kJ/mol} + 498.7 \text{ kJ/mol} = 1371.5 \text{ kJ/mol}$$
$$\text{total energy released} = 1840 \text{ kJ/mol}$$

Using Equation (9.3), we write

$$\Delta H° = 1371.5 \text{ kJ/mol} - 1840 \text{ kJ/mol} = -469 \text{ kJ/mol}$$

This result is only an estimate because the bond enthalpy of O—H is an average quantity. Alternatively, we can use Equation (6.18) and the data in Appendix 3 to calculate the enthalpy of reaction:

$$\Delta H° = 2\Delta H_f°(H_2O) - [2\Delta H_f°(H_2) + \Delta H_f°(O_2)]$$
$$= 2(-241.8 \text{ kJ/mol}) - 0 - 0$$
$$= -483.6 \text{ kJ/mol}$$

Check Note that the estimated value based on average bond enthalpies is quite close to the value calculated using $\Delta H_f°$ data. In general, Equation (9.3) works best for reactions that are either quite endothermic or quite exothermic, that is, reactions for which $\Delta H_{rxn}° > 100$ kJ/mol or for which $\Delta H_{rxn}° < -100$ kJ/mol.

Practice Exercise For the reaction

$$H_2(g) + C_2H_4(g) \longrightarrow C_2H_6(g)$$

(a) Estimate the enthalpy of reaction, using the bond enthalpy values in Table 9.4.

(b) Calculate the enthalpy of reaction, using standard enthalpies of formation. ($\Delta H_f°$ for H_2, C_2H_4, and C_2H_6 are 0, 52.3 kJ/mol, and -84.7 kJ/mol, respectively.)

Similar problem: 9.72.

Review of Concepts

Why does $\Delta H_{rxn}°$ calculated using bond enthalpies not always agree with that calculated using $\Delta H_f°$ values?

Key Equation

$\Delta H° = \Sigma BE(\text{reactants}) - \Sigma BE(\text{products})$ (9.3)   Calculating enthalpy change of a reaction from bond enthalpies.

Summary of Facts & Concepts

1. A Lewis dot symbol shows the number of valence electrons possessed by an atom of a given element. Lewis dot symbols are useful mainly for the representative elements.

2. The elements most likely to form ionic compounds have low ionization energies (such as the alkali metals and the alkaline earth metals, which form cations) or high electron affinities (such as the halogens and oxygen, which form anions).

3. An ionic bond is the product of the electrostatic forces of attraction between positive and negative ions. An ionic compound consists of a large network of ions in which positive and negative charges are balanced. The structure of a solid ionic compound maximizes the net attractive forces among the ions.

4. Lattice energy is a measure of the stability of an ionic solid. It can be calculated by means of the Born-Haber cycle, which is based on Hess's law.

5. In a covalent bond, two electrons (one pair) are shared by two atoms. In multiple covalent bonds, two or three pairs of electrons are shared by two atoms. Some covalently bonded atoms also have lone pairs, that is, pairs of valence electrons that are not involved in bonding.

The arrangement of bonding electrons and lone pairs in a molecule is represented by a Lewis structure.

6. Electronegativity is a measure of an atom's ability to attract electrons in a chemical bond.

7. The octet rule predicts that atoms form enough covalent bonds to surround themselves with eight electrons each. When one atom in a covalently bonded pair donates two electrons to the bond, the Lewis structure can include the formal charge on each atom as a means of keeping track of the valence electrons. There are exceptions to the octet rule, particularly for covalent beryllium compounds, elements in Group 3A, odd-electron molecules, and elements in the third period and beyond in the periodic table.

8. For some molecules or polyatomic ions, two or more Lewis structures based on the same skeletal structure satisfy the octet rule and appear chemically reasonable. Taken together, such resonance structures represent the molecule or ion more accurately than any single Lewis structure does.

9. The strength of a covalent bond is measured in terms of its bond enthalpy. Bond enthalpies can be used to estimate the enthalpy of reactions.

Key Words

Bond enthalpy, p. 398
Bond length, p. 379
Born-Haber cycle, p. 372
Coordinate covalent
    bond, p. 393
Coulomb's law, p. 372

Covalent bond, p. 377
Covalent compound, p. 377
Double bond, p. 378
Electronegativity, p. 380
Formal charge, p. 387
Ionic bond, p. 370

Lewis dot symbol, p. 369
Lewis structure, p. 378
Lone pair, p. 377
Multiple bond, p. 378
Octet rule, p. 378

Polar covalent bond, p. 380
Resonance, p. 390
Resonance structure, p. 390
Single bond, p. 378
Triple bond, p. 379

Questions & Problems

*Problems available in Connect Plus
Red numbered problems solved in Student Solutions Manual

Lewis Dot Symbols

Review Questions

9.1 What is a Lewis dot symbol? To what elements does the symbol mainly apply?

9.2 Use the second member of each group from Group 1A to Group 7A to show that the number of valence electrons on an atom of the element is the same as its group number.

• 9.3 Without referring to Figure 9.1, write Lewis dot symbols for atoms of the following elements: (a) Be, (b) K, (c) Ca, (d) Ga, (e) O, (f) Br, (g) N, (h) I, (i) As, (j) F.

• 9.4 Write Lewis dot symbols for the following ions: (a) Li^+, (b) Cl^-, (c) S^{2-}, (d) Sr^{2+}, (e) N^{3-}.

• 9.5 Write Lewis dot symbols for the following atoms and ions: (a) I, (b) I^-, (c) S, (d) S^{2-}, (e) P, (f) P^{3-}, (g) Na, (h) Na^+, (i) Mg, (j) Mg^{2+}, (k) Al, (l) Al^{3+}, (m) Pb, (n) Pb^{2+}.

The Ionic Bond
Review Questions

9.6   Explain what an ionic bond is.

9.7   Explain how ionization energy and electron affinity determine whether atoms of elements will combine to form ionic compounds.

9.8   Name five metals and five nonmetals that are very likely to form ionic compounds. Write formulas for compounds that might result from the combination of these metals and nonmetals. Name these compounds.

9.9   Name one ionic compound that contains only non-metallic elements.

9.10   Name one ionic compound that contains a polyatomic cation and a polyatomic anion (see Table 2.3).

9.11   Explain why ions with charges greater than 3 are seldom found in ionic compounds.

9.12   The term "molar mass" was introduced in Chapter 3. What is the advantage of using the term "molar mass" when we discuss ionic compounds?

● 9.13   In which of the following states would NaCl be electrically conducting? (a) solid, (b) molten (that is, melted), (c) dissolved in water. Explain your answers.

● 9.14   Beryllium forms a compound with chlorine that has the empirical formula $BeCl_2$. How would you determine whether it is an ionic compound? (The compound is not soluble in water.)

Problems

● 9.15   An ionic bond is formed between a cation A^+ and an anion B^-. How would the energy of the ionic bond [see Equation (9.2)] be affected by the following changes? (a) doubling the radius of A^+, (b) tripling the charge on A^+, (c) doubling the charges on A^+ and B^-, (d) decreasing the radii of A^+ and B^- to half their original values.

● 9.16   Give the empirical formulas and names of the compounds formed from the following pairs of ions: (a) Rb^+ and I^-, (b) Cs^+ and SO_4^{2-}, (c) Sr^{2+} and N^{3-}, (d) Al^{3+} and S^{2-}.

9.17   Use Lewis dot symbols to show the transfer of electrons between the following atoms to form cations and anions: (a) Na and F, (b) K and S, (c) Ba and O, (d) Al and N.

● 9.18   Write the Lewis dot symbols of the reactants and products in the following reactions. (First balance the equations.)
(a) $Sr + Se \longrightarrow SrSe$
(b) $Ca + H_2 \longrightarrow CaH_2$
(c) $Li + N_2 \longrightarrow Li_3N$
(d) $Al + S \longrightarrow Al_2S_3$

● 9.19   For each of the following pairs of elements, state whether the binary compound they form is likely to be ionic or covalent. Write the empirical formula and name of the compound: (a) I and Cl, (b) Mg and F.

● 9.20   For each of the following pairs of elements, state whether the binary compound they form is likely to be ionic or covalent. Write the empirical formula and name of the compound: (a) B and F, (b) K and Br.

Lattice Energy of Ionic Compounds
Review Questions

9.21   What is lattice energy and what role does it play in the stability of ionic compounds?

9.22   Explain how the lattice energy of an ionic compound such as KCl can be determined using the Born-Haber cycle. On what law is this procedure based?

● 9.23   Specify which compound in the following pairs of ionic compounds has the higher lattice energy: (a) KCl or MgO, (b) LiF or LiBr, (c) Mg_3N_2 or NaCl. Explain your choice.

● 9.24   Compare the stability (in the solid state) of the following pairs of compounds: (a) LiF and LiF_2 (containing the Li^{2+} ion), (b) Cs_2O and CsO (containing the O^- ion), (c) $CaBr_2$ and $CaBr_3$ (containing the Ca^{3+} ion).

Problems

● 9.25   Use the Born-Haber cycle outlined in Section 9.3 for LiF to calculate the lattice energy of NaCl. [The heat of sublimation of Na is 108 kJ/mol and $\Delta H_f^\circ(NaCl) = -411$ kJ/mol. Energy needed to dissociate $\frac{1}{2}$ mole of Cl_2 into Cl atoms = 121.4 kJ.]

● 9.26   Calculate the lattice energy of calcium chloride given that the heat of sublimation of Ca is 121 kJ/mol and $\Delta H_f^\circ(CaCl_2) = -795$ kJ/mol. (See Tables 8.2 and 8.3 for other data.)

The Covalent Bond
Review Questions

9.27   What is Lewis's contribution to our understanding of the covalent bond?

9.28   Use an example to illustrate each of the following terms: lone pairs, Lewis structure, the octet rule, bond length.

9.29   What is the difference between a Lewis dot symbol and a Lewis structure?

● 9.30   How many lone pairs are on the underlined atoms in these compounds? H<u>Br</u>, H<u>_2</u>S, <u>C</u>H... H<u>Br</u>, H<u>2S</u>, <u>C</u>H$_4$

9.31   Compare single, double, and triple bonds in a molecule, and give an example of each. For the same bonding atoms, how does the bond length change from single bond to triple bond?

9.32   Compare the properties of ionic compounds and covalent compounds.

Electronegativity and Bond Type
Review Questions

9.33 Define electronegativity, and explain the difference between electronegativity and electron affinity. Describe in general how the electronegativities of the elements change according to position in the periodic table.

9.34 What is a polar covalent bond? Name two compounds that contain one or more polar covalent bonds.

Problems

9.35 List the following bonds in order of increasing ionic character: the lithium-to-fluorine bond in LiF, the potassium-to-oxygen bond in K_2O, the nitrogen-to-nitrogen bond in N_2, the sulfur-to-oxygen bond in SO_2, the chlorine-to-fluorine bond in ClF_3.

9.36 Arrange the following bonds in order of increasing ionic character: carbon to hydrogen, fluorine to hydrogen, bromine to hydrogen, sodium to chlorine, potassium to fluorine, lithium to chlorine.

9.37 Four atoms are arbitrarily labeled D, E, F, and G. Their electronegativities are as follows: D = 3.8, E = 3.3, F = 2.8, and G = 1.3. If the atoms of these elements form the molecules DE, DG, EG, and DF, how would you arrange these molecules in order of increasing covalent bond character?

9.38 List the following bonds in order of increasing ionic character: cesium to fluorine, chlorine to chlorine, bromine to chlorine, silicon to carbon.

9.39 Classify the following bonds as ionic, polar covalent, or covalent, and give your reasons: (a) the CC bond in H_3CCH_3, (b) the KI bond in KI, (c) the NB bond in H_3NBCl_3, (d) the CF bond in CF_4.

9.40 Classify the following bonds as ionic, polar covalent, or covalent, and give your reasons: (a) the SiSi bond in $Cl_3SiSiCl_3$, (b) the SiCl bond in $Cl_3SiSiCl_3$, (c) the CaF bond in CaF_2, (d) the NH bond in NH_3.

Lewis Structure and the Octet Rule
Review Questions

9.41 Summarize the essential features of the Lewis octet rule. The octet rule applies mainly to the second-period elements. Explain.

9.42 Explain the concept of formal charge. Do formal charges represent actual separation of charges?

Problems

9.43 Write Lewis structures for the following molecules and ions: (a) NCl_3, (b) OCS, (c) H_2O_2, (d) CH_3COO^-, (e) CN^-, (f) $CH_3CH_2NH_3^+$.

9.44 Write Lewis structures for the following molecules and ions: (a) OF_2, (b) N_2F_2, (c) Si_2H_6, (d) OH^-, (e) CH_2ClCOO^-, (f) $CH_3NH_3^+$.

9.45 Write Lewis structures for the following molecules: (a) ICl, (b) PH_3, (c) P_4 (each P is bonded to three other P atoms), (d) H_2S, (e) N_2H_4, (f) $HClO_3$, (g) $COBr_2$ (C is bonded to O and Br atoms).

9.46 Write Lewis structures for the following ions: (a) O_2^{2-}, (b) C_2^{2-}, (c) NO^+, (d) NH_4^+. Show formal charges.

9.47 The following Lewis structures for (a) HCN, (b) C_2H_2, (c) SnO_2, (d) BF_3, (e) HOF, (f) HCOF, and (g) NF_3 are incorrect. Explain what is wrong with each one and give a correct structure for the molecule. (Relative positions of atoms are shown correctly.)

9.48 The skeletal structure of acetic acid shown below is correct, but some of the bonds are wrong. (a) Identify the incorrect bonds and explain what is wrong with them. (b) Write the correct Lewis structure for acetic acid.

The Concept of Resonance
Review Questions

9.49 Define bond length, resonance, and resonance structure. What are the rules for writing resonance structures?

9.50 Is it possible to "trap" a resonance structure of a compound for study? Explain.

Problems

9.51 Write Lewis structures for the following species, including all resonance forms, and show formal charges: (a) HCO_2^-, (b) $CH_2NO_2^-$. Relative positions of the atoms are as follows:

```
      O     H        O
  H  C            C  N
      O     H        O
```

9.52 Draw three resonance structures for the chlorate ion, ClO_3^-. Show formal charges.

406   Chapter 9 ▪ Chemical Bonding I: Basic Concepts

● 9.53   Write three resonance structures for hydrazoic acid, HN_3. The atomic arrangement is HNNN. Show formal charges.

● **9.54** Draw two resonance structures for diazomethane, CH_2N_2. Show formal charges. The skeletal structure of the molecule is

$$
\begin{array}{c}
H \\
 \quad C \quad N \quad N \\
H
\end{array}
$$

● 9.55   Draw three resonance structures for the molecule N_2O_3 (atomic arrangement is $ONNO_2$). Show formal charges.

● **9.56** Draw three reasonable resonance structures for the OCN^- ion. Show formal charges.

Exceptions to the Octet Rule
Review Questions

9.57   Why does the octet rule not hold for many compounds containing elements in the third period of the periodic table and beyond?

9.58   Give three examples of compounds that do not satisfy the octet rule. Write a Lewis structure for each.

9.59   Because fluorine has seven valence electrons ($2s^2 2p^5$), seven covalent bonds in principle could form around the atom. Such a compound might be FH_7 or FCl_7. These compounds have never been prepared. Why?

9.60   What is a coordinate covalent bond? Is it different from a normal covalent bond?

Problems

9.61   The AlI_3 molecule has an incomplete octet around Al. Draw three resonance structures of the molecule in which the octet rule is satisfied for both the Al and the I atoms. Show formal charges.

9.62 In the vapor phase, beryllium chloride consists of discrete $BeCl_2$ molecules. Is the octet rule satisfied for Be in this compound? If not, can you form an octet around Be by drawing another resonance structure? How plausible is this structure?

● 9.63   Of the noble gases, only Kr, Xe, and Rn are known to form a few compounds with O and/or F. Write Lewis structures for the following molecules: (a) XeF_2, (b) XeF_4, (c) XeF_6, (d) $XeOF_4$, (e) XeO_2F_2. In each case Xe is the central atom.

● 9.64   Write a Lewis structure for $SbCl_5$. Does this molecule obey the octet rule?

● 9.65   Write Lewis structures for SeF_4 and SeF_6. Is the octet rule satisfied for Se?

● 9.66   Write Lewis structures for the reaction

$$AlCl_3 + Cl^- \longrightarrow AlCl_4^-$$

What kind of bond joins Al and Cl in the product?

Bond Enthalpy
Review Questions

9.67   What is bond enthalpy? Bond enthalpies of polyatomic molecules are average values, whereas those of diatomic molecules can be accurately determined. Why?

9.68   Explain why the bond enthalpy of a molecule is usually defined in terms of a gas-phase reaction. Why are bond-breaking processes always endothermic and bond-forming processes always exothermic?

Problems

● 9.69   From the following data, calculate the average bond enthalpy for the N—H bond:

$$
\begin{array}{lll}
NH_3(g) \longrightarrow NH_2(g) + H(g) & \Delta H^\circ = 435 \text{ kJ/mol} \\
NH_2(g) \longrightarrow NH(g) + H(g) & \Delta H^\circ = 381 \text{ kJ/mol} \\
NH(g) \longrightarrow N(g) + H(g) & \Delta H^\circ = 360 \text{ kJ/mol}
\end{array}
$$

● **9.70** For the reaction

$$O(g) + O_2(g) \longrightarrow O_3(g) \quad \Delta H^\circ = -107.2 \text{ kJ/mol}$$

Calculate the average bond enthalpy in O_3.

● 9.71   The bond enthalpy of $F_2(g)$ is 156.9 kJ/mol. Calculate ΔH_f° for F(g).

● **9.72** For the reaction

$$2C_2H_6(g) + 7O_2(g) \longrightarrow 4CO_2(g) + 6H_2O(g)$$

(a) Predict the enthalpy of reaction from the average bond enthalpies in Table 9.4.

(b) Calculate the enthalpy of reaction from the standard enthalpies of formation (see Appendix 3) of the reactant and product molecules, and compare the result with your answer for part (a).

Additional Problems

● 9.73   Classify the following substances as ionic compounds or covalent compounds containing discrete molecules: CH_4, KF, CO, $SiCl_4$, $BaCl_2$.

9.74   Which of the following are ionic compounds? Which are covalent compounds? RbCl, PF_5, BrF_3, KO_2, CI_4

● 9.75   Match each of the following energy changes with one of the processes given: ionization energy, electron affinity, bond enthalpy, and standard enthalpy of formation.

(a) $F(g) + e^- \longrightarrow F^-(g)$
(b) $F_2(g) \longrightarrow 2F(g)$
(c) $Na(g) \longrightarrow Na^+(g) + e^-$
(d) $Na(s) + \frac{1}{2}F_2(g) \longrightarrow NaF(s)$

● **9.76** The formulas for the fluorides of the third-period elements are NaF, MgF_2, AlF_3, SiF_4, PF_5, SF_6, and ClF_3. Classify these compounds as covalent or ionic.

9.77 Use ionization energy (see Table 8.2) and electron affinity values (see Table 8.3) to calculate the energy change (in kJ/mol) for the following reactions:
(a) $Li(g) + I(g) \longrightarrow Li^+(g) + I^-(g)$
(b) $Na(g) + F(g) \longrightarrow Na^+(g) + F^-(g)$
(c) $K(g) + Cl(g) \longrightarrow K^+(g) + Cl^-(g)$

9.78 Describe some characteristics of an ionic compound such as KF that would distinguish it from a covalent compound such as benzene (C_6H_6).

9.79 Write Lewis structures for BrF_3, ClF_5, and IF_7. Identify those in which the octet rule is not obeyed.

9.80 Write three reasonable resonance structures for the azide ion N_3^- in which the atoms are arranged as NNN. Show formal charges.

9.81 The amide group plays an important role in determining the structure of proteins:

$$\begin{matrix} & & :\ddot{O}: \\ & & \| \\ -\overset{..}{N}-C- \\ & | \\ & H \end{matrix}$$

Draw another resonance structure for this group. Show formal charges.

9.82 Give an example of an ion or molecule containing Al that (a) obeys the octet rule, (b) has an expanded octet, and (c) has an incomplete octet.

9.83 Draw four reasonable resonance structures for the PO_3F^{2-} ion. The central P atom is bonded to the three O atoms and to the F atom. Show formal charges.

9.84 Attempts to prepare the compounds listed here as stable species under atmospheric conditions have failed. Suggest possible reasons for the failure. CF_2, LiO_2, $CsCl_2$, PI_5

9.85 Draw reasonable resonance structures for the following ions: (a) HSO_4^-, (b) PO_4^{3-}, (c) HSO_3^-, (d) SO_3^{2-}. (*Hint:* See comment on p. 396.)

9.86 Are the following statements true or false? (a) Formal charges represent actual separation of charges. (b) ΔH_{rxn}° can be estimated from the bond enthalpies of reactants and products. (c) All second-period elements obey the octet rule in their compounds. (d) The resonance structures of a molecule can be separated from one another.

9.87 A rule for drawing plausible Lewis structures is that the central atom is invariably less electronegative than the surrounding atoms. Explain why this is so. Why does this rule not apply to compounds like H_2O and NH_3?

9.88 Using the following information and the fact that the average C—H bond enthalpy is 414 kJ/mol, estimate the standard enthalpy of formation of methane (CH_4).

$$\begin{aligned} C(s) &\longrightarrow C(g) & \Delta H_{rxn}^\circ = 716 \text{ kJ/mol} \\ 2H_2(g) &\longrightarrow 4H(g) & \Delta H_{rxn}^\circ = 872.8 \text{ kJ/mol} \end{aligned}$$

9.89 Based on energy considerations, which of the following reactions will occur more readily?
(a) $Cl(g) + CH_4(g) \longrightarrow CH_3Cl(g) + H(g)$
(b) $Cl(g) + CH_4(g) \longrightarrow CH_3(g) + HCl(g)$
(*Hint:* Refer to Table 9.4, and assume that the average bond enthalpy of the C—Cl bond is 338 kJ/mol.)

9.90 Which of the following molecules has the shortest nitrogen-to-nitrogen bond? Explain. N_2H_4, N_2O, N_2, N_2O_4

9.91 Most organic acids can be represented as RCOOH, where COOH is the carboxyl group and R is the rest of the molecule. (For example, R is CH_3 in acetic acid, CH_3COOH.) (a) Draw a Lewis structure for the carboxyl group. (b) Upon ionization, the carboxyl group is converted to the carboxylate group, COO^-. Draw resonance structures for the carboxylate group.

9.92 Which of the following species are isoelectronic? NH_4^+, C_6H_6, CO, CH_4, N_2, $B_3N_3H_6$

9.93 The following species have been detected in interstellar space: (a) CH, (b) OH, (c) C_2, (d) HNC, (e) HCO. Draw Lewis structures for these species and indicate whether they are diamagnetic or paramagnetic.

9.94 The amide ion, NH_2^-, is a Brønsted base. Represent the reaction between the amide ion and water.

9.95 Draw Lewis structures for the following organic molecules: (a) tetrafluoroethylene (C_2F_4), (b) propane (C_3H_8), (c) butadiene ($CH_2CHCHCH_2$), (d) propyne (CH_3CCH), (e) benzoic acid (C_6H_5COOH). (To draw C_6H_5COOH, replace a H atom in benzene with a COOH group.)

9.96 The triiodide ion (I_3^-) in which the I atoms are arranged in a straight line is stable, but the corresponding F_3^- ion does not exist. Explain.

9.97 Compare the bond enthalpy of F_2 with the energy change for the following process:

$$F_2(g) \longrightarrow F^+(g) + F^-(g)$$

Which is the preferred dissociation for F_2, energetically speaking?

9.98 Methyl isocyanate (CH_3NCO) is used to make certain pesticides. In December 1984, water leaked into a tank containing this substance at a chemical plant, producing a toxic cloud that killed thousands of people in Bhopal, India. Draw Lewis structures for CH_3NCO, showing formal charges.

9.99 The chlorine nitrate molecule ($ClONO_2$) is believed to be involved in the destruction of ozone in the Antarctic stratosphere. Draw a plausible Lewis structure for this molecule.

9.100 Several resonance structures for the molecule CO_2 are shown next. Explain why some of them are likely to be of little importance in describing the bonding in this molecule.

(a) $\ddot{O}=C=\ddot{O}$

(b) $:\overset{+}{O}\equiv C-\ddot{\underset{..}{O}}:^-$

(c) $:O\equiv C\overset{\overset{..}{-}}{\underset{..}{}}\ddot{O}:$

(d) $:\overset{-}{\underset{..}{O}}\overset{2+}{\underset{}{-}}C\overset{-}{\underset{..}{-}}\ddot{O}:^-$

9.101 For each of the following organic molecules draw a Lewis structure in which the carbon atoms are bonded to each other by single bonds: (a) C_2H_6, (b) C_4H_{10}, (c) C_5H_{12}. For (b) and (c), show only structures in which each C atom is bonded to no more than two other C atoms.

9.102 Draw Lewis structures for the following chlorofluorocarbons (CFCs), which are partly responsible for the depletion of ozone in the stratosphere: (a) $CFCl_3$, (b) CF_2Cl_2, (c) CHF_2Cl, (d) CF_3CHF_2.

9.103 Draw Lewis structures for the following organic molecules. In each there is one $C=C$ bond, and the rest of the carbon atoms are joined by $C-C$ bonds. C_2H_3F, C_3H_6, C_4H_8

9.104 Calculate $\Delta H°$ for the reaction

$$H_2(g) + I_2(g) \longrightarrow 2HI(g)$$

using (a) Equation (9.3) and (b) Equation (6.18), given that $\Delta H_f°$ for $I_2(g)$ is 61.0 kJ/mol.

9.105 Draw Lewis structures for the following organic molecules: (a) methanol (CH_3OH); (b) ethanol (CH_3CH_2OH); (c) tetraethyllead [$Pb(CH_2CH_3)_4$], which was used in "leaded gasoline"; (d) methylamine (CH_3NH_2), which is used in tanning; (e) mustard gas ($ClCH_2CH_2SCH_2CH_2Cl$), a poisonous gas used in World War I; (f) urea [$(NH_2)_2CO$], a fertilizer; and (g) glycine (NH_2CH_2COOH), an amino acid.

9.106 Write Lewis structures for the following four isoelectronic species: (a) CO, (b) NO^+, (c) CN^-, (d) N_2. Show formal charges.

9.107 Oxygen forms three types of ionic compounds in which the anions are oxide (O^{2-}), peroxide (O_2^{2-}), and superoxide (O_2^-). Draw Lewis structures of these ions.

9.108 Comment on the correctness of the statement, "All compounds containing a noble gas atom violate the octet rule."

9.109 Write three resonance structures for (a) the cyanate ion (NCO^-) and (b) the isocyanate ion (CNO^-). In each case, rank the resonance structures in order of increasing importance.

9.110 (a) From the following data calculate the bond enthalpy of the F_2^- ion.

$$F_2(g) \longrightarrow 2F(g) \qquad \Delta H_{rxn}° = 156.9 \text{ kJ/mol}$$
$$F^-(g) \longrightarrow F(g) + e^- \qquad \Delta H_{rxn}° = 333 \text{ kJ/mol}$$
$$F_2^-(g) \longrightarrow F_2(g) + e^- \qquad \Delta H_{rxn}° = 290 \text{ kJ/mol}$$

(b) Explain the difference between the bond enthalpies of F_2 and F_2^-.

9.111 The resonance concept is sometimes described by analogy to a mule, which is a cross between a horse and a donkey. Compare this analogy with the one used in this chapter, that is, the description of a rhinoceros as a cross between a griffin and a unicorn. Which description is more appropriate? Why?

9.112 What are the other two reasons for choosing (b) in Example 9.7?

9.113 In the Chemistry in Action essay on p. 397, nitric oxide is said to be one of about 10 of the smallest stable molecules known. Based on what you have learned in the course so far, write all the diatomic molecules you know, give their names, and show their Lewis structures.

9.114 The N—O bond distance in nitric oxide is 115 pm, which is intermediate between a triple bond (106 pm) and a double bond (120 pm). (a) Draw two resonance structures for NO and comment on their relative importance. (b) Is it possible to draw a resonance structure having a triple bond between the atoms?

9.115 Write the formulas of the binary hydride for the second-period elements LiH to HF. Comment on the change from ionic to covalent character of these compounds. Note that beryllium behaves differently from the rest of the Group 2A metals (see p. 348).

9.116 Hydrazine borane, $NH_2NH_2BH_3$, has been proposed as a hydrogen storage material. When reacted with lithium hydride (LiH), hydrogen gas is released

$$NH_2NH_2BH_3 + LiH \longrightarrow LiNH_2NHBH_3 + H_2$$

Write Lewis structures for $NH_2NH_2BH_3$ and $NH_2NHBH_3^-$ and assign all formal charges.

9.117 Although nitrogen dioxide (NO_2) is a stable compound, there is a tendency for two such molecules to combine to form dinitrogen tetroxide (N_2O_4). Why? Draw four resonance structures of N_2O_4, showing formal charges.

9.118 Another possible skeletal structure for the CO_3^{2-} (carbonate) ion besides the one presented in Example 9.5 is O C O O. Why would we not use this structure to represent CO_3^{2-}?

9.119 Draw a Lewis structure for nitrogen pentoxide (N_2O_5) in which each N is bonded to three O atoms.

9.120 In the gas phase, aluminum chloride exists as a dimer (a unit of two) with the formula Al_2Cl_6. Its skeletal structure is given by

Complete the Lewis structure and indicate the coordinate covalent bonds in the molecule.

• 9.121 The hydroxyl radical (OH) plays an important role in atmospheric chemistry. It is highly reactive and has a tendency to combine with a H atom from other compounds, causing them to break up. Thus, OH is sometimes called a "detergent" radical because it helps to clean up the atmosphere. (a) Write the Lewis structure for the radical. (b) Refer to Table 9.4 and explain why the radical has a high affinity for H atoms. (c) Estimate the enthalpy change for the following reaction:

$$OH(g) + CH_4(g) \longrightarrow CH_3(g) + H_2O(g)$$

(d) The radical is generated when sunlight hits water vapor. Calculate the maximum wavelength (in nanometers) required to break an O—H bond in H_2O.

• 9.122 Experiments show that it takes 1656 kJ/mol to break all the bonds in methane (CH_4) and 4006 kJ/mol to break all the bonds in propane (C_3H_8). Based on these data, calculate the average bond enthalpy of the C—C bond.

9.123 Calculate ΔH_{rxn}° at 25°C of the reaction between carbon monoxide and hydrogen shown here using both bond enthalpy and ΔH_f° values.

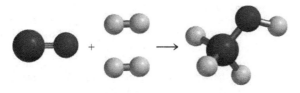

9.124 Calculate ΔH_{rxn}° at 25°C of the reaction between ethylene and chlorine shown here using both bond enthalpy and ΔH_f° values. (ΔH_f° for $C_2H_4Cl_2$ is −132 kJ/mol.)

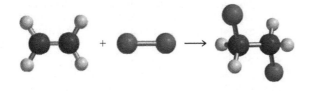

9.125 Draw three resonance structures of sulfur dioxide (SO_2). Indicate the most plausible structure(s).

9.126 Vinyl chloride (C_2H_3Cl) differs from ethylene (C_2H_4) in that one of the H atoms is replaced with a Cl atom. Vinyl chloride is used to prepare poly(vinyl chloride), which is an important polymer used in pipes. (a) Draw the Lewis structure of vinyl chloride. (b) The repeating unit in poly(vinyl chloride) is —CH_2—CHCl—. Draw a portion of the molecule showing three such repeating units. (c) Calculate the enthalpy change when 1.0×10^3 kg of vinyl chloride forms poly(vinyl chloride).

• 9.127 In 1998 scientists using a special type of electron microscope were able to measure the force needed to break a *single* chemical bond. If 2.0×10^{29} N was needed to break a C—Si bond, estimate the bond enthalpy in kJ/mol. Assume that the bond had to be stretched by a distance of 2 Å (2×10^{-10} m) before it is broken.

• 9.128 The American chemist Robert S. Mulliken suggested a different definition for the electronegativity (EN) of an element, given by

$$EN = \frac{IE + EA}{2}$$

where IE is the first ionization energy and EA the electron affinity of the element. Calculate the electronegativities of O, F, and Cl using the above equation. Compare the electronegativities of these elements on the Mulliken and Pauling scale. (To convert to the Pauling scale, divide each EN value by 230 kJ/mol.)

• 9.129 Among the common inhaled anesthetics are:

halothane: $CF_3CHClBr$

enflurane: $CHFClCF_2OCHF_2$

isoflurane: $CF_3CHClOCHF_2$

methoxyflurane: $CHCl_2CF_2OCH_3$

Draw Lewis structures of these molecules.

9.130 A student in your class claims that magnesium oxide actually consists of Mg^+ and O^- ions, not Mg^{2+} and O^{2-} ions. Suggest some experiments one could do to show that your classmate is wrong.

9.131 Shown here is a skeletal structure of borazine ($B_3N_3H_6$). Draw two resonance structures of the molecule, showing all the bonds and formal charges. Compare its properties with the isoelectronic molecule benzene.

$$\begin{array}{c} H \\ | \\ H-N \quad B \quad N-H \\ \quad \quad \quad \\ H-B \quad N \quad B-H \\ | \\ H \end{array}$$

9.132 Calculate the wavelength of light needed to carry out the reaction

$$H_2 \longrightarrow H^+ + H^-$$

9.133 Sulfuric acid (H_2SO_4), the most important industrial chemical in the world, is prepared by oxidizing sulfur to sulfur dioxide and then to sulfur trioxide. Although sulfur trioxide reacts with water to form sulfuric acid, it forms a mist of fine droplets of H_2SO_4 with water vapor that is hard to condense. Instead, sulfur trioxide is first dissolved in 98 percent sulfuric acid to form oleum ($H_2S_2O_7$). On treatment with water, concentrated sulfuric acid can be generated. Write equations for all the steps and draw Lewis structures of oleum based on the discussion in Example 9.11.

● **9.134** From the lattice energy of KCl in Table 9.1 and the ionization energy of K and electron affinity of Cl in Tables 8.2 and 8.3, calculate the $\Delta H°$ for the reaction

$$K(g) + Cl(g) \longrightarrow KCl(s)$$

● **9.135** The species H_3^+ is the simplest polyatomic ion. The geometry of the ion is that of an equilateral triangle. (a) Draw three resonance structures to represent the ion. (b) Given the following information

$$2H + H^+ \longrightarrow H_3^+ \quad \Delta H° = -849 \text{ kJ/mol}$$
and $$H_2 \longrightarrow 2H \quad \Delta H° = 436.4 \text{ kJ/mol}$$

calculate $\Delta H°$ for the reaction

$$H^+ + H_2 \longrightarrow H_3^+$$

● **9.136** The bond enthalpy of the C—N bond in the amide group of proteins (see Problem 9.81) can be treated as an average of C—N and C=N bonds. Calculate the maximum wavelength of light needed to break the bond.

9.137 In 1999 an unusual cation containing only nitrogen (N_5^+) was prepared. Draw three resonance structures of the ion, showing formal charges. (*Hint:* The N atoms are joined in a linear fashion.)

9.138 Nitroglycerin, one of the most commonly used explosives, has the following structure

$$CH_2ONO_2$$
$$|$$
$$CHONO_2$$
$$|$$
$$CH_2ONO_2$$

The decomposition reaction is

$$4C_3H_5N_3O_9(l) \longrightarrow$$
$$12CO_2(g) + 10H_2O(g) + 6N_2(g) + O_2(g)$$

The explosive action is the result of the heat released and the large increase in gaseous volume. (a) Calculate the $\Delta H°$ for the decomposition of one mole of nitroglycerin using both standard enthalpy of formation values and bond enthalpies. Assume that the two O atoms in the NO_2 groups are attached to N with one single bond and one double bond. (b) Calculate the combined volume of the gases at STP. (c) Assuming an initial explosion temperature of 3000 K, estimate the pressure exerted by the gases using the result from (b). (The standard enthalpy of formation of nitroglycerin is -371.1 kJ/mol.)

9.139 Give a brief description of the medical uses of the following ionic compounds: $AgNO_3$, $BaSO_4$, $CaSO_4$, KI, Li_2CO_3, $Mg(OH)_2$, $MgSO_4$, $NaHCO_3$, Na_2CO_3, NaF, TiO_2, ZnO. You would need to do a Web search of some of these compounds.

9.140 Use Table 9.4 to estimate the bond enthalpy of the C—C, N—N, and O—O bonds in C_2H_6, N_2H_4, and H_2O_2, respectively. What effect do lone pairs on adjacent atoms have on the strength of the particular bonds?

9.141 The isolated O^{2-} ion is unstable so it is not possible to measure the electron affinity of the O^- ion directly. Show how you can calculate its value by using the lattice energy of MgO and the Born-Haber cycle. [Useful information: $Mg(s) \rightarrow Mg(g)$ $\Delta H° = 148$ kJ/mol.]

9.142 When irradiated with light of wavelength 471.7 nm, the chlorine molecule dissociates into chlorine atoms. One Cl atom is formed in its ground electronic state while the other is in an excited state that is 10.5 kJ/mol above the ground state. What is the bond enthalpy of the Cl_2 molecule?

9.143 Recall from Chapter 8 that the product of the reaction between $Xe(g)$ and $PtF_6(g)$ was originally thought to be an ionic compound composed of Xe^+ cations and PtF_6^- anions (see Figure 8.22). This prediction was based on the theoretical enthalpy of formation of $XePtF_6$ calculated using a Born-Haber cycle. (a) The lattice energy for $XePtF_6$ was estimated to be 460 kJ/mol. Explain whether or not this value is consistent with the lattice energies in Table 9.1. (b) Calculate $\Delta H_f°$ for $XePtF_6$ given IE_1 for $Xe(g)$ is 1170 kJ/mol and EA_1 for $PtF_6(g)$ is 770 kJ/mol. Comment on the expected stability of $XePtF_6$ based on your calculation.

Interpreting, Modeling & Estimating

9.144 The reaction between fluorine (F_2) with ethane (C_2H_6) produces predominantly CF_4 rather than C_2F_6 molecules. Explain.

9.145 A new allotrope of oxygen, O_4, has been reported. The exact structure of O_4 is unknown, but the simplest possible structure would be a four-member ring consisting of oxygen-oxygen single bonds. The report speculated that the O_4 molecule might be useful as a fuel "because it packs a lot of oxygen in a small space, so it might be even more energy-dense than the liquefied ordinary oxygen used in rocket fuel." (a) Draw a Lewis structure for O_4 and write a balanced chemical equation for the reaction between ethane, $C_2H_6(g)$, and $O_4(g)$ to give carbon dioxide and water vapor. (b) Estimate $\Delta H°$ for the reaction. (c) Write a chemical equation illustrating the standard enthalpy of formation of $O_4(g)$ and estimate $\Delta H_f°$. (d) Assuming the oxygen allotropes are in excess, which will release more energy when reacted with ethane (or any other fuel): $O_2(g)$ or $O_4(g)$? Explain using your answers to parts (a)–(c).

9.146 Because bond formation is exothermic, when two gas-phase atoms come together to form a diatomic molecule it is necessary for a third atom or molecule to absorb the energy that is released. Otherwise the molecule will undergo dissociation. If two atoms of hydrogen combine to form $H_2(g)$, what would be the increase in velocity of a third hydrogen atom that absorbs the energy released from this process?

9.147 Estimate ΔH_f° for sodium astatide (NaAt) according to the equation

$$Na(s) + \tfrac{1}{2}At_2(s) \longrightarrow NaAt(s)$$

The information in Problem 8.147 may be useful.

Answers to Practice Exercises

9.1 $\cdot Ba \cdot + 2 \cdot H \longrightarrow Ba^{2+} \; 2H:^- \quad$ (or BaH_2)
    $[Xe]6s^2 \quad 1s^1 \qquad [Xe] \; [He]$

9.2 (a) Ionic, (b) polar covalent, (c) covalent.

9.3 $\ddot{S}=C=\ddot{S}$ **9.4** $H-\overset{\overset{\displaystyle :O:}{||}}{C}-\ddot{O}-H$ **9.5** $\left[\ddot{O}=N-\ddot{O}:\right]^-$

9.6 $\ddot{O}=\ddot{N}-\ddot{O}:^-$ **9.7** $H-C\equiv N:$

9.8 $\ddot{S}=C=\ddot{N}^- \longleftrightarrow {}^-:\ddot{S}-C\equiv N: \longleftrightarrow {}^+:S\equiv C-\ddot{N}:^{2-}$

The first structure is the most important; the last structure is the least important.

9.9 $:\ddot{F}-Be-\ddot{F}:$ **9.10** $:\ddot{F}-As\begin{smallmatrix}:\ddot{F}:\\|\\ \nearrow \ddot{F}:\\ \searrow \ddot{F}:\\|\\ :\ddot{F}:\end{smallmatrix}$

9.11 $H-\overset{\overset{\displaystyle :O:}{|}}{\underset{\underset{\displaystyle :O:}{|}}{S}}-\ddot{O}-H$ and $H-\overset{\overset{\displaystyle :\ddot{O}:^-}{|}}{\underset{\underset{\displaystyle :\ddot{O}:^-}{|}}{S^{2+}}}-\ddot{O}-H$

9.12 $\begin{smallmatrix}:\ddot{F} \quad\ddot{F}:\\ \diagdown \diagup\\ S\\ \diagup \diagdown\\ :\ddot{F} \quad \ddot{F}:\end{smallmatrix}$

9.13 (a) -543.1 kJ/mol, (b) -543.2 kJ/mol.

9.14 (a) -119 kJ/mol, (b) -137.0 kJ/mol.

CHAPTER

10

Chemical Bonding II

Molecular Geometry and Hybridization of Atomic Orbitals

The shape of molecules plays an important role in complex biochemical reactions such as those between protein and DNA molecules.

CHAPTER OUTLINE

A LOOK AHEAD

▶ We first examine the role of chemical bonds and lone pairs on the geometry of a molecule in terms of a simple approach called the VSEPR model. (10.1)

▶ We then learn the factors that determine whether a molecule possesses a dipole moment and how its measurement can help us in the study of molecular geometry. (10.2)

▶ Next, we learn a quantum mechanical approach, called the valence bond (VB) theory, in the study of chemical bonds. The VB theory explains why and how chemical bonds form in terms of atomic orbital overlaps. (10.3)

▶ We see that the VB approach, in terms of the concept of mixing or hybridization of atomic orbitals, accounts for both chemical bond formation and molecular geometry. (10.4 and 10.5)

▶ We then examine another quantum mechanical treatment of the chemical bond, called the molecular orbital (MO) theory. The MO theory considers the formation of molecular orbitals as a result of the overlap of atomic orbitals, and is able to explain the paramagnetism of the oxygen molecule. (10.6)

▶ We see that writing molecular orbital configuration is analogous to writing electron configuration for atoms in that both the Pauli exclusion principle and Hund's rule apply. Using homonuclear diatomic molecules as examples, we can learn about the strength of a bond as well as general magnetic properties from the molecular orbital configurations. (10.7)

▶ The concept of molecular orbital formation is extended to delocalized molecular orbitals, which cover three or more atoms. We see that these delocalized orbitals impart extra stability to molecules like benzene. (10.8)

In Chapter 9, we discussed bonding in terms of the Lewis theory. Here we will study the shape, or geometry, of molecules. Geometry has an important influence on the physical and chemical properties of molecules, such as density, melting point, boiling point, and reactivity. We will see that we can predict the shapes of molecules with considerable accuracy using a simple method based on Lewis structures.

The Lewis theory of chemical bonding, although useful and easy to apply, does not explain how and why bonds form. A proper understanding of bonding comes from quantum mechanics. Therefore, in the second part of the chapter we will apply quantum mechanics to the study of the geometry and stability of molecules.

10.1 Molecular Geometry

Molecular geometry is the three-dimensional arrangement of atoms in a molecule. A molecule's geometry affects its physical and chemical properties, such as melting point, boiling point, density, and the types of reactions it undergoes. In general, bond lengths and bond angles must be determined by experiment. However, there is a simple procedure that enables us to predict with considerable success the overall geometry of a molecule or ion if we know the number of electrons surrounding a central atom in its Lewis structure. The basis of this approach is the assumption that electron pairs in the valence shell of an atom repel one another. The *valence shell* is *the outermost electron-occupied shell of an atom; it holds the electrons that are usually involved in bonding.* In a covalent bond, a pair of electrons, often called the *bonding pair,* is responsible for holding two atoms together. However, in a polyatomic molecule, where there are two or more bonds between the central atom and the surrounding atoms, the repulsion between electrons in different bonding pairs causes them to remain as far apart as possible. The geometry that the molecule ultimately assumes (as defined by the positions of all the atoms) minimizes the repulsion. This approach to the study of molecular geometry is called the *valence-shell electron-pair repulsion (VSEPR) model,* because *it accounts for the geometric arrangements of electron pairs around a central atom in terms of the electrostatic repulsion between electron pairs.*

The term "central atom" means an atom that is not a terminal atom in a polyatomic molecule.

Two general rules govern the use of the VSEPR model:

VSEPR is pronounced "vesper."

Animation
VSEPR

Animation
VSEPR Theory

1. As far as electron-pair repulsion is concerned, double bonds and triple bonds can be treated like single bonds. This approximation is good for qualitative purposes. However, you should realize that in reality multiple bonds are "larger" than single bonds; that is, because there are two or three bonds between two atoms, the electron density occupies more space.

2. If a molecule has two or more resonance structures, we can apply the VSEPR model to any one of them. Formal charges are usually not shown.

With this model in mind, we can predict the geometry of molecules (and ions) in a systematic way. For this purpose, it is convenient to divide molecules into two categories, according to whether or not the central atom has lone pairs.

Molecules in Which the Central Atom Has No Lone Pairs

For simplicity we will consider molecules that contain atoms of only two elements, A and B, of which A is the central atom. These molecules have the general formula AB_x, where x is an integer 2, 3, ... (If $x = 1$, we have the diatomic

Table 10.1	Arrangement of Electron Pairs About a Central Atom (A) in a Molecule and Geometry of Some Simple Molecules and Ions in Which the Central Atom Has No Lone Pairs		
Number of Electron Pairs	Arrangement of Electron Pairs*	Molecular Geometry*	Examples
2	180° Linear	B—A—B Linear	$BeCl_2$, $HgCl_2$
3	120° Trigonal planar	Trigonal planar	BF_3
4	109.5° Tetrahedral	Tetrahedral	CH_4, NH_4^+
5	120° 90° Trigonal bipyramidal	Trigonal bipyramidal	PCl_5
6	90° 90° Octahedral	Octahedral	SF_6

*Bonds coming out of the page are represented as solid wedges. Bonds going into the page are represented as dashed wedges. Bonds in the plane of the page are represented as solid lines.

molecule AB, which is linear by definition.) In the vast majority of cases, x is between 2 and 6.

Table 10.1 shows five possible arrangements of electron pairs around the central atom A. As a result of mutual repulsion, the electron pairs stay as far from one another as possible. Note that the table shows arrangements of the electron pairs but not the positions of the atoms that surround the central atom. Molecules in which the central atom has no lone pairs have one of these five arrangements of bonding pairs. Using Table 10.1 as a reference, let us take a close look at the geometry of molecules with the formulas AB_2, AB_3, AB_4, AB_5, and AB_6.

AB$_2$: Beryllium Chloride (BeCl$_2$)

The Lewis structure of beryllium chloride in the gaseous state is

$$:\!\overset{\cdot\cdot}{\underset{\cdot\cdot}{Cl}}\!-\!Be\!-\!\overset{\cdot\cdot}{\underset{\cdot\cdot}{Cl}}\!:$$

Because the bonding pairs repel each other, they must be at opposite ends of a straight line in order for them to be as far apart as possible. Thus, the ClBeCl angle is predicted to be 180°, and the molecule is linear (see Table 10.1). The "ball-and-stick" model of BeCl$_2$ is

The blue and yellow spheres are for atoms in general.

AB$_3$: Boron Trifluoride (BF$_3$)

Boron trifluoride contains three covalent bonds, or bonding pairs.

$$\begin{array}{c} :\overset{\cdot\cdot}{F}: \\ | \\ B \\ \diagup \ \diagdown \\ :\overset{\cdot\cdot}{F} \qquad \overset{\cdot\cdot}{F}: \end{array}$$

In the most stable arrangement, the three BF bonds point to the corners of an equilateral triangle with B in the center of the triangle. According to Table 10.1, the geometry of BF$_3$ is trigonal planar because all four atoms lie in the same plane and the three end atoms form an equilateral triangle:

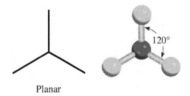

Planar

Thus, each of the three FBF angles is 120°.

AB$_4$: Methane (CH$_4$)

The Lewis structure of methane is

$$\begin{array}{c} H \\ | \\ H\!-\!C\!-\!H \\ | \\ H \end{array}$$

Because there are four bonding pairs, the geometry of CH$_4$ is tetrahedral (see Table 10.1). A *tetrahedron* has four sides (the prefix *tetra* means "four"), or faces, all of which are equilateral triangles. In a tetrahedral molecule, the central atom (C in this case) is located at the center of the tetrahedron and the other four atoms are at the corners. The bond angles are all 109.5°.

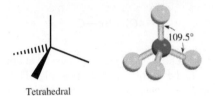

Tetrahedral

AB$_5$: Phosphorus Pentachloride (PCl$_5$)

The Lewis structure of phosphorus pentachloride (in the gas phase) is

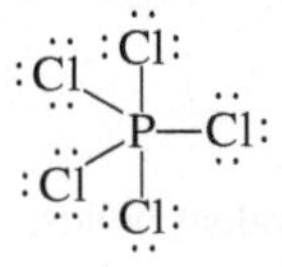

The only way to minimize the repulsive forces among the five bonding pairs is to arrange the PCl bonds in the form of a trigonal bipyramid (see Table 10.1). A trigonal bipyramid can be generated by joining two tetrahedrons along a common triangular base:

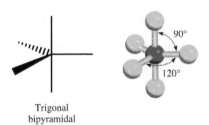

Trigonal
bipyramidal

The central atom (P in this case) is at the center of the common triangle with the surrounding atoms positioned at the five corners of the trigonal bipyramid. The atoms that are above and below the triangular plane are said to occupy *axial* positions, and those that are in the triangular plane are said to occupy *equatorial* positions. The angle between any two equatorial bonds is 120°; that between an axial bond and an equatorial bond is 90°, and that between the two axial bonds is 180°.

AB$_6$: Sulfur Hexafluoride (SF$_6$)

The Lewis structure of sulfur hexafluoride is

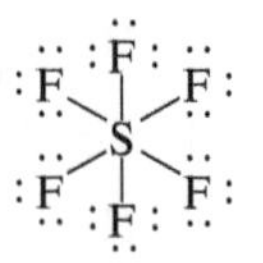

The most stable arrangement of the six SF bonding pairs is in the shape of an octahedron, as shown in Table 10.1. An octahedron has eight sides (the prefix *octa* means "eight"). It can be generated by joining two square pyramids on a common base. The central atom (S in this case) is at the center of the square base and the surrounding atoms are at the six corners. All bond angles are 90° except the one made by the bonds between the central atom and the pairs of atoms that are diametrically opposite each other. That angle is 180°. Because the six bonds are equivalent in an octahedral molecule, we cannot use the terms "axial" and "equatorial" as in a trigonal bipyramidal molecule.

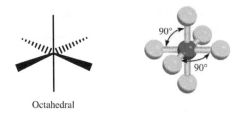

Octahedral

Molecules in Which the Central Atom Has One or More Lone Pairs

Determining the geometry of a molecule is more complicated if the central atom has both lone pairs and bonding pairs. In such molecules there are three types of repulsive forces—those between bonding pairs, those between lone pairs, and those between a bonding pair and a lone pair. In general, according to the VSEPR model, the repulsive forces decrease in the following order:

$$\text{lone-pair vs. lone-pair} > \text{lone-pair vs. bonding-} > \text{bonding-pair vs. bonding-}$$
$$\text{repulsion} \qquad \text{pair repulsion} \qquad \text{pair repulsion}$$

Electrons in a bond are held by the attractive forces exerted by the nuclei of the two bonded atoms. These electrons have less "spatial distribution" than lone pairs; that is, they take up less space than lone-pair electrons, which are associated with only one particular atom. Because lone-pair electrons in a molecule occupy more space, they experience greater repulsion from neighboring lone pairs and bonding pairs. To keep track of the total number of bonding pairs and lone pairs, we designate molecules with lone pairs as AB_xE_y, where A is the central atom, B is a surrounding atom, and E is a lone pair on A. Both x and y are integers; $x = 2, 3, \ldots$, and $y = 1, 2, \ldots$. Thus, the values of x and y indicate the number of surrounding atoms and number of lone pairs on the central atom, respectively. The simplest such molecule would be a triatomic molecule with one lone pair on the central atom and the formula is AB_2E.

As the following examples show, in most cases the presence of lone pairs on the central atom makes it difficult to predict the bond angles accurately.

For $x = 1$ we have a diatomic molecule, which by definition has a linear geometry.

AB_2E: Sulfur Dioxide (SO_2)

The Lewis structure of sulfur dioxide is

$$\ddot{O}=\ddot{S}=\ddot{O}$$

Because VSEPR treats double bonds as though they were single, the SO_2 molecule can be viewed as consisting of three electron pairs on the central S atom. Of these, two are bonding pairs and one is a lone pair. In Table 10.1 we see that the overall arrangement of three electron pairs is trigonal planar. But because one of the electron pairs is a lone pair, the SO_2 molecule has a "bent" shape.

$$\ddot{O}=\overset{\ddot{}}{S}=\ddot{O}$$

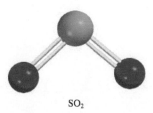

SO_2

418   **Chapter 10** ▪ Chemical Bonding II: Molecular Geometry and Hybridization of Atomic Orbitals

Because the lone-pair versus bonding-pair repulsion is greater than the bonding-pair versus bonding-pair repulsion, the two sulfur-to-oxygen bonds are pushed together slightly and the OSO angle is less than 120°.

AB₃E: Ammonia (NH₃)

The ammonia molecule contains three bonding pairs and one lone pair:

$$H—\overset{\cdot\cdot}{N}—H$$
$$|$$
$$H$$

As Table 10.1 shows, the overall arrangement of four electron pairs is tetrahedral. But in NH₃ one of the electron pairs is a lone pair, so the geometry of NH₃ is trigonal pyramidal (so called because it looks like a pyramid, with the N atom at the apex). Because the lone pair repels the bonding pairs more strongly, the three NH bonding pairs are pushed closer together:

$$H \cdots\cdots \overset{\cdot\cdot}{N} — H$$
$$H$$

Thus, the HNH angle in ammonia is smaller than the ideal tetrahedral angle of 109.5° (Figure 10.1).

AB₂E₂: Water (H₂O)

A water molecule contains two bonding pairs and two lone pairs:

$$H—\overset{\cdot\cdot}{\underset{\cdot\cdot}{O}}—H$$

The overall arrangement of the four electron pairs in water is tetrahedral, the same as in ammonia. However, unlike ammonia, water has two lone pairs on the central O atom. These lone pairs tend to be as far from each other as possible. Consequently,

Figure 10.1 *(a) The relative sizes of bonding pairs and lone pairs in CH₄, NH₃, and H₂O. (b) The bond angles in CH₄, NH₃, and H₂O. Note that the solid wedges represent electron pairs (bonding pairs or lone pairs) coming out above the plane of the paper, the dashed wedges represent electron pairs going back behind the plane of the paper, and the solid lines represent electron pairs in the plane of the paper.*

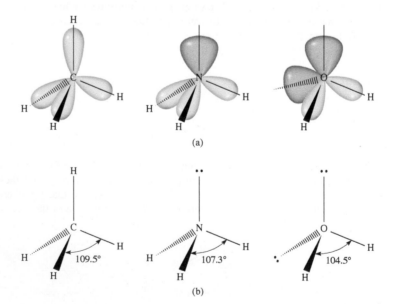

the two O—H bonding pairs are pushed toward each other, and we predict an even greater deviation from the tetrahedral angle than in NH_3. As Figure 10.1 shows, the HOH angle is 104.5°. The geometry of H_2O is bent:

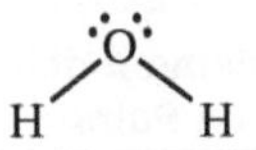

AB₄E: Sulfur Tetrafluoride (SF₄)

The Lewis structure of SF_4 is

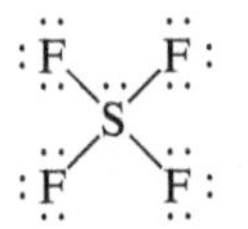

The central sulfur atom has five electron pairs whose arrangement, according to Table 10.1, is trigonal bipyramidal. In the SF_4 molecule, however, one of the electron pairs is a lone pair, so the molecule must have one of the following geometries:

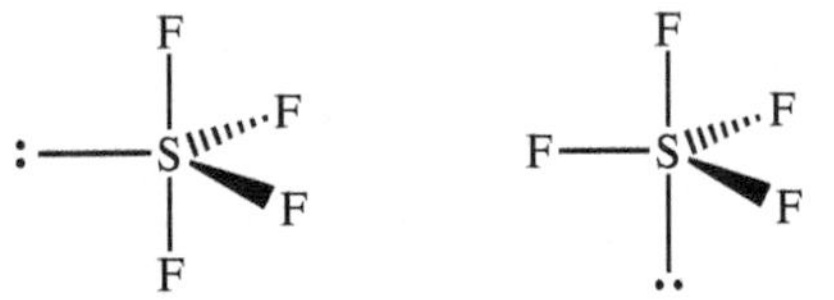

(a)   (b)

SF₄

In (a) the lone pair occupies an equatorial position, and in (b) it occupies an axial position. The axial position has three neighboring pairs at 90° and one at 180°, while the equatorial position has two neighboring pairs at 90° and two more at 120°. The repulsion is smaller for (a), and indeed (a) is the structure observed experimentally. This shape is sometimes described as a distorted tetrahedron (or seesaw if you turn the structure 90° to the right to view it). The angle between the axial F atoms and S is 173°, and that between the equatorial F atoms and S is 102°.

Table 10.2 shows the geometries of simple molecules in which the central atom has one or more lone pairs, including some that we have not discussed.

Geometry of Molecules with More Than One Central Atom

So far we have discussed the geometry of molecules having only one central atom. The overall geometry of molecules with more than one central atom is difficult to define in most cases. Often we can only describe the shape around each of the central atoms. For example, consider methanol, CH_3OH, whose Lewis structure is shown below:

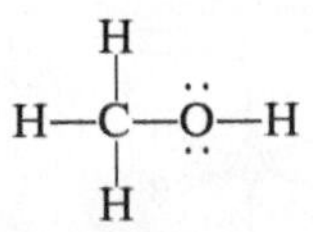

The two central (nonterminal) atoms in methanol are C and O. We can say that the three CH and the CO bonding pairs are tetrahedrally arranged about the C atom. The HCH and OCH bond angles are approximately 109°. The O atom here is like the one

Table 10.2	Geometry of Simple Molecules and Ions in Which the Central Atom Has One or More Lone Pairs					
Class of Molecule	Total Number of Electron Pairs	Number of Bonding Pairs	Number of Lone Pairs	Arrangement of Electron Pairs	Geometry of Molecule or Ion	Examples
AB_2E	3	2	1	Trigonal planar	Bent	SO_2
AB_3E	4	3	1	Tetrahedral	Trigonal pyramidal	NH_3
AB_2E_2	4	2	2	Tetrahedral	Bent	H_2O
AB_4E	5	4	1	Trigonal bipyramidal	Distorted tetrahedron (or seesaw)	SF_4
AB_3E_2	5	3	2	Trigonal bipyramidal	T-shaped	ClF_3
AB_2E_3	5	2	3	Trigonal bipyramidal	Linear	I_3^-
AB_5E	6	5	1	Octahedral	Square pyramidal	BrF_5
AB_4E_2	6	4	2	Octahedral	Square planar	XeF_4

in water in that it has two lone pairs and two bonding pairs. Therefore, the HOC portion of the molecule is bent, and the angle HOC is approximately equal to 105° (Figure 10.2).

Guidelines for Applying the VSEPR Model

Having studied the geometries of molecules in two categories (central atoms with and without lone pairs), let us consider some rules for applying the VSEPR model to all types of molecules:

1. Write the Lewis structure of the molecule, considering only the electron pairs around the central atom (that is, the atom that is bonded to more than one other atom).

2. Count the number of electron pairs around the central atom (bonding pairs and lone pairs). Treat double and triple bonds as though they were single bonds. Refer to Table 10.1 to predict the overall arrangement of the electron pairs.

3. Use Tables 10.1 and 10.2 to predict the geometry of the molecule.

4. In predicting bond angles, note that a lone pair repels another lone pair or a bonding pair more strongly than a bonding pair repels another bonding pair. Remember that in general there is no easy way to predict bond angles accurately when the central atom possesses one or more lone pairs.

The VSEPR model generates reliable predictions of the geometries of a variety of molecular structures. Chemists use the VSEPR approach because of its simplicity. Although there are some theoretical concerns about whether "electron-pair repulsion" actually determines molecular shapes, the assumption that it does leads to useful (and generally reliable) predictions. We need not ask more of any model at this stage in our study of chemistry. Example 10.1 illustrates the application of VSEPR.

Figure 10.2 *The geometry of* CH_3OH.

Example 10.1

Use the VSEPR model to predict the geometry of the following molecules and ions: (a) AsH_3, (b) OF_2, (c) $AlCl_4^-$, (d) I_3^-, (e) C_2H_4.

Strategy The sequence of steps in determining molecular geometry is as follows:

draw Lewis $\longrightarrow$ find arrangement of $\longrightarrow$ find arrangement $\longrightarrow$ determine geometry
structure   electron pairs   of bonding pairs   based on bonding pairs

Solution

(a) The Lewis structure of AsH_3 is

$$H-\overset{\cdot\cdot}{As}-H$$
$$\underset{H}{|}$$

There are four electron pairs around the central atom; therefore, the electron pair arrangement is tetrahedral (see Table 10.1). Recall that the geometry of a molecule is determined only by the arrangement of atoms (in this case the As and H atoms). Thus, removing the lone pair leaves us with three bonding pairs and a trigonal pyramidal geometry, like NH_3. We cannot predict the HAsH angle accurately, but we know that it is less than 109.5° because the repulsion of the bonding electron pairs in the As—H bonds by the lone pair on As is greater than the repulsion between the bonding pairs.

(b) The Lewis structure of OF_2 is

$$:\overset{\cdot\cdot}{\underset{\cdot\cdot}{F}}-\overset{\cdot\cdot}{\underset{\cdot\cdot}{O}}-\overset{\cdot\cdot}{\underset{\cdot\cdot}{F}}:$$

(Continued)

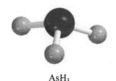

AsH_3

OF_2

There are four electron pairs around the central atom; therefore, the electron pair arrangement is tetrahedral (see Table 10.1). Recall that the geometry of a molecule is determined only by the arrangement of atoms (in this case the O and F atoms). Thus, removing the two lone pairs leaves us with two bonding pairs and a bent geometry, like H_2O. We cannot predict the FOF angle accurately, but we know that it must be less than 109.5° because the repulsion of the bonding electron pairs in the O—F bonds by the lone pairs on O is greater than the repulsion between the bonding pairs.

(c) The Lewis structure of $AlCl_4^-$ is

$$\left[\begin{array}{c} \ddot{:}\ddot{Cl}\ddot{:} \\ :\ddot{Cl}-Al-\ddot{Cl}: \\ :\ddot{Cl}: \end{array} \right]^-$$

$AlCl_4^-$

There are four electron pairs around the central atom; therefore, the electron pair arrangement is tetrahedral. Because there are no lone pairs present, the arrangement of the bonding pairs is the same as the electron pair arrangement. Therefore, $AlCl_4^-$ has a tetrahedral geometry and the ClAlCl angles are all 109.5°.

(d) The Lewis structure of I_3^- is

$$\left[:\ddot{I}-\ddot{I}-\ddot{I}: \right]^-$$

I_3^-

There are five electron pairs around the central I atom; therefore, the electron pair arrangement is trigonal bipyramidal. Of the five electron pairs, three are lone pairs and two are bonding pairs. Recall that the lone pairs preferentially occupy the equatorial positions in a trigonal bipyramid (see Table 10.2). Thus, removing the lone pairs leaves us with a linear geometry for I_3^-; that is, all three I atoms lie in a straight line.

(e) The Lewis structure of C_2H_4 is

$$\begin{array}{cc} H & H \\ \diagdown \; C=C \diagup \\ H & H \end{array}$$

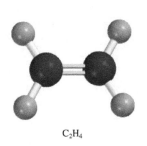

C_2H_4

The C=C bond is treated as though it were a single bond in the VSEPR model. Because there are three electron pairs around each C atom and there are no lone pairs present, the arrangement around each C atom has a trigonal planar shape like BF_3, discussed earlier. Thus, the predicted bond angles in C_2H_4 are all 120°.

$$\begin{array}{cc} H & 120° \quad H \\ \diagdown \quad C=C \quad 120° \\ H \quad 120° & H \end{array}$$

Comment (1) The I_3^- ion is one of the few structures for which the bond angle (180°) can be predicted accurately even though the central atom contains lone pairs. (2) In C_2H_4, all six atoms lie in the same plane. The overall planar geometry is not predicted by the VSEPR model, but we will see why the molecule prefers to be planar later. In reality, the angles are close, but not equal, to 120° because the bonds are not all equivalent.

Similar problems: 10.7, 10.8, 10.9.

Practice Exercise Use the VSEPR model to predict the geometry of (a) $SiBr_4$, (b) CS_2, and (c) NO_3^-.

Review of Concepts
Which of the following geometries has a greater stability for tin(IV) hydride (SnH₄)?

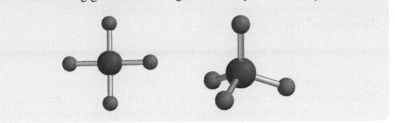

10.2 Dipole Moments

In Section 9.5 we learned that hydrogen fluoride is a covalent compound with a polar bond. There is a shift of electron density from H to F because the F atom is more electronegative than the H atom (see Figure 9.4). The shift of electron density is symbolized by placing a crossed arrow ($\longmapsto$) above the Lewis structure to indicate the direction of the shift. For example,

$$\overset{\longmapsto}{\text{H—}\ddot{\underset{\cdot\cdot}{\text{F}}}:}$$

The consequent charge separation can be represented as

$$\overset{\delta+\quad\delta-}{\text{H—}\ddot{\underset{\cdot\cdot}{\text{F}}}:}$$

where δ (delta) denotes a partial charge. This separation of charges can be confirmed in an electric field (Figure 10.3). When the field is turned on, HF molecules orient their negative ends toward the positive plate and their positive ends toward the negative plate. This alignment of molecules can be detected experimentally.

A quantitative measure of the polarity of a bond is its *dipole moment (μ)*, which is *the product of the charge Q and the distance r between the charges:*

$$\mu = Q \times r \tag{10.1}$$

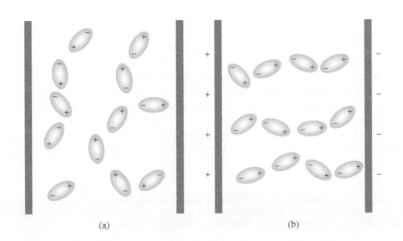

(a)   (b)

Figure 10.3 *Behavior of polar molecules (a) in the absence of an external electric field and (b) when the electric field is turned on. Nonpolar molecules are not affected by an electric field.*

424   **Chapter 10** ▪ Chemical Bonding II: Molecular Geometry and Hybridization of Atomic Orbitals

In a diatomic molecule like HF, the charge Q is equal to δ+ and δ−.

To maintain electrical neutrality, the charges on both ends of an electrically neutral diatomic molecule must be equal in magnitude and opposite in sign. However, in Equation (10.1), Q refers only to the magnitude of the charge and not to its sign, so μ is always positive. Dipole moments are usually expressed in debye units (D), named for Peter Debye.[†] The conversion factor is

$$1\ D = 3.336 \times 10^{-30}\ C\ m$$

where C is coulomb and m is meter.

▶▶ **Animation**
Polarity of Molecules

▶▶ **Animation**
Influence of Shape on Polarity

Diatomic molecules containing atoms of *different* elements (for example, HCl, CO, and NO) *have dipole moments* and are called **polar molecules.** Diatomic molecules containing atoms of the *same* element (for example, H_2, O_2, and F_2) are examples of **nonpolar molecules** because they *do not have dipole moments*. For a molecule made up of three or more atoms both the polarity of the bonds and the molecular geometry determine whether there is a dipole moment. Even if polar bonds are present, the molecule will not necessarily have a dipole moment. Carbon dioxide (CO_2), for example, is a triatomic molecule, so its geometry is either linear or bent:

resultant dipole moment

O=C=O
linear molecule
(no dipole moment)

bent molecule
(would have a dipole moment)

Each carbon-to-oxygen bond is polar, with the electron density shifted toward the more electronegative oxygen atom. However, the linear geometry of the molecule results in the cancellation of the two bond moments.

The arrows show the shift of electron density from the less electronegative carbon atom to the more electronegative oxygen atom. In each case, the dipole moment of the entire molecule is made up of two *bond moments,* that is, individual dipole moments in the polar C=O bonds. The bond moment is a *vector quantity,* which means that it has both magnitude and direction. The measured dipole moment is equal to the vector sum of the bond moments. The two bond moments in CO_2 are equal in magnitude. Because they point in opposite directions in a linear CO_2 molecule, the sum or resultant dipole moment would be zero. On the other hand, if the CO_2 molecule were bent, the two bond moments would partially reinforce each other, so that the molecule would have a dipole moment. Experimentally it is found that carbon dioxide has no dipole moment. Therefore, we conclude that the carbon dioxide molecule is linear. The linear nature of carbon dioxide has been confirmed through other experimental measurements.

The VSEPR model predicts that CO_2 is a linear molecule.

Next let us consider the NH_3 and NF_3 molecules shown in Figure 10.4. In both cases, the central N atom has a lone pair, whose charge density is away from the N atom. From Figure 9.5 we know that N is more electronegative than H, and F is more electronegative than N. For this reason, the shift of electron density in NH_3 is toward N and so contributes a larger dipole moment, whereas the NF bond moments are directed away from the N atom and so together they offset the contribution of the lone pair to the dipole moment. Thus, the resultant dipole moment in NH_3 is larger than that in NF_3.

Dipole moments can be used to distinguish between molecules that have the same formula but different structures. For example, the following molecules both exist; they

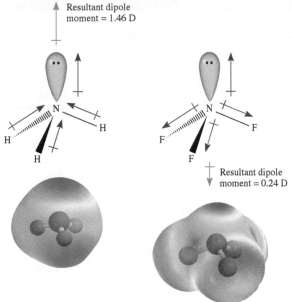

Resultant dipole moment = 1.46 D

Resultant dipole moment = 0.24 D

Figure 10.4 *Bond moments and resultant dipole moments in NH₃ and NF₃. The electrostatic potential maps show the electron density distributions in these molecules.*

have the same molecular formula ($C_2H_2Cl_2$), the same number and type of bonds, but different molecular structures:

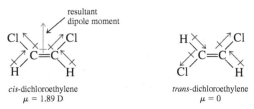

resultant dipole moment

cis-dichloroethylene
$\mu = 1.89$ D

trans-dichloroethylene
$\mu = 0$

Because *cis*-dichloroethylene is a polar molecule but *trans*-dichloroethylene is not, they can readily be distinguished by a dipole moment measurement. Additionally, as we will see in Chapter 11, the strength of intermolecular forces is partially determined by whether molecules possess a dipole moment. Table 10.3 lists the dipole moments of several polar molecules.

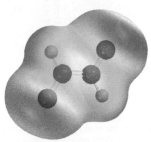

In cis-dichloroethylene (top), the bond moments reinforce one another and the molecule is polar. The opposite holds for trans-dichloroethylene and the molecule is nonpolar.

Table 10.3	Dipole Moments of Some Polar Molecules	
Molecule	**Geometry**	**Dipole Moment (D)**
HF	Linear	1.92
HCl	Linear	1.08
HBr	Linear	0.78
HI	Linear	0.38
H_2O	Bent	1.87
H_2S	Bent	1.10
NH_3	Trigonal pyramidal	1.46
SO_2	Bent	1.60

CHEMISTRY *in Action*

Microwave Ovens—Dipole Moments at Work

In the last 40 years the microwave oven has become a ubiquitous appliance. Microwave technology enables us to thaw and cook food much more rapidly than conventional appliances do. How do microwaves heat food so quickly?

In Chapter 7 we saw that microwaves are a form of electromagnetic radiation (see Figure 7.3). Microwaves are generated by a magnetron, which was invented during World War II when radar technology was being developed. The magnetron is

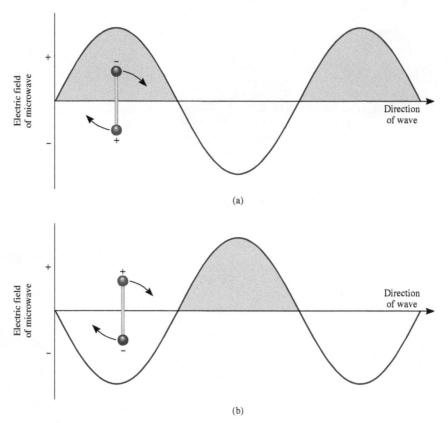

(a)

(b)

Interaction between the electric field component of the microwave and a polar molecule. (a) The negative end of the dipole follows the propagation of the wave (the positive region) and rotates in a clockwise direction. (b) If, after the molecule has rotated to the new position the radiation has also moved along to its next cycle, the positive end of the dipole will move into the negative region of the wave while the negative end will be pushed up. Thus, the molecule will rotate faster. No such interaction can occur with nonpolar molecules.

a hollow cylinder encased in a horseshoe-shaped magnet. In the center of the cylinder is a cathode rod. The walls of the cylinder act as an anode. When heated, the cathode emits electrons that travel toward the anode. The magnetic field forces the electrons to move in a circular path. This motion of charged particles generates microwaves, which are adjusted to a frequency of 2.45 GHz (2.45 × 10⁹ Hz) for cooking. A "waveguide" directs the microwaves into the cooking compartment. Rotating fan blades reflect the microwaves to all parts of the oven.

The cooking action in a microwave oven results from the interaction between the electric field component of the radiation with the polar molecules—mostly water—in food. All molecules rotate at room temperature. If the frequency of the radiation and that of the molecular rotation are equal, energy can be transferred from the microwave to the polar molecule. As a result, the molecule will rotate faster. This is what happens in a gas. In the condensed state (for example, in food), a molecule cannot execute the free rotation. Nevertheless, it still experiences a torque (a force that causes rotation) that tends to align its dipole moment with the oscillating field of the microwave. Consequently, there is friction between the molecules, which appears as heat in the food.

The reason that a microwave oven can cook food so fast is that the radiation is not absorbed by nonpolar molecules and can therefore reach different parts of food at the same time. (Depending on the amount of water present, microwaves can penetrate food to a depth of several inches.) In a conventional oven, heat can affect the center of foods only by conduction (that is, by transfer of heat from hot air molecules to cooler molecules in food in a layer-by-layer fashion), which is a very slow process.

The following points are relevant to the operation of a microwave oven. Plastics and Pyrex glasswares do not contain polar molecules and are therefore not affected by microwave radiation. (Styrofoam and certain plastics cannot be used in microwaves because they melt from the heat of the food.) Metals, however, reflect microwaves, thereby shielding the food and possibly returning enough energy to the microwave emitter to overload it. Because microwaves can induce a current in the metal, this action can lead to sparks jumping between the container and the bottom or walls of the oven. Finally, although water molecules in ice are locked in position and therefore cannot rotate, we routinely thaw food in a microwave oven. The reason is that at room temperature a thin film of liquid water quickly forms on the surface of frozen food and the mobile molecules in that film can absorb the radiation to start the thawing process.

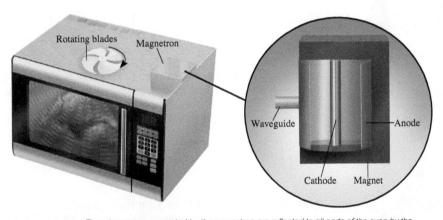

A microwave oven. The microwaves generated by the magnetron are reflected to all parts of the oven by the rotating fan blades.

Example 10.2 shows how we can predict whether a molecule possesses a dipole moment if we know its molecular geometry.

Example 10.2

Predict whether each of the following molecules has a dipole moment: (a) BrCl, (b) BF_3 (trigonal planar), (c) CH_2Cl_2 (tetrahedral).

Strategy Keep in mind that the dipole moment of a molecule depends on both the difference in electronegativities of the elements present and its geometry. A molecule can have polar bonds (if the bonded atoms have different electronegativities), but it may not possess a dipole moment if it has a highly symmetrical geometry.

Solution

(a) Because bromine chloride is diatomic, it has a linear geometry. Chlorine is more electronegative than bromine (see Figure 9.5), so BrCl is polar with chlorine at the negative end

$$Br\!-\!Cl$$

Thus, the molecule does have a dipole moment. In fact, all diatomic molecules containing different elements possess a dipole moment.

(b) Because fluorine is more electronegative than boron, each B—F bond in BF_3 (boron trifluoride) is polar and the three bond moments are equal. However, the symmetry of a trigonal planar shape means that the three bond moments exactly cancel one another:

An analogy is an object that is pulled in the directions shown by the three bond moments. If the forces are equal, the object will not move. Consequently, BF_3 has no dipole moment; it is a nonpolar molecule.

(c) The Lewis structure of CH_2Cl_2 (methylene chloride) is

$$\begin{array}{c} Cl \\ | \\ H\!-\!C\!-\!H \\ | \\ Cl \end{array}$$

This molecule is similar to CH_4 in that it has an overall tetrahedral shape. However, because not all the bonds are identical, there are three different bond angles: HCH, HCCl, and ClCCl. These bond angles are close to, but not equal to, 109.5°. Because chlorine is more electronegative than carbon, which is more electronegative than hydrogen, the bond moments do not cancel and the molecule possesses a dipole moment:

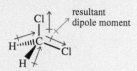

Thus, CH_2Cl_2 is a polar molecule.

Practice Exercise Does the $AlCl_3$ molecule have a dipole moment?

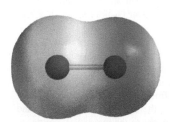

Electrostatic potential map of BrCl shows that the electron density is shifted toward the Cl atom.

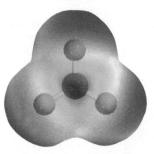

Electrostatic potential map shows that the electron density is symmetrically distributed in the BF_3 molecule.

Electrostatic potential map of CH_2Cl_2. The electron density is shifted toward the electronegative Cl atoms.

Similar problems: 10.21, 10.22, 10.23.

Review of Concepts

Carbon dioxide has a linear geometry and is nonpolar. Yet we know that the molecule executes bending and stretching motions that create a dipole moment. How would you reconcile these conflicting descriptions about CO_2?

10.3 Valence Bond Theory

The VSEPR model, based largely on Lewis structures, provides a relatively simple and straightforward method for predicting the geometry of molecules. But as we noted earlier, the Lewis theory of chemical bonding does not clearly explain why chemical bonds exist. Relating the formation of a covalent bond to the pairing of electrons was a step in the right direction, but it did not go far enough. For example, the Lewis theory describes the single bond between the H atoms in H_2 and that between the F atoms in F_2 in essentially the same way—as the pairing of two electrons. Yet these two molecules have quite different bond enthalpies and bond lengths (436.4 kJ/mol and 74 pm for H_2 and 150.6 kJ/mol and 142 pm for F_2). These and many other facts cannot be explained by the Lewis theory. For a more complete explanation of chemical bond formation we look to quantum mechanics. In fact, the quantum mechanical study of chemical bonding also provides a means for understanding molecular geometry.

At present, two quantum mechanical theories are used to describe covalent bond formation and the electronic structure of molecules. *Valence bond (VB) theory* assumes that the electrons in a molecule occupy atomic orbitals of the individual atoms. It enables us to retain a picture of individual atoms taking part in the bond formation. The second theory, called *molecular orbital (MO) theory,* assumes the formation of molecular orbitals from the atomic orbitals. Neither theory perfectly explains all aspects of bonding, but each has contributed something to our understanding of many observed molecular properties.

Let us start our discussion of valence bond theory by considering the formation of a H_2 molecule from two H atoms. The Lewis theory describes the H—H bond in terms of the pairing of the two electrons on the H atoms. In the framework of valence bond theory, the covalent H—H bond is formed by the *overlap* of the two $1s$ orbitals in the H atoms. By overlap, we mean that the two orbitals share a common region in space.

What happens to two H atoms as they move toward each other and form a bond? Initially, when the two atoms are far apart, there is no interaction. We say that the potential energy of this system (that is, the two H atoms) is zero. As the atoms approach each other, each electron is attracted by the nucleus of the other atom; at the same time, the electrons repel each other, as do the nuclei. While the atoms are still separated, attraction is stronger than repulsion, so that the potential energy of the system *decreases* (that is, it becomes negative) as the atoms approach each other (Figure 10.5). This trend continues until the potential energy reaches a minimum value. At this point, when the system has the lowest potential energy, it is most stable. This condition corresponds to substantial overlap of the $1s$ orbitals and the formation of a stable H_2 molecule. If the distance between nuclei were to decrease further, the potential energy would rise steeply and finally become positive as a result of the increased electron-electron and nuclear-nuclear repulsions. In accord with the law of conservation of energy, the decrease in potential energy as a result of H_2 formation must be accompanied by a release of energy. Experiments show that as a H_2 molecule is formed from two H atoms, heat is given off. The converse is also true. To break a H—H bond, energy must be supplied to the molecule. Figure 10.6 is another way of viewing the formation of a H_2 molecule.

Recall that an object has potential energy by virtue of its position.

Figure 10.5 *Change in potential energy of two H atoms with their distance of separation. At the point of minimum potential energy, the H_2 molecule is in its most stable state and the bond length is 74 pm. The spheres represent the 1s orbitals.*

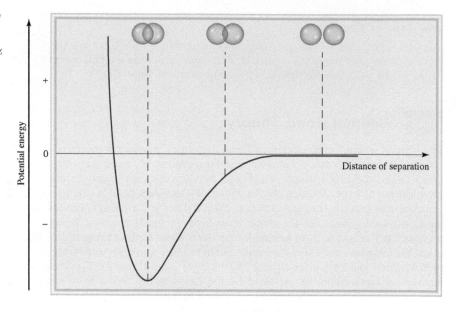

Figure 10.6 *Top to bottom: As two H atoms approach each other, their 1s orbitals begin to interact and each electron begins to feel the attraction of the other proton. Gradually, the electron density builds up in the region between the two nuclei (red color). Eventually, a stable H_2 molecule is formed with an internuclear distance of 74 pm.*

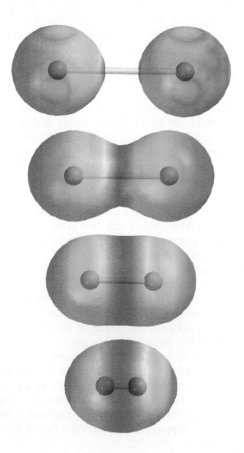

Thus, valence bond theory gives a clearer picture of chemical bond formation than the Lewis theory does. Valence bond theory states that a stable molecule forms from reacting atoms when the potential energy of the system has decreased to a minimum; the Lewis theory ignores energy changes in chemical bond formation.

The concept of overlapping atomic orbitals applies equally well to diatomic molecules other than H_2. Thus, a stable F_2 molecule forms when the $2p$ orbitals (containing the unpaired electrons) in the two F atoms overlap to form a covalent bond. Similarly, the formation of the HF molecule can be explained by the overlap of the $1s$ orbital in H with the $2p$ orbital in F. In each case, VB theory accounts for the changes in potential energy as the distance between the reacting atoms changes. Because the orbitals involved are not the same kind in all cases, we can see why the bond enthalpies and bond lengths in H_2, F_2, and HF might be different. As we stated earlier, Lewis theory treats *all* covalent bonds the same way and offers no explanation for the differences among covalent bonds.

The orbital diagram of the F atom is shown on p. 306.

Review of Concepts

Compare the Lewis theory and the valence bond theory of chemical bonding.

10.4 Hybridization of Atomic Orbitals

The concept of atomic orbital overlap should apply also to polyatomic molecules. However, a satisfactory bonding scheme must account for molecular geometry. We will discuss three examples of VB treatment of bonding in polyatomic molecules.

sp³ Hybridization

Consider the CH_4 molecule. Focusing only on the valence electrons, we can represent the orbital diagram of C as

Because the carbon atom has two unpaired electrons (one in each of the two $2p$ orbitals), it can form only two bonds with hydrogen in its ground state. Although the species CH_2 is known, it is very unstable. To account for the four C—H bonds in methane, we can try to promote (that is, energetically excite) an electron from the $2s$ orbital to the $2p$ orbital:

Now there are four unpaired electrons on C that could form four C—H bonds. However, the geometry is wrong, because three of the HCH bond angles would have to be 90° (remember that the three $2p$ orbitals on carbon are mutually perpendicular), and yet *all* HCH angles are 109.5°.

To explain the bonding in methane, VB theory uses hypothetical **hybrid orbitals,** which are *atomic orbitals obtained when two or more nonequivalent*

▶▶▶ Animation
Hybridization

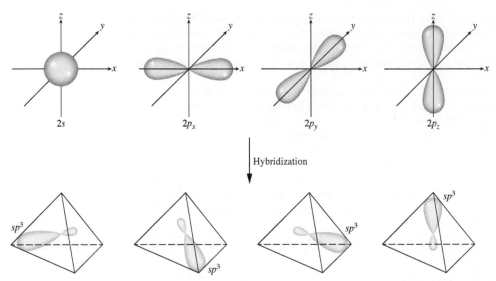

Figure 10.7 *Formation of four sp³ hybrid orbitals from one 2s and three 2p orbitals. The sp³ orbitals point to the corners of a tetrahedron.*

▶▶▶ Animation
Molecular Shape and Orbital Hybridization

orbitals of the same atom combine in preparation for covalent bond formation. **Hybridization** *is the term applied to the mixing of atomic orbitals in an atom (usually a central atom) to generate a set of hybrid orbitals.* We can generate four equivalent hybrid orbitals for carbon by mixing the $2s$ orbital and the three $2p$ orbitals:

sp^3 orbitals

sp^3 is pronounced "s-p three."

Because the new orbitals are formed from one s and three p orbitals, they are called sp^3 hybrid orbitals. Figure 10.7 shows the shape and orientations of the sp^3 orbitals. These four hybrid orbitals are directed toward the four corners of a regular tetrahedron. Figure 10.8 shows the formation of four covalent bonds between the carbon sp^3 hybrid orbitals and the hydrogen $1s$ orbitals in CH_4. Thus CH_4 has a tetrahedral shape, and all the HCH angles are 109.5°. Note that although energy is required to bring about hybridization, this input is more than compensated for by the energy released upon the formation of C—H bonds. (Recall that bond formation is an exothermic process.)

The following analogy is useful for understanding hybridization. Suppose that we have a beaker of a red solution and three beakers of blue solutions and that the volume of each is 50 mL. The red solution corresponds to one $2s$ orbital, the blue solutions represent three $2p$ orbitals, and the four equal volumes symbolize four separate orbitals. By mixing the solutions we obtain 200 mL of a purple solution, which can be divided into four 50-mL portions (that is, the hybridization process generates four sp^3 orbitals). Just as the purple color is made up of the red and blue components of the original solutions, the sp^3 hybrid orbitals possess both s and p orbital characteristics.

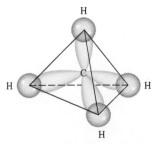

Figure 10.8 *Formation of four bonds between the carbon sp³ hybrid orbitals and the hydrogen 1s orbitals in CH₄. The smaller lobes are not shown.*

Another example of sp^3 hybridization is ammonia (NH_3). Table 10.1 shows that the arrangement of four electron pairs is tetrahedral, so that the bonding in NH_3 can be explained by assuming that N, like C in CH_4, is sp^3-hybridized. The ground-state electron configuration of N is $1s^2 2s^2 2p^3$, so that the orbital diagram for the sp^3 hybridized N atom is

sp^3 orbitals

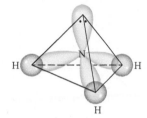

Figure 10.9 *The sp^3-hybridized N atom in NH_3. Three sp^3 hybrid orbitals form bonds with the H atoms. The fourth is occupied by nitrogen's lone pair.*

Three of the four hybrid orbitals form covalent N—H bonds, and the fourth hybrid orbital accommodates the lone pair on nitrogen (Figure 10.9). Repulsion between the lone-pair electrons and electrons in the bonding orbitals decreases the HNH bond angles from 109.5° to 107.3°.

It is important to understand the relationship between hybridization and the VSEPR model. We use hybridization to describe the bonding scheme only when the arrangement of electron pairs has been predicted using VSEPR. If the VSEPR model predicts a tetrahedral arrangement of electron pairs, then we assume that one s and three p orbitals are hybridized to form four sp^3 hybrid orbitals. The following are examples of other types of hybridization.

sp Hybridization

The beryllium chloride ($BeCl_2$) molecule is predicted to be linear by VSEPR. The orbital diagram for the valence electrons in Be is

$2s$ $2p$

We know that in its ground state, Be does not form covalent bonds with Cl because its electrons are paired in the $2s$ orbital. So we turn to hybridization for an explanation of Be's bonding behavior. First, we promote a $2s$ electron to a $2p$ orbital, resulting in

$2s$ $2p$

Now there are two Be orbitals available for bonding, the $2s$ and $2p$. However, if two Cl atoms were to combine with Be in this excited state, one Cl atom would share a $2s$ electron and the other Cl would share a $2p$ electron, making two nonequivalent BeCl bonds. This scheme contradicts experimental evidence. In the actual $BeCl_2$ molecule, the two BeCl bonds are identical in every respect. Thus, the $2s$ and $2p$ orbitals must be mixed, or hybridized, to form two equivalent sp hybrid orbitals:

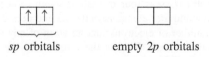

sp orbitals   empty $2p$ orbitals

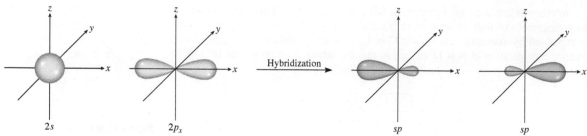

Figure 10.10 *Formation of sp hybrid orbitals.*

Figure 10.10 shows the shape and orientation of the *sp* orbitals. These two hybrid orbitals lie on the same line, the *x*-axis, so that the angle between them is 180°. Each of the BeCl bonds is then formed by the overlap of a Be *sp* hybrid orbital and a Cl 3*p* orbital, and the resulting BeCl$_2$ molecule has a linear geometry (Figure 10.11).

*sp*² Hybridization

Next we will look at the BF$_3$ (boron trifluoride) molecule, known to have a planar geometry. Considering only the valence electrons, the orbital diagram of B is

First, we promote a 2*s* electron to an empty 2*p* orbital:

*sp*² is pronounced "s-p two."

Mixing the 2*s* orbital with the two 2*p* orbitals generates three *sp*² hybrid orbitals:

These three *sp*² orbitals lie in the same plane, and the angle between any two of them is 120° (Figure 10.12). Each of the BF bonds is formed by the overlap of a boron *sp*² hybrid orbital and a fluorine 2*p* orbital (Figure 10.13). The BF$_3$ molecule is planar with all the FBF angles equal to 120°. This result conforms to experimental findings and also to VSEPR predictions.

You may have noticed an interesting connection between hybridization and the octet rule. Regardless of the type of hybridization, an atom starting with one *s* and three *p* orbitals would still possess four orbitals, enough to accommodate a total of eight electrons in a compound. For elements in the second period of the periodic table, eight is the maximum number of electrons that an atom of any of these elements can accommodate in the valence shell. This is the reason that the octet rule is usually obeyed by the second-period elements.

Figure 10.11 *The linear geometry of BeCl₂ can be explained by assuming that Be is sp-hybridized. The two sp hybrid orbitals overlap with the two chlorine 3p orbitals to form two covalent bonds.*

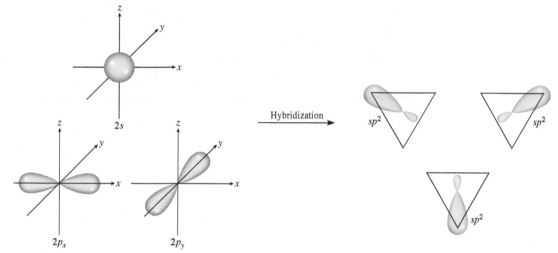

Figure 10.12 *Formation of sp² hybrid orbitals.*

The situation is different for an atom of a third-period element. If we use only the 3*s* and 3*p* orbitals of the atom to form hybrid orbitals in a molecule, then the octet rule applies. However, in some molecules the same atom may use one or more 3*d* orbitals, in addition to the 3*s* and 3*p* orbitals, to form hybrid orbitals. In these cases, the octet rule does not hold. We will see specific examples of the participation of the 3*d* orbital in hybridization shortly.

To summarize our discussion of hybridization, we note that

- The concept of hybridization is not applied to isolated atoms. It is a theoretical model used only to explain covalent bonding.

- Hybridization is the mixing of at least two nonequivalent atomic orbitals, for example, *s* and *p* orbitals. Therefore, a hybrid orbital is not a pure atomic orbital. Hybrid orbitals and pure atomic orbitals have very different shapes.

- The number of hybrid orbitals generated is equal to the number of pure atomic orbitals that participate in the hybridization process.

- Hybridization requires an input of energy; however, the system more than recovers this energy during bond formation.

- Covalent bonds in polyatomic molecules and ions are formed by the overlap of hybrid orbitals, or of hybrid orbitals with unhybridized ones. Therefore, the hybridization bonding scheme is still within the framework of valence bond theory; electrons in a molecule are assumed to occupy hybrid orbitals of the individual atoms.

Table 10.4 summarizes *sp*, *sp²*, and *sp³* hybridization (as well as other types that we will discuss shortly).

Procedure for Hybridizing Atomic Orbitals

Before going on to discuss the hybridization of *d* orbitals, let us specify what we need to know in order to apply hybridization to bonding in polyatomic molecules in general. In essence, hybridization simply extends Lewis theory and the VSEPR model.

Figure 10.13 *The sp² hybrid orbitals of boron overlap with the 2p orbitals of fluorine. The BF₃ molecule is planar, and all the FBF angles are 120°.*

436   **Chapter 10** ▪ Chemical Bonding II: Molecular Geometry and Hybridization of Atomic Orbitals

Table 10.4	Important Hybrid Orbitals and Their Shapes			
Pure Atomic Orbitals of the Central Atom	**Hybridization of the Central Atom**	**Number of Hybrid Orbitals**	**Shape of Hybrid Orbitals**	**Examples**
s, p	sp	2	Linear	$BeCl_2$
s, p, p	sp^2	3	Trigonal planar	BF_3
s, p, p, p	sp^3	4	Tetrahedral	CH_4, NH_4^+
s, p, p, p, d	sp^3d	5	Trigonal bipyramidal	PCl_5
s, p, p, p, d, d	sp^3d^2	6	Octahedral	SF_6

To assign a suitable state of hybridization to the central atom in a molecule, we must have some idea about the geometry of the molecule. The steps are as follows:

1. Draw the Lewis structure of the molecule.
2. Predict the overall arrangement of the electron pairs (both bonding pairs and lone pairs) using the VSEPR model (see Table 10.1).
3. Deduce the hybridization of the central atom by matching the arrangement of the electron pairs with those of the hybrid orbitals shown in Table 10.4.

Example 10.3 illustrates this procedure.

Example 10.3

Determine the hybridization state of the central (underlined) atom in each of the following molecules: (a) $\underline{Be}H_2$, (b) $\underline{Al}I_3$, and (c) $\underline{P}F_3$. Describe the hybridization process and determine the molecular geometry in each case.

Strategy The steps for determining the hybridization of the central atom in a molecule are:

draw Lewis structure of the molecule $\longrightarrow$ use VSEPR to determine the electron pair arrangement surrounding the central atom (Table 10.1) $\longrightarrow$ use Table 10.4 to determine the hybridization state of the central atom

Solution

(a) The ground-state electron configuration of Be is $1s^2 2s^2$ and the Be atom has two valence electrons. The Lewis structure of BeH_2 is

$$H{-}Be{-}H$$

BeH_2

There are two bonding pairs around Be; therefore, the electron pair arrangement is linear. We conclude that Be uses *sp* hybrid orbitals in bonding with H, because *sp* orbitals have a linear arrangement (see Table 10.4). The hybridization process can be imagined as follows. First, we draw the orbital diagram for the ground state of Be:

2s   2p

By promoting a 2s electron to the 2p orbital, we get the excited state:

2s   2p

The 2s and 2p orbitals then mix to form two hybrid orbitals:

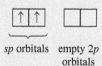

sp orbitals   empty 2p
                orbitals

The two Be—H bonds are formed by the overlap of the Be *sp* orbitals with the 1s orbitals of the H atoms. Thus, BeH_2 is a linear molecule.

(Continued)

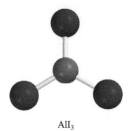

AlI₃

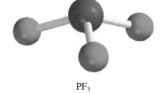

PF₃

Similar problems: 10.31, 10.33.

(b) The ground-state electron configuration of Al is $[Ne]3s^2 3p^1$. Therefore, the Al atom has three valence electrons. The Lewis structure of AlI₃ is

$$:\overset{\displaystyle ..}{\underset{\displaystyle ..}{I}}:$$
$$:\overset{..}{\underset{..}{I}}—Al—\overset{..}{\underset{..}{I}}:$$

There are three pairs of electrons around Al; therefore, the electron pair arrangement is trigonal planar. We conclude that Al uses sp^2 hybrid orbitals in bonding with I because sp^2 orbitals have a trigonal planar arrangement (see Table 10.4). The orbital diagram of the ground-state Al atom is

3s   3p

By promoting a 3s electron into the 3p orbital we obtain the following excited state:

3s   3p

The 3s and two 3p orbitals then mix to form three sp^2 hybrid orbitals:

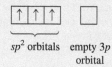

sp^2 orbitals   empty 3p
orbital

The sp^2 hybrid orbitals overlap with the 5p orbitals of I to form three covalent Al—I bonds. We predict that the AlI₃ molecule is trigonal planar and all the IAlI angles are 120°.

(c) The ground-state electron configuration of P is $[Ne]3s^2 3p^3$. Therefore, P atom has five valence electrons. The Lewis structure of PF₃ is

$$:\overset{..}{\underset{..}{F}}—\overset{..}{\underset{\displaystyle \underset{\displaystyle :\overset{..}{\underset{..}{F}}:}{|}}{P}—\overset{..}{\underset{..}{F}}:$$

There are four pairs of electrons around P; therefore, the electron pair arrangement is tetrahedral. We conclude that P uses sp^3 hybrid orbitals in bonding to F, because sp^3 orbitals have a tetrahedral arrangement (see Table 10.4). The hybridization process can be imagined to take place as follows. The orbital diagram of the ground-state P atom is

3s   3p

By mixing the 3s and 3p orbitals, we obtain four sp^3 hybrid orbitals.

sp^3 orbitals

As in the case of NH₃, one of the sp^3 hybrid orbitals is used to accommodate the lone pair on P. The other three sp^3 hybrid orbitals form covalent P—F bonds with the 2p orbitals of F. We predict the geometry of the molecule to be trigonal pyramidal; the FPF angle should be somewhat less than 109.5°.

Practice Exercise Determine the hybridization state of the underlined atoms in the following compounds: (a) <u>Si</u>Br₄ and (b) <u>B</u>Cl₃.

Hybridization of *s*, *p*, and *d* Orbitals

We have seen that hybridization neatly explains bonding that involves *s* and *p* orbitals. For elements in the third period and beyond, however, we cannot always account for molecular geometry by assuming that only *s* and *p* orbitals hybridize. To understand the formation of molecules with trigonal bipyramidal and octahedral geometries, for instance, we must include *d* orbitals in the hybridization concept.

Consider the SF_6 molecule as an example. In Section 10.1 we saw that this molecule has octahedral geometry, which is also the arrangement of the six electron pairs. Table 10.4 shows that the S atom is sp^3d^2-hybridized in SF_6. The ground-state electron configuration of S is $[Ne]3s^23p^4$. Focusing only on the valence electrons, we have the orbital diagram

Because the 3*d* level is quite close in energy to the 3*s* and 3*p* levels, we can promote 3*s* and 3*p* electrons to two of the 3*d* orbitals:

Mixing the 3*s*, three 3*p*, and two 3*d* orbitals generates six sp^3d^2 hybrid orbitals:

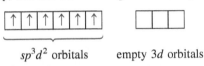

The six S—F bonds are formed by the overlap of the hybrid orbitals of the S atom with the 2*p* orbitals of the F atoms. Because there are 12 electrons around the S atom, the octet rule is violated. The use of *d* orbitals in addition to *s* and *p* orbitals to form an expanded octet (see Section 9.9) is an example of *valence-shell expansion*. Second-period elements, unlike third-period elements, do not have 2*d* energy levels, so they can never expand their valence shells. (Recall that when $n = 2$, $l = 0$ and 1. Thus, we can only have 2*s* and 2*p* orbitals.) Hence atoms of second-period elements can never be surrounded by more than eight electrons in any of their compounds.

Example 10.4 deals with valence-shell expansion in a third-period element.

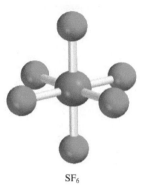

SF_6

sp^3d^2 is pronounced "s-p three d two."

Example 10.4

Describe the hybridization state of phosphorus in phosphorus pentabromide (PBr_5).

Strategy Follow the same procedure shown in Example 10.3.

Solution The ground-state electron configuration of P is $[Ne]3s^23p^3$. Therefore, the P atom has five valence electrons. The Lewis structure of PBr_5 is

$$\underset{\displaystyle :\!\!\ddot{Br}\!:}{\overset{\displaystyle :\!\!\ddot{Br}\!:}{\underset{\displaystyle :\!\ddot{Br}\!:}{:\!\ddot{Br}\!\diagdown\!\!\diagup\!P\!\!-\!\!\ddot{Br}\!:}}}$$

There are five pairs of electrons around P; therefore, the electron pair arrangement is trigonal bipyramidal. We conclude that P uses sp^3d hybrid orbitals in bonding to Br,

(Continued)

PBr_5

because sp^3d hybrid orbitals have a trigonal bipyramidal arrangement (see Table 10.4). The hybridization process can be imagined as follows. The orbital diagram of the ground-state P atom is

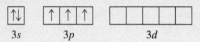

$$3s \qquad 3p \qquad 3d$$

Promoting a 3s electron into a 3d orbital results in the following excited state:

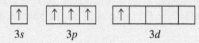

$$3s \qquad 3p \qquad 3d$$

Mixing the one 3s, three 3p, and one 3d orbitals generates five sp^3d hybrid orbitals:

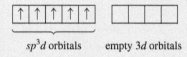

$$sp^3d \text{ orbitals} \qquad \text{empty } 3d \text{ orbitals}$$

These hybrid orbitals overlap the 4p orbitals of Br to form five covalent P—Br bonds. Because there are no lone pairs on the P atom, the geometry of PBr_5 is trigonal bipyramidal.

Practice Exercise Describe the hybridization state of Se in SeF_6.

Similar problem: 10.40.

Review of Concepts

What is the hybridization of Xe in XeF_4 (see Example 9.12 on p. 396)?

Ground state

Promotion of electron

sp^2-Hybridized state

Figure 10.14 *The sp² hybridization of a carbon atom. The 2s orbital is mixed with only two 2p orbitals to form three equivalent sp² hybrid orbitals. This process leaves an electron in the unhybridized orbital, the 2p_z orbital.*

▶▶▶ **Animation**
Sigma and Pi Bonds

10.5 Hybridization in Molecules Containing Double and Triple Bonds

The concept of hybridization is useful also for molecules with double and triple bonds. Consider the ethylene molecule, C_2H_4, as an example. In Example 10.1 we saw that C_2H_4 contains a carbon-carbon double bond and has planar geometry. Both the geometry and the bonding can be understood if we assume that each carbon atom is sp^2-hybridized. Figure 10.14 shows orbital diagrams of this hybridization process. We assume that only the $2p_x$ and $2p_y$ orbitals combine with the 2s orbital, and that the $2p_z$ orbital remains unchanged. Figure 10.15 shows that the $2p_z$ orbital is perpendicular to the plane of the hybrid orbitals. Now how do we account for the bonding of the C atoms? As Figure 10.16(a) shows, each carbon atom uses the three sp^2 hybrid orbitals to form two bonds with the two hydrogen 1s orbitals and one bond with the sp^2 hybrid orbital of the adjacent C atom. In addition, the two unhybridized $2p_z$ orbitals of the C atoms form another bond by overlapping sideways [Figure 10.16(b)].

A distinction is made between the two types of covalent bonds in C_2H_4. The three bonds formed by each C atom in Figure 10.16(a) are all ***sigma bonds (σ bonds),*** *covalent bonds formed by orbitals overlapping end-to-end, with the electron density concentrated between the nuclei of the bonding atoms.* The second type is called a ***pi bond (π bond),*** which is defined as *a covalent bond formed by sideways overlapping orbitals with electron density concentrated above and below the plane of the nuclei of the bonding atoms.* The two C atoms form a pi bond as shown in Figure 10.16(b).

It is this pi bond formation that gives ethylene its planar geometry. Figure 10.16(c) shows the orientation of the sigma and pi bonds. Figure 10.17 is yet another way of looking at the planar C_2H_4 molecule and the formation of the pi bond. Although we normally represent the carbon-carbon double bond as C==C (as in a Lewis structure), it is important to keep in mind that the two bonds are different types: One is a sigma bond and the other is a pi bond. In fact, the bond enthalpies of the carbon-carbon pi and sigma bonds are about 270 kJ/mol and 350 kJ/mol, respectively.

The acetylene molecule (C_2H_2) contains a carbon-carbon triple bond. Because the molecule is linear, we can explain its geometry and bonding by assuming that each C atom is sp-hybridized by mixing the $2s$ with the $2p_x$ orbital (Figure 10.18). As Figure 10.19 shows, the two sp hybrid orbitals of each C atom form one sigma bond with a hydrogen $1s$ orbital and another sigma bond with the other C atom. In addition, two pi bonds are formed by the sideways overlap of the unhybridized $2p_y$ and $2p_z$ orbitals. Thus, the C≡C bond is made up of one sigma bond and two pi bonds.

The following rule helps us predict hybridization in molecules containing multiple bonds: If the central atom forms a double bond, it is sp^2-hybridized; if it forms two double bonds or a triple bond, it is sp-hybridized. Note that this rule applies only to atoms of the second-period elements. Atoms of third-period elements and beyond that form multiple bonds present a more complicated picture and will not be dealt with here.

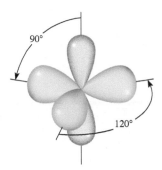

Figure 10.15 *Each carbon atom in the C_2H_4 molecule has three sp^2 hybrid orbitals (green) and one unhybridized $2p_z$ orbital (gray), which is perpendicular to the plane of the hybrid orbitals.*

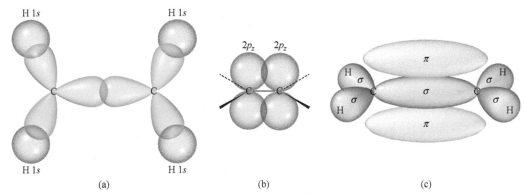

(a)   (b)   (c)

Figure 10.16 *Bonding in ethylene, C_2H_4. (a) Top view of the sigma bonds between carbon atoms and between carbon and hydrogen atoms. All the atoms lie in the same plane, making C_2H_4 a planar molecule. (b) Side view showing how the two $2p_z$ orbitals on the two carbon atoms overlap, leading to the formation of a pi bond. The solid, dashed, and wedged lines show the directions of the sigma bonds. (c) The interactions in (a) and (b) lead to the formation of the sigma bonds and the pi bond in ethylene. Note that the pi bond lies above and below the plane of the molecule.*

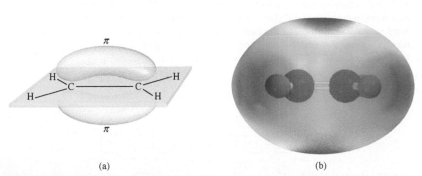

(a)   (b)

Figure 10.17 *(a) Another view of the pi bond in the C_2H_4 molecule. Note that all six atoms are in the same plane. It is the overlap of the $2p_z$ orbitals that causes the molecule to assume a planar structure. (b) Electrostatic potential map of C_2H_4.*

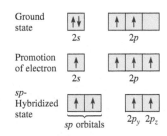

Figure 10.18 *The sp hybridization of a carbon atom. The 2s orbital is mixed with only one 2p orbital to form two sp hybrid orbitals. This process leaves an electron in each of the two unhybridized 2p orbitals, namely, the $2p_y$ and $2p_z$ orbitals.*

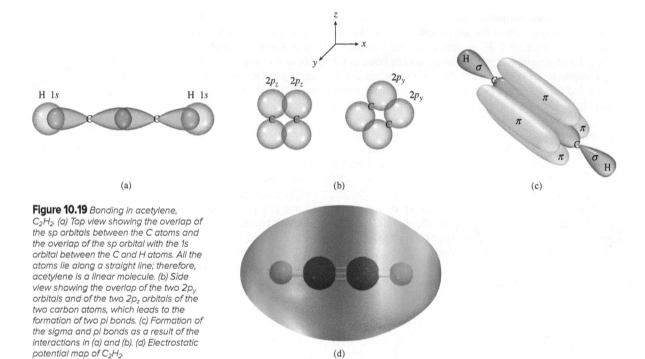

(a) (b) (c)

Figure 10.19 *Bonding in acetylene, C_2H_2. (a) Top view showing the overlap of the sp orbitals between the C atoms and the overlap of the sp orbital with the 1s orbital between the C and H atoms. All the atoms lie along a straight line; therefore, acetylene is a linear molecule. (b) Side view showing the overlap of the two $2p_y$ orbitals and of the two $2p_z$ orbitals of the two carbon atoms, which leads to the formation of two pi bonds. (c) Formation of the sigma and pi bonds as a result of the interactions in (a) and (b). (d) Electrostatic potential map of C_2H_2.*

(d)

Example 10.5

Describe the bonding in the formaldehyde molecule whose Lewis structure is

Assume that the O atom is sp^2-hybridized.

Strategy Follow the procedure shown in Example 10.3.

Solution There are three pairs of electrons around the C atom; therefore, the electron pair arrangement is trigonal planar. (Recall that a double bond is treated as a single bond in the VSEPR model.) We conclude that C uses sp^2 hybrid orbitals in bonding, because sp^2 hybrid orbitals have a trigonal planar arrangement (see Table 10.4). We can imagine the hybridization processes for C and O as follows:

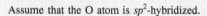

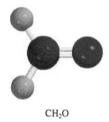

CH₂O

(Continued)

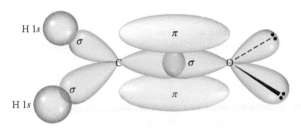

H 1s

H 1s

C

O

σ

σ

σ

π

π

Figure 10.20 *Bonding in the formaldehyde molecule. A sigma bond is formed by the overlap of the sp^2 hybrid orbital of carbon and the sp^2 hybrid orbital of oxygen; a pi bond is formed by the overlap of the $2p_z$ orbitals of the carbon and oxygen atoms. The two lone pairs on oxygen are placed in the other two sp^2 orbitals of oxygen.*

Carbon has one electron in each of the three sp^2 orbitals, which are used to form sigma bonds with the H atoms and the O atom. There is also an electron in the $2p_z$ orbital, which forms a pi bond with oxygen. Oxygen has two electrons in two of its sp^2 hybrid orbitals. These are the lone pairs on oxygen. Its third sp^2 hybrid orbital with one electron is used to form a sigma bond with carbon. The $2p_z$ orbital (with one electron) overlaps with the $2p_z$ orbital of C to form a pi bond (Figure 10.20).

Practice Exercise Describe the bonding in the hydrogen cyanide molecule, HCN. Assume that N is *sp*-hybridized.

Similar problems: 10.36, 10.37, 10.39.

Review of Concepts

Which of the following pairs of atomic orbitals on adjacent nuclei can overlap to form a sigma bond? a pi bond? Which cannot overlap (no bond)? Consider the x axis to be the internuclear axis. (a) 1s and 2s, (b) 1s and $2p_x$, (c) $2p_y$ and $2p_y$, (d) $3p_y$ and $3p_z$, (e) $2p_x$ and $3p_x$.

10.6 Molecular Orbital Theory

Valence bond theory is one of the two quantum mechanical approaches that explain bonding in molecules. It accounts, at least qualitatively, for the stability of the covalent bond in terms of overlapping atomic orbitals. Using the concept of hybridization, valence bond theory can explain molecular geometries predicted by the VSEPR model. However, the assumption that electrons in a molecule occupy atomic orbitals of the individual atoms can only be an approximation, because each bonding electron in a molecule must be in an orbital that is characteristic of the molecule as a whole.

In some cases, valence bond theory cannot satisfactorily account for observed properties of molecules. Consider the oxygen molecule, whose Lewis structure is

According to this description, all the electrons in O_2 are paired and oxygen should therefore be diamagnetic. But experiments have shown that the oxygen molecule has two unpaired electrons (Figure 10.21). This finding suggests a fundamental deficiency in valence bond theory, one that justifies searching for an alternative bonding approach that accounts for the properties of O_2 and other molecules that do not match the predictions of valence bond theory.

Magnetic and other properties of molecules are sometimes better explained by another quantum mechanical approach called *molecular orbital (MO) theory.* Molecular orbital theory describes covalent bonds in terms of **molecular orbitals,** which

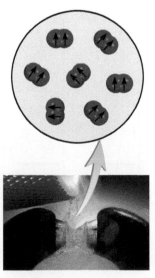

Figure 10.21 *Liquid oxygen caught between the poles of a magnet, because the O_2 molecules are paramagnetic, having two parallel spins.*

result from interaction of the atomic orbitals of the bonding atoms and are associated with the entire molecule. The difference between a molecular orbital and an atomic orbital is that an atomic orbital is associated with only one atom.

Review of Concepts

One way to account for the fact that an O_2 molecule contains two unpaired electrons is to draw the following Lewis structure:

$$\cdot\ddot{O}\text{—}\ddot{O}\cdot$$

Suggest two reasons why this structure is unsatisfactory.

Bonding and Antibonding Molecular Orbitals

According to MO theory, the overlap of the $1s$ orbitals of two hydrogen atoms leads to the formation of two molecular orbitals: one bonding molecular orbital and one antibonding molecular orbital. A **bonding molecular orbital** has *lower energy and greater stability than the atomic orbitals from which it was formed.* An **antibonding molecular orbital** has *higher energy and lower stability than the atomic orbitals from which it was formed.* As the names "bonding" and "antibonding" suggest, placing electrons in a bonding molecular orbital yields a stable covalent bond, whereas placing electrons in an antibonding molecular orbital results in an unstable bond.

In the bonding molecular orbital, the electron density is greatest between the nuclei of the bonding atoms. In the antibonding molecular orbital, on the other hand, the electron density decreases to zero between the nuclei. We can understand this distinction if we recall that electrons in orbitals have wave characteristics. A property unique to waves enables waves of the same type to interact in such a way that the resultant wave has either an enhanced amplitude or a diminished amplitude. In the former case, we call the interaction *constructive interference;* in the latter case, it is *destructive interference* (Figure 10.22).

The formation of bonding molecular orbitals corresponds to constructive interference (the increase in amplitude is analogous to the buildup of electron density between the two nuclei). The formation of antibonding molecular orbitals corresponds to destructive interference (the decrease in amplitude is analogous to the decrease in electron density between the two nuclei). The constructive and destructive interactions between the two $1s$ orbitals in the H_2 molecule, then, lead to the formation of a sigma bonding molecular orbital σ_{1s} and a sigma antibonding molecular orbital $\sigma_{1s}^{\star}$:

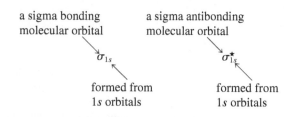

a sigma bonding molecular orbital σ_{1s} formed from $1s$ orbitals

a sigma antibonding molecular orbital $\sigma_{1s}^{\star}$ formed from $1s$ orbitals

where the star denotes an antibonding molecular orbital.

In a **sigma molecular orbital** (bonding or antibonding) *the electron density is concentrated symmetrically around a line between the two nuclei of the bonding atoms.* Two electrons in a sigma molecular orbital form a sigma bond (see Section 10.5). Remember that a single covalent bond (such as H—H or F—F) is almost always a sigma bond.

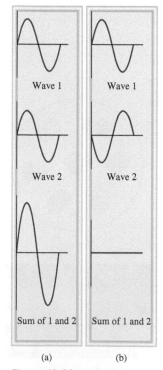

Wave 1

Wave 2

Sum of 1 and 2

Wave 1

Wave 2

Sum of 1 and 2

(a)   (b)

Figure 10.22 *Constructive interference (a) and destructive interference (b) of two waves of the same wavelength and amplitude.*

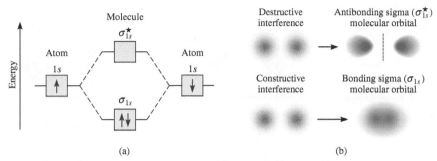

Figure 10.23 *(a) Energy levels of bonding and antibonding molecular orbitals in the H_2 molecule. Note that the two electrons in the σ_{1s} orbital must have opposite spins in accord with the Pauli exclusion principle. Keep in mind that the higher the energy of the molecular orbital, the less stable the electrons in that molecular orbital. (b) Constructive and destructive interferences between the two hydrogen 1s orbitals lead to the formation of a bonding and an antibonding molecular orbital. In the bonding molecular orbital, there is a buildup between the nuclei of electron density, which acts as a negatively charged "glue" to hold the positively charged nuclei together. In the antibonding molecular orbital, there is a nodal plane between the nuclei, where the electron density is zero.*

Figure 10.23 shows the *molecular orbital energy level diagram*—that is, the relative energy levels of the orbitals produced in the formation of the H_2 molecule—and the constructive and destructive interferences between the two 1s orbitals. Notice that in the antibonding molecular orbital there is a *nodal plane* between the nuclei that signifies zero electron density. The nuclei are repelled by each other's positive charges, rather than held together. Electrons in the antibonding molecular orbital have higher energy (and less stability) than they would have in the isolated atoms. On the other hand, electrons in the bonding molecular orbital have less energy (and hence greater stability) than they would have in the isolated atoms.

Although we have used the hydrogen molecule to illustrate molecular orbital formation, the concept is equally applicable to other molecules. In the H_2 molecule, we consider only the interaction between 1s orbitals; with more complex molecules we need to consider additional atomic orbitals as well. Nevertheless, for all s orbitals, the process is the same as for 1s orbitals. Thus, the interaction between two 2s or 3s orbitals can be understood in terms of the molecular orbital energy level diagram and the formation of bonding and antibonding molecular orbitals shown in Figure 10.23.

For *p* orbitals, the process is more complex because they can interact with each other in two different ways. For example, two 2p orbitals can approach each other end-to-end to produce a sigma bonding and a sigma antibonding molecular orbital, as shown in Figure 10.24(a). Alternatively, the two *p* orbitals can overlap sideways to generate a bonding and an antibonding pi molecular orbital [Figure 10.24(b)].

The two electrons in the sigma molecular orbital are paired. The Pauli exclusion principle applies to molecules as well as to atoms.

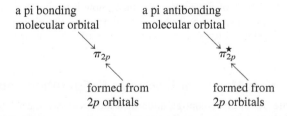

In a **pi molecular orbital** (bonding or antibonding), *the electron density is concentrated above and below a line joining the two nuclei of the bonding atoms.* Two

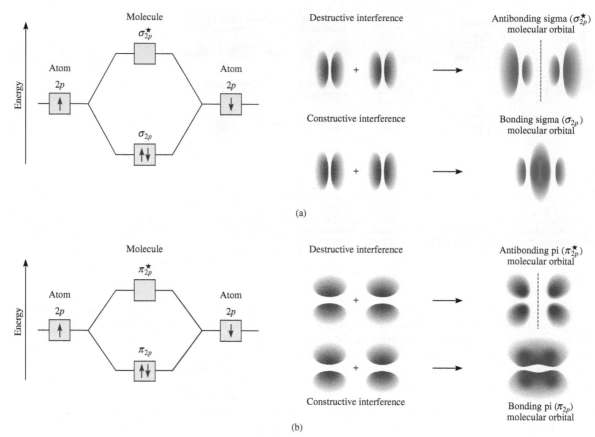

Figure 10.24 *Two possible interactions between two equivalent p orbitals and the corresponding molecular orbitals. (a) When the p orbitals overlap end-to-end, a sigma bonding and a sigma antibonding molecular orbital form. (b) When the p orbitals overlap side-to-side, a pi bonding and a pi antibonding molecular orbital form. Normally, a sigma bonding molecular orbital is more stable than a pi bonding molecular orbital, because side-to-side interaction leads to a smaller overlap of the p orbitals than does end-to-end interaction. We assume that the $2p_x$ orbitals take part in the sigma molecular orbital formation. The $2p_y$ and $2p_z$ orbitals can interact to form only π molecular orbitals. The behavior shown in (b) represents the interaction between the $2p_y$ orbitals or the $2p_z$ orbitals. In both cases, the dash line represents a nodal plane between the nuclei, where the electron density is zero.*

electrons in a pi molecular orbital form a pi bond (see Section 10.5). A double bond is almost always composed of a sigma bond and a pi bond; a triple bond is always a sigma bond plus two pi bonds.

10.7 Molecular Orbital Configurations

To understand properties of molecules, we must know how electrons are distributed among molecular orbitals. The procedure for determining the electron configuration of a molecule is analogous to the one we use to determine the electron configurations of atoms (see Section 7.8).

Rules Governing Molecular Electron Configuration and Stability

In order to write the electron configuration of a molecule, we must first arrange the molecular orbitals in order of increasing energy. Then we can use the following guidelines to fill the molecular orbitals with electrons. The rules also help us understand the stabilities of the molecular orbitals.

1. The number of molecular orbitals formed is always equal to the number of atomic orbitals combined.

2. The more stable the bonding molecular orbital, the less stable the corresponding antibonding molecular orbital.

3. The filling of molecular orbitals proceeds from low to high energies. In a stable molecule, the number of electrons in bonding molecular orbitals is always greater than that in antibonding molecular orbitals because we place electrons first in the lower-energy bonding molecular orbitals.

4. Like an atomic orbital, each molecular orbital can accommodate up to two electrons with opposite spins in accordance with the Pauli exclusion principle.

5. When electrons are added to molecular orbitals of the same energy, the most stable arrangement is predicted by Hund's rule; that is, electrons enter these molecular orbitals with parallel spins.

6. The number of electrons in the molecular orbitals is equal to the sum of all the electrons on the bonding atoms.

Hydrogen and Helium Molecules

Later in this section we will study molecules formed by atoms of the second-period elements. Before we do, it will be instructive to predict the relative stabilities of the simple species H_2^+, H_2, He_2^+, and He_2, using the energy-level diagrams shown in Figure 10.25. The σ_{1s} and $\sigma_{1s}^{\star}$ orbitals can accommodate a maximum of four electrons. The total number of electrons increases from one for H_2^+ to four for He_2. The Pauli exclusion principle stipulates that each molecular orbital can accommodate a maximum of two electrons with opposite spins. We are concerned only with the ground-state electron configurations in these cases.

To evaluate the stabilities of these species we determine their **bond order,** defined as

$$\text{bond order} = \frac{1}{2}\left(\begin{array}{c}\text{number of electrons}\\\text{in bonding MOs}\end{array} - \begin{array}{c}\text{number of electrons}\\\text{in antibonding MOs}\end{array}\right) \quad (10.2)$$

The bond order indicates the approximate strength of a bond. For example, if there are two electrons in the bonding molecular orbital and none in the antibonding molecular orbital, the bond order is one, which means that there is one covalent bond and that the molecule is stable. Note that the bond order can be a fraction, but a bond order of zero (or a negative value) means the bond has no stability and the molecule cannot exist. Bond order can be used only qualitatively for purposes of comparison. For example, a bonding sigma molecular orbital with two electrons and a bonding pi molecular orbital with two electrons would each have a bond order of one. Yet, these two bonds must differ in bond strength (and bond length) because of the differences in the extent of atomic orbital overlap.

The quantitative measure of the strength of a bond is bond enthalpy (see Section 9.10).

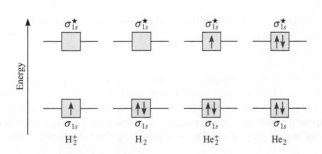

Figure 10.25 *Energy levels of the bonding and antibonding molecular orbitals in H_2^+, H_2, He_2^+, and He_2. In all these species, the molecular orbitals are formed by the interaction of two 1s orbitals.*

We are ready now to make predictions about the stability of H_2^+, H_2, He_2^+, and He_2 (see Figure 10.25). The H_2^+ molecular ion has only one electron in the σ_{1s} orbital. Because a covalent bond consists of two electrons in a bonding molecular orbital, H_2^+ has only half of one bond, or a bond order of $\frac{1}{2}$. Thus, we predict that the H_2^+ molecule may be a stable species. The electron configuration of H_2^+ is written as $(\sigma_{1s})^1$.

The superscript in $(\sigma_{1s})^1$ indicates that there is one electron in the sigma bonding molecular orbital.

The H_2 molecule has two electrons, both of which are in the σ_{1s} orbital. According to our scheme, two electrons equal one full bond; therefore, the H_2 molecule has a bond order of one, or one full covalent bond. The electron configuration of H_2 is $(\sigma_{1s})^2$.

As for the He_2^+ molecular ion, we place the first two electrons in the σ_{1s} orbital and the third electron in the $\sigma_{1s}^{\star}$ orbital. Because the antibonding molecular orbital is destabilizing, we expect He_2^+ to be less stable than H_2. Roughly speaking, the instability resulting from the electron in the $\sigma_{1s}^{\star}$ orbital is balanced by one of the σ_{1s} electrons. The bond order is $\frac{1}{2}(2 - 1) = \frac{1}{2}$ and the overall stability of He_2^+ is similar to that of the H_2^+ molecule. The electron configuration of He_2^+ is $(\sigma_{1s})^2(\sigma_{1s}^{\star})^1$.

In He_2 there would be two electrons in the σ_{1s} orbital and two electrons in the $\sigma_{1s}^{\star}$ orbital, so the molecule would have a bond order of zero and no net stability. The electron configuration of He_2 would be $(\sigma_{1s})^2(\sigma_{1s}^{\star})^2$.

To summarize, we can arrange our examples in order of decreasing stability:

$$H_2 > H_2^+, He_2^+ > He_2$$

We know that the hydrogen molecule is a stable species. Our simple molecular orbital method predicts that H_2^+ and He_2^+ also possess some stability, because both have bond orders of $\frac{1}{2}$. Indeed, their existence has been confirmed by experiment. It turns out that H_2^+ is somewhat more stable than He_2^+, because there is only one electron in the hydrogen molecular ion and therefore it has no electron-electron repulsion. Furthermore, H_2^+ also has less nuclear repulsion than He_2^+. Our prediction about He_2 is that it would have no stability, but in 1993 He_2 gas was found to exist. The "molecule" is extremely unstable and has only a transient existence under specially created conditions.

Review of Concepts

Estimate the bond enthalpy (kJ/mol) of the H_2^+ ion.

Homonuclear Diatomic Molecules of Second-Period Elements

We are now ready to study the ground-state electron configuration of molecules containing second-period elements. We will consider only the simplest case, that of **homonuclear diatomic molecules,** or *diatomic molecules containing atoms of the same elements.*

Figure 10.26 shows the molecular orbital energy level diagram for the first member of the second period, Li_2. These molecular orbitals are formed by the overlap of $1s$ and $2s$ orbitals. We will use this diagram to build up all the diatomic molecules, as we will see shortly.

The situation is more complex when the bonding also involves p orbitals. Two p orbitals can form either a sigma bond or a pi bond. Because there are three p orbitals for each atom of a second-period element, we know that one sigma and two pi molecular orbitals will result from the constructive interaction. The sigma molecular orbital is formed by the overlap of the $2p_x$ orbitals along the internuclear axis, that is, the

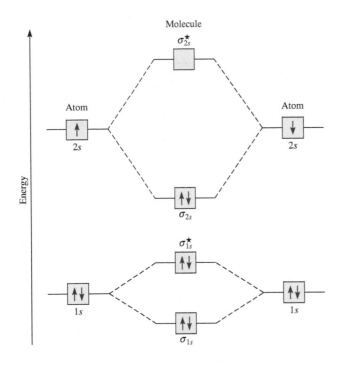

Molecule

Atom

Atom

Energy

Figure 10.26 *Molecular orbital energy level diagram for the Li$_2$ molecule. The six electrons in Li$_2$ (Li's electron configuration 1s^{2}2s^1) are in the σ_{1s}, $\sigma_{1s}^\star$, and σ_{2s} orbitals. Because there are two electrons each in σ_{1s} and $\sigma_{1s}^\star$ (just as in He$_2$), there is no net bonding or antibonding effect. Therefore, the single covalent bond in Li$_2$ is formed by the two electrons in the bonding molecular orbital σ_{2s}. Note that although the antibonding orbital ($\sigma_{1s}^\star$) has higher energy and is thus less stable than the bonding orbital (σ_{1s}), this antibonding orbital has less energy and greater stability than the σ_{2s} bonding orbital.*

x-axis. The $2p_y$ and $2p_z$ orbitals are perpendicular to the *x*-axis, and they will overlap sideways to give two pi molecular orbitals. The molecular orbitals are called σ_{2p_x}, π_{2p_y}, and π_{2p_z} orbitals, where the subscripts indicate which atomic orbitals take part in forming the molecular orbitals. As shown in Figure 10.24, overlap of the two *p* orbitals is normally greater in a σ molecular orbital than in a π molecular orbital, so we would expect the former to be lower in energy. However, the energies of molecular orbitals actually increase as follows:

$$\sigma_{1s} < \sigma_{1s}^\star < \sigma_{2s} < \sigma_{2s}^\star < \pi_{2p_y} = \pi_{2p_z} < \sigma_{2p_x} < \pi_{2p_y}^\star = \pi_{2p_z}^\star < \sigma_{2p_x}^\star$$

The inversion of the σ_{2p_x} orbital and the π_{2p_y} and π_{2p_z} orbitals is due to the interaction between the 2s orbital on one atom with the 2p orbital on the other. In MO terminology, we say there is mixing between these orbitals. The condition for mixing is that the 2s and 2p orbitals must be close in energy. This condition is met for the lighter molecules B$_2$, C$_2$, and N$_2$ with the result that the σ_{2p_x} orbital is raised in energy relative to the π_{2p_y} and π_{2p_z} orbitals as already shown. The mixing is less pronounced for O$_2$ and F$_2$ so the σ_{2p_x} orbital lies lower in energy than the π_{2p_y} and π_{2p_z} orbitals in these molecules.

With these concepts and Figure 10.27, which shows the order of increasing energies for 2p molecular orbitals, we can write the electron configurations and predict the magnetic properties and bond orders of second-period homonuclear diatomic molecules. We will consider a few examples.

The Lithium Molecule (Li$_2$)

The electron configuration of Li is 1s^{2}2s^1, so Li$_2$ has a total of six electrons. According to Figure 10.26, these electrons are placed (two each) in the σ_{1s}, $\sigma_{1s}^\star$, and σ_{2s} molecular orbitals. The electrons of σ_{1s} and $\sigma_{1s}^\star$ make no net contribution to the bonding in Li$_2$.

450   Chapter 10 ▪ Chemical Bonding II: Molecular Geometry and Hybridization of Atomic Orbitals

Figure 10.27 *General molecular orbital energy level diagram for the second-period homonuclear diatomic molecules Li_2, Be_2, B_2, C_2, and N_2. For simplicity, the σ_{1s} and σ_{2s} orbitals have been omitted. Note that in these molecules, the σ_{2p_x} orbital is higher in energy than either the π_{2p_y} or the π_{2p_z} orbitals. This means that electrons in the σ_{2p_x} orbitals are less stable than those in π_{2p_y} and π_{2p_z}. This abberation stems from the different interactions between the electrons in the σ_{2p_x} orbital, on one hand, and π_{2p_y} and π_{2p_z} orbitals, on the other hand, with the electrons in the lower-energy σ_s orbitals. For O_2 and F_2, the σ_{2p_x} orbital is lower in energy than π_{2p_y} and π_{2p_z}.*

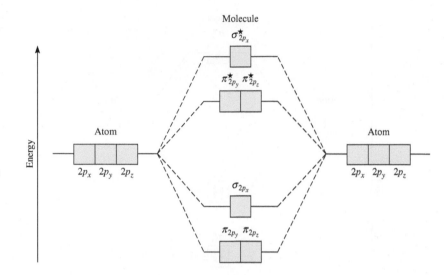

Thus, the electron configuration of the molecular orbitals in Li_2 is $(\sigma_{1s})^2(\sigma_{1s}^\star)^2(\sigma_{2s})^2$. Since there are two more electrons in the bonding molecular orbitals than in antibonding orbitals, the bond order is 1 [see Equation (10.2)]. We conclude that the Li_2 molecule is stable, and because it has no unpaired electron spins, it should be diamagnetic. Indeed, diamagnetic Li_2 molecules are known to exist in the vapor phase.

The Carbon Molecule (C_2)

The carbon atom has the electron configuration $1s^2 2s^2 2p^2$; thus, there are 12 electrons in the C_2 molecule. Referring to Figures 10.26 and 10.27, we place the last four electrons in the π_{2p_y} and π_{2p_z} orbitals. Therefore, C_2 has the electron configuration

$$(\sigma_{1s})^2(\sigma_{1s}^\star)^2(\sigma_{2s})^2(\sigma_{2s}^\star)^2(\pi_{2p_y})^2(\pi_{2p_z})^2$$

Its bond order is 2, and the molecule has no unpaired electrons. Again, diamagnetic C_2 molecules have been detected in the vapor state. Note that the double bonds in C_2 are both pi bonds because of the four electrons in the two pi molecular orbitals. In most other molecules, a double bond is made up of a sigma bond and a pi bond.

The Oxygen Molecule (O_2)

The ground-state electron configuration of O is $1s^2 2s^2 2p^4$; thus, there are 16 electrons in O_2. Using the order of increasing energies of the molecular orbitals discussed above, we write the ground-state electron configuration of O_2 as

$$(\sigma_{1s})^2(\sigma_{1s}^\star)^2(\sigma_{2s})^2(\sigma_{2s}^\star)^2(\sigma_{2p_x})^2(\pi_{2p_y})^2(\pi_{2p_z})^2(\pi_{2p_y}^\star)^1(\pi_{2p_z}^\star)^1$$

According to Hund's rule, the last two electrons enter the $\pi_{2p_y}^\star$ and $\pi_{2p_z}^\star$ orbitals with parallel spins. Ignoring the σ_{1s} and σ_{2s} orbitals (because their net effects on bonding are zero), we calculate the bond order of O_2 using Equation (10.2):

$$\text{bond order} = \tfrac{1}{2}(6 - 2) = 2$$

Therefore, the O_2 molecule has a bond order of 2 and oxygen is paramagnetic, a prediction that corresponds to experimental observations.

Table 10.5	Properties of Homonuclear Diatomic Molecules of the Second-Period Elements*						
	Li₂	**B₂**	**C₂**	**N₂**	**O₂**	**F₂**	
$\sigma^\star_{2p_x}$	☐	☐	☐	☐	☐	☐	$\sigma^\star_{2p_x}$
$\pi^\star_{2p_y}, \pi^\star_{2p_z}$	☐☐	☐☐	☐☐	☐☐	↑ ↑	↑↓ ↑↓	$\pi^\star_{2p_y}, \pi^\star_{2p_z}$
σ_{2p_x}	☐	☐	☐	↑↓	↑↓ ↑↓	↑↓ ↑↓	π_{2p_y}, π_{2p_z}
π_{2p_y}, π_{2p_z}	☐☐	↑ ↑	↑↓ ↑↓	↑↓ ↑↓	↑↓	↑↓	σ_{2p_x}
$\sigma^\star_{2s}$	☐	↑↓	↑↓	↑↓	↑↓	↑↓	$\sigma^\star_{2s}$
σ_{2s}	↑↓	↑↓	↑↓	↑↓	↑↓	↑↓	σ_{2s}
Bond order	1	1	2	3	2	1	
Bond length (pm)	267	159	131	110	121	142	
Bond enthalpy (kJ/mol)	104.6	288.7	627.6	941.4	498.7	156.9	
Magnetic properties	Diamagnetic	Paramagnetic	Diamagnetic	Diamagnetic	Paramagnetic	Diamagnetic	

*For simplicity the σ_{1s} and $\sigma^\star_{1s}$ orbitals are omitted. These two orbitals hold a total of four electrons. Remember that for O_2 and F_2, σ_{2p_x} is lower in energy than π_{2p_y} and π_{2p_z}.

Table 10.5 summarizes the general properties of the stable diatomic molecules of the second period.

Example 10.6 shows how MO theory can help predict molecular properties of ions.

Example 10.6

The N_2^+ ion can be prepared by bombarding the N_2 molecule with fast-moving electrons. Predict the following properties of N_2^+: (a) electron configuration, (b) bond order, (c) magnetic properties, and (d) bond length relative to the bond length of N_2 (is it longer or shorter?).

Strategy From Table 10.5 we can deduce the properties of ions generated from the homonuclear molecules. How does the stability of a molecule depend on the number of electrons in bonding and antibonding molecular orbitals? From what molecular orbital is an electron removed to form the N_2^+ ion from N_2? What properties determine whether a species is diamagnetic or paramagnetic?

Solution From Table 10.5 we can deduce the properties of ions generated from the homonuclear diatomic molecules.

(a) Because N_2^+ has one fewer electron than N_2, its electron configuration is

$$(\sigma_{1s})^2(\sigma^\star_{1s})^2(\sigma_{2s})^2(\sigma^\star_{2s})^2(\pi_{2p_y})^2(\pi_{2p_z})^2(\sigma_{2p_x})^1$$

(b) The bond order of N_2^+ is found by using Equation (10.2):

$$\text{bond order} = \tfrac{1}{2}(9 - 4) = 2.5$$

(c) N_2^+ has one unpaired electron, so it is paramagnetic.

(Continued)

(d) Because the electrons in the bonding molecular orbitals are responsible for holding the atoms together, N_2^+ should have a weaker and, therefore, longer bond than N_2. (In fact, the bond length of N_2^+ is 112 pm, compared with 110 pm for N_2.)

Check Because an electron is removed from a bonding molecular orbital, we expect the bond order to decrease. The N_2^+ ion has an odd number of electrons (13), so it should be paramagnetic.

Practice Exercise Which of the following species has a longer bond length: F_2 or F_2^-?

Similar problems: 10.57, 10.58.

10.8   Delocalized Molecular Orbitals

So far we have discussed chemical bonding only in terms of electron pairs. However, the properties of a molecule cannot always be explained accurately by a single structure. A case in point is the O_3 molecule, discussed in Section 9.8. There we overcame the dilemma by introducing the concept of resonance. In this section, we will tackle the problem in another way—by applying the molecular orbital approach. As in Section 9.8, we will use the benzene molecule and the carbonate ion as examples. Note that in discussing the bonding of polyatomic molecules or ions, it is convenient to determine first the hybridization state of the atoms present (a valence bond approach), followed by the formation of appropriate molecular orbitals.

The Benzene Molecule

Benzene (C_6H_6) is a planar hexagonal molecule with carbon atoms situated at the six corners. All carbon-carbon bonds are equal in length and strength, as are all carbon-hydrogen bonds, and the CCC and HCC angles are all 120°. Therefore, each carbon atom is sp^2-hybridized; it forms three sigma bonds with two adjacent carbon atoms and a hydrogen atom (Figure 10.28). This arrangement leaves an unhybridized $2p_z$ orbital on each carbon atom, perpendicular to the plane of the benzene molecule, or *benzene ring,* as it is often called. So far the description resembles the configuration of ethylene (C_2H_4), discussed in Section 10.5, except that in this case there are six unhybridized $2p_z$ orbitals in a cyclic arrangement.

Because of their similar shape and orientation, each $2p_z$ orbital overlaps two others, one on each adjacent carbon atom. According to the rules listed on p. 447, the interaction of six $2p_z$ orbitals leads to the formation of six pi molecular orbitals, of which three are bonding and three antibonding. A benzene molecule in the ground state therefore has six electrons in the three pi bonding molecular orbitals, two electrons with paired spins in each orbital (Figure 10.29).

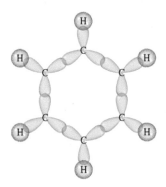

Figure 10.28 *The sigma bond framework in the benzene molecule. Each carbon atom is sp²-hybridized and forms sigma bonds with two adjacent carbon atoms and another sigma bond with a hydrogen atom.*

Figure 10.29 *(a) The six 2p_z orbitals on the carbon atoms in benzene. (b) The delocalized molecular orbital formed by the overlap of the 2p_z orbitals. The delocalized molecular orbital possesses pi symmetry and lies above and below the plane of the benzene ring. Actually, these 2p_z orbitals can combine in six different ways to yield three bonding molecular orbitals and three antibonding molecular orbitals. The one shown here is the most stable.*

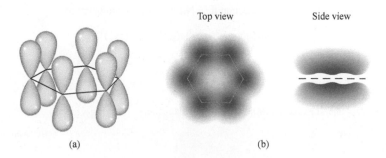

Top view   Side view

(a)   (b)

Unlike the pi bonding molecular orbitals in ethylene, those in benzene form **delocalized molecular orbitals,** which *are not confined between two adjacent bonding atoms, but actually extend over three or more atoms.* Therefore, electrons residing in any of these orbitals are free to move around the benzene ring. For this reason, the structure of benzene is sometimes represented as

in which the circle indicates that the pi bonds between carbon atoms are not confined to individual pairs of atoms; rather, the pi electron densities are evenly distributed throughout the benzene molecule. The carbon and hydrogen atoms are not shown in the simplified diagram.

We can now state that each carbon-to-carbon linkage in benzene contains a sigma bond and a "partial" pi bond. The bond order between any two adjacent carbon atoms is therefore between 1 and 2. Thus, molecular orbital theory offers an alternative to the resonance approach, which is based on valence bond theory. (The resonance structures of benzene are shown on p. 390.)

Electrostatic potential map of benzene shows the electron density (red color) above and below the plane of the molecule. For simplicity, only the framework of the molecule is shown.

The Carbonate Ion

Cyclic compounds like benzene are not the only ones with delocalized molecular orbitals. Let's look at bonding in the carbonate ion (CO_3^{2-}). VSEPR predicts a trigonal planar geometry for the carbonate ion, like that for BF_3. The planar structure of the carbonate ion can be explained by assuming that the carbon atom is sp^2-hybridized. The C atom forms sigma bonds with three O atoms. Thus, the unhybridized $2p_z$ orbital of the C atom can simultaneously overlap the $2p_z$ orbitals of all three O atoms (Figure 10.30). The result is a delocalized molecular orbital that extends over all four nuclei in such a way that the electron densities (and hence the bond orders) in the carbon-to-oxygen bonds are all the same. Molecular orbital theory therefore provides an acceptable alternative explanation of the properties of the carbonate ion as compared with the resonance structures of the ion shown on p. 390.

We should note that molecules with delocalized molecular orbitals are generally more stable than those containing molecular orbitals extending over only two atoms. For example, the benzene molecule, which contains delocalized molecular orbitals, is chemically less reactive (and hence more stable) than molecules containing "localized" C=C bonds, such as ethylene.

Review of Concepts

Describe the bonding in the nitrate ion (NO_3^-) in terms of resonance structures and delocalized molecular orbitals.

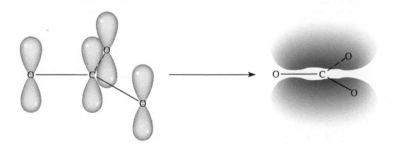

Figure 10.30 *Bonding in the carbonate ion. The carbon atom forms three sigma bonds with the three oxygen atoms. In addition, the $2p_z$ orbitals of the carbon and oxygen atoms overlap to form delocalized molecular orbitals, so that there is also a partial pi bond between the carbon atom and each of the three oxygen atoms.*

CHEMISTRY *in Action*

Buckyball, Anyone?

In 1985 chemists at Rice University in Texas used a high-powered laser to vaporize graphite in an effort to create unusual molecules believed to exist in interstellar space. Mass spectrometry revealed that one of the products was an unknown species with the formula C_{60}. Because of its size and the fact that it is pure carbon, this molecule has an exotic shape, which the researchers worked out using paper, scissors, and tape. Subsequent spectroscopic and X-ray measurements confirmed that C_{60} is shaped like a hollow sphere with a carbon atom at each of the 60 vertices. Geometrically, buckyball (short for "buckminsterfullerene") is the most symmetrical molecule known. In spite of its unique features, however, its bonding scheme is straightforward. Each carbon is sp^2-hybridized, and there are extensive delocalized molecular orbitals over the entire structure.

The discovery of buckyball generated tremendous interest within the scientific community. Here was a new allotrope of carbon with an intriguing geometry and unknown properties to investigate. Since 1985 chemists have created a whole class of *fullerenes,* with 70, 76, and even larger numbers of carbon atoms. Moreover, buckyball has been found to be a natural component of soot.

Buckyball and its heavier members represent a whole new concept in molecular architecture with far-reaching implications. For example, buckyball has been prepared with a helium atom trapped in its cage. Buckyball also reacts with potassium to give K_3C_{60}, which acts as a superconductor at 18 K. It is also possible

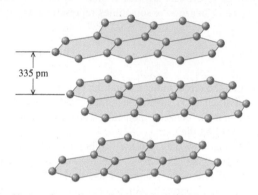

335 pm

Graphite is made up of layers of six-membered rings of carbon.

to attach transition metals to buckyball. These derivatives show promise as catalysts. Because of its unique shape, buckyball can be used as a lubricant.

One fascinating discovery, made in 1991 by Japanese scientists, was the identification of structural relatives of buckyball. These molecules are hundreds of nanometers long with a tubular shape and an internal cavity about 15 nm in diameter. Dubbed "buckytubes" or "nanotubes" (because of their size), these molecules have two distinctly different structures. One is a single sheet of graphite that is capped at both ends with a kind of truncated buckyball. The other is a scroll-like tube

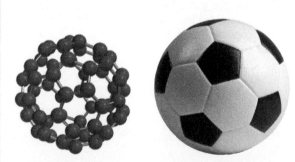

The geometry of a buckyball C_{60} (left) resembles a soccer ball (right). Scientists arrived at this structure by fitting together paper cutouts of enough hexagons and pentagons to accommodate 60 carbon atoms at the points where they intersect.

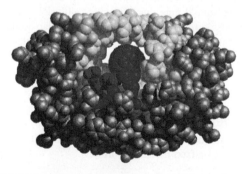

Computer-generated model of the binding of a buckyball derivative to the site of HIV-protease that normally attaches to a protein needed for the reproduction of HIV. The buckyball structure (purple color) fits tightly into the active site, thus preventing the enzyme from carrying out its function.

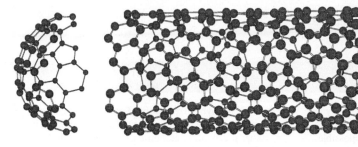

The structure of a buckytube that consists of a single layer of carbon atoms. Note that the truncated buckyball "cap," which has been separated from the rest of the buckytube in this view, has a different structure than the graphitelike cylindrical portion of the tube. Chemists have devised ways to open the cap in order to place other molecules inside the tube.

having anywhere from 2 to 30 graphitelike layers. Nanotubes are many times stronger than steel wires of similar dimensions. Numerous potential applications have been proposed for them, including conducting and high-strength materials, hydrogen storage media, molecular sensors, semiconductor devices, and molecular probes. The study of these materials has created a new field called *nanotechnology,* so called because scientists can manipulate materials on a molecular scale to create useful devices.

In the first biological application of buckyball, chemists at the University of California at San Francisco and Santa Barbara made a discovery in 1993 that could help in designing drugs to treat AIDS. The human immunodeficiency virus (HIV) that causes AIDS reproduces by synthesizing a long protein chain, which is cut into smaller segments by an enzyme called HIV-protease. One way to stop AIDS, then, might be to inactivate the enzyme. When the chemists reacted a water-soluble derivative of buckyball with HIV-protease, they found that it binds to the portion of the enzyme that would ordinarily cleave the reproductive protein, thereby preventing the HIV from reproducing. Consequently the virus could no longer infect the human cells they had grown in the laboratory. The buckyball compound itself is not a suitable drug for use against AIDS because of potential side effects and delivery difficulties, but it does provide a model for the development of such drugs.

In a recent development, scientists used a piece of adhesive tape (like Scotch tape) to peel off a flake of carbon from a piece of graphite (as is found in pencils) with the thickness of just one atom. This new-found material, called graphene, is a two-dimensional crystal with unusual electrical and optical properties. It is an excellent heat conductor. Graphene is

almost totally transparent yet the carbon atoms are packed so dense that not even helium, the smallest gaseous atom, can pass through it. It seems like many interesting and useful discoveries will come from the study of this unusual substance in the coming years.

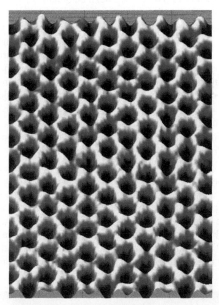

A micrograph of graphene showing honeycomb structure.

Key Equations

$\mu = Q \times r$ (10.1)   Expressing dipole moment in terms of charge (Q) and distance of separation (r) between charges.

$$\text{bond order} = \frac{1}{2}\left(\begin{array}{c}\text{number of electrons} \\ \text{in bonding MOs}\end{array} - \begin{array}{c}\text{number of electrons} \\ \text{in antibonding MOs}\end{array}\right) \text{ (10.2)}$$

Summary of Facts & Concepts

1. The VSEPR model for predicting molecular geometry is based on the assumption that valence-shell electron pairs repel one another and tend to stay as far apart as possible.

2. According to the VSEPR model, molecular geometry can be predicted from the number of bonding electron pairs and lone pairs. Lone pairs repel other pairs more forcefully than bonding pairs do and thus distort bond angles from the ideal geometry.

3. Dipole moment is a measure of the charge separation in molecules containing atoms of different electronegativities. The dipole moment of a molecule is the resultant of whatever bond moments are present. Information about molecular geometry can be obtained from dipole moment measurements.

4. There are two quantum mechanical explanations for covalent bond formation: valence bond theory and molecular orbital theory. In valence bond theory, hybridized atomic orbitals are formed by the combination and rearrangement of orbitals from the same atom. The hybridized orbitals are all of equal energy and electron density, and the number of hybridized orbitals is equal to the number of pure atomic orbitals that combine.

5. Valence-shell expansion can be explained by assuming hybridization of s, p, and d orbitals.

6. In sp hybridization, the two hybrid orbitals lie in a straight line; in sp^2 hybridization, the three hybrid orbitals are directed toward the corners of an equilateral triangle; in sp^3 hybridization, the four hybrid orbitals are directed toward the corners of a tetrahedron; in sp^3d hybridization, the five hybrid orbitals are directed toward the corners of a trigonal bipyramid; in sp^3d^2 hybridization, the six hybrid orbitals are directed toward the corners of an octahedron.

7. In an sp^2-hybridized atom (for example, carbon), the one unhybridized p orbital can form a pi bond with another p orbital. A carbon-carbon double bond consists of a sigma bond and a pi bond. In an sp-hybridized carbon atom, the two unhybridized p orbitals can form two pi bonds with two p orbitals on another atom (or atoms). A carbon-carbon triple bond consists of one sigma bond and two pi bonds.

8. Molecular orbital theory describes bonding in terms of the combination and rearrangement of atomic orbitals to form orbitals that are associated with the molecule as a whole.

9. Bonding molecular orbitals increase electron density between the nuclei and are lower in energy than individual atomic orbitals. Antibonding molecular orbitals have a region of zero electron density between the nuclei, and an energy level higher than that of the individual atomic orbitals.

10. We write electron configurations for molecular orbitals as we do for atomic orbitals, filling in electrons in the order of increasing energy levels. The number of molecular orbitals always equals the number of atomic orbitals that were combined. The Pauli exclusion principle and Hund's rule govern the filling of molecular orbitals.

11. Molecules are stable if the number of electrons in bonding molecular orbitals is greater than that in antibonding molecular orbitals.

12. Delocalized molecular orbitals, in which electrons are free to move around a whole molecule or group of atoms, are formed by electrons in p orbitals of adjacent atoms. Delocalized molecular orbitals are an alternative to resonance structures in explaining observed molecular properties.

Key Words

Antibonding molecular orbital, p. 444
Bond order, p. 447
Bonding molecular orbital, p. 444
Delocalized molecular orbital, p. 453

Dipole moment (μ), p. 423
Homonuclear diatomic molecule, p. 448
Hybrid orbital, p. 431
Hybridization, p. 432
Molecular orbital, p. 443
Nonpolar molecule, p. 424

Pi bond (π bond), p. 440
Pi molecular orbital, p. 445
Polar molecule, p. 424
Sigma bond (σ bond), p. 440
Sigma molecular orbital, p. 444
Valence shell, p. 413

Valence-shell electron-pair repulsion (VSEPR) model, p. 413

Questions & Problems

* Problems available in Connect Plus
Red numbered problems solved in Student Solutions Manual

Molecular Geometry
Review Questions

10.1   How is the geometry of a molecule defined and why is the study of molecular geometry important?

10.2   Sketch the shape of a linear triatomic molecule, a trigonal planar molecule containing four atoms, a tetrahedral molecule, a trigonal bipyramidal molecule, and an octahedral molecule. Give the bond angles in each case.

● 10.3   How many atoms are directly bonded to the central atom in a tetrahedral molecule, a trigonal bipyramidal molecule, and an octahedral molecule?

10.4   Discuss the basic features of the VSEPR model. Explain why the magnitude of repulsion decreases in the following order: lone pair-lone pair > lone pair-bonding pair > bonding pair-bonding pair.

10.5   In the trigonal bipyramidal arrangement, why does a lone pair occupy an equatorial position rather than an axial position?

10.6   The geometry of CH_4 could be square planar, with the four H atoms at the corners of a square and the C atom at the center of the square. Sketch this geometry and compare its stability with that of a tetrahedral CH_4 molecule.

Problems

● 10.7   Predict the geometries of the following species using the VSEPR method: (a) PCl_3, (b) $CHCl_3$, (c) SiH_4, (d) $TeCl_4$.

● **10.8**   Predict the geometries of the following species: (a) $AlCl_3$, (b) $ZnCl_2$, (c) $ZnCl_4^{2-}$.

● 10.9   Predict the geometry of the following molecules and ion using the VSEPR model: (a) CBr_4, (b) BCl_3, (c) NF_3, (d) H_2Se, (e) NO_2^-.

● **10.10**   Predict the geometry of the following molecules and ion using the VSEPR model: (a) CH_3I, (b) ClF_3, (c) H_2S, (d) SO_3, (e) SO_4^{2-}.

● 10.11   Predict the geometry of the following molecules using the VSEPR method: (a) $HgBr_2$, (b) N_2O (arrangement of atoms is NNO), (c) SCN^- (arrangement of atoms is SCN).

● **10.12**   Predict the geometries of the following ions: (a) NH_4^+, (b) NH_2^-, (c) CO_3^{2-}, (d) ICl_2^-, (e) ICl_4^-, (f) AlH_4^-, (g) $SnCl_5^-$, (h) H_3O^+, (i) BeF_4^{2-}.

● 10.13   Describe the geometry around each of the three central atoms in the CH_3COOH molecule.

● **10.14**   Which of the following species are tetrahedral? $SiCl_4$, SeF_4, XeF_4, CI_4, $CdCl_4^{2-}$

Dipole Moments
Review Questions

10.15   Define dipole moment. What are the units and symbol for dipole moment?

10.16   What is the relationship between the dipole moment and the bond moment? How is it possible for a molecule to have bond moments and yet be nonpolar?

10.17   Explain why an atom cannot have a permanent dipole moment.

10.18   The bonds in beryllium hydride (BeH_2) molecules are polar, and yet the dipole moment of the molecule is zero. Explain.

Problems

● 10.19   Referring to Table 10.3, arrange the following molecules in order of increasing dipole moment: H_2O, H_2S, H_2Te, H_2Se.

10.20   The dipole moments of the hydrogen halides decrease from HF to HI (see Table 10.3). Explain this trend.

● 10.21   List the following molecules in order of increasing dipole moment: H_2O, CBr_4, H_2S, HF, NH_3, CO_2.

10.22   Does the molecule OCS have a higher or lower dipole moment than CS_2?

● 10.23   Which of the following molecules has a higher dipole moment?

(a)   (b)

● **10.24**   Arrange the following compounds in order of increasing dipole moment:

(a)   (b)   (c)   (d)

Valence Bond Theory
Review Questions

10.25   What is valence bond theory? How does it differ from the Lewis concept of chemical bonding?

10.26   Use valence bond theory to explain the bonding in Cl_2 and HCl. Show how the atomic orbitals overlap when a bond is formed.

10.27   Draw a potential energy curve for the bond formation in F_2.

Hybridization

Review Questions

10.28   (a) What is the hybridization of atomic orbitals? Why is it impossible for an isolated atom to exist in the hybridized state? (b) How does a hybrid orbital differ from a pure atomic orbital? Can two $2p$ orbitals of an atom hybridize to give two hybridized orbitals?

10.29   What is the angle between the following two hybrid orbitals on the same atom? (a) sp and sp hybrid orbitals, (b) sp^2 and sp^2 hybrid orbitals, (c) sp^3 and sp^3 hybrid orbitals

10.30   How would you distinguish between a sigma bond and a pi bond?

Problems

● 10.31   Describe the bonding scheme of the AsH_3 molecule in terms of hybridization.

● 10.32   What is the hybridization state of Si in SiH_4 and in H_3Si—SiH_3?

● 10.33   Describe the change in hybridization (if any) of the Al atom in the following reaction:

$$AlCl_3 + Cl^- \longrightarrow AlCl_4^-$$

● 10.34   Consider the reaction

$$BF_3 + NH_3 \longrightarrow F_3B\!-\!NH_3$$

Describe the changes in hybridization (if any) of the B and N atoms as a result of this reaction.

● 10.35   What hybrid orbitals are used by nitrogen atoms in the following species? (a) NH_3, (b) H_2N—NH_2, (c) NO_3^-

● 10.36   What are the hybrid orbitals of the carbon atoms in the following molecules?
(a) H_3C—CH_3
(b) H_3C—CH=CH_2
(c) CH_3—C≡C—CH_2OH
(d) CH_3CH=O
(e) CH_3COOH

● 10.37   Specify which hybrid orbitals are used by carbon atoms in the following species: (a) CO, (b) CO_2, (c) CN^-.

● 10.38   What is the hybridization state of the central N atom in the azide ion, N_3^-? (Arrangement of atoms: NNN.)

● 10.39   The allene molecule H_2C=C=CH_2 is linear (the three C atoms lie on a straight line). What are the hybridization states of the carbon atoms? Draw

diagrams to show the formation of sigma bonds and pi bonds in allene.

● 10.40   Describe the hybridization of phosphorus in PF_5.

● 10.41   How many sigma bonds and pi bonds are there in each of the following molecules?

(a)   (b)   (c)

● 10.42   How many pi bonds and sigma bonds are there in the tetracyanoethylene molecule?

● 10.43   Give the formula of a cation comprised of iodine and fluorine in which the iodine atom is sp^3d-hybridized.

10.44   Give the formula of an anion comprised of iodine and fluorine in which the iodine atom is sp^3d^2-hybridized.

Molecular Orbital Theory

Review Questions

10.45   What is molecular orbital theory? How does it differ from valence bond theory?

10.46   Sketch the shapes of the following molecular orbitals: σ_{1s}, $\sigma_{1s}^{\star}$, π_{2p}, and $\pi_{2p}^{\star}$. How do their energies compare?

10.47   Compare the Lewis theory, valence bond theory, and molecular orbital theory of chemical bonding.

10.48   Explain the significance of bond order. Can bond order be used for quantitative comparisons of the strengths of chemical bonds?

Problems

10.49   Explain in molecular orbital terms the changes in H—H internuclear distance that occur as the molecular H_2 is ionized first to H_2^+ and then to H_2^{2+}.

10.50   The formation of H_2 from two H atoms is an energetically favorable process. Yet statistically there is less than a 100 percent chance that any two H atoms will undergo the reaction. Apart from energy considerations, how would you account for this observation based on the electron spins in the two H atoms?

● 10.51   Draw a molecular orbital energy level diagram for each of the following species: He_2, HHe, He_2^+. Compare their relative stabilities in terms of bond orders. (Treat HHe as a diatomic molecule with three electrons.)

10.52 Arrange the following species in order of increasing stability: Li_2, Li_2^+, Li_2^-. Justify your choice with a molecular orbital energy level diagram.

10.53 Use molecular orbital theory to explain why the Be_2 molecule does not exist.

10.54 Which of these species has a longer bond, B_2 or B_2^+? Explain in terms of molecular orbital theory.

10.55 Acetylene (C_2H_2) has a tendency to lose two protons (H^+) and form the carbide ion (C_2^{2-}), which is present in a number of ionic compounds, such as CaC_2 and MgC_2. Describe the bonding scheme in the C_2^{2-} ion in terms of molecular orbital theory. Compare the bond order in C_2^{2-} with that in C_2.

10.56 Compare the Lewis and molecular orbital treatments of the oxygen molecule.

10.57 Explain why the bond order of N_2 is greater than that of N_2^+, but the bond order of O_2 is less than that of O_2^+.

10.58 Compare the relative stability of the following species and indicate their magnetic properties (that is, diamagnetic or paramagnetic): O_2, O_2^+, O_2^- (superoxide ion), O_2^{2-} (peroxide ion).

10.59 Use molecular orbital theory to compare the relative stabilities of F_2 and F_2^+.

10.60 A single bond is almost always a sigma bond, and a double bond is almost always made up of a sigma bond and a pi bond. There are very few exceptions to this rule. Show that the B_2 and C_2 molecules are examples of the exceptions.

10.61 In 2009 the ion N_2^{3-} was isolated. Use a molecular orbital diagram to compare its properties (bond order and magnetism) with the isoelectronic ion O_2^-.

10.62 The following potential energy curve represents the formation of F_2 from two F atoms. Describe the state of bonding at the marked regions.

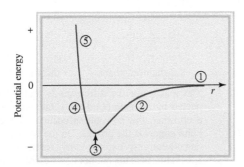

Delocalized Molecular Orbitals
Review Questions

10.63 How does a delocalized molecular orbital differ from a molecular orbital such as that found in H_2 or C_2H_4? What do you think are the minimum conditions (for example, number of atoms and types of orbitals) for forming a delocalized molecular orbital?

10.64 In Chapter 9 we saw that the resonance concept is useful for dealing with species such as the benzene molecule and the carbonate ion. How does molecular orbital theory deal with these species?

Problems

10.65 Both ethylene (C_2H_4) and benzene (C_6H_6) contain the C=C bond. The reactivity of ethylene is greater than that of benzene. For example, ethylene readily reacts with molecular bromine, whereas benzene is normally quite inert toward molecular bromine and many other compounds. Explain this difference in reactivity.

10.66 Explain why the symbol on the left is a better representation of benzene molecules than that on the right.

10.67 Determine which of these molecules has a more delocalized orbital and justify your choice.

(*Hint:* Both molecules contain two benzene rings. In naphthalene, the two rings are fused together. In biphenyl, the two rings are joined by a single bond, around which the two rings can rotate.)

10.68 Nitryl fluoride (FNO_2) is very reactive chemically. The fluorine and oxygen atoms are bonded to the nitrogen atom. (a) Write a Lewis structure for FNO_2. (b) Indicate the hybridization of the nitrogen atom. (c) Describe the bonding in terms of molecular orbital theory. Where would you expect delocalized molecular orbitals to form?

10.69 Describe the bonding in the nitrate ion NO_3^- in terms of delocalized molecular orbitals.

10.70 What is the state of hybridization of the central O atom in O_3? Describe the bonding in O_3 in terms of delocalized molecular orbitals.

Additional Problems

10.71 Which of the following species is not likely to have a tetrahedral shape? (a) $SiBr_4$, (b) NF_4^+, (c) SF_4, (d) $BeCl_4^{2-}$, (e) BF_4^-, (f) $AlCl_4^-$

10.72 Draw the Lewis structure of mercury(II) bromide. Is this molecule linear or bent? How would you establish its geometry?

10.73 Sketch the bond moments and resultant dipole moments for the following molecules: H_2O, PCl_3, XeF_4, PCl_5, SF_6.

460   Chapter 10 ▪ Chemical Bonding II: Molecular Geometry and Hybridization of Atomic Orbitals

10.74 Although both carbon and silicon are in Group 4A, very few Si=Si bonds are known. Account for the instability of silicon-to-silicon double bonds in general. (*Hint:* Compare the atomic radii of C and Si in Figure 8.5. What effect would the larger size have on pi bond formation?)

10.75 Acetaminophen is the active ingredient in Tylenol. (a) Write the molecular formula of the compound. (b) What is the hybridization state of each C, N, and O atom? (c) Describe the geometry about each C, N, and O atom.

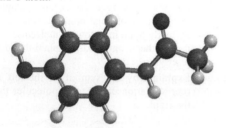

10.76 Caffeine is a stimulant drug present in coffee. (a) Write the molecular formula of the compound. (b) What is the hybridization state of each C, N, and O atom? (c) Describe the geometry about each C, N, and O atom.

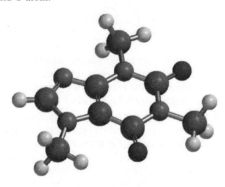

● **10.77** Predict the geometry of sulfur dichloride (SCl_2) and the hybridization of the sulfur atom.

● **10.78** Antimony pentafluoride, SbF_5, reacts with XeF_4 and XeF_6 to form ionic compounds, $XeF_3^+SbF_6^-$ and $XeF_5^+SbF_6^-$. Describe the geometries of the cations and anion in these two compounds.

● **10.79** Draw Lewis structures and give the other information requested for the following molecules: (a) BF_3. Shape: planar or nonplanar? (b) ClO_3^-. Shape: planar or nonplanar? (c) H_2O. Show the direction of the resultant dipole moment. (d) OF_2. Polar or nonpolar molecule? (e) NO_2. Estimate the ONO bond angle.

● **10.80** Predict the bond angles for the following molecules: (a) $BeCl_2$, (b) BCl_3, (c) CCl_4, (d) CH_3Cl, (e) Hg_2Cl_2 (arrangement of atoms: ClHgHgCl), (f) $SnCl_2$, (g) H_2O_2, (h) SnH_4.

10.81 Briefly compare the VSEPR and hybridization approaches to the study of molecular geometry.

● **10.82** Describe the hybridization state of arsenic in arsenic pentafluoride (AsF_5).

● **10.83** Draw Lewis structures and give the other information requested for the following: (a) SO_3. Polar or nonpolar molecule? (b) PF_3. Polar or nonpolar molecule? (c) F_3SiH. Show the direction of the resultant dipole moment. (d) SiH_3^-. Planar or pyramidal shape? (e) Br_2CH_2. Polar or nonpolar molecule?

● **10.84** Which of the following molecules and ions are linear? ICl_2^-, IF_2^+, OF_2, SnI_2, $CdBr_2$

● **10.85** Draw the Lewis structure for the $BeCl_4^{2-}$ ion. Predict its geometry and describe the hybridization state of the Be atom.

● **10.86** The N_2F_2 molecule can exist in either of the following two forms:

$$\underset{F}{\nearrow}N{=}N\underset{\searrow F}{}\qquad\underset{F}{}\overset{F}{\searrow}N{=}N\overset{F}{\nearrow}$$

(a) What is the hybridization of N in the molecule?

(b) Which structure has a dipole moment?

10.87 Cyclopropane (C_3H_6) has the shape of a triangle in which a C atom is bonded to two H atoms and two other C atoms at each corner. Cubane (C_8H_8) has the shape of a cube in which a C atom is bonded to one H atom and three other C atoms at each corner. (a) Draw Lewis structures of these molecules. (b) Compare the CCC angles in these molecules with those predicted for an sp^3-hybridized C atom. (c) Would you expect these molecules to be easy to make?

10.88 The compound 1,2-dichloroethane ($C_2H_4Cl_2$) is nonpolar, while *cis*-dichloroethylene ($C_2H_2Cl_2$) has a dipole moment:

$$\begin{array}{cc}\underset{H}{\overset{Cl}{|}}\ \underset{H}{\overset{Cl}{|}}\\ H{-}C{-}C{-}H\\ \underset{}{\overset{}{|}}\ \underset{}{\overset{}{|}}\end{array}\qquad\underset{H}{\overset{Cl}{\diagdown}}C{=}C\underset{H}{\overset{Cl}{\diagup}}$$

1,2-dichloroethane   *cis*-dichloroethylene

The reason for the difference is that groups connected by a single bond can rotate with respect to each other, but no rotation occurs when a double bond connects the groups. On the basis of bonding considerations, explain why rotation occurs in 1,2-dichloroethane but not in *cis*-dichloroethylene.

● **10.89** Does the following molecule have a dipole moment?

$$\underset{H}{\overset{Cl}{\diagdown}}C{=}C{=}C\underset{Cl}{\overset{H}{\diagup}}$$

(*Hint:* See the answer to Problem 10.39.)

• **10.90** So-called greenhouse gases, which contribute to global warming, have a dipole moment or can be bent or distorted into shapes that have a dipole moment. Which of the following gases are greenhouse gases? N_2, O_2, O_3, CO, CO_2, NO_2, N_2O, CH_4, $CFCl_3$

10.91 The bond angle of SO_2 is very close to 120°, even though there is a lone pair on S. Explain.

10.92 3'-azido-3'-deoxythymidine, shown here, commonly known as AZT, is one of the drugs used to treat acquired immune deficiency syndrome (AIDS). What are the hybridization states of the C and N atoms in this molecule?

• **10.93** The following molecules (AX_4Y_2) all have octahedral geometry. Group the molecules that are equivalent to each other.

(a)   (b)

(c)   (d)

10.94 The compounds carbon tetrachloride (CCl_4) and silicon tetrachloride ($SiCl_4$) are similar in geometry and hybridization. However, CCl_4 does not react with water but $SiCl_4$ does. Explain the difference in their chemical reactivities. (*Hint:* The first step of the reaction is believed to be the addition of a water molecule to the Si atom in $SiCl_4$.)

• **10.95** Write the ground-state electron configuration for B_2. Is the molecule diamagnetic or paramagnetic?

• **10.96** What are the hybridization states of the C and N atoms in this molecule?

10.97 Use molecular orbital theory to explain the difference between the bond enthalpies of F_2 and F_2^- (see Problem 9.110).

10.98 Referring to the Chemistry in Action essay on p. 426, answer the following questions: (a) If you wanted to cook a roast (beef or lamb), would you use a microwave oven or a conventional oven? (b) Radar is a means of locating an object by measuring the time for the echo of a microwave from the object to return to the source and the direction from which it returns. Would radar work if oxygen, nitrogen, and carbon dioxide were polar molecules? (c) In early tests of radar at the English Channel during World War II, the results were inconclusive even though there was no equipment malfunction. Why? (*Hint:* The weather is often foggy in the region.)

10.99 Which of the following molecules are polar?

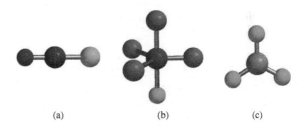

(a)   (b)   (c)

10.100 Which of the following molecules are polar?

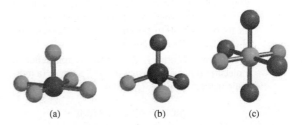

(a)   (b)   (c)

10.101 The stable allotropic form of phosphorus is P_4, in which each P atom is bonded to three other P atoms. Draw a Lewis structure of this molecule and describe its geometry. At high temperatures, P_4 dissociates to form P_2 molecules containing a P=P bond. Explain why P_4 is more stable than P_2.

462   **Chapter 10** • Chemical Bonding II: Molecular Geometry and Hybridization of Atomic Orbitals

10.102 Referring to Table 9.4, explain why the bond enthalpy for Cl_2 is greater than that for F_2. (*Hint:* The bond lengths of F_2 and Cl_2 are 142 pm and 199 pm, respectively.)

10.103 Use molecular orbital theory to explain the bonding in the azide ion (N_3^-). (Arrangement of atoms is NNN.)

• 10.104 The ionic character of the bond in a diatomic molecule can be estimated by the formula

$$\frac{\mu}{ed} \times 100\%$$

where μ is the experimentally measured dipole moment (in C m), e the electronic charge, and d the bond length in meters. (The quantity ed is the hypothetical dipole moment for the case in which the transfer of an electron from the less electronegative to the more electronegative atom is complete.) Given that the dipole moment and bond length of HF are 1.92 D and 91.7 pm, respectively, calculate the percent ionic character of the molecule.

• 10.105 Draw three Lewis structures for compounds with the formula $C_2H_2F_2$. Indicate which of the compound(s) are polar.

10.106 Greenhouse gases absorb (and trap) outgoing infrared radiation (heat) from Earth and contribute to global warming. The molecule of a greenhouse gas either possesses a permanent dipole moment or has a changing dipole moment during its vibrational motions. Consider three of the vibrational modes of carbon dioxide

$$\overleftarrow{O}=C=\overrightarrow{O} \qquad \overrightarrow{O}=\overleftarrow{C}=\overrightarrow{O} \qquad \overset{\uparrow}{O}=C=\underset{\downarrow}{O}$$

where the arrows indicate the movement of the atoms. (During a complete cycle of vibration, the atoms move toward one extreme position and then reverse their direction to the other extreme position.) Which of the preceding vibrations are responsible for CO_2 to behave as a greenhouse gas? Which of the following molecules can act as a greenhouse gas: N_2, O_2, CO, NO_2, and N_2O?

• 10.107 Aluminum trichloride ($AlCl_3$) is an electron-deficient molecule. It has a tendency to form a dimer (a molecule made of two $AlCl_3$ units):

$$AlCl_3 + AlCl_3 \rightarrow Al_2Cl_6$$

(a) Draw a Lewis structure for the dimer. (b) Describe the hybridization state of Al in $AlCl_3$ and Al_2Cl_6. (c) Sketch the geometry of the dimer. (d) Do these molecules possess a dipole moment?

10.108 The molecules *cis*-dichloroethylene and *trans*-dichloroethylene shown on p. 425 can be interconverted

by heating or irradiation. (a) Starting with *cis*-dichloroethylene, show that rotating the C=C bond by 180° will break only the pi bond but will leave the sigma bond intact. Explain the formation of *trans*-dichloroethylene from this process. (Treat the rotation as two stepwise 90° rotations.) (b) Account for the difference in the bond enthalpies for the pi bond (about 270 kJ/mol) and the sigma bond (about 350 kJ/mol). (c) Calculate the longest wavelength of light needed to bring about this conversion.

10.109 Progesterone is a hormone responsible for female sex characteristics. In the usual shorthand structure, each point where lines meet represent a C atom, and most H atoms are not shown. Draw the complete structure of the molecule, showing all C and H atoms. Indicate which C atoms are sp^2- and sp^3-hybridized.

• 10.110 For each pair listed here, state which one has a higher first ionization energy and explain your choice: (a) H or H_2, (b) N or N_2, (c) O or O_2, (d) F or F_2.

• 10.111 The molecule benzyne (C_6H_4) is a very reactive species. It resembles benzene in that it has a six-membered ring of carbon atoms. Draw a Lewis structure of the molecule and account for the molecule's high reactivity.

• 10.112 Assume that the third-period element phosphorus forms a diatomic molecule, P_2, in an analogous way as nitrogen does to form N_2. (a) Write the electronic configuration for P_2. Use $[Ne_2]$ to represent the electron configuration for the first two periods. (b) Calculate its bond order. (c) What are its magnetic properties (diamagnetic or paramagnetic)?

10.113 Consider a N_2 molecule in its first excited electronic state; that is, when an electron in the highest occupied molecular orbital is promoted to the lowest empty molecular orbital. (a) Identify the molecular orbitals involved and sketch a diagram to show the transition. (b) Compare the bond order and bond length of N_2^* with N_2, where the asterisk denotes the excited molecule. (c) Is N_2^* diamagnetic or paramagnetic? (d) When N_2^* loses its excess energy and converts to the ground state N_2, it emits a photon of wavelength 470 nm, which makes up part of the auroras lights. Calculate the energy difference between these levels.

10.114 As mentioned in the chapter, the Lewis structure for O_2 is

$$\overset{..}{O}=\overset{..}{O}$$

Use the molecular orbital theory to show that the structure actually corresponds to an excited state of the oxygen molecule.

10.115 Referring to Problem 9.137, describe the hybridization state of the N atoms and the overall shape of the ion.

10.116 Describe the geometry and hybridization for the reactants and product in the following reaction

$$ClF_3 + AsF_5 \longrightarrow [ClF_2^+][AsF_6^-]$$

10.117 Draw the Lewis structure of ketene (C_2H_2O) and describe the hybridization states of the C atoms. The molecule does not contain O—H bonds. On separate diagrams, sketch the formation of sigma and pi bonds.

10.118 TCDD, or 2,3,7,8-tetrachlorodibenzo-p-dioxin, is a highly toxic compound

It gained considerable notoriety in 2004 when it was implicated in the murder plot of a Ukrainian politician. (a) Describe its geometry and state whether the molecule has a dipole moment. (b) How many pi bonds and sigma bonds are there in the molecule?

10.119 Write the electron configuration of the cyanide ion (CN^-). Name a stable molecule that is isoelectronic with the ion.

10.120 Carbon monoxide (CO) is a poisonous compound due to its ability to bind strongly to Fe^{2+} in the hemoglobin molecule. The molecular orbitals of CO have the same energy order as those of the N_2 molecule. (a) Draw a Lewis structure of CO and assign formal charges. Explain why CO has a rather small dipole moment of 0.12 D. (b) Compare the bond order of CO with that from molecular orbital theory. (c) Which of the atoms (C or O) is more likely to form bonds with the Fe^{2+} ion in hemoglobin?

10.121 The geometries discussed in this chapter all lend themselves to fairly straightforward elucidation of bond angles. The exception is the tetrahedron, because its bond angles are hard to visualize. Consider the CCl_4 molecule, which has a tetrahedral geometry and is nonpolar. By equating the bond moment of a particular C—Cl bond to the resultant bond moments of the other three C—Cl bonds in opposite directions, show that the bond angles are all equal to 109.5°.

10.122 Carbon suboxide (C_3O_2) is a colorless pungent-smelling gas. Does it possess a dipole moment?

10.123 Which of the following ions possess a dipole moment? (a) ClF_2^+, (b) ClF_2^-, (c) IF_4^+, (d) IF_4^-.

10.124 Given that the order of molecular orbitals for NO is similar to that for O_2, arrange the following species in increasing bond orders: NO^{2-}, NO^-, NO, NO^+, NO^{2+}.

Interpreting, Modeling & Estimating

10.125 Shown here are molecular models of SX_4 for X = F, Cl, and Br. Comment on the trends in the bond angle between the axial S—X bonds in these molecules.

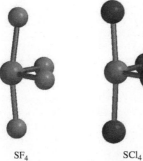

SF₄   SCl₄   SBr₄

10.126 Based on what you have learned from this chapter and Chapter 9, name a diatomic molecule that has the strongest known chemical bond and one with the weakest known chemical bond.

10.127 The stability of benzene is due to the fact that we can draw reasonable resonance structures for the molecule, which is equivalent to saying that there is electron delocalization. *Resonance energy* is a measure of how much more stable benzene is compared to the hypothetical molecule, which can be represented by just a single resonance structure. Shown on p. 464 are the enthalpies of hydrogenation (the addition of hydrogen) of cyclohexene (C_6H_{10}) to cyclohexane (C_6H_{12}) and benzene to cyclohexane.

464   **Chapter 10** ▪ Chemical Bonding II: Molecular Geometry and Hybridization of Atomic Orbitals

$$\Delta H° = -120 \text{ kJ/mol}$$

$$\Delta H° = -208 \text{ kJ/mol}$$

(In these simplified structures, each point where lines meet represents a C atom. There is a H atom

attached to a sp^2-hybridized C atom and there are two H atoms attached to a sp^3-hybridized C atom.) Estimate the resonance energy of benzene from these data.

10.128 How many carbon atoms are contained in one square centimeter of graphene (see the Chemistry in Action essay on p. 454 for a description of graphene)? What would be the mass of a 1-cm² section of graphene?

Answers to Practice Exercises

10.1 (a) Tetrahedral, (b) linear, (c) trigonal planar. **10.2** No. **10.3** (a) sp^3, (b) sp^2. **10.4** sp^3d^2. **10.5** The C atom is sp-hybridized. It forms a sigma bond with the H atom and another sigma bond with the N atom. The two unhybridized p orbitals on the C atom are used to form two pi bonds with the N atom. The lone pair on the N atom is placed in the sp orbital. **10.6** F_2^-.

Photo Credits

Front Matter

p. iii (top): Courtesy Margaret A. Chang; p. iii (bottom): Courtesy Nancy Goldsby; p. v: © Robert R. Johnson, Institute for Computational Molecular Science, Temple University; p. vi (top): © Mary Evans/Science Source; p. vi (bottom): © Derek Croucher/Alamy; p. vii (top): © OAR/ National Undersea Research Program (NURP)/ NOAA; p. vii (bottom): NASA; p. viii (top): © Sandia National Laboratories; p. viii (bottom): © Neil Setchfield/Alamy; p. ix (top): © SPL/ Science Source; p. ix (bottom): © Science Source; p. x (top): © Dr. Tim Evans/Science Source; p. x (bottom): © Layne Kennedy/ Corbis/Getty Images; p. xi: © Richard Megna/ Fundamental Photographs; p. xii (top): © U.S. Marine Corps photo by Lance Cpl. Ronald Stauffer; p. xii (center): © Michel Gangne/AFP/Getty Images; p. xii (bottom): © The McGraw-Hill Companies, Inc./Jill Braaten, photographer; p. xiii: © Robert Hoetink/ Alamy; p. xiv (top): © Feng Wei Photography/ Getty Images; p. xiv (bottom): © Sheila Terry/ Science Source; p. xv (top): © CERN/Fabienne Marcastel; p. xv (bottom): © View Stock RF/ age fotostock; p. xvi (top): © James L. Dye; p. xvi (bottom): © NASA/Science Source; p. xvii (top): © J. D. Barrie and C. H. Barrie, Jr.; p. xvii (bottom): © Jeff Gilbert/Alamy; p. xviii: Image courtesy of the Michigan Nonotechnology Institute for Medicine and Biological Sciences.

Chapter 1

Opener: © Robert R. Johnson, Institute for Computational Molecular Science, Temple University; 1.1a: © Jean Claude Revy/Phototake; 1.1b: Courtesy Richard B. Kaner; 1.1c: © David Parker/Seagate/ Science Source; 1.1d: Courtesy, Dr. Milt Gordon; 1.2: © B.A.E. Inc./Alamy; p. 6: © 2012 CERN, for the benefit of the CMS Collaboration (License: CC-BY-SA-4.0). Image courtesy Thomas McCauley and Lucas Taylor; 1.4a: © McGraw-Hill Higher Education Inc./Ken Karp, Photographer; 1.4b: © McGraw-Hill Higher Education Inc./Ken Karp, Photographer; 1.7: © Fritz Goro/Time & Life Pictures/Getty Images; p. 11: © McGraw-Hill Higher Education Inc./Ken Karp, Photographer; p. 13 (top): NASA; 1.9: BIPM (International Bureau of Weights and Measures/Bureau International des Poids et Mesures, www.bipm.org); p. 15 (top): © Tetra Images/Getty Images; p. 15 (bottom): © McGraw-Hill Higher Education Inc./Stephen Frisch, Photographer; p. 16: © iStockphoto/ Getty Images; p. 17: NASA/JPL-Caltech; 1.12: © James A. Prince/Science Source; p. 25: © Leonard Lessin/Science Source; p. 26: © Charles Falco/Science Source; p. 27: © Charles D. Winters/Science Source; p. 36: © Chris Butler/Science Photo Library/Science Source.

Chapter 2

Opener: © Mary Evans/Science Source; 2.4 (all): © The McGraw-Hill Companies, Inc./ Charles D. Winters/Timeframe Photography, Inc.; p. 45: © The Image Bank/Getty Images; 2.13 (c): © Charles D. Winters/Science Source; p. 54 (top): © Andrew Lambert/Science Source; p. 55: © 2009 George Resch/Fundamental Photographs; p. 57: © McGraw-Hill Higher Education Inc./Ken Karp, Photographer; 2.16: © McGraw-Hill Higher Education Inc./Ken Karp, Photographer.

Chapter 3

Opener: © Derek Croucher/Alamy; p. 77: © The McGraw-Hill Companies, Inc./Stephen Frisch, photographer; 3.1: © McGraw-Hill Higher Education Inc./Stephen Frisch, Photographer; p. 79: Courtesy National Scientific Balloon Facility/Palestine, Texas; p. 80: © Charles D. Winters/Science Source; p. 82: © Steve Allen/Getty Images RF; p. 83: © McGraw-Hill Higher Education Inc./Ken Karp, Photographer; p. 87: © The Natural History Museum/Alamy; p. 93: © McGraw-Hill Higher Education Inc./Ken Karp, Photographer; p. 98: © McGraw-Hill Higher Education Inc./Ken Karp, Photographer; p. 104: © Super Stock/age fotostock; p. 105: © Glyn Thomas/Alamy.

Chapter 4

Opener: © OAR/National Undersea Research Program (NURP)/NOAA; 4.1 (all): © McGraw-Hill Higher Education Inc./Ken Karp, Photographer; 4.3: © McGraw-Hill Higher Education Inc./ Charles Winter, Photographer; 4.4: © McGraw-Hill Higher Education Inc./Ken Karp, Photographer; 4.5: © McGraw-Hill Higher Education Inc./Charles Winter, Photographer; p. 124 (bottom): © McGraw-Hill Higher Education Inc./Ken Karp, Photographer; p. 126: © Sheila Terry/Science Source; 4.6: © McGraw-Hill Higher Education Inc./Ken Karp, Photographer; p. 129: © McGraw-Hill Higher Education Inc./Ken Karp, Photographer; 4.9, 4.10 (both), 4.12a: © McGraw-Hill Higher Education Inc./Ken Karp, Photographer; 4.12b: © Charles D. Winters/Science Source; 4.12c: © McGraw-Hill Higher Education Inc./Ken Karp, Photographer; 4.13a: © McGraw-Hill Higher Education Inc./Charles Winter, Photographer; 4.13b, 4.14a-b: © McGraw-Hill Higher Education Inc./Ken Karp, Photographer; 4.15a-c: © McGraw-Hill Higher Education Inc./Stephen Frisch, Photographer; 4.17: © Mula & Haramaty/Phototake; p. 144: © Jim Varney/Science Source; p. 146–147, 4.20a–c: © McGraw-Hill Higher Education Inc./Ken Karp, Photographer; p. 152 (top): © McGraw-Hill Higher Education Inc./Ken Karp, Photographer; 4.21a-b: © McGraw-Hill Higher Education Inc./Ken Karp, Photographer; 4.22:

© McGraw-Hill Higher Education Inc./Ken Karp, Photographer; p. 155 (bottom): © McGraw-Hill Higher Education Inc./Ken Karp, Photographer; p. 156: Historical photo courtesy of The Dow Chemical Company; p. 168: © Steve Warmowski/The Image Works; p. 171: © Dirck Halstead.

Chapter 5

Opener: NASA; p. 174: © McGraw-Hill Higher Education Inc./Ken Karp, Photographer; 5.11: © McGraw-Hill Higher Education Inc./Ken Karp, Photographer; p. 186: Courtesy, Industrial Refrigeration Service, Inc. & MTC Logistics; p. 187: Courtesy National Scientific Balloon Facility/Palestine, Texas; p. 188: © Mark Antman/The Image Works; p. 193: © McGraw-Hill Education/Charles D. Winters, photographer; p. 194: © fStop Images/Caspar Benson/Getty Images; p. 195: © Fred J. Maroon/Science Source; p. 201: © Comstock/Getty Images; p. 207: NASA-JPL; p. 208: © Mike Matthews, JILA; 5.20: © McGraw-Hill Higher Education Inc./Ken Karp, Photographer; p. 226 (left): Courtesy Sechrist Industries, Inc.; p. 229 (left): © PRNewsFoto/Huron Valley Travel/AP Images; p. 229 (right): © James Mattil/123RF.

Chapter 6

Opener: © Sandia National Laboratories; p. 231: © Jacques Jangoux/Science Source; p. 232: © Edward Kinsman/Science Source; p. 233 (bottom): © McGraw-Hill Higher Education Inc./Charles Winter, Photographer; 6.2: © akg-images/Newscom; p. 235: © 1994 Richard Megna, Fundamental Photographs, NYC; p. 240: © Sergey Podkolzin/Alamy; p. 243: © McGraw-Hill Higher Education Inc./Stephen Frisch, Photographer; p. 245: © Charles D. Winters/Science Source; p. 246: © McGraw-Hill Higher Education Inc./Stephen Frisch, Photographer; p. 250 (both): Diabetes. Jul 2009; 58(7): 1526–1531. Published online Apr 28, 2009. doi: 10.2337/db09-0530. © 2009 by the American Diabetes Association; p. 253 (top): © McGraw-Hill Higher Education Inc./Ken Karp, Photographer; p. 253 (bottom): © JewelryStock/Alamy RF; p. 255: © Charles D. Winters/Science Source; p. 256: © Courtesy of Thomas Eisner and Daniel Aneshansley/ Cornell University; p. 257: © Charles D. Winters/Science Source; p. 258: © Orgo-Thermite; p. 269: Courtesy Sofia Fernandez; p. 273: © McGraw-Hill Higher Education Inc./Ken Karp, Photographer.

Chapter 7

Opener: © Neil Setchfield/Alamy; 7.1: © Huw Jones/Getty Images; 7.4a (x-ray): © Ted Kinsman/Science Source; p. 282: © McGraw-Hill Higher Education Inc./Stephen Frisch,

C-2   Photo Credits

Photographer; 7.7: © 2010 Richard Megna/ Fundamental Photographs; 7.8: Courtesy of Wabash Instrument Corp.; p. 289: © Professor Ahmed H. Zewail/California Institute of Technology, Dept. of Chemistry; 7.14 (both): © Educational Development Center; p. 292: © Mary Martin/Science Source; p. 312: Courtesy, Prof. Dr. Horst Weller, University of Hamburg, Institute of Physical Chemistry; p. 313: © NIST; p. 325: © Francois Gohier/Science Source.

Chapter 8

Opener: © SPL/Science Source; p. 327: © McGraw-Hill Higher Education Inc./Charles Winter, Photographer; 8.10 (Na, Cl_2, Ar): © McGraw-Hill Higher Education Inc./Ken Karp, Photographer; 8.10 (Mg, Al, S_8): © L. V. Bergman/The Bergman Collection; 8.10 (Si): © PASIEKA/Science Photo Library/Getty Images; 8.10 (P_4): © Albert Fenn/Getty Images; 8.14 (Li, Na): © McGraw-Hill Higher Education Inc./Ken Karp, Photographer; 8.14 (K): © Albert Fenn/Getty Images; 8.14 (Rb, Cs): © L. V. Bergman/The Bergman Collection; 8.15 (Be, Mg, Ca, Sr, Ba): © L.V. Bergman/The Bergman Collection; 8.15 (Ra): Courtesy, Fred Bayer. Image from www. bayerf.de/pse; 8.16 (Ga): © McGraw-Hill Higher Education Inc./Charles Winter, Photographer; 8.16 (B, Al, In): © L. V. Bergman/ The Bergman Collection; 8.17 (Graphite): © McGraw-Hill Higher Education Inc./Ken Karp, Photographer; 8.17 (Diamond): © Jewelry Stock/Alamy; 8.17 (Si): © PASIEKA/Science Photo Library/Getty Images; 8.17 (Ge, Pb): © McGraw-Hill Higher Education Inc./ Ken Karp, Photographer; 8.17 (Sn): © L. V. Bergman/The Bergman Collection; 8.18 (P): © Albert Fenn/Getty Images; 8.18 (As, Sb, Bi): © L. V. Bergman/The Bergman Collection; 8.18 (N_2): © Charles D. Winter/ Science Source; 8.19 (S_8, Se_8): © L. V. Bergman/The Bergman Collection; 8.19 (Te): © McGraw-Hill Higher Education Inc./Ken Karp, Photographer; 8.20: © SPL/Science Source; 8.21 (all): © McGraw-Hill Higher Education Inc./Ken Karp, Photographer; 8.22a–b: © 2010 The Regents of the University of California, Lawrence Berkeley National Laboratory. Photo courtesy of Lawrence Berkeley National Laboratory; 8.23: © McGraw-Hill Higher Education Inc./Ken Karp, Photographer; p. 356 (top left): © NASA, ESA, J. Hester, A. Loll (ASU); p. 358: © Science Source.

Chapter 9

Opener: © Science Source; p. 370: © McGraw-Hill Higher Education Inc./Ken Karp, Photographer; p. 371: © Breck P. Kent/age fotostock; p. 376 (top): © Liane Enkelis; p. 376 (bottom): © Eckehard Schulz/AP Images; p. 387, 397: © McGraw-Hill Higher Education Inc./Ken Karp, Photographer.

Chapter 10

Opener: © Dr. Tim Evans/Science Source; 10.21: © Charles D. Winters/Science Source;

p. 454 (soccer ball): © Comstock/Alamy; p. 455: © Lawrence Berkeley National Laboratory/ Science Source.

Chapter 11

Opener: © Layne Kennedy/Corbis/Getty Images; 11.9: © McGraw-Hill Higher Education Inc./Ken Karp, Photographer; p. 473 (center): © Hermann Eisenbeiss/Science Source; p. 475: © The University of Queensland; 11.11: © McGraw-Hill Higher Education Inc./Ken Karp, Photographer; p. 478: © Alan Carey/The Image Works; 11.37a-d: © McGraw-Hill Higher Education Inc./Ken Karp, Photographer; p. 502: © McGraw-Hill Higher Education Inc./Ken Karp, Photographer; 11.42: © McGraw-Hill Higher Education Inc./Ken Karp, Photographer; p. 505: © Atsushi Tomura/ Getty Images; p. 507 (left): © Andrew McClenaghan/Science Photo Library/Science Source; p. 507 (right): © Alfred Benjamin/ Science Source; p. 514: © NaturaLight-No Release Needed/Alamy; p. 516 (left): © McGraw-Hill Higher Education Inc./Ken Karp, Photographer; p. 516 (right): © AFP Photo/Tony Ranze/Getty Images.

Chapter 12

Opener: © Richard Megna/Fundamental Photographs; 12.1 (all): © McGraw-Hill Higher Education Inc./Ken Karp, Photographer; p. 530: © McGraw-Hill Higher Education Inc./Ken Karp, Photographer; p. 531: © Bill Evans, U.S. Geological Survey; p. 537: © Hank Morgan/Science Source; p. 538: © McGraw-Hill Higher Education Inc./Ken Karp, Photographer; 12.13d (all): © David Phillips/Science Source; p. 541: © John Mead/Science Source; p. 546: © Beranger/ PhotoTake; 12.15: © Paul Weller; 12.16: © Bob van den Berg/Getty Images; p. 555 (both): © McGraw-Hill Higher Education Inc./Ken Karp, Photographer; p. 560: © David McNew/Getty Images.

Chapter 13

Opener: © U.S. Marine Corps photo by Lance Cpl. Ronald Stauffer; 13.3, 13.7: © McGraw-Hill Higher Education Inc./Ken Karp, Photographer; p. 577: © McGraw-Hill Higher Education Inc./Ken Karp, Photographer; p. 586: © Collection Roger-Viollet/The Image Works; 13.21: © McGraw-Hill Higher Education Inc./Ken Karp, Photographer; 13.25: © Courtesy of Jason Matthey; 13.27: © Dorling Kindersley Universal Images Group/Newscom.

Chapter 14

Opener: © Michel Gangne/AFP/Getty Images; p. 622 (both): © McGraw-Hill Higher Education Inc./Ken Karp, Photographer;

p. 630: © Collection Varin-Visage/Science Source; 14.7: © McGraw-Hill Higher Education Inc./Ken Karp, Photographer; 14.10a-b: © McGraw-Hill Higher Education Inc./Ken Karp, Photographer; 14.11: © McGraw-Hill Higher Education Inc./Ken Karp, Photographer; p. 651: © Barry Bishop/National Geographic Creative.

Chapter 15

Opener: © The McGraw-Hill Companies, Inc./Jill Braaten, Photographer; 15.2: © McGraw-Hill Higher Education Inc./Ken Karp, Photographer; p. 674: © McGraw-Hill Higher Education Inc./Stephen Frisch, Photographer; 15.9 (both): © McGraw-Hill Higher Education Inc./Ken Karp, Photographer; 15.10: © James H. Robinson/Science Source; 15.11: © McGraw-Hill Higher Education Inc./Ken Karp, Photographer; p. 707: © McGraw-Hill Higher Education Inc./Ken Karp, Photographer; p. 719: © Kristen Brochmann/Fundamental Photographs.

Chapter 16

Opener: © Robert Hoetink/Alamy; p. 724: © McGraw-Hill Higher Education Inc./Ken Karp, Photographer; 16.1, 16.3: © McGraw-Hill Higher Education Inc./Ken Karp, Photographer; p. 732: © Professors P. P. Botta and S. Correr/SPL/Science Source; 16.8: © McGraw-Hill Higher Education Inc./Ken Karp, Photographer; p. 742: © CNRI/SPL/Science Source; p. 745: © McGraw-Hill Higher Education Inc./Ken Karp, Photographer; p. 746 (both): © McGraw-Hill Higher Education Inc./Ken Karp, Photographer; p. 748: © Southern Illinois University/Science Source; p. 750, 753: © McGraw-Hill Higher Education Inc./Ken Karp, Photographer; 16.10–16.12: © McGraw-Hill Higher Education Inc./Ken Karp, Photographer; p. 760 (top left): © Judy Dole/Getty Images; p. 760 (top right): © Scientific American, March 1970, Vol. 222, No. 3, p. 88. Photo by A. R. Terepka; 16.13: © McGraw-Hill Higher Education Inc./Stephen Frisch, Photographer; p. 775 (both): © McGraw-Hill Higher Education Inc./Ken Karp, Photographer.

Chapter 17

Opener: © Feng Wei Photography/Getty Images; p. 778: © McGraw-Hill Higher Education Inc./Ken Karp, Photographer; p. 780: © Matthias K. Gebbert/University of Maryland, Baltimore County/Dept. of Mathematics and Statistics; p. 783: © McGraw-Hill Higher Education Inc./Ken Karp, Photographer; p. 793: © Dirk Wiersma/Photo Researchers/ Science Source; p. 795–796: © McGraw-Hill Higher Education Inc./Ken Karp, Photographer.

Chapter 18

Opener: © Sheila Terry/Science Source; 18.2: © McGraw-Hill Higher Education Inc./Ken Karp, Photographer; p. 835: © Michael Klinec/ Alamy; 18.12: NASA; p. 837: © Derek Lovely; 18.13a: © Fernando Arias/Getty Images; 18.13b: © McGraw-Hill Higher Education Inc./ Ken Karp, Photographer; 18.13c: © Wesley

Appendix 1

Derivation of the Names of Elements*

Element	Symbol	Atomic No.	Atomic Mass[†]	Date of Discovery	Discoverer and Nationality[‡]	Derivation
Actinium	Ac	89	(227)	1899	A. Debierne (Fr.)	Gr. *aktis*, beam or ray
Aluminum	Al	13	26.98	1827	F. Woehler (Ge.)	Alum, the aluminum compound in which it was discovered; derived from L. *alumen*, astringent taste
Americium	Am	95	(243)	1944	A. Ghiorso (USA) R. A. James (USA) G. T. Seaborg (USA) S. G. Thompson (USA)	The Americas
Antimony	Sb	51	121.8	Ancient		L. *antimonium* (*anti*, opposite of; *monium*, isolated condition), so named because it is a tangible (metallic) substance which combines readily; symbol L. *stibium*, mark
Argon	Ar	18	39.95	1894	Lord Raleigh (GB) Sir William Ramsay (GB)	Gr. *argos*, inactive
Arsenic	As	33	74.92	1250	Albertus Magnus (Ge.)	Gr. *aksenikon*, yellow pigment; L. *arsenicum*, orpiment; the Greeks once used arsenic trisulfide as a pigment
Astatine	At	85	(210)	1940	D. R. Corson (USA) K. R. MacKenzie (USA) E. Segre (USA)	Gr. *astatos*, unstable
Barium	Ba	56	137.3	1808	Sir Humphry Davy (GB)	barite, a heavy spar, derived from Gr. *barys*, heavy
Berkelium	Bk	97	(247)	1950	G. T. Seaborg (USA) S. G. Thompson (USA) A. Ghiorso (USA)	Berkeley, Calif.
Beryllium	Be	4	9.012	1828	F. Woehler (Ge.) A. A. B. Bussy (Fr.)	Fr. L. *beryl*, sweet

Source: Reprinted with permission from "The Elements and Derivation of Their Names and Symbols," G. P. Dinga, *Chemistry* **41** (2), 20–22 (1968). Copyright by the American Chemical Society.

*At the time this table was drawn up, only 103 elements were known to exist.

[†]The atomic masses given here correspond to the 1961 values of the Commission on Atomic Weights. Masses in parentheses are those of the most stable or most common isotopes.

[‡]The abbreviations are (Ar.) Arabic; (Au.) Austrian; (Du.) Dutch; (Fr.) French; (Ge.) German; (GB) British; (Gr.) Greek; (H.) Hungarian; (I.) Italian; (L.) Latin; (P.) Polish; (R.) Russian; (Sp.) Spanish; (Swe.) Swedish; (USA) American.

(Continued)

Element	Symbol	Atomic No.	Atomic Mass[†]	Date of Discovery	Discoverer and Nationality[‡]	Derivation
Bismuth	Bi	83	209.0	1753	Claude Geoffroy (Fr.)	Ge. *bismuth*, probably a distortion of *weisse masse* (white mass) in which it was found
Boron	B	5	10.81	1808	Sir Humphry Davy (GB) J. L. Gay-Lussac (Fr.) L. J. Thenard (Fr.)	The compound borax, derived from Ar. *buraq*, white
Bromine	Br	35	79.90	1826	A. J. Balard (Fr.)	Gr. *bromos*, stench
Cadmium	Cd	48	112.4	1817	Fr. Stromeyer (Ge.)	Gr. *kadmia*, earth; L. *cadmia*, calamine (because it is found along with calamine)
Calcium	Ca	20	40.08	1808	Sir Humphry Davy (GB)	L. *calx*, lime
Californium	Cf	98	(249)	1950	G. T. Seaborg (USA) S. G. Thompson (USA) A. Ghiorso (USA) K. Street, Jr. (USA)	California
Carbon	C	6	12.01	Ancient		L. *carbo*, charcoal
Cerium	Ce	58	140.1	1803	J. J. Berzelius (Swe.) William Hisinger (Swe.) M. H. Klaproth (Ge.)	Asteroid Ceres
Cesium	Cs	55	132.9	1860	R. Bunsen (Ge.) G. R. Kirchhoff (Ge.)	L. *caesium*, blue (cesium was discovered by its spectral lines, which are blue)
Chlorine	Cl	17	35.45	1774	K. W. Scheele (Swe.)	Gr. *chloros*, light green
Chromium	Cr	24	52.00	1797	L. N. Vauquelin (Fr.)	Gr. *chroma*, color (because it is used in pigments)
Cobalt	Co	27	58.93	1735	G. Brandt (Ge.)	Ge. *kobold*, goblin (because the ore yielded cobalt instead of the expected metal, copper, it was attributed to goblins)
Copper	Cu	29	63.55	Ancient		L. *cuprum*, copper, derived from *cyprium*, Island of Cyprus, the main source of ancient copper
Curium	Cm	96	(247)	1944	G. T. Seaborg (USA) R. A. James (USA) A. Ghiorso (USA)	Pierre and Marie Curie
Dysprosium	Dy	66	162.5	1886	Lecoq de Boisbaudran (Fr.)	Gr. *dysprositos*, hard to get at
Einsteinium	Es	99	(254)	1952	A. Ghiorso (USA)	Albert Einstein
Erbium	Er	68	167.3	1843	C. G. Mosander (Swe.)	Ytterby, Sweden, where many rare earths were discovered
Europium	Eu	63	152.0	1896	E. Demarcay (Fr.)	Europe

(Continued)

A-3   Appendix 1

Element	Symbol	Atomic No.	Atomic Mass†	Date of Discovery	Discoverer and Nationality‡	Derivation
Fermium	Fm	100	(253)	1953	A. Ghiorso (USA)	Enrico Fermi
Fluorine	F	9	19.00	1886	H. Moissan (Fr.)	Mineral fluorspar, from L. *fluere*, flow (because fluorspar was used as a flux)
Francium	Fr	87	(223)	1939	Marguerite Perey (Fr.)	France
Gadolinium	Gd	64	157.3	1880	J. C. Marignac (Fr.)	Johan Gadolin, Finnish rare earth chemist
Gallium	Ga	31	69.72	1875	Lecoq de Boisbaudran (Fr.)	L. *Gallia*, France
Germanium	Ge	32	72.59	1886	Clemens Winkler (Ge.)	L. *Germania*, Germany
Gold	Au	79	197.0	Ancient		L. *aurum*, shining dawn
Hafnium	Hf	72	178.5	1923	D. Coster (Du.) G. von Hevesey (H.)	L. *Hafnia*, Copenhagen
Helium	He	2	4.003	1868	P. Janssen (spectr) (Fr.) Sir William Ramsay (isolated) (GB)	Gr. *helios*, sun (because it was first discovered in the sun's spectrum)
Holmium	Ho	67	164.9	1879	P. T. Cleve (Swe.)	L. *Holmia*, Stockholm
Hydrogen	H	1	1.008	1766	Sir Henry Cavendish (GB)	Gr. *hydro*, water; *genes*, forming (because it produces water when burned with oxygen)
Indium	In	49	114.8	1863	F. Reich (Ge.) T. Richter (Ge.)	Indigo, because of its indigo blue lines in the spectrum
Iodine	I	53	126.9	1811	B. Courtois (Fr.)	Gr. *iodes*, violet
Iridium	Ir	77	192.2	1803	S. Tennant (GB)	L. *iris*, rainbow
Iron	Fe	26	55.85	Ancient		L. *ferrum*, iron
Krypton	Kr	36	83.80	1898	Sir William Ramsay (GB) M. W. Travers (GB)	Gr. *kryptos*, hidden
Lanthanum	La	57	138.9	1839	C. G. Mosander (Swe.)	Gr. *lanthanein*, concealed
Lawrencium	Lr	103	(257)	1961	A. Ghiorso (USA) T. Sikkeland (USA) A. E. Larsh (USA) R. M. Latimer (USA)	E. O. Lawrence (USA), inventor of the cyclotron
Lead	Pb	82	207.2	Ancient		Symbol, L. *plumbum*, lead, meaning heavy
Lithium	Li	3	6.941	1817	A. Arfvedson (Swe.)	Gr. *lithos*, rock (because it occurs in rocks)
Lutetium	Lu	71	175.0	1907	G. Urbain (Fr.) C. A. von Welsbach (Au.)	*Luteria*, ancient name for Paris
Magnesium	Mg	12	24.31	1808	Sir Humphry Davy (GB)	*Magnesia*, a district in Thessaly; possibly derived from L. *magnesia*
Manganese	Mn	25	54.94	1774	J. G. Gahn (Swe.)	L. *magnes*, magnet

(Continued)

Element	Symbol	Atomic No.	Atomic Mass[†]	Date of Discovery	Discoverer and Nationality[‡]	Derivation
Mendelevium	Md	101	(256)	1955	A. Ghiorso (USA) G. R. Choppin (USA) G. T. Seaborg (USA) B. G. Harvey (USA) S. G. Thompson (USA)	Mendeleev, Russian chemist who prepared the periodic chart and predicted properties of undiscovered elements
Mercury	Hg	80	200.6	Ancient		Symbol, L. *hydrargyrum*, liquid silver
Molybdenum	Mo	42	95.94	1778	G. W. Scheele (Swe.)	Gr. *molybdos*, lead
Neodymium	Nd	60	144.2	1885	C. A. von Welsbach (Au.)	Gr. *neos*, new; *didymos*, twin
Neon	Ne	10	20.18	1898	Sir William Ramsay (GB) M. W. Travers (GB)	Gr. *neos*, new
Neptunium	Np	93	(237)	1940	E. M. McMillan (USA) P. H. Abelson (USA)	Planet Neptune
Nickel	Ni	28	58.69	1751	A. F. Cronstedt (Swe.)	Swe. *kopparnickel*, false copper; also Ge. *nickel*, referring to the devil that prevented copper from being extracted from nickel ores
Niobium	Nb	41	92.91	1801	Charles Hatchett (GB)	Gr. *Niobe*, daughter of Tantalus (niobium was considered identical to tantalum, named after *Tantalus*, until 1884)
Nitrogen	N	7	14.01	1772	Daniel Rutherford (GB)	Fr. *nitrogene*, derived from L. *nitrum*, native soda, or Gr. *nitron*, native soda, and Gr. *genes*, forming
Nobelium	No	102	(253)	1958	A. Ghiorso (USA) T. Sikkeland (USA) J. R. Walton (USA) G. T. Seaborg (USA)	Alfred Nobel
Osmium	Os	76	190.2	1803	S. Tennant (GB)	Gr. *osme*, odor
Oxygen	O	8	16.00	1774	Joseph Priestley (GB) C. W. Scheele (Swe.)	Fr. *oxygene*, generator of acid, derived from Gr. *oxys*, acid, and L. *genes*, forming (because it was once thought to be a part of all acids)
Palladium	Pd	46	106.4	1803	W. H. Wollaston (GB)	Asteroid Pallas
Phosphorus	P	15	30.97	1669	H. Brandt (Ge.)	Gr. *phosphoros*, light bearing
Platinum	Pt	78	195.1	1735 1741	A. de Ulloa (Sp.) Charles Wood (GB)	Sp. *platina*, silver

(Continued)

A-5   Appendix 1

Element	Symbol	Atomic No.	Atomic Mass[†]	Date of Discovery	Discoverer and Nationality[‡]	Derivation
Plutonium	Pu	94	(242)	1940	G. T. Seaborg (USA) E. M. McMillan (USA) J. W. Kennedy (USA) A. C. Wahl (USA)	Planet Pluto
Polonium	Po	84	(210)	1898	Marie Curie (P.)	Poland
Potassium	K	19	39.10	1807	Sir Humphry Davy (GB)	Symbol, L. *kalium,* potash
Praseodymium	Pr	59	140.9	1885	C. A. von Welsbach (Au.)	Gr. *prasios,* green; *didymos,* twin
Promethium	Pm	61	(147)	1945	J. A. Marinsky (USA) L. E. Glendenin (USA) C. D. Coryell (USA)	Gr. mythology, *Prometheus,* the Greek Titan who stole fire from heaven
Protactinium	Pa	91	(231)	1917	O. Hahn (Ge.) L. Meitner (Au.)	Gr. *protos,* first; *actinium* (because it disintegrates into actinium)
Radium	Ra	88	(226)	1898	Pierre and Marie Curie (Fr., P.)	L. *radius,* ray
Radon	Rn	86	(222)	1900	F. E. Dorn (Ge.)	Derived from radium
Rhenium	Re	75	186.2	1925	W. Noddack (Ge.) I. Tacke (Ge.) Otto Berg (Ge.)	L. *Rhenus,* Rhine
Rhodium	Rh	45	102.9	1804	W. H. Wollaston (GB)	Gr. *rhodon,* rose (because some of its salts are rose-colored)
Rubidium	Rb	37	85.47	1861	R. W. Bunsen (Ge.) G. Kirchhoff (Ge.)	L. *rubidus,* dark red (discovered with the spectroscope, its spectrum shows red lines)
Ruthenium	Ru	44	101.1	1844	K. K. Klaus (R.)	L. *Ruthenia,* Russia
Samarium	Sm	62	150.4	1879	Lecoq de Boisbaudran (Fr.)	Samarskite, after Samarski, a Russian engineer
Scandium	Sc	21	44.96	1879	L. F. Nilson (Swe.)	Scandinavia
Selenium	Se	34	78.96	1817	J. J. Berzelius (Swe.)	Gr. *selene,* moon (because it resembles tellurium, named for the earth)
Silicon	Si	14	28.09	1824	J. J. Berzelius (Swe.)	L. *silex, silicis,* flint
Silver	Ag	47	107.9	Ancient		Symbol, L. *argentum,* silver
Sodium	Na	11	22.99	1807	Sir Humphry Davy (GB)	L. *sodanum,* headache remedy; symbol, L. *natrium,* soda
Strontium	Sr	38	87.62	1808	Sir Humphry Davy (GB)	Strontian, Scotland, derived from mineral strontionite

(Continued)

Element	Symbol	Atomic No.	Atomic Mass†	Date of Discovery	Discoverer and Nationality‡	Derivation
Sulfur	S	16	32.07	Ancient		L. *sulphurium* (Sanskrit, *sulvere*)
Tantalum	Ta	73	180.9	1802	A. G. Ekeberg (Swe.)	Gr. mythology, *Tantalus*, because of difficulty in isolating it
Technetium	Tc	43	(99)	1937	C. Perrier (I.)	Gr. *technetos*, artificial (because it was the first artificial element)
Tellurium	Te	52	127.6	1782	F. J. Müller (Au.)	L. *tellus*, earth
Terbium	Tb	65	158.9	1843	C. G. Mosander (Swe.)	Ytterby, Sweden
Thallium	Tl	81	204.4	1861	Sir William Crookes (GB)	Gr. *thallos*, a budding twig (because its spectrum shows a bright green line)
Thorium	Th	90	232.0	1828	J. J. Berzelius (Swe.)	Mineral thorite, derived from *Thor*, Norse god of war
Thulium	Tm	69	168.9	1879	P. T. Cleve (Swe.)	*Thule*, early name for Scandinavia
Tin	Sn	50	118.7	Ancient		Symbol, L. *stannum*, tin
Titanium	Ti	22	47.88	1791	W. Gregor (GB)	Gr. giants, the *Titans*, and L. *titans*, giant deities
Tungsten	W	74	183.9	1783	J. J. and F. de Elhuyar (Sp.)	Swe. *tung sten*, heavy stone; symbol, wolframite, a mineral
Uranium	U	92	238.0	1789 1841	M. H. Klaproth (Ge.) E. M. Peligot (Fr.)	Planet Uranus
Vanadium	V	23	50.94	1801 1830	A. M. del Rio (Sp.) N. G. Sefstrom (Swe.)	*Vanadis*, Norse goddess of love and beauty
Xenon	Xe	54	131.3	1898	Sir William Ramsay (GB) M. W. Travers (GB)	Gr. *xenos*, stranger
Ytterbium	Yb	70	173.0	1907	G. Urbain (Fr.)	Ytterby, Sweden
Yttrium	Y	39	88.91	1843	C. G. Mosander (Swe.)	Ytterby, Sweden
Zinc	Zn	30	65.39	1746	A. S. Marggraf (Ge.)	Ge. *zink*, of obscure origin
Zirconium	Zr	40	91.22	1789	M. H. Klaproth (Ge.)	Zircon, in which it was found, derived from Ar. *zargum*, gold color

Appendix 2

Units for the Gas Constant

In this appendix, we will see how the gas constant R can be expressed in units J/K · mol. Our first step is to derive a relationship between atm and pascal. We start with

$$\text{pressure} = \frac{\text{force}}{\text{area}}$$

$$= \frac{\text{mass} \times \text{acceleration}}{\text{area}}$$

$$= \frac{\text{volume} \times \text{density} \times \text{acceleration}}{\text{area}}$$

$$= \text{length} \times \text{density} \times \text{acceleration}$$

By definition, the standard atmosphere is the pressure exerted by a column of mercury exactly 76 cm high of density 13.5951 g/cm³, in a place where acceleration due to gravity is 980.665 cm/s². However, to express pressure in N/m² it is necessary to write

$$\text{density of mercury} = 1.35951 \times 10^4 \text{ kg/m}^3$$
$$\text{acceleration due to gravity} = 9.80665 \text{ m/s}^2$$

The standard atmosphere is given by

$$1 \text{ atm} = (0.76 \text{ m Hg})(1.35951 \times 10^4 \text{ kg/m}^3)(9.80665 \text{ m/s}^2)$$
$$= 101{,}325 \text{ kg m/m}^2 \cdot \text{s}^2$$
$$= 101{,}325 \text{ N/m}^2$$
$$= 101{,}325 \text{ Pa}$$

From Section 5.4 we see that the gas constant R is given by 0.082057 L · atm/K · mol. Using the conversion factors

$$1 \text{ L} = 1 \times 10^{-3} \text{ m}^3$$
$$1 \text{ atm} = 101{,}325 \text{ N/m}^2$$

we write

$$R = \left(0.082057 \frac{\text{L atm}}{\text{K mol}}\right)\left(\frac{1 \times 10^{-3} \text{ m}^3}{1 \text{ L}}\right)\left(\frac{101{,}325 \text{ N/m}^2}{1 \text{ atm}}\right)$$

$$= 8.314 \frac{\text{N m}}{\text{K mol}}$$

$$= 8.314 \frac{\text{J}}{\text{K mol}}$$

and

$$1 \text{ L} \cdot \text{atm} = (1 \times 10^{-3} \text{ m}^3)(101{,}325 \text{ N/m}^2)$$
$$= 101.3 \text{ N m}$$
$$= 101.3 \text{ J}$$

Appendix 3

Thermodynamic Data at 1 atm and 25°C*

Inorganic Substances

Substance	ΔH_f° (kJ/mol)	ΔG_f° (kJ/mol)	S° (J/K · mol)
$Ag(s)$	0	0	42.7
$Ag^+(aq)$	105.9	77.1	73.9
$AgCl(s)$	−127.0	−109.7	96.1
$AgBr(s)$	−99.5	−95.9	107.1
$AgI(s)$	−62.4	−66.3	114.2
$AgNO_3(s)$	−123.1	−32.2	140.9
$Al(s)$	0	0	28.3
$Al^{3+}(aq)$	−524.7	−481.2	−313.38
$AlCl_3(s)$	−705.6	−630.0	109.3
$Al_2O_3(s)$	−1669.8	−1576.4	50.99
$As(s)$	0	0	35.15
$AsO_4^{3-}(aq)$	−870.3	−635.97	−144.77
$AsH_3(g)$	171.5		
$H_3AsO_4(s)$	−900.4		
$Au(s)$	0	0	47.7
$Au_2O_3(s)$	80.8	163.2	125.5
$AuCl(s)$	−35.2		
$AuCl_3(s)$	−118.4		
$B(s)$	0	0	6.5
$B_2O_3(s)$	−1263.6	−1184.1	54.0
$H_3BO_3(s)$	−1087.9	−963.16	89.58
$H_3BO_3(aq)$	−1067.8	−963.3	159.8
$Ba(s)$	0	0	66.9
$Ba^{2+}(aq)$	−538.4	−560.66	12.55
$BaO(s)$	−558.2	−528.4	70.3
$BaCl_2(s)$	−860.1	−810.66	125.5
$BaSO_4(s)$	−1464.4	−1353.1	132.2
$BaCO_3(s)$	−1218.8	−1138.9	112.1
$Be(s)$	0	0	9.5
$BeO(s)$	−610.9	−581.58	14.1
$Br_2(l)$	0	0	152.3
$Br_2(g)$	30.91	3.11	245.3
$Br^-(aq)$	−120.9	−102.8	80.7
$HBr(g)$	−36.2	−53.2	198.48
$C(graphite)$	0	0	5.69
$C(diamond)$	1.90	2.87	2.4
$CO(g)$	−110.5	−137.3	197.9
$CO_2(g)$	−393.5	−394.4	213.6
$CO_2(aq)$	−412.9	−386.2	121.3

*The thermodynamic quantities of ions are based on the reference states that $\Delta H_f^\circ[H^+(aq)] = 0$, $\Delta G_f^\circ[H^+(aq)] = 0$, and $S^\circ[H^+(aq)] = 0$ (see p. 782).

(Continued)

A-9   Appendix 3

Substance	ΔH_f° (kJ/mol)	ΔG_f° (kJ/mol)	S° (J/K · mol)
$CO_3^{2-}(aq)$	−676.3	−528.1	−53.1
$HCO_3^-(aq)$	−691.1	−587.1	94.98
$H_2CO_3(aq)$	−699.7	−623.2	187.4
$CS_2(g)$	115.3	65.1	237.8
$CS_2(l)$	87.3	63.6	151.0
$HCN(aq)$	105.4	112.1	128.9
$CN^-(aq)$	151.0	165.69	117.99
$(NH_2)_2CO(s)$	−333.19	−197.15	104.6
$(NH_2)_2CO(aq)$	−319.2	−203.84	173.85
$Ca(s)$	0	0	41.6
$Ca^{2+}(aq)$	−542.96	−553.0	−55.2
$CaO(s)$	−635.6	−604.2	39.8
$Ca(OH)_2(s)$	−986.6	−896.8	83.4
$CaF_2(s)$	−1214.6	−1161.9	68.87
$CaCl_2(s)$	−794.96	−750.19	113.8
$CaSO_4(s)$	−1432.69	−1320.3	106.69
$CaCO_3(s)$	−1206.9	−1128.8	92.9
$Cd(s)$	0	0	51.46
$Cd^{2+}(aq)$	−72.38	−77.7	−61.09
$CdO(s)$	−254.6	−225.06	54.8
$CdCl_2(s)$	−389.1	−342.59	118.4
$CdSO_4(s)$	−926.17	−820.2	137.2
$Cl_2(g)$	0	0	223.0
$Cl^-(aq)$	−167.2	−131.2	56.5
$HCl(g)$	−92.3	−95.27	187.0
$Co(s)$	0	0	28.45
$Co^{2+}(aq)$	−67.36	−51.46	155.2
$CoO(s)$	−239.3	−213.38	43.9
$Cr(s)$	0	0	23.77
$Cr^{2+}(aq)$	−138.9		
$Cr_2O_3(s)$	−1128.4	−1046.8	81.17
$CrO_4^{2-}(aq)$	−863.16	−706.26	38.49
$Cr_2O_7^{2-}(aq)$	−1460.6	−1257.29	213.8
$Cs(s)$	0	0	82.8
$Cs^+(aq)$	−247.69	−282.0	133.05
$Cu(s)$	0	0	33.3
$Cu^+(aq)$	51.88	50.2	−26.4
$Cu^{2+}(aq)$	64.39	64.98	−99.6
$CuO(s)$	−155.2	−127.2	43.5
$Cu_2O(s)$	−166.69	−146.36	100.8
$CuCl(s)$	−134.7	−118.8	91.6
$CuCl_2(s)$	−205.85	?	?
$CuS(s)$	−48.5	−49.0	66.5
$CuSO_4(s)$	−769.86	−661.9	113.39
$F_2(g)$	0	0	203.34
$F^-(aq)$	−329.1	−276.48	−9.6
$HF(g)$	−271.6	−270.7	173.5
$Fe(s)$	0	0	27.2

(Continued)

Substance	ΔH_f° (kJ/mol)	ΔG_f° (kJ/mol)	S° (J/K · mol)
$Fe^{2+}(aq)$	−87.86	−84.9	−113.39
$Fe^{3+}(aq)$	−47.7	−10.5	−293.3
$FeCl_3(s)$	−400	−334	142.3
$FeO(s)$	−272.0	−255.2	60.8
$Fe_2O_3(s)$	−822.2	−741.0	90.0
$Fe(OH)_2(s)$	−568.19	−483.55	79.5
$Fe(OH)_3(s)$	−824.25	?	?
$H(g)$	218.2	203.2	114.6
$H_2(g)$	0	0	131.0
$H^+(aq)$	0	0	0
$OH^-(aq)$	−229.94	−157.30	−10.5
$H_2O(l)$	−285.8	−237.2	69.9
$H_2O(g)$	−241.8	−228.6	188.7
$H_2O_2(l)$	−187.6	−118.1	?
$Hg(l)$	0	0	77.4
$Hg^{2+}(aq)$		−164.38	
$HgO(s)$	−90.7	−58.5	72.0
$HgCl_2(s)$	−230.1		
$Hg_2Cl_2(s)$	−264.9	−210.66	196.2
$HgS(s)$	−58.16	−48.8	77.8
$HgSO_4(s)$	−704.17		
$Hg_2SO_4(s)$	−741.99	−623.92	200.75
$I_2(s)$	0	0	116.7
$I_2(g)$	62.25	19.37	260.6
$I(g)$	106.6	70.16	180.7
$I^-(aq)$	−55.9	−51.67	109.37
$HI(g)$	25.9	1.30	206.3
$K(s)$	0	0	63.6
$K^+(aq)$	−251.2	−282.28	102.5
$KOH(s)$	−425.85		
$KCl(s)$	−435.87	−408.3	82.68
$KClO_3(s)$	−391.20	−289.9	142.97
$KClO_4(s)$	−433.46	−304.18	151.0
$KBr(s)$	−392.17	−379.2	96.4
$KI(s)$	−327.65	−322.29	104.35
$KNO_3(s)$	−492.7	−393.1	132.9
$Li(s)$	0	0	28.0
$Li^+(aq)$	−278.46	−293.8	14.2
$Li_2O(s)$	−595.8	?	?
$LiOH(s)$	−487.2	−443.9	50.2
$Mg(s)$	0	0	32.5
$Mg^{2+}(aq)$	−461.96	−456.0	−117.99
$MgO(s)$	−601.8	−569.6	26.78
$Mg(OH)_2(s)$	−924.66	−833.75	63.1
$MgCl_2(s)$	−641.8	−592.3	89.5
$MgSO_4(s)$	−1278.2	−1173.6	91.6
$MgCO_3(s)$	−1112.9	−1029.3	65.69
$Mn(s)$	0	0	31.76

(Continued)

A-11   Appendix 3

Substance	ΔH_f° (kJ/mol)	ΔG_f° (kJ/mol)	S° (J/K · mol)
$Mn^{2+}(aq)$	−218.8	−223.4	−83.68
$MnO_2(s)$	−520.9	−466.1	53.1
$N_2(g)$	0	0	191.5
$N_3^-(aq)$	245.18	?	?
$NH_3(g)$	−46.3	−16.6	193.0
$NH_4^+(aq)$	−132.80	−79.5	112.8
$NH_4Cl(s)$	−315.39	−203.89	94.56
$NH_4NO_3(s)$	−365.6	−184.0	151
$NH_3(aq)$	−80.3	−26.5	111.3
$N_2H_4(l)$	50.4		
$NO(g)$	90.4	86.7	210.6
$NO_2(g)$	33.85	51.8	240.46
$N_2O_4(g)$	9.66	98.29	304.3
$N_2O(g)$	81.56	103.6	219.99
$HNO_2(aq)$	−118.8	−53.6	
$HNO_3(l)$	−173.2	−79.9	155.6
$NO_3^-(aq)$	−206.57	−110.5	146.4
$Na(s)$	0	0	51.05
$Na^+(aq)$	−239.66	−261.87	60.25
$Na_2O(s)$	−415.9	−376.56	72.8
$NaCl(s)$	−411.0	−384.0	72.38
$NaI(s)$	−288.0		
$Na_2SO_4(s)$	−1384.49	−1266.8	149.49
$NaNO_3(s)$	−466.68	−365.89	116.3
$Na_2CO_3(s)$	−1130.9	−1047.67	135.98
$NaHCO_3(s)$	−947.68	−851.86	102.09
$Ni(s)$	0	0	30.1
$Ni^{2+}(aq)$	−64.0	−46.4	−159.4
$NiO(s)$	−244.35	−216.3	38.58
$Ni(OH)_2(s)$	−538.06	−453.1	79.5
$O(g)$	249.4	230.1	160.95
$O_2(g)$	0	0	205.0
$O_3(aq)$	−12.09	16.3	110.88
$O_3(g)$	142.2	163.4	237.6
$P(white)$	0	0	44.0
$P(red)$	−18.4	13.8	29.3
$PO_4^{3-}(aq)$	−1284.07	−1025.59	−217.57
$P_4O_{10}(s)$	−3012.48		
$PH_3(g)$	9.25	18.2	210.0
$HPO_4^{2-}(aq)$	−1298.7	−1094.1	−35.98
$H_2PO_4^-(aq)$	−1302.48	−1135.1	89.1
$Pb(s)$	0	0	64.89
$Pb^{2+}(aq)$	1.6	−24.3	21.3
$PbO(s)$	−217.86	−188.49	69.45
$PbO_2(s)$	−276.65	−218.99	76.57
$PbCl_2(s)$	−359.2	−313.97	136.4
$PbS(s)$	−94.3	−92.68	91.2
$PbSO_4(s)$	−918.4	−811.2	147.28

(Continued)

Substance	ΔH_f° (kJ/mol)	ΔG_f° (kJ/mol)	S° (J/K · mol)
$Pt(s)$	0	0	41.84
$PtCl_4^{2-}(aq)$	−516.3	−384.5	175.7
$Rb(s)$	0	0	69.45
$Rb^+(aq)$	−246.4	−282.2	124.27
S(rhombic)	0	0	31.88
S(monoclinic)	0.30	0.10	32.55
$SO_2(g)$	−296.4	−300.4	248.5
$SO_3(g)$	−395.2	−370.4	256.2
$SO_3^{2-}(aq)$	−624.25	−497.06	43.5
$SO_4^{2-}(aq)$	−907.5	−741.99	17.15
$H_2S(g)$	−20.15	−33.0	205.64
$HSO_3^-(aq)$	−627.98	−527.3	132.38
$HSO_4^-(aq)$	−885.75	−752.87	126.86
$H_2SO_4(l)$	−811.3	?	?
$SF_6(g)$	−1096.2	?	?
$Si(s)$	0	0	18.70
$SiO_2(s)$	−859.3	−805.0	41.84
$Sr(s)$	0	0	54.39
$Sr^{2+}(aq)$	−545.5	−557.3	−39.33
$SrCl_2(s)$	−828.4	−781.15	117.15
$SrSO_4(s)$	−1444.74	−1334.28	121.75
$SrCO_3(s)$	−1218.38	−1137.6	97.07
$Zn(s)$	0	0	41.6
$Zn^{2+}(aq)$	−152.4	−147.2	−106.48
$ZnO(s)$	−348.0	−318.2	43.9
$ZnCl_2(s)$	−415.89	−369.26	108.37
$ZnS(s)$	−202.9	−198.3	57.7
$ZnSO_4(s)$	−978.6	−871.6	124.7

Organic Substances

Substance	Formula	ΔH_f° (kJ/mol)	ΔG_f° (kJ/mol)	S° (J/K · mol)
Acetic acid(l)	CH_3COOH	−484.2	−389.45	159.8
Acetaldehyde(g)	CH_3CHO	−166.35	−139.08	264.2
Acetone(l)	CH_3COCH_3	−246.8	−153.55	198.7
Acetylene(g)	C_2H_2	226.6	209.2	200.8
Benzene(l)	C_6H_6	49.04	124.5	172.8
Butane(g)	C_4H_{10}	−124.7	−15.7	310.0
Ethanol(l)	C_2H_5OH	−276.98	−174.18	161.0
Ethanol(g)	C_2H_5OH	−235.1	−168.5	282.7
Ethane(g)	C_2H_6	−84.7	−32.89	229.5
Ethylene(g)	C_2H_4	52.3	68.1	219.5
Formic acid(l)	$HCOOH$	−409.2	−346.0	129.0
Glucose(s)	$C_6H_{12}O_6$	−1274.5	−910.56	212.1
Methane(g)	CH_4	−74.85	−50.8	186.2
Methanol(l)	CH_3OH	−238.7	−166.3	126.8
Propane(g)	C_3H_8	−103.9	−23.5	269.9
Sucrose(s)	$C_{12}H_{22}O_{11}$	−2221.7	−1544.3	360.2

Appendix 4

Mathematical Operations

Logarithms

Common Logarithms

The concept of the logarithms is an extension of the concept of exponents, which is discussed in Chapter 1. The *common,* or base-10, logarithm of any number is the power to which 10 must be raised to equal the number. The following examples illustrate this relationship:

Logarithm	Exponent
$\log 1 = 0$	$10^0 = 1$
$\log 10 = 1$	$10^1 = 10$
$\log 100 = 2$	$10^2 = 100$
$\log 10^{-1} = -1$	$10^{-1} = 0.1$
$\log 10^{-2} = -2$	$10^{-2} = 0.01$

In each case, the logarithm of the number can be obtained by inspection.

Because the logarithms of numbers are exponents, they have the same properties as exponents. Thus, we have

Logarithm	Exponent
$\log AB = \log A + \log B$	$10^A \times 10^B = 10^{A+B}$
$\log \dfrac{A}{B} = \log A - \log B$	$\dfrac{10^A}{10^B} = 10^{A-B}$

Furthermore, $\log A^n = n \log A$.

Now suppose we want to find the common logarithm of 6.7×10^{-4}. On most electronic calculators, the number is entered first and then the log key is pressed. This operation gives us

$$\log 6.7 \times 10^{-4} = -3.17$$

Note that there are as many digits *after* the decimal point as there are significant figures in the original number. The original number has two significant figures and the "17" in -3.17 tells us that the log has two significant figures. The "3" in -3.17 serves only to locate the decimal point in the number 6.7×10^{-4}. Other examples are

Number	Common Logarithm
62	1.79
0.872	−0.0595
1.0×10^{-7}	−7.00

Sometimes (as in the case of pH calculations) it is necessary to obtain the number whose logarithm is known. This procedure is known as taking the antilogarithm; it is simply the reverse of taking the logarithm of a number. Suppose in a certain calculation we have pH = 1.46 and are asked to calculate $[H^+]$. From the definition of pH (pH $= -\log [H^+]$) we can write

$$[H^+] = 10^{-1.46}$$

Many calculators have a key labeled $\log^{-1}$ or INV log to obtain antilogs. Other calculators have a 10^x or y^x key (where x corresponds to -1.46 in our example and y is 10 for base-10 logarithm). Therefore, we find that $[H^+] = 0.035\ M$.

Natural Logarithms

Logarithms taken to the base e instead of 10 are known as natural logarithms (denoted by ln or $\log_e$); e is equal to 2.7183. The relationship between common logarithms and natural logarithms is as follows:

$$\begin{array}{ll} \log 10 = 1 & 10^1 = 10 \\ \ln 10 = 2.303 & e^{2.303} = 10 \end{array}$$

Thus,

$$\ln x = 2.303 \log x$$

To find the natural logarithm of 2.27, say, we first enter the number on the electronic calculator and then press the ln key to get

$$\ln 2.27 = 0.820$$

If no ln key is provided, we can proceed as follows:

$$\begin{aligned} 2.303 \log 2.27 &= 2.303 \times 0.356 \\ &= 0.820 \end{aligned}$$

Sometimes we may be given the natural logarithm and asked to find the number it represents. For example,

$$\ln x = 59.7$$

On many calculators, we simply enter the number and press the e key:

$$x = e^{59.7} = 8 \times 10^{25}$$

The Quadratic Equation

A quadratic equation takes the form

$$ax^2 + bx + c = 0$$

If coefficients a, b, and c are known, then x is given by

$$x = \frac{-b \pm \sqrt{b^2 - 4ac}}{2a}$$

Suppose we have the following quadratic equation:

$$2x^2 + 5x - 12 = 0$$

Solving for x, we write

$$\begin{aligned} x &= \frac{-5 \pm \sqrt{(5)^2 - 4(2)(-12)}}{2(2)} \\ &= \frac{-5 \pm \sqrt{25 + 96}}{4} \end{aligned}$$

Therefore,

$$x = \frac{-5 + 11}{4} = \frac{3}{2}$$

and

$$x = \frac{-5 - 11}{4} = -4$$

Glossary

The number in parentheses is the number of the section in which the term first appears.

A

absolute temperature scale. A temperature scale that uses the absolute zero of temperature as the lowest temperature. (5.3)

absolute zero. Theoretically the lowest attainable temperature. (5.3)

acceptor impurities. Impurities that can accept electrons from semiconductors. (21.3)

accuracy. The closeness of a measurement to the true value of the quantity that is measured. (1.8)

acid. A substance that yields hydrogen ions (H^+) when dissolved in water. (2.7)

acid ionization constant (K_a). The equilibrium constant for the acid ionization. (15.5)

actinide series. Elements that have incompletely filled $5f$ subshells or readily give rise to cations that have incompletely filled $5f$ subshells. (7.9)

activated complex. The species temporarily formed by the reactant molecules as a result of the collision before they form the product. (13.4)

activation energy (E_a). The minimum amount of energy required to initiate a chemical reaction. (13.4)

activity series. A summary of the results of many possible displacement reactions. (4.4)

actual yield. The amount of product actually obtained in a reaction. (3.10)

addition reaction. A reaction in which one molecule adds to another. (24.2)

adhesion. Attraction between unlike molecules. (11.3)

alcohol. An organic compound containing the hydroxyl group —OH. (24.4)

aldehydes. Compounds with a carbonyl functional group and the general formula RCHO, where R is an H atom, an alkyl, or an aromatic group. (24.4)

aliphatic hydrocarbons. Hydrocarbons that do not contain the benzene group or the benzene ring. (24.1)

alkali metals. The Group 1A elements (Li, Na, K, Rb, Cs, and Fr). (2.4)

alkaline earth metals. The Group 2A elements (Be, Mg, Ca, Sr, Ba, and Ra). (2.4)

alkanes. Hydrocarbons having the general formula C_nH_{2n+2}, where $n = 1,2, \ldots$ (24.2)

alkenes. Hydrocarbons that contain one or more carbon-carbon double bonds. They have the general formula C_nH_{2n}, where $n = 2,3, \ldots$ (24.2)

alkynes. Hydrocarbons that contain one or more carbon-carbon triple bonds. They have the general formula C_nH_{2n-2}, where $n = 2,3, \ldots$ (24.2)

allotropes. Two or more forms of the same element that differ significantly in chemical and physical properties. (2.6)

alloy. A solid solution composed of two or more metals, or of a metal or metals with one or more nonmetals. (21.2)

alpha particles. See alpha rays.

alpha (α) rays. Helium ions with a positive charge of $+2$. (2.2)

amalgam. An alloy of mercury with another metal or metals. (21.2)

amines. Organic bases that have the functional group —NR_2, where R may be H, an alkyl group, or an aromatic group. (24.4)

amino acids. A compound that contains at least one amino group and at least one carboxyl group. (25.3)

amorphous solid. A solid that lacks a regular three-dimensional arrangement of atoms or molecules. (11.7)

amphoteric oxide. An oxide that exhibits both acidic and basic properties. (8.6)

amplitude. The vertical distance from the middle of a wave to the peak or trough. (7.1)

anion. An ion with a net negative charge. (2.5)

anode. The electrode at which oxidation occurs. (18.2)

antibonding molecular orbital. A molecular orbital that is of higher energy and lower stability than the atomic orbitals from which it was formed. (10.6)

aqueous solution. A solution in which the solvent is water. (4.1)

aromatic hydrocarbon. A hydrocarbon that contains one or more benzene rings. (24.1)

atmospheric pressure. The pressure exerted by Earth's atmosphere. (5.2)

atom. The basic unit of an element that can enter into chemical combination. (2.1)

atomic mass. The mass of an atom in atomic mass units. (3.1)

atomic mass unit (amu). A mass exactly equal to $\frac{1}{12}$th the mass of one carbon-12 atom. (3.1)

atomic number (Z). The number of protons in the nucleus of an atom. (2.3)

atomic orbital. The wave function (Ψ) of an electron in an atom. (7.5)

atomic radius. One-half the distance between the two nuclei in two adjacent atoms of the same element in a metal. For elements that exist as diatomic units, the atomic radius is one-half the distance between the nuclei of the two atoms in a particular molecule. (8.3)

Aufbau principle. As protons are added one by one to the nucleus to build up the elements, electrons similarly are added to the atomic orbitals. (7.9)

Avogadro's law. At constant pressure and temperature, the volume of a gas is directly proportional to the number of moles of the gas present. (5.3)

Avogadro's number (N_A). 6.022×10^{23}; the number of particles in a mole. (3.2)

B

band theory. Delocalized electrons move freely through "bands" formed by overlapping molecular orbitals. (21.3)

barometer. An instrument that measures atmospheric pressure. (5.2)

base. A substance that yields hydroxide ions (OH^-) when dissolved in water. (2.7)

base ionization constant (K_b). The equilibrium constant for the base ionization. (15.6)

battery. A galvanic cell, or a series of combined galvanic cells, that can be used as a source of direct electric current at a constant voltage. (18.6)

beta particles. See beta rays.

beta (β) rays. Electrons. (2.2)

bimolecular reaction. An elementary step that involves two molecules. (13.5)

binary compounds. Compounds formed from just two elements. (2.7)

boiling point. The temperature at which the vapor pressure of a liquid is equal to the external atmospheric pressure. (11.8)

boiling-point elevation (ΔT_b). The boiling point of the solution (T_b) minus the boiling point of the pure solvent (T_b°). (12.6)

bond enthalpy. The enthalpy change required to break a bond in a mole of gaseous molecules. (9.10)

bond length. The distance between the nuclei of two bonded atoms in a molecule. (9.4)

bond order. The difference between the numbers of electrons in bonding molecular orbitals and antibonding molecular orbitals, divided by two. (10.7)

bonding molecular orbital. A molecular orbital that is of lower energy and greater stability than the atomic orbitals from which it was formed. (10.6)

Born-Haber cycle. The cycle that relates lattice energies of ionic compounds to ionization energies, electron affinities, heats of sublimation and formation, and bond enthalpies. (9.3)

boundary surface diagram. Diagram of the region containing a substantial amount of the electron density (about 90 percent) in an orbital. (7.7)

Boyle's law. The volume of a fixed amount of gas maintained at constant temperature is inversely proportional to the gas pressure. (5.3)

breeder reactor. A nuclear reactor that produces more fissionable materials than it uses. (19.5)

Brønsted acid. A substance capable of donating a proton. (4.3)

Brønsted base. A substance capable of accepting a proton. (4.3)

buffer solution. A solution of (a) a weak acid or base and (b) its salt; both components must be present. The solution has the ability to resist changes in pH upon the addition of small amounts of either acid or base. (16.3)

C

calorimetry. The measurement of heat changes. (6.5)

carbides. Ionic compounds containing the C_2^{2-} or C^{4-} ion. (22.3)

carboxylic acids. Acids that contain the carboxyl group —COOH. (24.4)

catalyst. A substance that increases the rate of a chemical reaction without itself being consumed. (13.6)

catenation. The ability of the atoms of an element to form bonds with one another. (22.3)

cathode. The electrode at which reduction occurs. (18.2)

cation. An ion with a net positive charge. (2.5)

cell voltage. Difference in electrical potential between the anode and the cathode of a galvanic cell. (18.2)

Charles' and Gay-Lussac's law. See Charles' law.

Charles' law. The volume of a fixed amount of gas maintained at constant pressure is directly proportional to the absolute temperature of the gas. (5.3)

chelating agent. A substance that forms complex ions with metal ions in solution. (23.3)

chemical energy. Energy stored within the structural units of chemical substances. (6.1)

chemical equation. An equation that uses chemical symbols to show what happens during a chemical reaction. (3.7)

chemical equilibrium. A state in which the rates of the forward and reverse reactions are equal. (14.1)

chemical formula. An expression showing the chemical composition of a compound in terms of the symbols for the atoms of the elements involved. (2.6)

chemical kinetics. The area of chemistry concerned with the speeds, or rates, at which chemical reactions occur. (13.1)

chemical property. Any property of a substance that cannot be studied without converting the substance into some other substance. (1.6)

chemical reaction. A process in which a substance (or substances) is changed into one or more new substances. (3.7)

chemistry. The study of matter and the changes it undergoes. (1.1)

chiral. Compounds or ions that are not superimposable with their mirror images. (23.4)

chlor-alkali process. The production of chlorine gas by the electrolysis of aqueous NaCl solution. (22.6)

closed system. A system that enables the exchange of energy (usually in the form of heat) but not mass with its surroundings. (6.2)

closest packing. The most efficient arrangements for packing atoms, molecules, or ions in a crystal. (11.4)

cohesion. The intermolecular attraction between like molecules. (11.3)

colligative properties. Properties of solutions that depend on the number of solute particles in solution and not on the nature of the solute particles. (12.6)

colloid. A dispersion of particles of one substance (the dispersed phase) throughout a dispersing medium made of another substance. (12.8)

combination reaction. A reaction in which two or more substances combine to form a single product. (4.4)

combustion reaction. A reaction in which a substance reacts with oxygen, usually with the release of heat and light, to produce a flame. (4.4)

common ion effect. The shift in equilibrium caused by the addition of a compound having an ion in common with the dissolved substances. (16.2)

complex ion. An ion containing a central metal cation bonded to one or more molecules or ions. (16.10)

compound. A substance composed of atoms of two or more elements chemically united in fixed proportions. (1.4)

concentration of a solution. The amount of solute present in a given quantity of solvent or solution. (4.5)

condensation. The phenomenon of going from the gaseous state to the liquid state. (11.8)

condensation reaction. A reaction in which two smaller molecules combine to form a larger molecule. Water is invariably one of the products of such a reaction. (24.4)

conductor. Substance capable of conducting electric current. (21.3)

conjugate acid-base pair. An acid and its conjugate base or a base and its conjugate acid. (15.1)

coordinate covalent bond. A bond in which the pair of electrons is supplied by one of the two bonded atoms; also called a dative bond. (9.9)

coordination compound. A neutral species containing one or more complex ions. (23.3)

coordination number. In a crystal lattice it is defined as the number of atoms (or ions) surrounding an atom (or ion) (11.4). In coordination compounds it is defined as the number of donor atoms surrounding the central metal atom in a complex. (23.3)

copolymer. A polymer containing two or more different monomers. (25.2)

core electrons. All nonvalence electrons in an atom. (8.2)

corrosion. The deterioration of metals by an electrochemical process. (18.7)

Coulomb's law. The potential energy between two ions is directly proportional to the product of their charges and inversely proportional to the distance between them. (9.3)

covalent bond. A bond in which two electrons are shared by two atoms. (9.4)

covalent compounds. Compounds containing only covalent bonds. (9.4)

critical mass. The minimum mass of fissionable material required to generate a self-sustaining nuclear chain reaction. (19.5)

critical pressure (P_c). The minimum pressure necessary to bring about liquefaction at the critical temperature. (11.8)

critical temperature (T_c). The temperature above which a gas will not liquefy. (11.8)

crystal field splitting (Δ). The energy difference between two sets of d orbitals in a metal atom when ligands are present. (23.5)

crystalline solid. A solid that possesses rigid and long-range order; its atoms, molecules, or ions occupy specific positions. (11.4)

crystallization. The process in which dissolved solute comes out of solution and forms crystals. (12.1)

cyanides. Compounds containing the CN^- ion. (22.3)

cycloalkanes. Alkanes whose carbon atoms are joined in rings. (24.2)

D

Dalton's law of partial pressures. The total pressure of a mixture of gases is just the sum of the pressures that each gas would exert if it were present alone. (5.6)

decomposition reaction. The breakdown of a compound into two or more components. (4.4)

delocalized molecular orbitals. Molecular orbitals that are not confined between two adjacent bonding atoms but actually extend over three or more atoms. (10.8)

denatured protein. Protein that does not exhibit normal biological activities. (25.3)

density. The mass of a substance divided by its volume. (1.6)

deoxyribonucleic acids (DNA). A type of nucleic acid. (25.4)

deposition. The process in which the molecules go directly from the vapor into the solid phase. (11.8)

diagonal relationship. Similarities between pairs of elements in different groups and periods of the periodic table. (8.6)

diamagnetic. Repelled by a magnet; a diamagnetic substance contains only paired electrons. (7.8)

diatomic molecule. A molecule that consists of two atoms. (2.5)

diffusion. The gradual mixing of molecules of one gas with the molecules of another by virtue of their kinetic properties. (5.7)

dilution. A procedure for preparing a less concentrated solution from a more concentrated solution. (4.5)

dipole moment (μ). The product of charge and the distance between the charges in a molecule. (10.2)

dipole-dipole forces. Forces that act between polar molecules. (11.2)

diprotic acid. Each unit of the acid yields two hydrogen ions upon ionization. (4.3)

dispersion forces. The attractive forces that arise as a result of temporary dipoles induced in the atoms or molecules; also called London forces. (11.2)

displacement reaction. An atom or an ion in a compound is replaced by an atom of another element. (4.4)

disproportionation reaction. A reaction in which an element in one oxidation state is both oxidized and reduced. (4.4)

donor atom. The atom in a ligand that is bonded directly to the metal atom. (23.3)

donor impurities. Impurities that provide conduction electrons to semiconductors. (21.3)

double bond. Two atoms are held together by two pairs of electrons. (9.4)

dynamic equilibrium. The condition in which the rate of a forward process is exactly balanced by the rate of a reverse process. (11.8)

E

effective nuclear charge (Z_{eff}). The nuclear charge felt by an electron when both the actual charge (Z) and the repulsive effect (shielding) of the other electrons are taken into account. (8.3)

effusion. A process by which a gas under pressure escapes from one compartment of a container to another by passing through a small opening. (5.7)

electrochemistry. The branch of chemistry that deals with the interconversion of electrical energy and chemical energy. (18.1)

electrolysis. A process in which electrical energy is used to cause a nonspontaneous chemical reaction to occur. (18.8)

electrolyte. A substance that, when dissolved in water, results in a solution that can conduct electricity. (4.1)

electrolytic cell. An apparatus for carrying out electrolysis. (18.8)

electromagnetic radiation. The emission and transmission of energy in the form of electromagnetic waves. (7.1)

electromagnetic wave. A wave that has an electric field component and a mutually perpendicular magnetic field component. (7.1)

electromotive force (emf) (E). The voltage difference between electrodes. (18.2)

electron. A subatomic particle that has a very low mass and carries a single negative electric charge. (2.2)

electron affinity (EA). The negative of the enthalpy change when an electron is accepted by an atom in the gaseous state to form an anion. (8.5)

electron configuration. The distribution of electrons among the various orbitals in an atom or molecule. (7.8)

electron density. The probability that an electron will be found at a particular region in an atomic orbital. (7.5)

electronegativity. The ability of an atom to attract electrons toward itself in a chemical bond. (9.5)

element. A substance that cannot be separated into simpler substances by chemical means. (1.4)

elementary steps. A series of simple reactions that represent the progress of the overall reaction at the molecular level. (13.5)

emission spectra. Continuous or line spectra emitted by substances. (7.3)

empirical formula. An expression showing the types of elements present and the simplest ratios of the different kinds of atoms. (2.6)

enantiomers. Optical isomers, that is, compounds and their nonsuperimposable mirror images. (23.4)

endothermic processes. Processes that absorb heat from the surroundings. (6.2)

end point. The pH at which the indicator changes color. (16.5)

energy. The capacity to do work or to produce change. (6.1)

enthalpy (H). A thermodynamic quantity used to describe heat changes taking place at constant pressure. (6.4)

enthalpy of reaction (ΔH_{rxn}). The difference between the enthalpies of the products and the enthalpies of the reactants. (6.4)

enthalpy of solution (ΔH_{soln}). The heat generated or absorbed when a certain amount of solute is dissolved in a certain amount of solvent. (6.7)

entropy (S). A measure of how dispersed the energy of a system is among the different ways that system can contain energy. (17.3)

enzyme. A biological catalyst. (13.6)

equilibrium constant (K). A number equal to the ratio of the equilibrium concentrations of products to the equilibrium concentrations of reactants, each raised to the power of its stoichiometric coefficient. (14.1)

equilibrium vapor pressure. The vapor pressure measured under dynamic equilibrium of condensation and evaporation at some temperature. (11.8)

equivalence point. The point at which the acid has completely reacted with or been neutralized by the base. (4.7)

esters. Compounds that have the general formula R'COOR, where R' can be H or an alkyl group or an aromatic group and R is an alkyl group or an aromatic group. (24.4)

ether. An organic compound containing the R—O—R' linkage, where R and R' are alkyl and/or aromatic groups. (24.4)

evaporation. The process in which a liquid is transformed into a gas; also called vaporization. (11.8)

excess reagents. One or more reactants present in quantities greater than necessary to react with the quantity of the limiting reagent. (3.9)

excited state (or level). A state that has higher energy than the ground state. (7.3)

exothermic processes. Processes that give off heat to the surroundings. (6.2)

extensive property. A property that depends on how much matter is being considered. (1.6)

F

family. The elements in a vertical column of the periodic table. (2.4)

Faraday constant. Charge contained in 1 mole of electrons, equivalent to 96,485.3 coulombs. (18.4)

ferromagnetic. Attracted by a magnet. The unpaired spins in a ferromagnetic substance are aligned in a common direction. (21.2)

first law of thermodynamics. Energy can be converted from one form to another, but cannot be created or destroyed. (6.3)

first-order reaction. A reaction whose rate depends on reactant concentration raised to the first power. (13.3)

formal charge. The difference between the valence electrons in an isolated atom and the number of electrons assigned to that atom in a Lewis structure. (9.7)

formation constant (K_f). The equilibrium constant for the complex ion formation. (16.10)

fractional crystallization. The separation of a mixture of substances into pure components on the basis of their different solubilities. (12.4)

fractional distillation. A procedure for separating liquid components of a solution that is based on their different boiling points. (12.6)

free energy (*G*). The energy available to do useful work. (17.5)

freezing point. The temperature at which the solid and liquid phases of a substance coexist at equilibrium. (11.8)

freezing-point depression (ΔT_f). The freezing point of the pure solvent (T_f°) minus the freezing point of the solution (T_f). (12.6)

frequency (ν). The number of waves that pass through a particular point per unit time. (7.1)

fuel cell. A galvanic cell that requires a continuous supply of reactants to keep functioning. (18.6)

functional group. That part of a molecule characterized by a special arrangement of atoms that is largely responsible for the chemical behavior of the parent molecule. (24.1)

G

galvanic cell. The experimental apparatus for generating electricity through the use of a spontaneous redox reaction. (18.2)

gamma (γ) rays. High-energy radiation. (2.2)

gas constant (*R*). The constant that appears in the ideal gas equation. It is usually expressed as 0.08206 L · atm/K · mol, or 8.314 J/K · mol. (5.4)

geometric isomers. Compounds with the same type and number of atoms and the same chemical bonds but different spatial arrangements; such isomers cannot be interconverted without breaking a chemical bond. (23.4)

Gibbs free energy. See free energy.

glass. The optically transparent fusion product of inorganic materials that has cooled to a rigid state without crystallizing. (11.7)

Graham's law of diffusion. Under the same conditions of temperature and pressure, rates of diffusion for gases are inversely proportional to the square roots of their molar masses. (5.7)

gravimetric analysis. An experimental procedure that involves the measurement of mass. (4.6)

greenhouse effect. Carbon dioxide and other gases' influence on Earth's temperature. (20.5)

ground state (or level). The lowest energy state of a system. (7.3)

group. The elements in a vertical column of the periodic table. (2.4)

H

half-cell reactions. Oxidation and reduction reactions at the electrodes. (18.2)

half-life ($t_{\frac{1}{2}}$). The time required for the concentration of a reactant to decrease to half of its initial concentration. (13.3)

half-reaction. A reaction that explicitly shows electrons involved in either oxidation or reduction. (4.4)

halogens. The nonmetallic elements in Group 7A (F, Cl, Br, I, and At). (2.4)

heat. Transfer of energy between two bodies that are at different temperatures. (6.2)

heat capacity (*C*). The amount of heat required to raise the temperature of a given quantity of the substance by one degree Celsius. (6.5)

heat of dilution. The heat change associated with the dilution process. (6.7)

heat of hydration (ΔH_{hydr}). The heat change associated with the hydration process. (6.7)

heat of solution. See enthalpy of solution.

Heisenberg uncertainty principle. It is impossible to know simultaneously both the momentum and the position of a particle with certainty. (7.5)

Henry's law. The solubility of a gas in a liquid is proportional to the pressure of the gas over the solution. (12.5)

Hess's law. When reactants are converted to products, the change in enthalpy is the same whether the reaction takes place in one step or in a series of steps. (6.6)

heterogeneous equilibrium. An equilibrium state in which the reacting species are not all in the same phase. (14.2)

heterogeneous mixture. The individual components of a mixture remain physically separated and can be seen as separate components. (1.4)

homogeneous equilibrium. An equilibrium state in which all reacting species are in the same phase. (14.2)

homogeneous mixture. The composition of a mixture, after sufficient stirring, is the same throughout the solution. (1.4)

homonuclear diatomic molecule. A diatomic molecule containing atoms of the same element. (10.7)

homopolymer. A polymer that is made from only one type of monomer. (25.2)

Hund's rule. The most stable arrangement of electrons in subshells is the one with the greatest number of parallel spins. (7.8)

hybrid orbitals. Atomic orbitals obtained when two or more nonequivalent orbitals of the same atom combine. (10.4)

hybridization. The process of mixing the atomic orbitals in an atom (usually the central atom) to generate a set of new atomic orbitals. (10.4)

hydrates. Compounds that have a specific number of water molecules attached to them. (2.7)

hydration. A process in which an ion or a molecule is surrounded by water molecules arranged in a specific manner. (4.1)

hydrocarbons. Compounds made up only of carbon and hydrogen. (24.1)

hydrogen bond. A special type of dipole-dipole interaction between the hydrogen atom bonded to an atom of a very electronegative element (F, N, O) and another atom of one of the three electronegative elements. (11.2)

hydrogenation. The addition of hydrogen, especially to compounds with double and triple carbon-carbon bonds. (22.2)

hydronium ion. The hydrated proton, H_3O^+. (4.3)

hydrophilic. Water-liking. (12.8)

hydrophobic. Water-fearing. (12.8)

hypothesis. A tentative explanation for a set of observations. (1.3)

I

ideal gas. A hypothetical gas whose pressure-volume-temperature behavior can be completely accounted for by the ideal gas equation. (5.4)

ideal gas equation. An equation expressing the relationships among pressure, volume, temperature, and amount of gas ($PV = nRT$, where R is the gas constant). (5.4)

ideal solution. Any solution that obeys Raoult's law. (12.6)

indicators. Substances that have distinctly different colors in acidic and basic media. (4.7)

induced dipole. The separation of positive and negative charges in a neutral atom (or a nonpolar molecule) caused by the proximity of an ion or a polar molecule. (11.2)

inert complex. A complex ion that undergoes very slow ligand exchange reactions. (23.6)

inorganic compounds. Compounds other than organic compounds. (2.7)

insulator. A substance incapable of conducting electricity. (21.3)

intensive property. A property that does not depend on how much matter is being considered. (1.6)

intermediate. A species that appears in the mechanism of the reaction (that is, the elementary steps) but not in the overall balanced equation. (13.5)

intermolecular forces. Attractive forces that exist among molecules. (11.2)

International System of Units (SI). A system of units based on metric units. (1.7)

intramolecular forces. Forces that hold atoms together in a molecule. (11.2)

ion. An atom or a group of atoms that has a net positive or negative charge. (2.5)

ion pair. One or more cations and one or more anions held together by electrostatic forces. (12.7)

ionic bond. The electrostatic force that holds ions together in an ionic compound. (9.2)

ionic compound. Any neutral compound containing cations and anions. (2.5)

ionic equation. An equation that shows dissolved species as free ions. (4.2)

ionic radius. The radius of a cation or an anion as measured in an ionic compound. (8.3)

ionization energy (*IE*). The minimum energy required to remove an electron from an isolated atom (or an ion) in its ground state. (8.4)

ion-dipole forces. Forces that operate between an ion and a dipole. (11.2)

ion-product constant. Product of hydrogen ion concentration and hydroxide ion concentration (both in molarity) at a particular temperature. (15.2)

ionosphere. The uppermost layer of the atmosphere. (20.1)

isoelectronic. Ions, or atoms and ions, that possess the same number of electrons, and hence the same ground-state electron configuration, are said to be isoelectronic. (8.2)

isolated system. A system that does not allow the transfer of either mass or energy to or from its surroundings. (6.2)

isotopes. Atoms having the same atomic number but different mass numbers. (2.3)

J

Joule (J). Unit of energy given by newtons × meters. (5.7)

K

kelvin. The SI base unit of temperature. (1.7)

Kelvin temperature scale. See absolute temperature scale.

ketones. Compounds with a carbonyl functional group and the general formula $RR'CO$, where R and R' are alkyl and/or aromatic groups. (24.4)

kinetic energy (KE). Energy available because of the motion of an object. (5.7)

kinetic molecular theory of gases. Treatment of gas behavior in terms of the random motion of molecules. (5.7)

L

labile complex. Complexes that undergo rapid ligand exchange reactions. (23.6)

lanthanide (rare earth) series. Elements that have incompletely filled $4f$ subshells or readily give rise to cations that have incompletely filled $4f$ subshells. (7.9)

lattice energy. The energy required to completely separate one mole of a solid ionic compound into gaseous ions. (6.7)

law. A concise verbal or mathematical statement of a relationship between phenomena that is always the same under the same conditions. (1.3)

law of conservation of energy. The total quantity of energy in the universe is constant. (6.1)

law of conservation of mass. Matter can be neither created nor destroyed. (2.1)

law of definite proportions. Different samples of the same compound always contain its constituent elements in the same proportions by mass. (2.1)

law of mass action. For a reversible reaction at equilibrium and a constant temperature, a certain ratio of reactant and product concentrations has a constant value, K (the equilibrium constant). (14.1)

law of multiple proportions. If two elements can combine to form more than one type of compound, the masses of one element that combine with a fixed mass of the other element are in ratios of small whole numbers. (2.1)

Le Châtelier's principle. If an external stress is applied to a system at equilibrium, the system will adjust itself in such a way as to partially offset the stress as the system reaches a new equilibrium position. (14.5)

Lewis acid. A substance that can accept a pair of electrons. (15.12)

Lewis base. A substance that can donate a pair of electrons. (15.12)

Lewis dot symbol. The symbol of an element with one or more dots that represent the number of valence electrons in an atom of the element. (9.1)

Lewis structure. A representation of covalent bonding using Lewis symbols. Shared electron pairs are shown either as lines or as pairs of dots between two atoms, and lone pairs are shown as pairs of dots on individual atoms. (9.4)

ligand. A molecule or an ion that is bonded to the metal ion in a complex ion. (23.3)

limiting reagent. The reactant used up first in a reaction. (3.9)

line spectra. Spectra produced when radiation is absorbed or emitted by substances only at some wavelengths. (7.3)

liter. The volume occupied by one cubic decimeter. (1.7)

lone pairs. Valence electrons that are not involved in covalent bond formation. (9.4)

M

macroscopic properties. Properties that can be measured directly. (1.7)

manometer. A device used to measure the pressure of gases. (5.2)

many-electron atoms. Atoms that contain two or more electrons. (7.5)

mass. A measure of the quantity of matter contained in an object. (1.6)

mass defect. The difference between the mass of an atom and the sum of the masses of its protons, neutrons, and electrons. (19.2)

mass number (*A*). The total number of neutrons and protons present in the nucleus of an atom. (2.3)

matter. Anything that occupies space and possesses mass. (1.4)

melting point. The temperature at which solid and liquid phases coexist in equilibrium. (11.8)

mesosphere. A region between the stratosphere and the ionosphere. (20.1)

metalloid. An element with properties intermediate between those of metals and nonmetals. (2.4)

metallurgy. The science and technology of separating metals from their ores and of compounding alloys. (21.2)

metals. Elements that are good conductors of heat and electricity and have the tendency to form positive ions in ionic compounds. (2.4)

metathesis reaction. A reaction that involves the exchange of parts between two compounds. (4.2)

microscopic properties. Properties that cannot be measured directly without the aid of a microscope or other special instrument. (1.7)

mineral. A naturally occurring substance with a range of chemical composition. (21.1)

miscible. Two liquids that are completely soluble in each other in all proportions are said to be miscible. (12.2)

mixture. A combination of two or more substances in which the substances retain their identity. (1.4)

moderator. A substance that can reduce the kinetic energy of neutrons. (19.5)

molality. The number of moles of solute dissolved in one kilogram of solvent. (12.3)

molar concentration. See molarity.

molar heat of fusion (ΔH_{fus}). The energy (in kilojoules) required to melt one mole of a solid. (11.8)

molar heat of sublimation (ΔH_{sub}). The energy (in kilojoules) required to sublime one mole of a solid. (11.8)

molar heat of vaporization (ΔH_{vap}). The energy (in kilojoules) required to vaporize one mole of a liquid. (11.8)

molar mass ($\mathcal{M}$). The mass (in grams or kilograms) of one mole of atoms, molecules, or other particles. (3.2)

molar solubility. The number of moles of solute in one liter of a saturated solution (mol/L). (16.6)

molarity (M). The number of moles of solute in one liter of solution. (4.5)

mole (mol). The amount of substance that contains as many elementary entities (atoms, molecules, or other particles) as there are atoms in exactly 12 grams (or 0.012 kilograms) of the carbon-12 isotope. (3.2)

mole fraction. Ratio of the number of moles of one component of a mixture to the total number of moles of all components in the mixture. (5.6)

mole method. An approach for determining the amount of product formed in a reaction. (3.8)

molecular equations. Equations in which the formulas of the compounds are written as though all species existed as molecules or whole units. (4.2)

molecular formula. An expression showing the exact numbers of atoms of each element in a molecule. (2.6)

molecular mass. The sum of the atomic masses (in amu) present in the molecule. (3.3)

molecular orbital. An orbital that results from the interaction of the atomic orbitals of the bonding atoms. (10.6)

molecularity of a reaction. The number of molecules reacting in an elementary step. (13.5)

molecule. An aggregate of at least two atoms in a definite arrangement held together by special forces. (2.5)

monatomic ion. An ion that contains only one atom. (2.5)

monomer. The single repeating unit of a polymer. (25.2)

monoprotic acid. Each unit of the acid yields one hydrogen ion upon ionization. (4.3)

multiple bonds. Bonds formed when two atoms share two or more pairs of electrons. (9.4)

N

Nernst equation. The relation between the emf of a galvanic cell and the standard emf and the concentrations of the oxidizing and reducing agents. (18.5)

net ionic equation. An equation that indicates only the ionic species that actually take part in the reaction. (4.2)

neutralization reaction. A reaction between an acid and a base. (4.3)

neutron. A subatomic particle that bears no net electric charge. Its mass is slightly greater than a proton's. (2.2)

newton (N). The SI unit for force. (5.2)

nitrogen fixation. The conversion of molecular nitrogen into nitrogen compounds. (20.1)

noble gas core. The electron configuration of the noble gas element that most nearly precedes the element being considered. (7.9)

noble gases. Nonmetallic elements in Group 8A (He, Ne, Ar, Kr, Xe, and Rn). (2.4)

node. The point at which the amplitude of the wave is zero. (7.4)

nonelectrolyte. A substance that, when dissolved in water, gives a solution that is not electrically conducting. (4.1)

nonmetals. Elements that are usually poor conductors of heat and electricity. (2.4)

nonpolar molecule. A molecule that does not possess a dipole moment. (10.2)

nonvolatile. Does not have a measurable vapor pressure. (12.6)

***n*-type semiconductors.** Semiconductors that contain donor impurities. (21.3)

nuclear binding energy. The energy required to break up a nucleus into its protons and neutrons. (19.2)

nuclear chain reaction. A self-sustaining sequence of nuclear fission reactions. (19.5)

nuclear fission. A heavy nucleus (mass number > 200) divides to form smaller nuclei of intermediate mass and one or more neutrons. (19.5)

nuclear fusion. The combining of small nuclei into larger ones. (19.6)

nuclear transmutation. The change undergone by a nucleus as a result of bombardment by neutrons or other particles. (19.1)

nucleic acids. High molar mass polymers that play an essential role in protein synthesis. (25.4)

nucleon. A general term for the protons and neutrons in a nucleus. (19.2)

nucleotide. The repeating unit in each strand of a DNA molecule which consists of a base-deoxyribose-phosphate linkage. (25.4)

nucleus. The central core of an atom. (2.2)

O

octet rule. An atom other than hydrogen tends to form bonds until it is surrounded by eight valence electrons. (9.4)

open system. A system that can exchange mass and energy (usually in the form of heat) with its surroundings. (6.2)

optical isomers. Compounds that are nonsuperimposable mirror images. (23.4)

ore. The material of a mineral deposit in a sufficiently concentrated form to allow economical recovery of a desired metal. (21.1)

organic chemistry. The branch of chemistry that deals with carbon compounds. (24.1)

organic compounds. Compounds that contain carbon, usually in combination with elements such as hydrogen, oxygen, nitrogen, and sulfur. (2.7)

osmosis. The net movement of solvent molecules through a semipermeable membrane from a pure solvent or from a dilute solution to a more concentrated solution. (12.6)

osmotic pressure (π). The pressure required to stop osmosis. (12.6)

overvoltage. The difference between the electrode potential and the actual voltage required to cause electrolysis. (18.8)

oxidation number. The number of charges an atom would have in a molecule if electrons were transferred completely in the direction indicated by the difference in electronegativity. (4.4)

oxidation reaction. The half-reaction that involves the loss of electrons. (4.4)

oxidation-reduction reaction. A reaction that involves the transfer of electron(s) or the change in the oxidation state of reactants. (4.4)

oxidation state. See oxidation number.

oxidizing agent. A substance that can accept electrons from another substance or increase the oxidation numbers in another substance. (4.4)

oxoacid. An acid containing hydrogen, oxygen, and another element (the central element). (2.7)

oxoanion. An anion derived from an oxoacid. (2.7)

P

paramagnetic. Attracted by a magnet. A paramagnetic substance contains one or more unpaired electrons. (7.8)

partial pressure. Pressure of one component in a mixture of gases. (5.6)

pascal (Pa). A pressure of one newton per square meter (1 N/m^2). (5.2)

Pauli exclusion principle. No two electrons in an atom can have the same four quantum numbers. (7.8)

percent by mass. The ratio of the mass of a solute to the mass of the solution, multiplied by 100 percent. (12.3)

percent composition by mass. The percent by mass of each element in a compound. (3.5)

percent ionization. Ratio of ionized acid concentration at equilibrium to the initial concentration of acid. (15.5)

percent yield. The ratio of actual yield to theoretical yield, multiplied by 100 percent. (3.10)

period. A horizontal row of the periodic table. (2.4)

periodic table. A tabular arrangement of the elements. (2.4)

pH. The negative logarithm of the hydrogen ion concentration. (15.3)

phase. A homogeneous part of a system in contact with other parts of the system but separated from them by a well-defined boundary. (11.1)

phase change. Transformation from one phase to another. (11.8)

phase diagram. A diagram showing the conditions at which a substance exists as a solid, liquid, or vapor. (11.9)

photochemical smog. Formation of smog by the reactions of automobile exhaust in the presence of sunlight. (20.7)

photoelectric effect. A phenomenon in which electrons are ejected from the surface of certain metals exposed to light of at least a certain minimum frequency. (7.2)

photon. A particle of light. (7.2)

physical equilibrium. An equilibrium in which only physical properties change. (14.1)

physical property. Any property of a substance that can be observed without transforming the substance into some other substance. (1.6)

pi bond (π). A covalent bond formed by sideways overlapping orbitals; its electron density is concentrated above and below the plane of the nuclei of the bonding atoms. (10.5)

pi molecular orbital. A molecular orbital in which the electron density is concentrated above and below the plane of the two nuclei of the bonding atoms. (10.6)

plasma. A gaseous mixture of positive ions and electrons. (19.6)

polar covalent bond. In such a bond, the electrons spend more time in the vicinity of one atom than the other. (9.5)

polar molecule. A molecule that possesses a dipole moment. (10.2)

polarimeter. The instrument for measuring the rotation of polarized light by optical isomers. (23.4)

polyatomic ion. An ion that contains more than one atom. (2.5)

polyatomic molecule. A molecule that consists of more than two atoms. (2.5)

polymer. A compound distinguished by a high molar mass, ranging into thousands and millions of grams, and made up of many repeating units. (25.1)

positron. A particle that has the same mass as the electron, but bears a +1 charge. (19.1)

potential energy. Energy available by virtue of an object's position. (6.1)

precipitate. An insoluble solid that separates from the solution. (4.2)

precipitation reaction. A reaction that results in the formation of a precipitate. (4.2)

precision. The closeness of agreement of two or more measurements of the same quantity. (1.8)

pressure. Force applied per unit area. (5.2)

product. The substance formed as a result of a chemical reaction. (3.7)

protein. Polymers of amino acids. (25.3)

proton. A subatomic particle having a single positive electric charge. The mass of a proton is about 1840 times that of an electron. (2.2)

p-type semiconductors. Semiconductors that contain acceptor impurities. (21.3)

pyrometallurgy. Metallurgical processes that are carried out at high temperatures. (21.2)

Q

qualitative. Consisting of general observations about the system. (1.3)

qualitative analysis. The determination of the types of ions present in a solution. (16.11)

quantitative. Comprising numbers obtained by various measurements of the system. (1.3)

quantitative analysis. The determination of the amount of substances present in a sample. (4.5)

quantum. The smallest quantity of energy that can be emitted (or absorbed) in the form of electromagnetic radiation. (7.1)

quantum numbers. Numbers that describe the distribution of electrons in hydrogen and other atoms. (7.6)

R

racemic mixture. An equimolar mixture of the two enantiomers. (23.4)

radiant energy. Energy transmitted in the form of waves. (6.1)

radiation. The emission and transmission of energy through space in the form of particles and/or waves. (2.2)

radical. Any neutral fragment of a molecule containing an unpaired electron. (19.8)

radioactive decay series. A sequence of nuclear reactions that ultimately result in the formation of a stable isotope. (19.3)

radioactivity. The spontaneous breakdown of an atom by emission of particles and/or radiation. (2.2)

Raoult's law. The vapor pressure of the solvent over a solution is given by the product of the vapor pressure of the pure solvent and the mole fraction of the solvent in the solution. (12.6)

rare earth series. See lanthanide series.

rate constant (k). Constant of proportionality between the reaction rate and the concentrations of reactants. (13.1)

rate law. An expression relating the rate of a reaction to the rate constant and the concentrations of the reactants. (13.2)

rate-determining step. The slowest step in the sequence of steps leading to the formation of products. (13.5)

reactants. The starting substances in a chemical reaction. (3.7)

reaction mechanism. The sequence of elementary steps that leads to product formation. (13.5)

reaction order. The sum of the powers to which all reactant concentrations appearing in the rate law are raised. (13.2)

reaction quotient (Q_c). A number equal to the ratio of product concentrations to reactant concentrations, each raised to the power of its stoichiometric coefficient at some point other than equilibrium. (14.4)

reaction rate. The change in the concentration of reactant or product with time. (13.1)

redox reaction. A reaction in which there is either a transfer of electrons or a change in the oxidation numbers of the substances taking part in the reaction. (4.4)

reducing agent. A substance that can donate electrons to another substance or decrease the oxidation numbers in another substance. (4.4)

reduction reaction. The half-reaction that involves the gain of electrons. (4.4)

representative elements. Elements in Groups 1A through 7A, all of which have incompletely filled s or p subshell of highest principal quantum number. (8.2)

resonance. The use of two or more Lewis structures to represent a particular molecule. (9.8)

resonance structure. One of two or more alternative Lewis structures for a molecule that cannot be described fully with a single Lewis structure. (9.8)

reversible reaction. A reaction that can occur in both directions. (4.1)

ribonucleic acid (RNA). A form of nucleic acid. (25.4)

root-mean-square (rms) speed (u_{rms}). A measure of the average molecular speed at a given temperature. (5.7)

S

salt. An ionic compound made up of a cation other than H^+ and an anion other than OH^- or O^{2-}. (4.3)

salt hydrolysis. The reaction of the anion or cation, or both, of a salt with water. (15.10)

saponification. Soapmaking. (24.4)

saturated hydrocarbons. Hydrocarbons that contain the maximum number of hydrogen atoms that can bond with the number of carbon atoms present. (24.2)

saturated solution. At a given temperature, the solution that results when the maximum amount of a substance has dissolved in a solvent. (12.1)

scientific method. A systematic approach to research. (1.3)

second law of thermodynamics. The entropy of the universe increases in a spontaneous process and remains unchanged in an equilibrium process. (17.4)

second-order reaction. A reaction whose rate depends on reactant concentration raised to the second power or on the concentrations of two different reactants, each raised to the first power. (13.3)

semiconductors. Elements that normally cannot conduct electricity, but can have their conductivity greatly enhanced either by raising the temperature or by adding certain impurities. (21.3)

semipermeable membrane. A membrane that enables solvent molecules to pass through, but blocks the movement of solute molecules. (12.6)

sigma bond (σ). A covalent bond formed by orbitals overlapping end-to-end; its electron density is concentrated between the nuclei of the bonding atoms. (10.5)

sigma molecular orbital. A molecular orbital in which the electron density is concentrated around a line between the two nuclei of the bonding atoms. (10.6)

significant figures. The number of meaningful digits in a measured or calculated quantity. (1.8)

single bond. Two atoms are held together by one electron pair. (9.4)

solubility. The maximum amount of solute that can be dissolved in a given quantity of solvent at a specific temperature. (4.2, 16.6)

solubility product (K_{sp}). The product of the molar concentrations of the constituent ions, each raised to the power of its stoichiometric coefficient in the equilibrium equation. (16.6)

solute. The substance present in smaller amount in a solution. (4.1)

solution. A homogeneous mixture of two or more substances. (4.1)

solvation. The process in which an ion or a molecule is surrounded by solvent molecules arranged in a specific manner. (12.2)

solvent. The substance present in larger amount in a solution. (4.1)

specific heat (s). The amount of heat energy required to raise the temperature of one gram of a substance by one degree Celsius. (6.5)

spectator ions. Ions that are not involved in the overall reaction. (4.2)

spectrochemical series. A list of ligands arranged in increasing order of their abilities to split the d-orbital energy levels. (23.5)

standard atmospheric pressure (1 atm). The pressure that supports a column of mercury exactly 76 cm high at 0°C at sea level. (5.2)

standard emf ($E°$). The difference of the standard reduction potential of the substance that undergoes reduction and the standard reduction potential of the substance that undergoes oxidation. (18.3)

standard enthalpy of formation ($\Delta H_f°$). The heat change that results when one mole of a compound is formed from its elements in their standard states. (6.6)

standard enthalpy of reaction ($\Delta H_{rxn}°$). The enthalpy change when the reaction is carried out under standard-state conditions. (6.6)

standard entropy of reaction ($\Delta S_{rxn}°$). The entropy change when the reaction is carried out under standard-state conditions. (17.4)

standard free-energy of formation ($\Delta G_f°$). The free-energy change when 1 mole of a compound is synthesized from its elements in their standard states. (17.5)

standard free-energy of reaction ($\Delta G_{rxn}°$). The free-energy change when the reaction is carried out under standard-state conditions. (17.5)

standard reduction potential. The voltage measured as a reduction reaction occurs at the electrode when all solutes are 1 M and all gases are at 1 atm. (18.3)

standard solution. A solution of accurately known concentration. (4.7)

standard state. The condition of 1 atm of pressure. (6.6)

standard temperature and pressure (STP). 0°C and 1 atm. (5.4)

state function. A property that is determined by the state of the system. (6.3)

state of a system. The values of all pertinent macroscopic variables (for example, composition, volume, pressure, and temperature) of a system. (6.3)

stereoisomers. Compounds that are made up of the same types and numbers of atoms bonded together in the same sequence but with different spatial arrangements. (23.4)

stoichiometric amounts. The exact molar amounts of reactants and products that appear in the balanced chemical equation. (3.9)

stoichiometry. The quantitative study of reactants and products in a chemical reaction. (3.8)

stratosphere. The region of the atmosphere extending upward from the troposphere to about 50 km from Earth. (20.1)

strong acids. Strong electrolytes which are assumed to ionize completely in water. (15.4)

strong bases. Strong electrolytes which are assumed to ionize completely in water. (15.4)

structural formula. A chemical formula that shows how atoms are bonded to one another in a molecule. (2.6)

structural isomers. Molecules that have the same molecular formula but different structures. (24.2)

sublimation. The process in which molecules go directly from the solid into the vapor phase. (11.8)

substance. A form of matter that has a definite or constant composition (the number and type of basic units present) and distinct properties. (1.4)

substitution reaction. A reaction in which an atom or group of atoms replaces an atom or groups of atoms in another molecule. (24.3)

supercooling. Cooling of a liquid below its freezing point without forming the solid. (11.8)

supersaturated solution. A solution that contains more of the solute than is present in a saturated solution. (12.1)

surface tension. The amount of energy required to stretch or increase the surface of a liquid by a unit area. (11.3)

surroundings. The rest of the universe outside a system. (6.2)

system. Any specific part of the universe that is of interest to us. (6.2)

T

termolecular reaction. An elementary step that involves three molecules. (13.5)

ternary compounds. Compounds consisting of three elements. (2.7)

theoretical yield. The amount of product predicted by the balanced equation when all of the limiting reagent has reacted. (3.10)

theory. A unifying principle that explains a body of facts and the laws that are based on them. (1.3)

thermal energy. Energy associated with the random motion of atoms and molecules. (6.1)

thermochemical equation. An equation that shows both the mass and enthalpy relations. (6.4)

thermochemistry. The study of heat changes in chemical reactions. (6.2)

thermodynamics. The scientific study of the interconversion of heat and other forms of energy. (6.3)

thermonuclear reactions. Nuclear fusion reactions that occur at very high temperatures. (19.6)

thermosphere. The region of the atmosphere in which the temperature increases continuously with altitude. (20.1)

third law of thermodynamics. The entropy of a perfect crystalline substance is zero at the absolute zero of temperature. (17.4)

titration. The gradual addition of a solution of accurately known concentration to another solution of unknown concentration until the chemical reaction between the two solutions is complete. (4.7)

tracers. Isotopes, especially radioactive isotopes, that are used to trace the path of the atoms of an element in a chemical or biological process. (19.7)

transition metals. Elements that have incompletely filled d subshells or readily give rise to cations that have incompletely filled d subshells. (7.9)

transition state. See activated complex.

transuranium elements. Elements with atomic numbers greater than 92. (19.4)

triple bond. Two atoms are held together by three pairs of electrons. (9.4)

triple point. The point at which the vapor, liquid, and solid states of a substance are in equilibrium. (11.9)

triprotic acid. Each unit of the acid yields three protons upon ionization. (4.3)

troposphere. The layer of the atmosphere which contains about 80 percent of the total mass of air and practically all of the atmosphere's water vapor. (20.1)

U

unimolecular reaction. An elementary step in which only one reacting molecule participates. (13.5)

G-9   Glossary

unit cell. The basic repeating unit of the arrangement of atoms, molecules, or ions in a crystalline solid. (11.4)

unsaturated hydrocarbons. Hydrocarbons that contain carbon-carbon double bonds or carbon-carbon triple bonds. (24.2)

unsaturated solution. A solution that contains less solute than it has the capacity to dissolve. (12.1)

V

valence electrons. The outer electrons of an atom, which are those involved in chemical bonding. (8.2)

valence shell. The outermost electron-occupied shell of an atom, which holds the electrons that are usually involved in bonding. (10.1)

valence-shell electron-pair repulsion (VSEPR) model. A model that accounts for the geometrical arrangements of shared and unshared electron pairs around a central atom in terms of the repulsions between electron pairs. (10.1)

van der Waals equation. An equation that describes the P, V, and T of a nonideal gas. (5.8)

van der Waals forces. The dipole-dipole, dipole-induced dipole, and dispersion forces. (11.2)

van't Hoff factor (i). The ratio of actual number of particles in solution after dissociation to the number of formula units initially dissolved in solution. (12.7)

vaporization. The escape of molecules from the surface of a liquid; also called evaporation. (11.8)

viscosity. A measure of a fluid's resistance to flow. (11.3)

volatile. Has a measurable vapor pressure. (12.6)

volume. It is the length cubed. (1.6)

W

wave. A vibrating disturbance by which energy is transmitted. (7.1)

wavelength (λ). The distance between identical points on successive waves. (7.1)

weak acids. Weak electrolytes that ionize only to a limited extent in water. (15.4)

weak bases. Weak electrolytes that ionize only to a limited extent in water. (15.4)

weight. The force that gravity exerts on an object. (1.7)

work. Directed energy change resulting from a process. (6.1)

X

X-ray diffraction. The scattering of X rays by the units of a regular crystalline solid. (11.5)

Answers to Even-Numbered Problems

Chapter 1

1.4 (a) Hypothesis. (b) Law. (c) Theory. **1.12** (a) Physical change. (b) Chemical change. (c) Physical change. (d) Chemical change. (e) Physical change. **1.14** (a) Cs. (b) Ge. (c) Ga. (d) Sr. (e) U. (f) Se. (g) Ne. (h) Cd. **1.16** (a) Homogeneous mixture. (b) Element. (c) Compound. (d) Homogeneous mixture. (e) Heterogeneous mixture. (f) Heterogeneous mixture. (g) Element. **1.22** 71.2 g. **1.24** (a) 41°C. (b) 11.3°F. (c) 1.1×10^{4}°F. (d) 233°C. **1.26** (a) -196°C. (b) -269°C. (c) 328°C. **1.30** (a) 0.0152. (b) 0.0000000778. **1.32** (a) 1.8×10^{-2}. (b) 1.14×10^{10}. (c) -5×10^{4}. (d) 1.3×10^{3}. **1.34** (a) One. (b) Three. (c) Three. (d) Four. (e) Two or three. (f) One. (g) One or two. **1.36** (a) 1.28. (b) 3.18×10^{-3} mg. (c) 8.14×10^{7} dm. (d) 3.8 m/s. **1.38** Tailor X's measurements are the most precise. Tailor Y's measurements are the least accurate and least precise. Tailor Z's measurements are the most accurate. **1.40** (a) 1.10×10^{8} mg. (b) 6.83×10^{-5} m^{3}. (c) 7.2×10^{3} L. (d) 6.24×10^{-8} lb. **1.42** 3.1557×10^{7} s. **1.44** (a) 118 in/s. (b) 1.80×10^{2} m/min. (c) 10.8 km/h. **1.46** 178 mph. **1.48** 3.7×10^{-3} g Pb. **1.50** (a) 1.5×10^{2} lb. (b) 4.4×10^{17} s. (c) 2.3 m. (d) 8.86×10^{4} L. **1.52** 6.25×10^{-4} g/cm^{3}. **1.54** (a) Chemical. (b) Chemical. (c) Physical. (d) Physical. (e) Chemical. **1.56** 2.6 g/cm^{3}. **1.58** 9.20 cm. **1.60** 767 mph. **1.62** Liquid must be less dense than ice; temperature below 0°C. **1.64** 2.3×10^{3} cm^{3}. **1.66** 6.4¢. **1.68** 73°S. **1.70** (a) 8.6×10^{3} L air/day. (b) 0.018 L CO/day. **1.72** 26,700,000 basketballs. **1.74** 7.0×10^{20} L. **1.76** 88 lb; 40 kg. **1.78** O: 4.0×10^{4} g; C: 1.1×10^{4} g; H: 6.2×10^{3} g; N: 2×10^{3} g; Ca: 9.9×10^{2} g; P: 7.4×10^{2} g. **1.80** 4.6×10^{2}°C; 8.6×10^{2}°F. **1.82** 2.4×10^{12}. **1.84** 5.4×10^{22} Fe atoms. **1.86** 29 times. **1.88** 1.450×10^{-2} mm. **1.90** 1.3×10^{3} mL. **1.92** (a) 11.063 mL. (b) 0.78900 g/mL. (c) 7.140 g/mL. **1.94** 0.88 s. **1.96** (a) 327 L CO. (b) 5.0×10^{-8} g/L. (c) 1.20×10^{3} μg/mL. **1.98** 0.853 cm. **1.100** 4.97×10^{4} g. **1.102** 2.413 g/mL. **1.104** The glass bottle would crack.

Chapter 2

2.8 0.12 mi. **2.14** 145. **2.16** N(7,8,7); S(16,17,16); Cu(29,34,29); Sr(38,46,38); Ba(56,74,56); W(74,112,74); Hg(80,122,80). **2.18** (a) $^{186}_{74}$W. (b) $^{201}_{80}$Hg. **2.24** (a) Metallic character increases down a group. (b) Metallic character decreases from left to right. **2.26** F and Cl; Na and K; P and N. **2.32** (a) Diatomic molecule and compound. (b) Polyatomic molecule and compound. (c) Polyatomic molecule and element. **2.34** (a) H$_2$ and F$_2$. (b) HCl and CO. (c) S$_8$ and P$_4$. (d) H$_2$O and C$_{12}$H$_{22}$O$_{11}$ (sucrose). **2.36** (protons, electrons) K$^+$(19,18); Mg^{2+}(12,10); Fe^{3+}(26,23); Br$^-$(35,36); Mn^{2+}(25,23); C^{4-}(6,10); Cu^{2+}(29,27). **2.44** (a) CuBr. (b) Mn$_2$O$_3$. (c) Hg$_2$I$_2$. (d) Mg$_3$(PO$_4$)$_2$. **2.46** (a) AlBr$_3$. (b) NaSO$_2$. (c) N$_2$O$_5$. (d) K$_2$Cr$_2$O$_7$. **2.48** C$_2$H$_6$O. **2.50** Ionic: NaBr, BaF$_2$, CsCl. Molecular: CH$_4$, CCl$_4$, ICl, NF$_3$. **2.58** (a) Potassium hypochlorite. (b) Silver carbonate. (c) Iron(II) chloride. (d) Potassium permanganate. (e) Cesium chlorate. (f) Hypoiodous acid. (g) Iron(II) oxide. (h) Iron(III) oxide. (i) Titanium(IV) chloride. (j) Sodium hydride. (k) Lithium nitride. (l) Sodium oxide. (m) Sodium peroxide. (n) Iron(III) chloride hexahydrate. **2.60** (a) CuCN. (b) Sr(ClO$_2$)$_2$. (c) HBrO$_4$.

(d) HI(*aq*). (e) Na$_2$(NH$_4$)PO$_4$. (f) PbCO$_3$. (g) SnF$_2$. (h) P$_4$S$_{10}$. (i) HgO. (j) Hg$_2$I$_2$. (k) SeF$_6$. **2.62** (a) Dinitrogen pentoxide (N$_2$O$_5$). (b) Boron trifluoride (BF$_3$). (c) Dialuminum hexabromide (Al$_2$Br$_6$). **2.64** (a) $^{52}_{25}$Mn. (b) $^{22}_{10}$Ne. (c) $^{107}_{47}$Ag. (d) $^{127}_{53}$I. (e) $^{239}_{94}$Pu. **2.66** (c) Changing the electrical charge of an atom usually has a major effect on its chemical properties. **2.68** I$^-$. **2.70** NaCl is an ionic compound. It does not form molecules. **2.72** Element: (b), (c), (e), (f), (g), (j), (k). Molecules but not compounds: (b), (f), (g), (k). Compounds but not molecules: (i), (l). Compounds and molecules: (a), (d), (h). **2.74** (a) Ne: 10 p, 10 n. (b) Cu: 29 p, 34 n. (c) Ag: 47 p, 60 n. (d) W: 74 p, 108 n. (e) Po: 84 p, 119 n. (f) Pu: 94 p, 140 n. **2.76** (a) Cu. (b) P. (c) Kr. (d) Cs. (e) Al. (f) Sb. (g) Cl. (h) Sr. **2.78** (a) The magnitude of a particle scattering depends on the number of protons present. (b) Density of nucleus: 3.25×10^{14} g/cm^3; density of space occupied by electrons: 3.72×10^{-4} g/cm^3. The result supports Rutherford's model. **2.80** The empirical and molecular formulas of acetaminophen are both C$_8$H$_9$NO$_2$. **2.82** (a) Tin(IV) chloride. (b) Copper(I) oxide. (c) Cobalt(II) nitrate. (d) Sodium dichromate. **2.84** (a) Ionic compounds formed between metallic and nonmetallic elements. (b) Transition metals, lanthanides, and actinides. **2.86** ^{23}Na. **2.88** Hg and Br$_2$. **2.90** H$_2$, N$_2$, O$_2$, F$_2$, Cl$_2$, He, Ne, Ar, Kr, Xe, Rn. **2.92** Unreactive. He, Ne, and Ar are chemically inert. **2.94** Ra is a radioactive decay product of U-238. **2.96** ^{77}Se^{2-}. **2.98** (a) NaH, sodium hydride. (b) B$_2$O$_3$, diboron trioxide. (c) Na$_2$S, sodium sulfide. (d) AlF$_3$, aluminum fluoride. (e) OF$_2$, oxygen difluoride. (f) SrCl$_2$, strontium chloride. **2.100** NF$_3$ (nitrogen trifluoride), PBr$_5$ (phosphorus pentabromide), SCl$_2$ (sulfur dichloride). **2.102** 1st row: Mg^{2+}, HCO$_3^-$, Mg(HCO$_3$)$_2$. 2nd row: Sr^{2+}, Cl$^-$, strontium chloride. 3rd row: Fe(NO$_2$)$_3$, iron(III) nitrite. 4th row: Mn^{2+}, ClO$_3^-$, Mn(ClO$_3$)$_2$. 5th row: Sn^{4+}, Br$^-$, tin(IV) bromide. 6th row: Co$_3$(PO$_4$)$_2$, cobalt(II) phosphate. 7th row: Hg$_2$I$_2$, mercury(I) iodide. 8th row: Cu$^+$, CO$_3^{2-}$, copper(I) carbonate. 9th row: Li$^+$, N^{3-}, Li$_3$N. 10th row: Al$_2$S$_3$, aluminum sulfide. **2.104** 1.91×10^{-8} g. Mass is too small to be detected. **2.106** (a) Volume of a sphere is given by $V = (4/3)\pi r^3$. Volume is also proportional to the number of neutrons and protons present, or the mass number A. Therefore, $r^3 \propto A$ or $r \propto A^{1/3}$. (b) 5.1×10^{-44} m^3. (c) The nucleus occupies only 3.5×10^{-13}% of the atom's volume. The result supports Rutherford's model. **2.108** (a) Yes. (b) Ethane: CH$_3$ and C$_2$H$_6$. Acetylene: CH and C$_2$H$_2$. **2.110** Manganese (Mn). **2.112** From left to right: chloric acid, nitrous acid, hydrocyanic acid, and sulfuric acid. **2.114** XY$_2$. X is likely in Group 4B or Group 4A and Y is likely in Group 6A. Examples: titanium(IV) oxide (TiO$_2$), tin(IV) oxide (SnO$_2$), and lead(IV) oxide (PbO$_2$).

Chapter 3

3.6 7.5% and 92.5%. **3.8** 5.1×10^{24} amu. **3.12** 5.8×10^{3} light-yr. **3.14** 9.96×10^{-15} mol Co. **3.16** 3.01×10^{3} g Au. **3.18** (a) 1.244×10^{-22} g/As atom. (b) 9.746×10^{-23} g/Ni atom. **3.20** 6.0×10^{20} Cu atoms. **3.22** Pb. **3.24** (a) 73.89 g. (b) 76.15 g. (c) 119.37 g. (d) 176.12 g. (e) 101.11 g. (f) 100.95 g. **3.26** 6.69×10^{21} C$_2$H$_6$ molecules. **3.28** C: 1.10×10^{26} atoms; S: 5.50×10^{25} atoms;

H: 3.30×10^{26} atoms; O: 5.50×10^{25} atoms. **3.30** 8.56×10^{22} molecules. **3.34** 7. **3.40** C: 10.06%; H: 0.8442%; Cl: 89.07%. **3.42** NH_3. **3.44** $C_2H_3NO_5$. **3.46** 39.3 g S. **3.48** 5.97 g F. **3.50** (a) CH_2O. (b) KCN. **3.52** C_6H_6. **3.54** $C_5H_8O_4NNa$. **3.60** (a) $2N_2O_5 \longrightarrow 2N_2O_4 + O_2$. (b) $2KNO_3 \longrightarrow 2KNO_2 + O_2$. (c) $NH_4NO_3 \longrightarrow N_2O + 2H_2O$. (d) $NH_4NO_2 \longrightarrow N_2 + 2H_2O$. (e) $2NaHCO_3 \longrightarrow Na_2CO_3 + H_2O + CO_2$. (f) $P_4O_{10} + 6H_2O \longrightarrow 4H_3PO_4$. (g) $2HCl + CaCO_3 \longrightarrow CaCl_2 + H_2O + CO_2$. (h) $2Al + 3H_2SO_4 \longrightarrow Al_2(SO_4)_3 + 3H_2$. (i) $CO_2 + 2KOH \longrightarrow K_2CO_3 + H_2O$. (j) $CH_4 + 2O_2 \longrightarrow CO_2 + 2H_2O$. (k) $Be_2C + 4H_2O \longrightarrow 2Be(OH)_2 + CH_4$. (l) $3Cu + 8HNO_3 \longrightarrow 3Cu(NO_3)_2 + 2NO + 4H_2O$. (m) $S + 6HNO_3 \longrightarrow H_2SO_4 + 6NO_2 + 2H_2O$. (n) $2NH_3 + 3CuO \longrightarrow 3Cu + N_2 + 3H_2O$. **3.64** (d). **3.66** 1.01 mol. **3.68** 20 mol. **3.70** (a) $2NaHCO_3 \longrightarrow Na_2CO_3 + CO_2 + H_2O$. (b) 78.3 g. **3.72** 255.9 g; 0.324 L. **3.74** 0.294 mol. **3.76** (a) $NH_4NO_3 \longrightarrow N_2O + 2H_2O$. (b) 20 g. **3.78** 18.0 g. **3.82** 1 mole H_2 left and 6 moles NH_3 produced. **3.84** (a) $2NH_3 + H_2SO_4 \longrightarrow (NH_4)_2SO_4$. (b) 5.23 g NH_3; 21.0 g H_2SO_4. **3.86** HCl; 23.4 g. **3.90** (a) 7.05 g. (b) 92.9%. **3.92** 3.48×10^3 g. **3.94** 8.55 g; 76.6%. **3.96** ^{85}Rb: 72.1%; ^{87}Rb: 27.9%. **3.98** (b). **3.100** (a) $C_5H_{12} + 8O_2 \longrightarrow 5CO_2 + 6H_2O$. (b) $NaHCO_3 + HCl \longrightarrow CO_2 + NaCl + H_2O$. (c) $6Li + N_2 \longrightarrow 2Li_3N$. (d) $PCl_3 + 3H_2O \longrightarrow H_3PO_3 + 3HCl$. (e) $3CuO + 2NH_3 \longrightarrow 3Cu + N_2 + 3H_2O$. **3.102** Cl_2O_7. **3.104** 18.7 g. **3.106** (a) 0.212 mol. (b) 0.424 mol. **3.108** 18. **3.110** 2.4×10^{23} atoms. **3.112** 65.4 amu; Zn. **3.114** 89.5%. **3.116** CH_2O; $C_6H_{12}O_6$. **3.118** 51.9 g/mol; Cr. **3.120** 1.6×10^4 g/mol. **3.122** NaBr: 24.03%; Na_2SO_4: 75.97%. **3.124** $C_3H_8 + 5O_2 \longrightarrow 3CO_2 + 4H_2O$. **3.126** Ca: 38.76%; P: 19.97%; O: 41.27%. **3.128** Yes. **3.130** 2.01×10^{21} molecules. **3.132** 16.00 amu. **3.134** (e). **3.136** $PtCl_2$; $PtCl_4$. **3.138** (a) 12 g; 28 mL. (b) 15 g. **3.140** (a) X: MnO_2; Y: Mn_3O_4. (b) $3MnO_2 \longrightarrow Mn_3O_4 + O_2$. **3.142** 6.1×10^5 tons. **3.144** $C_3H_2ClF_5O$. C: 19.53%; H: 1.093%; Cl: 19.21%; F: 51.49%; O: 8.672%. **3.146** Mg_3N_2 (magnesium nitride). **3.148** PbC_8H_{20}. **3.150** (a) 4.3×10^{22} atoms. (b) 1.6×10^2 pm. **3.152** 28.97 g/mol. **3.154** (a) $Fe_2O_3 + 6HCl \longrightarrow 2FeCl_3 + 3H_2O$. (b) 396 g $FeCl_3$. **3.156** (a) $C_3H_8 + 3H_2O \longrightarrow 3CO + 7H_2$. (b) 9.09×10^2 kg. **3.158** (a) There is only one reactant so the use of "limiting reagent" is unnecessary. (b) The term "limiting reagent" usually applies only to one reactant. **3.160** (a) \$0.47/kg. (b) 0.631 kg K_2O. **3.162** $BaBr_2$. **3.164** NaCl: 32.17%; Na_2SO_4: 20.09%; $NaNO_3$: 47.75%.

Chapter 4

4.8 (c). **4.10** (a) Strong electrolyte. (b) Nonelectrolyte. (c) Weak electrolyte. (d) Strong electrolyte. **4.12** (b) and (c). **4.14** HCl does not ionize in benzene. **4.18** (b). **4.20** (a) Insoluble. (b) Soluble. (c) Soluble. (d) Insoluble. (e) Soluble. **4.22** (a) Ionic: $2Na^+ + S^{2-} + Zn^{2+} + 2Cl^- \longrightarrow ZnS + 2Na^+ + 2Cl^-$. Net ionic: $Zn^{2+} + S^{2-} \longrightarrow ZnS$. (b) Ionic: $6K^+ + 2PO_4^{3-} + 3Sr^{2+} + 6NO_3^- \longrightarrow Sr_3(PO_4)_2 + 6KNO_3$. Net ionic: $3Sr^{2+} + 2PO_4^{3-} \longrightarrow Sr_3(PO_4)_2$. (c) Ionic: $Mg^{2+} + 2NO_3^- + 2Na^+ + 2OH^- \longrightarrow Mg(OH)_2 + 2Na^+ + 2NO_3^-$. Net ionic: $Mg^{2+} + 2OH^- \longrightarrow Mg(OH)_2$. **4.24** (a) Add chloride ions. (b) Add hydroxide ions. (c) Add carbonate ions. (d) Add sulfate ions. **4.32** (a) Brønsted base. (b) Brønsted base. (c) Brønsted acid. (d) Brønsted base and Brønsted acid. **4.34** (a) Ionic: $CH_3COOH + K^+ + OH^- \longrightarrow K^+ + CH_3COO^- + H_2O$; Net ionic: $CH_3COOH + OH^- \longrightarrow CH_3COO^- + H_2O$. (b) Ionic: $H_2CO_3 + 2Na^+ + 2OH^- \longrightarrow 2Na^+ + CO_3^{2-} + 2H_2O$; Net ionic: $H_2CO_3 + 2OH^- \longrightarrow CO_3^{2-} + 2H_2O$. (c) Ionic: $2H^+ + 2NO_3^- + Ba^{2+} + 2OH^- \longrightarrow Ba^{2+} + 2NO_3^- + 2H_2O$; Net ionic: $H^+ + OH^- \longrightarrow H_2O$. **4.44** (a) Fe $\longrightarrow Fe^{3+} + 3e^-$; $O_2 + 4e^- \longrightarrow 2O^{2-}$. Oxidizing agent: O_2; reducing agent: Fe. (b) $2Br^- \longrightarrow Br_2 + 2e^-$; $Cl_2 + 2e^- \longrightarrow 2Cl^-$.

Oxidizing agent: Cl_2; reducing agent: Br^-. (c) Si $\longrightarrow Si^{4+} + 4e^-$; $F_2 + 2e^- \longrightarrow 2F^-$. Oxidizing agent: F_2; reducing agent: Si. (d) $H_2 \longrightarrow 2H^+ + 2e^-$; $Cl_2 + 2e^- \longrightarrow 2Cl^-$. Oxidizing agent: Cl_2; reducing agent: H_2. **4.46** (a) +5. (b) +1. (c) +3. (d) +5. (e) +5. (f) +5. **4.48** All are zero. **4.50** (a) −3. (b) −1/2. (c) −1. (d) +4. (e) +3. (f) −2. (g) +3. (h) +6. **4.52** Li and Ca. **4.54** (a) No reaction. (b) No reaction. (c) $Mg + CuSO_4 \longrightarrow MgSO_4 + Cu$. (d) $Cl_2 + 2KBr \longrightarrow Br_2 + 2KCl$. **4.56** (a) Combination. (b) Decomposition. (c) Displacement. (d) Disproportionation. **4.58** O_2^+. **4.62** Dissolve 15.0 g $NaNO_3$ in enough water to make up 250 mL. **4.64** 10.8 g. **4.66** (a) 1.37 M. (b) 0.426 M. (c) 0.716 M. **4.68** (a) 6.50 g. (b) 2.45 g. (c) 2.65 g. (d) 7.36 g. (e) 3.95 g. **4.70** 11.83 g. **4.74** 0.0433 M. **4.76** 126 mL. **4.78** 1.09 M. **4.82** 35.73%. **4.84** 0.00975 M. **4.90** 0.217 M. **4.92** (a) 6.00 mL. (b) 8.00 mL. **4.96** 9.44×10^{-3} g. **4.98** 0.06020 M. **4.100** 6.15 mL. **4.102** 0.232 mg. **4.104** (i) Only oxygen supports combustion. (ii) Only CO_2 reacts with $Ca(OH)_2(aq)$ to form $CaCO_3$ (white precipitate). **4.106** 1.26 M. **4.108** (a) 15.6 g $Al(OH)_3$. (b) $[Al^{3+}] = 0.250 M$, $[NO_3^-] = 2.25 M$, $[K^+] 1.50 M$. **4.110** 0.171 M. **4.112** 0.115 M. **4.114** Ag: 1.25 g; Zn: 2.12 g. **4.116** 0.0721 M NaOH. **4.118** 24.0 g/mol; Mg. **4.120** 2. **4.122** 1.72 M. **4.124** Only Fe(II) is oxidized by $KMnO_4$ solution and can therefore change the purple color to colorless. **4.126** Ions are removed as the $BaSO_4$ precipitate. **4.128** $FeCl_2 \cdot 4H_2O$. **4.130** (i) Conductivity test. (ii) Only NaCl reacts with $AgNO_3$ to form AgCl precipitate. **4.132** The Cl^- ion cannot accept any electrons. **4.134** Reaction is too violent. **4.136** Use sodium bicarbonate: $HCO_3^- + H^+ \longrightarrow H_2O + CO_2$. NaOH is a caustic substance and unsafe to use in this manner. **4.138** (a) Conductivity. Reaction with $AgNO_3$ to form AgCl. (b) Soluble in water. Nonelectrolyte. (c) Possesses properties of acids. (d) Soluble. Reacts with acids to give CO_2. (e) Soluble, strong electrolyte. Reacts with acids to give CO_2. (f) Weak electrolyte and weak acid. (g) Soluble in water. Reacts with NaOH to produce $Mg(OH)_2$ precipitate. (h) Strong electrolyte and strong base. (i) Characteristic odor. Weak electrolyte and weak base. (j) Insoluble. Reacts with acids. (k) Insoluble. Reacts with acids to produce CO_2. **4.140** NaCl: 44.11%; KCl: 55.89%. **4.142** (a) $AgOH(s) + HNO_3(aq) \longrightarrow AgNO_3(aq) + H_2O(l)$. **4.144** 1.33 g. **4.146** 56.18%. **4.148** (a) 1.40 M. (b) 4.96 g. **4.150** (a) $NH_4^+ + OH^- \longrightarrow NH_3 + H_2O$. (b) 97.99%. **4.152** Zero. **4.154** 0.224%. Yes. **4.156** (a) $Zn + H_2SO_4 \longrightarrow ZnSO_4 + H_2$. (b) $2KClO_3 \longrightarrow 2KCl + 3O_2$. (c) $Na_2CO_3 + 2HCl \longrightarrow 2NaCl + CO_2 + H_2O$. (d) $NH_4NO_2 \longrightarrow N_2 + 2H_2O$. **4.158** Yes. **4.160** (a) $8.316 \times 10^{-7} M$. (b) 3.286×10^{-5} g. **4.162** $[Fe^{2+}] = 0.0920 M$, $[Fe^{3+}] = 0.0680 M$. **4.164** (a) Precipitation: $Mg^{2+} + 2OH^- \longrightarrow Mg(OH)_2$; acid-base: $Mg(OH)_2 + 2HCl \longrightarrow MgCl_2 + 2H_2O$; redox: $MgCl_2 \longrightarrow Mg + Cl_2$. (b) NaOH is more expensive than CaO. (c) Dolomite provides additional Mg. **4.166** D < A < C < B. D = Au, A = Cu, C = Zn, B = Mg. **4.168** (a) $Cu^{2+} + SO_4^{2-} + Ba^{2+} + 2OH^- \longrightarrow Cu(OH)_2 + BaSO_4$. (b) 14.6 g $Cu(OH)_2$, 35.0 g $BaSO_4$. $[Cu^{2+}] = [SO_4^{2-}] = 0.0417 M$.

Chapter 5

5.14 0.797 atm; 80.8 kPa. **5.18** (1) b. (2) a. (3) c. (4) a. **5.20** 53 atm. **5.22** (a) 0.69 L. (b) 61 atm. **5.24** 1.3×10^2 K. **5.26** ClF_3. **5.32** 6.2 atm. **5.34** 745 K. **5.36** 1.9 atm. **5.38** 0.82 L. **5.40** 45.1 L. **5.42** 6.1×10^{-3} atm. **5.44** 35.1 g/mol. **5.46** N_2: 2.1×10^{22}; O_2: 5.7×10^{21}; Ar: 3×10^{20}. **5.48** 2.98 g/L. **5.50** SF_4. **5.52** F_2: 59.7%; Cl_2: 40.3%. **5.54** 370 L. **5.56** 88.9%. **5.58** $M + 3HCl \longrightarrow (3/2)H_2 + MCl_3$; M_2O_3, $M_2(SO_4)_3$. **5.60** 2.84×10^{-2} mol CO_2; 94.7%. The impurities must not react with HCl to produce CO_2.

5.62 1.71×10^3 L. **5.64** 86.0%. **5.68** (a) 0.89 atm. (b) 1.4 L. **5.70** 349 mmHg. **5.72** 19.8 g. **5.74** H_2: 650 mmHg; N_2: 217 mmHg. **5.76** (a) Box on right. (b) Box on left. **5.82** N_2: 472 m/s; O_2: 441 m/s; O_3: 360 m/s. **5.84** 2.8 m/s; 2.7 m/s. Squaring favors the larger values. **5.86** 1.0043. **5.88** 4. **5.94** No. **5.96** Ne. **5.98** C_6H_6. **5.100** 445 mL. **5.102** (a) 9.53 atm. (b) $Ni(CO)_4$ decomposes to give CO, which increases the pressure. **5.104** 1.30×10^{22} molecules; CO_2, O_2, N_2, H_2O. **5.106** 5.25×10^{18} kg. **5.108** 0.0701 M. **5.110** He: 0.16 atm; Ne: 2.0 atm. **5.112** HCl dissolves in the water, creating a partial vacuum. **5.114** 7. **5.116** (a) 61.2 m/s. (b) 4.58×10^{-4} s. (c) 328 m/s; 366 m/s. The velocity 328 m/s is that of a particular atom and u_{rms} is an average value. **5.118** 2.09×10^4 g; 1.58×10^4 L. **5.120** Higher partial pressure of C_2H_4 inside the paper bag. **5.122** To equalize the pressure as the amount of ink decreases. **5.124** (a) $NH_4NO_3 \longrightarrow N_2O + 2H_2O$. (b) 0.0821 L · atm/K · mol. **5.126** C_6H_6. **5.128** The low atmospheric pressure caused the harmful gases (CO, CO_2, CH_4) to flow out of the mine, and the man suffocated. **5.130** Br_2 (159.8 g/mol; red); SO_3 (80.07 g/mol; yellow); N_2 (28.02 g/mol; green); CH_4 (16.04 g/mol; blue). **5.132** (a) 5×10^{-22} atm. (b) 5×10^{20} L/g H. **5.134** 91%. **5.136** 1.7×10^{12} molecules. **5.138** 4.66 L. **5.140** 3.8×10^{-3} m/s; 1.0×10^{-30} J. **5.142** 2.3×10^3 L. **5.144** 1.8×10^2 mL. **5.146** (a) 1.09×10^{44} molecules. (b) 1.18×10^{22} molecules/breath. (c) 2.60×10^{30} molecules. (d) 2.39×10^{-14}; 3×10^8 molecules. (e) Complete mixing of air; no molecules escaped to the outer atmosphere; no molecules used up during metabolism, nitrogen fixation, etc. **5.148** 3.7 nm; 0.31 nm. **5.150** 0.54 atm. **5.152** H_2: 0.5857; D_2: 0.4143. **5.154** 53.4%. **5.156** CO: 54.4%; CO_2: 45.6%. **5.158** CH_4: 0.789; C_2H_6: 0.211. **5.160** (a) $8(4\pi r^3/3)$. (b) $(16/3)N_A\pi r^3$. The excluded volume is 4 times the volumes of the atoms. **5.162** CH_4. **5.164** NO. **5.166** (a) 8.0 atm. (c) 5.3 atm. (ii) $P_T = 5.3$ atm, $P_A = 2.65$ atm. $P_B = 2.65$ atm. **5.170** CH_4: 2.3 atm. C_2H_6: 0.84 atm. C_3H_8: 1.4 atm.

Chapter 6

6.16 (a) 0. (b) -9.5 J. (c) -18 J. **6.18** 48 J. **6.20** -3.1×10^3 J. **6.26** 1.57×10^4 kJ. **6.28** -553.8 kJ/mol. **6.32** 0.237 J/g · °C. **6.34** 3.31 kJ. **6.36** 98.6 g. **6.38** 22.39°C. **6.46** O_2. **6.48** (a) $\Delta H_f^\circ[Br_2(l)] = 0$; $\Delta H_f^\circ[Br_2(g)] > 0$. (b) $\Delta H_f^\circ[I_2(s)] = 0$; $\Delta H_f^\circ[I_2(g)] > 0$. **6.50** Measure ΔH° for the formation of Ag_2O from Ag and O_2 and of $CaCl_2$ from Ca and Cl_2. **6.52** (a) -167.2 kJ/mol. (b) -56.2 kJ/mol. **6.54** (a) -1411 kJ/mol. (b) -1124 kJ/mol. **6.56** 218.2 kJ/mol. **6.58** 71.58 kJ/g. **6.60** 2.70×10^2 kJ. **6.62** -84.6 kJ/mol. **6.64** -847.6 kJ/mol. **6.72** 11 kJ. **6.74** -2.90×10^2 kJ/mol. **6.76** (a) -336.5 kJ/mol. (b) NH_3. **6.78** 26.5 kJ/mol. **6.80** 43.6 kJ. **6.82** 0. **6.84** -350.7 kJ/mol. **6.86** -558.2 kJ/mol. **6.88** 0.492 J/g · °C. **6.90** The first (exothermic) reaction can be used to promote the second (endothermic) reaction. **6.92** 1.09×10^4 kJ. **6.94** 4.10 L. **6.96** 5.60 kJ/mol. **6.98** (a). **6.100** (a) 0. (b) -9.1 J. (c) 2.4 L; -48 J. **6.102** (a) A more fully packed freezer has a greater mass and hence a larger heat capacity. (b) Tea or coffee has a greater amount of water, which has a higher specific heat than noodles. **6.104** 1.84×10^3 kJ. **6.106** 3.0×10^9. **6.108** 5.35 kJ/°C. **6.110** -5.2×10^6 kJ. **6.112** (a) 3.4×10^5 g. (b) -2.0×10^8 J. **6.114** -86.7 kJ/mol. **6.116** (a) 1.4×10^2 kJ. (b) 3.9×10^2 kJ. **6.118** (a) -65.2 kJ/mol. (b) -9.0 kJ/mol. **6.120** -110.5 kJ/mol. It will form both CO and CO_2. **6.122** (a) 0.50 J. (b) 32 m/s. (c) 0.12°C. **6.124** -277.0 kJ/mol. **6.126** 104 g. **6.128** 296 kJ. **6.130** 9.9×10^8 J; 304°C. **6.132** (a) $CaC_2 + 2H_2O \longrightarrow C_2H_2 + Ca(OH)_2$. (b) 1.51×10^3 kJ. **6.134** $\Delta U = -5153$ kJ/mol; $\Delta H = -5158$ kJ/mol. **6.136** -564.2 kJ/mol. **6.138** 96.21%. **6.140** (a) CH. (b) 49 kJ/mol.

6.142 (a) Heating water at room temperature to its boiling point. (b) Heating water at its boiling point. (c) A chemical reaction taking place in a bomb calorimeter (an isolated system) where there is no heat exchange with the surroundings. **6.144** -101.3 J. Yes, because in a cyclic process, the change in a state function must be zero. **6.146** (a) Exothermic. (b) No clear conclusion. It is a balance between the energy needed to break the ionic bond and the energy released during hydration. (c) No clear conclusion. It is a balance between the energy needed to break the A—B bond and the energy released when the A—C bond is formed. (d) Endothermic.

Chapter 7

7.8 (a) 6.58×10^{14}/s. (b) 1.22×10^8 nm. **7.10** 2.5 min. **7.12** 4.95×10^{14}/s. **7.16** (a) 4.0×10^2 nm. (b) 5.0×10^{-19} J. **7.18** 1.2×10^2 nm (UV). **7.20** (a) 3.70×10^2 nm. (b) UV. (c) 5.38×10^{-19} J. **7.22** 8.16×10^{-19} J. **7.26** Use a prism. **7.28** Compare the emission spectra with those on Earth of known elements. **7.30** 3.027×10^{-19} J. **7.32** 6.17×10^{14}/s. 486 nm. **7.34** 5. **7.40** 1.37×10^{-6} nm. **7.42** 1.7×10^{-23} nm. **7.56** $\ell = 2$: $m_\ell = -2, -1, 0, 1, 2$. $\ell = 1$: $m_\ell = -1, 0, 1$. $\ell = 0$: $m_\ell = 0$. **7.58** (a) $n = 3$, $\ell = 0$, $m_\ell = 0$. (b) $n = 4$, $\ell = 1$, $m_\ell = -1, 0, 1$. (c) $n = 3$, $\ell = 2$, $m_\ell = -2, -1, 0, 1, 2$. In all cases, $m_s = +1/2$ or $-1/2$. **7.60** Differ in orientation only. **7.62** $6s$, $6p$, $6d$, $6f$, $6g$, and $6h$. **7.64** $2n^2$. **7.66** (a) 3. (b) 6. (c) 0. **7.68** There is no shielding in an H atom. **7.70** (a) $2s < 2p$. (b) $3p < 3d$. (c) $3s < 4s$. (d) $4d < 5f$. **7.76** Al: $1s^22s^22p^63s^23p^1$. B: $1s^22s^22p^1$. F: $1s^22s^22p^5$. **7.78** B(1), Ne(0), P(3), Sc(1), Mn(5), Se(2), Kr(0), Fe(4), Cd(0), I(1), Pb(2). **7.88** $[Kr]5s^24d^5$. **7.90** Ge: $[Ar]4s^23d^{10}4p^2$. Fe: $[Ar]4s^23d^6$. Zn: $[Ar]4s^23d^{10}$. Ni: $[Ar]4s^23d^8$. W: $[Xe]6s^24f^{14}5d^4$. Tl: $[Xe]6s^24f^{14}5d^{10}6p^1$. **7.92** S^+. **7.94** 6.68×10^{16} photons. **7.96** (a) Incorrect. (b) Correct. (c) Incorrect. **7.98** (a) $4e$: An e in a $2s$ and an e in each $2p$ orbital. (b) $6e$: $2e$ each in a $4p$, a $4d$, and a $4f$ orbital. (c) $10e$: $2e$ in each of the five $3d$ orbitals. (d) $1e$: An e in a $2s$ orbital. (e) $2e$: $2e$ in a $4f$ orbital. **7.100** Wave properties. **7.102** (a) 1.05×10^{-25} nm. (b) 8.86 nm. **7.104** (a) $n = 2$. The possible ℓ values are from 0 to $(n - 1)$ integer values. (b) Possible ℓ values are 0, 1, 2, or 3. Possible m_ℓ values range from $-\ell$ to $+\ell$ integer values. **7.106** (a) 1.20×10^{18} photons. (b) 3.76×10^8 W. **7.108** 419 nm. Yes. **7.110** Ne. **7.112** He^+: 164 nm, 121 nm, 109 nm, 103 nm (all in the UV region). H: 657 nm, 487 nm, 434 nm, 411 nm (all in the visible region). **7.114** 1.2×10^2 photons. **7.116** 2.5×10^{17} photons. **7.118** Yellow light will generate more electrons; blue light will generate electrons with greater kinetic energy. **7.120** (a) He. (b) N. (c) Na. (d) As. (e) Cl. See Table 7.3 for ground-state electron configurations. **7.122** They might have discovered the wave properties of electrons. **7.124** 7.39×10^{-2} nm. **7.126** (a) False. (b) False. (c) True. (d) False. (e) True. **7.128** 2.0×10^{-5} m/s. **7.130** (a) and (f) violate Pauli exclusion principle; (b), (d), and (e) violate Hund's rule. **7.132** 2.8×10^6 K. **7.134** 2.76×10^{-11} m. **7.136** 17.4 pm. **7.138** 0.929 pm; 3.23×10^{20}/s. **7.140** $n_i = 5$ to $n_f = 3$. **7.142** (a) B: $4 \longrightarrow 2$; C: $5 \longrightarrow 2$. (b) A: 41.1 nm; B: 30.4 nm. (c) 2.18×10^{-18} J. (d) At high values of n, the energy levels are very closely spaced, leading to a continuum of lines. **7.144** $n = 1$: 1.96×10^{-17} J; $n = 5$: 7.85×10^{-19} J. 10.6 nm. **7.146** 9.5×10^3 m/s. **7.148** 3.87×10^5 m/s. **7.150** Photosynthesis and vision. **7.152** 1.06 nm. **7.154** (a) 1.12 pm. (b) Smaller than the molecule.

Chapter 8

8.20 (a) $1s^22s^22p^63s^23p^5$. (b) Representative. (c) Paramagnetic. **8.22** (a) and (d); (b) and (e); (c) and (f). **8.24** (a) Group 1A. (b) Group 5A. (c) Group 8A. (d) Group 8B. **8.26** Fe. **8.28** (a) [Ne].

(b) [Ne]. (c) [Ar]. (d) [Ar]. (e) [Ar]. (f) $[Ar]3d^6$. (g) $[Ar]3d^9$.
(h) $[Ar]3d^{10}$. **8.30** (a) Cr^{3+}. (b) Sc^{3+}. (c) Rh^{3+}. (d) Ir^{3+}. **8.32** Be^{2+}
and He; F^- and N^{3-}; Fe^{2+} and Co^{3+}; S^{2-} and Ar. **8.38** Na >
Mg > Al > P > Cl. **8.40** F. **8.42** The effective nuclear charge that
the outermost electrons feel increases across the period.
8.44 $Mg^{2+} < Na^+ < F^- < O^{2-} < N^{3-}$. **8.46** Te^{2-}. **8.48** H^- is
larger. **8.52** K < Ca < P < F < Ne. **8.54** The single $3p$ electron in
Al is well shielded by the $1s$, $2s$, and $3s$ electrons. **8.56** $1s^2 2s^2 2p^6$:
2080 kJ/mol. **8.58** 8.40×10^6 kJ/mol. **8.62** Greatest: Cl; least: He.
8.64 The ns^1 configuration enables them to accept another
electron. **8.68** Fr should be the most reactive toward water and
oxygen, forming FrOH and Fr_2O, Fr_2O_2, and FrO_2. **8.70** The
Group 1B elements have higher ionization energies due to the
incomplete shielding of the inner d electrons. **8.72** (a) Li_2O +
$H_2O \longrightarrow 2LiOH$. (b) CaO + $H_2O \longrightarrow Ca(OH)_2$. (c) SO_3 +
$H_2O \longrightarrow H_2SO_4$. **8.74** BaO. **8.76** (a) Bromine. (b) Nitrogen.
(c) Rubidium. (d) Magnesium. **8.78** P^{3-}, S^{2-}, Cl^-, K^+, Ca^{2+}, Sc^{3+},
Ti^{4+}, V^{5+}, Cr^{6+}, Mn^{7+}. **8.80** M is K; X is Br. **8.82** N and O^+; Ne
and N^{3-}; Ar and S^{2-}; Zn and As^{3+}; Cs^+ and Xe. **8.84** (a) and (d).
8.86 Yellow-green gas: F_2; yellow gas: Cl_2; red liquid: Br_2; dark
solid: I_2. **8.88** (a) $\Delta H = 1532$ kJ/mol. (b) $\Delta H = 12,405$ kJ/mol.
8.90 Fluorine. **8.92** H^-. **8.94** Li_2O (basic); BeO (amphoteric);
B_2O_3 (acidic); CO_2 (acidic); N_2O_5 (acidic). **8.96** It forms both the
H^+ and H^- ions; H^+ is a single proton. **8.98** 0.65. **8.100** 79.9%.
8.102 418 kJ/mol. Use maximum wavelength. **8.104** 7.28×10^3
kJ/mol. **8.106** X: Sn or Pb; Y: P; Z: alkali metal. **8.108** 495.9
kJ/mol. **8.110** 343 nm (UV). **8.112** 604.3 kJ/mol. **8.114** K_2TiO_4.
8.116 $2K_2MnF_6 + 4SbF_5 \longrightarrow 4KSbF_6 + 2MnF_3 + F_2$.
8.118 N_2O (+1), NO (+2), N_2O_3 (+3), NO_2 and N_2O_4 (+4),
N_2O_5 (+5). **8.120** The larger the effective nuclear charge, the more
tightly held are the electrons. The atomic radius will be small and
the ionization energy will be large. **8.122** m.p.: 6.3°C; b.p.: 74.9°C.
8.124 An alkaline earth metal. **8.126** (a) It was discovered that the
periodic table was based on atomic number, not atomic mass.
(b) Ar: 39.95 amu; K: 39.10 amu. **8.128** Z = 119;
$[Rn]7s^2 5f^{14} 6d^{10} 7p^6 8s^1$. **8.130** Group 3A. **8.132** (a) SiH_4, GeH_4,
SnH_4, PbH_4. (b) RbH more ionic. (c) Ra + $2H_2O \longrightarrow Ra(OH)_2$ +
H_2. (d) Be. **8.134** Mg^{2+} is the smallest cation and has the largest
charge density and is closest to the negative ion. Ba^{2+} is just the
opposite. Thus, Mg^{2+} binds the tightest and Ba^{2+} the least.
8.136 See chapter. **8.138** Carbon (diamond). **8.140** 419 nm.
8.142 The first ionization energy of He is less than twice the ionization
of H because the radius of He is greater than that of H and the
shielding in He makes Z_{eff} less than 2. In He^+, there is no shielding
and the greater nuclear attraction makes the second ionization of He
greater than twice the ionization energy of H. **8.144** Z_{eff}: Li (1.26);
Na (1.84); K (2.26). Z_{eff}/n: Li (0.630); Na (0.613); K (0.565). Z_{eff}
increases as n increases. Thus, Z_{eff}/n remains fairly constant.
8.146 Go to the recommended website. Click on "Biology" tab
above the periodic table and then click on each of the listed elements.
A brief summary of the biological role of each element is provided.

Chapter 9

9.16 (a) RbI, rubidium iodide. (b) Cs_2SO_4, cesium sulfate.
(c) Sr_3N_2, strontium nitride. (d) Al_2S_3, aluminum sulfide.

9.18 (a) $\cdot Sr \cdot + \cdot \ddot{Se} \cdot \longrightarrow Sr^{2+} : \ddot{Se} :^{2-}$

(b) $\cdot Ca \cdot + 2H \cdot \longrightarrow Ca^{2+} \ 2H :^-$

(c) $3Li \cdot + \cdot \ddot{N} \cdot \longrightarrow 3Li^+ : \ddot{N} :^{3-}$

(d) $2 \cdot \ddot{Al} \cdot + 3 \cdot \ddot{S} \cdot \longrightarrow 2Al^{3+} \ 3 : \ddot{S} :^{2-}$

9.20 (a) BF_3, covalent. Boron triflouride. (b) KBr, ionic. Potassium
bromide. **9.26** 2195 kJ/mol. **9.36** C—H < Br—H < F—H <
Li—Cl < Na—Cl < K—F. **9.38** Cl—Cl < Br—Cl < Si—C <
Cs—F. **9.40** (a) Covalent. (b) Polar covalent. (c) Ionic. (d) Polar
covalent.

9.44 (a) $: \ddot{F} - \ddot{O} - \ddot{F} :$ (b) $: \ddot{F} - \ddot{N} = \ddot{N} - \ddot{F} :$

(c) Lewis structure of $H-Si(H)(H)-Si(H)(H)-H$ (d) $^- : \ddot{O} - H$

(e) Lewis structure with H—C—C—O, carbonyl O, Cl, negative charge   (f) Lewis structure $H-C(H)(H)-N^+(H)(H)-H$

9.46 (a) $^- : \ddot{O} - \ddot{O} :^-$ (b) $^- : C \equiv C :^-$ (c) $: N \equiv O :^+$

9.48 (a) The double bond between C and H; the single bond
between C and the end O; the lone pair on C atom.
(b) Lewis structure $H-C(H)-C(:O:)-O-H$

9.52 $\ddot{O} = \ddot{Cl} - \ddot{O} :^- \longleftrightarrow {}^- : \ddot{O} - \ddot{Cl} = \ddot{O} \longleftrightarrow \ddot{O} = \ddot{Cl} = \ddot{O}$

9.54 $H - C = \overset{+}{N} = \ddot{N}^- \longleftrightarrow H - \ddot{C} - \overset{+}{N} \equiv N :$

9.56 $\ddot{O} = C = \ddot{N}^- \longleftrightarrow {}^- : \ddot{O} - C \equiv N : \longleftrightarrow : \ddot{O} \equiv C - \ddot{N} :^{2-}$

9.62 $^+ \ddot{Cl} = \overset{2-}{Be} = \ddot{Cl}^+$ Not plausible.

9.64 $Cl - \overset{Cl}{\underset{Cl}{Sb}} - Cl$ The octet rule is not obeyed.

9.66 $Cl - \overset{Cl}{\underset{Cl}{Al}} = Cl$ Coordinate covalent bond.

9.70 303.0 kJ/mol. **9.72** (a) −2759 kJ/mol. (b) −2855 kJ/mol.
9.74 Ionic: RbCl, KO_2; covalent: PF_5, BrF_3, CI_4. **9.76** Ionic: NaF,
MgF_2, AlF_3; covalent: SiF_4, PF_5, SF_6, ClF_3. **9.78** KF: ionic, high
melting point, soluble in water, its melt and solution conduct
electricity. C_6H_6: covalent and discrete molecule, low melting
point, insoluble in water, does not conduct electricity.

9.80 $\ddot{N} = \overset{+}{N} = \ddot{N}^- \longleftrightarrow : N \equiv \overset{+}{N} - \ddot{N} :^{2-} \longleftrightarrow {}^{2-} : \ddot{N} - \overset{+}{N} \equiv N :$

9.82 (a) $AlCl_4^-$. (b) AlF_6^{3-}. (c) $AlCl_3$. **9.84** CF_2: violates the octet
rule; LiO_2: lattice energy too low; $CsCl_2$: second ionization energy
too high to produce Cs^{2+}; PI_5: I atom too bulky to fit around P.
9.86 (a) False. (b) True. (c) False. (d) False. **9.88** −67 kJ/mol.
9.90 N_2. **9.92** NH_4^+ and CH_4; CO and N_2; $B_3N_3H_6$ and C_6H_6.

9.94

$$H-\overset{\displaystyle\cdot\cdot}{N}:^- + H-\overset{\displaystyle\cdot\cdot}{O}: \longrightarrow H-\overset{\displaystyle\underset{|}{N}}{\underset{H}{|}}-H + {}^-:\overset{\displaystyle\cdot\cdot}{\underset{H}{O}}-H$$

9.96 F_3^- violates the octet rule.

9.98 $CH_3-\overset{\displaystyle\cdot\cdot}{N}=C=\overset{\displaystyle\cdot\cdot}{O} \longleftrightarrow CH_3-\overset{\displaystyle +}{N}\equiv C-\overset{\displaystyle\cdot\cdot}{O}:$

9.100 (c) No bond between C and O. (d) Large formal charges.

9.102 (a)

$$F-\underset{\underset{Cl}{|}}{\overset{\overset{Cl}{|}}{C}}-Cl$$

(b)

$$F-\underset{\underset{Cl}{|}}{\overset{\overset{Cl}{|}}{C}}-F$$

(c)

$$H-\underset{\underset{Cl}{|}}{\overset{\overset{F}{|}}{C}}-F$$

(d)

$$F-\underset{\underset{F}{|}}{\overset{\overset{F}{|}}{C}}-\underset{\underset{F}{|}}{\overset{\overset{H}{|}}{C}}-F$$

9.104 (a) -9.2 kJ/mol. (b) -9.2 kJ/mol. **9.106** (a) $:C\equiv O:^+$ (b) $:N\equiv O:^+$ (c) $^-:C\equiv N:$ (d) $:N\equiv N:$. **9.108** True.
9.110 (a) 114 kJ/mol. (b) Extra electron increases repulsion between F atoms. **9.112** Lone pair on C and negative formal charge on C.

9.114 (a) $:\overset{\displaystyle\cdot\cdot}{N}=\overset{\displaystyle\cdot\cdot}{O} \longleftrightarrow \overset{\displaystyle\cdot\cdot}{N}=\overset{\displaystyle\cdot\cdot}{O}^+$ (b) No.

9.116

$$:N-\underset{\underset{H}{|}}{\overset{\overset{H}{|}}{\underset{}{N}}}{}^+-\underset{\underset{H}{|}}{\overset{\overset{H}{|}}{B}}-H \qquad :N-\underset{\underset{H}{|}}{\overset{\overset{H}{|}}{\overset{\cdot\cdot}{N}}}-\underset{\underset{H}{|}}{\overset{\overset{H}{|}}{B}}-H$$

9.118 The OCOO structure leaves a lone pair and a negative charge on C.

9.120

$$\underset{Cl}{\overset{Cl}{Al}}\diagdown\underset{Cl}{\overset{Cl}{\underset{}{Al}}}\diagup\overset{Cl}{\underset{Cl}{}}$$

The arrows indicate coordinate covalent bonds.

9.122 347 kJ/mol.
9.124 From bond enthalpies: -140 kJ/mol; from standard enthalpies of formation: -184 kJ/mol.

9.126 (a)

$$\underset{\underset{H}{|}}{\overset{\overset{H}{|}}{C}}=\underset{\underset{Cl}{|}}{\overset{\overset{H}{|}}{C}}$$

(b)

$$-\underset{\underset{H}{|}}{\overset{\overset{H}{|}}{C}}-\underset{\underset{Cl}{|}}{\overset{\overset{H}{|}}{C}}-\underset{\underset{H}{|}}{\overset{\overset{H}{|}}{C}}-\underset{\underset{Cl}{|}}{\overset{\overset{H}{|}}{C}}-$$

(c) -1.2×10^6 kJ.

9.128 O: 3.16; F: 4.37; Cl: 3.48. **9.130** (1) The MgO solid containing Mg^+ and O^- ions would be paramagnetic. (2) The lattice energy would be like NaCl (too low). **9.132** 71.5 nm. **9.134** -629 kJ/mol. **9.136** 268 nm. **9.138** (a) From bond enthalpies: -1937 kJ/mol; from standard enthalpies of formation: -1413.9 kJ/mol. (b) 162 L. (c) 11.0 atm. **9.140** The repulsion between lone pairs on adjacent atoms weakens the bond. There are two lone pairs on each O atom in H_2O_2. The repulsion is the greatest; it has the smallest bond enthalpy (about 142 kJ/mol). There is one lone pair on each N atom in N_2H_4; it has the intermediate bond enthalpy (about 193 kJ/mol). There are no lone pairs on the C atoms in C_2H_6; it has the greatest bond enthalpy (about 347 kJ/mol). **9.142** 244 kJ/mol.

Chapter 10

10.8 (a) Trigonal planar. (b) Linear. (c) Tetrahedral.
10.10 (a) Tetrahedral. (b) T-shaped. (c) Bent. (d) Trigonal planar. (e) Tetrahedral. **10.12** (a) Tetrahedral. (b) Bent. (c) Trigonal planar. (d) Linear. (e) Square planar. (f) Tetrahedral. (g) Trigonal bipyramidal. (h) Trigonal pyramidal. (i) Tetrahedral. **10.14** $SiCl_4$, CI_4, $CdCl_4^{2-}$. **10.20** Electronegativity decreases from F to I. **10.22** Larger. **10.24** (b) = (d) < (c) < (a). **10.32** sp^3 for both.

10.34 B: sp^2 to sp^3; N: remains at sp^3. **10.36** From left to right. (a) sp^3. (b) sp^3, sp^2, sp^2. (c) sp^3, sp, sp, sp^3. (d) sp^3, sp^2. (e) sp^3, sp^2. **10.38** sp. **10.40** sp^3d. **10.42** 9 pi bonds and 9 sigma bonds. **10.44** IF_4^-. **10.50** Electron spins must be paired in H_2. **10.52** $Li_2^- = Li_2^+ < Li_2$. **10.54** B_2^+. **10.56** MO theory predicts O_2 is paramagnetic. **10.58** $O_2^{2-} < O_2^- < O_2 < O_2^+$. **10.60** B_2 contains a pi bond; C_2 contains 2 pi bonds. **10.62** (1) Atoms far apart. No interaction. (2) The $2p$ orbitals begin to overlap. Attractive forces operating. (3) The system at its most stable state. The potential energy reaches a minimum. (4) As the distance decreases further, nuclear-nuclear and electron-electron repulsion increase. (5) Further decrease in distance leads to instability of F_2 molecule. **10.66** The circle shows electron delocalization.

10.68 (a)

$$\overset{\displaystyle\cdot\cdot}{\overset{\displaystyle:F:}{\underset{|}{O}}}=\underset{+}{\overset{}{N}}-\overset{\displaystyle\cdot\cdot}{O}:^- \longleftrightarrow {}^-:\overset{\displaystyle\cdot\cdot}{O}-\underset{+}{\overset{\displaystyle\overset{:F:}{|}}{N}}=\overset{\displaystyle\cdot\cdot}{O}$$

(b) sp^2. (c) N forms sigma bonds with F and O atoms. There is a pi molecular orbital delocalized over N and O atoms. **10.70** sp^2. **10.72** Linear. Dipole moment measurement. **10.74** The large size of Si results in poor sideways overlap of p orbitals to form pi bonds. **10.76** (a) $C_8H_{10}N_4O_2$. (b) C atoms in the ring and O are sp^2. C atom in CH_3 group is sp^3. Double-bonded N is sp^2; single-bonded N is sp^3. (c) Geometry about the sp^2 C and N atoms is trigonal planar. Geometry about sp^3 C and N atom is tetrahedral. **10.78** XeF_3^+: T-shaped; XeF_5^+: square pyramidal; SbF_6^-: octahedral. **10.80** (a) 180°. (b) 120°. (c) 109.5°. (d) About 109.5°. (e) 180°. (f) About 120°. (g) About 109.5°. (h) 109.5°. **10.82** sp^3d. **10.84** ICl_2^- and $CdBr_2$. **10.86** (a) sp^2. (b) Molecule on the right. **10.88** The pi bond in *cis*-dichloroethylene prevents rotation. **10.90** O_3, CO, CO_2, NO_2, N_2O, CH_4, $CFCl_3$. **10.92** C: all single-bonded C atoms are sp^3, the double-bonded C atoms are sp^2; N: single-bonded N atoms are sp^3, N atoms that form one double bond are sp^2, N atom that forms two double bonds is sp. **10.94** Si has $3d$ orbitals so water can add to Si (valence shell expansion). **10.96** C: sp^2; N: N atom that forms a double bond is sp^2, the others are sp^3. **10.98** (a) Use a conventional oven. (b) No. Polar molecules would absorb microwaves. (c) Water molecules absorb part of microwaves. **10.100** (a) and (b) are polar. **10.102** The small size of F results in a shorter bond and greater lone pair repulsion. **10.104** 43.6%. **10.106** Second and third vibrations. CO, NO_2, N_2O. **10.108** (a) The two 90° rotations will break and make the pi bond and convert *cis*-dichloroethylene to *trans*-dichloroethylene. (b) The pi bond is weaker because of the lesser extent of sideways orbital overlap. (c) 444 nm. **10.110** (a) H_2. The electron is removed from the more stable bonding molecular orbital. (b) N_2. Same as (a). (c) O. The atomic orbital in O is more stable than the antibonding molecular orbital in O_2. (d) The atomic orbital in F is more stable than the antibonding molecular orbital in F_2. **10.112** (a) $[Ne_2](\sigma_{3s})^2(\sigma_{3s}^\star)^2(\pi_{3p_y})^2(\pi_{3p_z})^2(\sigma_{3p_x})^2$. (b) 3. (c) Diamagnetic. **10.114** For all the electrons to be paired in O_2 (see Table 10.5), energy is needed to flip the spin of one of the electrons in the antibonding molecular orbitals. This arrangement is less stable according to Hund's rule. **10.116** ClF_3: T-shaped; sp^3d. AsF_5: Trigonal bipyramidal; sp^3d; ClF_2^+: bent; sp^3; AsF_6^-: Octahedral; sp^3d^2. **10.118** (a) Planar and no dipole moment. (b) 20 sigma bonds and 6 pi bonds. **10.120** (a) The negative formal charge is placed on the less electronegative carbon, so there is less charge separation and a smaller dipole moment. (b) Both the Lewis structure and the molecular orbital treatment predicts a triple bond. (c) C. **10.122** O=C=C=C=O. The molecule is linear and nonpolar. **10.124** $NO^{2-} < NO^- < NO = NO^{2+} < NO^+$.

Chapter 11

11.8 Methane. **11.10** (a) Dispersion forces. (b) Dispersion and dipole-dipole forces. (c) Same as (b). (d) Dispersion and ion-ion forces. (e) Same as (a). **11.12** (e). **11.14** Only 1-butanol can form hydrogen bonds. **11.16** (a) Xe. (b) CS_2. (c) Cl_2. (d) LiF. (e) NH_3. **11.18** (a) Hydrogen bond and dispersion forces. (b) Dispersion forces. (c) Dispersion forces. (d) Covalent bond. **11.20** The compound on the left can form an intramolecular hydrogen bond, reducing intermolecular hydrogen bonding. **11.32** Between ethanol and glycerol. **11.38** scc: 1; bcc: 2; fcc: 4. **11.40** 6.20×10^{23} Ba atoms/mol. **11.42** 458 pm. **11.44** XY_3. **11.48** 0.220 nm. **11.52** Molecular solid. **11.54** Molecular solids: Se_8, HBr, CO_2, P_4O_6, SiH_4. Covalent solids: Si, C. **11.56** Each C atom in diamond is covalently bonded to four other C atoms. Graphite has delocalized electrons in two dimensions. **11.76** 2.67×10^3 kJ. **11.78** 47.03 kJ/mol. **11.80** Freezing, sublimation. **11.82** When steam condenses at 100°C, it releases heat equal to heat of vaporization. **11.84** 331 mmHg. **11.86** The small amount of liquid nitrogen will evaporate quickly, extracting little heat from the skin. Boiling water will release much more heat to the skin as it cools. Water has a high specific heat. **11.90** Initially ice melts because of the increase in pressure. As the wire sinks into the ice, the water above it refreezes. In this way, the wire moves through the ice without cutting it in half. **11.92** (a) Ice melts. (b) Water vapor condenses to ice. (c) Water boils. **11.94** (d). **11.96** Covalent crystal. **11.98** Orthorhombic. **11.100** 760 mmHg. **11.102** It is the critical point. **11.104** Crystalline SiO_2. **11.106** (c) and (d). **11.108** (a), (b), (d). **11.110** 8.3×10^{-3} atm. **11.112** (a) K_2S. Ionic. (b) Br_2. Dispersion. **11.114** SO_2. It is a polar molecule. **11.116** 62.4 kJ/mol. **11.118** 304°C. **11.120** Small ions have more concentrated charges and are more effective in ion-dipole interaction, resulting in a greater extent of hydration. The distance of separation between cation and anion is also shorter. **11.122** (a) 30.7 kJ/mol. (b) 192.5 kJ/mol. **11.124** (a) Decreases. (b) No change. (c) No change. **11.126** (a) 1 Cs^+ ion and 1 Cl^- ion. (b) 4 Zn^{2+} ions and 4 S^{2-} ions. (c) 4 Ca^{2+} ions and 8 F^- ions. **11.128** $CaCO_3(s) \longrightarrow CaO(s) + CO_2(g)$. Three phases. **11.130** SiO_2 is a covalent crystal. CO_2 exists as discrete molecules. **11.132** 66.8%. **11.134** scc: 52.4%; bcc: 68.0%; fcc: 74.0%. **11.136** 1.69 g/cm^3. **11.138** (a) Two (diamond/graphite/liquid and graphite/liquid/vapor). (b) Diamond. (c) Apply high pressure at high temperature. **11.140** Molecules in the cane are held together by intermolecular forces. **11.142** When the tungsten filament is heated to a high temperature (ca. 3000°C), it sublimes and condenses on the inside walls. The inert pressurized Ar gas retards sublimation. **11.144** When methane burns in air, it forms CO_2 and water vapor. The latter condenses on the outside of the cold beaker. **11.146** 6.019×10^{23} Fe atoms/mol. **11.148** Na (186 pm and 0.965 g/cm^3). **11.150** (d). **11.152** 0.833 g/L. Hydrogen bonding in the gas phase.

Chapter 12

12.10 Cyclohexane cannot form hydrogen bonds. **12.12** The longer chains become more nonpolar. **12.16** (a) 25.9 g. (b) 1.72×10^3 g. **12.18** (a) 2.68 m. (b) 7.82 m. **12.20** 0.010 m. **12.22** 5.0×10^2 m; 18.3 M. **12.24** (a) 2.41 m. (b) 2.13 M. (c) 0.0587 L. **12.28** 45.9 g. **12.36** CO_2 pressure is greater at the bottom of the mine. **12.38** 0.28 L. **12.50** 1.3×10^3 g. **12.52** Ethanol: 30.0 mmHg; 1-propanol: 26.3 mmHg. **12.54** 128 g. **12.56** 0.59 m. **12.58** 120 g/mol. $C_4H_8O_4$. **12.60** −8.6°C. **12.62** 4.3×10^2 g/mol. $C_{24}H_{20}P_4$. **12.64** 1.75×10^4 g/mol. **12.66** 343 g/mol. **12.70** Boiling point, vapor pressure, osmotic pressure. **12.72** 0.50 m glucose > 0.50 m

acetic acid > 0.50 m HCl. **12.74** 0.9420 m. **12.76** 7.6 atm. **12.78** 1.6 atm. **12.82** (c). **12.84** 3.5 atm. **12.86** (a) 104 mmHg. (b) 116 mmHg. **12.88** 2.95×10^3 g/mol. **12.90** 12.5 g. **12.92** No. **12.94** No. $AlCl_3$ dissociates into Al^{3+} and 3 Cl^- ions. **12.96** O_2: 4.7×10^{-6}; N_2: 9.7×10^6. The mole fraction of O_2 compared to the mole fraction of N_2 in water is greater compared to that in air. **12.98** The molar mass in B (248 g/mol) is twice as large as that in A (124 g/mol). A dimerization process. **12.100** (a) Last alcohol. (b) Methanol. (c) Last alcohol. **12.102** I_2-water: weak dipole−induced dipole; I_3^--water: favorable ion-dipole interaction. **12.104** (a) Same NaCl solution on both sides. (b) Only water would move from left to right. (c) Normal osmosis. **12.106** 12.3 M. **12.108** 14.2%. **12.110** (a) and (d). **12.112** (a) Decreases with increasing lattice energy. (b) Increases with increasing polarity of solvent. (c) Increases with increasing enthalpy of hydration. **12.114** 1.80 g/mL. 5.0×10^2 m. **12.116** 0.815. **12.118** NH_3 can form hydrogen bonds with water. **12.120** 3%. **12.122** 1.2×10^2 g/mol. It forms a dimer in benzene. **12.124** (a) 1.1 m. (b) The protein prevents the formation of ice crystals. **12.126** It is due to the precipitated minerals that refract light and create an opaque appearance. **12.128** 1.9 m. **12.130** (a) $X_A = 0.524$, $X_B = 0.476$. (b) A: 50 mmHg; B: 20 mmHg. (c) $X_A = 0.71$, $X_B = 0.29$. $P_A = 67$ mmHg. $P_B = 12$ mmHg. **12.132** 2.7×10^{-3}. **12.134** From $n = kP$ and $PV = nRT$, show that $V = kRT$. **12.136** −0.737°C. **12.138** The polar groups (C=O) can bind the K^+ ions. The exterior is nonpolar (due to the —CH_3 groups), which enables the molecule to pass through the cell membranes containing nonpolar lipids. **12.140** The string is wetted and laid on top of the ice cube. Salt is shaken onto the top of the ice cube and the moistened string. The presence of salt lowers the freezing point of the ice, resulting in the melting of the ice on the surface. Melting is an endothermic process. The water in the moist string freezes, and the string becomes attached to the ice cube. The ice cube can now be lifted out of the glass.

Chapter 13

13.6 (a) Rate $= -(1/2)\Delta[H_2]/\Delta t = -\Delta[O_2]/\Delta t = (1/2)\Delta[H_2O]/\Delta t$. (b) Rate $= -(1/4)\Delta[NH_3]/\Delta t = -(1/5)\Delta[O_2]/\Delta t = (1/4)\Delta[NO]/\Delta t = (1/6)\Delta[H_2O]/\Delta t$. **13.8** (a) 0.049 M/s. (b) 0.025 M/s. **13.14** 2.4×10^{-4} M/s. **13.16** (a) Third order. (b) 0.38 M/s. **13.18** (a) 0.046 s^{-1}. (b) 0.13/$M \cdot$ s. **13.20** First order. 1.08×10^{-3} s^{-1}. **13.26** (a) 0.0198 s^{-1}. (b) 151 s. **13.28** 3.6 s. **13.30** (a) The relative rates for (i), (ii), and (iii) are 4:3:6. (b) The relative rates would be unaffected, but each of the absolute rates would decrease by 50%. (c) The relative half-lives are 1:1:1. **13.38** 135 kJ/mol. **13.40** 103 kJ/mol. **13.42** 644 K. **13.44** 9.25×10^3 s^{-1}. **13.46** 51.0 kJ/mol. **13.56** (a) Rate $= k[X_2][Y]$. (b) Reaction is zero order in Z. (c) $X_2 + Y \longrightarrow XY + X$ (slow). $X + Z \longrightarrow XZ$ (fast). **13.58** Mechanism I. **13.66** Rate $= (k_1k_2/k_{-1})[E][S]$. **13.68** This is a first-order reaction. The rate constant is 0.046 min^{-1}. **13.70** Temperature, energy of activation, concentration of reactants, catalyst. **13.72** 22.6 cm^2; 44.9 cm^2. The large surface area of grain dust can result in a violent explosion. **13.74** (a) Third order. (b) 0.38/$M^2 \cdot$ s. (c) $H_2 + 2NO \longrightarrow N_2 + H_2O + O$ (slow); $O + H_2 \longrightarrow H_2O$ (fast). **13.76** Water is present in excess so its concentration does not change appreciably. **13.78** 10.7/$M \cdot$ s. **13.80** 2.63 atm. **13.82** M^{-2} s^{-1}. **13.84** 56.4 min. **13.86** rate $= k[A][B]^2$. **13.88** (b), (d), (e). **13.90** 9.8×10^{-4}. **13.92** (a) Increase. (b) Decrease. (c) Decrease. (d) Increase. **13.94** 0.0896 min^{-1}. **13.96** 1.12×10^3 min. **13.98** (a) I_2 absorbs visible light to form I atoms. (b) UV light is needed to dissociate H_2. **13.100** (a) Rate $= k[X][Y]^2$. (b) $1.9 \times 10^{-2}/M \cdot$ s. **13.102** Second order.

$2.4 \times 10^7/M \cdot s$. **13.104** Because the engine is relatively cold so the exhaust gases will not fully react with the catalytic converter. **13.106** $H_2(g) + ICl(g) \longrightarrow HCl(g) + HI(g)$ (slow). $HI(g) + ICl(g) \longrightarrow HCl(g) + I_2(g)$ (fast). **13.108** 5.7×10^5 yr. **13.110** (a) Mn^{2+}; Mn^{3+}; first step. (b) Without the catalyst, reaction would be termolecular. (c) Homogeneous. **13.112** 0.45 atm. **13.114** (a) $k_1[A] - k_2[B]$. (b) $[B] = (k_1/k_2)[A]$. **13.116** (a) 2.47×10^{-2} yr^{-1}. (b) 9.8×10^{-4}. (c) 186 yr. **13.118** (a) 3. (b) 2. (c) $C \longrightarrow D$. (d) Exothermic. **13.120** 1.8×10^3 K. **13.122** (a) 2.5×10^{-5} M/s. (b) Same as (a). (c) 8.3×10^{-6} M. **13.126** (a) 1.13×10^{-3} M/min. (b) 6.83×10^{-4} M/min; 8.8×10^{-3} M. **13.128** Second order. $0.42/M \cdot$ min. **13.130** 60% increase. The result shows the profound effect of an exponential dependence. **13.132** 2.6×10^{-4} M/s. **13.134** 404 kJ/mol. **13.136** (a) Rate = $k[NO]^2[O_2]$. (b) Rate = $k_{obs}[NO]^2$. (c) 1.3×10^3 min.

Chapter 14

14.14 (a) $A + C \rightleftharpoons AC$. (b) $A + D \rightleftharpoons AD$. **14.16** 1.08×10^7. **14.18** 3.5×10^{-7}. **14.20** (a) 0.082. (b) 0.29. **14.22** 0.105; 2.05×10^{-3}. **14.24** 7.09×10^{-3}. **14.26** 3.3. **14.28** 0.0353. **14.30** 4.0×10^{-6}. **14.32** 5.6×10^{23}. **14.36** $0.64/M^2 \cdot$ s. **14.40** $[NH_3]$ will increase and $[N_2]$ and $[H_2]$ will decrease. **14.42** NO: 0.50 atm; NO_2: 0.020 atm. **14.44** $[I] = 8.58 \times 10^{-4}$ M; $[I_2] = 0.0194$ M. **14.46** (a) 0.52. (b) $[CO_2] = 0.48$ M, $[H_2] = 0.020$ M, $[CO] = 0.075$ M, $[H_2O] = 0.065$ M. **14.48** $[H_2] = [CO_2] = 0.05$ M, $[H_2O] = [CO] = 0.11$ M. **14.54** (a) Shift position of equilibrium to the right. (b) No effect. (c) No effect. **14.56** (a) No effect. (b) No effect. (c) Shift the position of equilibrium to the left. (d) No effect. (e) To the left. **14.58** (a) To the right. (b) To the left. (c) To the right. (d) To the left. (e) No effect. **14.60** No change. **14.62** (a) More CO_2 will form. (b) No change. (c) No change. (d) Some CO_2 will combine with CaO to form $CaCO_3$. (e) Some CO_2 will react with NaOH so equilibrium will shift to the right. (f) HCl reacts with $CaCO_3$ to produce CO_2. Equilibrium will shift to the left. (g) Equilibrium will shift to the right. **14.64** (a) NO: 0.24 atm; Cl_2: 0.12 atm. (b) 0.017. **14.66** $[A_2] = [B_2] = 0.040$ M. $[AB] = 0.020$ M. **14.68** (a) No effect. (b) More CO_2 and H_2O will form. **14.70** (a) 8×10^{-44}. (b) The reaction has a very large activation energy. **14.72** (a) 1.7. (b) A: 0.69 atm, B: 0.81 atm. **14.74** 1.5×10^5. **14.76** H_2: 0.28 atm, Cl_2: 0.049 atm, HCl: 1.67 atm. **14.78** 5.0×10^1 atm. **14.80** 3.84×10^{-2}. **14.82** 3.13. **14.84** N_2: 0.860 atm; H_2: 0.366 atm; NH_3: 4.40×10^{-3} atm. **14.86** (a) 1.16. (b) 53.7%. **14.88** (a) 0.49 atm. (b) 0.23. (c) 0.037. (d) Greater than 0.037 mol. **14.90** $[H_2] = 0.070$ M, $[I_2] = 0.182$ M, $[HI] = 0.825$ M. **14.92** (c). **14.94** (a) 4.2×10^{-4}. (b) 0.83. (c) 1.1. (d) In (b): 2.3×10^3; in (c): 0.021. **14.96** 0.0231; 9.60×10^{-4}. **14.98** NO_2: 1.2 atm; N_2O_4: 0.12 atm. $K_P = 12$. **14.100** (a) $K_c = 33.3$. (b) $Q_c = 2.8$. Shift to the right. (c) $Q_c = 169$. Shift to the left. **14.102** (a) The equilibrium will shift to the right. (b) To the right. (c) No change. (d) No change. (e) No change. (f) To the left. **14.104** NO_2: 0.100 atm; N_2O_4: 0.09 atm. **14.106** (a) 1.03 atm. (b) 0.39 atm. (c) 1.67 atm. (d) 0.620. **14.108** (a) $K_P = 2.6 \times 10^{-6}$; $K_c = 1.1 \times 10^{-7}$. (b) 22 mg/m^3. Yes. **14.110** Temporary dynamic equilibrium between the melting ice cubes and the freezing of the water between the ice cubes. **14.112** $[NH_3] = 0.042$ M, $[N_2] = 0.086$ M, $[H_2] = 0.26$ M. **14.114** 1.3 atm. **14.116** PCl_5: 0.683 atm; PCl_3: 1.11 atm; Cl_2: 0.211 atm. **14.118** -115 kJ/mol. **14.120** SO_2: 2.71 atm; Cl_2: 2.71 atm; SO_2Cl_2: 3.58 atm. **14.122** 4.0. **14.124** (a) The plot curves toward higher pressure at low values of $1/V$. (b) The plot curves toward higher volume as T increases.

Chapter 15

15.4 (a) NO_2^-. (b) HSO_4^-. (c) HS^-. (d) CN^-. (e) $HCOO^-$. **15.6** (a) H_2S. (b) H_2CO_3. (c) HCO_3^-. (d) H_3PO_4. (e) $H_2PO_4^-$. (f) HPO_4^{2-}. (g) H_2SO_4. (h) HSO_4^-. (i) HSO_3^-. **15.8** (a) CH_2ClCOO^-. (b) IO_4^-. (c) $H_2PO_4^-$. (d) HPO_4^{2-}. (e) PO_4^{3-}. (f) HSO_4^-. (g) SO_4^{2-}. (h) IO_3^-. (i) SO_3^{2-}. (j) NH_3. (k) HS^-. (l) S^{2-}. (m) OCl^-. **15.16** 1.6×10^{-14} M. **15.18** (a) 10.74. (b) 3.28. **15.20** (a) 6.3×10^{-6} M. (b) 1.0×10^{-16} M. (c) 2.7×10^{-6} M. **15.22** (a) Acidic. (b) Neutral. (c) Basic. **15.24** 1.98×10^{-3} mol. 0.444. **15.26** 0.118. **15.32** (1) c. (2) b and d. **15.34** (a) Strong. (b) Weak. (c) Weak. (d) Weak. (e) Strong. **15.36** (b) and (c). **15.38** No. **15.44** $[H^+] = [CH_3COO^-] = 5.8 \times 10^{-4}$ M, $[CH_3COOH] = 0.0181$ M. **15.46** 2.3×10^{-3} M. **15.48** (a) 3.5%. (b) 33%. (c) 79%. Percent ionization increases with dilution. **15.50** (a) 3.9%. (b) 0.30%. **15.54** (c) < (a) < (b). **15.56** 7.1×10^{-7}. **15.58** 1.5%. **15.64** HCl: 1.40; H_2SO_4: 1.31. **15.66** $[H^+] = [HCO_3^-] = 1.0 \times 10^{-4}$ M, $[CO_3^{2-}] = 4.8 \times 10^{-11}$ M. **15.70** (a) $H_2SO_4 > H_2SeO_4$. (b) $H_3PO_4 > H_3AsO_4$. **15.72** The conjugate base of phenol can be stabilized by resonance. **15.78** (a) Neutral. (b) Basic. (c) Acidic. (d) Acidic. **15.80** HZ < HY < HX. **15.82** 4.82. **15.84** Basic. **15.88** (a) $Al_2O_3 < BaO < K_2O$. (b) $CrO_3 < Cr_2O_3 < CrO$. **15.90** $Al(OH)_3 + OH^- \longrightarrow Al(OH)_4^-$. Lewis acid-base reaction. **15.94** $AlCl_3$ is the Lewis acid, Cl^- is the Lewis base. **15.96** CO_2 and BF_3. **15.98** 0.0094 M. **15.100** 0.106 L. **15.102** No. **15.104** No, volume is the same. **15.106** CrO is basic and CrO_3 is acidic. **15.108** 4.0×10^{-2}. **15.110** 7.00. **15.112** NH_3. **15.114** (a) 7.43. (b) pD < 7.43. (c) pD + pOD = 14.87. **15.116** 1.79. **15.118** F^- reacts with HF to form HF_2^-, thereby shifting the ionization of HF to the right. **15.120** (b) 6.80. **15.122** $[H^+] = [H_2PO_4^-] = 0.0239$ M, $[H_3PO_4] = 0.076$ M, $[HPO_4^{2-}] = 6.2 \times 10^{-8}$ M, $[PO_4^{3-}] = 1.2 \times 10^{-18}$ M. **15.124** Pyrex glass contains 10–25% B_2O_3, an acidic oxide. **15.126** $[Na^+] = 0.200$ M, $[HCO_3^-] = [OH^-] = 4.6 \times 10^{-3}$ M, $[H_2CO_3] = 2.4 \times 10^{-8}$ M, $[H^+] = 2.2 \times 10^{-12}$ M. **15.128** The H^+ ions convert CN^- to HCN, which escapes as a gas. **15.130** 0.25 g. **15.132** -0.20. **15.134** (a) Equilibrium will shift to the right. (b) To the left. (c) No effect. (d) To the right. **15.136** The amines are converted to their salts RNH_3^+. **15.138** 1.4×10^{-4}. **15.140** 4.40. **15.142** In a basic medium, the ammonium salt is converted to the pungent-smelling ammonia. **15.144** (c). **15.146** 21 mL. **15.148** HX is the stronger acid. **15.150** Mg. **15.152** 1.57. $[CN^-] = 1.8 \times 10^{-8}$ M in 1.00 M HF and 2.2×10^{-5} M in 1.00 M HCN. HF is a stronger acid than HCN. **15.154** 6.02. **15.156** 1.18. **15.158** (a) pH = 7.24. (b) 10,000 H_3O^+ ions for every OH^- ion. **15.160** Both are -55.9 kJ/mol because they have the same net ionic equation.

Chapter 16

16.6 (a) 11.28. (b) 9.08. **16.10** (a), (b), and (c). **16.12** 4.74 for both. (a) is more effective because it has a higher concentration. **16.14** 7.03. **16.16** 10. More effective against the acid. **16.18** (a) 4.82. (b) 4.64. **16.20** HC. **16.22** (l) (a): 5.10. (b): 4.82. (c): 5.22. (d): 5.00. (2) 4.90. (3) 5.22. **16.24** 0.53 mole. **16.28** 90.1 g/mol. **16.30** 0.467 M. **16.32** $[H^+] = 3.0 \times 10^{-13}$ M, $[OH^-] = 0.0335$ M, $[Na^+] = 0.0835$ M, $[CH_3COO^-] = 0.0500$ M, $[CH_3COOH] = 8.4 \times 10^{-10}$ M. **16.34** 8.23. **16.36** (a) 11.36. (b) 9.55. (c) 8.95. (d) 5.19. (e) 1.70. **16.38** (1) (c). (2) (a). (3) (d). (4) (b). pH < 7 at the equivalence point. **16.40** 6.0×10^{-6}. **16.44** CO_2 dissolves in water to form H_2CO_3, which neutralizes NaOH. **16.46** 5.70. **16.54** (a) 7.8×10^{-10}. (b) 1.8×10^{-18}. **16.56** 1.80×10^{-10}. **16.58** 2.2×10^{-4} M. **16.60** 2.3×10^{-9}. **16.62** $[Na^+] = 0.045$ M, $[NO_3^-] = 0.076$ M, $[Sr^{2+}] = 0.016$ M, $[F^-] = 1.1 \times 10^{-4}$ M. **16.64** pH greater than 3.34 and less than

8.11. **16.68** (a) 0.013 M. (b) 2.2×10^{-4} M. (c) 3.3×10^{-3} M.
16.70 (a) 1.0×10^{-5} M. (b) 1.1×10^{-10} M. **16.72** (b), (c), (d), and
(e). **16.74** (a) 0.016 M. (b) 1.6×10^{-6} M. **16.76** Yes. **16.80** $[Cd^{2+}] =$
1.1×10^{-18} M, $[Cd(CN)_4^{2-}] = 4.2 \times 10^{-3}$ M, $[CN^-] = 0.48$ M.
16.82 3.5×10^{-5} M. **16.84** (a) $Cu^{2+} + 4NH_3 \rightleftharpoons Cu(NH_3)_4^{2+}$.
(b) $Ag^+ + 2CN^- \rightleftharpoons Ag(CN)_2^-$. (c) $Hg^{2+} + 4Cl^- \rightleftharpoons HgCl_4^{2-}$.
16.88 0.011 M. **16.90** Use Cl^- ions or flame test. **16.92** From 2.51
to 4.41. **16.94** 1.8×10^2 mL. **16.96** 1.28 M. **16.98** $[H^+] = 3.0 \times$
10^{-13} M, $[OH^-] = 0.0335$ M, $[HCOO^-] = 0.0500$ M, $[HCOOH] =$
8.8×10^{-11} M, $[Na^+] = 0.0835$ M. **16.100** 9.97 g. pH = 13.04.
16.102 6.0×10^3. **16.104** 0.036 g/L. **16.106** (a) 1.37. (b) 5.97.
(c) 10.24. **16.108** Original precipitate was HgI_2. In the presence
of excess KI, it redissolves as HgI_4^{2-}. **16.110** 7.82 − 10.38.
16.112 (a) 3.60. (b) 9.69. (c) 6.07. **16.114** (a) $MCO_3 + 2HCl \longrightarrow$
$MCl_2 + H_2O + CO_2$. $HCl + NaOH \longrightarrow NaCl + H_2O$.
(b) 24.3 g/mol. Mg. **16.116** 2. **16.118** (a) 12.6. (b) 8.8×10^{-6} M.
16.120 (a) Sulfate. (b) Sulfide. (c) Iodide. **16.122** They are
insoluble. **16.124** The ionized polyphenols have a dark color. The
H^+ ions from lemon juice shift the equilibrium to the light color
acid. **16.126** Yes. **16.128** (c). **16.130** (a) 1.7×10^{-7} M. (b) $MgCO_3$
is more soluble than $CaCO_3$. (c) 12.40. (d) 1.9×10^{-8} M. (e) Ca^{2+}
because it is present in larger amount. **16.132** pH = 1.0, fully
protonated; pH = 7.0, dipolar ion; pH = 12.0, fully ionized.
16.134 (a) 8.4 mL. (b) 12.5 mL. (c) 27.0 mL. **16.136** (a) 4.74
before and after dilution. (b) 2.52 before and 3.02 after dilution.
16.138 4.75. **16.140** (a) 0.0085 g. (b) 2.7×10^{-8} g. (c) 1.2×10^{-4} g.
16.142 (1) The initial pH of acid (a) is lower. (2) The pH at half-
way to the equivalence point is lower for (a). (3) The pH at the
equivalence point is lower for acid (a), indicating that (a) forms a
weaker conjugate base than (b). Thus, (a) is the stronger acid.
16.144 $[Cu^{2+}] = 1.8 \times 10^{-7}$ M. $[OH^-] = 3.6 \times 10^{-7}$ M. $[Ba^{2+}] =$
$[SO_4^{2-}] = 1.0 \times 10^{-5}$ M.

Chapter 17

17.6 (a) 0.25. (b) 8×10^{-31}. (c) ≈ 0. For a macroscopic system,
the probability is practically zero that all the molecules will be
found only in one bulb. **17.10** (c) < (d) < (e) < (a) < (b). Solids
have smaller entropies than gases. More complex structures have
higher entropies. **17.12** (a) 47.5 J/K · mol. (b) −12.5 J/K · mol.
(c) −242.8 J/K · mol. **17.14** (a) $\Delta S < 0$. (b) $\Delta S > 0$. (c) $\Delta S > 0$.
(d) $\Delta S < 0$. **17.18** (a) −1139 kJ/mol. (b) −140.0 kJ/mol.
(c) −2935.0 kJ/mol. **17.20** (a) At all temperatures. (b) Below
111 K. **17.24** 8.0×10^1 kJ/mol. **17.26** 4.572×10^2 kJ/mol. $7.2 \times$
10^{-81}. **17.28** (a) −24.6 kJ/mol. (b) −1.33 kJ/mol. **17.30** −341
kJ/mol. **17.32** −2.87 kJ/mol. The process has a high activation
energy. **17.36** 1×10^3. glucose + ATP $\longrightarrow$ glucose 6-phosphate +
ADP. 1×10^3. **17.38** (a) 0. (b) 4.0×10^4 J/mol. (c) -3.2×10^4
J/mol. (d) 6.4×10^4 J/mol. **17.40** Positive. **17.42** (a) No reaction is
possible because $\Delta G > 0$. (b) The reaction has a very large
activation energy. (c) Reactants and products already at their
equilibrium concentrations. **17.44** In all cases $\Delta H > 0$ and $\Delta S >$
0. $\Delta G < 0$ for (a), = 0 for (b), and > 0 for (c). **17.46** $\Delta S > 0$.
17.48 (a) Most liquids have similar structure so the changes in
entropy from liquid to vapor are similar. (b) ΔS_{vap} are larger for
ethanol and water because of hydrogen bonding (there are fewer
microstates in these liquids). **17.50** (a) $2CO + 2NO \longrightarrow 2CO_2 +$
N_2. (b) Oxidizing agent: NO; reducing agent: CO. (c) 3×10^{120}.
(d) 1.2×10^{18}. From left to right. (e) No. **17.52** 2×10^{-10}.
17.54 2.6×10^{-9}. **17.56** 976 K. **17.58** $\Delta S < 0$; $\Delta H < 0$.
17.60 55 J/K · mol. **17.62** Increase in entropy of the surroundings
offsets the decrease in entropy of the system. **17.64** 56 J/K.
17.66 4.5×10^5. **17.68** 4.8×10^{-75} atm. **17.70** (a) True. (b) True.

(c) False. **17.72** $C + CuO \rightleftharpoons CO + Cu$. 6.1. **17.74** 673.2 K.
17.76 (a) 7.6×10^{14}. (b) 4.1×10^{-12}. **17.78** (a) A reverse
disproportionation reaction. (b) 8.2×10^{15}. Yes, a large K makes
this an efficient process. (c) Less effective. **17.80** 1.8×10^{70}.
Reaction has a large activation energy. **17.82** Heating the ore alone
is not a feasible process. −214.3 kJ/mol. **17.84** $K_P = 36$. 981 K.
No. **17.86** Negative. **17.88** Mole percents: butane = 30%;
isobutane = 70%. Yes. **17.90** (a) $Na(l)$: 99.69 J/K · mol.
(b) $S_2Cl_2(g)$: 331.5 J/K · mol. (c) $FeCl_2(s)$: 117.9 J/K · mol.
17.92 Mole fractions are: CO = 0.45, CO_2 = 0.55. Use ΔG_f°
values at 25°C for 900°C. **17.94** 617 J/K. **17.96** 3×10^{-13} s.
17.98 ΔS_{sys} = −327 J/K · mol, ΔS_{surr} = 1918 J/K · mol, ΔS_{univ} =
1591 J/K · mol. **17.100** q, w. **17.102** $\Delta H < 0$, $\Delta S < 0$, $\Delta G < 0$.
17.104 (a) 5.76 J/K. (b) The orientation is not totally
random. **17.106** ΔH° = 33.89 kJ/mol; ΔS° = 96.4 J/K · mol;
ΔG° = 5.2 kJ/mol. This is an endothermic liquid to vapor process
so both ΔH° and ΔS° are positive. ΔG° is positive because the
temperature is below the boiling point of benzene (80.1°C).
17.108 ΔG° = 62.5 kJ/mol; ΔH° = 157.8 kJ/mol; ΔS° = 109
J/K · mol. **17.110** Slightly larger than 0.052 atm.

Chapter 18

18.2 (a) $Mn^{2+} + H_2O_2 + 2OH^- \longrightarrow MnO_2 + 2H_2O$.
(b) $2Bi(OH)_3 + 3SnO_2^{2-} \longrightarrow 2Bi + 3H_2O + 3SnO_3^{2-}$.
(c) $Cr_2O_7^{2-} + 14H^+ + 3C_2O_4^{2-} \longrightarrow 2Cr^{3+} + 6CO_2 + 7H_2O$.
(d) $2Cl^- + 2ClO_3^- + 4H^+ \longrightarrow Cl_2 + 2ClO_2 + 2H_2O$. **18.12** 2.46 V.
$Al + 3Ag^+ \longrightarrow 3Ag + Al^{3+}$. **18.14** $Cl_2(g)$ and $MnO_4^-(aq)$.
18.16 Only (a) and (d) are spontaneous. **18.18** (a) Li. (b) H_2.
(c) Fe^{2+}. (d) Br^-. **18.20** −1.79 V. **18.24** 0.368 V.
18.26 (a) −432 kJ/mol, 5×10^{75}. (b) −104 kJ/mol, 2×10^{18}.
(c) −178 kJ/mol, 1×10^{31}. (d) −1.27 $\times 10^3$ kJ/mol, 8×10^{211}.
18.28 0.37 V, −36 kJ/mol, 2×10^6. **18.32** (a) 2.23 V, 2.23 V, −430
kJ/mol. (b) 0.02 V, 0.04 V, −23 kJ/mol. **18.34** 0.083 V. **18.36** 0.010
V. **18.40** 1.09 V. **18.48** (b) 0.64 g. **18.50** (a) 2.10×10^3. (b) 2.46
$\times 10^3$. (c) 4.70×10^3. **18.52** (a) 0.14 mol. (b) 0.121 mol. (c) 0.10
mol. **18.54** (a) $Ag^+ + e^- \longrightarrow Ag$. (b) $2H_2O \longrightarrow O_2 + 4H^+ +$
$4e^-$. (c) 6.0×10^2 C. **18.56** (a) 0.589 Cu. (b) 0.133 A. **18.58** 2.3 h.
18.60 9.66×10^4 C. **18.62** 0.0710 mol. **18.64** (a) Anode: $Cu(s)$
$\longrightarrow Cu^{2+}(aq) + 2e^-$. Cathode: $Cu^{2+}(aq) + 2e^- \longrightarrow Cu(s)$.
(b) 2.4×10^2 g. (c) Copper is more easily oxidized than Ag and
Au. Copper ions (Cu^{2+}) are more easily reduced than Fe^{2+} and
Zn^{2+}. **18.66** 0.0296 V. **18.68** 0.156 M. $Cr_2O_7^{2-} + 6Fe^{2+} +$
$14H^+ \longrightarrow 2Cr^{3+} + 6Fe^{3+} + 7H_2O$. **18.70** 45.1%. **18.72** (a)
$2MnO_4^- + 16H^+ + 5C_2O_4^{2-} \longrightarrow 2Mn^{2+} + 10CO_2 + 8H_2O$.
(b) 5.40%. **18.74** 0.231 mg Ca^{2+}/mL blood. **18.76** (a) 0.80 V.
(b) $2Ag^+ + H_2 \longrightarrow 2Ag + 2H^+$. (c) (i) 0.92 V. (ii) 1.10 V.
(d) The cell operates as a pH meter. **18.78** Fluorine gas reacts with
water. **18.80** 2.5×10^2 h. **18.82** Hg_2^{2+}. **18.84** $[Mg^{2+}]$ = 0.0500 M,
$[Ag^+] = 7 \times 10^{-55}$ M, 1.44 g. **18.86** (a) 0.206 L H_2. (b) 6.09
$\times 10^{23}$/mol e^-. **18.88** (a) −1356.8 kJ/mol. (b) 1.17 V. **18.90** +3.
18.92 6.8 kJ/mol, 0.064. **18.94** In both cells, the anode is on
the left and the cathode is on the right. In the galvanic cell, the
anode is negatively charged and the cathode is positively charged.
The opposite holds for the electrolytic cell. Electrons flow from
the anode in the galvanic cell to the cathode in the electrolytic
cell and electrons flow from the anode in the electrolytic cell
to the cathode in the galvanic cell. **18.96** 1.4 A. **18.98** +4. **18.100**
1.60×10^{-19} C/e^-. **18.102** A cell made of Li^+/Li and F_2/F^-
gives the maximum voltage of 5.92 V. Reactive oxidizing and
reducing agents are hard to handle. **18.104** 0.030 V. **18.106**
2×10^{20}. **18.108** (a) E° for X is negative; E° for Y is positive.
(b) 0.59 V. **18.110** (a) The reduction potential of O_2 is insufficient

to oxidize gold. (b) Yes. (c) $2Au + 3F_2 \longrightarrow 2AuF_3$. **18.112** $[Fe^{2+}] = 0.0920\ M$, $[Fe^{3+}] = 0.0680\ M$. **18.114** $E° = 1.09\ V$. Spontaneous. **18.116** (a) Ni. (b) Pb. (c) Zn. (d) Fe. **18.118** (a) Unchanged. (b) Unchanged. (c) Squared. (d) Doubled. (e) Doubled. **18.120** Stronger. **18.122** 4.4×10^2 atm. **18.124** (a) Zn $\longrightarrow Zn^{2+} + 2e^-$; $(1/2)O_2 + 2e^- \longrightarrow O^{2-}$. 1.65 V. (b) 1.63 V. (c) 4.87×10^3 kJ/kg. (d) 62 L. **18.126** -3.05 V. **18.128** 1×10^{-14}. **18.130** (b) 104 A · h. The concentration of H_2SO_4 keeps decreasing. (c) 2.01 V; -3.88×10^2 kJ/mol. **18.132** \$217. **18.134** -0.037 V. **18.136** 2×10^{37}. **18.138** 5 mol ATP. **18.140** 2.87 V.

Chapter 19

19.6 (Z,N,A) $_2^4\alpha$ decay: $(-2, -2, -4)$. $_{-1}^{0}\beta$ decay: $(+1, -1, 0)$. $_{+1}^{0}\beta$ decay: $(-1, +1, 0)$. e^- capture: $(-1, +1, 0)$. **19.8** (a) $_{-1}^{0}\beta$. (b) $_{20}^{40}Ca$. (c) $_2^4\alpha$. (d) $_0^1n$. **19.16** (a) $_3^9Li$. (b) $_{11}^{25}Na$. (c) $_{21}^{48}Sc$. **19.18** (a) $_{10}^{17}Ne$. (b) $_{20}^{45}Ca$. (c) $_{43}^{92}Tc$. (d) $_{80}^{195}Hg$. (e) $_{96}^{242}Cm$. **19.20** 6×10^9 kg/s. **19.22** (a) 4.55×10^{-12} J; 1.14×10^{-12} J/nucleon. (b) 2.36×10^{-10} J; 1.28×10^{-12} J/nucleon. **19.26** 0.251 d^{-1}. 2.77 d. **19.28** 2.7 d. **19.30** $_{82}^{208}Pb$. **19.32** A: 0; B: 0.25 mole; C: 0; D: 0.75 mole. **19.34** $_{88}^{224}Ra$. **19.38** (a) $_{34}^{80}Se + _1^2H \longrightarrow _1^1p + _{34}^{81}Se$. (b) $_4^9Be + _1^1H \longrightarrow 2_1^1p + _3^9Li$. (c) $_5^{10}B + _0^1n \longrightarrow _2^4\alpha + _3^7Li$. **19.40** $_{80}^{198}Hg + _0^1n \longrightarrow _{79}^{198}Au + _1^1p$. **19.52** IO_3^- is only formed from IO_4^-. **19.54** Incorporate Fe-59 into a person's body. After a few days isolate red blood cells and monitor radioactivity from the hemoglobin molecules. **19.56** (a) $_{25}^{50}Mn \longrightarrow _{24}^{50}Cr + _{+1}^{0}\beta$. (b) Three half-lives. **19.58** An analogous Pauli exclusion principle for nucleons. **19.60** (a) 0.343 mCi. (b) $_{93}^{237}Np \longrightarrow _2^4\alpha + _{91}^{233}Pa$. **19.62** (a) 1.040×10^{-12} J/nucleon. (b) 1.111×10^{-12} J/nucleon. (c) 1.199×10^{-12} J/nucleon. (d) 1.410×10^{-12} J/nucleon. **19.64** $_7^{18}N \longrightarrow _8^{18}O + _{-1}^{0}\beta$. **19.66** Radioactive dating. **19.68** (a) $_{83}^{209}Bi + _2^4\alpha \longrightarrow _{85}^{211}At + 2_0^1n$. (b) $_{83}^{209}Bi(\alpha,2n)_{85}^{211}At$. **19.70** The sun exerts a much greater gravity on the particles. **19.72** 2.77×10^3 yr. **19.74** (a) $_{19}^{40}K \longrightarrow _{18}^{40}Ar + _{+1}^{0}\beta$. (b) 3.0×10^9 yr. **19.76** (a) ^{90}Sr: 5.59×10^{-15} J; ^{90}Y: 2.84×10^{-13} J. (b) 0.024 mole. (c) 4.26×10^6 kJ. **19.78** 2.7×10^{14} I-131 atoms. **19.80** 5.9×10^{23}/mol. **19.82** All except gravitational. **19.84** U-238 and Th-232. Long half-lives. **19.86** 8.3×10^{-4} nm. **19.88** $_1^3H$. **19.90** The reflected neutrons induced a nuclear chain reaction. **19.92** 2.1×10^2 g/mol. **19.94** First step: $_{90}^{234}Th \longrightarrow _{91}^{234}Pa + _{-1}^{0}\beta$. Second step: $_{91}^{234}Pa \longrightarrow _{92}^{234}U + _{-1}^{0}\beta$. Third step: $_{92}^{234}U \longrightarrow _{90}^{230}Th + _2^4\alpha$. Fourth step: $_{90}^{230}Th \longrightarrow _{88}^{226}Ra + _2^4\alpha$. Fifth step: $_{88}^{226}Ra \longrightarrow _{86}^{222}Rn + _2^4\alpha$. **19.96** (a) $_{94}^{238}Pu \longrightarrow _2^4\alpha + _{92}^{234}U$. (b) $t = 0$: 0.58 mW; $t = 10$ yr: 0.53 mW. **19.98** 0.49 rem. **19.100** The high temperature attained during the chain reaction causes a small-scale nuclear fusion: $_1^2H + _1^3H \longrightarrow _2^4He + _0^1n$. The additional neutrons will result in a more powerful fission bomb. **19.102** 21.5 mL. **19.104** No. According to Equation (19.1), energy and mass are interconvertible. **19.106** (a) 1.69×10^{-12} J. (b) 1.23×10^{-12} J. Because a proton feels the repulsion from other protons, it has a smaller binding energy than a neutron.

Chapter 20

20.6 3.3×10^{-4} atm. **20.8** N_2: 3.96×10^{18} kg; O_2: 1.22×10^{18} kg; CO_2: 2.63×10^{15} kg. **20.12** 3.57×10^{-19} J. **20.22** 5.2×10^6 kg/day. 5.6×10^{14} kJ. **20.24** The wavelength is not short enough. **20.26** 434 nm. Both.

20.28

F—C—C—Cl   F—C—C—H   **20.40** 1.3×10^{10} kg.

20.42 Ethane and propane are greenhouse gases. **20.50** 4.34. **20.58** 1.2×10^{-11} M/s. **20.60** (b). **20.66** 0.12%. **20.68** Endothermic. **20.70** O_2. **20.72** 5.72. **20.74** 394 nm. **20.76** It has a high activation energy. **20.78** Size of tree rings are related to CO_2 content. Age of CO_2 in ice can be determined by radiocarbon dating. **20.80** 165 kJ/mol. **20.82** 5.1×10^{20} photons. **20.84** (a) 62.6 kJ/mol. (b) 38 min. **20.86** 5.6×10^{23}. **20.88** H—Ö—Ö—Ö ·

Chapter 21

21.12 111 h. **21.14** Roast the sulfide followed by reduction of the oxide with coke or carbon monoxide. **21.16** (a) 8.9×10^{12} cm^3. (b) 4.0×10^8 kg. **21.18** Iron does not need to be produced electrolytically. **21.28** (a) $2Na + 2H_2O \longrightarrow 2NaOH + H_2$. (b) $2NaOH + CO_2 \longrightarrow Na_2CO_3 + H_2O$. (c) $Na_2CO_3 + 2HCl \longrightarrow 2NaCl + CO_2 + H_2O$. (d) $NaHCO_3 + HCl \longrightarrow NaCl + CO_2 + H_2O$. (e) $2NaHCO_3 \longrightarrow Na_2CO_3 + CO_2 + H_2O$. (f) No reaction. **21.30** 5.59 L. **21.34** First react Mg with HNO_3 to form $Mg(NO_3)_2$. On heating, $2Mg(NO_3)_2 \longrightarrow 2MgO + 4NO_2 + O_2$. **21.36** The third electron is removed from the neon core. **21.38** Helium has a closed-shell noble gas configuration. **21.40** (a) CaO. (b) $Ca(OH)_2$. (c) An aqueous suspension of $Ca(OH)_2$. **21.44** 60.7 h. **21.46** (a) 1.03 V. (b) 3.32×10^4 kJ/mol. **21.48** $4Al(NO_3)_3 \longrightarrow 2Al_2O_3 + 12NO_2 + 3O_2$. **21.50** Because Al_2Cl_6 dissociates to form $AlCl_3$. **21.52** From sp^3 to sp^2. **21.54** 65.4 g/mol. **21.56** No. **21.58** (a) 1482 kJ/mol. (b) 3152.8 kJ/mol. **21.60** Magnesium reacts with nitrogen to form magnesium nitride. **21.62** (a) Al^{3+} hydrolyzes in water to produce H^+ ions. (b) $Al(OH)_3$ dissolves in a strong base to form $Al(OH)_4^-$. **21.64** $CaO + 2HCl \longrightarrow CaCl_2 + H_2O$. **21.66** Electronic transitions (in the visible region) between closely spaced energy levels. **21.68** NaF: toothpaste additive; Li_2CO_3: to treat mental illness; $Mg(OH)_2$: antacid; $CaCO_3$: antacid; $BaSO_4$: for X-ray diagnostic of digestive system; $Al(OH)_2NaCO_3$: antacid. **21.70** (i) Both Li and Mg form oxides. (ii) Like Mg, Li forms nitride. (iii) The carbonates, fluorides, and phosphates of Li and Mg have low solubilities. **21.72** Zn. **21.74** D < A < C < B. **21.76** 727 atm.

Chapter 22

22.12 (a) Hydrogen reacts with alkali metals to form hydrides. (b) Hydrogen reacts with oxygen to form water. **22.14** Use palladium metal to separate hydrogen from other gases. **22.16** 11 kg. **22.18** (a) $H_2 + Cl_2 \longrightarrow 2HCl$. (b) $N_2 + 3H_2 \longrightarrow 2NH_3$. (c) $2Li + H_2 \longrightarrow 2LiH$, $LiH + H_2O \longrightarrow LiOH + H_2$. **22.26** $:C≡C:^{2-}$. **22.28** (a) $2NaHCO_3 \longrightarrow Na_2CO_3 + H_2O + CO_2$. (b) CO_2 reacts with $Ca(OH)_2$ solution to form a white precipitate ($CaCO_3$). **22.30** On heating, the bicarbonate ion decomposes: $2HCO_3^- \longrightarrow CO_3^{2-} + H_2O + CO_2$. Mg^{2+} ions combine with CO_3^{2-} ions to form $MgCO_3$. **22.32** First, $2NaOH + CO_2 \longrightarrow Na_2CO_3 + H_2O$. Then, $Na_2CO_3 + CO_2 + H_2O \longrightarrow 2NaHCO_3$. **22.34** Yes. **22.40** (a) $2NaNO_3 \longrightarrow 2NaNO_2 + O_2$. (b) $NaNO_3 + C \longrightarrow NaNO_2 + CO$. **22.42** $2NH_3 + CO_2 \longrightarrow (NH_2)_2CO + H_2O$. At high pressures. **22.44** NH_4Cl decomposes to form NH_3 and HCl. **22.46** N is in its highest oxidation state ($+5$) in HNO_3. **22.48** Favored reaction: $4Zn + NO_3^- + 10H^+ \longrightarrow 4Zn^{2+} + NH_4^+ + 3H_2O$. **22.50** Linear. **22.52** -1168 kJ/mol. **22.54** P_4. 125 g/mol. **22.56** $P_4O_{10} + 4HNO_3 \longrightarrow 2N_2O_5 + 4HPO_3$. 60.4 g. **22.58** sp^3. **22.66** -198.3 kJ/mol, 6×10^{34}, 6×10^{34}. **22.68** 0; -1. **22.70** 4.4×10^{11} mol; 1.4×10^{13} g. **22.72** 79.1 g. **22.74** Cl, Br, and I atoms are too bulky around the S atom. **22.76** 35 g. **22.78** $9H_2SO_4 + 8NaI \longrightarrow H_2S + 4I_2 + 4H_2O + 8NaHSO_4$. **22.82** $H_2SO_4 + NaCl \longrightarrow HCl + NaHSO_4$.

The HCl gas escapes, driving the equilibrium to the right. **22.84** 25.3 L. **22.86** Sulfuric acid oxidizes sodium bromide to molecular bromine. **22.88** 2.81 L. **22.90** $I_2O_5 + 5CO \longrightarrow I_2 + 5CO_2$. C is oxidized; I is reduced. **22.92** (a) $SiCl_4$. (b) F^-. (c) F. (d) CO_2. **22.94** No change. **22.96** (a) $2Na + D_2O \longrightarrow 2NaOD + D_2$. (b) $2D_2O \longrightarrow 2D_2 + O_2$ (electrolysis). $D_2 + Cl_2 \longrightarrow 2DCl$. (c) $Mg_3N_2 + 6D_2O \longrightarrow 3Mg(OD)_2 + 2ND_3$. (d) $CaC_2 + 2D_2O \longrightarrow C_2D_2 + Ca(OD)_2$. (e) $Be_2C + 4D_2O \longrightarrow 2Be(OD)_2 + CD_4$. (f) $SO_3 + D_2O \longrightarrow D_2SO_4$. **22.98** (a) At elevated pressure, water boils above 100°C. (b) So the water is able to melt a larger area of sulfur deposit. (c) Sulfur deposits are structurally weak. Conventional mining would be dangerous. **22.100** The C—D bond breaks at a slower rate. **22.102** Molecular oxygen is a powerful oxidizing agent, reacting with substances such as glucose to release energy for growth and function. Molecular nitrogen (containing the nitrogen-to-nitrogen triple bond) is too unreactive at room temperature to be of any practical use. **22.104** 25°C: 9.61×10^{-22}; 1000°C: 138. High temperature favors the formation of CO. **22.106** 1.18.

Chapter 23

23.12 (a) +3. (b) 6. (c) oxalate. **23.14** (a) Na: +1, Mo: +6. (b) Mg: +2, W: +6. (c) Fe: 0. **23.16** (a) *cis*-dichlorobis(ethylenediamine)cobalt(III). (b) pentaamminechloroplatinum(IV) chloride. (c) pentaamminechlorocobalt(III) chloride. **23.18** (a) $[Cr(en)_2Cl_2]^+$. (b) $Fe(CO)_5$. (c) $K_2[Cu(CN)_4]$. (d) $[Co(NH_3)_4(H_2O)Cl]Cl_2$. **23.24** (a) 2. (b) 2. **23.26** (a) Two geometric isomers:

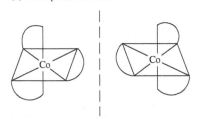

trans   *cis*

(b) Two optical isomers:

23.34 CN^- is a strong-field ligand. Absorbs near UV (blue) so appears yellow. **23.36** (a) Orange. (b) 255 kJ/mol. **23.38** $[Co(NH_3)_4Cl_2]Cl$. 2 moles. **23.42** Use $^{14}CN^-$ label (in NaCN). **23.44** First $Cu(CN)_2$ (white) is formed. It redissolves as $Cu(CN)_4^{2-}$. **23.46** 1.4×10^2. **23.48** Mn^{3+}. The $3d^3$ electron configuration of Cr^{3+} is stable. **23.50** Ti: +3; Fe: +3. **23.52** Four Fe atoms per hemoglobin molecule. 1.6×10^4 g/mol. **23.54** (a) $[Cr(H_2O)_6]Cl_3$. (b) $[Cr(H_2O)_5Cl]Cl_2 \cdot H_2O$. (c) $[Cr(H_2O)_4Cl_2]Cl \cdot 2H_2O$. Compare electrical conductance with solutions of NaCl, $MgCl_2$, and $FeCl_3$ of the same molar concentration. **23.56** -1.8×10^2 kJ/mol; 6×10^{30}. **23.58** Iron is more abundant. **23.60** Oxyhemoglobin is low spin and therefore absorbs higher energy light. **23.62** All except Fe^{2+}, Cu^{2+}, and Co^{2+}. The colorless ions have electron configurations d^0 and d^{10}. **23.64** Dipole moment measurements. **23.66** EDTA sequesters essential metal ions (Ca^{2+}, Mg^{2+}). **23.68** 3. **23.70** 1.0×10^{-18} M. **23.72** 2.2×10^{-20} M. **23.74** (a) 2.7×10^6. (b) Cu^+ ions are unstable in solution. **23.76** (a) Cu^{3+} is unstable in solution because it can be easily reduced. (b) Potassium hexafluorocuprate(III). Octahedral. Paramagnetic. (c) Diamagnetic.

Chapter 24

24.12 $CH_3CH_2CH_2CH_2CH_2Cl$. $CH_3CH_2CH_2CHClCH_3$. $CH_3CH_2CHClCH_2CH_3$.

24.14

24.16 (a) Alkene or cycloalkane. (b) Alkyne. (c) Alkane. (d) Like (a). (e) Alkyne. **24.18** No, too much strain. **24.20** (a) is alkane and (b) is alkene. Only an alkene reacts with a hydrogen halide and hydrogen. **24.22** −630.8 kJ/mol. **24.24** (a) *cis*-1,2-dichlorocylopropane. (b) *trans*-1,2-dichlorocylopropane. **24.26** (a) 2-methylpentane. (b) 2,3,4-trimethylhexane. (c) 3-ethylhexane. (d) 3-methyl-1,4-pentadiene. (e) 2-pentyne. (f) 3-phenyl-1-pentene.

24.28 (a)   (b)

(c)   (d)

24.32 (a) 2,4-dichloro-1-methylbenzene. (b) 2-ethyl-1,4-dinitrobenzene. (c) 1,2,4,5-tetramethylbenzene. **24.36** (a) Ether. (b) Amine. (c) Aldehyde. (d) Ketone. (e) Carboxylic acid. (f) Alcohol. (g) Amino acid. **24.38** $HCOOH + CH_3OH \longrightarrow HCOOCH_3 + H_2O$. Methyl formate. **24.40** $(CH_3)_2CH—O—CH_3$. **24.42** (a) Ketone. (b) Ester. (c) Ether. **24.44** −174 kJ/mol. **24.46** (a), (c), (d), (f). **24.48** (a) Rubbing alcohol. (b) Vinegar. (c) Moth balls. (d) Organic synthesis. (e) Organic synthesis. (f) Antifreeze. (g) Natural gas. (h) Synthetic polymer. **24.50** (a) 3. (b) 16. (c) 6. **24.52** (a) C: 15.81 mg, H: 1.33 mg, O: 3.49 mg. (b) C_6H_6O.

(c) Phenol.

24.54 Empirical and molecular formula: $C_5H_{10}O$. 88.7 g/mol.

CH_2=CH—CH_2—O—CH_2—CH_3. **24.56** (a) The C atoms bonded to the methyl group and the amino group and the H atom. (b) The C atoms bonded to Br. **24.58** CH_3CH_2CHO. **24.60** (a) Alcohol. (b) Ether. (c) Aldehyde. (d) Carboxylic acid. (e) Amine. **24.62** The acids in lemon juice convert the amines to the ammonium salts, which have very low vapor pressures. **24.64** Methane (CH_4), ethanol (C_2H_5OH), methanol (CH_3OH), isopropanol (C_3H_7OH), ethylene glycol (CH_2OHCH_2OH), naphthalene ($C_{10}H_8$), acetic acid (CH_3COOH). **24.66** (a) 1. (b) 2. (c) 5. **24.68** Br_2 dissociates into Br atoms, which react with CH_4 to form CH_3Br and HBr.

24.70 (a)
$$CH_3-\overset{\overset{\displaystyle OH}{|}}{\underset{\underset{\displaystyle H}{|}}{C}}-CH_2-CH_3$$
. The compound is chiral.

(b) The product is a racemic mixture.

24.72 $CH_3CH_2CH_2OH$ or
$$CH_3-\overset{\overset{\displaystyle OH}{|}}{CH}-CH_3$$
. **24.74** (a) Reaction between glycerol and carboxylic acid (formation of an ester). (b) Fat or oil (shown in problem) + NaOH $\longrightarrow$ Glycerol + $3RCOO^-Na^+$ (soap). (c) Molecules having more C=C bonds are harder to pack tightly. Consequently, they have a lower melting point. (d) H_2 gas with a homogeneous or heterogeneous catalyst. (e) 123.

Chapter 25

25.8 —(CH_2—CHCl—CH_2—CCl_2)—. **25.10** By an addition reaction involving styrene monomers.

25.12 (a) CH_2=CH—CH=CH_2. (b) $HO_2C(CH_2)_6NH_2$. **25.22** At 35°C the enzyme begins to denature. **25.28** Proteins are made of 20 amino acids. Nucleic acids are made of four building blocks (purines, pyrimidines, sugar, phosphate group) only. **25.30** C-G base pairs have three hydrogen bonds and higher boiling point; A-T base pairs have two hydrogen bonds. **25.32** Leg muscles are active, have a high metabolic rate and hence a high concentration of myoglobin. The iron content in Mb makes the meat look dark. **25.34** Insects have blood that contains no hemoglobin. It is unlikely that a human-sized insect could obtain sufficient oxygen for metabolism by diffusion. **25.36** There are four Fe atoms per hemoglobin molecule. 1.6×10^4 g/mol. **25.38** Mostly dispersion forces. **25.40** Gly-Ala-Phe-Glu-His-Gly-Ala-Leu-Val. **25.42** No. Enzymes only act on one of the two optical isomers of a compound. **25.44** 315 K. **25.46** Hydrogen bonding. **25.48** (a) The —COOH group. (b) pH = 1.0: The valine is in the fully protonated form. pH = 7.0: Only the —COOH group is ionized. pH = 12.0: Both groups are ionized. (c) 5.97. **25.50** (a) $\overline{M}_n$ = 3.6 kg/mol; $\overline{M}_w$ = 4.3 kg/mol. (b) $\overline{M}_n$ = 5 kg/mol; $\overline{M}_w$ = 5 kg/mol. (c) If $\overline{M}_n$ and $\overline{M}_w$ are close in value, that indicates a small spread in the distribution of polymer sizes. (d) The four subunits in hemoglobin molecule dissociate in solution, giving a distribution of molar masses. There are no subunits in myoglobin or cytochrome c, so no distribution of molar masses.

Index

I-14   Index

Periodic Table of the Elements

Key:

11
Na — Atomic number
Sodium
22.99 — Atomic mass

1 1A	2 2A	3 3B	4 4B	5 5B	6 6B	7 7B	8 8B	9 8B	10 8B	11 1B	12 2B	13 3A	14 4A	15 5A	16 6A	17 7A	18 8A
1 **H** Hydrogen 1.008																	2 **He** Helium 4.003
3 **Li** Lithium 6.941	4 **Be** Beryllium 9.012											5 **B** Boron 10.81	6 **C** Carbon 12.01	7 **N** Nitrogen 14.01	8 **O** Oxygen 16.00	9 **F** Fluorine 19.00	10 **Ne** Neon 20.18
11 **Na** Sodium 22.99	12 **Mg** Magnesium 24.31											13 **Al** Aluminum 26.98	14 **Si** Silicon 28.09	15 **P** Phosphorus 30.97	16 **S** Sulfur 32.07	17 **Cl** Chlorine 35.45	18 **Ar** Argon 39.95
19 **K** Potassium 39.10	20 **Ca** Calcium 40.08	21 **Sc** Scandium 44.96	22 **Ti** Titanium 47.88	23 **V** Vanadium 50.94	24 **Cr** Chromium 52.00	25 **Mn** Manganese 54.94	26 **Fe** Iron 55.85	27 **Co** Cobalt 58.93	28 **Ni** Nickel 58.69	29 **Cu** Copper 63.55	30 **Zn** Zinc 65.39	31 **Ga** Gallium 69.72	32 **Ge** Germanium 72.59	33 **As** Arsenic 74.92	34 **Se** Selenium 78.96	35 **Br** Bromine 79.90	36 **Kr** Krypton 83.80
37 **Rb** Rubidium 85.47	38 **Sr** Strontium 87.62	39 **Y** Yttrium 88.91	40 **Zr** Zirconium 91.22	41 **Nb** Niobium 92.91	42 **Mo** Molybdenum 95.94	43 **Tc** Technetium (98)	44 **Ru** Ruthenium 101.1	45 **Rh** Rhodium 102.9	46 **Pd** Palladium 106.4	47 **Ag** Silver 107.9	48 **Cd** Cadmium 112.4	49 **In** Indium 114.8	50 **Sn** Tin 118.7	51 **Sb** Antimony 121.8	52 **Te** Tellurium 127.6	53 **I** Iodine 126.9	54 **Xe** Xenon 131.3
55 **Cs** Cesium 132.9	56 **Ba** Barium 137.3	57 **La** Lanthanum 138.9	72 **Hf** Hafnium 178.5	73 **Ta** Tantalum 180.9	74 **W** Tungsten 183.9	75 **Re** Rhenium 186.2	76 **Os** Osmium 190.2	77 **Ir** Iridium 192.2	78 **Pt** Platinum 195.1	79 **Au** Gold 197.0	80 **Hg** Mercury 200.6	81 **Tl** Thallium 204.4	82 **Pb** Lead 207.2	83 **Bi** Bismuth 209.0	84 **Po** Polonium (210)	85 **At** Astatine (210)	86 **Rn** Radon (222)
87 **Fr** Francium (223)	88 **Ra** Radium (226)	89 **Ac** Actinium (227)	104 **Rf** Rutherfordium (257)	105 **Db** Dubnium (260)	106 **Sg** Seaborgium (263)	107 **Bh** Bohrium (262)	108 **Hs** Hassium (265)	109 **Mt** Meitnerium (266)	110 **Ds** Darmstadtium (269)	111 **Rg** Roentgenium (272)	112 **Cn** Copernicium (285)	113	114 **Fl** Flerovium (289)	115	116 **Lv** Livermorium (293)	117	118

Lanthanides:

58 **Ce** Cerium 140.1	59 **Pr** Praseodymium 140.9	60 **Nd** Neodymium 144.2	61 **Pm** Promethium (147)	62 **Sm** Samarium 150.4	63 **Eu** Europium 152.0	64 **Gd** Gadolinium 157.3	65 **Tb** Terbium 158.9	66 **Dy** Dysprosium 162.5	67 **Ho** Holmium 164.9	68 **Er** Erbium 167.3	69 **Tm** Thulium 168.9	70 **Yb** Ytterbium 173.0	71 **Lu** Lutetium 175.0

Actinides:

90 **Th** Thorium 232.0	91 **Pa** Protactinium (231)	92 **U** Uranium 238.0	93 **Np** Neptunium (237)	94 **Pu** Plutonium (242)	95 **Am** Americium (243)	96 **Cm** Curium (247)	97 **Bk** Berkelium (247)	98 **Cf** Californium (249)	99 **Es** Einsteinium (254)	100 **Fm** Fermium (253)	101 **Md** Mendelevium (256)	102 **No** Nobelium (254)	103 **Lr** Lawrencium (257)

Legend:

- Metals
- Metalloids
- Nonmetals

The 1–18 group designation has been recommended by the International Union of Pure and Applied Chemistry (IUPAC) but is not yet in wide use. In this text we use the standard U.S. notation for group numbers (1A–8A and 1B–8B). No names have been assigned for elements 113, 115, 117, and 118. In 2011 IUPAC revised the atomic masses of some elements. The changes are minor and they are not adopted in the present edition of this text.

List of the Elements with Their Symbols and Atomic Masses*

Element	Symbol	Atomic Number	Atomic Mass†	Element	Symbol	Atomic Number	Atomic Mass†
Actinium	Ac	89	(227)	Manganese	Mn	25	54.94
Aluminum	Al	13	26.98	Meitnerium	Mt	109	(266)
Americium	Am	95	(243)	Mendelevium	Md	101	(256)
Antimony	Sb	51	121.8	Mercury	Hg	80	200.6
Argon	Ar	18	39.95	Molybdenum	Mo	42	95.94
Arsenic	As	33	74.92	Neodymium	Nd	60	144.2
Astatine	At	85	(210)	Neon	Ne	10	20.18
Barium	Ba	56	137.3	Neptunium	Np	93	(237)
Berkelium	Bk	97	(247)	Nickel	Ni	28	58.69
Beryllium	Be	4	9.012	Niobium	Nb	41	92.91
Bismuth	Bi	83	209.0	Nitrogen	N	7	14.01
Bohrium	Bh	107	(262)	Nobelium	No	102	(253)
Boron	B	5	10.81	Osmium	Os	76	190.2
Bromine	Br	35	79.90	Oxygen	O	8	16.00
Cadmium	Cd	48	112.4	Palladium	Pd	46	106.4
Calcium	Ca	20	40.08	Phosphorus	P	15	30.97
Californium	Cf	98	(249)	Platinum	Pt	78	195.1
Carbon	C	6	12.01	Plutonium	Pu	94	(242)
Cerium	Ce	58	140.1	Polonium	Po	84	(210)
Cesium	Cs	55	132.9	Potassium	K	19	39.10
Chlorine	Cl	17	35.45	Praseodymium	Pr	59	140.9
Chromium	Cr	24	52.00	Promethium	Pm	61	(147)
Cobalt	Co	27	58.93	Protactinium	Pa	91	(231)
Copernicium	Cn	112	(285)	Radium	Ra	88	(226)
Copper	Cu	29	63.55	Radon	Rn	86	(222)
Curium	Cm	96	(247)	Rhenium	Re	75	186.2
Darmstadtium	Ds	110	(269)	Rhodium	Rh	45	102.9
Dubnium	Db	105	(260)	Roentgenium	Rg	111	(272)
Dysprosium	Dy	66	162.5	Rubidium	Rb	37	85.47
Einsteinium	Es	99	(254)	Ruthenium	Ru	44	101.1
Erbium	Er	68	167.3	Rutherfordium	Rf	104	(257)
Europium	Eu	63	152.0	Samarium	Sm	62	150.4
Fermium	Fm	100	(253)	Scandium	Sc	21	44.96
Flerovium	Fl	114	(289)	Seaborgium	Sg	106	(263)
Fluorine	F	9	19.00	Selenium	Se	34	78.96
Francium	Fr	87	(223)	Silicon	Si	14	28.09
Gadolinium	Gd	64	157.3	Silver	Ag	47	107.9
Gallium	Ga	31	69.72	Sodium	Na	11	22.99
Germanium	Ge	32	72.59	Strontium	Sr	38	87.62
Gold	Au	79	197.0	Sulfur	S	16	32.07
Hafnium	Hf	72	178.5	Tantalum	Ta	73	180.9
Hassium	Hs	108	(265)	Technetium	Tc	43	(99)
Helium	He	2	4.003	Tellurium	Te	52	127.6
Holmium	Ho	67	164.9	Terbium	Tb	65	158.9
Hydrogen	H	1	1.008	Thallium	Tl	81	204.4
Indium	In	49	114.8	Thorium	Th	90	232.0
Iodine	I	53	126.9	Thulium	Tm	69	168.9
Iridium	Ir	77	192.2	Tin	Sn	50	118.7
Iron	Fe	26	55.85	Titanium	Ti	22	47.88
Krypton	Kr	36	83.80	Tungsten	W	74	183.9
Lanthanum	La	57	138.9	Uranium	U	92	238.0
Lawrencium	Lr	103	(257)	Vanadium	V	23	50.94
Lead	Pb	82	207.2	Xenon	Xe	54	131.3
Lithium	Li	3	6.941	Ytterbium	Yb	70	173.0
Livermorium	Lv	116	(293)	Yttrium	Y	39	88.91
Lutetium	Lu	71	175.0	Zinc	Zn	30	65.39
Magnesium	Mg	12	24.31	Zirconium	Zr	40	91.22

*All atomic masses have four significant figures. These values are recommended by the Committee on Teaching of Chemistry, International Union of Pure and Applied Chemistry.
†Approximate values of atomic masses for radioactive elements are given in parentheses.

Fundamental Constants

Avogadro's number	6.0221413×10^{23}
Electron charge (e)	$1.60217653 \times 10^{-19}$ C
Electron mass	$9.1093826 \times 10^{-28}$ g
Faraday constant (F)	96,485.3383 C/mol e^-
Gas constant (R)	8.314472 J/K $\cdot$ mol (0.082057 L $\cdot$ atm/K $\cdot$ mol)
Neutron mass	$1.67492728 \times 10^{-24}$ g
Planck's constant (h)	$6.6260693 \times 10^{-34}$ J $\cdot$ s
Proton mass	1.672621×10^{-24} g
Rydberg constant (R_H)	2.179872×10^{-18} J
Speed of light in vacuum	2.99792458×10^8 m/s

Useful Conversion Factors and Relationships

1 lb = 453.6 g

1 gal = 3.785 L = 4 quarts

1 in = 2.54 cm (exactly)

1 mi = 1.609 km

1 km = 0.6215 mi

1 pm = 1×10^{-12} m = 1×10^{-10} cm

1 atm = 760 mmHg = 760 torr = 101,325 N/m^2 = 101,325 Pa

1 cal = 4.184 J (exactly)

1 L atm = 101.325 J

1 J = 1 C $\times$ 1 V

$$?°C = (°F - 32°F) \times \frac{5°C}{9°F}$$

$$?°F = \frac{9°F}{5°C} \times (°C) + 32°F$$

$$?K = (°C + 273.15°C)\left(\frac{1\ K}{1°C}\right)$$

Color Codes for Molecular Models

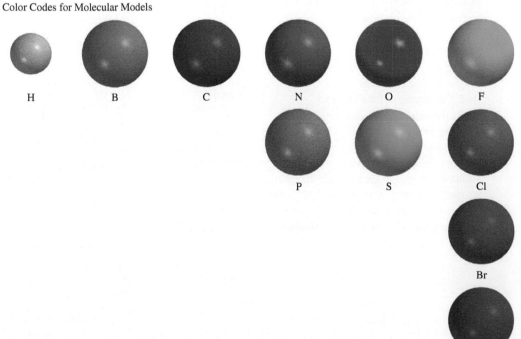

H   B   C   N   O   F

P   S   Cl

Br

I

Some Prefixes Used with SI Units

tera (T)	10^{12}	centi (c)	10^{-2}
giga (G)	10^{9}	milli (m)	10^{-3}
mega (M)	10^{6}	micro (μ)	10^{-6}
kilo (k)	10^{3}	nano (n)	10^{-9}
deci (d)	10^{-1}	pico (p)	10^{-12}

Index of Important Figures and Tables

Credits

Online Supplements

Connect One-Semester Online Access for Chemistry, 12th Edition

McGraw-Hill Connect is a digital teaching and learning environment that improves performance over a variety of critical outcomes. With Connect, instructors can deliver assignments, quizzes and tests easily online. Students can practice important skills at their own pace and on their own schedule.

HOW TO REGISTER

Using a Print Book?

To register and activate your Connect account, simply follow these easy steps:

1. **Go to the Connect course web address provided by your instructor or visit the Connect link set up on your instructor's course within your campus learning management system.**
2. **Click on the link to register.**
3. **When prompted, enter the Connect code found on the inside back cover of your book and click Submit. Complete the brief registration form that follows to begin using Connect.**

Using an eBook?

To register and activate your Connect account, simply follow these easy steps:

1. **Upon purchase of your eBook, you will be granted automatic access to Connect.**
2. **Go to the Connect course web address provided by your instructor or visit the Connect link set up on your instructor's course within your campus learning management system.**
3. **Sign in using the same email address and password you used to register on the eBookstore. Complete your registration and begin using Connect.**

Note: Access Code is for one use only. If you did not purchase this book new, the access code included in this book is no longer valid.

Need help? Visit mhhe.com/support